The Adventures
in Literature Program

Adventures for Readers: Book One
Test Booklet
*Steps to Better Reading: Book 1**
Teacher's Manual
Many Voices 7, a longplay record

Adventures for Readers: Book Two
Test Booklet
*Steps to Better Reading: Book 2**
Teacher's Manual
Many Voices 8, a longplay record

Adventures in Reading
Test Booklet
*Steps to Better Reading: Book 3**
Teacher's Manual
Many Voices 9, a two-record
(longplay) album

Adventures in Appreciation
Test Booklet
*Steps to Reading Literature: Book 1**
Teacher's Manual
Many Voices 10A, a longplay record
Many Voices 10B, a longplay record
of *Julius Caesar*

Adventures in American Literature
Test Booklet
*Steps to Reading Literature: Book 2**
Teacher's Manual
Many Voices 11, a two-record
(longplay) album

Adventures in English Literature
Test Booklet
*Steps to Reading Literature: Book 3**
Teacher's Manual
Many Voices 12A, a longplay record
Many Voices 12B, a longplay record
of *Macbeth*

* Programed Instruction

ADVENTURES

LAUREATE
EDITION

Harcourt, Brace & World, Inc.

New York Chicago Atlanta Dallas Burlingame

IN READING

EVAN LODGE

MARJORIE BRAYMER

Series Editor: MARY RIVES BOWMAN

Reading Consultant: HERBERT POTELL

EVAN LODGE, a native of Ohio, has been since 1946 supervisor of English for the junior and senior high schools of Cleveland. His career in education has been extensive, particularly in the field of secondary education. From 1930 until 1946 he was a teacher in five different Cleveland schools, and for eight of those years he was chairman of the English Department at East High School. Born in the town of Columbiana, Ohio, he was educated at Mount Union College and later at Western Reserve University. Evan Lodge is co-editor of two earlier editions of *Adventures in Reading*.

MARJORIE BRAYMER has been a teacher of English and history at Sequoia High School in Redwood City, California, since 1946. Born in Chicago, Illinois, she was educated at the University of Chicago and at Ohio State University. In 1944 she was a Morris Fellow in Education at Teachers College, Columbia University. With Mr. Lodge she was co-editor of the Olympic edition of *Adventures in Reading*. In addition to her work as a teacher and editor, Marjorie Braymer is the author of the prize-winning biography of Heinrich Schliemann, *The Walls of Windy Troy*, which she wrote especially for young people.

The Series Editor, MARY RIVES BOWMAN, holds degrees in English (B.A.) from the University of Texas and the University of Chicago (M.A.) and has also done graduate work in English at the University of Colorado and at East Texas State College. She has been active in various professional organizations and has devoted much of her time to the training and supervision of high school English teachers. She was co-editor of the last three editions of *Adventures in American Literature* and of two editions of *Adventures for Readers, Books 1 and 2*.

HERBERT POTELL is Reading Co-ordinator and teacher of English at the New Utrecht High School, Brooklyn, New York. A graduate of Brooklyn College, he has done graduate work in English at Columbia University. He has served as reading consultant on two editions of the Adventures in Literature Series, and is co-author of the ninth and tenth grade books in the Companion Series — *Adventures for Today* and *Adventures in Living*.

FRONTISPIECE: *Glazed Brick Lion from the wall of the procession street of Babylon; Babylonian, period of Nebuchadnezzar, 605–352* B.C. The Metropolitan Museum of Art, Fletcher Fund, 1931.

Artists who have contributed illustrations to this book are: Don Bolognese, Joseph Cellini, Herbert Danska, Harvey Dinnerstein, Ati Forberg, Milton Glaser, Eugene Karlin, Howard Koslow, Whitold Mars, Tom O'Sullivan, Isidore Seltzer, Edward Shenton, Robert Shore, Joseph Weishar.

CONTENTS

Short Stories

Nonfiction

MAN'S CONQUEST OF THE AIR (A THEMATIC UNIT)

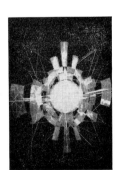

Poetry

BY WAY OF INTRODUCTION

Drama

The Epic Tale

* Special classroom edition.

The Novel

ADVENTURES IN READING

Short Stories

Good stories are always good, and the passing of time affects them very little. The ancient Greek fables about the fox and the grapes, or about the greedy dog that saw his image in the brook, are centuries old, yet they still entertain and have meaning for us in our own time.

Fables, in the sense that they have tales to tell, are examples of the very oldest kind of story. In the earliest days, stories were told by word of mouth, and because the rhythm and rhyme of poetry made listening more enjoyable, these stories were told in verse. Even after writing had become a part of man's accomplishments, verse was still used for story-telling. The only literature written in prose consisted of histories and biographies. Then, with the invention of the printing press, a great new audience of readers was created. For this new audience, other forms of prose writing — works that would offer the reader excitement, adventure, and imaginative characters — needed to be developed. Stories and tales were no longer confined to verse; at last they were presented in prose — or fiction, as it was called. In this way, the new and rapidly expanding audience of readers brought about the appearance of novels and, ultimately, of short stories.

It was in America that the short story as we know it today had its origin. Today's modern short story can be directly traced to the tales and sketches of such early American authors as Washington Irving and Nathaniel Hawthorne. One of the first writers of short stories was Edgar Allan Poe, whose classic story "The Tell-Tale Heart" is to be found in this section of the anthology. Poe not only was the author of some of the best short stories ever written, but he also set forth rules for judging this

◀ Riding toward you from the sixteenth century is this shining symbol of the adventure and high craftsmanship which marked that age: a suit of armor for knight and horse.

new form of fiction. Poe's feeling was that a story, among other things, should be short enough to be read at a single sitting, should have a single line of action (novels may have subplots), and should have an ending toward which every incident or event in the story moves without interruption. There are, of course, exceptions to any set of rules, but in giving thought to the qualities that make up a well-written story, Edgar Allan Poe was doing what you, as readers of short stories, should do: he was asking himself what made a story good.

The question of why a certain story is good cannot be completely answered. For example, it would be difficult to say precisely why Eric Knight's "Lassie Come-Home," which you will read in this section, is more memorable than other well-written dog stories, and yet it is. A good story has an "extra" quality that is hard to pin down. All stories, however, are made up of the same basic elements of *plot, character, setting,* and *theme.* It is by studying these elements and learning to evaluate them that the reader can find most of the "whys" of a good story. That is one of the aims of this section you are about to begin: to offer you good stories and the opportunity to explore the reasons for their merits.

You will find here a variety of stories, written by different authors over a wide period of time. There are stories by authors from France, Sweden, England, and Canada, as well as from nearly every region of America. The settings of the stories vary from ancient Pompeii to medieval Sweden to present-day Pennsylvania. You will meet a number of memorable characters in these stories, many of them young like yourselves — a Yorkshire lad, a Masai warrior stretching toward manhood, a lean, hard Colorado rancher and his son. Many of the stories are the work of current authors, while others have been favorites for years.

In reading such a variety and range of stories, you will have the chance to observe the different ways in which authors handle the elements of plot, character, setting, and theme. You will deal with literary terms, such as *crisis, climax,* and *resolution,* which help to chart the way a story is developed and "shaped" by an author. A good story, you will discover, is good for many specific reasons. And you will find that there is one characteristic shared by all good stories, which is perhaps the best reason for reading them: they are entertaining!

Conflict and Action:
Stories of Plot

ACTION

①   In Picture No. 1 a man is shown walking along a stretch of rugged terrain. If we were to use this man as the main character in a story, we would be starting out with something that is necessary to all stories: *action.* But the mere action of walking is not, in itself, very exciting, is it? Where is the man going? Why? These are the questions that add interest to the action. If we attempt to answer such questions, we will have the beginning of a story.

CONFLICT

②   Wait a moment. Perhaps we are finding answers to our questions. In Picture No. 2 the man is no longer simply walking; he has come to a mountain and is embarked on the dangerous task of climbing it. He is pitting his strength against the mountain, and between these two opposing forces — the man and the mountain — a struggle will ensue. The action in the story has suddenly become more interesting. It has achieved more interest because *conflict* has been introduced. Action alone cannot create a story. Some sort of conflict — a struggle between opposing forces — must be present also. And now that the story has both action and conflict, we may have the beginning of what we call a *plot*. To find out more about what plot is, let us continue to follow the man on his journey up the mountain.

ACTION PLUS CONFLICT   COMPLICATION

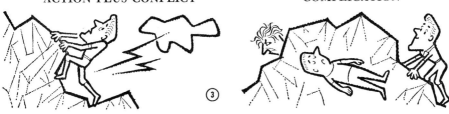

In Picture No. 3 the man is shown fighting his way up the mountain. His struggle to climb the mountain has given our story action and conflict, but so far we are still without a plot. Something more needs to happen. Will there be trouble ahead? What will happen to the mountain climber? Let us consider this last question for a moment. The working out of a plot for a story consists, really, of deciding what is to happen as a result of the conflict. If we wished, we could construct a plot centered solely on the man's struggle to climb the mountain. What are the various events which could occur during his attempt to scale the mountain?

The man has pitted himself against a treacherous, unyielding mass of stone and ice. Perhaps as he straddles a dangerous crevice, a fierce wind might catch him and threaten his balance. For a moment it might seem as if all is lost. Then, in the final split second before falling, he might somehow maintain his footing and continue the ascent . . . until the next incident occurs. Devising other incidents in which to involve the hero would give us a workable plot, for that is what plot consists of: the series of incidents which confront the main characters during the course of a story. For our plot we could use, as we have said, the mountain itself and the incidents which could arise in the man's attempt to conquer it. But look at Picture No. 4. We see that another man is lying at the top of the mountain, apparently injured. With the introduction of this new character, the story can take a different turn. The first man, it is now disclosed, has another purpose in climbing the mountain. His purpose is to rescue an injured friend at the top. He is now the "hero" in an important struggle; the plot has now widened to include another character, who is dependent on the actions of the hero. But are there further developments? Look again at Picture No. 4. Hiding on the mountain is a third man. Why is this third person hiding? What will happen? The plot is already more complicated, and, before it is concluded, it must answer these questions.

CRISIS	CLIMAX, RESOLUTION

Here, in Picture No. 5, the hero is shown approaching his injured friend. The hero is nearing his goal. Victory seems within reach; only a few more feet of treacherous mountain need to be traversed. Now, some new incident is about to take place. The third man creeps from his hiding place, as if ready to attack the others. Will the hero suffer defeat or victory? The plot has begun to create *suspense*. Events will soon reach a *crisis*. The term *crisis* in a story refers to an incident or situation which could change the events to follow. If the third man is successful in his attack on the other two men, the outcome of the story would be radically changed. The plot would follow an entirely different direction. What will the outcome be here? Picture No. 6 provides the answer. The villain loses his footing — another new incident — and is sent hurtling below. This new incident provides the story with a *climax*. The action in the story has arrived at a turning point which will decide the way the story is to end. The hero can now rescue his friend, and this final action brings the plot to its *resolution*. The defeat of the villain and victory for the hero in rescuing his friend — that is the resolution of the story.

Thus you see that plot is the arrangement of a story's incidents in such a manner that the action and conflict can develop and reach a satisfactory conclusion. In the five stories that follow, the element of plot is especially noteworthy. Prepare for action — and conflict!

Dive Right In

B. J. CHUTE

Conflict and action stories often involve the attempts of a person to solve a problem. In this case the problem-solver is a boy, and the problem concerns a friend's stage fright. The solution is psychological — and funny, too.

S<small>KEETS</small> R<small>OGERS</small> breezed into the lodge room at Camp Timberlake. He slammed the door behind him.

"Well, here I am," he shouted cheerily.

No one answered him or paid any attention. Skeets looked around the room.

"What's the trouble?" he said. "Why all this gloom on a beautiful summer morning?"

Five other camp boys were in the room.

"Do you have to be so cheerful?" asked one, Bill Anderson, in a weak voice.

"Nature is one glorious smile," said Skeets. "I feel cheerful."

"Well, go away and feel cheerful somewhere else," said Bill. "I can't stand it."

Skeets helped himself to a chair. He sat down.

"What's the trouble now?" he asked. "Tell Uncle Skeets all about it."

All the boys started to talk at once. Skeets waved for them to stop talking.

"Bill can tell me," he said. "After all, he's chairman of the committee for the swimming meet."

"We've got trouble, Skeets," said Bill. "You knew that Bunty Richards was our man in the high diving?"

"Yup," said Skeets.

"Well, he's out," went on Bill. "This morning he was playing tennis. He tripped and hurt his ankle — badly."

"I see," said Skeets thoughtfully.

Relating Character to Plot. In a sports story like this one, the action has to move along swiftly. To do so, the story needs a main character capable of swift action. Pay close attention to the character of Skeets in this story. Note what he does or does not do to solve the problems he faces. Consider this question: Is Skeets a good choice for a main character in a story in which fast action is important?

"Dive Right In" by B. J. Chute. Reprinted by permission of the author and *Boys' Life,* published by the Boy Scouts of America.

"Well, after all, there are other boys who can dive. What about John Clark?"

"Look, dopey," answered Bill, "you know what happens to John when he tries to dive in front of people. He gets stage fright. He's hopeless. He looks around at the crowd. Then he dives — just like a bale of hay."

"Stage fright — that can be cured," said Skeets. "Once I read an article on psychology. It said that stage fright can be overcome."

"I wish you'd stop reading. Reading upsets your brain," said Bill.

Skeets paid no attention to Bill. He went right on explaining. "I'll tell you what to do. Enter John for the swimming meet. I will promise to cure him of stage fright. And in time to win the diving for you. John is good enough to beat Andy Farrell, isn't he? Andy is going to dive for Camp Playfair."

"Oh, John's good enough to beat anyone," answered Bill. "He can dive just like a dream. But still, he — "

"Leave it all to me," Skeets said. "I don't know much about high diving. But when it comes to psychology — I'm really great."

"Brag is your middle name," said Bill.

"Now stop worrying, my dear old pals," Skeets said. "Everything is under perfect control. I'll go and find John now. I'll start working on him."

Skeets went out the door so fast that Bill couldn't think up an answer.

Skeets had a long, hot search. Finally he found John sitting under a tree eating an apple and playing with a beetle. He was teaching the beetle to dive off a blade of grass.

"Bunty Richards hurt his ankle this morning," Skeets said, flopping down on the ground beside John. John nodded. He had already heard the news.

"Which means," said Skeets firmly, "that you have to take his place in the swimming meet."

"I — you know how I — " began John, shaking his head.

"Yes, I know. You don't need to tell me how you get stage fright. But I'm going to cure you. And by the way," he went on, "I entered your name for the high dive."

"Skeets!" wailed John, jumping to his feet. "You didn't — ! I can't — !"

"There is no such word as can't," said Skeets.

"Oh, yes, there is!" cried John. "You just don't know how it feels when you're going to dive. Everybody's looking at you. All of a sudden you feel awful. You feel as if you had an earthquake inside you."

"Your pet earthquake — now isn't that silly?" said Skeets. "You'd feel worse if we lose the swimming meet, wouldn't you? Now look. I read an article on psychology. It said there are several ways to cure stage fright. All I want is your help."

John said he would co-operate till he popped. But he knew it wouldn't do any good. Skeets didn't pay much attention to John's doubt in the matter.

"I have to study your case," Skeets told him. "Now how many people does it take to give you stage fright? I've seen you diving off the high tower. The other fellows were watching — It didn't seem to make any difference then."

"Yes, but they're friends! Nobody cares — "

"Friends," said Skeets wisely. "You have to feel that all the people are your friends. How many friends at a time can you stand without getting nervous?"

"Maybe four or five," John said carefully.

Skeets looked down. Then he took a deep breath and felt better. "Well, we'll just have to make you feel more confident. Look here, John. I want you to be at the diving tower tomorrow morning at ten o'clock. I'll be on the raft. Just me. No one else — see? I'm going to study you."

"Oh," said John weakly.

"And now, old pal, I must leave you," said Skeets, getting to his feet. "I have a few little plans to make. Hey, is this your beetle?"

"Yes," said John, "I'm teaching it to dive. I was just trying to get it over its stage fright." He laughed sadly.

Next morning, Skeets was lying on the diving raft. He looked up to the top of the high-diving tower. John was standing on the edge of the diving board. Then John sprang out and up. His arms were spread in a perfect swan dive. He sailed through the air. He cut into the water with hardly a splash.

"Oh, purty, purty!" Skeets called. John swam over to the raft where Skeets was lying. "Now, go back and do it again."

"Why?" asked John.

"Because I say so," said Skeets.

John shrugged his shoulders. But he turned and swam back to the diving tower. Then Skeets smiled secretly to himself. He faced the shore and lifted both hands. He gave a signal to the other boys. All at once, the boys began to pop out from behind the trees and rocks. Soon there was a small crowd of campers along the water.

John did not know that others besides Skeets were watching him. He climbed the diving tower. He walked again to the edge of the diving board and stood there. Since he was looking down at Skeets, his back was to the boys watching him. And they were very quiet.

"Okay," Skeets shouted to John. "Now dive again."

John dived again, like a well-trained arrow in perfect flight. His body cut the water clean. As his head came up above the water, the group of boys on the shore broke into a cheer. John's head shot under the water again. Skeets, reaching an arm over the side of the raft, pulled John on board.

"Glug," said John, gulping.

"See?" said Skeets, pounding John on the back. "Look what you did! You dived in front of an audience."

"Gubble," said John. "Didn't know they were there."

"That's just the point," said Skeets. "You didn't know they were there. And you dived anyhow. According to psychology, I have cured your fear of a crowd. The article said if you do it once, you're almost cured. Now your only job is to go back and do it once more. See? It's simple."

"Hm-m-m-m-m," said John, breathing deeply.

"Go on," urged Skeets. "You know you can do it now."

John looked doubtful, but he was anxious to please. Again he climbed the diving tower as the other boys watched. They knew that John's high dive would probably win or lose the swimming meet. It was now only a week away.

John walked to the edge of the diving board. He stood there looking down at the water. Then he turned and looked at the crowd of boys.

"Go ahead! You did it once in front of them. Do it again," called Skeets.

John looked at the water again. Then something happened to his legs. They shook so much that he could hardly stand up. He gulped. He tried to take a deep breath. His hands were ice-cold.

"Come on!" yelled Skeets, getting anxious.

"I did it before," John whispered to himself, sinking back on his heels. "But

I didn't know they were there." Skeets was yelling again, something about will power.

John pulled himself up on his toes. He spread his arms and gave a mighty pull. He threw himself off the diving board. The dive was like that of an elephant. John went into the water with a great splash.

The crowd of boys groaned. Skeets groaned.

"You see?" said John, coming out of the water. He pointed his finger at Skeets.

"I see all right," said Skeets. "I'd better get a new article on psychology. I'll feed the other one to the fish."

During the week that followed, John never had a minute's peace. Skeets read one psychology book after another. The day before the swimming meet, both boys were nervous wrecks.

"It's worse than ever," John said sadly. He was sitting on a rock, holding his head in his hands. "Before, I used to get stage fright at diving. Now I get stage fright about getting stage fright. I can't dive at the meet tomorrow, Skeets. It's awful!"

"But you've got to," said Skeets. "You're our only entry in the high dive. You've just got to win."

"I'll go smack on my face," John warned him.

"But where's your will power?" Skeets asked, still reading a psychology book.

"It's all very well for you to talk about will power —"

"Hey!" yelled Skeets, looking up. "This book says in case of stage fright, take the person's mind off what he's doing. Hey, do you know any poems by heart?"

"No, I don't," said John crossly. "What's that got to do with diving? If you think I am going to recite poems on the edge of the diving board,

you're crazy!"

"The idea is to get your mind off diving. You could say the multiplication tables."

"I can just see myself," John snorted. "Two times two is four won't take my mind off the people. I couldn't even hear myself anyway, the way my knees would be knocking."

"But if someone else reads it to you —" began Skeets, thinking to himself.

"Reads it to me!" John nearly fell off the rock. "When I'm standing on the high-diving board? Skeets, you are crazy!"

"But if everything else fails," said Skeets, "I'm going to try it." He patted the book on psychology. Chapter Ten also said to make the person angry — then he would use his will power and forget himself.

The day of the swimming meet was a beautiful one. The sun shone, and the lake sparkled. Camp Timberlake's boys all looked good. Skeets felt that John was angry enough to forget himself in front of a crowd. So Skeets felt good as John climbed up the high tower. Andy Farrell, the diver for Camp Playfair, was right behind John.

The first dive from the high tower was Andy's. Both Timberlake Camp and Playfair cheered as Andy slid into the water. Skeets smiled to himself. He knew that John could do better than Andy — if his nerves behaved.

Skeets had his eyes glued to the diving board where John stood, ready for the dive. John waited. The judges waited. Everyone waited. Skeets gulped. Then one of the judges waved for John to go ahead and dive. John rose on his toes. Then he fell back on his heels.

"Gurk," said Skeets.

John rose to his toes again. He cast a wild glance about him. Then he dived.

Skeets closed his eyes. Then came the grand splash as John walloped into the water. Skeets opened his eyes.

"You and your psychology!" yelled one boy to Skeets. "We'd have done better not to enter anybody in the high dive."

"I'll be right back!" yelled Skeets suddenly.

He turned and ran. On the diving tower, Andy and John climbed the ladder again. Poor John! His shoulders were sagging, and he looked hopeless.

Skeets raced madly to the edge of the dock. He was waving a book in his hands. He snatched a boat tied to the dock. He leaped into the boat and set off with a great splash for the diving tower. Once there, he seized the ladder and hurried up to the top.

Gazing sadly at the water below, John stood there, head down.

"Hi ya, pal," said Skeets to him. "Aren't you glad to see me?"

Andy Farrell was about to dive. He stopped on the edge of the platform. "Well, what do you know?" he said. "Visitors!" Andy laughed, then he sailed off into space with a perfect dive.

"What is the trouble?" asked John weakly.

"You," said Skeets. "I'm going to read poetry to you."

Before John could say another word, Skeets pushed him toward the diving board. He had one hand firmly on John's shoulder. In the other hand was a small book of poems.

"Now you just listen to me closely," Skeets said, "and relax."

Skeets cleared his throat. He paid no attention to the crowd below.

"*Once upon a midnight dreary —*" Skeets began to read.

"Oh, Skeets!" John wailed. "Stop it, please."

"You don't like that one?" Skeets asked. "Well, I don't blame you. Too sad. Here's another." He turned the pages of the book. "*I wandered lonely as a cloud,*" he began. "Are you relaxing, John?"

"No," said John wildly.

"Here's one — listen — *Grow old along with me. The best is yet to be.*"

"Oh, Skeets," wailed John, "go away! Please go away!"

"Here's one," said Skeets, paying no attention. "*Each sting that bids nor sit nor stand, but go!*"

Skeets looked at John standing there wildly.

"*Go!*" yelled Skeets again. He flung his arms wide. In doing this, Skeets threw himself off balance. The diving board was a narrow one. For a wild minute, it looked as if Skeets might manage to stay on the diving board. But he didn't.

"Help! Help!" Skeets shrieked as he pitched off.

"Hey!" yelled John, grabbing for Skeets too late.

"Hold on, Skeets, I'm coming!" he yelled. Then he dived to rescue Skeets. He wanted to help.

The two boys came up together. John towed Skeets back to the diving tower.

"Boy, the lake is as hard as cement!" gulped Skeets. Then he seized John's arms and shook him. "John, look, you dived! You dived in front of an audience. No stage fright at all! You did it!"

"Gee, you're right," said John.

"Go and do it again, pal," Skeets told him.

So John did.

There was a big party at Camp Timberlake that night. But the hero of all the heroes was John.

"You're thanking the wrong person, fellows," said John. "If it hadn't been for Skeets here, I'd have gone flat on my face again. It was Skeets who made me enter the high dive in the first place. It was Skeets who finally cured me of stage fright. And if Skeets hadn't fallen off the diving board — "

John broke off. He motioned for Skeets to stand up. Skeets stood, looking a bit nervous himself. There was a loud clapping of hands and laughing.

"Speech! Speech!" yelled the campers.

Skeets looked all around him. There were all the boys, looking at him. There seemed to be hundreds of people, and they were all waiting for him to say something. He wanted to say that his fall off the diving board was not an accident. He wanted to say that he planned it all to get John's mind off his stage fright.

But Skeets's hands had turned to ice. His voice would not come.

"I — " he began weakly. Then he sat down. Skeets had stage fright.

THINKING IT OVER

1. The author does not tell how the swimming meet came out, but the results are suggested in the events that follow. Which team won, and why, and what are your reasons for thinking so?

2. A swimming race is determined by the order in which the swimmers finish. How is a diving contest judged?

3. Frequently an author works out a double surprise near the end of a story. What are the two surprises here?

4. Psychology is the study of the mind and why human beings (and animals too) act as they do. It is put to use in all sorts of ways — in advertising, in sports and other school activities, in home life, in the training or raising of animals, in politics, and in civic undertakings. Can you give some illustrations?

RELATING CHARACTER TO PLOT

1. "Breezed," "slammed" — these are two words used to describe Skeets's actions in the very first paragraph of the story. What do these words suggest about his character? Find other words in the story that give you a picture of him.

2. When the other boys tell Skeets that Bunty Richards is out of the diving competition, what is the first thought he has? What is his reaction to the news that John Clark has stage fright? What is his next step? When he locates John, what precaution has he taken about the diving competition that prevents John from backing out?

3. What is your conclusion about Skeets and whether he helps the story to move swiftly? Explain your conclusion.

PEN AND PAPER

Whom would you rather have for a friend, Skeets or John, and why? Use "I'll Take —— " as your title. Or write, if you'd rather, a half- or three-quarter-page composition on the subject "Stage Fright and I."

ABOUT THE AUTHOR

B. J. Chute (1913–) began her literary career at the age of eighteen. That's right — *her* career. The initials stand for Beatrice Joy, but she dislikes her given names and never uses them. Born near Minneapolis, she has lived for some years in New York City with her mother and a sister, Marchette, who is also a well-known writer. Miss Chute has worked a great deal with young people in some of the poorer sections of the city, and much of her writing has been about boys and sports. Her popular novel *Greenwillow* was published in 1956.

Which Scene Is It? →

Obviously this painting by Tom O'Sullivan is of a scene from "Dive Right In." There are two diving scenes in the story, however. Can you find the details in the illustration that indicate which diving scene this is? What importance does the scene have in the plot of the story?

Catherine and the Winter Wheat

P. B. HUGHES

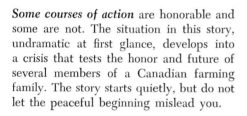

Some courses of action are honorable and some are not. The situation in this story, undramatic at first glance, develops into a crisis that tests the honor and future of several members of a Canadian farming family. The story starts quietly, but do not let the peaceful beginning mislead you.

THIS IS the winter wheat that is being hauled along the roads in late July or early August in southern Ontario, the winter wheat, the fall wheat — have it how you will.

It is sown in September, about the time of the equinox,[1] when the wind blows northwesterly, or used to, across Star-of-the-Sea, and the heavy rain has not come. It stands through the winter, withering under the snow like common

[1] **equinox** (ē′kwĭ·nŏks): the time when the sun crosses the equator and days and nights are everywhere of equal length. There are two such times, coming about March 21 and September 23.

grass, blazing emerald in spring, and by early June it is breast-high, fading in color and heading up, as the farmers say, looking to their binders against July, when the field will be yellow gold and heavy with grain.

It was our sole cash crop, and the brief season when we hauled wheat to the mill was always associated with new clothes and toys and coins in our pockets when my sisters and I were children.

One year before the war we carried our wheat, as we always did, to the mill at Streetsville on the Credit River. I was in my first teens. Before the war, the 1914 war, long ago now. I rode on the sacks, sitting beside my sister Catherine, who was sixteen now, or nearly, while my father drove the team and Emily, the oldest of us, seventeen, sat beside him and spelled him with the reins.

Following the Plot. This is a "double story." That is, there are two problems and two distinct plot threads. As you read, notice how the two plots are developed separately. Observe how these separate plots gradually interweave, and how the solution of one problem helps to bring about the solution of the other problem.

That way the trip took hours, though you'd cover it in a few minutes today in a car. But the sun was bright and the day fresh and beautiful after all the rain and humid heat of the summer, and I talked away to Catherine and thought of the delight to come, of lying under the trees at the miller's while we waited our turn to unload and my father chatted with the men and smoked his pipe, and the greatest delight of all, when the wagon was empty and my father would give us money and tell us to get about our shopping.

Catherine paid no attention to what I said. Dark and stormy she sat on the jolting wagon, for all the glory of this most glorious day.

She had the letter shoved into her blouse, the letter she'd written the night before when everyone was in bed, a secret portentous letter, probably misspelled, but still one of those papers which shape the history of the world.

Oh, I heard the lamp being lit and saw the shadowy figure scratching away, and I knew all about her and Tom Skaife, and what would be in the letter, so I went to sleep again. Skaife's was only a mile out of Streetsville. For certain I'd be dispatched to deliver it personally and privately to Tom before we all set out home again, and Tom would be along one night to get her, and the two of them off to be married at Hamilton, where Tom worked at the iron works except in the harvest season.

That's the way it was, and the reason Catherine's singing was muted that summer and she so fiery and quick to take the corn broom to a boy that got in her way about the place. There wasn't anything against Tom. It was just a matter of their both being so young, and the two years of waiting demanded of them so intolerably too

much. Catherine and I were close to one another, and I think I could tell what she was thinking. That is how I knew what was in the letter. I never saw it.

So Catherine brooded on the top of the rumbling wagonload, and I grieved beside her that I was to lose her, but I was a lad brought up on the land and aware already that all life was ordered in awful cycles of growth and generation and decay, and go she must, soon or late. And today there would be the long ride in the sun, which was far-travel to me, the stream of grain as the sacks were emptied, and money rattling in my pocket, and I could not keep on with grieving and regretting when I contemplated these things.

This summer, this trip to the Credit River, this harvest, are special in my memory. There was Catherine and Tom Skaife. Then there was the wetness of the July and the heat. The two factors got strangely mixed up during the course of the day, which is a trick Nature is playing all the time while she is weaving away at the destinies of men. My father, unaware of this letter writing, was unusually preoccupied, worrying about the condition of the wheat he carried, for grain is sensitive to the weather in which it has matured and been harvested.

We knew that a good deal of wheat had been turned away at the mill in the last week for toughness, which is a matter of moisture content and difficult to deal with, though they do have drying equipment now at the mills which takes care of a lot of doubtful stuff. You daren't bin it tough. Heating and spoilage is an ever-present risk.

At that time you hauled it home again, and you might dry it out with untold labor by spreading it out on the floor in the threshold of the barn, and keep it or sell it degraded for feed. Then, too, your barn was stuffed with hay and with straw from the threshing so you hadn't any floor to spread it on.

My father pondered the matter as he drove, and Emily, sensitive to the moods of others, was quiet. Catherine was wrapped in her own thoughts. Only I was possessed of the high spirits proper to the occasion.

There wasn't much waiting around at the mill. Some years all the farmers seemed to arrive together and you might be four or five hours in line, and other times the season was strung out so you could get a load in when you brought it. We all went into the miller's office together. Old Mr. Jonathan remembered all our names, inquired for my mother, and complained of his rheumatism, the hard times, the cost of labor, the sad wheat he'd been brought and how much he'd had to refuse. It was the same each year, but this year it was the toughness of the wheat he grumbled about most.

"Well, William," he said at last, "dump her off. No need to sample Laughlin's wheat, anyway."

The girls and I looked at each other with relief. I felt like jumping up and down, for there is no doubt the worry about selling the wheat had been urgent in the last hour. My father and his father, the old Laughlin who bought Star-of-the-Sea from the O'Rourkes who built it in '69, were staunch men, and men of substance, but the substance was seldom cash.

My father stood there quite still, and the rest of us, starting for the door of the office, halted when he did not turn to go.

"No, Jonathan," he said, after a little pause, "I guess we'd better sample this. It's not been a good summer."

The miller got up, a little surprised. "H'm. All right. Thought it mightn't have been so bad your way."

They went out together, and we followed without speaking to each other, and my father and the miller opened a lot of the sacks, and talked as they pushed their hands into the wheat. Then they carried a couple of sample tins into the office and remained there for what seemed hours to us. At last my father came out and when we saw his face, our hearts sank. He didn't say anything but climbed back onto the wagon, and we got up beside him and around behind him, and he worked the wagon around and we started back toward the road.

At the road, he swung the team down toward the town and halted under the trees in front of the post office. Then he pulled a dollar out of his pocket and told Emily to get something for her mother and some ice cream for us while the horses were rested and watered.

But we didn't move at once. The blow had been heavy. I thought: Catherine is going to give me that letter now to take to Tom while Father is seeing to the horses. Then suddenly there were tears in Emily's eyes and she turned on my father, hurt and passionate.

"Oh, why couldn't you have unloaded the wheat when he told you to? Why haven't you got the money for it? What did you say it had to be tested for?"

My father looked at her and at us. Three pairs of eyes were upon him, wide-open, puzzled, accusing, in that moment or two before he spoke. Actually he said very little by way of answer.

Only, "Children, you'd better remember this all your lives."

I think we must have stared at him a long time before we turned away,

ashamed, realizing the enormity of what had been in our minds, of what Emily had expressed. We got down slowly off the wheat, leaving Father, and went into the shop and ate ice-cream cones, not talking and not looking at each other.

Suddenly Catherine pulled out the letter and tore it across and across, again and again, until it was only small wads of paper too thick to tear. She pushed the bits into her pocket and ran out without a word, her face wet with tears, to where my father was tending the horses.

Emily and I went and got some bit of something for Mother, and eventually we all got back on the wagon and went home with the sun setting in front of us, and that is all there was to that day — but I have remembered.

THINKING IT OVER

1. Who is the narrator in this story — a younger, or older, brother or sister? Find the point in the story where the narrator's identity is fully revealed. Were you surprised by it, or did you expect it? Why?

2. Early in the story, what information suggests the character of each of Mr. Laughlin's children? Did this information give you a clear picture of them?

3. What would have been the easy way out for Mr. Laughlin in his dilemma? How would the Catherine–Tom Skaife situation have ended if Mr. Laughlin had made a different decision?

4. What is the significance of the sentence, "My father and his father . . . were . . . men of substance, but the substance was seldom cash"? What decision of Mr. Laughlin's bears out this statement?

5. What lesson did his children learn from Mr. Laughlin's decision?

FOLLOWING THE PLOT

1. A story usually begins with a problem. In this story, there are two problems. What is Catherine's? What is the other problem?

2. Make a list of the steps covered by each of the two plots in the story. The plot steps involving Catherine might begin: (a) Catherine rides angrily into town; (b) Catherine has a secret letter to Tom Skaife concerning an elopement. Can you complete this list and then enumerate the steps of the other plot?

3. What action of Catherine's provides the solution to her problem? What is the solution to the other problem?

4. Which of the plots would you say is more important — that is, which does the story depend on in order to exist? Try to think of a good title for each of the two plots.

LOOKING AT SYMBOLISM

When you see a picture of an eagle, it very likely makes you think of America. This is because the eagle represents, or is a *symbol* of, our country. Symbolism — the use of one thing to represent or give special meaning to something else — is a literary device much used by authors. In this story, the use of symbolism effectively points up the story's meaning. What does the testing of the wheat symbolize? What else was tested? Explain.

ABOUT THE AUTHOR

P. B. Hughes (1906–   ) was born in Montreal and writes chiefly of Canadian scenes and places. Once a one-voyage deck hand on an ocean freighter, he admits that it took him twenty-five years to convert this experience into writing — a piece about three hundred words long. At present Mr. Hughes is an assistant professor of engineering at the University of Toronto.

Setting and Character

The photograph on page 15 of a wheat field helps to illustrate the effect that setting can have on character in a story. If you picture Catherine in such a setting — the unbroken expanse of wheat stretching into the lonely distance, with no neighboring houses nearby — what explanation might you find for the drastic action she contemplates taking in this story?

The Apprentice

DOROTHY CANFIELD

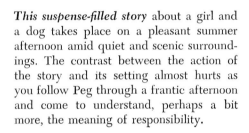

This suspense-filled story about a girl and a dog takes place on a pleasant summer afternoon amid quiet and scenic surroundings. The contrast between the action of the story and its setting almost hurts as you follow Peg through a frantic afternoon and come to understand, perhaps a bit more, the meaning of responsibility.

T HE DAY had been one of the unbearable ones, when every sound had set her teeth on edge like chalk creaking on a blackboard, when every word her father or mother said to her or did not say to her seemed an intentional injustice. And of course it would happen, as the fitting end to such a day, that just as the sun went down back of the mountain and the long twilight began, she noticed that Rollie was not around.

Tense with exasperation at what her mother would say, she began to call him in a carefully casual tone — she would simply explode if Mother got going: "Here, Rollie! He-ere, boy! Want to go for a walk, Rollie?" Whistling to him cheerfully, her heart full of wrath at the way the world treated her, she made the rounds of his haunts: the corner of the woodshed, where he liked to curl up on the wool of Father's discarded old sweater; the hay barn, the cow barn, the sunny spot on the side porch. No Rollie.

Perhaps he had sneaked upstairs to lie on her bed, where he was not supposed to go — not that *she* would have minded! That rule was a part of Mother's fussiness, part, too, of Mother's bossiness. It was *her* bed, wasn't it? But was she allowed the say-so about it? Not on your life. They *said* she could have things the way she wanted in her own room, now she was in her teens, but — Her heart burned at unfairness as

Noting Important Details. To follow the plot changes in a story, it is often necessary to keep track of the changes in the main characters. In this story, for example, it is important to note the changes in Peg. Watch for the details the author has supplied to show Peg's changing moods of *resentment, puzzled concern, frantic concern, sudden relief, anger, responsibility, forgiveness,* and *happiness.*

she took the stairs stormily, two steps at a time, her pigtails flopping up and down on her back. If Rollie was there, she was just going to let him stay there, and Mother could say what she wanted to.

But he was not there. The bedspread and pillow were crumpled, but that was where she had flung herself down to cry that afternoon. Every nerve in her had been twanging discordantly, but she couldn't cry. She could only lie there, her hands doubled up hard, furious that she had nothing to cry about. Not really. She was too big to cry just over Father's having said to her, severely, "I told you if I let you take the chess set, you were to put it away when you got through with it. One of the pawns was on the floor of our bedroom this morning. I stepped on it. If I'd had my shoes on, I'd have broken it."

Well, he *had* told her that. And he hadn't said she mustn't ever take the set again. No, the instant she thought about that, she knew she couldn't cry about it. She could be, and was, in a rage about the way Father kept on talking long after she'd got his point: "It's not that I care so much about the chess set. It's because if you don't learn how to take care of things, you yourself will suffer for it. You'll forget or neglect something that will be really important for *you*. We *have* to try to teach you to be responsible for what you've said you'll take care of. If we —" on and on.

She stood there, dry-eyed, by the bed that Rollie had not crumpled and thought, *I hope Mother sees the spread and says something about Rollie — I just hope she does.*

She heard her mother coming down the hall, and hastily shut her door. She had a right to shut the door to her own room, hadn't she? She had *some* rights, she supposed, even if she was only thir-

teen and the youngest child. If her mother opened it to say, "What are you doing in here that you don't want me to see?" she'd say — she'd just say —

But her mother did not open the door. Her feet went steadily on along the hall, and then, carefully, slowly, down the stairs. She probably had an armful of winter things she was bringing down from the attic. She was probably thinking that a tall, thirteen-year-old daughter was big enough to help with a chore like that. But she wouldn't *say* anything. She would just get out that insulting look of a grownup silently putting up with a crazy, unreasonable kid. She had worn that expression all day; it was too much to be endured.

Up in her bedroom behind her closed door the thirteen-year-old stamped her foot in a gust of uncontrollable rage, none the less savage and heartshaking because it was mysterious to her.

But she had not located Rollie. She would be cut into little pieces before she would let her father and mother know she had lost sight of him, forgotten about him. They would not scold her, she knew. They would do worse; they would look at her. And in their silence she would hear, droning on reproachfully, what they had said when she had been begging to keep for her own the sweet, woolly collie puppy in her arms.

How warm he had felt! Astonishing how warm and alive a puppy was compared with a doll! She had never liked her dolls much after she had held Rollie, feeling him warm against her breast, warm and wriggling, bursting with life, reaching up to lick her face. He had loved her from that first instant. As he felt her arms around him, his liquid, beautiful eyes had melted in trusting sweetness. And they did now, whenever he looked at her. Her dog was the only creature in the world who *really* loved her, she thought passionately.

And back then, at the very minute when, as a darling baby dog, he was beginning to love her, her father and mother were saying, so cold, so reasonable — gosh, how she *hated* reasonableness! — "Now, Peg, remember that, living where we do, with sheep on the farms around us, it is a serious responsibility to have a collie dog. If you keep him, you've got to be the one to take care of him. You'll have to be the one to train him to stay at home. We're too busy with you children to start bringing up a puppy, too."

Rollie, nestling in her arms, let one hind leg drop awkwardly. It must be uncomfortable. She looked down at him tenderly, tucked his leg up under him, and gave him a hug. He laughed up in her face — he really did laugh, his mouth stretched wide in a cheerful grin. Now he was snug in a warm little ball.

Her parents were saying, "If you want him, you can have him. But you must be responsible for him. If he gets to running sheep, he'll just have to be shot, you know that."

They had not said, aloud, "Like the Wilsons' collie." They never mentioned that awfulness — her racing unsuspectingly down across the fields just at the horrible moment when Mr. Wilson shot his collie, caught in the very act of killing sheep. They probably thought that if they never spoke about it, she would forget it — *forget* the crack of that rifle, and the collapse of the great beautiful dog! Forget the red, red blood spurting from the hole in his head. She hadn't forgotten. She never would. She knew as well as they did how important it was to train a collie puppy about sheep. They didn't have to rub it in like that. They always rubbed everything in. She had told them, fervently, indignantly,

that of *course* she would take care of him, be responsible for him, teach him to stay at home. Of course. Of course. *She* understood!

And now, when he was six months old, tall, rangy, powerful, standing up far above her knee, nearly to her waist, she didn't know where he was. But of course he must be somewhere around. He always was. She composed her face to look natural and went downstairs to search the house. He was probably asleep somewhere. She looked every room over carefully. Her mother was nowhere visible. It was safe to call him again, to give the special piercing whistle which always brought him racing to her, the white-feathered plume of his tail waving in elation that she wanted him.

But he did not answer. She stood still on the front porch to think.

Could he have gone up to their special place in the edge of the field where

the three young pines, their branches growing close to the ground, made a triangular, walled-in space, completely hidden from the world? Sometimes he went up there with her, and when she lay down on the dried grass to dream he, too, lay down quietly, his head on his paws, his beautiful eyes fixed adoringly on her. He entered into her every mood. If she wanted to be quiet, all right, he did too. It didn't seem as though he would have gone alone there. Still — She loped up the steep slope of the field rather fast, beginning to be anxious.

No, he was not there. She stood irresolutely in the roofless, green-walled triangular hide-out, wondering what to do next.

Then, before she knew what thought had come into her mind, its emotional impact knocked her down. At least her knees crumpled under her. The Wilsons had, last Wednesday, brought their sheep down from the far upper pasture to the home farm! They were — she herself had seen them on her way to school, and like an idiot had not thought of Rollie — on the river meadow.

She was off like a racer at the crack of the starting pistol, her long, strong legs stretched in great leaps, her pigtails flying. She took the short cut, regardless of the brambles. Their thorn-spiked, wiry stems tore at her flesh, but she did not care. She welcomed the pain. It was something she was doing for Rollie, for her Rollie.

She was in the pine woods now, rushing down the steep, stony path, tripping over roots, half falling, catching herself just in time, not slackening her speed. She burst out on the open knoll above the river meadow, calling wildly, "Rollie, here, Rollie, here, boy! Here! Here!" She tried to whistle, but she was crying too hard to pucker her lips.

There was nobody to see or hear her. Twilight was falling over the bare, grassy knoll. The sunless evening wind slid down the mountain like an invisible river, engulfing her in cold. Her teeth began to chatter. "Here, Rollie, here, boy, here!" She strained her eyes to look down into the meadow to see if the sheep were there. She could not be sure. She stopped calling him as she would a dog, and called out his name despairingly as if he were her child, "Rollie! Oh, *Rollie,* where are you?"

The tears ran down her cheeks in streams. She sobbed loudly, terribly; she did not try to control herself, since there was no one to hear. "Hou! Hou! Hou!" she sobbed, her face contorted grotesquely. "Oh, Rollie! Rollie! Rollie!" She had wanted something to cry about. Oh, how terribly now she had something to cry about.

She saw him as clearly as if he were there beside her, his muzzle and gaping mouth all smeared with the betraying blood (like the Wilsons' collie). "But he didn't *know* it was wrong!" she screamed like a wild creature. "Nobody *told* him it was wrong. It was my fault. I should have taken better care of him. I will now. I will!"

But no matter how she screamed, she could not make herself heard. In the cold gathering darkness, she saw him stand, poor, guiltless victim of his ignorance, who should have been protected from his own nature, his beautiful soft eyes looking at her with love, his splendid plumed tail waving gently. "It was my fault. I promised I would bring him up. I should have *made* him stay at home. I was responsible for him. It was my fault."

But she could not make his executioners hear her. The shot rang out. Rollie sank down, his beautiful liquid eyes glazed, the blood spurting from the hole in his head — like the Wilsons' collie. She gave a wild shriek, long, soul-satisfying, frantic. It was the scream at sudden, unendurable tragedy of a mature, full-blooded woman. It drained dry the girl of thirteen. She came to herself. She was standing on the knoll, trembling and quaking with cold, the darkness closing in on her.

Her breath had given out. For once in her life she had wept all the tears there were in her body. Her hands were so stiff with cold she could scarcely close them. How her nose was running! Simply streaming down her upper lip. And she had no handkerchief. She lifted her skirt, fumbled for her slip, stooped, blew her nose on it, wiped her eyes, drew a long quavering breath — and heard something! Far off in the distance, a faint sound, like a dog's muffled bark.

She whirled on her heels and bent her head to listen. The sound did not come from the meadow below the knoll. It came from back of her, from the Wilsons' maple grove higher up. She held her breath. Yes, it came from there. She began to run again, but now she was not sobbing. She was silent, absorbed in her effort to cover ground. If she could only live to get there, to see if it really were Rollie. She ran steadily till she came to the fence, and went over this in a great plunge. Her skirt caught on a nail. She impatiently pulled at it, not hearing or not heeding the long sibilant [1] tear as it came loose. She was in the dusky maple woods, stumbling over the rocks as she ran. As she tore on up the slope, she knew it was Rollie's bark.

She stopped short and leaned weakly against a tree, sick with the breathlessness of her straining lungs, sick in the reaction of relief, sick with anger at Rollie, who had been here having a

[1] **sibilant** (sĭb′ĭ-lănt): with a hissing sound.

wonderful time while she had been dying, just dying in terror about him.

For she could now not only hear that it was Rollie's bark; she could hear, in the dog language she knew as well as he, what he was saying in those excited yips; that he had run a woodchuck into a hole in the tumbled stone wall, that he almost had him, that the intoxicating wild-animal smell was as close to him — almost — as if he had his jaws on his quarry. Yip! Woof! Yip! Yip!

The wild, joyful quality of the dog talk enraged the girl. She was trembling in exhaustion, in indignation. So that was where he had been, when she was killing herself trying to take care of him. Plenty near enough to hear her calling and whistling to him, if he had paid attention. Just so set on having his foolish good time, he never thought to listen for her call.

She stooped to pick up a stout stick. She would teach him! It was time he had something to make him remember to listen. She started forward.

But she stopped, stood thinking. One of the things to remember about collies — everybody knew that — was their sensitiveness. A collie who had been beaten was never "right" again. His spirit was broken. "Anything but a broken-spirited collie," the farmers often said. They were no good after that.

She threw down her stick. Anyhow, she thought, he was too young to know, really, that he had done wrong. He was still only a puppy. Like all puppies, he got perfectly crazy over wild-animal smells. Probably he really and truly hadn't heard her calling and whistling.

All the same, all the same — she stared intently into the twilight — he couldn't be let to grow up just as he wanted to. She would have to make him understand that he mustn't go off this way by himself. He must be trained to

know how to do what a good dog does — not because *she* wanted him to, but for his own sake.

She walked on now, steady, purposeful, gathering her inner strength together, Olympian [1] in her understanding of the full meaning of the event.

When he heard his own special young god approaching, he turned delightedly and ran to meet her, panting, his tongue hanging out. His eyes shone. He jumped up on her in an ecstasy of welcome and licked her face.

But she pushed him away. Her face and voice were grave. "No, Rollie, *no!*" she said severely. "You're *bad*. You know you're not to go off in the woods without me! You are — a — *bad* — *dog*."

He was horrified. Stricken into misery. He stood facing her, frozen, the gladness going out of his eyes, the erect waving plume of his tail slowly lowered to slinking, guilty dejection.

"I know you were all wrapped up in that woodchuck. But that's no excuse. You *could* have heard me calling you, whistling for you, if you'd paid attention," she went on. "You've got to learn, and I've got to teach you."

[1] **Olympian** (ô·lĭm′pĭ·ăn): godlike.

With a shudder of misery he lay down, his tail stretched out limp on the ground, his head flat on his paws, his ears drooping — ears ringing with doomsday awfulness of the voice he so loved and revered. He must have been utterly wicked. He trembled and turned his head away from her august look of blame, groveling in remorse for whatever mysterious sin he had committed.

She sat down by him, as miserable as he. "I don't *want* to scold you. But I have to! I have to bring you up right, or you'll get shot, Rollie. You *mustn't* go away from the house without me, do you hear, *never!*"

Catching, with his sharp ears yearning for her approval, a faint overtone of relenting affection in her voice, he lifted his eyes to her, humbly, soft in imploring fondness.

"Oh, Rollie!" she said, stooping low over him. "I *do* love you. I do. But I *have* to bring you up. I'm responsible for you, don't you see?"

He did not see. Hearing sternness or something else he did not recognize in the beloved voice, he shut his eyes tight in sorrow, and made a little whimpering lament in his throat.

She had never heard him cry before. It was too much. She sat down by him and drew his head to her, rocking him in her arms, soothing him with inarticulate small murmurs.

He leaped in her arms and wriggled happily as he had when he was a baby; he reached up to lick her face as he had then. But he was no baby now. He was half as big as she, a great, warm, pulsing, living armful of love. She clasped him closely. Her heart was brimming full, but calmed, quiet. The blood flowed in equable [2] gentleness all over her body. She was deliciously warm.

[2] **equable** (ĕk′wȧ·b'l): even, smooth.

Her nose was still running a littie. She sniffed and wiped it on her sleeve.

It was almost dark now. "We'll be late to supper, Rollie," she said responsibly. Pushing him gently off, she stood up. "Home, Rollie, home!"

Here was a command he could understand. At once he trotted along the path toward home. His plumed tail, held high, waved cheerfully. His short dog memory had dropped into oblivion the suffering just back of him.

Her human memory was longer. His prancing gait was as carefree as a young child's. Plodding heavily like a serious adult, she trod behind him. Her very shoulders seemed bowed by what she had lived through. She felt, she thought, like an old, old woman of thirty. But it was all right now. She knew she had made an impression on him.

When they came out into the open pasture, Rollie ran back to get her to play with him. He leaped around her in circles, barking in cheerful yawps, jumping up on her, inviting her to run a race with him, to throw him a stick, to come alive.

His high spirits were ridiculous. But infectious. She gave one little leap to match his. Rollie pretended that this was a threat to him, planted his forepaws low, and barked loudly at her, laughing between yips. He was so funny, she thought, when he grinned that way. She laughed back and gave another mock-threatening leap at him. Radiant that his sky was once more clear, he sprang high on his spring-steel muscles in an explosion of happiness, and bounded in circles around her.

Following him, not noting in the dusk where she was going, she felt the grassy slope drop steeply. Oh, yes, she knew where she was. They had come to the rolling-down hill just back of the house.

All the kids rolled down there, even the little ones, because it was soft grass without a stone. She had rolled down that slope a million times — years and years ago, when she was a kid herself. It was fun. She remembered well the whirling dizziness of the descent, all the world turning over and over crazily. And the delicious giddy staggering when you first stood up, the earth still spinning under your feet.

"All right, Rollie, let's go," she cried, and flung herself down in the rolling position, her arms straight up over her head.

Rollie had never seen this skylarking before. It threw him into almost hysterical amusement. He capered around the rapidly rolling figure, half scared, mystified, enchanted.

His wild frolicsome barking might have come from her own throat, so accurately did it sound the way she felt — crazy, foolish, like a little kid no more than five years old, the age she had been when she had last rolled down that hill.

At the bottom she sprang up, on muscles as steel-strong as Rollie's. She staggered a little, and laughed aloud.

The living-room windows were just

before them. How yellow lighted windows looked when you were in the darkness going home. How nice and yellow. Maybe Mother had waffles for supper. She was a swell cook, Mother was, and she certainly gave her family all the breaks, when it came to meals.

"Home, Rollie, home!" She burst open the door to the living room. "Hi, Mom, what you got for supper?"

From the kitchen her mother announced coolly, "I hate to break the news to you, but it's waffles."

"Oh, *Mom!*" she shouted in ecstasy.

Her mother could not see her. She did not need to. "For goodness' sakes, go and wash," she called.

In the long mirror across the room she saw herself, her hair hanging wild, her long bare legs scratched, her broadly smiling face dirt-streaked, her torn skirt dangling, her dog laughing up at her. Gosh, was it a relief to feel your own age, just exactly thirteen years old!

THINKING IT OVER

1. Is Peg a typical thirteen-year-old? What reasons have you for your answers?

2. What is your estimate of Peg's parents? What difficulties did they face in dealing with their daughter?

3. At one point Peg remembers having heard her parents say: "We're too busy with you children to start bringing up a puppy, too." Why are other children not mentioned anywhere else in the story?

4. Explain the title and just who the apprentice is. Check the term in a dictionary to be sure you know the background of the word.

5. Peg's roll down the hill symbolized her return to her happier, untroubled mood. By this act, which she had last performed when she was five, she put the troubles of the afternoon completely behind her — almost as easily as Rollie had forgotten his troubles. What lasting effects of the afternoon might there be for her? for Rollie?

NOTING IMPORTANT DETAILS

1. Point out the details that illustrate the moods you were asked to watch for when you began the story: *resentment, puzzled concern, frantic concern, sudden relief, anger, responsibility, forgiveness,* and *happiness.*

2. Point out some details in the opening paragraphs of the story which suggest that Peg might be exaggerating her feelings of persecution beyond what is warranted by the situation.

3. What details show that Peg's parents are fair? What is she chiefly in revolt against? What details tell you this?

4. What details did you note concerning the training of dogs?

5. Point out details that show Peg's change of feeling toward her mother.

6. What details show you that the author has a rather good understanding of young people? of parents? of dogs?

ABOUT THE AUTHOR

Dorothy Canfield (1879–1958), born in Kansas, has used New England, where her later life was spent, as the setting for most of her stories. She has written a number of distinguished stories and books; usually the characters in her tales are plain, everyday people. You may be acquainted with her long-time favorites, *Understood Betsy* and *The Bent Twig,* or with the many collections of short stories which she has had published.

The Mind's Eye ➤

Sometimes an event that happens only in our imagination can be as real and meaningful as an actual occurrence. In Joseph Cellini's painting, the artist has depicted a scene from "The Apprentice" which occurs solely in Peg's mind — the terrible vision of Rollie being shot for attacking the Wilsons' sheep. Point out other instances where Peg's active imagination plays an important part in this story. Do you think Peg suffered more from what she imagined to be true than from what actually happened? Explain your answer.

The Ransom of Red Chief

O. HENRY

Unusual plots, unconventional characters, and lively action were trademarks of O. Henry. All are present in this story. The fact that it is also one of the funniest stories ever written is proof that action and conflict can spell out laughter, too.

I T LOOKED like a good thing: but wait till I tell you. We were down South, in Alabama — Bill Driscoll and myself — when this kidnaping idea struck us. It was, as Bill afterward expressed it, "during a moment of temporary mental apparition";[1] but we didn't find that out till later.

There was a town down there, as flat as a flannel cake, and called Summit, of course. It contained inhabitants of as undeleterious[2] and self-satisfied a class of peasantry as ever clustered around a Maypole.

Bill and me had a joint capital of about six hundred dollars, and we needed just two thousand dollars more to pull off a fraudulent town-lot scheme in western Illinois with. We talked it over on the front steps of the hotel. Philoprogenitiveness,[3] says we, is strong in semirural communities; therefore, and for other reasons, a kidnaping project ought to do better there than in the radius of newspapers that send reporters out in plain clothes to stir up talk about such things. We knew that Summit couldn't get after us with anything stronger than constables and, maybe, some lackadaisical bloodhounds and a diatribe[4] or two in the *Weekly Farmers' Budget*. So, it looked good.

We selected for our victim the only child of a prominent citizen named Ebenezer Dorset. The father was respectable and tight, a mortgage fancier and a stern, upright collection-plate passer and forecloser. The kid was a boy of

---

[1] **apparition** (ăp′*a*·rĭsh′*ŭn*): misused for *aberration* (ăb′ĕr·*a*′shŭn), a lapse or departure from the normal.
[2] **undeleterious** (ŭn′dĕl·ê·tēr′ĭ·*ŭs*): incapable of doing harm; harmless.
[3] **philoprogenitiveness** (fĭl′ò·prò·jĕn′ĭ·tĭv·nĕs): love of parents for their children.
[4] **diatribe** (dī′*a*·trīb): an abusive speech or piece of writing.

ten, with bas-relief [1] freckles, and hair the color of the cover of the magazine you buy at the newsstand when you want to catch a train. Bill and me figured that Ebenezer would melt down for a ransom of two thousand dollars to a cent. But wait till I tell you.

About two miles from Summit was a little mountain, covered with a dense cedar brake. [2] On the rear elevation of this mountain was a cave. There we stored provisions.

One evening after sundown, we drove in a buggy past old Dorset's house. The kid was in the street, throwing rocks at a kitten on the opposite fence.

"Hey, little boy!" says Bill, "would you like to have a bag of candy and a nice ride?"

The boy catches Bill neatly in the eye with a piece of brick.

"That will cost the old man an extra five hundred dollars," says Bill, climbing over the wheel.

That boy put up a fight like a welterweight cinnamon bear; but, at last, we got him down in the bottom of the buggy and drove away. We took him up to the cave, and I hitched the horse in the cedar brake. After dark I drove the buggy to the little village, three miles away, where we had hired it, and walked back to the mountain.

Bill was pasting court plaster over the scratches and bruises on his features. There was a fire burning behind the big rock at the entrance of the cave, and the boy was watching a pot of boiling coffee, with two buzzard tail feathers stuck in his red hair. He points a stick at me when I come up, and says:

"Ha! cursèd paleface, do you dare to enter the camp of Red Chief, the terror of the plains?"

"He's all right now," says Bill, rolling up his trousers and examining some bruises on his shins. "We're playing Indian. We're making Buffalo Bill's show looks like magic-lantern views of Palestine in the town hall. I'm Old Hank, the Trapper, Red Chief's captive, and I'm to be scalped at daybreak. By Geronimo! [3] that kid can kick hard."

Yes, sir, that boy seemed to be having the time of his life. The fun of camping out in a cave had made him forget that he was a captive himself. He immediately christened me Snake-eye, the Spy, and announced that, when his braves returned from the warpath, I was to be broiled at the stake at the rising of the sun.

Then we had supper; and he filled his mouth full of bacon and bread and gravy, and began to talk. He made a during-dinner speech something like this:

"I like this fine. I never camped out before; but I had a pet possum once, and I was nine last birthday. I hate to go to school. Rats ate up sixteen of Jimmy Talbot's aunt's speckled hen's eggs. Are there any real Indians in these woods? I want some more gravy. Does the trees moving make the wind blow? We had five puppies. What makes your nose so red, Hank? My father has lots of money. Are the stars hot? I whipped Ed Walker twice, Saturday. I don't like girls. You dassent catch toads unless with a string. Do oxen make any noise? Why are oranges round? Have you got beds to sleep on in this cave? Amos Murray has got six toes. A parrot can talk, but a monkey or a fish can't. How many does it take to make twelve?"

Every few minutes he would remember that he was a pesky redskin, and

[1] **bas-relief** (bä′rê·lêf′): raised slightly from a background, like some kinds of wall sculpture.

[2] **cedar brake:** a thicket of young cedars.

[3] **Geronimo** (jĕ·rŏn′ĭ·mō): a famous Apache chieftain.

pick up his stick rifle and tiptoe to the mouth of the cave to rubber for the scouts of the hated paleface. Now and then he would let out a war whoop that made Old Hank the Trapper shiver. That boy had Bill terrorized from the start.

"Red Chief," says I to the kid, "would you like to go home?"

"Aw, what for?" says he. "I don't have any fun at home. I hate to go to school. I like to camp out. You won't take me back home again, Snake-eye, will you?"

"Not right away," says I. "We'll stay here in the cave a while."

"All right!" says he. "That'll be fine. I never had such fun in all my life."

We went to bed about eleven o'clock. We spread down some wide blankets and quilts and put Red Chief between us. We weren't afraid he'd run away. He kept us awake for three hours, jumping up and reaching for his rifle and screeching: "Hist! pard," in mine and Bill's ears, as the fancied crackle of a twig or the rustle of a leaf revealed to his young imagination the stealthy approach of the outlaw band. At last, I fell into a troubled sleep, and dreamed that I had been kidnaped and chained to a tree by a ferocious pirate with red hair.

Just at daybreak, I was awakened by a series of awful screams from Bill. They weren't yells, or howls, or shouts, or whoops, or yawps, such as you'd expect from a manly set of vocal organs — they were simply indecent, terrifying, humiliating screams, such as women emit when they see ghosts or caterpillars. It's an awful thing to hear a strong, desperate, fat man scream incontinently [1] in a cave at daybreak.

I jumped up to see what the matter was. Red Chief was sitting on Bill's chest, with one hand twined in Bill's

[1] **incontinently** (ĭn·kŏn′tĭ·nĕnt·lĭ): without restraint.

hair. In the other he had the sharp case knife we used for slicing bacon; and he was industriously and realistically trying to take Bill's scalp, according to the sentence that had been pronounced upon him the evening before.

I got the knife away from the kid and made him lie down again. But, from that moment, Bill's spirit was broken. He laid down on his side of the bed, but he never closed an eye again in sleep as long as that boy was with us. I dozed off for a while, but along toward sunup I remembered that Red Chief had said I was to be burned at the stake at the rising of the sun. I wasn't nervous or afraid; but I sat up and lit my pipe and leaned against a rock.

"What you getting up so soon for, Sam?" asked Bill.

"Me?" says I. "Oh, I got a kind of a pain in my shoulder. I thought sitting up would rest it."

"You're a liar!" says Bill. "You're afraid. You was to be burned at sunrise, and you was afraid he'd do it. And he would, too, if he could find a match. Ain't it awful, Sam? Do you think anybody will pay out money to get a little imp like that back home?"

"Sure," said I. "A rowdy kid like that is just the kind that parents dote on. Now, you and the Chief get up and cook breakfast, while I go up on the top of this mountain and reconnoiter."

I went up on the peak of the little mountain and ran my eye over the contiguous vicinity. Over toward Summit I expected to see the sturdy yeomanry of the village armed with scythes and pitchforks beating the countryside for the dastardly kidnapers. But what I saw was a peaceful landscape dotted with one man plowing with a dun mule. Nobody was dragging the creek; no couriers dashed hither and yon, bringing tidings of no news to the distracted parents. There was a sylvan [1] attitude of somnolent [2] sleepiness pervading that section of the external outward surface of Alabama that lay exposed to my view. "Perhaps," says I to myself, "it has not yet been discovered that the wolves have borne away the tender lambkin from the fold. Heaven help the wolves!" says I, and I went down the mountain to breakfast.

When I got to the cave, I found Bill backed up against the side of it, breathing hard, and the boy threatening to smash him with a rock half as big as a coconut.

"He put a red-hot boiled potato down my back," explained Bill, "and then mashed it with his foot; and I boxed his ears. Have you got a gun about you, Sam?"

I took the rock away from the boy and kind of patched up the argument. "I'll fix you," says the kid to Bill. "No man ever yet struck the Red Chief but what he got paid for it. You better beware!"

After breakfast the kid takes a piece of leather with strings wrapped around it out of his pocket and goes outside the cave unwinding it.

"What's he up to now?" says Bill anxiously. "You don't think he'll run away, do you, Sam?"

"No fear of it," says I. "He don't seem to be much of a homebody. But we've got to fix up some plan about the ransom. There don't seem to be much excitement around Summit on account of his disappearance, but maybe they haven't realized yet that he's gone. His folks may think he's spending the night with Aunt Jane or one of the neighbors. Anyhow, he'll be missed today. Tonight we must get a message to his father de-

manding the two thousand dollars for his return."

Just then we heard a kind of war whoop, such as David might have emitted when he knocked out the champion Goliath. It was a sling that Red Chief had pulled out of his pocket, and he was whirling it around his head.

I dodged, and heard a heavy thud and a kind of a sigh from Bill, like a horse gives out when you take his saddle off. A rock the size of an egg had caught Bill just behind his left ear. He loosened himself all over and fell in the fire across the frying pan of hot water for washing the dishes. I dragged him out and poured cold water on his head for half an hour.

By and by, Bill sits up and feels behind his ear and says: "Sam, do you know who my favorite Biblical character is?"

"Take it easy," says I. "You'll come to your senses presently."

"King Herod," [3] says he. "You won't go away and leave me here alone, will you, Sam?"

---

[1] **sylvan:** woodsy; rustic.
[2] **somnolent** (sŏm'nō·lĕnt): drowsy.

[3] **King Herod:** the king who, according to the Bible story, ordered the killing of all male children under two in Bethlehem in an effort to slay the infant Jesus.

I went out and caught that boy and shook him until his freckles rattled.

"If you don't behave," says I, "I'll take you straight home. Now, are you going to be good, or not?"

"I was only funning," says he sullenly. "I didn't mean to hurt Old Hank. But what did he hit me for? I'll behave, Snake-eye, if you won't send me home, and if you'll let me play the Black Scout today."

"I don't know the game," says I. "That's for you and Mr. Bill to decide. He's your playmate for the day. I'm going away for a while, on business. Now, you come in and make friends with him and say you are sorry for hurting him, or home you go, at once."

I made him and Bill shake hands, and then I took Bill aside and told him I was going to Poplar Cove, a little village three miles from the cave, and find out what I could about how the kidnaping had been regarded in Summit. Also, I thought it best to send a peremptory letter to old man Dorset that day, demanding the ransom and dictating how it should be paid.

"You know, Sam," says Bill, "I've stood by you without batting an eye in earthquakes, fire, and flood — in poker games, dynamite outrages, police raids, train robberies, and cyclones. I never lost my nerve yet till we kidnaped that two-legged skyrocket of a kid. He's got me going. You won't leave me long with him, will you, Sam?"

"I'll be back some time this afternoon," says I. "You must keep the boy amused and quiet till I return. And now we'll write the letter to old Dorset."

Bill and I got paper and pencil and worked on the letter while Red Chief, with a blanket wrapped around him, strutted up and down, guarding the mouth of the cave. Bill begged me tearfully to make the ransom fifteen hundred dollars instead of two thousand. "I ain't attempting," says he, "to decry the celebrated moral aspect of parental affection, but we're dealing with humans, and it ain't human for anybody to give up two thousand dollars for that forty-pound chunk of freckled wildcat. I'm willing to take a chance at fifteen hundred dollars. You can charge the difference up to me."

So, to relieve Bill, I acceded, and we collaborated a letter that ran this way:

EBENEZER DORSET, ESQ.:

We have your boy concealed in a place far from Summit. It is useless for you or the most skillful detectives to attempt to find him. Absolutely, the only terms on which you can have him restored to you are these: We demand fifteen hundred dollars in large bills for his return; the money to be left at midnight tonight at the same spot and in the same box as your reply — as hereinafter described. If you agree to these terms, send your answer in writing by a solitary messenger tonight at half-past eight o'clock. After crossing Owl Creek, on the road to Poplar Cove, there are three large trees about a hundred yards apart, close to the fence of the wheat field on the right-hand side. At the bottom of the fence post, opposite the third tree, will be found a small pasteboard box.

The messenger will place the answer in this box and return immediately to Summit.

If you attempt any treachery or fail to comply with our demand as stated, you will never see your boy again.

If you pay the money as demanded, he will be returned to you safe and well within three hours. These terms are final, and if you do not accede to them no further communication will be attempted.

Two Desperate Men.

I addressed this letter to Dorset, and put it in my pocket. As I was about to start, the kid comes up to me and says:

"Aw, Snake-eye, you said I could play the Black Scout while you was gone."

"Play it, of course," says I. "Mr. Bill will play with you. What kind of a game is it?"

"I'm the Black Scout," says Red Chief, "and I have to ride to the stockade to warn the settlers that the Indians are coming. I'm tired of playing Indian myself. I want to be the Black Scout."

"All right," says I. "It sounds harmless to me. I guess Mr. Bill will help you foil the pesky savages."

"What am I to do?" asks Bill, looking at the kid suspiciously.

"You are the hoss," says Black Scout. "Get down on your hands and knees. How can I ride to the stockade without a hoss?"

"You'd better keep him interested," said I, "till we get the scheme going. Loosen up."

Bill gets down on his all fours, and a look comes in his eye like a rabbit's when you catch it in a trap.

"How far is it to the stockade, kid?" he asks, in a husky manner of voice.

"Ninety miles," says the Black Scout.

"And you have to hump yourself to get there on time. Whoa, now!" The Black Scout jumps on Bill's back and digs his heels in his side.

"For heaven's sake," says Bill, "hurry back, Sam, as soon as you can. I wish we hadn't made the ransom more than a thousand. Say, you quit kicking me or I'll get up and warm you good."

I walked over to Poplar Cove and sat around the post office and store talking with the chaw-bacons that came in to trade. One whiskerando says that he hears Summit is all upset on account of Elder Ebenezer Dorset's boy having been lost or stolen. That was all I wanted to know. I bought some smoking tobacco, referred casually to the price of black-eyed peas, posted my letter surreptitiously,[1] and came away. The postmaster said the mail carrier would come by in an hour to take the mail on to Summit.

When I got back to the cave, Bill and the boy were not to be found. I explored the vicinity of the cave and risked a yodel or two, but there was no response.

So I lighted my pipe and sat down on

---

[1] **surreptitiously** (sŭr′ĕp·tĭsh′ŭs·lĭ): secretly, stealthily.

a mossy bank to await developments.

In about half an hour I heard the bushes rustle, and Bill wabbled out into the little glade in front of the cave. Behind him was the kid, stepping softly like a scout, with a broad grin on his face. Bill stopped, took off his hat, and wiped his face with a red handkerchief. The kid stopped about eight feet behind him.

"Sam," says Bill, "I suppose you'll think I'm a renegade, but I couldn't help it. I'm a grown person with masculine proclivities[1] and habits of self-defense, but there is a time when all systems of egotism and predominance fail. The boy is gone. I have sent him home. All is off. There was martyrs in old times," goes on Bill, "that suffered death rather than give up the particular graft they enjoyed. None of 'em ever was subjugated to such supernatural tortures as I have been. I tried to be faithful to our articles of depredation,[2] but there came a limit."

"What's the trouble, Bill?" I asks him.

"I was rode," says Bill, "the ninety miles to the stockade, not barring an inch. Then, when the settlers was rescued, I was given oats. Sand ain't a palatable substitute. And then, for an hour I had to try to explain to him why there was nothin' in holes, how a road can run both ways, and what makes the grass green. I tell you, Sam, a human can only stand so much. I takes him by the neck of his clothes and drags him down the mountain. On the way he kicks my legs black-and-blue from the knees down; and I've got to have two or three bites on my thumb and hand cauterized.[3]

"But he's gone" — continues Bill —

[1] **proclivities** (prŏ·klĭv′ĭ·tĭz): natural traits.
[2] **depredation** (dĕp′rĕ·dā′shŭn): plundering.
[3] **cauterized** (kô′tĕr·īzd): burned with a hot iron or chemical to stop spread of infection.

"gone home. I showed him the road to Summit and kicked him about eight feet nearer there at one kick. I'm sorry we lose the ransom, but it was either that or Bill Driscoll to the madhouse."

Bill is puffing and blowing, but there is a look of ineffable peace and growing content on his rose-pink features.

"Bill," says I, "there isn't any heart disease in your family, is there?"

"No," says Bill, "nothing chronic except malaria and accidents. Why?"

"Then you might turn around," says I, "and have a look behind you."

Bill turns and sees the boy, and loses his complexion and sits down plump on the ground and begins to pluck aimlessly at grass and little sticks. For an hour I was afraid for his mind. And then I told him that my scheme was to put the whole job through immediately and that we would get the ransom and be off with it by midnight if old Dorset fell in with our proposition. So Bill braced up enough to give the kid a weak sort of a smile and a promise to play the Russian in a Japanese war with him as soon as he felt a little better.

I had a scheme for collecting that ransom without danger of being caught by counterplots that ought to commend itself to professional kidnapers. The tree under which the answer was to be left — and the money later on — was close to the road fence with big, bare fields on all sides. If a gang of constables should be watching for anyone to come for the note, they could see him a long way off crossing the fields or in the road. But no, siree! At half-past eight I was up in that tree as well hidden as a tree toad, waiting for the messenger to arrive.

Exactly on time, a half-grown boy rides up the road on a bicycle, locates the pasteboard box at the foot of the fence post, slips a folded piece of paper into it, and pedals away again back toward Summit.

I waited an hour and then concluded the thing was square. I slid down the tree, got the note, slipped along the fence till I struck the woods, and was back at the cave in another half an hour. I opened the note, got near the lantern, and read it to Bill. It was written with a pen in a crabbed hand, and the sum and substance of it was this:

TWO DESPERATE MEN.

Gentlemen: I received your letter today by post, in regard to the ransom you ask for the return of my son. I think you are a little high in your demands, and I hereby make you a counterproposition, which I am inclined to believe you will accept. You bring Johnny home and pay me two hundred and fifty dollars in cash, and I agree to take him off your hands. You had better come at night, for the neighbors believe he is lost, and I couldn't be responsible for what they would do to anybody they saw bringing him back.
Very respectfully,
EBENEZER DORSET.

"Great pirates of Penzance!" says I; "of all the impudent — "

But I glanced at Bill and hesitated. He had the most appealing look in his eyes I ever saw on the face of a dumb or a talking brute.

"Sam," says he, "what's two hundred and fifty dollars, after all? We've got the money. One more night of this kid will send me to a bed in Bedlam.[1] Besides being a thorough gentleman, I think Mr. Dorset is a spendthrift for making us such a liberal offer. You ain't going to let the chance go, are you?"

"Tell you the truth, Bill," says I, "this little he ewe lamb has somewhat got on my nerves too. We'll take him home,

¹ **Bedlam** (bĕd'lăm): a very early London hospital for lunatics; its correct name was Bethlehem.

pay the ransom, and make our getaway."

We took him home that night. We got him to go by telling him that his father had bought a silver-mounted rifle and a pair of moccasins for him, and we were going to hunt bears the next day.

It was just twelve o'clock when we knocked at Ebenezer's front door. Just at the moment when I should have been abstracting the fifteen hundred dollars from the box under the tree, according to the original proposition, Bill was counting out two hundred and fifty dollars into Dorset's hand.

When the kid found out we were going to leave him at home, he started up a howl like a calliope ² and fastened himself as tight as a leech to Bill's leg. His father peeled him away gradually, like a porous plaster.

"How long can you hold him?" asks Bill.

"I'm not as strong as I used to be," says old Dorset, "but I think I can promise you ten minutes."

"Enough," says Bill. "In ten minutes I shall cross the Central, Southern, and Middle Western States and be legging it trippingly for the Canadian border."

And, as dark as it was, and as fat as Bill was, and as good a runner as I am, he was a good mile and a half out of Summit before I could catch up with him.

² **calliope** (kă·lī'ô·pê): a mechanical organ with a shrill whistling sound. Sam probably pronounced it kăl'ĭ·ōp.

THINKING IT OVER

1. What signs tell you, early in the story, that the events are going to be funny rather than tragic?

2. The speech and writing of Sam and Bill are a strange mixture of educated

and uneducated usage. Find and read a few such passages. What is the author's purpose?

3. Set up the steps of the plot as a series of newspaper headlines, the first being "Two Men Kidnap Boy," perhaps followed by "Boy Bites Back." Try to capture the story's humor in your headlines.

4. Make a chalkboard list of the character traits of Ebenezer Dorset.

LOOKING AT IRONY

What a speech or a sentence seems to say and what it *really* says can be two different matters. "The day's beginning fine," you might remark, upon stubbing your toe as you get up in the morning. Actually, you mean the opposite of what you are saying. This is called *irony*. Irony — saying one thing but meaning another —is used extensively in literature. In this story, Sam and Bill sign the ransom note "Two Desperate Men." Can you explain the irony in their signature? Point out at least five other examples in the story where irony is used. How is the very plot of the story ironic in itself?

FOR YOUR VOCABULARY: WORD ORIGINS

The English language developed chiefly from Germanic beginnings, with the Angles and Saxons (two German tribes) giving it its first spoken form. Most of the words we use in our daily conversation come from Anglo-Saxon, yet perhaps 80 per cent of the words in an unabridged dictionary are borrowed from other languages.

Your dictionary probably lists at least these abbreviations for borrowed words: *Ar., AS., D., F., G., Gr., Heb., It., Jap., L., Per.,* and *Sp.* (see entry below).

mag′a·zine′ (măg′á·zēn′; *in sense* 4, *often* măg′á·zēn; 2), *n.* [F. *magasin*, through OF. & It., fr. Ar. *makhāzin*, pl. of *makhzan* storehouse, granary, cellar.] **1.** A warehouse, storehouse, or depot, esp. for military stores. **2. a** The room in which powder is kept in a fort or a ship. **b** A district rich in natural products. **c** A reservoir or supply chamber for a stove, battery, camera, or other apparatus. **d** A chamber in a gun for holding cartridges to be fed to the piece. **3.** The contents of a storehouse; as: **a** An accumulation of munitions of war. **b** A stock of provisions or goods. **4.** A periodical containing miscellaneous articles, stories, poems, etc. **5.** In France, a store, or shop.

Without looking them up, what languages do you think these refer to? (By the way, an *O.* in front of one of these means *Old,* and *M.* means *Middle,* and an *L.* means *Late; fr.* means *from.*)

Look up the following words — all appearing in the first ten paragraphs of the story — to see what languages they come from: *candy, cinnamon, clustered, dollars, forecloser, kitten, mortgage, project, rocks,* and *thousand.*

ABOUT THE AUTHOR

O. Henry (1862–1910), whose real name was William Sydney Porter, was one of America's most prolific and best-loved short story writers. He had a varied career that included a prison term on the charge of embezzling some money from a bank in which he had worked in Texas. The details of the case are not entirely clear, but there is some evidence that he may have been protecting another person. In any event it was during this period in prison that he seriously set about developing his skill as a writer of short stories and, while still behind bars, became famous.

More of O. Henry ➔

Depicted by artist Joseph Cellini on the opposite page are scenes from three other O. Henry stories — (*top*) "Mammon and the Archer," (*center*) "After Twenty Years," and (*bottom*) "The Last Leaf." Each of the three scenes has for its setting New York City, where O. Henry spent the last eight years of his life. The picturesque streets of Greenwich Village and Irving Place in the 1900's — this was the New York O. Henry came to know and cherish. It was a world made up of ordinary people — shopgirls, waiters, policemen, horse-cab drivers. He wrote about this world in many of his stories, along with the small-town South of "The Ransom of Red Chief" and the West, two other regions where he resided earlier in his life. A mixture of tragedy and comedy, with the unexpected always about to happen, the unique world of O. Henry is worth your further exploration.

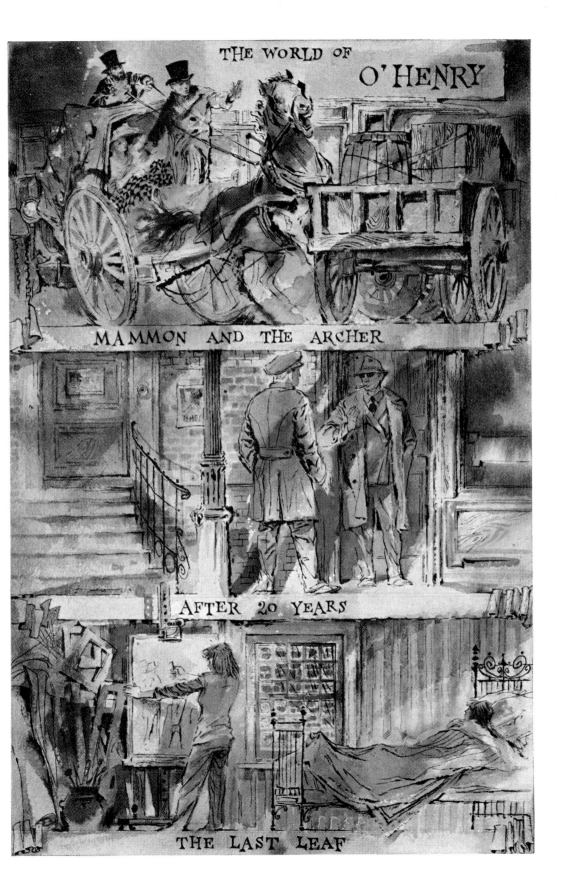

THE WORLD OF

O'HENRY

MAMMON AND THE ARCHER

AFTER 20 YEARS

THE LAST LEAF

The Adventure of the Dying Detective

SIR ARTHUR CONAN DOYLE

Today's detective stories generally have more violence in their plots and heroes who are frequently less admirable than the great Sherlock Holmes. But these stories owe much to Arthur Conan Doyle, the creator of Sherlock Holmes. Certainly there are no better-written "whodunits" nor a more intriguing hero than the man you are about to meet.

Mrs. Hudson, the landlady of Sherlock Holmes, was a long-suffering woman. Not only was her first-floor flat invaded at all hours by throngs of singular and often undesirable characters, but her remarkable lodger showed an eccentricity and irregularity in his life which must have sorely tried her patience. His incredible untidiness, his addiction to music at strange hours, his occasional revolver practice within doors, his weird and often malodorous scientific experiments, and the atmos-phere of violence and danger which hung around him made him the very worst tenant in London. On the other hand, his payments were princely. I have no doubt that the house might have been purchased at the price which Holmes paid for his rooms during the years that I was with him.

The landlady stood in the deepest awe of him, and never dared to interfere with him, however outrageous his proceedings might seem. She was fond of him, too, for he had a remarkable gentleness and courtesy in his dealings with women. He disliked and distrusted the sex, but he was always a chivalrous opponent. Knowing how genuine was her regard for him, I listened earnestly to her story when she came to my rooms in the second year of my married life and told me of the sad condition to which my poor friend was reduced.

"He's dying, Dr. Watson," said she.

Anticipating Outcome. The fun of a mystery story is, of course, in trying to guess the solution. To aid and at the same time to confuse you, the author provides clues, which he challenges the reader to piece together. Be on the alert for the clues Conan Doyle presents here; see if they lead you to the solution — or away from it!

"For three days he has been sinking, and I doubt if he will last the day. He would not let me get a doctor. This morning when I saw his bones sticking out of his face and his great bright eyes looking at me, I could stand no more of it. 'With your leave or without it, Mr. Holmes, I am going for a doctor this very hour,' said I. 'Let it be Watson, then,' said he. I wouldn't waste an hour in coming to him, sir, or you may not see him alive."

I was horrified, for I had heard nothing of his illness. I need not say that I rushed for my coat and my hat. As we drove back, I asked for the details.

"There is little I can tell you, sir. He has been working at a case down at Rotherhithe,[1] in an alley near the river, and he has brought this illness back with him. He took to his bed on Wednesday afternoon and has never moved since. For these three days neither food nor drink has passed his lips."

"Good grief! Why did you not call in a doctor?"

"He wouldn't have it, sir. You know how masterful he is. I didn't dare to disobey him. But he's not long for this world, as you'll see for yourself the moment that you set eyes on him."

He was indeed a deplorable spectacle. In the dim light of a foggy November day the sickroom was a gloomy spot, but it was that gaunt, wasted face staring at me from the bed which sent a chill to my heart. His eyes had the brightness of fever, there was a hectic flush upon either cheek, and dark crusts clung to his lips; the thin hands upon the coverlet twitched incessantly, his voice was croaking and spasmodic. He lay listlessly as I entered the room, but the sight of me brought a gleam of recognition to his eyes.

[1] **Rotherhithe** (rŏth′ĕr·hĭth): a district in southeast London near the docks.

"Well, Watson, we seem to have fallen upon evil days," said he, in a feeble voice, but with something of his old carelessness of manner.

"My dear fellow!" I cried, approaching him.

"Stand back! Stand right back!" said he, with the sharp imperiousness which I had associated only with moments of crisis. "If you approach me, Watson, I shall order you out of the house."

"But why?"

"Because it is my desire. Is that not enough?"

Yes, Mrs. Hudson was right. He was more masterful than ever. It was pitiful, however, to see his exhaustion.

"I only wished to help," I explained.

"Exactly! You will help best by doing what you are told."

"Certainly, Holmes."

He relaxed the austerity of his manner.

"You are not angry?" he asked, gasping for breath.

Poor devil, how could I be angry when I saw him lying in such a plight before me?

"It's for your own sake, Watson," he croaked.

"For my sake?"

"I know what is the matter with me. It is a coolie disease from Sumatra — a thing that the Dutch know more about than we, though they have made little of it up to date. One thing only is certain. It is infallibly deadly, and it is horribly contagious."

He spoke now with a feverish energy, the long hands twitching and jerking as he motioned me away.

"Contagious by touch, Watson — that's it, by touch. Keep your distance and all is well."

"Good heavens, Holmes! Do you suppose that such a consideration weighs with me for an instant? It would not affect me in the case of a stranger. Do you imagine it would prevent me from doing my duty to so old a friend?"

Again I advanced, but he repulsed me with a look of furious anger.

"If you will stand there, I will talk. If you do not, you must leave the room."

I have so deep a respect for the extraordinary qualities of Holmes that I have always deferred to his wishes, even when I least understood them. But now all my professional instincts were aroused. Let him be my master elsewhere, I at least was his in a sickroom.

"Holmes," said I, "you are not yourself. A sick man is but a child, and so I will treat you. Whether you like it or not, I will examine your symptoms and treat you for them."

He looked at me with venomous eyes.

"If I am to have a doctor whether I will or not, let me at least have someone in whom I have confidence," said he.

"Then you have none in me?"

"In your friendship, certainly. But facts are facts, Watson, and after all you are only a general practitioner with very limited experience and mediocre qualifications. It is painful to have to say these things, but you leave me no choice."

I was bitterly hurt.

"Such a remark is unworthy of you, Holmes. It shows me very clearly the state of your own nerves. But if you have no confidence in me, I would not intrude my services. Let me bring Sir Jasper Meek or Penrose Fisher, or any of the best men in London. But someone you must have, and that is final. If you think that I am going to stand here and see you die without either helping you myself or bringing anyone else to help you, then you have mistaken your man."

"You mean well, Watson," said the sick man, with something between a sob and a groan. "Shall I demonstrate your own ignorance? What do you know, pray, of Tapanuli [1] fever? What do you know of the black Formosa corruption?"

"I have never heard of either."

"There are many problems of disease, many strange pathological [2] possibilities, in the East, Watson." He paused after each sentence to collect his failing strength. "I have learned so much during some recent researches which have a medicocriminal aspect. It was in the course of them that I contracted this complaint. You can do nothing."

"Possibly not. But I happen to know that Dr. Ainstree, the greatest living authority upon tropical disease, is now in London. All remonstrance is useless, Holmes. I am going this instant to fetch him." I turned resolutely to the door.

Never have I had such a shock! In an instant, with a tiger-spring, the dying man had intercepted me. I heard the sharp snap of a twisted key. The next moment he had staggered back to his bed, exhausted and panting after his one tremendous outflame of energy.

"You won't take the key from me by force, Watson. I've got you, my friend. Here you are, and here you will stay until I will otherwise. But I'll humor you." (All this in little gasps, with terrible struggles for breath between.) "You've only my own good at heart. Of course I know that very well. You shall have your way, but give me time to get my strength. Not now, Watson; not now. It's four o'clock. At six you can go."

"This is insanity, Holmes."

"Only two hours, Watson. I promise you will go at six. Are you content to wait?"

[1] **Tapanuli** (tä'pä·nōō'lē): area in Sumatra.
[2] **pathological** (păth'ô·lŏj'ĭ·k*ă*l): disease-connected.

"I seem to have no choice."

"None in the world, Watson. Thank you, I need no help in arranging the clothes. You will please keep your distance. Now, Watson, there is one other condition that I would make. You will seek help, not from the man you mention, but from the one that I choose."

"By all means."

"The first three sensible words that you have uttered since you entered this room, Watson. You will find some books over there. I am somewhat exhausted; I wonder how a battery feels when it pours electricity into a nonconductor? At six, Watson, we resume our conversation."

But it was destined to be resumed long before that hour, and in circumstances which gave me a shock hardly second to that caused by his spring to the door. I had stood for some minutes looking at the silent figure in the bed. His face was almost covered by the clothes, and he appeared to be asleep. Then, unable to settle down to reading, I walked slowly round the room, examining the pictures of celebrated criminals with which every wall was adorned. Finally, in my aimless perambulation, I came to the mantelpiece. A litter of pipes, tobacco pouches, penknives, revolver cartridges, and other debris was scattered over it. In the midst of these was a small black and white ivory box with a sliding lid. It was a neat little thing, and I had stretched out my hand to examine it more closely, when —

It was a dreadful cry that he gave — a yell which might have been heard down the street. My skin went cold and my hair bristled at that horrible scream. As I turned, I caught a glimpse of a convulsed face and frantic eyes. I stood paralyzed, with the little box in my hand.

"Put it down! Down, this instant, Watson! This instant, I say!" His head sank back upon the pillow and he gave a deep sigh of relief as I replaced the box upon the mantelpiece. "I hate to have my things touched, Watson. You know that I hate it. You fidget me beyond endurance. You, a doctor — you are enough to drive a patient into an asylum. Sit down, man, and let me have my rest!"

The incident left a most unpleasant impression upon my mind. The violent and causeless excitement, followed by this brutality of speech, so far removed from his usual suavity, showed me how deep was the disorganization of his mind. Of all ruins, that of a noble mind is the most deplorable. I sat in silent dejection until the stipulated time had passed. He seemed to have been watching the clock as well as I, for it was hardly six before he began to talk with the same feverish animation as before.

"Now, Watson," said he. "Have you any change in your pocket?"

"Yes."

"Any silver?"

"A good deal."

"How many half-crowns?"

"I have five."

"Ah, too few! Too few! How very unfortunate, Watson! However, such as they are, you can put them in your watch pocket. And all the rest of your money in your left trouser pocket. Thank you. It will balance you so much better like that."

This was raving insanity. He shuddered and again made a sound between a cough and a sob.

"You will now light the gas, Watson, but you will be very careful that not for one instant shall it be more than half on. I implore you to be careful, Watson. Thank you, that is excellent.

No, you need not draw the blind. Now you will have the kindness to place some letters and papers upon this table within my reach. Thank you. Now some of that litter from the mantelpiece. Excellent, Watson! There is a sugar tongs there. Kindly raise that small ivory box with its assistance. Place it here among the papers. Good! You can now go and fetch Mr. Culverton Smith, of 13, Lower Burke Street."

To tell the truth, my desire to fetch a doctor had somewhat weakened, for poor Holmes was so obviously delirious that it seemed dangerous to leave him. However, he was as eager now to consult the person named as he had been obstinate in refusing.

"I never heard the name," said I.

"Possibly not, my good Watson. It may surprise you to know that the man upon earth who is best versed in this disease is not a medical man, but a planter. Mr. Culverton Smith is a well-known resident of Sumatra, now visiting London. An outbreak of the disease upon his plantation, which was distant from medical aid, caused him to study it himself, with some rather far-reaching consequences. He is a very methodical person, and I did not desire you to start before six because I was well aware that you would not find him in his study. If you could persuade him to come here and give us the benefit of his unique experience of this disease, the investigation of which has been his dearest hobby, I cannot doubt that he could help me."

I give Holmes's remarks as a consecutive whole, and will not attempt to indicate how they were interrupted by gaspings for breath and those clutchings of his hands which indicated the pain from which he was suffering. His appearance had changed for the worse during the few hours that I had been with him. Those hectic spots were more pronounced, the eyes shone more brightly out of darker hollows, and a cold sweat glimmered upon his brow. He still retained, however, the jaunty gallantry of his speech. To the last gasp he would always be the master.

"You will tell him exactly how you have left me," said he. "You will convey the very impression which is in your own mind — a dying man — a dying and delirious man. Indeed, I cannot think why the whole bed of the ocean is not one solid mass of oysters, so prolific the creatures seem. Ah, I am wandering! Strange how the brain controls the brain! What was I saying, Watson?"

"My directions for Mr. Culverton Smith."

"Ah, yes, I remember. My life depends upon it. Plead with him, Watson. There is no good feeling between us. His nephew, Watson — I had suspicions of foul play and I allowed him to see it. The boy died horribly. He has a grudge against me. You will soften him, Watson. Beg him, pray him, get him here by any means. He can save me — only he!"

"I will bring him in a cab, if I have to carry him down to it."

"You will do nothing of the sort. You will persuade him to come. And then you will return in front of him. Make any excuse so as not to come with him. Don't forget, Watson. You won't fail me. You never did fail me. No doubt there are natural enemies which limit the increase of the creatures. You and I, Watson, we have done our part. Shall the world, then, be overrun by oysters? No, no; horrible! You'll convey all that is in your mind."

I left him full of the image of this magnificent intellect babbling like a foolish child. He had handed me the key, and with a happy thought I took it with me lest he should lock himself in. Mrs. Hudson was waiting, trembling and weeping, in the passage. Behind me as I passed from the flat I heard Holmes's high, thin voice in some delirious chant. Below, as I stood whistling for a cab, a man came on me through the fog.

"How is Mr. Holmes, sir?" he asked.

It was an old acquaintance, Inspector Morton, of Scotland Yard, dressed in unofficial tweeds.

"He is very ill," I answered.

He looked at me in a most singular fashion. Had it not been too fiendish, I could have imagined that the gleam of the fanlight showed exultation in his face.

"I heard some rumor of it," said he.

The cab had driven up, and I left him.

Lower Burke Street proved to be a line of fine houses lying in the vague borderland between Notting Hill and Kensington.[1] The particular one at which my cabman pulled up had an air of smug and demure respectability in its old-fashioned iron railings, its massive folding door, and its shining brasswork. All was in keeping with a solemn butler who appeared framed in the pink radiance of a tinted electric light behind him.

"Yes, Mr. Culverton Smith is in. Dr. Watson! Very good, sir, I will take up your card."

My humble name and title did not appear to impress Mr. Culverton Smith. Through the half-open door I heard a high, petulant, penetrating voice.

"Who is this person? What does he want? Dear me, Staples, how often have I said that I am not to be disturbed in my hours of study?"

There came a gentle flow of soothing explanation from the butler.

"Well, I won't see him, Staples. I can't have my work interrupted like this. I am not at home. Say so. Tell him to come in the morning if he really must see me."

Again the gentle murmur.

"Well, well, give him that message. He can come in the morning, or he can stay away. My work must not be hindered."

I thought of Holmes tossing upon his bed of sickness and counting the minutes, perhaps, until I could bring help to him. It was not a time to stand upon ceremony. His life depended upon my promptness. Before the apologetic butler had delivered his message, I had pushed past him and was in the room.

With a shrill cry of anger a man rose from a reclining chair beside the fire. I saw a great yellow face, coarse-grained and greasy, with heavy double chin, and two sullen, menacing gray eyes which glared at me from under tufted and sandy brows. A high bald head had a small velvet smoking-cap poised coquettishly upon one side of its pink curve. The skull was of enormous capacity, and yet as I looked down I saw to my amazement that the figure of the man was small and frail, twisted in the shoulders and back like one who has suffered from rickets in his childhood.

"What's this?" he cried, in a high, screaming voice. "What is the meaning of this intrusion? Didn't I send you word that I would see you tomorrow morning?"

"I am sorry," said I, "but the matter cannot be delayed. Mr. Sherlock Holmes — "

The mention of my friend's name had an extraordinary effect upon the little man. The look of anger passed in an

[1] **Notting Hill** and **Kensington** (kĕn'zĭng-tŭn): two neighboring districts in the northwest of London.

instant from his face. His features became tense and alert.

"Have you come from Holmes?" he asked.

"I have just left him."

"What about Holmes? How is he?"

"He is desperately ill. That is why I have come."

The man motioned me to a chair and turned to resume his own. As he did so, I caught a glimpse of his face in the mirror over the mantelpiece. I could have sworn that it was set in a malicious and abominable smile. Yet I persuaded myself that it must have been some nervous contraction which I had surprised, for he turned to me an instant later with genuine concern upon his features.

"I am sorry to hear this," said he. "I only know Mr. Holmes through some business dealings which we have had, but I have every respect for his talents and his character. He is an amateur of crime, as I am of disease. For him the villain, for me the microbe. There are my prisons," he continued, pointing to a row of bottles and jars which stood upon a side table. "Among those gelatine cultivations some of the very worst offenders in the world are now doing time."

"It was on account of your special knowledge that Mr. Holmes desired to see you. He has a high opinion of you, and thought that you were the one man in London who could help him."

The little man started, and the jaunty smoking-cap slid to the floor.

"Why?" he asked. "Why should Mr. Holmes think that I could help him in his trouble?"

"Because of your knowledge of Eastern diseases."

"But why should he think that this disease which he has contracted is Eastern?"

"Because, in some professional inquiry, he has been working among Chinese sailors down in the docks."

Mr. Culverton Smith smiled pleasantly and picked up his smoking-cap.

"Oh, that's it — is it?" said he. "I trust the matter is not so grave as you suppose. How long has he been ill?"

"About three days."

"Is he delirious?"

"Occasionally."

"Tut, tut! This sounds serious. It would be inhuman not to answer his call. I very much resent any interruption to my work, Dr. Watson, but this case is certainly exceptional. I will come with you at once."

I remembered Holmes's injunction.[1]

"I have another appointment," said I.

"Very good. I will go alone. I have a note of Mr. Holmes's address. You can rely upon my being there within half an hour at most."

It was with a sinking heart that I reentered Holmes's bedroom. For all that I knew the worst might have happened in my absence. To my enormous relief, he had improved greatly in the interval. His appearance was as ghastly as ever, but all trace of delirium had left him. He spoke in a feeble voice, it is

[1] **injunction:** order or command.

true, but with even more than his usual crispness and lucidity.

"Well, did you see him, Watson?"

"Yes; he is coming."

"Admirable, Watson! Admirable! You are the best of messengers."

"He wished to return with me."

"That would never do, Watson. That would be obviously impossible. Did he ask what ailed me?"

"I told him about the Chinese in the East End."

"Exactly! Well, Watson, you have done all that a good friend could. You can now disappear from the scene."

"I must wait and hear his opinion, Holmes."

"Of course you must. But I have reasons to suppose that this opinion would be very much more frank and valuable if he imagines that we are alone. There is just room behind the head of my bed, Watson."

"My dear Holmes!"

"I fear there is no alternative, Watson. The room does not lend itself to concealment, which is as well, as it is the less likely to arouse suspicion. But just there, Watson, I fancy that it could be done." Suddenly he sat up with a rigid intentness upon his haggard face. "There are the wheels, Watson. Quick, man, if you love me! And don't budge, whatever happens — whatever happens, do you hear? Don't speak! Don't move! Just listen with all your ears." Then in an instant his sudden access of strength departed, and his masterful, purposeful talk droned away into the low, vague murmurings of a semidelirious man.

From the hiding place into which I had been so swiftly hustled, I heard the footfalls upon the stair, with the opening and the closing of the bedroom door. Then, to my surprise, there came a long silence, broken only by the heavy breathings and gaspings of the sick man. I could imagine that our visitor was standing by the bedside and looking down at the sufferer. At last that strange hush was broken.

"Holmes!" he cried. "Holmes!" in the insistent tone of one who awakens a sleeper. "Can't you hear me, Holmes?" There was a rustling, as if he had shaken the sick man roughly by the shoulder.

"Is that you, Mr. Smith?" Holmes whispered. "I hardly dared hope that you would come."

The other laughed.

"I should imagine not," he said. "And yet, you see, I am here. Coals of fire, Holmes — coals of fire!"

"It is very good of you — very noble of you. I appreciate your special knowledge."

Our visitor sniggered.

"You do. You are, fortunately, the only man in London who does. Do you know what is the matter with you?"

"The same," said Holmes.

"Ah! You recognize the symptoms?"

"Only too well."

"Well, I shouldn't be surprised, Holmes. I shouldn't be surprised if it were the same. A bad look-out for you if it is. Poor Victor was a dead man on the fourth day — a strong, hearty young fellow. It was certainly, as you said, very surprising that he should have contracted an out-of-the-way Asiatic disease in the heart of London — a disease, too, of which I had made such a very special study. Singular coincidence, Holmes. Very smart of you to notice it, but rather uncharitable to suggest that it was cause and effect."

"I knew that you did it."

"Oh, you did, did you? Well, you couldn't prove it, anyhow. But what do you think of yourself spreading reports about me like that, and then crawling to me for help the moment you are in trouble? What sort of a game is that — eh?"

I heard the rasping, labored breathing of the sick man. "Give me the water!" he gasped.

"You're precious near your end, my friend, but I don't want you to go till I have had a word with you. That's why I give you water. There, don't slop it about! That's right. Can you understand what I say?"

Holmes groaned.

"Do what you can for me. Let bygones be bygones," he whispered. "I'll put the words out of my head — I swear I will. Only cure me, and I'll forget it."

"Forget what?"

"Well, about Victor Savage's death. You as good as admitted just now that you had done it. I'll forget it."

"You can forget it or remember it, just as you like. I don't see you in the witness box. Quite another shaped box, my good Holmes, I assure you. It matters nothing to me that you should know how my nephew died. It's not him we are talking about. It's you."

"Yes, yes."

"The fellow who came for me— I've forgotten his name — said that you contracted it down in the East End among the sailors."

"I could only account for it so."

"You are proud of your brains, Holmes, are you not? Think yourself smart, don't you? You came across someone who was smarter this time. Now cast your mind back, Holmes. Can you think of no other way you could have got this thing?"

"I can't think. My mind is gone. For Heaven's sake, help me!"

"Yes, I will help you. I'll help you to understand just where you are and how you got there. I'd like you to know before you die."

"Give me something to ease my pain."

"Painful, is it? Yes, the coolies used to do some squealing toward the end. Takes you as cramp, I fancy."

"Yes, yes; it is cramp."

"Well, you can hear what I say, anyhow. Listen now! Can you remember any unusual incident in your life just about the time your symptoms began?"

"No, no; nothing."

"Think again."

"I'm too ill to think."

"Well, then, I'll help you. Did anything come by post?"

"By post?"

"A box, by chance?"

"I'm fainting — I'm gone!"

"Listen, Holmes!" There was a sound as if he was shaking the dying man, and it was all that I could do to hold myself quiet in my hiding place. "You must hear me. You shall hear me. Do you remember a box — an ivory box? It came on Wednesday. You opened it — Do you remember?"

"Yes, yes, I opened it. There was a sharp spring inside it. Some joke— "

"It was no joke, as you will find to your cost. You fool, you would have it, and you have got it. Who asked you to cross my path? If you had left me alone, I would not have hurt you."

"I remember," Holmes gasped. "The spring! It drew blood. This box — this on the table."

"The very one, by George! And it may as well leave the room in my pocket. There goes your last shred of evidence. But you have the truth now, Holmes, and you can die with the knowledge that I killed you. You knew too much of the fate of Victor Savage, so I have sent you to share it. You are very near your end, Holmes. I will sit here and I will watch you die."

Holmes's voice had sunk to an almost inaudible whisper.

"What is that?" said Smith. "Turn up the gas? Ah, the shadows begin to fall, do they? Yes, I will turn it up, that I may see you the better." He crossed the room and the light suddenly brightened. "Is there any other little service that I can do you, my friend?"

"A match and a cigarette."

I nearly called out in my joy and my amazement. He was speaking in his natural voice — a little weak, perhaps, but the very voice I knew. There was a long pause, and I felt that Culverton Smith was standing in silent amazement looking down at his companion.

"What's the meaning of this?" I heard him say at last, in a dry, rasping tone.

"The best way of successfully acting a part is to be it," said Holmes. "I give you my word that for three days I have tasted neither food nor drink until you were good enough to pour me out that glass of water. But it is the tobacco which I find most irksome. Ah, here are some cigarettes." I heard the striking of a match. "That is very much better. Halloa! Halloa! Do I hear the step of a friend?"

There were footfalls outside, the door opened, and Inspector Morton appeared.

"All is in order and this is your man," said Holmes.

The officer gave the usual cautions.

"I arrest you on the charge of the murder of one Victor Savage," he concluded.

"And you might add of the attempted murder of one Sherlock Holmes," remarked my friend with a chuckle. "To save an invalid trouble, inspector, Mr. Culverton Smith was good enough to give our signal by turning up the gas. By the way, the prisoner has a small box in the right-hand pocket of his coat which it would be as well to remove. Thank you. I would handle it gingerly if I were you. Put it down here. It may play its part in the trial."

There was a sudden rush and a scuffle, followed by the clash of iron and a cry of pain.

"You'll only get yourself hurt," said the inspector. "Stand still, will you?" There was the click of the closing handcuffs.

"A nice trap!" cried the high, snarling voice. "It will bring you into the dock, Holmes, not me. He asked me to come here to cure him. I was sorry for him and I came. Now he will pretend, no doubt, that I have said anything which he may invent which will corroborate his insane suspicions. You can lie as you like, Holmes. My word is always as good as yours."

"Good heavens!" cried Holmes. "I had totally forgotten him. My dear Watson, I owe you a thousand apologies. To think that I should have overlooked you! I need not introduce you to Mr. Culverton Smith, since I understand that you met somewhat earlier in the evening. Have you the cab below? I will follow you when I am dressed, for I may be of some use at the station.

"I never needed it more," said Holmes, as he refreshed himself with a glass of claret and some biscuits in the intervals of his toilet. "However, as you know, my habits are irregular, and such a feat means less to me than to most men. It was very essential that I should impress Mrs. Hudson with the reality of my condition, since she was to convey it to you, and you in turn to him. You won't be offended, Watson? You will realize that among your many talents dissimulation [1] finds no place, and that if you had shared my secret, you would never have been able to impress Smith with the urgent necessity of his presence, which was the vital point of the whole scheme. Knowing his vindictive nature, I was perfectly certain that he would come to look upon his handiwork."

"But your appearance, Holmes — your ghastly face?"

"Three days of absolute fast does not improve one's beauty, Watson. For the rest, there is nothing which a sponge may not cure. With Vaseline upon one's forehead, belladonna [2] in one's eyes, rouge over the cheekbones, and crusts of beeswax round one's lips, a very satisfying effect can be produced. Malingering [3] is a subject upon which I have sometimes thought of writing a monograph. [4] A little occasional talk about half-crowns, oysters, or any other extraneous subject produces a pleasing effect of delirium."

"But why would you not let me near you, since there was in truth no infection?"

"Can you ask, my dear Watson? Do you imagine that I have no respect for your medical talents? Could I fancy that your astute judgment would pass a dying man who, however weak, had no rise of pulse or temperature? At four yards, I could deceive you. If I failed to do so, who would bring my Smith within my grasp? No, Watson, I would not touch that box. You can just see if you look at it sideways where the sharp spring like a viper's tooth emerges as

you open it. I dare say it was some such device that poor Savage, who stood between this monster and a reversion, [5] was done to death. My correspondence, however, is, as you know, a varied one, and I am somewhat upon my guard against any packages which reach me. It was clear to me, however, that by pretending that he had really succeeded in his design I might surprise a confession. That pretense I have carried out with the thoroughness of the true artist. Thank you, Watson; you must help me on with my coat. When we have finished at the police station, I think that something nutritious at Simpson's would not be out of place."

[5] **reversion** (rē·vûr′shŭn): return of an estate.

THINKING IT OVER

1. What do the first two paragraphs of the story tell you about the character of Sherlock Holmes? Give at least six of the details which create the vivid picture of him.

2. The same two paragraphs provide no description of Watson, yet his character is also established. How does he listen to the landlady's story? What does this suggest about him as a whole?

3. Make a chalkboard list of as many characteristics of Holmes and Watson as you can provide, based on the story. Which of the two would you rather have for a friend of the family. Why?

4. A good detective story makes skillful use of setting and atmosphere to build an air of mystery. Consider this sentence from the story: "In the dim light of a foggy November day the sickroom was a gloomy spot. . . ." Find other descriptive passages which you think create a mood.

5. This story would make an ideal television play. Make an outline for the script by listing the different scenes and the characters in them. *Scene I*, for example, would read: *Watson's apartment. Mrs. Hudson and Watson.*

[1] **dissimulation** (dǐ·sǐm′ů·lā′shŭn): deception, pretending.
[2] **belladonna** (běl′à·dǒn′à): a drug which causes the pupil of the eye to dilate or enlarge.
[3] **malingering** (má·lǐng′gēr·ǐng): pretending illness to avoid work.
[4] **monograph** (mǒn′ō·grȧf): a scientific paper or article.

ANTICIPATING OUTCOME

1. Explain what the following clues may have led you to deduce about the plot: (a) Holmes's refusal to see a doctor, despite his condition; (b) his refusal to let Watson examine him; (c) the ivory box.

2. When Watson discovers Inspector Morton outside Holmes's door, he almost imagines that Morton's face shows exultation on learning of Holmes's "illness." What are the implications that you read into this?

3. List the other important clues given prior to the solution. Explain whether you think these clues were cleverly handled. Did you guess the solution, and, if so, what tipped you off?

4. A favorite scheme of a detective is to bait a trap for a suspected criminal. What is unusual about the bait in this trap?

5. Why could Holmes himself not arrest Culverton Smith? And why was Watson's hidden presence necessary?

USING CONTEXT CLUES

Even though you may speak only one language, you have *three* vocabularies. They consist of the words you use in speaking, writing, and reading, and they are all quite different. You can understand many words that you read which you would normally not use in your conversation or writing. In reading, you can find the meaning of a word by examining the words around it, which make up the sentence or passage; that is, you can study the word in its particular *context*.

For example, you are familiar with *singular* and *plural* nouns, but what does *singular* mean in the context of the second sentence of this story? In the third sentence, what is the meaning of *malodorous*? Study the context of the sentence before you decide. By using context clues where possible, you can add to your working vocabulary.

ABOUT THE AUTHOR

Sir Arthur Conan Doyle (1859–1930) drew upon his study of medicine in many of his stories. He was a doctor who was chiefly interested in writing; when he needed a foil for his great detective, Sherlock Holmes, he created a fictitious doctor to "tell" all the stories. Within a few years these stories became popular all over the world. When the author grew weary of inventing new mysteries for his hero to solve and let him "die," the public clamor was such that he had to bring Holmes back to life again! Conan Doyle was by no means the first writer of detective stories — some notable ones had been written before he was born — but his name is most often credited with the growth of this kind of story. He also wrote novels, plays, and historical books. If you like stories of knighthood in the time of the Crusades, you will enjoy *The White Company*.

RELATING THE STORIES

1. One of the main requirements for a good plot is conflict. To have conflict, there must be "opposing forces" present in a story. For example, the opposing forces in "Dive Right In" might be listed as "John's stage fright versus Skeets's use of psychology." Can you state the opposing forces in the other stories in this group?

2. Select from the group the story you enjoyed most and explain the reasons for your choice. What did you like about its plot?

The World of Sherlock Holmes

Conan Doyle wrote a total of fifty-six stories and four full-length novels about Sherlock Holmes. The fictitious world created in these works has become for many readers as real as if Holmes himself — called by one critic "the most famous character in English literature" — had actually lived. Today, visitors to London still ask to be shown "221–B" Baker Street, the mythical address assigned the detective by Conan Doyle. On the following pages are London scenes that have become associated with the world of Sherlock Holmes.

Holmes's London

Shown above is Scotland Yard, a place much "visited" by Sherlock Holmes; below is a view of the dock area in London's East End, a district referred to in "The Adventure of the Dying Detective."

On exhibit in London is Holmes's living room, above, reconstructed from descriptions given by Conan Doyle in the stories.

A view of Wyndham Place ▶ — just around the corner from "221–B" Baker Street.

Character and Setting: People and Places

The elements of character and setting can have varying importance in short stories. A story may have an engrossing plot, one in which the incidents and events involve the reader fully and cause him anxiously to await the outcome. The same story, however, can sometimes possess another element which proves to be even more absorbing. A character in the story will become so interesting to the reader that the plot assumes a secondary importance. Perhaps the author of the story has made the character especially unusual or amusing or remarkably real; or the character might be so appealing that the reader's sympathy and concern are strongly aroused. Things happen in the story because of this character; the action and plot of the story all seem to grow out of the character's traits and behavior. The reader finds that the character dominates the story; without this particular character, behaving in this particular manner, there would *be* no story. As the story progresses, the reader is concerned about how it will end, but mostly about how the ending will affect this character. And long after the story is finished, it will be the character — the fictitious person brought vividly to life by the author — that the reader will remember and think about. There are many stories of this kind, in which *character* becomes the most significant element. You will find examples of such stories in this next group of selections.

The element of *setting* — the time and place of a story — can also be of high importance. A story's setting can perform many functions. It can explain much about the behavior of a character in a story. In real life, the climate or conditions of a particular region — extreme heat or cold, for example, or rough, mountainous terrain — will partially determine the way in which the people of that region live. The characters in a story can be similarly affected by setting. An example of this is "The Long Winter," a story in this group; here, the character of Ralph McKeever has been largely shaped by the harsh demands of life on a Colorado ranch. Sometimes, the action of a story could not have occurred in any other time or place; then setting performs an even more vital function. "The Dog of Pompeii," another selection in this group, is an illustration of such a story. Neither the time period nor the setting of "The Dog of Pompeii" could be changed; the entire story is dependent on the element of setting.

A high school girl afraid of being jobless, a young African tribesman and the wise lion he challenges in combat — these are some of the other characters you will meet in these stories. And you will see, too, the key role played by setting in each story.

The Dog of Pompeii

LOUIS UNTERMEYER

Writers often go far beyond the borders of their own country or time for the setting and characters of a story. These elements then require research and imagination to make them believable and real. Here is such a story about a dog and a boy, set in the ancient city of Pompeii just before its destruction by earthquake and volcano in A.D. 79.

Tito and his dog Bimbo lived (if you could call it living) under the wall where it joined the inner gate. They really didn't live there; they just slept there. They lived anywhere. Pompeii [1] was one of the gayest of the old Latin towns, but although Tito was never an unhappy boy, he was not exactly a merry one. The streets were always lively with shining chariots and bright red trappings; the open-air theaters rocked with laughing crowds; sham battles and athletic sports were free for the asking in the great stadium. Once a year the Caesar [2] visited the pleasure city and the fireworks lasted for days; the sacrifices in the Forum were better than a show.

But Tito saw none of these things. He was blind — had been blind from birth. He was known to everyone in the poorer quarters. But no one could say how old he was, no one remembered his parents, no one could tell where he came from. Bimbo was another mystery. As long as people could remember seeing Tito — about twelve or thirteen years — they had seen Bimbo. Bimbo had never left his side. He was not only dog, but nurse, pillow, playmate, mother and father to Tito.

Did I say Bimbo never left his master? (Perhaps I had better say comrade, for if anyone was the master, it was Bimbo.) I was wrong. Bimbo did trust Tito alone exactly three times a day. It was a fixed routine, a custom understood between boy and dog since the beginning of their friendship, and the way it worked was this: Early in the morning, shortly after dawn, while

[1] **Pompeii** (pŏm·pā′ē): an ancient Italian city near Mount Vesuvius.

[2] **Caesar** (sē′zēr): the title given to the ruler of the Roman Empire.

Tito was still dreaming, Bimbo would disappear. When Tito awoke, Bimbo would be sitting quietly at his side, his ears cocked, his stump of a tail tapping the ground, and a fresh-baked bread — more like a large round roll — at his feet. Tito would stretch himself; Bimbo would yawn; then they would breakfast. At noon, no matter where they happened to be, Bimbo would put his paw on Tito's knee and the two of them would return to the inner gate. Tito would curl up in the corner (almost like a dog) and go to sleep, while Bimbo, looking quite important (almost like a boy), would disappear again. In half an hour he'd be back with their lunch. Sometimes it would be a piece of fruit or a scrap of meat, often it was nothing but a dry crust. But sometimes there would be one of those flat rich cakes, sprinkled with raisins and sugar, that Tito liked so much. At suppertime the same thing happened, although there was a little less of everything, for things were hard to snatch in the evening with the streets full of people. Besides, Bimbo didn't approve of too much food before going to sleep. A heavy supper made boys too restless and dogs too stodgy — and it was the business of a dog to sleep lightly with one ear open and muscles ready for action.

But, whether there was much or little, hot or cold, fresh or dry, food was always there. Tito never asked where it came from and Bimbo never told him. There was plenty of rain water in the hollows of soft stones; the old egg woman at the corner sometimes gave him a cupful of strong goat's milk; in the grape season the fat wine maker let him have drippings of the mild juice. So there was no danger of going hungry or thirsty. There was plenty of everything in Pompeii — if you knew where to find it — and if you had a dog like Bimbo.

As I said before, Tito was not the merriest boy in Pompeii. He could not romp with the other youngsters and play Hare-and-Hounds and I-Spy and Follow-Your-Master and Ball-Against-the-Building and Jackstones and Kings-and-Robbers with them. But that did not make him sorry for himself. If he could not see the sights that delighted the lads of Pompeii, he could hear and smell things they never noticed. He could really see more with his ears and nose than they could with their eyes. When he and Bimbo went out walking, he knew just where they were going and exactly what was happening.

"Ah," he'd sniff and say, as they passed a handsome villa,[1] "Glaucus Pansa is giving a grand dinner tonight. They're going to have three kinds of bread, and roast pigling, and stuffed goose, and a great stew — I think bear stew — and a fig pie." And Bimbo would note that this would be a good place to visit tomorrow.

Or, "H'm," Tito would murmur, half through his lips, half through his nostrils. "The wife of Marcus Lucretius is expecting her mother. She's shaking out every piece of goods in the house; she's going to use the best clothes — the ones she's been keeping in pine needles and camphor — and there's an extra girl in the kitchen. Come, Bimbo, let's get out of the dust!"

Or, as they passed a small but elegant dwelling opposite the public baths, "Too bad! The tragic poet is ill again. It must be a bad fever this time, for they're trying smoke fumes instead of medicine. Whew! I'm glad I'm not a tragic poet!"

Or, as they neared the Forum,

[1] villa (vĭl'á): a large house.

"Mm-m! What good things they have in the Macellum today!" (It really was a sort of butcher-grocer-market place, but Tito didn't know any better. He called it the Macellum.) "Dates from Africa, and salt oysters from sea caves, and cuttlefish, and new honey, and sweet onions, and — ugh! — water-buffalo steaks. Come, let's see what's what in the Forum." And Bimbo, just as curious as his comrade, hurried on. Being a dog, he trusted his ears and nose (like Tito) more than his eyes. And so the two of them entered the center of Pompeii.

The Forum was the part of the town to which everybody came at least once during the day. It was the Central Square, and everything happened here. There were no private houses; all was public — the chief temples, the gold and red bazaars, the silk shops, the town hall, the booths belonging to the weavers and jewel merchants, the wealthy woolen market, the shrine of the household gods. Everything glittered here. The buildings looked as if they were new — which, in a sense, they were. The earthquake of twelve years ago had brought down all the old stuctures and, since the citizens of Pompeii were ambitious to rival Naples and even Rome, they had seized the opportunity to rebuild the whole town. And they had done it all within a dozen years. There was scarcely a building that was older than Tito.

Tito had heard a great deal about the earthquake, though being about a year old at the time, he could scarcely remember it. This particular quake had been a light one — as earthquakes go. The weaker houses had been shaken down, parts of the outworn wall had been wrecked; but there was little loss of life, and the brilliant new Pompeii had taken the place of the old. No one

knew what caused these earthquakes. Records showed they had happened in the neighborhood since the beginning of time. Sailors said that it was to teach the lazy city folk a lesson and make them appreciate those who risked the dangers of the sea to bring them luxuries and protect their town from invaders. The priests said that the gods took this way of showing their anger to those who refused to worship properly and who failed to bring enough sacrifices to the altars and (though they didn't say it in so many words) presents to the priests. The tradesmen said that the foreign merchants had corrupted the ground and it was no longer safe to traffic in imported goods that came from strange places and carried a curse with them. Everyone had a different explanation and everyone's explanation was louder and sillier than his neighbor's.

They were talking about it this afternoon as Tito and Bimbo came out of the side street into the public square. The

Forum was the favorite promenade for rich and poor. What with the priests arguing with the politicians, servants doing the day's shopping, tradesmen crying their wares, women displaying the latest fashions from Greece and Egypt, children playing hide-and-seek among the marble columns, knots of soldiers, sailors, peasants from the provinces — to say nothing of those who merely came to lounge and look on — the square was crowded to its last inch. His ears even more than his nose guided Tito to the place where the talk was loudest. It was in front of the Shrine of the Household Gods that, naturally enough, the householders were arguing.

"I tell you," rumbled a voice which Tito recognized as bath master Rufus', "there won't be another earthquake in my lifetime or yours. There may be a tremble or two, but earthquakes, like lightnings, never strike twice in the same place."

"Do they not?" asked a thin voice Tito had never heard. It had a high,

sharp ring to it and Tito knew it as the accent of a stranger. "How about the two towns of Sicily that have been ruined three times within fifteen years by the eruptions of Mount Etna? And were they not warned? And does that column of smoke above Vesuvius mean nothing?"

"That?" Tito could hear the grunt with which one question answered another. "That's always there. We use it for our weather guide. When the smoke stands up straight, we know we'll have fair weather; when it flattens out, it's sure to be foggy; when it drifts to the east — "

"Yes, yes," cut in the edged voice. "I've heard about your mountain barometer. But the column of smoke seems hundreds of feet higher than usual and it's thickening and spreading like a shadowy tree. They say in Naples — "

"Oh, Naples!" Tito knew this voice by the little squeak that went with it. It was Attilio the cameo cutter. "They talk while we suffer. Little help we got from them last time. Naples commits the crimes and Pompeii pays the price. It's become a proverb with us. Let them mind their own business."

"Yes," grumbled Rufus, "and others', too."

"Very well, my confident friends," responded the thin voice which now sounded curiously flat. "We also have a proverb — and it is this: *Those who will not listen to men must be taught by the gods.* I say no more. But I leave a last warning. Remember the holy ones. Look to your temples. And when the smoke tree above Vesuvius grows to the shape of an umbrella pine, look to your lives."

Tito could hear the air whistle as the speaker drew his toga about him and the quick shuffle of feet told him the stranger had gone.

"Now what," said the cameo cutter, "did he mean by that?"

"I wonder," grunted Rufus. "I wonder."

Tito wondered, too. And Bimbo, his head at a thoughtful angle, looked as if he had been doing a heavy piece of pondering. By nightfall the argument had been forgotten. If the smoke had increased, no one saw it in the dark. Besides, it was Caesar's birthday and the town was in holiday mood. Tito and Bimbo were among the merrymakers, dodging the charioteers who shouted at them. A dozen times they almost upset baskets of sweets and jars of Vesuvian wine, said to be as fiery as the streams inside the volcano, and a dozen times they were cursed and cuffed. But Tito never missed his footing. He was thankful for his keen ears and quick instinct — most thankful of all for Bimbo.

They visited the uncovered theater and, though Tito could not see the faces of the actors, he could follow the play better than most of the audience, for their attention wandered — they were distracted by the scenery, the costumes, the byplay, even by themselves — while Tito's whole attention was centered in what he heard. Then to the city walls, where the people of Pompeii watched a mock naval battle in which the city was attacked by the sea and saved after thousands of flaming arrows had been exchanged and countless colored torches had been burned. Though the thrill of flaring ships and lighted skies was lost to Tito, the shouts and cheers excited him as much as any and he cried out with the loudest of them.

The next morning there were two of the beloved raisin and sugar cakes for his breakfast. Bimbo was unusually active and thumped his bit of a tail until Tito was afraid he would wear it out. The boy could not imagine whether Bimbo was urging him to some sort of game or was trying to tell something. After a while, he ceased to notice Bimbo. He felt drowsy. Last night's late hours had tired him. Besides, there was a heavy mist in the air — no, a thick fog rather than a mist — a fog that got into his throat and scraped it and made him cough. He walked as far as the marine gate to get a breath of the sea. But the blanket of haze had spread all over the bay and even the salt air seemed smoky.

He went to bed before dusk and slept. But he did not sleep well. He had too many dreams — dreams of ships lurching in the Forum, of losing his way in a screaming crowd, of armies marching across his chest, of being pulled over every rough pavement of Pompeii.

He woke early. Or, rather, he was pulled awake. Bimbo was doing the pulling. The dog had dragged Tito to his feet and was urging the boy along.

Somewhere. Where, Tito did not know. His feet stumbled uncertainly; he was still half asleep. For a while he noticed nothing except the fact that it was hard to breathe. The air was hot. And heavy. So heavy that he could taste it. The air, it seemed, had turned to powder — a warm powder that stung his nostrils and burned his sightless eyes.

Then he began to hear sounds. Peculiar sounds. Like animals under the earth. Hissings and groanings and muffled cries that a dying creature might make dislodging the stones of his underground cave. There was no doubt of it now. The noises came from underneath. He not only heard them — he could feel them. The earth twitched; the twitching changed to an uneven shrugging of the soil. Then, as Bimbo half pulled, half coaxed him across, the ground jerked away from his feet and he was thrown against a stone fountain.

The water — hot water — splashing in his face revived him. He got to his feet, Bimbo steadying him, helping him on again. The noises grew louder; they came closer. The cries were even more animal-like than before, but now they came from human throats. A few people, quicker of foot and more hurried by fear, began to rush by. A family or two — then a section — then, it seemed, an army broken out of bounds. Tito, bewildered though he was, could recognize Rufus as he bellowed past him, like a water buffalo gone mad. Time was lost in a nightmare.

It was then the crashing began. First a sharp crackling, like a monstrous snapping of twigs; then a roar like the fall of a whole forest of trees; then an explosion that tore earth and sky. The heavens, though Tito could not see them, were shot through with continual flickerings of fire. Lightnings above were answered by thunders beneath. A

house fell. Then another. By a miracle the two companions had escaped the dangerous side streets and were in a more open space. It was the Forum. They rested here awhile — how long he did not know.

Tito had no idea of the time of day. He could feel it was black — an unnatural blackness. Something inside — perhaps the lack of breakfast and lunch — told him it was past noon. But it didn't matter. Nothing seemed to matter. He was getting drowsy, too drowsy to walk. But walk he must. He knew it. And Bimbo knew it; the sharp tugs told him so. Nor was it a moment too soon. The sacred ground of the Forum was safe no longer. It was beginning to rock, then to pitch, then to split. As they stumbled out of the square, the earth wriggled like a caught snake and all the columns of the temple of Jupiter came down. It was the end of the world — or so it seemed. To walk was not enough now. They must run. Tito was too frightened to know what to do or where to go. He had lost all sense of direction. He started to go back to the inner gate; but Bimbo, straining his back to the last inch, almost pulled his clothes from him. What did the creature want? Had the dog gone mad?

Then suddenly, he understood. Bimbo was telling him the way out — urging him there. The sea gate, of course. The sea gate — and then the sea. Far from falling buildings, heaving ground. He turned, Bimbo guiding him across open pits and dangerous pools of bubbling mud, away from buildings that had caught fire and were dropping their burning beams. Tito could no longer tell whether the noises were made by the shrieking sky or the agonized people. He and Bimbo ran on — the only silent beings in a howling world.

New dangers threatened. All Pompeii

seemed to be thronging toward the marine gate and, squeezing among the crowds, there was the chance of being trampled to death. But the chance had to be taken. It was growing harder and harder to breathe. What air there was choked him. It was all dust now — dust and pebbles, pebbles as large as beans. They fell on his head, his hands — pumice stones from the black heart of Vesuvius. The mountain was turning itself inside out. Tito remembered a phrase that the stranger had said in the Forum two days ago: "Those who will not listen to men must be taught by the gods." The people of Pompeii had refused to heed the warnings; they were being taught now — if it was not too late.

Suddenly it seemed too late for Tito. The red-hot ashes blistered his skin, the stinging vapors tore his throat. He could not go on. He staggered toward a small tree at the side of the road and fell. In a moment Bimbo was beside him. He coaxed. But there was no answer. He licked Tito's hands, his feet, his face. The boy did not stir. Then Bimbo did the last thing he could — the last thing he wanted to do. He bit his comrade, bit him deep in the arm. With a cry of pain, Tito jumped to his feet, Bimbo after him. Tito was in despair, but Bimbo was determined. He drove the boy on, snapping at his heels, worrying his way through the crowd; barking, baring his teeth, heedless of kicks or falling stones. Sick with hunger, half dead with fear and sulfur fumes, Tito pounded on, pursued by Bimbo. How long, he never knew. At last he staggered through the marine gate and felt soft sand under him. Then Tito fainted. . . .

Someone was dashing sea water over him. Someone was carrying him toward a boat.

"Bimbo," he called. And then louder, "Bimbo!" But Bimbo had disappeared.

Voices jarred against each other. "Hurry — hurry!" "To the boats!" "Can't you see the child's frightened and starving!" "He keeps calling for someone!" "Poor boy, he's out of his mind." "Here, child — take this!"

They tucked him in among them. The oarlocks creaked; the oars splashed; the boat rode over toppling waves. Tito was safe. But he wept continually.

"Bimbo!" he wailed. "Bimbo! Bimbo!"

He could not be comforted.

Eighteen hundred years passed. Scientists were restoring the ancient city; excavators were working their way through the stones and trash that had buried the entire town. Much had already been brought to light — statues, bronze instruments, bright mosaics, household articles; even delicate paintings had been preserved by the fall of ashes that had taken over two thousand lives. Columns were dug up, and the Forum was beginning to emerge.

It was at a place where the ruins lay deepest that the Director paused.

"Come here," he called to his assistant. "I think we've discovered the remains of a building in good shape. Here are four huge millstones that were most likely turned by slaves or mules — and here is a whole wall standing with shelves inside it. Why! It must have been a bakery. And here's a curious thing. What do you think I found under this heap where the ashes were thickest? The skeleton of a dog!"

"Amazing!" gasped his assistant. "You'd think a dog would have had sense enough to run away at the time. And what is that flat thing he's holding between his teeth? It can't be a stone."

"No. It must have come from this bakery. You know it looks to me like some sort of cake hardened with the years. And, bless me, if those little black pebbles aren't raisins. A raisin cake almost two thousand years old! I wonder what made him want it at such a moment?"

"I wonder," murmured the assistant.

THINKING IT OVER

1. In writing a story of this kind, an author must combine historical research with his own imagination. Point out passages in the story that show research as well as some that show imagination.

2. A very few real facts often serve as the basis for a work of fiction. What are the "facts" that might have led to the writing of this story? What is the *irony* in the scientists' interpretations?

3. In paragraph 3 of the story, after supplying facts about Tito's past life, the author describes Bimbo and his relationship to the blind boy. What does this description also tell about Tito's character?

4. For possibly a thousand years the very site of the city of Pompeii was forgotten. Excavations on it began two hundred years ago, in 1763, and the complex operation continues even now. Make a guess as to what happened to Pompeii and then consult an encyclopedia.

PEN AND PAPER

Think over some of the qualities that apply to Bimbo. He was faithful, resourceful, intelligent, and he had a grave sense of responsibility. Write a paragraph with the title "Bimbo" and a topic sentence that begins "The thing I liked most about Bimbo was his . . ." Stick to the characteristic you have selected and back up your statements by referring to incidents in the story.

FOR YOUR VOCABULARY

You might not guess it by looking at them, but the following words, all in this story, have something in common: *approve, appreciate, accent, assistant*. It's not the double letter, but the double letter is involved. These words all have the prefix *ad–* or one of its variant forms. It means "to," or "toward," or "nearness." The forms it appears under are *ad–, ac–, a–,* and *ag–*. Check a dictionary for the situations under which these different forms are used and make a list of ten words from the dictionary, two for each variant form, but not using words found in the definition of *ad–*.

ABOUT THE AUTHOR

Louis Untermeyer (1885–   ) was born in New York City. As a youth his main interest was centered in music, and for a number of years it was his ambition to become a concert pianist. He gave this up, however, when he decided that he lacked sufficient musical talent. After he completed high school, Louis Untermeyer worked for his father, who had a jewelry business in New York. He became an avid reader, especially of poetry, and eventually was writing his own poems, as well as stories and articles. It is as the editor of a number of distinguished anthologies of both prose and poetry that he is best known.

Pompeii Today →

The photograph opposite is of present-day Pompeii, showing the ancient Temple of Apollo as it now stands. In the background can be seen the silent shape of Mt. Vesuvius. It is easy to place Tito and his dog in this scene, as they hear, in the distance, the ominous rumbling of the volcano.

Mr. Brownlee's Roses

ELSIE SINGMASTER

Have you wondered and worried sometimes about just what you will do when you've finished school, and whether you'll be able to succeed? Perhaps the future might depend more on character — on what you *are* — than on skills or aptitude tests. Perhaps your chance will come, as in this story, at a most unexpected moment.

As JENNIE SWENSON closed the outer door of her mother's kitchen, pulling with all her strength against the wind, she heard far up the street a man's loud singing.

> I took my girl to a ball one night,
>   It was a fancy hop;
> We danced until the lights went out,
>   And the music it did stop.

Stanislaus Sobieski, usually called Stan Sobski, night fireman at Mr. Brownlee's greenhouse, was going to

his work. His song was old; new songs, he said, did not fit his voice. He was apparently not disturbed by the fact that work began at six o'clock and it was now seven.

To Jennie, Mr. Brownlee's greenhouse was paradise; she did not understand how anyone could be late for work there. All else in the mining town was black and grim; there was no money for paint, and there was no time for cultivating gardens. At each end of Main Street towered a frame structure called a breaker, to whose lofty summit ran cars filled with coal. Beside each breaker rose a mountain of black refuse, separated from the coal as it descended in long chutes.

There had been a third mine along the hillside, and its owner, Mr. Brownlee's father, had built a small greenhouse for his own pleasure. As the mine

---

Inferring Character. Sometimes an author tells us directly about a character in a story. Chiefly, however, we learn about a character from his speech and actions, and from what the other characters in the story say and do about him. Speech and action are clues from which we *infer* the sort of person a character is. These clues begin at the very start of a story. Notice the first two paragraphs (consider Stan's song as part of the first paragraph) of "Mr. Brownlee's Roses." What do these details tell you about Stan? Watch for clues about the other characters in the story.

---

grew lean, he began to sell flowers. Presently he was shipping a thousand American Beauties each night to New York. The present Mr. Brownlee was shipping three thousand before he went to war. Now he and his sister were once more sending roses, five thousand in a night — not American Beauties, but newer and more fashionable varieties: Premier and Columbia and Radiance, in various shades of rose and pink; Talisman, a blending of pink and apricot and gold; double white Killarneys and long yellow buds of Souvenir de Claudius Pernet.[1]

Jennie did not know their names or even their distinct and lovely odors; she knew only their colors, seen when she walked slowly by, looking eagerly for panes of glass on which the white paint was worn away. She often watched Mr. Brownlee and his sister. He was tall and a little lame, and his hair was slightly gray; Miss Brownlee was short and broad, but not stout. She had clear blue eyes, wavy hair, and a broad white forehead. Her brother could do no strenuous work; but she worked from morning till night, directing the laborers, inspecting rows of plants, and superintending the packing of roses.

At the same instant that Jennie heard Stan singing, she wound her scarf more tightly around her neck, locked the door, and hung the key behind a shutter. For hours a light snow had been falling, and now an east wind was beginning to blow. Stan had now reached the middle of his song.

And this is what she ate:
A dozen raw, a plate of slaw,
A chicken and a roast,
Some oyster stew and ice cream too,
And several quail on toast.

In the moment while she waited for Stan to pass, Jennie was tempted to turn back to the kitchen and study. There was a good light and perfect quiet — for Mrs. Swenson, a nurse, was on a case, and Jennie's sisters, Anna and Gertrude, lived in Wilkes-Barre.[2]

But what Jennie required for study was not quiet — it was company. There were incomprehensible passages in her Latin lesson; insoluble problems in her algebra. If she did not graduate in June, she could not get a position. Better the storm and the long walk to Hilda Yonson's kitchen, where there were no less than eight younger children, than peace and quiet and blankness of mind.

Gertrude and Anna were astonished at her dullness. She could not be a stenographer because she was too slow; she could not teach because she was too dull; she could not be a nurse because she was too timid. The teachers gave aptitude tests, but she showed no aptitude for anything. When she was excited or embarrassed her Swedish tongue refused to say "j"; it refused now.

"I *must* get a yob!" wailed Jennie aloud to the storm.

She stepped from the boardwalk, already swept bare, into a drift up to her knees. Instantly she laughed and shook the tears out of her eyes. She was a true Swede, tall and broad and strong. She started briskly down the street. The lights in the neighbors' houses were dimmed by whirling snow, but far above them hung a light at the top of the breaker.

She heard a shrill bell which heralded the rising of the elevator from the mine. In a moment a line of tired men would pass the corner. Five years ago

[1] **Souvenir de Claudius Pernet** (sōōv·nĕr′ dē klô′dĭ·ŭs pĕr·nä′).

[2] **Wilkes-Barre** (wĭlks′bär′ē): a city in Pennsylvania.

there had been an evening when the loud whistle blew and everyone went running and crying to the pit head. Mrs. Swenson had been the first to get there and first to know that she was widowed.

At the third corner Jennie halted. There were two ways to the Yonson house: one down Main Street; the other through side streets, past Mr. Brownlee's greenhouse. Jennie took a step in that direction; then, laughing at herself, ran on down Main Street, then up a sharp hill.

From the Yonsons' porch the whole of the Wyoming Valley was visible in daylight — cities and towns and roads, churches and schools and factories; and in every town and village a towering breaker. A part of the valley had a strange and solemn name, "The Shades of Death," a memorial of Colonial war and massacre.

Tim Yonson sat before the stove, in a coal-blackened rocker reserved for his use. His face and hands were clean, but they were not white. He smoked a long pipe and talked to Mrs. Yonson, who was washing dishes. There was a child on each side of the table, each pair of eyes on a book.

"Good efening, Yennie," said Tim.

"Good efening," said Mrs. Yonson.

Hilda looked up. "Hello! Thought you weren't coming."

As Jennie unwound her scarf, Mrs. Yonson set a large plate of Swedish cookies on the table to lighten the evening's labors, and it was not until half-past nine that Jennie rose to leave. Mr. Yonson had gone to bed and so had five or six children.

"I certainly am grateful," sighed Jennie.

Mrs. Yonson had difficulty with many English letters. "Come efery night till you are old, and Hilda will not yet pay

what your moder done for us."

Jennie had expected to have the wind in her face, but it blew from every direction in turn. Regardless of the stinging snow, she turned down the dark street which led to Mr. Brownlee's greenhouse. A new section had been added, and the low, dimly lighted buildings occupied a solid block.

She walked slowly past. There they were, the pinks, the yellows, the shades of rose! She stood still, though the wind seemed to blow through her. The snow hissed against the glass. How could this thin protection keep the roses safe?

The office was furnished with two broad desks, a half-dozen chairs, a bookcase, and many files. Neither of the Brownlees was in sight; but Mr. Brownlee's gray overcoat hung on a hook, his soft gray hat above it, and a crumpled newspaper lay on the floor beside his chair. At the back of the room a door opened on a stairway leading to the boiler room. The door was ajar; perhaps he was down there with Stan. Probably he would stay in the greenhouse all night. She would, in his place!

In ten minutes she was at home. The house rocked a little in the wind. She shook down the fire, put on fresh coal, and, while it caught, undressed near the stove.

Though she was warm in bed, she could not sleep. She shut her eyes, determined not to open them again; then, startled by a sound, she sat up. "Mother?" she called.

There was no answer. The sound came from outside and grew each moment louder.

"I took my girl to a ball one night!" shouted Stan Sobieski at the gate. "To a ball! Fifty cents!"

Jennie was terrified. But Stan was an honest fellow — he would not break into a house! That is, when he was sober!

She sprang out of bed and went to the window. She could not see him, but she could hear him. "I took my girl to a social hop!"

He was not going toward the greenhouse; he was going in the opposite direction!

"And this is what she ate! And this is what she ate —" he yelled, from far away. "She ate — "

It was not until Jennie had one knee on her bed and was about to creep back that she was really awake. It was a bitter night, and Mr. Brownlee's roses were in the midst of their most profitable bloom. Suppose the fires should go out? But Mr. Brownlee was there! But suppose Mr. Brownlee had gone home?

Foolish though it seemed, she put on her slippers and went downstairs. In the pale glow from the fire she could see her clothes spread on the chair; they seemed to say, "Put us on! Put us on!"

"How silly!" said Jennie. "I'm going back to bed."

Instantly she had another delusion; she saw thousands of roses standing with drooping heads. No, as plants froze they got stiffer and stiffer and held their heads straight. It was only after the sun came out that they got limp and black.

"I don't care if I am crazy," she said, and began to dress.

As she opened the door, the wind seemed to drag her out, rather than drive her back. It blew with a roaring sound, far above her head. She heard a loud crash, as though the roof of a house had been blown off. She could see the breaker light when the clouds of snow blew away, but no other.

She laughed hysterically and ran. Stan had another old song — "I don't know where I'm going, but I'm on my way."

"That's me!" said Jennie.

The great area of dim light was as it had been. She slowed her step; there were the roses, beautiful and unchanged. The office was brightly lighted and still empty of human beings; but Mr. Brownlee's coat hung on its hook, and the door to the boiler room was open.

"It's all right!" thought Jennie.

Above Mr. Brownlee's desk hung a clock with a large face. "Look at me, Jennie!" it seemed to say. It was half-past one! At the same instant she saw that Mr. Brownlee's crumpled newspaper lay exactly where it had been at half-past nine.

Jennie went up the step and opened the door. How warm it was, how sweet, how like paradise!

"Mr. Brownlee!" she called faintly.

There was no answer.

"Mr. Brownlee!" Alarm sharpened her voice.

"Who is there?" Undoubtedly it was Mr. Brownlee, speaking from the boiler room.

"Jennie Swenson." She could not help giggling. What did "Jennie Swenson" mean to Mr. Brownlee?

"In the name of mercy, Jennie Swenson, come down here!"

The words were pitiful, yet there was an undertone of amusement. Trembling, Jennie went down the steps. The room was low and paved with brick. At one end was a huge boiler; along one side were coalbins and piles of wood, and along the other shelves filled with cans and bottles of insecticides and sprays. Before the boiler stood an old couch, and on it lay Mr. Brownlee.

"Open that firebox door quick, will you, and pile in wood."

Jennie picked up a chunk as she dashed to the furnace.

"Finer pieces, plenty of them! Pretty low, isn't it?"

"Not so very bad," said Jennie.

"What are you crying for?"

"Will they die?"

"Humph!" said Mr. Brownlee. "Go to my desk and take the flashlight you'll find there; then go to the farthest corner of every greenhouse and read the thermometers. And you might pray as you go!"

"Did Stan tie you?" asked Jennie, running up the stairs swiftly.

"Lumbago tied me."

Jennie came running back. The wood in the firebox was burning briskly. Mr. Brownlee's eyes shone like points of fire.

"Forty-eight degrees is the lowest."

Mr. Brownlee threw up his arm. It covered his eyes and mouth. "What did you say your name is?"

"Jennie Swenson."

"Where do you come from?"

"Up the street."

"You come from heaven!" Mr. Brownlee still kept his eyes covered. "Can you put coal on the fire?"

"Sure!"

"Have you no father who may be out looking for you? No mother who is anxious? Are you real?"

"My father was killed in Shaft Eighteen. I guess you remember that time."

"Remember!" exclaimed Mr. Brownlee.

"My mother's a nurse, Mrs. Swenson. She has a case all night. I heard Stan Sobieski going home and I thought of the flowers. He was singing loud."

"Close that lower door," ordered Mr. Brownlee. "Then make the rounds with your flashlight. When you come back, bring yourself a chair."

"The lowest is now above forty-eight," reported Jennie a few minutes later.

"Sit down, Jennie," said Mr. Brownlee. "Now tell me again how you happen to be here."

"I vas" — excited and embarrassed, Jennie spoke rapidly — "I vas studying mine lesson by Hilda Yonson, and I vas coming past so I could see the flowers." Then she recovered her English. "There was no one in the office, but a newspaper was lying all mussed on the floor. When I was in bed, I heard Stan going home."

"He wasn't here," said Brownlee. "He never came. I was shoveling coal when this attack of lumbago caught me. It's happened before. All I could do was lie down on Stan's couch. It'll take a stretcher to get me home. My sister is in New York; otherwise she would have been here long ago. Now go on. So you heard Stan going home?"

"Then I came," said Jennie.

"Then you came," repeated Mr. Brownlee. "You got up in the middle of the night in a blizzard and you came."

"I saw the newspaper in the same place," she explained, "and I felt something was wrong."

Again Mr. Brownlee covered his eyes. "Better make another round, Jennie, and you might fetch my overcoat along."

"It's now fifty at the lowest," she reported on her return. "I'll cover you up. I can hear water bubbling in the pipe. I could take a few of those bottles, fill them with hot water, and put them behind you."

"Why, so you could! Open that spigot and you can fill them. Do you go to school?"

"Yes." Jennie sat down in her chair. "But I'm not good at Latin and algebra and geometry. I don't know if I can graduate in June. And I don't know if I can find a" — this time Jennie knew that she had made a slip — "a yob. I'm strong, but I'm not bright."

"No?" said Mr. Brownlee. "Will you kindly take another look at the thermometers?"

"Fifty-two everywhere," she told him jubilantly. "It's three o'clock now, not long till daylight."

"At five-forty my sister's train is due. She'll see the light in the office as they come into the station. Whatever has been our pain and anxiety, Jennie, we shall have the fun of seeing her come down those stairs. While I was at war, you know, the government shut down on luxuries. We couldn't use our own coal to run our own greenhouse, and we lost sixteen thousand plants in one night."

"I have heard of that," Jennie wept.

"You've got to keep the houses fifty-seven at night and fifty-five by day. Below forty-eight is blight and mildew. Will you please put more coal on, and make another round?"

"Sure!"

At six o'clock that morning the outer door opened, and there was a brisk tap of feet on the linoleum.

"Dick!" called a frightened voice. "Where are you?"

Already Miss Brownlee was on the steps. At the bottom she stood looking from her brother to his guest. Jennie rose, the flashlight in her hand.

"You might take that flash, Alice, and read the thermometers," said Mr. Brownlee in a tired voice.

Like an old woman, Miss Brownlee crept up the steps. Then she ran.

"It's fifty-seven everywhere," she cried, returning. "Have you lumbago? You've been shoveling coal! Where's Stan? What's the matter?"

"Alice, this is Jennie Swenson, Harriet Swenson's daughter," said Mr. Brownlee. "Last night at one o'clock,

lying in her bed, she heard Stan going home, singing as he went. Now Jennie is something of a prowler herself. She comes here — has been coming for a good many years — to peer in at our windows. She looks at the roses; she doesn't handle them, she doesn't even smell them. She has never been in the greenhouse. But, hearing Stan yelling, she dressed and came down, just to look in and see that everything was all right. She says that she's dull, but she observed that my newspaper was lying exactly where she had seen it at nine-thirty."

"I'll put on a little more coal," offered Jennie.

Miss Brownlee looked hard at her. "You certainly have common sense, and you're certainly strong, and you certainly love flowers," she said at last. "Would you come here and work as an assistant? I would teach you all I know."

"When school closes, you mean," put in Mr. Brownlee. "In the meantime we'll help her with her Latin, her Greek, her Hebrew, her calculus, and her what not."

If he thought Jennie would laugh, he was mistaken. She lifted her hand to cover her trembling lips.

"Sure I'd come!" said she.

At half-past six Jennie went up the street. The snow was whirling through the air. Traveling was uncertain because you stepped now on bare, slippery flagstones, now into deep drifts. Jennie had a box on her arm; she carried it as though it were a baby.

Jennie opened the kitchen door of her home. The light was burning and her mother sat before the fire, taking off her shoes. She turned with a start. She had pleasant, tired eyes and a braid of thick light hair.

"Why, Yennie!" she exclaimed.

"Where were you out in the night? What have you?"

Jennie sat down, the box in her arms.

"I've got roses in this box," she said. "Red and pink and white and yellow. They have long, long stems. And — moder — oh, moder! I've got a yob!"

THINKING IT OVER

1. How would you state the theme of this story? Examine the third and fourth paragraphs. Explain the contrast the author makes in the two paragraphs and tell how it is related to the theme.

2. Throughout the story, Jennie has to make many decisions. Staying home or going to the Yonsons' was one decision. Give at least five others that she made. What was the crucial decision that could have changed the story entirely? How was this the result of the earlier decisions?

3. Do you know of any successful persons who did not have much schooling, for one reason or another, or who had trouble with their school work? Why do you think they became successful?

4. Make a chalkboard list of qualities that do not depend upon book knowledge but are important to success. Which of these qualities would you credit to Jennie? What school subjects will help you to gain a useful place in the world? What are some important factors you should consider in trying to fit yourself into a job?

INFERRING CHARACTER

1. Stan's song (paragraph 1) should have told you that he was a happy-go-lucky person. What do you learn about his sense of responsibility in the second paragraph?

2. What do you learn about Jennie's love of beauty in paragraph 2? What tells you in this same paragraph that her sense of responsibility is different from Stan's?

3. When Jennie left the house, she was in a discouraged mood. Then she stepped into a snowdrift, and "Instantly she laughed and shook the tears out of her eyes." What does this incident show?

4. Find the paragraph that describes Tim Yonson as he sits in the kitchen. Explain what sort of person you think he is, judging from the paragraph. What does Mrs. Yonson do that suggests her whole character? What do you think is the reason for her treatment of Jennie?

5. "The words were pitiful, yet there was an undertone of amusement." What does that description of Mr. Brownlee's call for help tell you about him? Can you find other details that convey his character?

6. What characteristic showed when Jennie said, "I'm strong, but I'm not bright"?

7. What are her characteristics as reported in the speeches of Mr. Brownlee and his sister on page 65?

ABOUT THE AUTHOR

Elsie Singmaster (1878–) is a native of Pennsylvania. A long-time resident of Gettysburg, she has written much about that historic locale and about the people in other parts of her state. In particular, she is known for her local-color stories of the Pennsylvania Dutch and of the people in the many mining towns of Pennsylvania. Her first published story doesn't have happy recollections. It was printed in a teacher's journal when she was eleven, and she says, "The plot was not wholly original; when the story was printed, my conscience began to trouble me and has ever since."

As the Artist Sees It ➤

The painting on the facing page is artist Tom O'Sullivan's interpretation of Mr. Brownlee's greenhouse and the mining town where "all else . . . was black and grim." The artist has shown the greenhouse contrasted against the towering black coal shaft and the dark streets of the town. The town and the mine shaft are dark, and in the darkness the bright-colored roses, tended by Jennie, seem to glow like jewels. Can you explain how this scene of contrast reveals something of the theme of the story — and of the character of Jennie as well?

Pride of Seven

ROBERT W. KREPPS

The test of character often comes in a crisis. Faced with danger or a threat, the quality most people wish for is courage. But there are different kinds of courage. What a young African warrior and an old lion do in a time of crisis make this story exciting and memorable.

THE SHEEP was my friend, and I was worried about him. For related reasons I felt uneasy about the lions. Sooner or later one of these problems would be solved, and I honestly couldn't make up my mind which one I wanted it to be. You see, if The Sheep killed a lion, the first worry would be over; whereas if he didn't kill a lion, that would finish the second.

I was living upcountry with the Masai;[1] or perhaps I should say I was spending half my time with them and half with the lions. The Masai are a nomadic people of great pride, much beauty, and a congenital dislike for work of any sort. As a general thing, they despise anyone who hasn't had the luck to be born Masai, but for one

¹ Masai (mä·sī′).

reason and another they tolerated me. I spoke their language — learned it before I ever came to their country, from a fellow down at the Cape — and that pleased them no end, especially when they found I wasn't a missionary but a loafer like themselves. I was actually working on a book about South Africa, but you can't explain that to a Masai.

Well, I settled down in one of their long, low, mud-plastered wood houses, which are unlike other native huts in that they are divided into private apartments. I had the women fix me a neat brushwood bed with soft hides for blankets; I acquired a cooking pot and some gourds for milk, and bought a cow. I used to sit in the sun with the warriors and the old men, swapping awful lies and making notes for the book, and sometimes it would strike me that I'd never been more contented in my life.

There was one man whom I particularly liked, a wiry, well-made youth with finely cut features, whose looks were marred only by the usual lack of two lower front teeth; the Masai have been knocking these teeth out ever since the days when lockjaw was prevalent among them and a way had to be found to feed the victims. It's a mark of elegance with them now, like the frightful stretched lips of the old-time Ubangi. This young fellow, though quite intelligent and presentable, seemed to be held in scorn by the warriors and, worse, by the girls. I began our friendship in pity, and soon discovered a calmly philosophical spirit in him that was most pleasing. His name, or perhaps nickname, was En-gerr: The Sheep.

He had recently gone through the ceremonies that take a Masai from the ranks of the boys and make him a warrior, *il-muran*. He carried a long-bladed spear and a leaf-shaped sword, wore a goat-stomach cap and a vulture-feather cape, ankle fringes of white monkey's fur, and the horn arm clamp which none but a fighter may wear. The only thing missing in his costume was the great headdress of ostrich feathers and a lion's mane. He had never killed a lion. That was the reason he was disdained.

I couldn't believe that he was a coward. When I had known him a while, I asked him bluntly why he had not sought out his lion (in the bad old days it used to be a man you had to kill) and proved himself worthy to be called a warrior. Looking me straight in the eyes, he said, "I have not felt like it." It was unorthodox in a Masai, but I knew it was the truth. En-gerr simply had a mind of his own.

If he'd been a member of another tribe, this delay wouldn't have mattered a scrap. The Masai *muran,* however, since he cannot now legally slay men, concentrates all his arrogant manhood in his prowess with lions. A warrior who puts off his first fight is little better than a woman.

I've mentioned the lions, the ones I was worried about. I had been living in the village for about three weeks when I discovered them. After that I spent a good deal of my time stretched out on the warm grass of a hilltop, in the shade of a couple of thorny, broad-crowned acacia trees, watching them. When the Masai found how I was occupying my days, they were more convinced than ever that I was a natural-born drone.

I'd go out around ten in the morning, wearing red-lined khaki drill [1] and a double-brimmed felt hat to keep out the sun, with heelless Dutch veldschoen [2] of cowhide that made no noise when I walked; I'd take some dried fruit to munch on, and maybe a gourd of sweet milk. Making a wide circle, I would come to my hill from the opposite side to the lions' lolling place. It took a while to climb it, for it was steep and tricky. At last I would reach the top and sprawl out under the acacias [3] and look down at the bowl of cool, damp bush below me, and there would be the lions. Rarely was I disappointed. They were nearly always there, the whole pride of seven.

Pride is an old word for a troop of lions, and may even be obsolete, for all I know, but I like it. What other word befits the king so well?

There are many places in Africa where the lion still reigns. One of these — to my mind the finest of the lot — is the great rolling savanna of East Africa inhabited by the Masai. Hot on the hills, cool in the valleys, all greens from olive to emerald, it pulses with its strange alien life beneath a sky that is higher and more blue than you ever see it else-

---

[1] **drill**: a heavy fabric.
[2] **veldschoen** (vĕlt′sko͞on′): shoes made of untanned hide, without nails.
[3] **acacias** (á·kā′shåz): trees with white or yellow blossoms, generally found in warm climates.

where. Hundreds of millions of animals darken the land, eating and breeding and traveling and dying from year's end to year's end. Over these inexhaustible hordes rules the lion.

The leader of my pride was a tawny beast, not of the really golden shade, but more the color of a well-used bar of yellow laundry soap. He was big — nearly five hundred pounds, I judged him — with a thick, tangled mane that flung back grandly from his forehead, and a hogshead of a chest all seamed with long-healed scars. He was a superb creature, just going into the last years of his prime. Ordinarily I deplore the gratuitous giving of names to wild animals, names that are often coy and silly; but in his case I couldn't say merely "the old one" or "the big fellow," so I called him El Asfar, which is Algerian Arabic for a tawny lion. It sounded rather grand. Arabic does — especially if, like me, you understand no more than a dozen words.

He had a pair of wives, fine large beauties both. Then there was a young-er male, brown with a black mane, smaller and lighter on his feet and more restless than El Asfar. He had a wife too, a scrubby dun-colored lioness with a walleye, who nagged and fought with him. There was a very old sway-backed female who was probably a relative, for lions have a strong family instinct and take care of their own. To round out the pride, there was a cub that was just learning to kill for himself, a beast who would be a walloping giant when he got his growth, which was slow com-ing, for although he was well over a year old his paws were still too big for him.

They never did much of anything during the day, just lazed around and talked to themselves and stared at but-terflies, and such little activities; but I

loved to watch them. As a flawlessly organized apparatus of energy, combin-ing tremendous brawn with graceful beauty and nimble intelligence, the lion has no peer in Africa. How could one tire of viewing perfection?

I used to lie there until the sun had touched the rim of the plain, and then have to hurry home to the village be-fore the lions set out to stalk their night's meal. So long as I stayed on the hilltop I was perfectly safe, for a lion almost never looks up; besides, they would have had to scale a long stretch of bare rock to get at me, and sun-cooked rock burns a lion's pad till he nearly goes mad. In case of a show-down, of course, I always had my rifle handy, but it never came to that.

I did, indeed, run slap into El Asfar one morning, as he was ambling home from an all-night gorge of zebra. Had it been the younger, nervous Black Mane, I think I would have shot at once, for I never trusted his looks; but since it was the patriarch, I just stopped in my tracks to stare at a fluff of cloud and whistle a small tuneless tune, as though the last thing in my mind was the possibility of a lion being within fifty miles. By and by El Asfar gave a grunt and walked round me, and I watched him go, full belly flopping from side to side, until he had disap-peared. This trick of ignoring a sur-prised lion I learned from an old hun-ter, who said it would work nine times out of ten. The tenth lion is the one to dread.

When I told the warriors about this incident — bragging is an honorable pastime among the Masai — my stock rose with them, because they said I ob-viously had the true feeling for lions. My friend En-gerr seemed fascinated by the story and made me tell him all over again about the seven big cats who lay

up below the hill. We were having a noon snack: rice and tea for me and a noisome concoction of warm blood and milk, which forms the basic Masai diet, for En-gerr. Nothing would satisfy him but that we take our weapons and go out immediately to have a look at the pride. So off we went, The Sheep and I, to a chorus of jeering yells: "Observe, En-gerr goes to stare from a distance upon *ol-ngatuny*,[1] whom he dares not face in battle!" and much more of the same savage small-boy humor. My friend ignored them with equanimity.

We came to the hill and climbed it and, lying flat on our bellies, we peered over the edge together. All seven of my lions were at the retreat. I looked over at En-gerr and saw his lean, clever face alight with pleasure. He, too, had the feeling for lions, not only the sportsmanlike respect for a worthy rival that is common among his people, but also, I thought, a kind of reverence for the lithe, perfect kings of the cat tribe, a heathen fealty paid to these master-

works of the gods. His brown eyes were wide and worshiping. I was glad that I had brought him.

We stayed on the hill for a couple of hours, and we were rewarded by a sight I should not like to have missed.

For some time I had had the uncomfortable feeling that the black-maned male was the real boss of the troop, for all the size and majesty of El Asfar, because Black Mane was as cocky and insolent a brute as ever drew breath. He would stalk round and round the lying-in place, growling and making eyes at the old man's wives, and El Asfar, with his paws curled in like a kitten's, would blink and yawn and look bored. I feared that, for all his obvious strength, he must be past his prime or he would never have endured such impudence.

Today he had brought home a bloody haunch of eland,[2] a meat to which his clan is very partial. (Don't tell me that a lion never carries off part of his kill. There is nothing that a lion *never* does, unless it be flying.) He had been gnaw-

[1] *ol-ngatuny* (ôl·ngät′ōōn·ĭ): the lion.

[2] **eland** (ē′lănd): a large antelope.

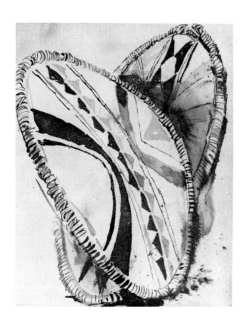

ing thoughtfully at this trophy and then, growing thirsty, had gone off to the stream to lap up a little warm water. Returning, he discovered that the nervy Black Mane had appropriated the eland haunch.

"Now we will see who is chief," En-gerr whispered in my ear.

El Asfar trotted over and lowered his head until his flaring nostrils were within six inches of Black Mane's face. Then he roared, simply roared.

The chances are that you have never heard a lion roar. You may have heard them calling in the zoos, and that noise is only a grunt, fearful though it seems to you. The lion's cough, too, is a full-bodied boom of sound. Yet his vocal cords, marvelous instruments backed by the great echo chamber of his barrel, can do much more than grunt and cough; they can produce a roar that would make a thunderclap envious.

El Asfar, as I say, roared. It was a shattering crash of a roar, an angry blast that literally shook the air where we were lying, thirty yards above his head.

Rocks began to fall down the hillside; the very earth seemed to quiver. It felt and sounded as though someone had set off a charge of dynamite.

Black Mane laid his ears flat to his skull, opened his eyes till the whites showed plain, dropped the stolen tidbit and got himself out of there, crawling backward as fast as he could go. There was no longer a doubt, in his mind or in mine, as to who was the leader of the pride.

On the way home, En-gerr was silent and abstracted. Then, as we came to the tall fence of thorn bushes that circled the village, he spoke.

"My friend, I have found the lion which I must kill. He is the great yellow chieftain."

My heart actually gave a jump, for I was very fond of my pride of seven, and particularly fond of El Asfar. "Why do you choose him?"

"He is the finest lion I have ever seen. None lesser should be my first kill."

I had overestimated The Sheep. He was, after all, a typical Masai in his thinking; the highest compliment he could pay a lion was to meet it in fair fight. Merely to watch and admire it, as I did, couldn't give his esteem full expression. No, he had to oil himself up and whet his spear and go out to try to butcher it.

That was when I started to worry about the lions. Heretofore I'd been unhappy about En-gerr.

Now it seemed that my concern over his softness was to be drowned in the blood of my friend El Asfar. I had twin troubles, and I couldn't decide which one I most desired to see ended.

The days went by and aside from telling his intentions to the other *murani*, who laughed at him, En-gerr did nothing.

I stopped watching the lions, because it saddened me to think of their family breaking up. I have shot lions and likely will again; but there's a great difference in killing a lion with whom you have no acquaintance and seeing one killed whom you have long known and liked. I suppose you might say I was overly sentimental about El Asfar, but then how many men are not sentimental about some animal or other? Would you like to live with the knowledge that a savage African was going to murder your favorite dog?

The days went on, and still The Sheep did nothing.

When I had not seen my big cats for a week, their fascination dimmed a little, so that I found myself brooding more over the young warrior than over the catastrophe darkening El Asfar's future. En-gerr was, after all, my good friend, and my inherent human sympathies were with him. His intelligence should have been making him an honored place in the tribe, and the girls should have been serving him beef and brewing him honey wine. Instead he was the butt of crude jokes and a sorrow to his family. Was he not eighteen, of sound wind and tough limb? Then what was he doing here in the village, lying idle with his feet against a post like the father of many sons?

At last, one evening as we were watching the sun go down in a glory of gold-rimmed purple clouds athwart the dusky blue sky, I took a firm stand. "En-gerr, my friend," I said, "you must stop this spineless dawdling. You must slay your lion."

He was quiet for a moment, while we followed a flight of little chirruping birds with our eyes. Then he said, "I am ready. It shall be tomorrow."

I felt a brief pang for El Asfar; but where a man's whole career and reputa-

tion are at stake, even a lion must take a back seat. "Why have you waited?" I asked him.

"You are over thirty," he said. "Have you taken a wife?"

"No."

"Have you thought of taking a wife?"

"Many times."

"And did you rush heedlessly into marriage on the first day you thought of it? No, you sat down and smoked and brooded for a long time about it." He looked over at me, handsome eyes slanted in what passes with the Masai for a wink. "Is a man's first lion then less important than his first wife, my friend? Or should he not concentrate his mind on *ol-ngatuny* for many days, weighing the beast's worth, and his own readiness, and the method of the slaying?"

"*Aiya!*" I said. "That is so. A woman is only a woman, but a good lion is the eighth wonder of the world."

"And that is the truth. A man remembers his first lion all his life. When he is old, he gathers his grandchildren and refights the animal with words for their benefit. As he dies, he feels its claws again and takes pride in the long-ago kill." He stood up. The vivid African stars were already blazing above us. "Tomorrow I take my first lion."

"And must it surely be the yellow one? He is a noble beast."

"That is why it must be the yellow lion," En-gerr explained.

He went away to polish his weapons. I sat there by myself, feeling moody and old and lonesome.

The next morning we assembled for the hunt. Now that En-gerr had made up his mind, he was the hero of the hour. The contrast with his former indolence had produced a sharp reaction in the tribe. All the young warriors were eager to go with him, to act as beaters. The elders were giving him last-minute advice, and the women were throwing grass and spitting at him to bring luck. The Sheep himself was bedecked to the hilt. His all but naked body was greased with ocher [1] clay and fat; his fur anklets were lustrous, his pigtail was plaited with fresh leather strips, and his horn arm clamp shone with much rubbing.

He was in a hysterical temper, froth on his lips, his eyes dilated and shot with red. He had been nursing this passion for hours, so that it was at its peak. Unable to stand still, he bounded about, flourishing his sword, shouting unintelligibly, and gnashing his teeth in a horrible fashion. He was no longer my calm, sensible friend, but a fanatical, dangerous killer. Yet truly I couldn't grieve over the change, for his race is hard on nonconformists. His life would be easier after this display of conventional Masai madness.

As we started out — I was going with them, of course — I passed his father, who smiled proudly. "He is like a hyena's sinew, so tough he will never know defeat," he said to me.

"Hoi!" I said admiringly.

We headed for the lying-up place of the seven, flung out in a wide-spaced line that spanned the rolling plain from the rocky outcrop of a chain of hills to the green palms that marked a watercourse. The warriors chanted and sang. En-gerr marched in the center, with me beside him, my heavy rifle slung over my shoulder. A little duikerbok [2] bounced out of the grass ahead of us and dived away into a hidden pothole. Myriads of insects made their drowsy noises. A bold silver-speckled lizard ran up my leg and leaped off again.

"There is the hill of the lion chief," shouted The Sheep at last. "There waits the yellow one, waits for my spear to

[1] ocher (ō′kẽr): yellow.
[2] duikerbok (dī′kẽr·bŏk′): a small antelope.

kiss his breast!"

Poor old El Asfar, I said to myself; what an end to his placid, powerful life. I couldn't doubt that this raving barbarian next to me must surely conquer him.

We approached the secret bowl of cool green bush, and one of the lionesses came out and looked at us inquiringly and disappeared. The warriors set up a howling. En-gerr shook his weapons and snapped like an angry dog.

The lioness must have told El Asfar about us, for a few minutes later his own broad muzzle poked out between the leaves that half hid the entrance to his lair. He studied our noisy gang a moment, and then withdrew, coughing. Suddenly the thought occurred to me: this beast knows what he's about; he has seen the lines of men come over the plains before. I don't know what put the idea into my head. I simply believed it, all at once, and felt sure that such an old stager as El Asfar must be wise in the ways of the Masai. "By the gods," I said aloud in English, "I'll bet he won't be there when we hit the place!"

And he wasn't. The bowl was empty of life save for an iridescent blue jay, who scolded us peevishly as we broke through the brush. "He flies from my wrath," shrieked En-gerr, although to me the withdrawal of the pride was more in the nature of a lot of dignified giants leaving the vicinity of an annoying mosquito swarm. "He trembles with fear!"

With two or three companions En-gerr went on across the bowl, while the others skirted it, and I scrambled up the almost sheer rock face of the hill for twenty feet or so, to have a look at the country.

On the side opposite to that from which we had come, the plain was

quite flat, cut by a single shallow dry gully, the only one within sight. It could not have been more than half a yard deep and was filled with thick grass. Along this meager cut El Asfar was shepherding his troop. They were going on their bellies, heads low and tails dragging. The females were in the lead, then the cub, with Black Mane and the big fellow at the rear. It was a most orderly retreat, and I could have wagered my rifle that the expressions on their faces were irritable but in no way afraid.

The Masai gathered in a loose mob near the lair, and began jumping up and down, trying to locate the lions. They did not shout to me. If they had, I really don't know whether I'd have told them where El Asfar was. My loyalties were divided that day and all in a hopeless muddle. I only know that I was immensely excited.

The Masai started to cast out from the hill like hounds at fault. I was surprised that they could not see the quarry. A lion can hide himself in a patch of grass which you'd swear wouldn't harbor a dozen quail, but it seemed to me that En-gerr and his men should at least have noticed the gully. However, they were at the pitch of their hunting frenzy, their eyes suffused with blood, and I imagine their sight was none too keen. It looked as though they were going to lose their lion for good.

Then, away in the invisible distances, an ostrich boomed hollowly like a lost kettledrum; and that chuckleheaded Black Mane raised his head and answered with a reverberating grunt.

I groaned in disgust.

The four females, followed by the clumsy yearling, shot out of the gully and ran for the nearest hill, which was about half a mile farther on.

Black Mane watched them go, his whole body expressing astonishment. You might have thought he didn't have the intellect of a bumblebee.

As for the leader, I expected to see him turn at bay, to keep the Masai from following his charges.

Not he! Patient with the other's top-lofty airs in time of peace, he would not bear insubordination in the face of the enemy. He stood up slowly. Giving a brief but ear-splitting bellow, he launched his great body full at Black Mane. He had not even glanced back at the warriors, who had been racing toward him, but who now dug in their heels and skidded to a halt, spreading out to watch the fight.

And it was a fight. None of the petulant slapping and half-hearted nips that lion gives lion when they're quarreling over the choice cuts of a dead buffalo, but terrible smashes with the forearms that might have splintered a plank, lightning-fast stabs with the fangs, and quick short rips with the claws that lacerated hide wherever they touched. Their first tangle was like an explosion, their movement too quick to follow. Then they drew back, and for the briefest part of a minute held off, snarling fiercely, their eyes never leaving one another. There might have been no human enemy near.

El Asfar pounced again. Black Mane met him halfway, and they rolled over and over, locked in a cruel embrace. Their hind feet were searching for the tender bellies, and it was a wonder that one or the other was not disemboweled. Probably the flailing legs parried reciprocally.[1] The younger beast went for El Asfar's throat, and they broke apart once more. Both of them were striped and splashed with blood.

Circling, they made ferocious little assaults, not closing until El Asfar, with a full-chested roar, rose to his hind feet, challenging the other to do the same. There they stood, reared up like boxers, El Asfar full eight feet tall and Black Mane not much less; balancing thus,

[1] parried reciprocally: blocked each other.

they beat mercilessly at each other's heads with those brawn-corded arms and steel-tipped paws. I had never seen anything so ragingly fearless.

I feared that the old fellow's years would tell against him in such a slug-fest. I needn't have worried. Prime muscles answering a shrewd and vastly experienced brain and yellow eyes quicker than a fencer's, combined with an utter lack of the nerves that plagued his enemy, gave El Asfar the victory within seconds of their heaving erect. The climax was incredibly swift and violent. Black Mane had got in a very good swat on his chops that appeared to madden the king. El Asfar's right paw crashed against the younger brute's ear with a jolt that rocked him back and sideways; as Black Mane was falling, dazed and sick, El Asfar's left forefoot, claws fully extended, made an arc and caught him a terrific bang under the jowl. Never was the old one-two used to better advantage. Black Mane went down like a ton of loose bones.

His punishment administered, the great lion lost all anger; he began to prod Black Mane with his nose, whining at him to rouse himself and scat out of there. Black Mane obviously did not feel lively. He managed to sit up, his hind legs stretched out to one side, his head drooping and wagging tipsily. Several times he made an attempt to get to his feet, but it was two or three minutes before he was able to make it.

The *murani* were shouting like devils. I went down the hillside and walked over to join them. There was something gone from their voices. I realized what it was: the hysterical note of the dedicated lion killer. There is much sportsmanship in the Masai; they love a good fight. I wondered what the end would be. If En-gerr declined to slay his lion, it would seem just and proper to all of them at this moment, yet later the name of coward might be hurled at him, when his comrades had forgotten their own emotions on the plain of battle.

By the time I had reached my friend's side, Black Mane had succeeded in standing and was starting off after the distant lionesses, his chin touching the grass as he went. He looked like a beast who had learned a valuable lesson — the hard way.

El Asfar watched him until he had gone a fair way and then faced round and looked at us inquiringly. I thought he would charge, for his brawling blood must be up, but he merely stood there quite silently, running his tongue in and out of the front of his mouth. Then he lifted a bruised paw and licked it.

The warriors glanced at En-gerr, two or three of them hefting their spears in a halfhearted manner.

Then The Sheep did a magnificent thing, the bravest, daftest act imaginable. Instinctively he did it with great dramatic presence. Lifting his weapons in both hands, he cast them down at his feet, first the spear, then the razor-sharp sword. He didn't say a word. Leaning over, he plucked a handful of grass, a sacred symbol of his race, and holding it in his right hand as the Masai do when making a truce, he walked toward the yellow lion. His face was set in a calm, almost cold, expression, and he walked neither too fast nor too slowly. I unslung my rifle and threw a shell into the chamber. None of the *murani* moved.

En-gerr approached the animal at his steady pace until no more than fifteen feet separated them. El Asfar stared at him, his head cocked and his ears pricked forward, for all the world like a puzzled dog.

En-gerr raised his hand and waved the grass. The lion looked at it. Keen for battle, he should, I thought, have leaped on the presumptuous creature who faced him so boldly and torn his throat out. But all he moved was his head. The whole business was uncanny.

"It is peace, chieftain," En-gerr said in a clear, carrying voice. "You are my first lion, and it is peace between us."

He tossed the grass down before El Asfar, and turned and came back toward us. The warriors began to murmur. Soon they would break into cheers, clustering around to carry The Sheep home in triumph. The tale of his insane audacity would be told in the village throughout his lifetime and beyond. And incidentally, both of my own worries would be wiped away as though they had never existed — if El Asfar did not decide to charge. He took two steps forward, lowered his muzzle to sniff at the scattered tuft of grass, then stared at the young man's retreating back.

Now, I thought, surely he'll attack. He's been making up his involved feline mind, and now he'll charge. I could not believe in this incredible peacemaking. I clung to my doubts until the very moment when En-gerr rejoined us, when the cheering arose and my friend The Sheep shook himself and blinked and broke into a sweat, grinning half in shame and half in pride; while El Asfar wheeled and padded off to catch up with his troop. I slung my rifle again. Suddenly I wanted a drink of water. My throat was like a tube of alum.[1]

I should have known, I said to myself as we turned toward home. Good will calls to good will, and courage shall recognize courage the world over, in fearless man or in the brute creation.

[1] alum (ăl′ŭm): a mineral salt that has a puckering effect on the mouth when tasted.

THINKING IT OVER

1. How was The Sheep regarded by others at the beginning of the story — by the men? the girls of the village? the author? Try to justify their views.

2. In this story the killing of a lion with a spear was a test or initiation. What tests do Boy Scouts and Girl Scouts have to pass? What do you think of such tests — and school tests as well — as a preparation for life?

3. There are two prominent animal characters in this story. Contrast the characters of El Asfar and Black Mane.

4. What earlier acts of either The Sheep or El Asfar make the unusual ending believable?

5. Name a few worth-while facts which you learned about lions and about the Masai of this story.

6. Find the theme of this story, stated at the end, and tell what you think of it as a solution for school, civic, or international problems.

7. A member of the class might like to do some reading about the Masai and report about these interesting people to the other students.

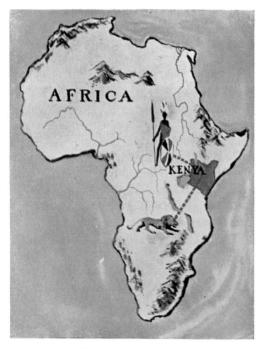

FOR YOUR VOCABULARY: THE "–SOME" SUFFIX

At one point in the story when En-gerr is described as drinking a *"noisome* concoction," it was a mixture that was annoying to the senses or smelled bad, but not one that was noisy! The *–some* suffix indicates a considerable degree of the quality shown in the first part of the word. With this to help you, try to define the following in your own words:

> a *wearisome* program
> a *bothersome* duty
> a *quarrelsome* player
> a *venturesome* boy

Check an unabridged dictionary for additional interesting *–some* words. How is *threesome* defined, for example?

ABOUT THE AUTHOR

Robert W. Krepps (1919–   ) is happiest when he is writing about Africa. Several novels and most of his short stories (more than four hundred have been printed) have African settings. "Pride of Seven" is a favorite of his, and he has written that he is happy to see it in a school anthology because he made up his mind to become a writer while he was in high school. Born in Pittsburgh, Pennsylvania, Mr. Krepps has been writing professionally ever since his graduation from Westminster College in 1941.

◄ *The Landscape of Africa* ►

The location of Kenya, which is the setting for "Pride of Seven," is indicated on the decorative map of Africa shown at the left. On the opposite page is a photograph, taken in Kenya, of Kilimanjaro, the highest mountain in Africa. Over 19,000 feet high, rising out of vast stretches of plains and jungles teeming with wildlife, snow-capped Kilimanjaro lies on the border of Kenya and its neighbor to the south, Tanganyika. Can you find passages in the story which create for you other pictures of the colorful African landscape? Perhaps a class member might locate and bring in more photographs of Kenya.

The Long Winter

WALTER HAVIGHURST

At the start of this story, your sympathies will lie entirely with young Dan McKeever. The actions of his father will anger and puzzle you. But you are asked to postpone your judgment of Ralph McKeever until you learn the reason for his behavior.

A THIN, cold rain was falling, and the air came down cold from the snow fields on Sheep Mountain. It felt like March, not the middle of May; winter couldn't let go this year. So it looked good to Dan, when he rode into the little park ringed with dripping spruce, to see his father and Gus already dismounted and blue smoke rising in the gray air. Gus threw down an armload of sticks where big Ralph McKeever was feeding a reluctant fire, fanning it with his Stetson.

The boy broke through the fringe of trees, and his father called, "Drag up one of those dead branches, Dan."

He pulled the horse over to a stunted spruce and grasped a dead limb. The wood splintered as he leaned against it, bracing himself in the stirrups. At the rending noise Diablo shied, and the boy was already off balance. He fell hard, with the broken spruce branch under him.

His father, still fanning the fire, didn't look around. "Can't you learn to stay on a horse?" he said.

Dan got up slowly, pushing the dead limb away. Gus dropped his new load of sticks and splashed across the little stream. He headed off the horse, throwing up his right arm — the one with an iron hook on the wrist — while his good hand caught the reins. In a quick hitch he tied them around a sapling.

Drawing Conclusions. All stories, not just detective or mystery tales, contain clues. And, like a good sleuth, the careful reader is on the alert for these clues. He draws conclusions based on evidence gathered along the way, and stands ready to change his conclusions when new evidence comes to light. As you read this story, stop now and again to draw some conclusions about the character of Ralph McKeever — then see whether new evidence causes you to change your conclusions.

He looked around. "Hurt, Dan?" he asked.

The boy shook his head.

At the fire his father straightened up slowly, putting the Stetson on his head. As he approached, Dan limped away, his thin jaw set. His father went back to the fire. While he fanned the blue smoke into a blaze, the boy came up, dragging the spruce limb.

The rancher snapped off the wood and tossed it on the fire. "Hungry?" he said.

"Yes," Dan answered.

"Hurt yourself?"

"No."

"When I was your age . . . going on fifteen . . ."

The boy reached up for another branch. He was almost as tall as the big man in the blue work jacket, now stained dark with drizzle, but he did not have his father's big hands nor his wide shoulders. Dan pulled at the stubborn limb.

"We've got enough wood now," his father said. "You want to camp here all day and all night?"

The boy didn't answer. He jammed his stiff hands into his pockets.

Gus came up from the creek with the coffeepot dripping. With his good hand he dumped the coffee in and set the pot in the crackling fire.

"What do you think I saw down there, boss?"

The rancher looked around.

"That young bull's track – fresh," Gus said.

Ralph McKeever scowled at his son. "You must have rode right past them," he said. "Didn't you see anything?"

"They're half in the creek," the foreman said quickly.

"Which way is he headed?"

"Couldn't tell," Gus answered. "Only shows where he crossed over. But I'd

say he was heading down."

"We'll separate then," the rancher said, "after we've had some coffee." He went to his horse and unbuckled the saddlebag.

The rain was letting up, and the fire burned briskly around the blackened coffeepot. He laid out the sandwiches and boiled eggs that Indian Mary, muttering to herself, had fixed at daylight.

A brown froth boiled over and hissed onto the fire. Gus pulled the pot off with his hook and poured smoking coffee into the tin cups.

"We'll make a sweep down the mountain," the rancher said. "I'll go over and catch the other fork of the creek. Gus, you take this fork. You drop down the canyon, Son, and follow Sheep Creek. One of us ought to pick him up on the way. We'll meet down at the flats."

Gus rinsed out the coffeepot, scouring it in the sand. He stomped on the fire and doused it with creek water, though the woods were dripping.

"You know where to go, Son?" the rancher said.

"Down the canyon."

"And keep your eyes open. That bull is worth a lot of money."

The rain began to come down harder as the rancher rode off, his slicker gleaming above the wet flank of his horse.

For a little way the foreman and young Dan rode together. Gus had the reins wrapped around his hook; his good hand pointed. "There's his track," he said, "but it don't tell much about where he was going. It fades right out after he got across."

"We might pick it up again," the boy said, "if he followed the creek."

"That's right."

For a minute there was only the crunch of hoofs and the creak of leather. Gus fingered a pinch of tobacco out of his breast pocket and crammed it into his mouth. "Saw you limping," he said. "That foot bother you?"

Dan shook his head. "It caught in the stirrup when I fell," he said. "It just got twisted."

"That canyon trail is rough. Maybe you better take this fork. I'll go down the canyon."

The boy swung around, his thin face tense under the wide brim of his hat. "Dad wouldn't — He told me to take the canyon. I can make it."

"Oh, sure," the foreman said. "But Diablo's spooking[1] today. And your foot — "

"It'll be all right."

"You sure, Danny?"

The boy sat rigid in the saddle. Danny — that was what his mother had always called him. He hadn't heard it since that gray day, with the snow swirling furiously against her bedroom window, a week before Christmas.

"I'm all right," he said. He dug his heels in, and Diablo jumped ahead. The spruce boughs rained on him as he made for the head of the canyon.

"See you at the flats," the foreman called.

Ralph McKeever had forded the noisy water and come out on the green flats when Gus appeared, driving the yearling bull ahead of him. Dan was not there. They waited awhile in the rain, looking through the drizzle toward the canyon mouth, letting the horses pull at the wet grass.

"He ought to be here," the rancher said. "It's shorter down the canyon."

"Rougher too," Gus said.

The big man grunted. "That's why I sent him that way," he said. "When I was his age, I knew every gulch be-

[1] spooking: being frightened, or pretending fright.

tween here and Granite Peak. I knew every foot of that canyon — could ride it in the dark. He's got to learn."

Gus put a wad of tobacco into his mouth.

"You know how it was last winter," the rancher said, looking off in the rain. "He took it hard. For a month after Christmas he wouldn't do a thing but tend that colt in the stable — blankets and hot water, ground oats and warm bran mash!" He turned to the slouching foreman. "But he's growing up now. Did you see him up there by the creek when he fell? It hurt all right, with that dead branch under him. But he wouldn't let me come near." The rancher smiled. "He got up and walked away. Did you see him?"

Gus nodded. "I saw him." He spat a brown stream past his horse's ear.

Daylight was nearly gone; a heavy sky was pressing down on the high, bare slopes.

"Let's be moving," the rancher said. "If he looks around any, he'll see we've been here."

They jogged on along the creek, up a draw,[2] across the big pasture. Through the dusk came a light drumming of hoofs. Then a yearling colt raced beside them, head up, showing the white feather between his pointed ears.

"That colt," the foreman said. "You wouldn't think he'd been sick all winter. I guess Dan wasn't wasting his time. Look at that stride. See how he puts his feet down. He'll make us a horse."

"He looks all right," the rancher said, "if he's got stamina."

They rode through scattered pines to the corral, and when they turned the horses out, the yellow lamplight showed from the house. They washed up at the pump, with a good smell of supper

[2] draw: a small valley or gully.

coming from the kitchen door and the radio going. Before they went in, Gus looked across the pasture where the horses were standing in the thin, cold rain.

Old Franz, his wrinkled, red face freshly scrubbed, was already sitting up against the radio that was on full blast. Soon he would take the sheep up to the high parks, where there would be no sound but the wind pouring down the pass and the sheep blatting. He got up and hobbled over to the table. "Where's young Dan?"

"In the box canyon," the rancher said. "He probably lost the trail and had to pick his way."

Indian Mary set food on the table, and they ate with the radio shouting. Ralph made a motion over his shoulder, and Mary turned the knob. Then they ate in silence. When she padded around again, filling the coffee cups, she stopped at the empty place next to the end of the table where Ellen McKeever had sat.

"That boy always hungry," she said, nodding her head so that her big shadow moved slowly on the wall. "He never get full."

"He's empty now," Gus said.

Old Franz nodded. "Hungry as a sheep," he said.

Ralph buttered a square of corn bread before he spoke. "When I was his age, I was out for days in these mountains. He has to learn."

Indian Mary stalked back to the kitchen, and there was only the noise Old Franz made, working his toothless gums and swilling coffee. They kept waiting for the sound of footsteps outside, for the door to burst open and a voice half bass and half treble to say, "I'm starved!" But when Old Franz pushed his plate back, there was only the steady dripping outside the window

and a rattle in the kitchen, where Mary was poking wood into the stove.

After the cheese and pie and another round of the coffeepot, Old Franz turned on the radio again. "Not so loud," Gus shouted around the stem of his pipe. Ralph leafed through the Durango *Herald-Democrat* and then tossed it down. He filled his pipe, stared at the dark window, and began talking about horses.

"You know why our colts bring the price we get, Gus. They survive on their own."

"That colt, Feather — " the foreman began.

The rancher went right on. "Foaled on the range, born maybe in a snowstorm, chased by coyotes and bobcats before they're a week old — they learn how to take care of themselves. Sure we lose some, but the ones that grow up are real horseflesh. They'll always have stamina."

In the slanting lamplight his face was harsh. One hand held the dead pipe in his mouth, and the other twisted a tobacco pouch till the leather was white. He was talking about horses, but even Indian Mary, moving around the table laying out the breakfast places, knew there were other things in his thoughts. There was his loneliness, his confused concern for the son he had cut himself off from, his memory of Ellen McKeever playing the upright piano at the edge of the lamplight. She had insisted on going to Durango to buy Danny's Christmas present, a bridle for the colt he was raising. She was already coughing when they started, and that trip was too much, the long cold ride back made longer when the chains broke in the deepening snow and Ralph worked with numb hands in bitter silence, mending them with a snarl of baling wire. That night, when she began to toss with fever, the telephone was dead. Somewhere in the cold woods the wire was down, though a doctor could never have got there through the drifting snow. All because of a Christmas gift.

Ralph held it against his son. And when the boy seemed lost without his mother, Ralph held that against him, too. Now he sat with a dead pipe clamped in his jaw staring at the black window.

"Shut off the radio," Gus said.

When Old Franz didn't stir, Gus jumped up, pushed him out of the way, and turned the knob. Outside, through the dripping rain, came a high-pitched whinny.

"That's Diablo," Ralph said.

Gus was already in the kitchen. He took the lantern from the wall, scratched a match on his metal hand, and turned up the wick. Then he went outside.

Ralph came out after him. At the corral gate they found Dan's horse, with raveled reins and a scarred saddle.

"Fell off again," the rancher said.

"He had a bad foot," Gus said. "It twisted when he fell this noon." He lowered the lantern and looked at the horse's ragged hoofs. "There's a rough stretch halfway up the canyon — that new rockslide."

The rain fell cold on their faces.

"We can't get up there tonight," the rancher said. "We'll have to wait for daylight."

Gus pulled off the scratched saddle and the sodden blanket, and then slipped the bridle off Diablo's head. His good hand made a flat sound on the wet rump, and the horse trotted off in the darkness. Gus heaved the saddle into the dark tack room.[1]

As they walked back to the house,

[1] **tack room:** storage room.

the rancher began, "When I was his age — "

Gus cut in. "He's got matches, and there's shelter in the canyon. He won't try to travel on a bad foot. He's hungry, though; that's sure."

"Do him good," Ralph said sharply. "The kid's got to learn to take care of himself."

Old Franz stuck his head out of the bunkhouse door. "Where's Dan?"

"His horse came in alone," Gus said.

"Where you think he is?" Old Franz insisted.

"He's still in the canyon," the rancher said. "Saddle three horses in the morning. We'll start up as soon as there's daylight."

At breakfast, while darkness was thinning outside the window, Old Franz hobbled in, excited.

"We lost a colt, boss — that new one, out of the roan mare."

"Dead?" Ralph asked.

"Dead as a sheep. Throat slit wide open. And that other colt, Feather — " the old man pushed his battered hat back — "he's cut up bad. Part of the fence is down, above the creek. I found the colt there, scared as a sheep, with the wire cuts on him."

Gus got up. "Where is he?" he asked.

"In the corral," Franz answered. "I brought him in with the others."

In the kitchen Mary had a package of sandwiches ready and a Thermos jug of smoking coffee. "That boy be hungry," she said.

"Better fill a jug of water, too," Gus said. The rancher followed him outside.

As they crossed the yard, Gus pointed. The sky was brightening, a band of pale blue spreading over the long saddle of snow on Sheep Mountain. But what Gus pointed to was a thread of smoke showing against the dark spruce slopes above the canyon.

"Halfway up the canyon," Ralph said. "He didn't get far."

Gus nodded. "By that rockslide. Right there is where you'll find him."

The rancher looked around. "You not going?" he asked.

"I figured to look at this colt."

The clatter of hoofs began as the men opened the heavy gate. The colt ran stiff-legged, head up, ears rigid, eyes rolling. He stopped on the far side of the corral and stood there sweating in the raw air. When he turned, they saw the torn forequarters and the blackened stripes down his legs.

The rancher went toward him. Snorting, tossing his thin head, the colt ran to the far corner. "Whoa, now! Whoa!" the rancher called, closing in on him. The colt bolted. The man waved his hat, and the colt dodged back, slammed into the fence, and fell. The rancher stepped up, but the colt got his blackened legs on the ground and scrambled up. "Whoa, now! Whoa!" Ralph said again. But the colt flew past him, flinging mud.

Ralph walked back to the gate. "Better turn him out," he said, pushing the hat back on his head.

But Gus stood waiting with a hackamore[1] hooked on his metal hand. "He's hurt bad," he said quietly, his eyes on the trembling colt. "He needs some help."

"It's a waste of time," Ralph said.

Gus walked up slowly, holding his good hand out. "Easy, boy, easy. Easy now." Twice the colt jerked past him, and still Gus followed, his voice going on in that steady, quiet horse talk.

"It's no use, Gus." The rancher went to the tie rack and buckled the saddlebags behind his saddle. When he

[1] **hackamore** (hăk′a·mōr): a rope halter.

looked around, Gus had the hackamore on the colt and was studying the trembling forelegs.

"Three deep cuts," he said. "I hope they don't go through those muscles." Still muttering quietly to the colt, he tied the hackamore to the rail.

"Turn him out," Ralph said.

"I'll get some tar on him." Gus hooked the blackened bucket with his metal hand.

"You're wasting time," Ralph said again. There was a new sharpness in his voice. "Turn him out, I said. Let him heal up himself. If he can't, he'll never be my kind of horse."

Gus looked up, the blue eyes thoughtful in his leathery face. "What's galling you, Ralph? Any other time — before last winter — you'd be doing this yourself. What's wrong with you?"

The tall man's face was harsher than ever, and his voice was savage. "Nothing is wrong with me. But you can't make a sound horse out of a soft one. Let him heal himself, if he can."

Gus set the bucket down. For a minute he stood scowling across the corral. Then he pulled back his sleeve and held up his right arm. It showed a worn harness strapped to his elbow and holding a leather collar onto his wrist, with the hook anchored in it. "Your father didn't talk like that when I lost a hand with a stick of his blasting powder," he said. "I was just a boy, and I thought I'd never be any good around horses or cattle with my right hand gone. I was ready to blow. But your father wouldn't let me. He made me think I could be as good as any man." Gus spat at a fence post and turned back to the colt.

"It's a waste of time," the rancher repeated.

"Then I'll do it on my own time. Take it out of my wages." Gus's blue eyes blazed as he hooked up the bucket.

Ralph climbed into his saddle. In a grim silence he rode out the gate, tugging the lead horse[1] behind him.

At the canyon mouth he waded his animals across Sheep Creek and urged them up to high ground on the far side. He stopped there, his eyes searching. The sky was clearing, there was a thin sun now, and all along the west slope the wet spruce glistened. Finally he found the gray-blue thread, thinner now but unmistakable. In the windless air the smoke went straight up, across the pale swath of aspens[2] on the mountain shoulder and the high snows on the ridge. Impatiently he nudged his horse ahead. He was not exactly worried about his son, but something was nagging him.

As he moved on up the canyon, his mind kept going back — not to last winter or any time before that — just back an hour ago, when he had ridden away in anger from the corral gate. Now he saw, as though they were there before him, a calm man and a frightened colt.

[1] the lead horse: the horse being led.
[2] swath of aspens: a row of poplar trees.

He saw a maimed hand holding the hackamore and a good hand dabbing a tarred brush at the torn forequarters. He heard a patient voice say: "Easy, boy, easy. Steady, now, steady, steady, steady." In that clear picture, Ralph saw the yearling flinch and stand. He was a proud colt, though he had been frail and awkward. He was a hurt and frightened animal, but he had courage. After this morning he'd be marked, but he'd be strengthened, too.

As Ralph rode on, he heard his own voice following him like an echo. "Let him heal himself. . . . You're only wasting time." And he saw the flash of scorn in the foreman's eyes. He was wrong, dead wrong. And Gus was right.

A realization came to him, and it was like the end of a long and numbing pain: *They don't have to survive alone. They can count on help.* The colts and horses . . . Gus and young Dan . . . even grim Ralph McKeever himself.

The sun had burned the ground haze off, and now he looked up at the washed blue sky. He nudged his horse and jogged through a scattering of cedars. In the clear again, he searched for the thread of smoke. All he saw was the rimrock and the huge sweep of the upper slopes.

He cupped a hand to his mouth and called: "Dan! . . . Dan!"

The fading echo went from wall to wall. Then there was only the small noise of Sheep Creek in the canyon's silence.

He urged his horses up a sharp grade and around a jutting boulder. As it climbed, the trail grew rougher. Then there was no trail at all. There was only a chaos of shattered rock studded by snapped and broken cedars.

"Dan!" he called. "Dan!" Now there was a pleading in his voice.

No answer came except the mocking echo. But his narrowed eyes fixed on an unshattered pine beside a massive boulder. He dismounted, unstrapped the saddlebag, and picked his way over the slide of rock.

He called again, "Dan . . ."

This time his voice was different, but the huddled figure in the huge rock's shelter did not stir. He stepped across the charred sticks and bent over. "Dan," he said quietly.

At his touch the boy awoke. For an instant his startled eyes showed white. He scrambled to his feet, but at the first step he collapsed. Then Ralph saw the bruised and blackened foot bursting out of a tattered sock.

He slit the sock with his knife and pulled it off. He opened the saddlebag, poured cold water on the sock, and bathed the swollen joint. The boy's eyes opened. He looked at his father as if from a distance.

The older man said, "You've got a bad foot, Dan."

"It — it doesn't hurt."

"Hurt? Why, sure it hurts. It hurts plenty," he said, pouring fresh water on the sock. "It's as big as a feed bag."

The boy looked down and his eyes widened.

"But it won't stay that way," Ralph said. "In a few days we'll have you as good as ever."

The boy sank back.

"What I don't see," the older man said, "is how you got this far. Every lurch in the saddle would throw you on this foot."

"I fell off," Dan answered.

"Right here? Where you had firewood and this rock for shelter? That was lucky, Dan."

"No. I crawled here."

The man looked again at his son, and now he saw the scarred hands and the torn clothing. As he dabbed at the ankle, a muscle quivered in his cheek. "We — we saw your smoke first thing this morning."

"Can I have a drink of water?" Dan asked. "I'm thirsty."

"Sure you can. I'm forgetting everything. There's hot coffee here, and sandwiches. Mary knew you would be hungry."

As Ralph unwrapped the package, a grimy hand reached out. The first sandwich went in three huge bites.

"I kept looking for the bull, Dad. Did you find him?"

"Yes, we did. Gus picked him up halfway down the gulch."

"Where is Gus?"

"In the corral. Doctoring your colt Feather. He cut himself on the new fence."

"Bad?" Dan asked.

"Yes, pretty bad. But we can take care of him. He was scared and hurt, but we'll get him over it."

The boy seemed to forget the food in his hands. Slowly his eyes went up to his father. "Dad, if we help him — will he — will he have stamina?"

Again the muscle quivered in the man's gaunt cheek. His deep-set eyes looked squarely at the boy. "Yes, he will, Dan. More than ever."

The boy swallowed the last of the sandwich. He rubbed his stomach. "I'm still hungry," he said.

"Well, Mary will know what to do about that. We'd better start home. I'm going to carry you to the horses." His arms cradled the boy. "Easy now. Take it easy. Just put your arm around my shoulder."

Ralph stepped carefully through the broken rock and lifted the boy into the saddle. They started down the trail, taking it slowly, the sun warm as a blanket on their backs.

"You all right?" the man asked. "We can stop and rest — anywhere."

"I'm all right," Dan answered.

They forded the creek and came out on the wide green flats, where the wet grass gleamed in the sun.

A magpie flew over, showing its white chevrons,[1] and from somewhere a bobolink sang his bubbling, ding-dong song over and over.

"Summer is getting here at last," the rancher said. "It's a late season. We had a long winter, but it's over now." He turned in the saddle. "You're not saying much, Danny. What's on your mind?"

The boy smiled. "Oatmeal and corn bread," he said, "bacon and pancakes. I'm starved."

[1] chevrons (shĕv'rŭnz): distinguishing markings. The term usually refers to the markings which indicate military rank or length of service.

THINKING IT OVER

1. Would you say this story is mainly about (a) cruelty, (b) the dangers of ranch life, or (c) a man's discovery about himself?

2. Why was Gus the foreman necessary in this story?

3. What role does Feather the colt play in the reunion of father and son? And in what sense is this a reunion?

4. Is Feather used as a symbol in the story? A symbol of what? What symbolism is there in the next-to-last paragraph in the story? Think about this in connection with the title and the events of the story up to this point.

5. Check the definitions for *climax* and *crisis* on page 4. What was the climax of the story? Point out several crises that led to the climax of the story. What is the story's resolution?

DRAWING CONCLUSIONS

1. Review the conclusions you made about Ralph McKeever as you read the story. Tell what you concluded about him when you reached this point in the story: "The boy didn't answer. He jammed his stiff hands into his pockets" (page 81). What evidence influenced your conclusion?

2. At the point in the story, " 'See you at the flats,' the foreman called" (page 82), you did not know much more about the reasons for Mr. McKeever's behavior, but you had learned something more about the family circle. Explain the significance in the paragraph beginning "The boy sat rigid in the saddle" (page 82).

3. By the time you reached "We'll start up as soon as there's daylight" (page 84), the rest of the evidence had been supplied, though there was no apparent change in Ralph McKeever. What was the motivation behind his actions?

4. Examine the point in the story "A realization came to him . . . The colts and horses . . . even grim Ralph McKeever himself" (page 86) and answer this question: What can you predict about the action to follow?

5. Consider this statement made by Ralph McKeever: "It's a late season. We had a long winter, but it's over now" (page 88). What change does this signify about McKeever's character?

ABOUT THE AUTHOR

Walter Havighurst (1901–) is a distinguished writer whose special field has been the Middle West. Born in Wisconsin, he attended high school in Illinois, was graduated from the University of Denver in Colorado, and has been a professor of English at Miami University in Oxford, Ohio, since 1928. Two of his better-known books are *The Quiet Shore* and *Annie Oakley of the Wild West*.

Illustrating Mood ➜

In the pen-and-ink drawing of a Colorado landscape opposite, artist Edward Shenton has sought to express the mood of "The Long Winter." Point out some details in the drawing which for you suggest the mood of the story.

The Tell-Tale Heart

EDGAR ALLAN POE

No group of stories highlighting character and setting would be complete without a contribution from Edgar Allan Poe. He was a master at setting a scene and creating startling characters. In this tale of shock and suspense he takes you inside the mind of a — But the opening sentence tells you that the narrator is *not* insane. What are you to believe?

TRUE! — nervous — very, very dreadfully nervous I had been and am; but why will you say that I am mad? The disease had sharpened my senses — not destroyed — not dulled them. Above all was the sense of hearing acute. I heard all things in the heaven and in the earth. I heard many things in hell. How, then, am I mad? Hearken! and observe how healthily — how calmly I can tell you the whole story.

It is impossible to say how first the idea entered my brain; but once conceived, it haunted me day and night. Object there was none. Passion there was none. I loved the old man. He had never wronged me. He had never given me insult. For his gold I had no desire. I think it was his eye! Yes, it was this! One of his eyes resembled that of a vulture — a pale blue eye, with a film over it. Whenever it fell upon me, my blood ran cold; and so by degrees — very gradually — I made up my mind to take the life of the old man, and thus rid myself of the eye forever.

Now this is the point. You fancy me mad. Madmen know nothing. But you should have seen me. You should have seen how wisely I proceeded — with what caution — with what foresight — with what dissimulation I went to work! I was never kinder to the old man than during the whole week before I killed him. And every night, about midnight, I turned the latch of his door and opened it — oh, so gently! And then, when I had made an opening sufficient for my head, I put in a dark lantern, all closed, closed, so that no light shone out, and then I thrust in my head. Oh, you would have laughed to see how cunningly I thrust it in! I moved it slowly — very, very slowly, so that I might not disturb the old man's sleep. It took me an hour to place my whole head within the opening so far that I could see him as he lay upon his bed. Ha! — would a madman have been so wise as this? And then, when my head was well in the room, I undid the lantern cautiously — oh, so cautiously — cautiously (for the hinges creaked) — I undid it just so much that a single thin ray fell upon the vulture eye. And this I did for seven long nights — every night just at midnight — but I found the eye always closed; and so it was impossible to do the work; for it was not the old man who vexed me, but his Evil Eye. And every morning, when the day broke, I went boldly into the chamber and spoke courageously to him, calling him by name in a hearty tone, and inquiring how he had passed the night. So you see he would have been a very profound old man, indeed, to suspect that every night, just at twelve, I looked in upon him while he slept.

Upon the eighth night I was more than usually cautious in opening the door. A watch's minute hand moves more quickly than did mine. Never before that night had I felt the extent of my own powers — of my sagacity. I could scarcely contain my feelings of triumph. To think that there I was, opening the door, little by little, and he not even to dream of my secret deeds or thoughts. I fairly chuckled at the idea; and perhaps he heard me; for he moved on the bed suddenly, as if startled. Now you may think that I drew back — but no. His room was as black as pitch with the thick darkness (for the shutters were close-fastened, through fear of robbers), and so I

knew that he could not see the opening of the door, and I kept pushing it on steadily, steadily.

I had my head in and was about to open the lantern, when my thumb slipped upon the tin fastening, and the old man sprang up in the bed, crying out — "Who's there?"

I kept quite still and said nothing. For a whole hour I did not move a muscle, and in the meantime I did not hear him lie down. He was still sitting up in the bed listening — just as I had done, night after night, hearkening to the deathwatches [1] in the wall.

Presently I heard a slight groan, and I knew it was the groan of mortal terror. It was not a groan of pain or of grief — oh, no! — it was the low stifled sound that arises from the bottom of the soul when overcharged with awe. I knew the sound well. Many a night, just at midnight, when all the world slept, it has welled up from my own bosom, deepening, with its dreadful echo, the terrors that distracted me. I say I knew it well. I knew what the old man felt, and pitied him, although I chuckled at heart. I knew that he had been lying awake ever since the first slight noise, when he had turned in the bed. His fears had been ever since growing upon him. He had been trying to fancy them causeless, but could not. He had been saying to himself — "It is nothing but the wind in the chimney — it is only a mouse crossing the floor," or "It is merely a cricket which has made a single chirp." Yes, he had been trying to comfort himself with these suppositions; but he had found all in vain. All in vain; because Death, in approaching him, had stalked with his black shadow before

[1] **deathwatches:** small insects which make a ticking sound believed by the superstitious to be a forewarning of death.

him, and enveloped the victim. And it was the mournful influence of the unperceived shadow that caused him to feel — although he neither saw nor heard — to feel the presence of my head within the room.

When I had waited a long time, very patiently, without hearing him lie down, I resolved to open a little — a very, very little crevice in the lantern. So I opened it — you cannot imagine how stealthily, stealthily — until, at length, a single dim ray, like the thread of the spider, shot from out the crevice and full upon the vulture eye.

It was open — wide, wide open — and I grew furious as I gazed upon it. I saw it with perfect distinctness — all a dull blue, with a hideous veil over it that chilled the very marrow in my bones; but I could see nothing else of the old man's face or person: for I had directed the ray as if by instinct, precisely upon the damned spot.

And now have I not told you that what you mistake for madness is but overacuteness of the senses? — now, I say, there came to my ears a low, dull, quick sound, such as a watch makes when enveloped in cotton. I knew that sound well, too. It was the beating of the old man's heart. It increased my fury, as the beating of a drum stimulates the soldier into courage.

But even yet I refrained and kept still. I scarcely breathed. I held the lantern motionless. I tried how steadily I could maintain the ray upon the eye. Meantime the hellish tattoo of the heart increased. It grew quicker and quicker, and louder and louder every instant. The old man's terror must have been extreme! It grew louder, I say, louder every moment! — do you mark me well? I have told you that I am nervous: so I am. And now at the dead hour of the night, amid the dreadful

silence of that old house, so strange a noise as this excited me to uncontrollable terror. Yet for some minutes longer I refrained and stood still. But the beating grew louder, louder! I thought the heart must burst. And now a new anxiety seized me — the sound would be heard by a neighbor! The old man's hour had come! With a loud yell, I threw open the lantern and leaped into the room. He shrieked once — once only. In an instant I dragged him to the floor and pulled the heavy bed over him. I then smiled gaily, to find the deed so far done. But, for many minutes the heart beat on with a muffled sound. This, however, did not vex me; it would not be heard through the wall. At length it ceased. The old man was dead. I removed the bed and examined the corpse. Yes, he was stone, stone-dead. I placed my hand upon the heart and held it there many minutes. There was no pulsation. He was stone-dead. His eye would trouble me no more.

If still you think me mad, you will think so no longer when I describe the wise precautions I took for the concealment of the body. The night waned, and I worked hastily, but in silence. First of all I dismembered the corpse. I cut off the head and the arms and the legs.

I then took up three planks from the flooring of the chamber, and deposited all between the scantlings.[1] I then replaced the boards so cleverly, so cunningly, that no human eye — not even his — could have detected anything wrong. There was nothing to wash out — no stain of any kind — no blood spot whatever. I had been too wary for that. A tub had caught all — ha! ha!

When I had made an end of these labors, it was four o'clock — still dark

[1] **scantlings:** crosspieces.

as midnight. As the bell sounded the hour, there came a knocking at the street door. I went down to open it with a light heart — for what had I now to fear? There entered three men, who introduced themselves, with perfect suavity, as officers of the police. A shriek had been heard by a neighbor during the night; suspicion of foul play had been aroused; information had been lodged at the police office, and they (the officers) had been deputed to search the premises.

I smiled — for what had I to fear? I bade the gentlemen welcome. The shriek, I said, was my own in a dream. The old man, I mentioned, was absent in the country. I took my visitors all over the house. I bade them search — search well. I led them, at length, to his chamber. I showed them his treasures, secure, undisturbed. In the enthusiasm of my confidence, I brought chairs into the room, and desired them here to rest from their fatigues, while I myself, in the wild audacity of my perfect triumph, placed my own seat upon the very spot beneath which reposed the corpse of the victim.

The officers were satisfied. My manner had convinced them. I was singularly at ease. They sat, and while I answered cheerily, they chatted familiar things. But, ere long, I felt myself getting pale and wished them gone. My head ached, and I fancied a ringing in my ears: but still they sat and still chatted. The ringing became more distinct; it continued and became more distinct. I talked more freely to get rid of the feeling, but it continued and gained definitiveness — until, at length, I found that the noise was not within my ears.

No doubt I now grew very pale; but I talked more fluently, and with a heightened voice. Yet the sound increased — and what could I do? It was a low, dull, quick sound — much such a sound as a watch makes when enveloped in cotton. I gasped for breath — and yet the officers heard it not. I talked more quickly — more vehemently; but the noise steadily increased. I arose and argued about trifles, in a high key and with violent gesticulations, but the noise steadily increased. Why would they not be gone? I paced the floor to and fro with heavy strides, as if excited to fury by the observation of the men — but the noise steadily increased. Oh, God! What could I do? I foamed — I raved — I swore! I swung the chair upon which I had been sitting, and grated it upon the boards, but the noise arose over all and continually increased. It grew louder — louder — louder! And still the men chatted pleasantly and smiled. Was it possible they heard not? Almighty God! — no, no! They heard! — they suspected! — they knew! — they were making a mockery of my horror! — this I thought, and this I think. But anything was better than this agony! Anything was more tolerable than this derision! I could bear those hypocritical smiles no longer! I felt that I must scream or die! — and now — again! — hark! louder! louder! louder! louder!

"Villains!" I shrieked. "Dissemble no more! I admit the deed! — tear up the planks! here, here! — it is the beating of his hideous heart!"

THINKING IT OVER

1. The murder itself is described rather sketchily. Just how was the old man killed? Is this scene believable?

2. If you were an attorney appointed by the court to defend the murderer, what defense would you make? How could you use this story to assist your defense instead of to damage it?

3. Why not have three members of the class — not necessarily all boys — actually pretend to be the police officers in the story. The scene is back at the station and the captain (the fourth member of the cast) begins something like this: "All right, men, now let's have your story just as it happened." One officer should be the spokesman, with the others correcting and adding to the story and with the captain occasionally asking to have things clarified. When the end of the story as Poe has told it has been reached, see if any of the cast can continue the action and relate what happened *after* the narrator's sudden confession.

READING WITH QUESTIONS IN MIND

1. The first sentence of this story provides an immediate question: "Is the narrator insane?" What is your conclusion on the evidence of the first paragraph alone?

2. The first sentence of the second paragraph poses another question: "What is going to happen?" That question is answered in the last sentence of the paragraph. In between those two sentences, however, you have probably begun to suspect the answer because of several other questions that the story has raised: Why does the narrator say there was no object, no passion, to his crime? Why is there this emphasis on the eye? Why does he say he loved the old man?

3. Finally, of course, you must ask yourself the summing-up question: Has the author made the story real and convincing for me? Did he make me believe in the situation and its outcome?

LOOKING AT STYLE

"True! — nervous — very, very dreadfully nervous I had been and am; but why will you say that I am mad?" This opening sentence from the story is a perfect illustration of Poe's unique style of writing. Notice how he sets off the very first word with an exclamation point — True! — giving the story an immediate dramatic impact. Notice his use of dashes in the sentence, which make the reader almost hear the frantic agitation of the narrator. The word *nervous* is used twice; in its second usage, Poe adds the adverbs *very, very dreadfully*, which seem to in-

crease the narrator's nervousness right before the reader's eye. The sentence ends with a question — "but why will you say that I am mad?" By then, the reader already knows the answer, and the violent atmosphere of the story has already been achieved. Find other passages from the story where the words and phrases, the punctuation, and the rhythm of the words all contribute to the tension and horror of the tale. In his use of rhythm, Poe was building toward a particular effect. What do you think it is?

ABOUT THE AUTHOR

Edgar Allan Poe (1809–1849) died at the early age of forty, but in his brief lifetime he had a profound effect on American literature and especially on the short story. Adopted into a wealthy family in Richmond, Virginia, he was a brilliant student but erratic in behavior. His stories in a Southern literary magazine were so widely read that the magazine's circulation rose from 700 to 50,000 copies. His poetry and stories gained fame both here and abroad, and he was an able magazine editor and critic.

RELATING THE STORIES

1. The stories in this group make use of a wide variety of settings. Look over each story and explain how the setting was important to the story.

2. Select one story and point out very briefly how the nature of the main character or one of the main characters was instrumental in determining the action of the story — that is, show how *character* caused *action* in the story.

As the Artist Sees It ➤

Poe used words to establish the forbidding atmosphere of "The Tell-Tale Heart." In the illustration opposite, artist Robert Shore has used a painter's tools to create the same atmosphere. Notice how the orange-lavender-black color scheme captures the story's sense of horror and tension. What details in the drawing suggest the mental state of the narrator?

Theme: Ideas in Stories

The word *theme* would seem, perhaps, not to belong in an analysis of the short story. For you the word probably represents something quite removed from the fiction world of stories. No doubt in your school career you have practiced the writing of themes. Your English teacher assigns the class a topic or a list of topics from which to make a selection. From such a list, you choose the one which appeals to you the most. It is something that you care about, a topic that concerns and interests you. In the theme that you write, you try to express your thoughts and ideas about the topic. You end with a conclusion: this is what you think about the topic; this is your final word, your summary. You might not have been aware of it, but the author of a short story provides a conclusion similar to that of a theme. In the story itself will be found the author's ideas regarding the subject with which he is dealing. The ending of the story — happy or sad, with the hero either triumphing or suffering defeat — will indicate the author's final word on the subject.

The element of *theme* is as present in a story as are the elements of plot, character, and setting. A story, any story, is always *about* something. To determine the theme of a story, the reader asks himself: What point does this story make? Does it express an opinion or belief? The author might be expressing an idea about courage or love or loyalty. The author might be saying, in effect, that "Courage can endure," or that "True loyalty cannot be bought or sold." This is the underlying idea of a story, expressed by the author in terms of a plot and characters. All stories have themes. The difference lies in a matter of degree. Certain stories contain a passionate, deeply felt conviction about something. That conviction is felt in every line of the story. The author might be expressing his ideas in terms of humor or irony, or his tone might be grave and serious. But the conviction, the theme, will be there. In such stories theme becomes a major element.

The stories which make up this next group all contain particular ideas about life and the world. As you read, look for these ideas which the authors are expressing. What is the author saying? What are his feelings on the subject? What does the outcome of the story indicate about his feelings? These are the questions to ask yourself. You will enjoy the plots of these stories. The settings, which include a modern high school in California as well as a school for knights back in the days when people believed in dragons, will be of interest to you, as will the characters in the stories. Most of the characters, incidentally, are young people like yourselves, so you will have a good deal in common with them. But each of the five stories has a strong theme, or underlying idea. It is that element which you will want to talk over and think about.

A Man Who Had No Eyes

MacKINLAY KANTOR

The person who has more "can" power than "can't" in his make-up will succeed in spite of difficulties and physical handicaps. That's the theme of this story. Now see how the author develops it into a startling climax.

A BEGGAR was coming down the avenue just as Mr. Parsons emerged from his hotel.

He was a blind beggar, carrying the traditional battered cane and thumping his way before him with the cautious, half-furtive effort of the sightless. He was a shaggy, thick-necked fellow; his coat was greasy about the lapels and pockets, and his hand splayed over the cane's crook with a futile sort of clinging. He wore a black pouch slung over his shoulder. Apparently he had something to sell.

The air was rich with spring; sun was warm and yellowed on the asphalt. Mr. Parsons, standing there in front of his hotel and noting the clack-clack approach of the sightless man, felt a sudden and foolish sort of pity for all blind creatures.

And, thought Mr. Parsons, he was very glad to be alive. A few years ago he had been little more than a skilled laborer; now he was successful, respected, admired. . . . Insurance . . . And he had done it alone, unaided, struggling beneath handicaps. . . . And he was still young. The blue air of spring, fresh from its memories of windy pools and lush shrubbery, could thrill him with eagerness.

He took a step forward just as the tap-tapping blind man passed him by. Quickly the shabby fellow turned.

"Listen, guv'nor. Just a minute of your time."

Mr. Parsons said, "It's late. I have an appointment. Do you want me to give you something?"

"I ain't no beggar, guv'nor. You bet

Drawing Conclusions. Beginning with the first paragraph, notice the little details that the author has furnished to tell you about the two main characters. Paying attention to these details will enable you to draw conclusions about the two men even before the author has provided all the facts about their characters and previous lives.

I ain't. I got a handy little article here" — he fumbled until he could press a small object into Mr. Parsons' hand — "that I sell. One buck. Best cigarette lighter made."

Mr. Parsons stood there, somewhat annoyed and embarrassed. He was a handsome figure, with his immaculate gray suit and gray hat and malacca stick.[1] Of course the man with the cigarette lighters could not see him. . . . "But I don't smoke," he said.

"Listen. I bet you know plenty people who smoke. Nice little present," wheedled the man. "And, mister, you wouldn't mind helping a poor guy out?" He clung to Mr. Parsons' sleeve.

Mr. Parsons sighed and felt in his vest pocket. He brought out two half dollars and pressed them into the man's hand. "Certainly. I'll help you out. As you say, I can give it to someone. Maybe the elevator boy would — " He hesitated, not wishing to be boorish and inquisitive, even with a blind peddler. "Have you lost your sight entirely?"

The shabby man pocketed the two half dollars. "Fourteen years, guv'nor." Then he added with an insane sort of pride: "Westbury, sir. I was one of 'em."

"Westbury," repeated Mr. Parsons. "Ah, yes. The chemical explosion. . . . The papers haven't mentioned it for years. But at the time it was supposed to be one of the greatest disasters in — "

"They've all forgot about it." The fellow shifted his feet wearily. "I tell you, guv'nor, a man who was in it don't forget about it. Last thing I ever saw was C shop going up in one grand smudge, and that awful gas pouring in at all the busted windows."

Mr. Parsons coughed. But the blind

peddler was caught up with the train of his one dramatic reminiscence. And, also, he was thinking that there might be more half dollars in Mr. Parsons' pocket.

"Just think about it, guv'nor. There was a hundred and eight people killed, about two hundred injured, and over fifty of them lost their eyes. Blind as bats — " He groped forward until his dirty hand rested against Mr. Parsons' coat. "I tell you, sir, there wasn't nothing worse than that in the war. If I had lost my eyes in the war, okay. I would have been well took care of. But I was just a workman, working for what was in it. And I got it. You're so right I got it, while the capitalists were making their dough! They was insured, don't worry about that. They — "

"Insured," repeated his listener. "Yes. That's what I sell — "

"You want to know how I lost my eyes?" cried the man. "Well, here it is!" His words fell with the bitter and studied drama of a story often told, and told for money. "I was there in C shop, last of all the folks rushing out. Out in the air there was a chance, even with buildings exploding right and left. A lot of guys made it safe out the door and got away. And just when I was about there, crawling along between those big vats, a guy behind me grabs my leg. He says, 'Let me past, you ——!' Maybe he was nuts. I dunno. I try to forgive him in my heart, guv'nor. But he was bigger than me. He hauls me back and climbs right over me! Tramples me into the dirt. And he gets out, and I lie there with all that poison gas pouring down on all sides of me, and flame and stuff. . . ." He swallowed — a studied sob — and stood dumbly expectant. He could imagine the next words: Tough luck, my man. Awfully tough. Now, I want to — "That's the story, guv'nor."

[1] malacca stick: a cane made from the wood of palm trees found in Malaya.

The spring wind shrilled past them, damp and quivering.

"Not quite," said Mr. Parsons.

The blind peddler shivered crazily. "Not quite? What you mean, you — ?"

"The story is true," Mr. Parsons said, "except that it was the other way around."

"Other way around?" He croaked unamiably. "Say, guv'nor — "

"I was in C shop," said Mr. Parsons. "It was the other way around. You were the fellow who hauled back on me and climbed over me. You were bigger than I was, Markwardt."

The blind man stood for a long time, swallowing hoarsely. He gulped: "Parsons. By heaven! By heaven! I thought you — " And then he screamed fiendishly: "Yes. Maybe so. Maybe so. But I'm blind! I'm blind, and you've been standing here letting me spout to you, and laughing at me every minute! I'm blind!"

People in the street turned to stare at him.

"You got away, but I'm blind! Do you hear? I'm — "

"Well," said Mr. Parsons, "don't make such a row about it, Markwardt. . . . So am I."

THINKING IT OVER

1. Try to state the theme of this story in different wording than was used in the introduction. Do you agree with the theme? Explain your answer.

2. Many stories carry a surprise at the end, but this one has two surprises. What are they?

3. Find some details in the first four paragraphs that suggest Mr. Parsons' condition without actually stating it.

4. What is the earliest evidence you can find which indicates that Mr. Parsons might have had more than second-hand knowledge of the industrial disaster?

5. Do you know any real-life story of a blind person who succeeded in spite of his handicap? If so, be ready to tell the class about this person. Later in this book you will read Karsten Ohnstad's autobiographical selection, "The World at My Finger Tips" (page 280), which is a true account of what it is like to be blind.

DRAWING CONCLUSIONS

1. Does the second paragraph cause you to admire or to distrust the beggar? What are the descriptive words or phrases which make you draw some tentative conclusions about him?

2. How does paragraph 3 make you feel about Mr. Parsons? What does his reaction to the approach of the beggar make you conclude about at least one aspect of his character?

3. Examine the first three speeches of the beggar. What more do you conclude about him from his speech?

4. Even though the description of the beggar and his speech have probably made you believe that he is not very admirable, your final conclusion about him comes through the speech of Mr. Parsons. What is this damaging revelation?

5. If the beggar had been self-reliant and Mr. Parsons rude and unkind, how would the theme of the story have been affected?

PEN AND PAPER

The beggar in the story is not too admirable, but even so he is pitiable. Imagine that he is to be tried for some minor criminal offense, and that you are his defense attorney. Write out your defense of him, citing the factors which you believe should entitle him to mercy.

ABOUT THE AUTHOR

MacKinlay Kantor (1904–) knew early in life that he wanted to be a writer. At seventeen he had a full-time job as a reporter on his home-town newspaper in Webster City, Iowa, and at eighteen he won first prize in a short story contest. His early ambition has carried him through journalism, free-lance writing, motion picture scenario work, and a stretch as a war correspondent in World War II. Of his many novels, you are most likely to be acquainted with *The Voice of Bugle Ann*.

As Ye Sow, So Shall Ye Reap

JESSE STUART

Trying to get even with someone just doesn't pay. Usually the opposite happens. That's the title and that's the theme of this Kentucky mountain story about some boyish vandalism and the poetic justice that catches up with the culprits.

I WANT you to know that I didn't plan it. I'd've never thought of doing such a thing to a neighbor if it hadn't been for my cousin Winn . . . Winn Shelton. . . . He's the one that has idears about gettin' even with people. When anybody does 'im a wrong once, he never forgets it. He goes back after 'im if it is a year, two years, or ten years later. I'm not like that. I never was like that.

"Knucklehead," Winn said to me when we stood in the barn loft with empty lard cans. "What's th' matter with you? Are you a-goin' to get cold feet?"

"But this ain't right, Winn!" I told 'im. "Something down deep in me tells me it's wrong!"

"That's not the way you talked when old Jeff made you play on one side the creek and Martha on the other," Winn said, showing two missin' teeth as he

laughed. "He never thought enough o' you to let you go with 'er. You know that! And you know you love 'er too!"

Winn knew just what to say to make me warm under the collar. I was in love with Martha and when I went to Skinner's shack on Sundays to play with Eddie and Tom, Jeff Skinner, Martha's Pappie, would get himself a chair and sit under the peach-tree shade with an open Bible on his lap. He'd pretend that he's a-readin' his Bible, but all the time he'd have his eye on me. He'd make us boys play on one side the little creek that flowed down past his house. He'd make his girls play on the other side. Though Minnie and Mary were mighty pretty, Martha was the one for me. She was so pretty, she hurt my eyes.

"Well, why don't you say something?" Winn asked me as he put his lard cans down on the barn-loft floor. "You know what I got against th' Skinners! Tom and Eddie double-teamed on me and whopped me, but I'll make 'em pay for it. I'll make 'em do a lot o' diggin'. I thought you'd want to get even with 'em too."

"But I tell you, I'm afraid. They've

got shotguns and rifles in th' house and they're all good shots!"

"But they'll never see us," Winn said, shaking his long index finger under my nose. "They'll all be in bed asleep. You're a coward! You've got cold feet! Let Martha's Pappie push you around any old way and you don't do anything about it!"

When Winn reminded me again of the way Martha's Pappie had treated me, he didn't have to say another word. That's why I started scooping up double handfuls of mixed timothy, redtop, orchard grass, blue grass, and Johnson grass from the hay where Uncle Mel had forked it to feed his cattle.

"Now, you're a working fellow," Winn said, working to fill his can first. But as I worked, I thought about Martha and I beat Winn. Winn is right after all, I thought. I ought to get even with old Jeff Skinner. He has never been a friend to me. Long ago when Martha and I were smaller, he used to invite me to come to his house and stay all night with his boys. And now that Martha is fifteen and I'm sixteen, he won't do that. But he didn't know I had my eye on Martha when I was smaller and that I've never taken it off'n her since.

Just as soon as Winn had filled his can, we climbed down the barn-loft ladder and took off up the hill through the bushes and briers. But it wasn't as bad as you'd think, for Winn had made a little path to Jeff Skinner's strawberry patch.

"Since they didn't invite me to their fresh strawberries this spring, I had to invite myself," Winn grunted, getting his second wind as we climbed the winding path, over the rocks, around the trees, and through the briers with our loads restin' on our shoulders.

I'd never heard that anybody was a-takin' Jeff Skinner's strawberries either. When anything like this happens on the creek where I live, everybody knows about it and everybody's a-talkin' about it. One thing the people on th' creek where I live don't like, and that's a thief. And I didn't know my cousin was a thief. If anybody'd a-told me that he'd a-stolen strawberries, I wouldn't've believed 'im. And if I'd've known it in time, I wouldn't've been headin' toward Jeff Skinner's strawberry patch with a load o' grass seeds either.

"Oh, boy, ain't this wonderful," Winn said as we broke through the trees into the big clearin' surrounded by trees. "Here's where we do th' work! A pretty berry patch, ain't it? Look how pretty and clean! But in a couple o' weeks it'll be pretty grassy!"

A moon, brighter than a shined brass button and bigger than a wagon wheel, looked from a low blue sky on us. And it lighted up the berry patch until we could see the grass seeds we were broadcastin'.[1] Each took a row of strawberries at a time, like Winn planned it.

"It'll take a lot of grass seeds to sow all this field," I whispered to Winn. "It'll take us to midnight if we sow it a row at th' time."

"We've got plenty o' seed in our barn loft," Winn said, "and we've got all night to do it. We must not leave any spot without seeds upon it."

And the strawberry patch was just right for sowin' in grass, since Skinners had gone through it with their hoes and had cut th' sprouts and pulled each little sprig of grass with their hands from around their strawberries. The ground was clean around the plants as a hound dog's tooth. And it was as soft where they had used garden rakes to

[1] **broadcastin':** scattering seed in all directions.

AS YE SOW, SO SHALL YE REAP   **101**

harrow the tiny clods as a lettuce bed. I knew that grass would come up almost overnight and sod the berry patch if Skinners didn't get down on their knees and pull it out.

And they will know the kind of grass it is, too, I thought. They will know the kinds of hay Uncle Mel Shelton feeds his cattle. They will know where the seeds come from. And something Mom used to tell me went through my head: As ye sow, so shall ye reap. And when I thought of these words, I trembled as we went down the path for more grass seeds.

We'd carried eleven loads of grass seeds to Skinner's strawberry patch and had broadcast 'em row by row so as to be sure there would be enough seed on the ground. And this was enough seed, the way Uncle Mel and Pa had sowed our pasture fields, to have sowed forty acres. That's what I tried to tell Winn as we went after the twelfth and last load. That would make us twenty-four lard cans of seeds sowed on less than four acres. But Winn would have it his way, and I was so tired I could hardly walk.

As I climbed the hill with my twelfth lard can, my legs felt weak and trembly. And all over the country the roosters started crowin' for midnight. That's why I know it was after midnight, for we'd reached the field and had just finished the little rows in the topmost corner of the field when it happened.

"It's a good job well done," Winn said as he scraped his last handful of seed from the bottom of his can and sowed 'em on a spot he'd sowed before just to be sure. "Now I can go home and sleep in peace since I'm even with Eddie and Tom. They'll lose more sweat diggin' out this grass than I lost on them. They'll take more of a beatin' in this field than they gave me. I'll slip up here

and peep from the bushes when they start diggin' up this grass and I'll laugh to myself as I watch 'em work! You'll come along too, won't you?"

"No, I don't think I will," I said, sowing my last handful. "I'll be glad to get away from here. I'll never want to see this field again; I'm tired. I want to go home and go to bed!"

"I thought you'd enjoy seeing old Jeff bend his back over his hoe handle," Winn said. "I thought you'd like to see 'im get down on his prayer bones and pull grass."

And then Winn laughed loud enough for anybody to hear 'im.

"What is that, Winn?" I asked, pointing to something white and black a-comin' into the berry patch.

"It's a dog," Winn said, partly holding his breath. "And I believe it's a mad dog. Look how it's a-comin' in an even trot not lookin' to right nor left!"

It had come up the path Winn had made to the berry patch. That is the reason I saw it. We'd started back and we were facin' th' path.

"I believe it's a mad dog, too," I screamed as it came toward us. "Which way'll we go? We can't make th' path! We'll have to pass it!"

"This way," Winn screamed, takin' off with the lard can a-bangin' against his leg as he went. "Follow me!"

I was right at Winn's heels with my cap in one hand and my lard can in th' other, liftin' my feet so high my heels were a-hittin' me in the back.

"This way," Winn screamed, hurdlin' a pile of logs at the far end of the berry patch. I ran over the logs and crashed into the brush and was through it like a rabbit. I was on Winn's heels when he reached th' loggin' road that led to my house.

"Head for my house," I screamed as we sailed like two birds down the broad loggin' road that had a few low stumps just right to catch our toes. And one did catch Winn's toe before he reached the foot of the hill, and he must've scooted fifteen feet flat on his stomach, his lard can rolling ahead.

"The dog's on our heels," I screamed as Winn jumped to his feet and grabbed his lard can. "Come on!"

I passed Winn up when he fell, but I didn't hold my gain long. His legs were a little longer than mine and he pulled up beside me and we ran side by side almost a half mile. Then I looked back 'r I might've stayed beside Winn. . . .

"He's behind us, Winn," I screamed. "Can we take to a tree?"

"No," Winn shouted. "Let's get to your house and get a gun!"

How we did it, I don't know. I was tired when we started. But you let a mad dog get after you and you see what happens! Just something in you, no matter if your legs are tired, trembly and shaky, that lifts you up and makes you almost fly. And this was a time when I wished that I was a bird with wings! My breath came hard and then it got easy again. And then it came hard again. And just as we reached a pair of drawbars,[1] I saw Winn throw his lard can and sail over 'em like a bird, his body bent forward, his hands almost touchin' his toes as he went over with the seat of his pants barely missin' th' top drawbar. I turned and threw my lard can at the mad dog and then dove headforemost between two bars, hittin' th' ground on my stomach.

When I got to my feet, I looked behind me and here came the mad dog. His shoulders were at an even pace and he didn't look to th' left nor th' right.

"Come, come, Shan!" Winn screamed.

[1] drawbars: removable bars in a fence, making a crude gate.

"Maybe we can make it!"

"You'll make it," I yelled. "But he's about to get me!"

Winn shouted to me: "Save your breath. You can do it!"

We had one more pair of bars and then we had to cross over a little gap where the road went over from the hollow to our house. I don't know how I did it, but I laid my hand on the top drawbar just as Winn had done seconds before. I hand-sprung th' drawbars and hit runnin' with all the breath I had left and all the strength in my body, for we'd run nearly two miles. The mad dog was twenty feet or less behind me as I climbed the grade between the cliffs in the gap and coasted down the other side to our house. Winn beat me and hit our door like a ton of rocks.

"Mad dog!" he screamed. "Mad dog! Uncle Mick, fetch the gun!"

Winn held to the doorknob to stand up and I pitched headlong on the grass, scootin' on my stomach over the wet grass up to where my head hit the log wall of our house and it jarred me all over.

Pa come out o' th' house in his nightshirt with a double-barreled shotgun in his hand.

"Where is he?" Pa shouted.

"We've barely escaped 'im," I grunted from where I lay on the grass. "He come nigh t' a-bitin' both o' us!"

Just then we heard Black Boy start growlin' and Pa took off barefooted around th' house.

"Be keerful, Uncle," Winn grunted with a half breath.

"But I'll get 'im," Pa said. "And in a hurry, too!"

We waited in silence for him to shoot.

"Behave yourself, Black Boy," we heard 'im say.

And then the two dogs stopped growlin'.

"What color was that dog?" Pa asked as he came back around the corner with th' double barrel across his shoulder and a disappointed look on his face.

"White and black," I said.

"That's Jeff Skinner's dog," Pa said. "He's around there a-arguin' with Black Boy over a bone! He's not mad! Mad dogs don't eat! They don't fuss over a bone! They bite!"

"Why did he run us if he wasn't mad?" Winn asked.

"Skinners don't have a dog like that," I said.

"Oh, yes they do," Pa said. "I was over there Wednesday and Jeff showed me his new dog. He's a trained dog for thieves, and somebody's been a-gettin' into Jeff's berries."

I got up to my feet and looked at Winn. He stopped leanin' against th' house and looked at me.

"He's trained, so Jeff told me, just to run people," Pa said. "And if one tries to make a tree, he really works on 'im as he goes up th' tree. Or if he stops on the road, he'll mighty nigh take a leg off. I suppose Jeff and his boys're a-comin' somewhere along th' road behind him now!"

Winn didn't speak and I didn't speak, but I heard his heart poundin' and I know he heard mine poundin' faster than it did when the dog was behind me.

"Don't suppose you boys were in his berry patch?"

I didn't answer, for the words wouldn't come. They choked in my gullet. Winn looked down at the ground. I looked at Pa, but I didn't see him. I could see Winn in front with his long-handled gooseneck hoe as he went up the path toward the berry patch. And I could feel my hoe handle in my hand as I followed 'im. I could see the green meadow before us we would have to hoe, weed, and clean while Jeff Skinner came to the field each day to see if we were doin' it right. And I could see Eddie and Tom sittin' in the shade and I could hear 'em laughin' at Winn down on his prayer bones. Martha, I could see her too. So pretty she hurt my eyes. Maybe she'd know I'd done it for her.

THINKING IT OVER

1. To understand why two boys would do all the hard work involved in the story, you need some exposition from the author. In other words, you need to know what happened *before* the barn scene in paragraph 2. What is the exposition given for Winn? for Shan? Find the passages in the story that supply this information. With this information you will understand the motivation behind the boys' act.

2. To build a suspenseful climax, an author often throws a series of hurdles into the path of his main characters as they struggle to overcome their difficulties. Name at least five hurdles Winn and Shan must scale in their flight from the berry patch.

3. Point out some differences in character between the two boys. Then try to answer this question: Does Shan deserve the same punishment as Winn?

4. How do you explain the final sentence in the story? Which of the two boys do you think learned a lesson from the experience?

ABOUT THE AUTHOR

Jesse Stuart (1907–   ) was born in a one-room coal miner's shack in the Kentucky mountains. It was in high school that a teacher gave him a book of Robert Burns's poems to read, an experience which made him determined to be a writer someday. When Jesse Stuart was twenty-seven, he saw published his first book of poems, *Man with a Bull-Tongue Plow*. Since then he has written novels, articles, and many short stories, and has been a teacher and farmer as well. You will become better acquainted with Jesse Stuart in his autobiographical selection "The Thread That Runs So True" on page 240.

Trademark

JESSAMYN WEST

Just having a goal and working toward it brings satisfaction to a person. But sometimes there's the problem of choosing the right goal. This story is about a girl, her goal, and the way her plans turned out.

M<small>RS.</small> D<small>ELAHANTY</small> went to the door of Crescent's room to remind her that it was time to set the table for supper. It was a fine Saturday afternoon in November, and ordinarily Cress would have been outside, up in the hills with friends, or helping her father with the irrigation; or just walking about under the pepper and eucalyptus [1] trees in the yard, deep in a world which found significance in the parchmentlike bark peeled from a eucalyptus tree or in a bunch of berries (thirteen berries, exactly the number of years she had been alive — what was the meaning of that?) dropped from the pepper tree. But this afternoon Cress had spent in her room in spite of the clear warm weather, and Mrs. Delahanty examined her daughter's stubby, somewhat boyish profile

[1] **eucalyptus** (ū′kà·lĭp′tŭs): a tree, native to Australia but common in California.

outlined against the golden light of the west windows with considerable curiosity.

"What are you writing, Cress?"

Cress looked up from the sheets of paper spread before her on the drop leaf of the rickety bamboo desk she had bought for herself that summer and said, "I'm not exactly writing, Mother." The sheets had words on them and Cress had a pencil in her hand and, as if aware of this contradiction between appearance and truth, she added, "I'm making a list."

At this Mrs. Delahanty smiled. In school she had learned that ontogeny recapitulates phylogeny [2] and, while she had always been somewhat hazy as to the meaning of that sentence, still it had stayed in her memory and was, amended, her formula for accounting for her daughter: Cress recapitulates John. Since she loved and approved her

[2] **ontogeny recapitulates phylogeny** (ŏn·tŏj′é·nĭ rē′kà·pĭt′ů·lāts fĭ·lŏj′é·nĭ): the life history of an individual recapitulates, or repeats, the life history of the species. That is, a human being passes through stages in the development of the species before he is born.

husband, believing him to be not only handsome but as often as not wise and sensible as well, she was glad this was so. Yet it was strange, as now, to see the gestures and habits of a large dark thirty-eight-year-old rancher recapitulated in a medium-sized tow-haired girl.

How much simpler my life would have been, she thought, easing her shoulders against the door jamb, if Cress had recapitulated me, instead of John. Nor was she helped any in understanding Cress's activity, by the fact that it was one she had witnessed in John for fifteen years. More than fifteen years.

"What are you making a list of, Cress?" she asked.

She had no fear that she was intruding in private matters. One of John's greatest pleasures was the sharing of his lists. After two or three evenings hunched over catalogues and sheets of paper he would look up, about bedtime, and say, "See what you think of this, Gertrude," and begin to read from a list headed, "Supplies Needed for a Prolonged Trip in Sub-Zero Weather."

Cress looked up from *her* list and answered, "I'm making a list of traits, Mother."

"Traits?" Mrs. Delahanty asked.

"Good and bad traits," Cress said, and then explained further. "For school, that is."

"You mean personal traits?" Mrs. Delahanty asked.

"Kind of," Cress replied.

Mrs. Delahanty wondered anew. "Traits like honesty, kindness, cheerfulness?" she asked.

"Well, like them," Cress said, "but they aren't on it. This is a list of traits useful for school."

"Isn't honesty useful for school?"

"Nobody at school I ever heard of was popular for honesty," Cress said.

After Mrs. Delahanty had considered this in silence for some seconds Cress asked, "Did you ever hear anybody say, 'I'm just crazy about her, she's so honest'? Did you?"

"No," Mrs. Delahanty admitted, "I guess I never did."

"Me either," Cress said. "It's all right to be honest," Cress reassured her, "but there's nothing very outstanding about it."

"Oh, I don't know," Mrs. Delahanty said, trying to keep a foothold in this conversation which she felt to be, in spite of its subject matter, pretty slippery. "Look at Diogenes.[1] We've remembered him all these years."

Cress sniffed. "He was hunting for an honest man; not being one. And it was his lantern that was outstanding. That was his trademark. That and his barrel."

"There have been a lot of people with lanterns and barrels we've forgotten, I expect."

Cress agreed. "The trademark's got to stand for something. But if you get a good gag and it stands for something" — for all her conviction of tone Cress looked uncertain — "you're fixed, don't you think?"

Cress put down her pencil with melancholy finality. "At present," she said, "I don't have a trademark. Not of any kind."

That night after supper Mr. Delahanty, who had been up at five irrigating, and who was put out with a climate so tardy with its rains that irrigating this late in November was necessary, said to his wife, "I think I'll just stay home and read tonight. I have to

[1] **Diogenes** (dī·ŏj′ê·nēz): an ancient Greek philosopher who was said to have lived in a cask and who went about in daylight with a lantern searching for an honest man.

reset the water at ten anyway. You and Cress go ahead into town if you want to."

"I don't want to go," Cress said. "I'm busy."

"I'm not busy," Mrs. Delahanty admitted, "but I'm not enough interested in what happens when a lady mayor meets a male mayor to drive to the movies alone to find out."

"I can tell you what happens anyway," Mr. Delahanty said. "Same thing like when a lady pearl diver meets gentleman pearl diver. Or lady surgeon meets male surgeon."

Cress listened to this exchange with an unsmiling face, then went to her room where Mrs. Delahanty heard the lid of the bamboo desk at once creak open. The evening had cooled, and at eight Mrs. Delahanty lit a fire of eucalyptus chunks, then challenged her husband to a game of Russian bank.[1] Mr. Delahanty accepted the challenge, but he did not care whether he won or lost, and Mrs. Delahanty wished for Cress, who followed the fall of each card with the intensity of a player who has the home ranch up at stake. At nine Cress came out, advised her father to his benefit on his play, but refused to play herself. "No, I just came out because of the fire. I've got work to do," she said and took her papers to the dining-room table.

At nine thirty, after losing his second game, Mr. Delahanty said, "Anybody want to go out and reset the water for me?" When no one answered, he said, "Woman's work is from sun to sun but man's work is never done," and went outside cheerfully whistling "Swanee River."

Mrs. Delahanty, who knew what he would want when he came back to the

[1] **Russian bank:** a card game for two players.

house, went to the kitchen and made a pot of chocolate and a plate of toasted cheese sandwiches. Cress wandered out, watched her whip the chocolate to a foam and put the sandwiches in the oven, refused anything to eat, then picked up a large wedge of cheese and went off toward her room nibbling gloomily.

Mrs. Delahanty had planned to take the food in by the fire, but Mr. Delahanty said as he pulled off his muddy boots, "Let's have it on the dining-room table where there's room to spread out." He carried the tray in himself and had the chocolate poured by the time Mrs. Delahanty, who had forgotten the napkins, came to the table.

"What's this?" he asked, gesturing with a cheese sandwich toward the sheet of paper beside his chocolate cup.

Mrs. Delahanty, who had an idea, answered only, "What does it say?"

Mr. Delahanty read, stared, drank chocolate, and finally said in a voice in which disbelief and sorrowful understanding mingled, "It says here, 'Useful Traits for School. I. Personality, A. Unusual, 1. Witty.'" He put the sheet down. "What's the meaning of this?"

"It's a list," Mrs. Delahanty said. "You ought to understand if anybody would."

Mr. Delahanty ate half a sandwich, then picked up a second sheet. "'My Trademark. Isn't she Crazy!' is the heading here," he said thoughtfully. "'Isn't she Crazy' is in quotes," he explained. "Under it is, 'Useful Gags for Craziness. I. Clothes, A. Shoes, 1. Unmatched.'"

He put the second sheet face down on the first and covered both with the sandwich plate. He finished his cheese sandwich, then said, "My heavens, what a dark world."

"You do understand it, then?" Mrs. Delahanty asked.

"Certainly I understand it. I lived there for a year."

"What year?"

"The year I was thirteen."

Mrs. Delahanty had not known her husband until he was fifteen, and these hints of an earlier life always enthralled her. She saw him at thirteen, a big solemn boy with soft dark hair, inquiring eyes, and a sensitive mouth.

"You don't know who you are then, or what you can do. You've got to make a hundred false starts. You've got to make your mark, without knowing what your mark is. Are you a coward or a hero? How do you know without involving yourself in dangerous situations? So you walk ridge poles and visit cemeteries. How do you know you're even alive at that age if you aren't noticed?"

"It's the dark time of life," Mr. Delahanty said again. "It turns my stomach now, but at thirteen I too had a trademark."

"A trademark!"

Mr. Delahanty grimaced. "Spitting. At thirteen I was a professional spitter. I used to give exhibitions. Distance and accuracy. Power and control. I had everything. And I hated it. And I still hate anybody now from grammar school days who calls me 'Spit' Delahanty."

"I don't ever remember seeing you spit."

"At fifteen I was far past that, an ex-spitter. By that time I had taken up —" He stopped in mid-sentence. "Cress," he said.

Cress, in her pink-sprigged seersucker pajamas, the cheek that had been against the pillow pinker than the other, stood in the opening between living room and dining room. "Did we wake you up with our talk?"

Cress sat down in the chair her father pushed out for her. "No," she said, "you didn't wake me up because I hadn't gone to sleep yet."

Mrs. Delahanty had the feeling that Cress had left her lists out on purpose, had given them time to read them and would now like to have their opinion of craziness as a trademark. But she was loath to speak of them unless Cress did; and Cress was silent, and John went on as if he had never heard of trademarks — or craziness; or spitting, for that matter, either.

"How's school?" Mr. Delahanty asked his daughter. "Classes, teachers, kids? Edwin? Honor Gallagher? Everything turning out as well as you thought it would?"

"Everything's all right," Cress said, opening a cheese sandwich, then closing it like a book she didn't care to read. "Did I tell you I'm probably going to be freshman editor of the yearbook?"

"No," said Mr. Delahanty, "you didn't. That's fine. Congratulations."

"I'm not editor yet," Cress reminded him.

"But spoken of for the job. Spoken of favorably for the job."

Cress admitted it. "And it's a tradition that the person who is freshman editor is editor in chief his senior year."

"Congratulations," Mr. Delahanty said again; then, shaking the chocolate pot, "Have some cocoa? It's soporific. Just what you need to put you to sleep."

"I read the other day it wasn't," Cress said. "I read it had every bit as much caffein in it as coffee."

"Where? Where'd you read that?"

"In the newspaper."

"The newspaper!" scoffed Mr. Delahanty. "You can read anything in the newspapers. Let's consult the authority." He sprang from his chair with the enthusiasm which the search for a fact always gave him and came back to the table bearing Volume IV of the *Britannica*, Bishārīn to Calgary. Cress got up and leaned across his shoulder as he flipped the pages. Mrs. Delahanty, while the two of them pursued the word, took the thing itself — caffein or no caffein — to the kitchen to reheat for Cress.

The campaign, "Craziness as a Trademark," seemed to be going well in spite of Mrs. Delahanty's doubts. Cress, as November wore on, had never seemed more happy. Certainly she had never been more active or engrossed — and her activities engaged Mrs. Delahanty's energies as well as her own.

"Life now," Mrs. Delahanty reported to her husband one gray day at lunch, "is very full for me. It is like being property manager for a vaudeville star. It takes a good deal of equipment and thought to achieve the effect of craziness when actually you're as sober as a judge."

"Cress isn't and never was sober as a judge," Mr. Delahanty said. "Clowning comes naturally to her."

"Not this clowning," Mrs. Delahanty said. "She memorizes lines. She gathers up equipment. She teaches kids their cues. It's exactly as spontaneous as a vaudeville act, and I think we ought to put a stop to it."

"How?" Mr. Delahanty asked.

"Just tell her it's silly and to stop it."

"And for the rest of her life she'd blame us for keeping her from finding out who she really was."

"Well, there's no use her finding out the hard way when we could tell her that she suits us just as she is."

"Cress is trying out her wings for a little flight from the us-nest."

"She is trying the wrong wings then, John. Do you know what she did this morning?" Mrs. Delahanty didn't wait for any reply from her husband. "She wore her bedroom slippers to the bus and carried her oxfords. She had to have new bedroom slippers for this, by the way, the old ones wouldn't do for a public appearance. Do you know what the gag is there?"

This time she waited for Mr. Delahanty's answer. "No," he said, "I don't."

"The gag is that she has figured that it takes three minutes' time to put on her oxfords. Time on the bus is waste time. So, if she puts them on there, that three minutes is saved. Three minutes a day is fifteen minutes a week, an hour a month, nine hours in a school year. The whole busload will have it reported at school ten minutes after they've arrived. 'Hear the latest about Cress Delahanty? That crazy kid. She's figured out how to save nine hours a year — by putting on her shoes in the bus. What a girl! What a card!'"

Mrs. Delahanty's imitation of the high school crowd did not awaken her husband from his musing. "Nine hours," he murmured thoughtfully. "A whole work day. I suppose she can sleep that much longer?"

"John Delahanty," Mrs. Delahanty said, "you surely — " But in the midst of that she changed her tack. "Did you hear her phoning last night?"

"With one ear. I was busy at the time."

"It would've paid you to listen."

Mr. Delahanty looked up from his Spanish rice. "Why?" he asked.

"She makes this call every night. Her algebra teacher made the sad mistake of saying in class that he couldn't possibly rest at night for wondering whether the class had done its homework. So Cress calls him."

"What does she say?"

"She says," Mrs. Delahanty said crisply, " 'This is Crescent Delahanty reporting, Mr. Holcomb. I have finished my homework. I hope you will sleep well now.' " About this exploit Mrs. Delahanty, feeling that such a lily needed no gilding, made no comment.

Mr. Delahanty appeared to choke a little on his Spanish rice. "More red pepper than usual in this today," he said.

Mrs. Delahanty said, "I have been making that dish for seventeen years and I put exactly the same amount of red pepper in it now as I did then."

"Maybe my mouth is getting more sensitive with the years."

"Maybe so," Mrs. Delahanty agreed. "But I doubt it."

"I suppose that really was carrying things a little far?"

Mrs. Delahanty waited for a more adequate summing up of the situation.

"I should think Mr. Holcomb would be over any night now to strangle her," Mr. Delahanty said.

This seemed quite a lot more likely to Mrs. Delahanty, and she relaxed

somewhat, pleased to find that the family still contained two sane members. Mr. Delahanty's sudden whoop of laughter, however, dispelled this happy supposition.

With that laugh still in her mind's ear, Mrs. Delahanty handed her husband the *Tenant Hi-Lights* at lunch a few days later. "Cress gave this to me this morning before she left for school," she said. "I think maybe she thought we would like some time alone to digest it." The paper was folded to the column called, "The Hi-Light's on —," by I. Marcum. This week's Hi-Light was on "Cress Delahanty, That Crazy Freshman," and there was a drawing of her in the center of the column in her fur-topped bedroom slippers holding an oxford in each hand. "Read it out loud," Mrs. Delahanty said. "I want to be sure I wasn't seeing things when I read it."

After some preliminary smoothing and folding, which the *Hi-Lights* didn't need, Mr. Delahanty read in an expressionless voice, "Crazy or Cagy? Freshman girl sole discoverer of way never to be on her uppers, and you are a heel if you suggest that this is not the last word on this soulful subject. Personally, the ice-blonde freshman can vamp us any time she wants to." Mr. Delahanty stopped reading. "Gertrude, do you really want me to go on with this?"

"Yes," Mrs. Delahanty said, "I do."

Mr. Delahanty took up the *Hi-Lights* again, but before continuing he said, "Ice blonde! Why, Cress is nothing but a mere child."

"A color is a color, I suppose," Mrs. Delahanty answered mildly, "regardless of age."

"Ice blonde is something more than a color," Mr. Delahanty argued, but when Mrs. Delahanty asked him to explain, he could do no more than mention two or three movie stars.

"Go on reading," Mrs. Delahanty urged. "There's a good deal more."

Mr. Delahanty gave the *Hi-Lights* a couple more of the flattening whacks it did not require and continued. "Personally the ice-blonde freshman can vamp us any time she wants to. We get a boot out of Delahanty. We pumped Cress, and this is her version of what she calls 'Delahanty's Law,' or, to add our own interpretation, 'What You Do on the Bus Doesn't Count.'"

Mr. Delahanty paused once more and Mrs. Delahanty waited expectantly, but about Delahanty's Law and its interpretation he had nothing to say.

"It goes on, Gertrude, as you doubtless remember, this way," he said. "No nit-wit she, Cress, and we quote, thus explained her discovery while we listened, tongue hanging out, so to speak, and all unlaced with interest. 'I, in my tireless search for efficiency, discovered that I spent fifteen minutes a week putting on and tying my shoes. Now if I did this on the bus, time ordinarily lost, as all bus riders know, in useless chatter, I would gain one hour a month, or one full working day a year.'

"Asked what she intended doing with this 'saved' time, Cress answered demurely, 'Study.' Asked what, she replied, 'Algebra. Mr. Holcomb, you know, can't rest nights if the homework for his class isn't done.' (See next week's *Hi-Lights* for the Holcomb-Delahanty story. Adv't.) Asked what her ultimate goal was, Cress said, 'Oxford.'

"Excuse us please now while we pull on our own Congressional Gaiters (not on a bus, thus losing, according to Delahanty's Law, three minutes). We're going to hotfoot it over to Cress's. Got a little equation we want help with. Delahanty + I. Marcum = ? See next week's column for answer (Adv't.)"

Mr. Delahanty folded the *Tenant Hi-Lights* into a compact oblong and threw it toward the fireplace, which he missed. "What have we got for dessert?" he asked.

"It's right there before you," Mrs. Delahanty said, indicating the raisin pie by his plate. Mr. Delahanty grunted and began slowly to eat.

Mrs. Delahanty didn't feel like raisin pie herself. "John," she asked, "what's your opinion of that?"

"My opinion is that I. Marcum will go far. We'll turn on the radio any day now and hear I. Marcum's report on the love life of Lana Turner."

"What do you really think, John?"

"I think it's a pity and a crying shame."

"You'll speak to Cress then?"

"It wouldn't do any good. What can we say to her? Stop saying and doing funny things?"

"Yes, we can."

"Sure, we can. But in the first place we can't stop her, and in the second place if we could stop her, Cress would hate us for the rest of her life. I tell you, she's finding out who she is. At that age the only way to know whether craziness is your trademark is to *be* crazy. It's something you've got to do."

"I didn't have to."

"No, Gertrude, you didn't."

"Once on a dare I wore a dress to school hindside foremost."

"Gertrude," Mr. Delahanty said, "you never had to bother trying on attitudes. You were born wearing one that fit beautifully."

Still, and startled at this sudden turning of the conversation, Mrs. Delahanty watched her husband eat raisin pie. He paused to ask, "Don't you want to know its name?"

Mrs. Delahanty nodded, mutely.

"Radiant loving-kindness."

This unexpected and extravagant compliment made Mrs. Delahanty feel shy. It was too extraordinary for her to deal with instantaneously, and she put it aside for later consideration. "Whatever you think about Cress, John, I'm going to speak to her. I think it's my duty and I'm going to warn her at the first opportune minute."

The first opportune minute came that very afternoon, and Cress, after being warned, went in tears to her room. She came out, ate her supper wordlessly, then went again to her room. When Mrs. Delahanty heard the lid of the bamboo desk creak down, she said to her husband, "There is Cress writing out a list of reasons for hating me."

"What now?" Mr. Delahanty asked, and Mrs. Delahanty with no heart for dishwashing said, "Come on in by the fire and I'll tell you."

Mr. Delahanty settled himself in the Morris chair, which had been his father's, and Mrs. Delahanty stood in front of the fireplace, close to the fire until her calves began to scorch, then on the edge of the hearth until they cooled.

"This afternoon," she said, "Cress came skipping and hopping home from the bus clapping those two horrible bedroom slippers together over her head like castanets."

"Cymbals," said Mr. Delahanty.

"Together, anyway, and happy as a lark. It seems they had an assembly to-day — "

"Assemblies, assemblies," said Mr. Delahanty. "Bird imitations, football rallies, talent shows. When do the kids go to school?"

"Assemblies," said Mrs. Delahanty, who went to P.T.A., "provide the chil-dren opportunity for participation in life situations."

"Is that thought to be a good thing? A life situation, if you ask me, is just about to engulf Cress. If you ask me, a little participation in something unlife-like on the order of ancient history or the ablative case is what Cress has a crying need for. A little more life par-ticipation, and she'll burst apart at the seams. I can hear them — "

"John," Mrs. Delahanty said, "I just want to tell you what Cress told me. And what I told her. I don't give a whit one way or another about assemblies. The point is, they had one. And when Mr. DuMont came out on the stage — "

"Who is this Mr. DuMont? A bird imitator?"

"Mr. DuMont is the vice-principal in charge of student activities. He has pre-mature gray hair, a beautiful tan, and sings 'On the Road to Mandalay' so, Cress says, you can feel the waves ris-ing and falling beneath you. He . . ."

"That's enough about DuMont," Mr. Delahanty said.

"John, please try just to listen. All I want to do is tell you what happened."

"O.K.," Mr. Delahanty said, "I'm lis-tening. Tell me."

He had the look of a man who has not yet had his say out, but Mrs. Dela-hanty went on in spite of it. "On his way out, Mr. DuMont stumbled over a pair of tennis shoes somebody had left on the stage. He stooped, picked them up by the strings, swung them back and forth, and then said in what Cress re-ports as being a perfectly dead-pan, sidesplitting way: 'I see Delahanty has been here.' Like Kilroy has been here,[1] you know."

[1] **Kilroy has been here:** a variation of "Kil-roy was here," which American soldiers in World War II used to write on the walls of buildings in far-off places they visited.

"I know," Mr. Delahanty said.

"Then when everyone had stopped laughing at that, he said: 'They look like my size, but as a student of Delahanty's Law I intend to wait until I'm on a bus to try them on.'"

"Mr. DuMont's trademark appears to be craziness too," Mr. Delahanty remarked.

"The kids seem to love him."

"Why not?" asked Mr. Delahanty. "The kids are one with Mr. DuMont."

"I thought you approved of craziness. I thought that was what we've been arguing about."

"Gertrude, I haven't been arguing, and what I approve of is not craziness but freedom to find out who and what you are."

"Well, Cress thinks she's found out. She thinks she's a wit. Or a wag. Or the school jester. She says that about Delahanty's Law really panicked them and that not an eye in the auditorium but was on her. Even though she was sitting in an obscure spot under the balcony in the midst of one hundred and seventy-two other freshmen and practically invisible."

"She didn't say anything about standing up, or whistling and waving her handkerchief to help them see her, did she?"

"Now, John. Anyway, when she finished, and I hated to do it because she was as happy as —"

"A prima donna?"[1] suggested Mr. Delahanty.

"Oh, no! A baby who's picked its first flower. Well, when she finished, I told her everything I've been thinking. I told her to stop it at once. That it was cheap and silly to play to the grandstand that way and that she was going to regret

[1] **prima donna** (prē'mȧ dŏn'ȧ): the principal woman singer in an opera. The phrase is used to suggest anyone who is temperamental.

getting a reputation as a harebrained clown when she was really a good, sweet, solid, sensible child." Mrs. Delahanty was unable to keep her voice from trembling.

"What did Cress say?"

"She said, 'Good, solid, sensible, sweet,' as if I had — as if I had reviled her. She said 'child' as if I had called her — a name. Then she began to cry."

Mr. Delahanty nodded and nodded as if this were all an old story to him.

"Then she stopped crying long enough to say that I didn't understand a thing. Not her. Not school. Not young people in general. Not Mr. DuMont. Not I. Marcum. And she said her constant prayer was that when she grew up and had children that she would not forget what it was like to be young. The way I have. And she said that for three months at school she *had* been sweet, solid, and sensible. And where had it gotten her? At the end of three months of that, she had been a complete nonentity and not a soul at school could've told you who Crescent Delahanty was. And now at the end of three weeks of planned living, with craziness for her trademark, she is a great success and she doubts there is even a custodian at school who has not heard of Crescent Delahanty and Delahanty's Law. 'In fact,' I said, 'you are now a character.' She said yes, she was, and proud of it. Then she went to her room. But before she left she said, 'Anyway, my father understands me.' And now she is there making a list headed, 'What's Wrong with Mother.' But I don't care. I had to tell her."

Mr. Delahanty caught at the edge of Mrs. Delahanty's skirt as she switched away from the fire and toward him, and pulled her down onto his lap. "Don't try to comfort me," she said, struggling to get up. "You think one way and I think another. That's all there is to it."

"I think just what you think, Gertrude — except that I think Cress will have to find it out for herself. She'll wake up pretty soon, and it'll be a painful awakening, but it's bound to come."

Mrs. Delahanty, in spite of herself, was settling back and relaxing. "You believe that?"

"Of course. You don't think our daughter's a fool, do you?"

"No," Mrs. Delahanty said, letting her head, finally, rest at ease against her husband's shoulder. "No, how could I? Cress recapitulates you."

The "awakening," as Mr. Delahanty had named it, came the first week in December. The rains which had held off through the whole of November arrived the minute the November leaf on the calendar was torn off and made up by their abundance for their lateness. On Friday afternoon Mr. Delahanty, happily housebound by the downpour, sat before a drowsy fire working on his electrification lists.

On the other side of the fire Mrs. Delahanty was shelling English walnuts preparatory to sugaring them for annual Christmas gifts to eastern relatives. She listened to the pleasant blend of sounds, fire sighing, pen scratching, nutshells cracking, and behind and giving body to the blend the fine heavy sound of the constant rain. She was, she thought, reasonably happy. Then, as the pile of walnut kernels rose in the crock on the floor by her side, she decided that there is no such thing as reasonable happiness since happiness, like love, is without reason. A reasonable happiness is usually simply all the reasons one can think of for not being unhappy.

"I am not unhappy because my family is in good health, and I myself am well, and a good and needed rain is falling, and we have a tight roof over our heads, and the fire is drawing beautifully." No, she thought, that is not enough. Happiness, like love, fills the heart and does not need to be accounted for. She was analyzing now. That was the reason she knew she was not happy. And continuing to analyze, she knew she would not be until Cress was herself once again.

Cress came in from the bus, as Mrs. Delahanty recognized this fact; but she was neither the old Cress, solid and sensible, nor the new one, crazy and showoff. This Cress had been crying. She had on a hooded raincoat, but she had walked up from the bus with the hood hanging down her shoulders, and her hair, soaked to the scalp, was lank and mousy. She was no ice blonde now. I. Marcum would scarcely recognize her. Water dripped from her cheeks and beaded her eyelashes and stood in the corners of her mouth, which she held with unchildlike firmness. She went without a word to the fireplace and stood there with her back to her parents while occasional drops of water hissed off her raincoat onto the andirons. Then she turned around to face them, and it was the first time Mrs. Delahanty had ever heard adult resignation in her daughter's voice, adult acceptance of the fact that the source of one's joy is also often the source of one's sorrow. I may have forgotten what it's like to be a girl, she thought, but Cress is learning what it's like to be a parent.

"You have a perfect right to say I told you so now if you want to, Mother," Cress said. "You told me I was getting to be a character and I was, all right."

"What do you mean, Cress?" her father asked.

"I mean I'm a Character," Cress said bleakly. "I'm 'Irresponsible Delahanty,' I'm that 'Crazy Kid.' If I said I was dying, people would laugh." Water ran out of her hair and across her face and dripped off her chin, but she scorned to wipe it away.

"I made a good speech to the Student Council, and they laughed at every word I said. They laughed and held their sides and rolled in their chairs like loons."

"What speech was this, Cress?"

"The speech everybody who is a candidate for an office has to make to them. Then if they like you, they nominate you. I was a candidate for freshman editor. What they nominated me for was *Josh* editor. A two-year-old can be Josh editor. All you need to be Josh editor is a pair of scissors to cut out jokes with. I wouldn't be Josh editor if they shot me for not being. It's a silly job."

"Take off your coat, Cress," Mrs. Delahanty said, and Cress, not ceasing to speak, began also to unbutton. "I would've been a good editor, and I told them the reasons — like I was responsible, knew the meaning of time, would see that the assignments were in on time, and so forth. They laughed like hyenas," she said, not bitterly but reflectively. "They said, 'This is the richest thing yet. Delahanty is a real character.' So they nominated me for Josh editor, and I'm branded for life."

She threw her raincoat, which she had finished unbuttoning, onto the floor, said, "I have ruined my life," and walked out of the room, no longer trying to hide the fact that she was crying.

Mr. and Mrs. Delahanty still held the positions they had had when Cress entered; Mr. Delahanty, pen above his list; Mrs. Delahanty, nutcracker in one hand, cracked unshelled nut in the other. Mr. Delahanty said, "I guess you were right. I guess it would've been better to have forbidden it."

"I did forbid it," Mrs. Delahanty said, "in so far as I could, and you can see what came of that." Mechanically she picked the kernel from the nut she still held, then got up and threw the pan of shells into the fire. Mr. Delahanty had gone back to his list making and she felt almost the first wave of dislike she had ever known for her husband. That was really carrying objectiveness a little too far. Electrification at a time like this. She herself was going to Cress. She looked coldly down at Mr. Delahanty's list as she passed and saw what had been, and was, in the process of being written there. "Spit. Spit. Spit Delahanty. Big Spit Delahanty. Spit. Spit."

John saw her look and let her take his hand. "I told you it was a dark time," he said quietly.

"John — you still remember? It still matters?"

All he said was, "You go on in to Cress. She's your youngest baby."

She let go his hand and went toward Cress's room. She didn't know what she would or could say when she got there. Maybe, "Cress, people like you and your father have to try on more than one way of being and doing to see who you are. And you're bound to make mistakes." Maybe she would say, "My sweet, sensible daughter." But she would surely hug her and kiss her. Her arms, as she heard through the closed door those catching sobs, already felt that stocky body grow quiet. She opened the door and said, "Cress, honey."

THINKING IT OVER

1. To see how much attention you gave the details in the story, can you answer: (a) How old is Cress? (b) Mr. Delahanty? (c) What is the name of Cress's school paper? (d) Who is I. Marcum?

2. In what ways did Mr. and Mrs. Delahanty differ in their approach to helping Cress solve her problem?

3. The introduction stated that the story concerned a girl, her goal, and the way her plans turned out. What is the theme of the story?

4. There are some wise observations about life in this story — comments on the problems of adolescence, the necessity for "trying on attitudes," the value of assemblies, happiness, the connection between joy and sorrow. Find these observations and comment on them.

5. At the beginning of the story, Cress says that she had never heard of anyone who was "popular for honesty." Explain whether you think she learned the value of honesty, and why. Discuss how honesty is to be valued in school affairs; between friends; at home; and in adult life and careers. What is the result of dishonesty in these areas of life?

6. You can't say that this story has a happy ending for Cress, but is it the *right* ending? Go back to the auditorium incident in which Cress made her speech. Do you think your schoolmates would have reacted the same way? Why?

FOR YOUR VOCABULARY: WORD HISTORIES

Mr. Delahanty *grimaced* (gri·māst′) when he revealed his own youthful trademark. That is, he made a wry face. The word *grimace* came into English from the French language, and into French from the Spanish. In the dictionary this is shown as F., fr. Sp. *grimazo*.

1. To see how some common English words have been "borrowed" from other languages, look up the origin of the following words, all taken from this story: *algebra, bamboo, chocolate, pepper tree, ranch, school, scoffed, seersucker, skirt,* and *supper.*

2. To demonstrate the extent that spoken English depends upon words of Anglo-Saxon origin (AS. in your dictionary), select a short example of dialogue, five or six lines in length, from the story and look up in the dictionary every word in the dialogue. In one column, list the "AS." words, and in another, list those which are "NOT AS."

PEN AND PAPER

On half or three quarters of a sheet of paper, tell *your* story of a plan that did not work out right, or a goal that you once had or that you are now working toward. Begin with a sentence like "Plans do not always work out the way you think they will," or "Once I wanted to be a cowboy."

ABOUT THE AUTHOR

Jessamyn West came of Indiana Quaker stock and her earliest stories were about the Friends of that state. Her first book, *The Friendly Persuasion,* appeared in 1945 and was later made into a motion picture. If you are interested in the problems of movie making and the struggle to make a film both artistic and realistic, read *To See the Dream,* her account of the filming of *The Friendly Persuasion.* "Conestoga Wagons," one of the poems in this book, is from a play of Jessamyn West's based on the life of the painter Audubon. Her long residence in California has given her the setting for many of her stories.

An Imaginary Situation →

In the illustration, artist Tom O'Sullivan has pictured Cress Delahanty and her parents in an imaginary situation: choosing a party dress for Cress. Evidently the choice has narrowed down to three dresses, and a decision is at hand. See what you have learned about the personalities of Cress and her parents by applying your knowledge of them to this imaginary situation. Which dress, for example, do you think each of the Delahantys is voting for, and why? Why do you suppose Mr. Delahanty is present at the selection? What might be Cress's reason for needing the dress, and which dress do you think she will finally buy? Perhaps you can even supply the conversation that is taking place among the three Delahantys.

Lassie
Come-Home

ERIC KNIGHT

Loyalty is one of the finest character traits a person can have — but fortunately most of us never have our loyalties put to that supreme test, the risking of one's life. Here is a story which concerns a dog and a poor Yorkshire family. The loyalty of both was painfully tested, though in different ways.

THE DOG had met the boy by the school gate for five years. Now she couldn't understand that times were changed and she wasn't supposed to be there any more. But the boy knew.

So when he opened the door of the cottage, he spoke before he entered.

"Mother," he said, "Lassie's come home again."

He waited a moment, as if in hope of something. But the man and woman inside the cottage did not speak.

He held open the door, and the tri-color collie walked in obediently. Going head down, as a collie does when it knows something is wrong, it went to the rug and lay down before the hearth, a black-white-and-gold aristocrat. The man, sitting on a low stool by the fireside, kept his eyes turned away. The woman went to the sink and busied herself there.

"She were waiting at school for me, just like always," the boy went on. He spoke fast, as if racing against time. "She must ha' got away again. I thought, happen this time, we might just — "

"No!" the woman exploded.

The boy's carelessness dropped. His voice rose in pleading.

"But this time, Mother! Just this time. We could hide her. They wouldn't ever know."

Anticipating Outcomes. In every story there are certain details which the alert reader notices and wonders about. These details are like clues or hints. Sometimes a detail, added to what has happened already, can give you a definite idea of what is going to happen. Learn to watch for these hints which signal the events that lie ahead in the story. In this way you can often anticipate the outcome of a situation or plot complication in a story and add to your enjoyment of it.

"Dogs, dogs, dogs!" the woman cried. The words poured from her as if the boy's pleading had been a signal gun for her own anger. "I'm sick o' hearing about tykes [1] round this house. Well, she's sold and gone and done with, so the quicker she's taken back, the better. Now get her back quick, or first thing ye know we'll have Hynes round here again. Mr. Hynes!"

Her voice sharpened in imitation of the Cockney accent of the south: " 'Hi know you Yorkshiremen and yer come- 'ome dogs. Training yer dogs to come 'ome so's yer can sell 'em hover and hover again.'

"Well, she's sold, so ye can take her out o' my house and home to them as bought her!"

The boy's bottom lip crept out suddenly, and there was silence in the cottage. Then the dog lifted its head and nudged the man's hand, as a dog will when asking for patting. But the man drew away and stared, silently, into the fire.

The boy tried again, with the ceaseless guile of a child, his voice coaxing.

"Look, Feyther, she wants thee to bid her welcome. Aye, she's that glad to be home. Happen they don't tak' good care on her up there? Look, her coat's a bit poorly, don't ye think? A bit o' linseed strained through her drinking water — that's what I'd gi' her."

Still looking in the fire, the man nodded. But the woman, as if perceiving the boy's new attack, sniffed.

"Aye, tha wouldn't be a Carraclough if tha didn't know more about tykes nor breaking eggs wi' a stick. Nor a Yorkshireman. My goodness, it seems to me sometimes tha chaps in this village thinks more on their tykes nor they do o' their own flesh and blood. They'll sit by their firesides and let their own

[1] tykes: dogs.

bairns [2] starve so long as t' dog gets fed."

The man stirred, suddenly, but the boy cut in quickly.

"But she does look thin. Look, truly — they're not feeding her right. Just look!"

"Aye," the woman chattered. "I wouldn't put it past Hynes to steal t' best part o' t' dog meat for himself. And Lassie always was a strong eater."

"She's fair thin now," the boy said.

Almost unwillingly the man and woman looked at the dog for the first time.

"By gum, she is off a bit," the woman said. Then she caught herself. "Ma goodness, I suppose I'll have to fix her a bit o' summat. She can do wi' it. But soon as she's fed, back she goes. And never another dog I'll have in my house. Never another. Cooking and nursing for 'em and as much trouble to bring up as a bairn!"

So, grumbling and chatting as a village woman will, she moved about, warming a pan of food for the dog. The man and boy watched the collie eat. When it was done, the boy took from the mantelpiece a folded cloth and brush, and began prettying the collie's coat. The man watched for several minutes, and then could stand it no longer.

"Here," he said.

He took the cloth and brush from the boy and began working expertly on the dog, rubbing the rich deep coat, then brushing the snowy whiteness of the full ruff and the apron, bringing out the heavy legging on the forelegs. He lost himself in his work, and the boy sat on the rug, watching contentedly. The woman stood it as long as she could.

"Now will ye please tak' that tyke out o' here?"

The man flared in anger.

[2] **bairns** (bârnz): children.

"Well, ye wouldn't have me tak' her back looking like a mucky Monday wash, wouldta?"

He bent again, and began fluffing out the collie's petticoats.

"Joe!" the woman pleaded. "Will ye tak' her out o' here? Hynes'll be nosing round afore ye know it. And I won't have that man in my house. Wearing his hat inside, and going on like he's the duke himself — him and his leggings!"

"All right, lass."

"And this time, Joe, tak' young Joe wi' ye."

"What for?"

"Well, let's get the business done and over with. It's him that Lassie runs away for. She comes for young Joe. So if he went wi' thee, and told her to stay, happen she'd be content and not run away no more, and then we'd have a little peace and quiet in the home — though heaven knows there's not much hope o' that these days, things being like they are." The woman's voice trailed away, as if she would soon cry in weariness.

The man rose. "Come, Joe," he said. "Get thy cap."

The Duke of Rudling walked along the gravel paths of his place with his granddaughter, Philippa. Philippa was a bright and knowing young woman, allegedly the only member of the duke's family he could address in unspotted language. For it was also alleged that the duke was the most irascible, vile-tempered old man in the three Ridings [1] of Yorkshire.

"Country going to pot!" the duke roared, stabbing at the walk with his great blackthorn stick. "When I was a young man! Hah! Women today not as

[1] **Ridings:** divisions of Yorkshire — North Riding, West Riding, and East Riding.

pretty. Horses today not as fast. As for dogs — ye don't see dogs today like — "

Just then the duke and Philippa came round a clump of rhododendrons and saw a man, a boy, and a dog.

"Ah," said the duke, in admiration. Then his brow knotted. "Carraclough! What are ye doing with my dog?"

He shouted it as if the others were in the next county, for it was also the opinion of the Duke of Rudling that people were not nearly so keen of hearing as they used to be when he was a young man.

"It's Lassie," Carraclough said. "She runned away again, and I brought her back."

Carraclough lifted his cap and poked the boy to do the same, not in any servile gesture, but to show that they were as well brought up as the next.

"Ran away again!" the duke roared. "And I told that utter nincompoop Hynes to — where is he? Hynes! Hynes! Hynes, what're ye hiding for?"

"Coming, your lordship!" sounded a voice, far away behind the shrubberies. And soon Hynes appeared, a sharp-faced man in check coat, riding breeches, and the cloth leggings that grooms wear.

"Take this dog," roared the duke, "and pen her up! And, if she breaks out again, I'll — I'll —"

The duke waved his great stick threateningly, and then, without so much as a thank you or kiss the back of my hand to Joe Carraclough, he went stamping and muttering away.

"I'll pen 'er up," Hynes muttered, when the duke was gone. "And if she ever gets awye agyne, I'll — "

He made as if to grab the dog, but Joe Carraclough's hobnailed boot trod heavily on Hynes's foot.

"I brought my lad wi' me to bid her stay, so we'll pen her up this time. Eigh

— sorry! I didn't see I were on thy foot. Come, Joe, lad."

They walked down the crunching gravel path, along by the neat kennel buildings. When Lassie was behind the closed door, she raced into the high wire run where she could see them as they went. She pressed close against the wire, waiting.

The boy stood close, too, his fingers through the meshes touching the dog's nose.

"Go on, lad," his father ordered. "Bid her stay!"

The boy looked around, as if for help that he did not find. He swallowed and then spoke, low and quickly.

"Stay here, Lassie, and don't come home no more," he said. "And don't come to school for me no more. Because I don't want to see ye no more. 'Cause tha's a bad dog, and we don't love thee no more, and we don't want thee. So stay there forever and leave us be, and don't never come home no more."

Then he turned, and because it was hard to see the path plainly, he stumbled. But his father, who was holding his head very high as they walked away from Hynes, shook him savagely, and snapped roughly: "Look where tha's going!"

Then the boy trotted beside his father. He was thinking that he'd never be able to understand why grownups sometimes were so bad-tempered with you, just when you needed them most.

After that, there were days and days that passed, and the dog did not come to the school gate any more. So then it was not like old times. There were so many things that were not like old times.

The boy was thinking that as he came wearily up the path and opened the cottage door and heard his father's voice, tense with anger: ". . . walk my feet off. If tha thinks I like — "

Then they heard his opening of the door, and the voice stopped, and the cottage was silent.

That's how it was now, the boy thought. They stopped talking in front of you. And this, somehow, was too much for him to bear.

He closed the door, ran into the night, and onto the moor, that great flat expanse of land where all the people of that village walked in lonesomeness when life and its troubles seemed past bearing.

A long while later, his father's voice cut through the darkness.

"What's tha doing out here, Joe lad?"

"Walking."

"Aye."

They went on together, aimlessly, each following his own thoughts. And they both thought about the dog that had been sold.

"Tha maun't think we're hard on thee, Joe," the man said at last. "It's just that a chap's for to be honest. There's that to it. Sometimes, when a chap doesn't have much, he clings right hard to what he's got. And honest is honest, and there's no two ways about it.

"Why, look, Joe. Seventeen year I worked in that Clarabelle Pit till she shut down, and a good collier too. Seventeen year! And butties [1] I've had by the dozen, and never one of 'em can ever say that Joe Carraclough kept what wasn't his; nor spoke what wasn't true. Not a man in this Riding can ever call a Carraclough mishonest.

"And when ye've sold a man summat, and ye've taken his brass, and ye've spent it — well, then done's done. That's all. And ye've got to stand by that."

"But Lassie was — "

[1] **butties:** means the same as *buddies*.

"Now, Joe! Ye can't alter it, ever. It's done — and happen it's for t' best. No two ways, Joe, she were getting hard to feed. Why, ye wouldn't want Lassie to be going around peaked and pined, like some chaps round here keep their tykes. And if ye're fond of her, then just think on it that now she's got lots to eat, and a private kennel, and a good run to herself, and living like a veritable princess, she is. Ain't that best for her?"

"We wouldn't pine her. We've always got lots to eat."

The man blew his breath, angrily: "Eigh, Joe, nowt pleases thee. Well then, tha might as well have it. Tha'll never see Lassie no more. She run home once too often, so the duke's taken her wi' him up to his place in Scotland, and there she'll stay. So it's good-by and good luck to her, and she'll never come home no more, she won't. Now, I weren't off to tell thee, but there it is, so put it in thy pipe and smoke it, and let's never say a word about it no more — especially in front of thy mother."

The boy stumbled on in the darkness. Then the man halted.

"We ought to be getting back, lad. We left thy mother alone."

He turned the boy about, and then went on, but as if he were talking to himself.

"Tha sees, Joe, women's not like men. They have to stay home and manage best they can, and just spend the time in wishing. And when things don't go right, well, they have to take it out in talk. But it don't mean nowt, really, so tha shouldn't mind when thy mother talks hard.

"Ye just got to learn to be patient, and let 'em talk, and just let it go up t' chimney wi' th' smoke."

Then they were quiet, until, over the rise, they saw the lights of the village. Then the boy spoke: "How far away is Scotland, Feyther?"

"Nay, lad, it's a long, long road."

"But how far, Feyther?"

"I don't know — but it's a longer road than thee or me'll ever walk. Now, lad. Don't fret no more, and try to be a man — and don't plague thy mother no more, wilta?"

Joe Carraclough was right. It is a long road, as they say in the North, from Yorkshire to Scotland. Much too far for a man to walk — or a boy. And though the boy often thought of it, he remembered his father's words on the moor, and he put the thought behind him.

But there is another way of looking at it; and that's the distance from Scotland to Yorkshire. And that is just as far as from Yorkshire to Scotland. A matter of about four hundred miles, it would be, from the Duke of Rudling's place far up in the Highlands to the village of Holdersby. That would be for a man, who could go fairly straight.

To an animal, how much farther would it be? For a dog can study no maps, read no signposts, ask no directions. It could only go blindly, by instinct, knowing that it must keep on to the south, to the south. It would wander and err, quest and quarter, run into firths and lochs [1] that would send it sidetracking and backtracking before it could go again on its way — south.

A thousand miles, it would be, going that way — a thousand miles over strange terrain.

There would be moors to cross, and burns [2] to swim. And then those great, long lochs that stretch almost from one side of that dour land to another would bar the way and send a dog questing a hundred miles before it could find a

---

[1] **firths and lochs:** bays and lakes.
[2] **burns** (bûrnz): streams.

crossing that would allow it to go south.

And, too, there would be rivers to cross, wide rivers like the Forth and the Clyde, the Tweed and the Tyne, where one must go miles to find bridges. And the bridges would be in towns. And in the towns there would be officials — like the one in Lanarkshire. In all his life he had never let a captured dog get away — except one. That one was a gaunt, snarling collie that whirled on him right in the pound itself, and fought and twisted loose to race away down the city street — going south.

But there are also kind people, too; ones knowing and understanding in the ways of dogs. There was an old couple in Durham who found a dog lying exhausted in a ditch one night — lying there with its head to the south. They took that dog into their cottage and warmed it and fed it and nursed it. And because it seemed an understanding, wise dog, they kept it in their home, hoping it would learn to be content. But, as it grew stronger, every afternoon toward four o'clock it would go to the door and whine, and then begin pacing back and forth between the door and the window, back and forth as the animals do in their cages at the zoo.

They tried every wile and every kind-

ness to make it bide with them, but finally, when the dog began to refuse food, the old people knew what they must do. Because they understood dogs, they opened the door one afternoon, and they watched a collie go, not down the road to the right, or to the left, but straight across a field toward the south; going steadily at a trot, as if it knew it still had a long, long road to travel.

Ah, a thousand miles of tor and brae,[1] of shire and moor, of path and road and plowland, of river and stream and burn and brook and beck,[2] of snow and rain and fog and sun is a long way, even for a human being. But it would seem too far — much, much too far — for any dog to travel blindly and win through.

And yet — and yet — who shall say why, when so many weeks had passed that hope against hope was dying, a boy coming out of school, out of the cloakroom that always smelled of damp wool drying, across the concrete play yard with the black, waxed slides, should turn his eyes to a spot by the school gate from force of five years of habit, and see there a dog? Not a dog, this one, that lifted glad ears above a proud, slim head with its black-and-

[1] **tor and brae** (tôr; brā): hill and slope.
[2] **brook and beck**: brook and brooklet.

gold mask; but a dog that lay weakly, trying to lift a head that would no longer lift, trying to wag a tail that was torn and blotched and matted with dirt and burs, and managing to do nothing much except to whine in a weak, happy, crying way as a boy on his knees threw arms about it, and hands touched it that had not touched it for many a day.

Then who shall picture the urgency of a boy, running awkwardly, with a great dog in his arms, running through the village, past the empty mill, past the Labor Exchange, where the men looked up from their deep ponderings on life and the dole?[1] Or who shall describe the high tone of a voice — a boy's voice calling as he runs up a path: "Mother! Oh, Mother! Lassie's come home! Lassie's come home!"

Nor does anyone who ever owned a dog need to be told the sound a man makes as he bends over a dog that has been his for many years, nor how a woman moves quickly, preparing food — which might be the family's condensed milk stirred into warm water; nor how the jowl of a dog is lifted so that raw egg and brandy, bought with precious pence, should be spooned in;

[1] dole: money paid to the unemployed.

nor how bleeding pads are bandaged, tenderly.

That was one day. There was another day when the woman in the cottage sighed with pleasure, for a dog lifted itself to its feet for the first time to stand over a bowl of oatmeal, putting its head down and lapping again and again while its pinched flanks quivered.

And there was another day when the boy realized that, even now, the dog was not to be his again. So the cottage rang again with protests and cries, and a woman shrilling: "Is there never to be no more peace in my house and home?" Long after he was in bed that night the boy heard the rise and fall of the woman's voice, and the steady, reiterative tone of the man's. It went on long after he was asleep.

In the morning the man spoke, not looking at the boy, saying the words as if he had long rehearsed them.

"Thy mother and me have decided upon it that Lassie shall stay here till she's better. Anyhow, nobody could nurse her better than us. But the day that t' duke comes back, then back she goes, too. For she belongs to him, and that's honest, too. Now tha has her for a while, so be content."

In childhood, "for a while" is such a great stretch of days when seen from one end. It is a terribly short time seen from the other.

The boy knew how short it was that morning as he went to school and saw a motorcar driven by a young woman. And in the car was a gray-thatched, terrible old man, who waved a cane and shouted: "Hi! Hi, there! Lad! You there! Hi!"

Then it was no use running, for the car could go faster than you, and soon it was beside you, and the man was saying: "Philippa, will you make this smelly thing stand still a moment? Hi, lad!"

"Yes, sir."

"You're What's-'is-Name's lad, aren't you?"

"Ma feyther's Joe Carraclough."

"I know. I know. Is he home now?"

"No, sir. He's away to Allerby. A mate spoke for him at the pit, and he's gone to see if there's a chance."

"When'll he be back?"

"I don't know. I think about tea."

"Eh, yes. Well, yes. I'll drop round about fivish to see that father of yours. Something important."

It was hard to pretend to listen to lessons. There was only waiting for noon. Then the boy ran home.

"Mother! T' duke is back, and he's coming to take Lassie away."

"Eigh, drat my buttons. Never no peace in this house. Is tha sure?"

"Aye. He stopped me. He said tell Feyther he'll be round at five. Can't we hide her? Oh, Mother."

"Nay, thy feyther —"

"Won't you beg him? Please, please. Beg Feyther to —"

"Young Joe, now it's no use. So stop thy teasing! Thy feyther'll not lie. That much I'll give him. Come good, come bad, he'll not lie."

"But just this once, Mother. Please beg him, just this once. Just one lie wouldn't hurt him. I'll make it up to him. I will. When I'm growed up, I'll get a job. I'll make money. I'll buy him things — and you, too. I'll buy you both anything you want if you'll only —"

For the first time in his trouble the boy became a child, and the mother, looking over, saw the tears that ran openly down his contorted face. She turned her face to the fire, and there was a pause. Then she spoke.

"Joe, tha mustn't," she said softly. "Tha must learn never to want nothing in life like that. It don't do, lad. Tha mustn't want things bad, like tha wants Lassie."

The boy shook his clenched fists in impatience.

"It ain't that, Mother. Ye don't understand. Don't yer see — it ain't me that wants her. It's her that wants us! Tha's wha made her come all them miles. It's her that wants us, so terrible bad!"

The woman turned and stared. It was as if, in that moment, she were seeing this child, this boy, this son of her own, for the first time in many years. She turned her head down toward the table. It was surrender.

"Come and eat, then," she said. "I'll talk to him. I will that, all right. I feel sure he won't lie. But I'll talk to him, all right. I'll talk to Mr. Joe Carraclough. I will indeed."

At five that afternoon, the Duke of Rudling, fuming and muttering, got out of a car at a cottage gate to find a boy barring his way. This was a boy who stood, stubbornly, saying fiercely: "Away wi' thee! Thy tyke's net here!"

"Philippa, th' lad's touched," the duke said. "He is. He's touched."

Scowling and thumping his stick, the old duke advanced until the boy gave way, backing down the path out of the

reach of the waving blackthorn stick.

"The tyke's net here," the boy protested.

"What's he saying?" the girl asked.

"Says my dog isn't here. You going deaf? I'm supposed to be deaf, and I hear him plainly enough. Now, ma lad, what tyke o' mine's net here?"

As he turned to the boy, the duke spoke in broadest Yorkshire, as he did always to the people of the cottages — a habit which the Duchess of Rudling, and many more members of the duke's family, deplored.

"Coom, coom, ma lad. What tyke's net here?"

"No tyke o' thine. Us hasn't got it." The words began running faster and faster as the boy backed away from the fearful old man who advanced. "No tyke could have done it. No tyke can come all them miles. It isn't Lassie. It's another one that looks like her. It isn't Lassie!"

"Why, bless ma heart and sowl," the duke puffed. "Where's thy father, ma lad?"

The door behind the boy opened, and a woman's voice spoke.

"If it's Joe Carraclough ye want, he's out in the shed — and been there shut up half the afternoon."

"What's this lad talking about — a dog of mine being here?"

"Nay," the woman snapped quickly. "He didn't say a tyke o' thine was here. He said it wasn't here."

The woman swallowed and looked about as if for help. The duke stood, peering from under his jutting eyebrows. Her answer, truth or lie, was never spoken, for then they heard the rattle of a door opening, and a man making a pursing sound with his lips, as he will when he wants a dog to follow, and then Joe Carraclough's voice said: "This is t' only tyke us has here.

Does it look like any dog that belongs to thee?"

With his mouth open to cry one last protest, the boy turned. And his mouth stayed open. For there he saw his father, Joe Carraclough, the collie fancier, standing with a dog at his heels — a dog that sat at his left heel patiently, as any well-trained dog should do — as Lassie used to do. But this dog was not Lassie. In fact, it was ridiculous to think of it at the same moment as you thought of Lassie.

For where Lassie's skull was aristocratic and slim, this dog's head was clumsy and rough. Where Lassie's ears stood in twin-lapped symmetry, this dog had one ear draggling and the other standing up Alsatian fashion in a way to give any collie breeder the cold shivers. Where Lassie's coat was rich tawny gold, this dog's coat had ugly patches of black; and where Lassie's apron was a billowing stretch of snow-white, this dog had puddles of off-color blue-merle mixture. Besides, Lassie had four white paws, and this one had one paw white, two dirty-brown, and one almost black.

That is the dog they all looked at as Joe Carraclough stood there, having told no lie, having only asked a question. They all stood, waiting the duke's verdict.

But the duke said nothing. He only walked forward, slowly, as if he were seeing a dream. He bent beside the collie, looking with eyes that were as knowing about dogs as any Yorkshireman alive. And those eyes did not waste themselves upon twisted ears, or blotched marking, or rough head. Instead they were looking at a paw that the duke lifted, looking at the underside of the paw, staring intently at five black pads, crossed and recrossed with the scars where thorns had lacerated, and stones had torn.

For a long time the duke stared, and when he got up, he did not speak in Yorkshire accents any more. He spoke as a gentleman should, and he said: "Joe Carraclough. I never owned this dog. 'Pon my soul, she's never belonged to me. Never!"

Then he turned and went stumping down the path, thumping his cane and saying: "Bless my soul. Four hundred miles! Wouldn't ha' believed it. Five hundred miles!"

He was at the gate when his granddaughter whispered to him fiercely.

"Of course," he cried. "Mind your own business. Exactly what I came for. Talking about dogs made me forget. Carraclough! Carraclough! What're ye hiding for?"

"I'm still here, sir."

"Ah, there you are. You working?"

"Eigh, now. Working," Joe said. That's the best he could manage.

"Yes, working, working!" The duke fumed.

"Well, now — " Joe began.

Then Mrs. Carraclough came to his rescue, as a good housewife in Yorkshire will.

"Why, Joe's got three or four things that he's been considering," she said, with proper display of pride. "But he hasn't quite said yes or no to any of them yet."

"Then say no, quick," the old man puffed. "Had to sack Hynes. Didn't know a dog from a drunken filly. Should ha' known all along no Londoner could handle dogs fit for Yorkshire taste. How much, Carraclough?"

"Well, now," Joe began.

"Seven pounds a week, and worth every penny," Mrs. Carraclough chipped in. "One of them other offers may come up to eight," she lied, expertly. For there's always a certain amount of lying to be done in life, and when a wom-

an's married to a man who has made a lifelong cult of being honest, then she's got to learn to do the lying for two.

"Five," roared the duke — who, after all, was a Yorkshireman, and couldn't help being a bit sharp about things that pertained to money.

"Six," said Mrs. Carraclough.

"Five pound ten," bargained the duke, cannily.

"Done," said Mrs. Carraclough, who would have been willing to settle for three pounds in the first place. "But, o' course, us gets the cottage too."

"All right," puffed the duke. "Five pounds ten and the cottage. Begin Monday. But — on one condition. Carraclough, you can live on my land, but I won't have that thick-skulled, screw-lugged, gay-tailed eyesore of a misshapen mongrel on my property. Now never let me see her again. You'll get rid of her?"

He waited, and Joe fumbled for words. But it was the boy who answered, happily, gaily: "Oh, no, sir. She'll be waiting at school for me most o' the time. And, anyway, in a day or so we'll have her fixed up and coped [1] up so's ye'd never, never recognize her."

"I don't doubt that," puffed the duke, as he went to the car. "I don't doubt ye could do just exactly that."

It was a long time afterward, in the car, that the girl said: "Don't sit there like a lion on the Nelson column. [2] And I thought you were supposed to be a hard man."

"Fiddlesticks, m'dear. I'm a ruthless realist. For five years I've sworn I'd have that dog by hook or crook, and

[1] coped: shaped.
[2] Nelson column: a London monument honoring Lord Horatio Nelson, the British naval hero.

now, egad, at last I've got her."

"Pooh! You had to buy the man before you could get his dog."

"Well, perhaps that's not the worst part of the bargain."

THINKING IT OVER

1. Did that hyphen in the title bother you at all? Find the reason for its use in one of the early speeches of Mrs. Carraclough.

2. From her first speeches, what were your impressions of Mrs. Carraclough? And just where did you begin to feel a bit differently about her?

3. Explain the meaning of the speech of his father's that young Joe overhears: ". . . walk my feet off. If tha thinks I like — " What background does this furnish concerning the critical problem faced by the Carracloughs?

4. Someone who knows dogs might explain the ruff, apron, and leggings that are mentioned in the early description of Lassie.

5. Make a chalkboard list of the character traits of the Duke and Mr. Carraclough. Be able to justify each trait.

6. Mr. and Mrs. Carraclough felt they must be loyal to a code of behavior beyond their loyalty to Lassie. What was the code? What changed their attitude? Discuss which of the two loyalties you think is greater.

7. There are many loyalties demanded of us. A person, each to his degree, is loyal to some group, person, idea, or institution. Name some of these loyalties and explain the kind of loyalty you feel should be given to each.

ANTICIPATING OUTCOMES

1. What signal of future trouble do you get in paragraph 1?

2. Early in the story, in the scene ending with "Get thy cap," find two hints that the quarreling between husband and wife will be continued.

3. Near the end of the scene in which Joe and his father are walking off their troubles on the moor, there is a definite

hint of Lassie's future long trip home. Find these sentences.

4. Try to find the earliest point at which you are certain that it is Lassie who is making the brave journey that the author describes.

5. What action do you anticipate when you read the sentence, "But the day that t' duke comes back, then back she goes, too"?

6. What speech of Mrs. Carraclough's tells you that this time something will be done to keep Lassie?

7. When are you assured that there will be no more attempts to separate Lassie and young Joe? This hint is in a speech of the Duke's.

ABOUT THE AUTHOR

Eric Knight (1897–1943) was born in Yorkshire, England, the setting for this tale. He fought as a private in the Canadian Army in World War I and later became an American citizen. A major in the United States Army in World War II, he was killed in an airplane crash while on an official mission. "Lassie Come-Home" is probably the best-known of Knight's works. It has appeared also as a novel, a motion picture, and as a television series. If you enjoy the Yorkshire flavor of the story, you will want to read his humorous book *The Flying Yorkshireman*, which concerns the colorful and lively adventures of the remarkable Sam Small, another memorable character created by Eric Knight.

As the Artist Sees It ➤

The scene on the opposite page, as interpreted by artist Harvey Dinnerstein, is taken from a brief but memorable sequence in "Lassie Come-Home." The old couple who give shelter to Lassie on her homeward journey are not described by the author in any detail. Yet the few details given form a picture for the reader. The sequence is complete in other ways, too, and is almost like a story-within-a-story, with its own beginning, middle, and end. Which part of the sequence has the artist depicted in his drawing? Point out the details that reveal the answer.

The Fifty–first Dragon

HEYWOOD BROUN

A *story* can sometimes have two different levels of meaning. One level is simply the series of events that form the plot. The second level uses these events in order to make various comments on life. Usually, the comments will be of a serious nature, even though the author presents them in a humorous manner. This is a story with two such levels. The subjects taught at the "knight school" — a course on how to kill dragons, for example — will entertain you, as will many fantastic events. But if you read carefully, you will get more than entertainment.

O F ALL the pupils at the knight school Gawaine le Cœur-Hardy [1] was among the least promising. He was tall and sturdy, but his instructors soon discovered that he lacked spirit. He would hide in the woods when the jousting class was called, although his companions and members of the faculty sought to appeal to his better nature by shouting to him to come out and break his

[1] **Gawaine le Cœur-Hardy** (gä′wȧn lĕ kûr′-här′dĭ): Gawaine the Boldhearted; *Cœur* means *heart*.

neck like a man. Even when they told him that the lances were padded, the horses no more than ponies, and the field unusually soft for late autumn, Gawaine refused to grow enthusiastic. The Headmaster and the Assistant Professor of Pleasance were discussing the case one spring afternoon, and the Assistant Professor could see no remedy but expulsion.

"No," said the Headmaster, as he looked out at the purple hills which ringed the school, "I think I'll train him to slay dragons."

"He might be killed," objected the Assistant Professor.

"So he might," replied the Headmaster brightly, "but," he added, more soberly, "we must consider the greater good. We are responsible for the formation of this lad's character."

"Are the dragons particularly bad this year?" interrupted the Assistant Professor. This was characteristic. He always seemed restive when the head of the school began to talk ethics and the ideals of the institution.

"I've never known them worse," replied the Headmaster. "Up in the hills to the south last week they killed a number of peasants, two cows, and a prize pig. And if this dry spell holds, there's no telling when they may start a forest fire simply by breathing around indiscriminately."

"Would any refund on the tuition fee be necessary in case of an accident to young Cœur-Hardy?"

"No," the principal answered, judicially, "that's all covered in the contract. But as a matter of fact, he won't be killed. Before I send him up in the hills, I'm going to give him a magic word."

"That's a good idea," said the Professor. "Sometimes they work wonders."

From that day on Gawaine specialized in dragons. His course included both theory and practice. In the morning there were long lectures on the history, anatomy, manners, and customs of dragons. Gawaine did not distinguish himself in these studies. He had a marvelously versatile gift for forgetting things. In the afternoon he showed to better advantage, for then he would go down to the South Meadow and practice with a battle-ax. In this exercise he was truly impressive, for he had enormous strength as well as speed and grace. He even developed a deceptive display of ferocity. Old alumni say that it was a thrilling sight to see Gawaine charging across the field toward the dummy paper dragon which had been set up for his practice. As he ran he would brandish his ax and shout "A murrain [1] on thee!" or some other vivid bit of campus slang. It never took him more than one stroke to behead the dummy dragon.

Gradually his task was made more

difficult. Paper gave way to papier-mâché [2] and finally to wood, but even the toughest of these dummy dragons had no terrors for Gawaine. One sweep of the ax always did the business. There were those who said that, when the practice was protracted until dusk and the dragons threw long, fantastic shadows across the meadow, Gawaine did not charge so impetuously nor shout so loudly. It is possible there was malice in this charge. At any rate, the Headmaster decided by the end of June that it was time for the test. Only the night before a dragon had come close to the school grounds and had eaten some of the lettuce from the garden. The faculty decided that Gawaine was ready. They gave him a diploma and a new battle-ax and the Headmaster summoned him to a private conference.

"Sit down," said the Headmaster. "Have a cigarette."

Gawaine hesitated.

"Oh, I know it's against the rules," said the Headmaster. "But after all, you have received your preliminary degree. You are no longer a boy. You are a man. Tomorrow you will go out into the world, the great world of achievement."

Gawaine took a cigarette. The Headmaster offered him a match, but he produced one of his own and began to puff away with a dexterity which quite amazed the principal.

"Here you have learned the theories of life," continued the Headmaster, resuming the thread of his discourse, "but after all, life is not a matter of theories. Life is a matter of facts. It calls on the young and the old alike to face these facts, even though they are hard and sometimes unpleasant. Your problem, for example, is to slay dragons."

[1] **murrain** (mûr'ĭn): plague.

[2] **papier-mâché** (pā'pēr-mȧ-shā'): a hard material made of paper pulp mixed with glue or rosin.

"They say that those dragons down in the south wood are five hundred feet long," ventured Gawaine timorously.

"Stuff and nonsense!" said the Headmaster. "The curate saw one last week from the top of Arthur's Hill. The dragon was sunning himself down in the valley. The curate didn't have an opportunity to look at him very long because he felt it was his duty to hurry back to make a report to me. He said the monster — or, shall I say, the big lizard? — wasn't an inch over two hundred feet. But the size has nothing at all to do with it. You'll find the big ones even easier than the little ones. They're far slower on their feet and less aggressive, I'm told. Besides, before you go I'm going to equip you in such fashion that you need have no fear of all the dragons in the world."

"I'd like an enchanted cap," said Gawaine.

"What's that?" answered the Headmaster testily.

"A cap to make me disappear," explained Gawaine.

The Headmaster laughed indulgently. "You mustn't believe all those old wives' stories," he said. "There isn't any such thing. A cap to make you disappear, indeed! What would you do with it? You haven't even appeared yet. Why, my boy, you could walk from here to London, and nobody would so much as look at you. You're nobody. You couldn't be more invisible than that."

Gawaine seemed dangerously close to a relapse into his old habit of whimpering. The Headmaster reassured him: "Don't worry; I'll give you something much better than an enchanted cap. I'm going to give you a magic word. All you have to do is to repeat this magic charm once, and no dragon can possibly harm a hair of your head. You can cut off his head at your leisure."

He took a heavy book from the shelf behind his desk and began to run through it. "Sometimes," he said, "the charm is a whole phrase or even a sentence. I might, for instance, give you 'To make the' — No, that might not do. I think a single word would be best for dragons."

"A short word," suggested Gawaine.

"It can't be too short or it wouldn't be potent. There isn't so much hurry as all that. Here's a splendid magic word: 'Rumplesnitz.' Do you think you can learn that?"

Gawaine tried and in an hour or so he seemed to have the word well in hand. Again and again he interrupted the lesson to inquire, "And if I say 'Rumplesnitz,' the dragon can't possibly hurt me?" And always the Headmaster replied, "If you only say 'Rumplesnitz,' you are perfectly safe."

Toward morning Gawaine seemed resigned to his career. At daybreak the Headmaster saw him to the edge of the forest and pointed him to the direction in which he should proceed. About a mile away to the southwest a cloud of steam hovered over an open meadow in the woods, and the Headmaster assured Gawaine that under the steam he would find a dragon. Gawaine went forward slowly. He wondered whether it would be best to approach the dragon on the run as he did in his practice in the South Meadow or to walk slowly toward him, shouting "Rumplesnitz" all the way.

The problem was decided for him. No sooner had he come to the fringe of the meadow than the dragon spied him and began to charge. It was a large dragon, and yet it seemed decidedly aggressive in spite of the Headmaster's statement to the contrary. As the dragon charged, it released huge clouds of hissing steam through its nostrils. It was almost as if a gigantic teapot had gone mad. The dragon came forward so fast and Gawaine was so frightened that he had time to say "Rumplesnitz" only once. As he said it, he swung his battle-ax and off popped the head of the dragon. Gawaine had to admit that it was even easier to kill a real dragon than a wooden one if only you said "Rumplesnitz."

Gawaine brought the ears home and a small section of the tail. His schoolmates and the faculty made much of him, but the Headmaster wisely kept him from being spoiled by insisting that he go on with his work. Every clear day Gawaine rose at dawn and went out to kill dragons. The Headmaster kept him at home when it rained, because he said the woods were damp and unhealthy at such times and that he didn't want the boy to run needless risks. Few good days passed in which Gawaine failed to get a dragon. On one particularly fortunate day he killed three, a husband and wife and a visiting relative. Gradually he developed a technique. Pupils who sometimes watched him from the hilltops a long way off said that he often allowed the dragon to come within a few feet before he said "Rumplesnitz." He came to say it with a mocking sneer. Occasionally he did stunts. Once when an excursion party from London was watching him he went into action with his right hand tied behind his back. The dragon's head came off just as easily.

As Gawaine's record of killings mounted higher, the Headmaster found it impossible to keep him completely in hand. He fell into the habit of stealing out at night and engaging in long drinking bouts at the village tavern. It was after such a debauch that he rose a little before dawn one fine August morning and started out after his fiftieth dragon. His head was heavy and his mind sluggish. He was heavy in other respects as well, for he had adopted the somewhat vulgar practice of wearing his medals, ribbons and all, when he went out dragon hunting. The decorations began on his chest and ran all the way down to his abdomen. They must have weighed at least eight pounds.

Gawaine found a dragon in the same meadow where he had killed the first one. It was a fair-sized dragon, but evidently an old one. Its face was wrinkled, and Gawaine thought he had never seen so hideous a countenance. Much to the lad's disgust, the monster refused to charge, and Gawaine was obliged to walk toward him. He whistled as he went. The dragon regarded him hopelessly, but craftily. Of course it had heard of Gawaine. Even when the lad raised his battle-ax, the dragon made no move. It knew that there was no salvation in the quickest thrust of the head, for it had been informed that this hunter was protected by an enchantment. It merely waited, hoping something would turn up. Gawaine raised the battle-ax and suddenly lowered it again. He had grown very pale, and he trembled violently. The dragon suspected a trick. "What's the matter?" it asked, with false solicitude.

"I've forgotten the magic word," stammered Gawaine.

"What a pity," said the dragon. "So that was the secret. It doesn't seem quite sporting to me, all this magic stuff, you know. Not cricket, as we used to say when I was a little dragon; but after all, that's a matter of opinion."

Gawaine was so helpless with terror that the dragon's confidence rose immeasurably and it could not resist the temptation to show off a bit.

"Could I possibly be of any assistance?" it asked. "What's the first letter of the magic word?"

"It begins with an 'r,'" said Gawaine weakly.

"Let's see," mused the dragon, "that doesn't tell us much, does it? What sort of a word is this? Is it an epithet, do you think?"

Gawaine could do no more than nod.

"Why, of course," exclaimed the dragon, "reactionary Republican."

Gawaine shook his head.

"Well, then," said the dragon, "we'd better get down to business. Will you surrender?"

With the suggestion of a compromise Gawaine mustered up enough courage to speak.

"What will you do if I surrender?" he asked.

"Why, I'll eat you," said the dragon.

"And if I don't surrender?"

"I'll eat you just the same."

"Then it doesn't mean any difference, does it?" moaned Gawaine.

"It does to me," said the dragon with a smile. "I'd rather you didn't surrender. You'd taste much better if you didn't."

The dragon waited for a long time for Gawaine to ask "Why?" but the boy was too frightened to speak. At last the dragon had to give the explanation

without his cue line. "You see," he said, "if you don't surrender, you'll taste better because you'll die game."

This was an old and ancient trick of the dragon's. By means of some such quip he was accustomed to paralyze his victims with laughter and then to destroy them. Gawaine was sufficiently paralyzed as it was, but laughter had no part in his helplessness. With the last word of the joke the dragon drew back his head and struck. In that second there flashed into the mind of Gawaine the magic word "Rumplesnitz," but there was no time to say it. There was time only to strike and, without a word, Gawaine met the onrush of the dragon with a full swing. He put all his back and shoulders into it. The impact was terrific, and the head of the dragon flew away almost a hundred yards and landed in a thicket.

Gawaine did not remain frightened very long after the death of the dragon. His mood was one of wonder. He was enormously puzzled. He cut off the ears of the monster almost in a trance. Again and again he thought to himself, "I didn't say 'Rumplesnitz'!" He was sure of that, and yet there was no question that he had killed the dragon. In fact, he had never killed one so utterly. Never before had he driven a head for anything like the same distance. Twenty-five yards was perhaps his best previous record. All the way back to the knight school he kept rumbling about in his mind seeking an explanation for what had occurred. He went to the Headmaster immediately and after closing the door told him what had happened. "I didn't say 'Rumplesnitz,'" he explained with great earnestness.

The Headmaster laughed. "I'm glad you've found out," he said. "It makes you ever so much more of a hero. Don't you see that? Now you know that it was you who killed all these dragons and not that foolish little word 'Rumplesnitz.'"

Gawaine frowned. "Then it wasn't a magic word after all?" he asked.

"Of course not," said the Headmaster, "you ought to be too old for such foolishness. There isn't any such thing as a magic word."

"But you told me it was magic," protested Gawaine. "You said it was magic, and now you say it isn't."

"It wasn't magic in a literal sense," answered the Headmaster, "but it was much more wonderful than that. The word gave you confidence. It took away your fears. If I hadn't told you that, you might have been killed the very first time. It was your battle-ax did the trick."

Gawaine surprised the Headmaster by his attitude. He was obviously distressed by the explanation. He interrupted a long philosophic and ethical discourse by the Headmaster with, "If I hadn't of hit 'em all mighty hard and fast, any one of 'em might have crushed me like a, like a —" He fumbled for a word.

"Eggshell," suggested the Headmaster.

"Like a eggshell," assented Gawaine, and he said it many times. All through the evening meal people who sat near him heard him muttering, "Like a eggshell, like a eggshell."

The next day was clear, but Gawaine did not get up at dawn. Indeed, it was almost noon when the Headmaster found him cowering in bed, with the clothes pulled over his head. The principal called the Assistant Professor of Pleasance, and together they dragged the boy toward the forest.

"He'll be all right as soon as he gets a couple more dragons under his belt," explained the Headmaster.

The Assistant Professor of Pleasance agreed. "It would be a shame to stop such a fine run," he said. "Why, counting that one yesterday, he's killed fifty dragons."

They pushed the boy into a thicket above which hung a meager cloud of steam. It was obviously quite a small dragon. But Gawaine did not come back that night or the next. In fact, he never came back. Some weeks afterward brave spirits from the school explored the thicket, but they could find nothing to remind them of Gawaine except the metal parts of his medals. Even the ribbons had been devoured.

The Headmaster and the Assistant Professor of Pleasance agreed that it would be just as well not to tell the school how Gawaine had achieved his record and still less how he came to die. They held that it might have a bad effect on school spirit. Accordingly, Gawaine has lived in the memory of the school as its greatest hero. No visitor succeeds in leaving the building today without seeing a great shield which hangs on the wall of the dining hall. Fifty pairs of dragons' ears are mounted upon the shield and underneath in gilt letters is "Gawaine le Cœur-Hardy," followed by the simple inscription, "He killed fifty dragons." The record has never been equaled.

THINKING IT OVER

1. The story is about killing dragons with the aid of a secret charm, but what else is it about? State the theme. Probably the class will have different ideas about the theme and what it means. List all the suggestions on the chalkboard, then decide as a group which statement comes closest to expressing what the author had in mind. Explain how you think Gawaine would have fared without a magic word.

2. The second level of the story develops the theme in the form of the author's comments. To recognize this, can you find at least one statement in the first paragraph which might be a comment from the author? Explain what comment, if any, is made in the sentence beginning "Even when they told him that . . ." (page 130).

3. Answers to these questions will help you to check how carefully you read the story: (a) What made the Headmaster decide to train Gawaine to slay dragons? (b) What circumstances prompted him to decide that Gawaine was ready for battle? (c) What magic aid did Gawaine request to help him face the dragons? (d) What effect did success have on Gawaine?

4. Explain the irony in the inscription, "He killed fifty dragons," which appeared on the shield displayed by the school in memory of Gawaine.

5. A part of the fun in this story comes from the description of an imaginary "knight school" as if it were a school of today. What are some of these humorous touches?

WORDS IN CONTEXT

1. You may not have been familiar with *jousting* in paragraph 1, but by studying this word in its context and looking through the paragraph for clues to the meaning of the word, you would have learned that (a) jousting just might involve a broken neck, (b) lances are used, and (c) horses are used. From these "context clues" you could reasonably conclude that *jousting* is combat on horseback using lances.

2. Now that you know the method, try to get yourself past any other unfamiliar words in the story — without skipping! And when you come across unfamiliar words in your future reading, look for context clues which might help you uncover the meaning of the words. *Then* you can check your conclusion in the dictionary.

ABOUT THE AUTHOR

Heywood Broun (1888–1939) first began writing as a student at the Horace Mann School in New York, where he edited the school paper. After attending Harvard University, he joined the staff of the New York *Telegraph* as a sports writer and also gained attention as the author of some baseball stories. He served as a magazine drama critic, but it was when he became a syndicated newspaper columnist that he achieved fame. His column "It Seems to Me" was a leading feature of American newspapers for nearly twenty-five years, and such was its popularity that Heywood Broun became a national figure as a result. A man of strong opinions, he never hesitated to say what he felt; it was this characteristic which distinguished his literary career. "The Fifty-first Dragon" discloses Heywood Broun in a lighter mood and is perhaps his most enduring work.

RELATING THE STORIES

1. Review the stories in your mind and decide which theme is best described by each of the following words, and to which story it properly belongs:

> self-reliance
> enterprise
> paying
> faithfulness
> self-realization

2. Which theme reflected in the five stories meant the most to you? Which theme would you call the most important? the least important? the most memorable?

3. Name the story which, in your opinion, best stated its theme.

Variety in Reading: Forms and Techniques

If you have followed the sequence in which these stories have thus far been grouped, you will have seen by now that all stories are made up of certain common elements. As you have observed, different uses of these elements can be made by the author of a short story. You have read examples of stories which derive their chief excitement from the use of plot, and stories wherein the stress was placed more on character and setting. There were other stories which boasted strong plots and excellent characterizations, and which had, as an outstanding feature, a particular theme or an idea. All of the stories used the common elements of plot, character, setting, and theme, but used these elements with varying degrees of emphasis. Different authors, you learned, tell their stories in different ways.

In this final group are some stories which can be grouped together for another reason. Each of these stories has some special characteristic. Reading them will allow you to observe the different forms and techniques that can be used in short stories.

You will find here an example of the "short-short" story, one which also happens to represent the very popular science-fiction school of writing. The term "short-short" refers, of course, to length, which is kept to a minimum in this kind of story. There is a famous "surprise-ending" story that will make you blink twice. Be prepared for the last paragraph; if you anticipate it, you will have done better than most of us. For those among you who enjoy puzzles, there is a "question-mark" (or what-*really*-happened?) story that has been fascinating readers for years. Undoubtedly, you will enjoy piecing together your own answer to the puzzle presented in this celebrated story. Included in the group is a story written in the style of a fable; it makes delightful reading as it takes hold of reality and proceeds to turn it upside down. You will read, too, an example of the "framework" story, which will impress you with its unusual and striking qualities. Within the outer frame of this story, a second story is told — a story-within-a-story.

Three of the five stories in the group are classics; that is, they are of recognized, long-standing excellence. In reading "The Lady or the Tiger?", "The Necklace," and "The Silver Mine," you will find it interesting — and revealing — to decide why you think these stories have become classics. The other two stories in the group exemplify the very best of their kind. All of them will help point out to you, as the other selections have done, the many intriguing avenues down which the short story beckons you to travel.

The Lady
or
the Tiger?

FRANK R. STOCKTON

Here is a story which became famous almost the instant it was published. It is a question-mark, or "what-really-happened?" story, and undoubtedly a classic. The title even includes a question mark, for reasons you will soon understand.

IN THE very olden time, there lived a semibarbaric king, who was a man of exuberant fancy and of an authority so irresistible that, at his will, he turned his varied fancies into facts. He was greatly given to self-communing, and when he and himself agreed upon anything, the thing was done. When everything moved smoothly, his nature was bland and genial; but whenever there was a little hitch, he was blander and more genial still, for nothing pleased him so much as to make the crooked straight, and crush down uneven places.

Among his borrowed notions was that of the public arena, in which, by exhibitions of manly and beastly valor, the minds of his subjects were refined and cultured.

But even here the exuberant and bar-baric fancy asserted itself. This vast amphitheater,[1] with its encircling galleries, its mysterious vault, and its unseen passages, was an agent of poetic justice, in which crime was punished, or virtue rewarded, by the decrees of an impartial and incorruptible chance.

When a subject was accused of a crime of sufficient importance to interest the king, public notice was given that on an appointed day the fate of the accused person would be decided in the king's arena.

When all the people had assembled in the galleries, and the king, surrounded by his court, sat high up on his throne of royal state on one side of the arena, he gave a signal, a door beneath him opened, and the accused subject stepped out into the amphitheater. Directly opposite him, on the other side of the enclosed space, were two doors, exactly alike and side by side. It was the duty and the privilege of the person on trial to walk directly to these doors and open one of them. He could open either

[1] **amphitheater** (ăm'fĭ·thē'*à*·tẽr): an oval or circular arena with rising tiers of seats.

"The Lady or the Tiger?" by Frank Stockton, published by Charles Scribner's Sons.

door he pleased. He was subject to no guidance or influence but that of the aforementioned impartial and incorruptible chance. If he opened the one, there came out of it a hungry tiger, the fiercest and most cruel that could be procured, which immediately sprang upon him and tore him to pieces as a punishment for his guilt. The moment that the case of the criminal was thus decided, doleful iron bells were clanged, great wails went up from the hired mourners posted on the outer rim of the arena, and the vast audience, with bowed heads and downcast hearts, wended slowly their homeward way, mourning greatly that one so young and fair, or so old and respected, should have merited so dire a fate.

But if the accused person opened the other door, there came forth from it a lady, the most suitable to his years and station that His Majesty could select among his fair subjects; and to this lady he was immediately married, as a reward of his innocence. It mattered not that he might already possess a wife and family, or that his affections might be engaged upon an object of his own selection. The king allowed no such arrangements to interfere with his great scheme of punishment and reward. The exercises, as in the other instance, took place immediately, and in the arena. Another door opened beneath the king, and a priest, followed by a band of choristers, and dancing maidens blowing joyous airs on golden horns, advanced to where the pair stood side by side, and the wedding was promptly and cheerily solemnized. Then the gay brass bells rang forth their merry peals, and the people shouted glad hurrahs, and the innocent man, preceded by children strewing flowers on his path, led his bride to his home.

This was the king's semibarbaric method of administering justice. Its perfect fairness is obvious. The criminal could not know out of which door would come the lady. He opened either he pleased, without having the slightest idea whether, in the next instant, he was to be devoured or married. On some occasions the tiger came out of one door, and on some, out of the other. The decisions were not only fair — they were positively decisive. The accused person was instantly punished if he found himself guilty, and if innocent, he was rewarded on the spot, whether he liked it or not. There was no escape from the judgments of the king's arena.

The institution was a very popular one. When the people gathered together on one of the great trial days, they never knew whether they were to witness a bloody slaughter or a hilarious wedding. This element of uncertainty lent an interest to the occasion which it could not otherwise have attained. Thus the masses were entertained and pleased, and the thinking part of the community could bring no charge of unfairness against this plan; for did not the accused person have the whole matter in his own hands?

This semibarbaric king had a daughter as blooming as his most rosy fancies, and with a soul as fervent and imperious as his own. As is usual in such cases, she was the apple of his eye, and was loved by him above all humanity. Among his courtiers was a young man of that fineness of blood and lowness of station common to the heroes of romance who love royal maidens. This royal maiden was well satisfied with her lover, for he was handsome and brave to a degree unsurpassed in all this kingdom, and she loved him with an ardor that had enough of barbarism in it to make it exceedingly warm and strong. This love affair moved on happily for many months, until, one day, the king happened to discover its existence. He did not hesitate nor waver in regard to his duty. The youth was immediately cast into prison, and a day was appointed for his trial in the king's arena. This, of course, was an especially important occasion, and His Majesty, as well as all the people, was greatly interested in the workings and development of this trial. Never before had such a case occurred — never before had a subject dared to love the daughter of a king. In afteryears such things became commonplace enough, but then they were, in no slight degree, novel and startling.

The tiger cages of the kingdom were searched for the most savage and relentless beasts, from which the fiercest monster might be selected for the arena, and the ranks of maiden youth and beauty throughout the land were carefully surveyed by competent judges, in order that the young man might have a fitting bride in case fate did not determine for him a different destiny. Of course, everybody knew that the deed with which the accused was charged had been done. He had loved the princess, and neither he, she, nor anyone else thought of denying the fact. But the king would not think of allowing any fact of this kind to interfere with the workings of the court of judgment, in which he took such great delight and satisfaction. No matter how the affair turned out, the youth would be disposed of, and the king would take pleasure in watching the course of events which would determine whether or not the young man had done wrong in allowing himself to love the princess.

The appointed day arrived. From far and near the people gathered and thronged the great galleries of the arena, while crowds, unable to gain admittance, massed themselves against its outside walls. The king and his court were in their places, opposite the twin doors — those fateful portals, so terrible in their similarity!

All was ready. The signal was given. A door beneath the royal party opened, and the lover of the princess walked into the arena. Tall, beautiful, fair, his appearance was greeted with a low hum of admiration and anxiety. Half the audience had not known so grand a youth had lived among them. No wonder the princess loved him! What a terrible thing for him to be there!

As the youth advanced into the arena, he turned, as the custom was, to bow to the king. But he did not think at all of that royal personage; his eyes were fixed upon the princess, who sat to the right of her father. Had it not been for the barbarism in her nature, it is probable that lady would not have been there. But her intense and fervid soul would not allow her to be absent on an occasion in which she was so terribly interested. From the moment that the decree had gone forth that her lover should decide his fate in the king's arena, she had thought of nothing, night or day, but this great event and the various subjects connected with it. Possessed of more power, influence, and force of character than anyone who had ever before been interested in such a case, she had done what no other person had done — she had possessed herself of the secret of the doors. She knew in which of the two rooms behind those doors stood the cage of the tiger, with its open front, and in which waited the lady. Through these thick doors, heavily curtained with skins on the inside, it was impossible that any noise or suggestion should come from within to the person who should approach to raise the latch of one of them. But gold, and the power of a woman's will, had brought the secret to the princess.

Not only did she know in which room stood the lady, ready to emerge, all blushing and radiant, should her door be opened, but she knew who the lady was. It was one of the fairest and loveliest of the damsels of the court who had been selected as the reward of the accused youth, should he be proved innocent of the crime of aspiring to one so far above him; and the princess hated her. Often had she seen, or imagined that she had seen, this fair creature throwing glances of admiration upon the person of her lover, and sometimes she thought these glances were perceived and even returned. Now and then she had seen them talking together. It was but for a moment or two, but much can be said in a brief space. It may have been on most unimportant topics, but how could she know that? The girl was lovely, but she had dared to raise her eyes to the loved one of the princess, and, with all the intensity of the savage blood transmitted to her through long lines of wholly barbaric ancestors, she hated the woman who blushed and trembled behind that silent door.

When her lover turned and looked at her, and his eye met hers as she sat there paler and whiter than anyone in the vast ocean of anxious faces about her, he saw, by that power of quick perception which is given to those whose souls are one, that she knew behind which door crouched the tiger, and behind which stood the lady. He had expected her to know it. He understood her nature, and his soul was assured that she would never rest until she had made plain to herself this thing, hidden to all other lookers-on, even to the king. The only hope for the youth in which there was any element of certainty was based upon the success of

the princess in discovering this mystery, and the moment he looked upon her, he saw she had succeeded.

Then it was that his quick and anxious glance asked the question, "Which?" It was as plain to her as if he shouted it from where he stood. There was not an instant to be lost. The question was asked in a flash; it must be answered in another.

Her right arm lay on the cushioned parapet [1] before her. She raised her hand, and made a slight, quick movement toward the right. No one but her lover saw her. Every eye but his was fixed on the man in the arena.

He turned, and with a firm and rapid step he walked across the empty space. Every heart stopped beating, every breath was held, every eye was fixed immovably upon that man. Without the slightest hesitation, he went to the door on the right and opened it.

Now, the point of the story is this: Did the tiger come out of that door, or did the lady?

The more we reflect upon this question, the harder it is to answer. It involves a study of the human heart which leads us through roundabout pathways of passion, out of which it is difficult to find our way. Think of it, fair reader, not as if the decision of the question depended upon yourself, but upon that hot-blooded, semibarbaric princess, her soul at a white heat beneath the combined fires of despair and jealousy. She had lost him, but who should have him?

How often, in her waking hours and in her dreams, had she started in wild horror and covered her face with her hands as she thought of her lover opening the door on the other side of which waited the cruel fangs of the tiger!

But how much oftener had she seen

[1] **parapet** (păr′*á*·pĕt): a low wall or railing.

him at the other door! How in her grievous reveries had she gnashed her teeth and torn her hair when she saw his start of rapturous delight as he opened the door of the lady! How her soul had burned in agony when she had seen him rush to meet that woman, with her flushing cheek and sparkling eye of triumph; when she had seen him lead her forth, his whole frame kindled with the joy of recovered life; when she had heard the glad shouts from the multitude, and the wild ringing of the happy bells; when she had seen the priest, with his joyous followers, advance to the couple, and make them man and wife before her very eyes; and when she had seen them walk away together upon their path of flowers, followed by the tremendous shouts of the hilarious multitude, in which her one despairing shriek was lost and drowned!

Would it not be better for him to die at once, and go to wait for her in the blessed regions of semibarbaric futurity?

And yet, that awful tiger, those shrieks, that blood!

Her decision had been indicated in an instant, but it had been made after days and nights of anguished deliberation. She had known she would be asked, she had decided what she would answer, and without the slightest hesitation, she had moved her hand to the right.

The question of her decision is one not to be lightly considered, and it is not for me to presume to set up myself as the one person able to answer it. So I leave it with all of you: Which came out of the opened door — the lady or the tiger?

THINKING IT OVER

1. What is *your* answer to the question mark posed by the story? Explain your theory. It might be fun to hold a class debate.

2. Point out some details in the first two sentences that establish the absolute authority of the king. What is your opinion of the king's method of justice as a means of solving important problems? Are there any places in the world today where a ruler has this much power?

3. The author says of the king's method of dispensing justice: "Its perfect fairness is obvious." Do you think he believes this? Tell why or why not.

4. In a number of civilized nations in the world, parents, even today, arrange the marriages of their children. What can you say *in defense* of this kind of social custom?

5. The chief effect of the story lies in the reader's understanding of the nature of the princess. What is there in her character or background that makes her an especially unpredictable person?

ABOUT THE AUTHOR

Francis Richard Stockton (1834–1902) was born in Philadelphia. Shortly after graduating from high school in that city, he began a career in wood engraving, and when he turned to writing, he used his own engravings as illustrations. He served on the staff of several magazines (including the famous *St. Nicholas*). His writing falls into a number of categories. He has written science fiction, fairy tales, outdoor yarns, historical romances, and love stories.

Visualizing the Story ➤

On the facing page is artist Whitold Mars's interpretation of the climactic scene in "The Lady or the Tiger?" A good reader performs a function similar to that of the illustrator of a story: the reader takes the author's words and uses his imagination to visualize what these words describe. A reader who really uses his imagination can visualize details beyond those the author has supplied. For example, can you visualize what the king's palace in this story might have looked like, based on what you know about him? What about the princess' rooms? her clothing and interests?

The Necklace

GUY DE MAUPASSANT

You will have a lot to think about as you read this, one of the great surprise-ending stories in literature. The fate of the two main characters will raise questions in your mind that are not easily answered, and you will not easily forget the theme of the story.

SHE WAS one of those pretty and charming girls, born, as if by an accident of fate, into a family of clerks. With no dowry, no prospects, no way of any kind of being met, understood, loved, and married by a man both prosperous and famous, she was finally married to a minor clerk in the Ministry of Education.

She dressed plainly because she could not afford fine clothes, but was as unhappy as a woman who has come down in the world; for women have no family rank or social class. With them, beauty, grace, and charm take the place of birth and breeding. Their natural poise, their instinctive good taste, and their mental cleverness are the sole guiding principles which make daughters of the common people the equals of ladies in high society.

She grieved incessantly, feeling that she had been born for all the little niceties and luxuries of living. She grieved over the shabbiness of her apartment, the dinginess of the walls, the worn-out appearance of the chairs, the ugliness of the draperies. All these things, which another woman of her class would not even have noticed, gnawed at her and made her furious The sight of the little Breton [1] girl who did her humble housework roused in her disconsolate regrets and wild daydreams. She would dream of silent chambers, draped with Oriental tapestries and lighted by tall bronze floor lamps, and of two handsome butlers in knee breeches, who, drowsy from the heavy warmth cast by the central stove,[2] dozed in large overstuffed armchairs.

She would dream of great reception halls hung with old silks, of fine furni-

[1] **Breton** (brĕt′ŭn): a native of Brittany, a province in northwestern France.
[2] **central stove**: At the time of this story, rooms were heated by large stoves usually placed in the center of the room.

"The Necklace" by Guy de Maupassant. Translated by Newbury LeB. Morse.

ture filled with priceless curios, and of small, stylish, scented sitting rooms just right for the four o'clock chat with intimate friends, with distinguished and sought-after men whose attention every woman envies and longs to attract.

When dining at the round table, covered for the third day with the same cloth, opposite her husband who would raise the cover of the soup tureen, declaring delightedly, "Ah! a good stew! There's nothing I like better . . ." she would dream of fashionable dinner parties, of gleaming silverware, of tapestries making the walls alive with characters out of history and strange birds in a fairyland forest; she would dream of delicious dishes served on wonderful china, of gallant compliments whispered and listened to with a sphinxlike smile as one eats the rosy flesh of a trout or nibbles at the wings of a grouse.

She had no evening clothes, no jewels, nothing. But those were the things she wanted; she felt that was the kind of life for her. She so much longed to please, be envied, be fascinating and sought after.

She had a well-to-do friend, a classmate of convent-school days whom she would no longer go to see, simply because she would feel so distressed on returning home. And she would weep for days on end from vexation, regret, despair, and anguish.

Then one evening, her husband came home proudly holding out a large envelope.

"Look," he said, "I've got something for you."

She excitedly tore open the envelope and pulled out a printed card bearing these words:

"The Minister of Education and Mme Georges Ramponneau[1] beg M. and Mme Loisel[2] to do them the honor of attending an evening reception at the ministerial mansion on Friday, January 18."

Instead of being delighted, as her husband had hoped, she scornfully tossed the invitation on the table, murmuring, "What good is that to me?"

"But, my dear, I thought you'd be thrilled to death. You never get a chance to go out, and this is a real affair, a wonderful one! I had an awful time getting a card. Everybody wants one; it's much sought after, and not many clerks have a chance at one. You'll see all the most important people there."

She gave him an irritated glance, and burst out impatiently, "What do you think I have to go in?"

He hadn't given that a thought. He stammered, "Why, the dress you wear when we go to the theater. That looks quite nice, I think."

He stopped talking, dazed and distracted to see his wife burst out weeping. Two large tears slowly rolled from the corners of her eyes to the corners of her mouth; he gasped, "Why, what's the matter? What's the trouble?"

By sheer will power she overcame her outburst and answered in a calm voice while wiping the tears from her wet cheeks:

"Oh, nothing. Only I don't have an evening dress and therefore I can't go to that affair. Give the card to some friend at the office whose wife can dress better than I can."

He was stunned. He resumed, "Let's see, Mathilde.[3] How much would a suitable outfit cost — one you could wear for other affairs too — something very simple?"

[1] Mme Georges Ramponneau (ma·dam' zhôrzh rän·pò·nō').

[2] M. . . . Mme Loisel (mē·syû' . . . lwä·zĕl').

[3] Mathilde (ma·tēld').

She thought it over for several seconds, going over her allowance and thinking also of the amount she could ask for without bringing an immediate refusal and an exclamation of dismay from the thrifty clerk.

Finally, she answered hesitatingly, "I'm not sure exactly, but I think with four hundred francs [1] I could manage it."

He turned a bit pale, for he had set aside just that amount to buy a rifle so that, the following summer, he could join some friends who were getting up a group to shoot larks on the plain near Nanterre.[2]

However, he said, "All right. I'll give you four hundred francs. But try to get a nice dress."

As the day of the party approached, Mme Loisel seemed sad, moody, and ill at ease. Her outfit was ready, however. Her husband said to her one evening, "What's the matter? You've been all out of sorts for three days."

And she answered, "It's embarrassing not to have a jewel or a gem — nothing to wear on my dress. I'll look like a pauper: I'd almost rather not go to that party."

He answered, "Why not wear some flowers? They're very fashionable this season. For ten francs you can get two or three gorgeous roses."

She wasn't at all convinced. "No . . . There's nothing more humiliating than to look poor among a lot of rich women."

But her husband exclaimed, "My, but you're silly! Go see your friend Mme Forestier [3] and ask her to lend you some jewelry. You and she know each other well enough for you to do that."

She gave a cry of joy, "Why, that's so! I hadn't thought of it."

The next day she paid her friend a visit and told her of her predicament.

Mme Forestier went toward a large closet with mirrored doors, took out a large jewel box, brought it over, opened it, and said to Mme Loisel: "Pick something out, my dear."

At first her eyes noted some bracelets, then a pearl necklace, then a Venetian cross, gold and gems, of marvelous workmanship. She tried on these adornments in front of the mirror, but hesitated, unable to decide which to part with and put back. She kept on asking, "Haven't you something else?"

"Oh, yes, keep on looking. I don't know just what you'd like."

All at once she found, in a black satin box, a superb diamond necklace; and her pulse beat faster with longing. Her hands trembled as she took it up. Clasping it around her throat, outside her high-necked dress, she stood in ecstasy looking at her reflection.

Then she asked, hesitatingly, pleading, "Could I borrow that, just that and nothing else?"

"Why, of course."

She threw her arms around her friend, kissed her warmly, and fled with her treasure.

[1] **four hundred francs:** about $80 then.

[2] **Nanterre** (näN·târ′): a French town near Paris.

[3] **Forestier** (fô·rĕ·styā′).

The day of the party arrived. Mme Loisel was a sensation. She was the prettiest one there, fashionable, gracious, smiling, and wild with joy. All the men turned to look at her, asked who she was, begged to be introduced. All the cabinet officials wanted to waltz with her. The minister took notice of her.

She danced madly, wildly, drunk with pleasure, giving no thought to anything in the triumph of her beauty, the pride of her success, in a kind of happy cloud composed of all the adulation, of all the admiring glances, of all the awakened longings, of a sense of complete victory that is so sweet to a woman's heart.

She left around four o'clock in the morning. Her husband, since midnight, had been dozing in a small empty sitting room with three other gentlemen whose wives were having too good a time.

He threw over her shoulders the wraps he had brought for going home, modest garments of everyday life whose shabbiness clashed with the stylishness of her evening clothes. She felt this and longed to escape, unseen by the other women who were draped in expensive furs.

Loisel held her back.

"Hold on! You'll catch cold outside. I'll call a cab."

But she wouldn't listen to him and went rapidly down the stairs. When they were on the street, they didn't find a carriage; and they set out to hunt for one, hailing drivers whom they saw going by at a distance.

They walked toward the Seine,[1] disconsolate and shivering. Finally on the docks they found one of those carriages

that one sees in Paris only after nightfall, as if they were ashamed to show their drabness during daylight hours.

It dropped them at their door in the Rue des Martyrs, and they climbed wearily up to their apartment. For her, it was all over. For him, there was the thought that he would have to be at the ministry at ten o'clock.

Before the mirror, she let the wraps fall from her shoulders to see herself once again in all her glory. Suddenly she gave a cry. The necklace was gone.

Her husband, already half undressed, said, "What's the trouble?"

She turned toward him despairingly, "I . . . I . . . I don't have Mme Forestier's necklace."

"What! You can't mean it! It's impossible!"

They hunted everywhere, through the folds of the dress, through the folds of the coat, in the pockets. They found nothing.

He asked, "Are you sure you had it when leaving the dance?"

"Yes, I felt it when I was in the hall of the ministry."

"But, if you had lost it on the street we'd have heard it drop. It must be in the cab."

"Yes. Quite likely. Did you get its number?"

[1] **Seine** (sān): a river which runs through Paris.

"No. Didn't you notice it either?"

"No."

They looked at each other aghast. Finally Loisel got dressed again.

"I'll retrace our steps on foot," he said, "to see if I can find it."

And he went out. She remained in her evening clothes, without the strength to go to bed, slumped in a chair in the unheated room, her mind a blank.

Her husband came in about seven o'clock. He had had no luck.

He went to the police station, to the newspapers to post a reward, to the cab companies, everywhere the slightest hope drove him.

That evening Loisel returned, pale, his face lined; still he had learned nothing.

"We'll have to write your friend," he said, "to tell her you have broken the catch and are having it repaired. That will give us a little time to turn around."

She wrote to his dictation.

At the end of a week, they had given up all hope.

And Loisel, looking five years older, declared, "We must take steps to replace that piece of jewelry."

The next day they took the case to the jeweler whose name they found inside. He consulted his records. "I didn't sell that necklace, madame," he said. "I only supplied the case."

Then they went from one jeweler to another hunting for a similar necklace, going over their recollections, both sick with despair and anxiety.

They found, in a shop in Palais Royal,[1] a string of diamonds which seemed exactly like the one they were seeking. It was priced at forty thousand francs. They could get it for thirty-six.

They asked the jeweler to hold it for them for three days. And they reached

an agreement that he would take it back for thirty-four thousand if the lost one was found before the end of February.

Loisel had eighteen thousand francs he had inherited from his father. He would borrow the rest.

He went about raising the money, asking a thousand francs from one, four hundred from another, a hundred here, sixty there. He signed notes, made ruinous deals, did business with loan sharks, ran the whole gamut of moneylenders. He compromised the rest of his life, risked his signature without knowing if he'd be able to honor it, and then, terrified by the outlook for the future, by the blackness of despair about to close around him, by the prospect of all the privations of the body and tortures of the spirit, he went to claim the new necklace with the thirty-six thousand francs which he placed on the counter of the shopkeeper.

When Mme Loisel took the necklace back, Mme Forestier said to her frostily, "You should have brought it back sooner; I might have needed it."

She didn't open the case, an action her friend was afraid of. If she had noticed the substitution, what would she have thought? What would she have said? Would she have thought her a thief?

Mme Loisel experienced the horrible life the needy live. She played her part, however, with sudden heroism. That frightful debt had to be paid. She would pay it. She dismissed her maid; they rented a garret under the eaves.

She learned to do the heavy housework, to perform the hateful duties of cooking. She washed dishes, wearing down her shell-pink nails scouring the grease from pots and pans; she scrubbed dirty linen, shirts, and clean-

[1] **Palais Royal** (pà·lā′ rwȧ·äl′): a section with many stores.

ing rags which she hung on a line to dry; she took the garbage down to the street each morning and brought up water, stopping on each landing to get her breath. And, clad like a peasant woman, basket on arm, guarding sou[1] by sou her scanty allowance, she bargained with the fruit dealers, the grocer, the butcher, and was insulted by them.

Each month notes had to be paid, and others renewed to give more time.

Her husband labored evenings to balance a tradesman's accounts, and at night, often, he copied documents at five sous a page.

And this went on for ten years.

Finally, all was paid back, everything including the exorbitant rates of the loan sharks and accumulated compound interest.

Mme Loisel appeared an old woman, now. She became heavy, rough, harsh, like one of the poor. Her hair untended, her skirts askew, her hands red, her voice shrill, she even slopped water on her floors and scrubbed them herself. But, sometimes, while her husband was at work, she would sit near the window and think of that long-ago evening when, at the dance, she had been so beautiful and admired.

What would have happened if she had not lost that necklace? Who knows? Who can say? How strange and unpredictable life is! How little there is between happiness and misery!

Then one Sunday when she had gone for a walk on the Champs Élysées[2] to relax a bit from the week's labors, she suddenly noticed a woman strolling with a child. It was Mme Forestier, still young-looking, still beautiful, still charming.

Mme Loisel felt a rush of emotion. Should she speak to her? Of course. And now that everything was paid off, she would tell her the whole story. Why not?

She went toward her. "Hello, Jeanne."

The other, not recognizing her, showed astonishment at being spoken to so familiarly by this common person. She stammered, "But . . . madame . . . I don't recognize . . . You must be mistaken."

"No, I'm Mathilde Loisel."

Her friend gave a cry, "Oh, my poor Mathilde, how you've changed!"

"Yes, I've had a hard time since last seeing you. And plenty of misfortunes — and all on account of you!"

"Of me . . . How do you mean?"

"Do you remember that diamond necklace you loaned me to wear to the dance at the ministry?"

"Yes, but what about it?"

"Well, I lost it."

"You lost it! But you returned it."

"I brought you another just like it. And we've been paying for it for ten years now. You can imagine that wasn't easy for us who had nothing. Well, it's over now, and I am glad of it."

Mme Forestier stopped short. "You mean to say you bought a diamond necklace to replace mine?"

"Yes. You never noticed, then? They were quite alike."

And she smiled with proud and simple joy.

Mme Forestier, quite overcome, clasped her by the hands, "Oh, my poor Mathilde. But mine was only paste.[3] Why, at most it was worth only five hundred francs!"

---

[1] **sou** (soo): a coin then worth about one cent.

[2] **Champs Élysées** (shäṉ'-zā'lē'zā'): a well-known avenue.

[3] **paste:** a brilliant, glassy material used in making imitation diamonds.

THINKING IT OVER

1. State the theme of this story. Do you agree with the way the author has worked it out in terms of the fate of the Loisels — or would you have allowed them a less cruel fate? Defend your position.

2. If Mme Loisel had not lost the necklace, what sort of future would you predict for her? State whether you think it might have been happy or just as tragic, and explain why.

3. It is interesting to go back over a surprise-ending story and hunt for the place where you might have been tricked. At what point in the story did Mme Loisel and her husband make the mistake that cost them so dearly? Did you realize it was a mistake? What would you have done in their place?

4. Mme Loisel's foolish extravagance was caused by her poor sense of values. She was interested in what today we would call "status symbols" — possessions which, when displayed publicly, give their owners a feeling of importance. What are some status symbols that you have observed among adults? among students?

5. Mme Loisel wanted pretty clothes, a more attractive home, and a position in society. Is it wrong to want these things? Suppose you, as an older and valued family friend, had to listen to her incessant grieving (paragraph 3). What advice would you give her? What are the chances that she would have followed your advice?

FOR YOUR VOCABULARY: THE "–IVE" SUFFIX

In this story there are such descriptive words as "*instinctive* good taste" and "*expensive* furs." The –ive suffix means "having the nature or quality of a thing." For example, *active* means "having the nature or quality of action." See whether you can form the –ive words for the following. Be sure to spell them correctly. Then give a definition for each.

derision	excess
invention	progress
meditation	compete
protection	illustrate
argument	narrate
combat	preserve

PEN AND PAPER

Write a "happy ending" for the story that you think is possible and believable. To do this, you will probably want to continue briefly the scene in the park between the two women and then add a final scene between Mme Loisel and her husband — or perhaps you have other ideas.

ABOUT THE AUTHOR

Guy de Maupassant [1] (1850–1893) has written many world-renowned stories in addition to "The Necklace." A Frenchman, he was born in the province of Normandy but spent most of his life in Paris, where he studied under the great French novelist, Gustave Flaubert. As a literary artist Maupassant concentrated on an objective, cameralike presentation of life. This was a new kind of realism. Maupassant's style has served as a model for many writers, none of whom has equaled his mastery.

[1] **Guy de Maupassant** (gē dē mō'pä'sän').

Great Art as Illustration ➤

"Pont Neuf" — the title of the painting opposite — is the work of the great French artist, Pierre Auguste Renoir (1841–1919). Renoir belongs to a famous school of painters called "Impressionists." The attempt of these artists was to capture the effects of light on the colors of the objects they painted; thus their canvases conveyed an impression of a scene rather than a literal representation of it. Pont Neuf is a famous bridge which spans the Seine River in Paris, connecting the two main areas of the city, the Left Bank and the Right Bank. The scene painted by Renoir is of Paris in the 1870's, the period which forms the setting of "The Necklace." Across the bridge stroll groups of elegant, well-dressed Parisiennes. In your mind, picture the Loisels among the strollers. From what you know of Mme Loisel's character as it was at the beginning of the story, how might such a scene have affected her? Would the Mme Loisel at the end of the story have had a different reaction to the scene? If so, explain.

The Silver Mine

SELMA LAGERLÖF

In this unusual story the coach in which a king is traveling has an accident, forcing him to make a stopover in a small village. There, the king listens to a tale — a story-within-the-story — told by a man who is a stranger to him. You will know the secret long before King Gustaf does, but you will wonder how and when he will discover it, too.

KING GUSTAF III[1] was traveling through Dalecarlia.[2] He was pressed for time, and all the way he wanted to drive like lightning. Although they drove with such speed that the horses were extended like stretched rubber bands and the coach cleared the turns on two wheels, the King poked his head out of

---

[1] **Gustaf III** (gŭs'täv): king of Sweden from 1611 to 1632.
[2] **Dalecarlia** (dăl'ĕ·kär'lĭ·á): a region in west central Sweden.

the window and shouted to the postilion,[3] "Why don't you go ahead? Do you think you are driving over eggs?"

Since they had to drive over poor country roads at such a mad pace, it would have been almost a miracle had the harness and wagon held together! And they didn't, either; for at the foot of a steep hill the pole broke — and there the King sat! The courtiers sprang from the coach and scolded the driver, but this did not lessen the damage done. There was no possibility of continuing until the coach was mended.

When the courtiers looked around to try to find something with which the King could amuse himself while he waited, they noticed a church spire looming high above the trees in a grove a short distance ahead. They intimated to the King that he might step into

---

[3] **postilion** (pōs·tǐl'yŭn): a rider on one of the leading horses on a coach team.

Inferring Character. As you know, the speech and actions of a character can tell you a great deal about him. You can also gain additional information about him from the speech and actions of others in the story. In this story, try to be aware of all the ways in which you can infer character from clues of this kind.

---

one of the coaches in which the attendants were riding and drive up to the church. It was a Sunday, and the King might attend services to pass the time until the royal coach was ready.

The King accepted the proposal and drove toward the church. He had been traveling for hours through dark forest regions; but here it looked more cheerful, with fairly large meadows and villages, and with the Dal River gliding on light and pretty, between thick rows of alder bushes.

But the King had ill luck to this extent: the bell ringer took up the recessional chant just as the King was stepping from the coach on the church knoll and the people were coming out from the service. But when they came walking past him, the King remained standing, with one foot in the wagon and the other on the footstep. He did not move from the spot — only stared at them. They were the finest lot of folk he had ever seen. All the men were above the average height, with intelligent and earnest faces, and the women were dignified and stately, with an air of Sabbath peace about them.

The whole of the preceding day the King had talked only of the desolate tracts he was passing through, and had said to his courtiers again and again, "Now I am certainly driving through the very poorest part of my kingdom!" But now, when he saw the people, garbed in the picturesque dress of this section of the country, he forgot to think of their poverty; instead his heart warmed, and he remarked to himself, "The King of Sweden is not so badly off as his enemies think. So long as my subjects look like this, I shall probably be able to defend both my faith and my country."

He commanded the courtiers to make known to the people that the stranger who was standing among them was their King and that they should gather around him, so he could talk to them.

And then the King made a speech to the people. He spoke from the high steps outside the vestry, and the narrow step upon which he stood is there even today.

The King gave an account of the sad plight in which the kingdom was placed. He said that the Swedes were threatened with war by both Russians and Danes. Under ordinary circumstances it would not be such a serious matter; but now the army was filled with traitors, and he did not dare depend upon it. Therefore there was no other course for him to take than to go himself into the country settlements and ask his subjects if they would be loyal to their King and help him with men and money, so he could save the Fatherland.

The peasants stood quietly while the King was speaking to them, and when he had finished they gave no sign either of approval or disapproval.

The King himself thought that he had spoken well. The tears had sprung to his eyes several times while he was speaking. But when the peasants stood there all the while, troubled and undecided, and could not make up their minds to answer him, the King frowned and looked displeased.

The peasants understood that it was becoming monotonous for the King to wait, and finally one of them stepped out from the crowd.

"Now, you must know, King Gustaf, that we were not expecting a royal visit in the parish today," said the peasant, "and therefore we are not prepared to answer you at once. I advise you to go into the vestry and speak with our pastor, while we discuss among ourselves this matter which you have laid before us."

The King apprehended that a more satisfactory response was not to be had immediately, so he felt that it would be best for him to follow the peasant's advice.

When he came into the vestry, he found no one there but a man who looked like a peasant. He was tall and rugged, with big hands, toughened by labor, and he wore neither cassock nor collar, but leather breeches and a long white homespun coat, like all the other men.

He rose and bowed to the King when the latter entered.

"I thought I should find the parson in here," said the King.

The man grew somewhat red in the face. He thought it annoying to mention the fact that he was the parson of

this parish, when he saw that the King had mistaken him for a peasant. "Yes," said he, "the parson is usually on hand in here."

The King dropped into a large armchair which stood in the vestry at that time and which stands there today, looking exactly like itself, with this difference: the congregation has had a gilded crown attached to the back of it.

"Have you a good parson in this parish?" asked the King, who wanted to appear interested in the welfare of the peasants.

When the King questioned him in this manner, the parson felt that he couldn't possibly tell who he was. "It's better to let him go on believing that I'm only a peasant," thought he, and replied that the parson was good enough. He preached a pure and clear gospel and tried to live as he taught.

The King thought that this was a good commendation, but he had a sharp ear and marked a certain doubt in the tone. "You sound as if you were not quite satisfied with the parson," said the King.

"He's a bit arbitrary," said the man, thinking that, if the King should find out later who he was, he would not think that the parson had been standing here and blowing his own horn; therefore he wished to come out with a little faultfinding also. "There are some, no doubt, who say the parson wants to be the only one to counsel and rule in this parish," he continued.

"Then, at all events, he has led and managed in the best possible way," said the King. He didn't like it that the peasant complained of one who was placed above him. "To me it appears as though good habits and old-time simplicity were the rule here."

"The people are good enough," said the curate, "but then they live in poverty and isolation. Human beings here would certainly be no better than others if this world's temptations came closer to them."

"But there's no fear of anything of the sort happening," said the King, with a shrug.

He said nothing further, but began thrumming on the table with his fingers. He thought he had exchanged a sufficient number of gracious words with this peasant and wondered when the others would be ready with their answer.

"These peasants are not very eager to help their King," thought he. "If I only had my coach, I would drive away from them and their palaver!" [1]

The pastor sat there troubled, debating with himself as to how he should decide an important matter which he must settle. He was beginning to feel happy because he had not told the King who he was. Now he felt that he could speak with him about matters which otherwise he could not have placed before him.

After a while the parson broke the silence and asked the King if it was an actual fact that enemies were upon them and that the kingdom was in danger.

The King thought this man ought to have sense enough not to trouble him further. He simply glared at him and said nothing.

"I ask because I was standing in here and could not hear very well," said the parson. "But if this is really the case, I want to say to you that the pastor of this congregation might perhaps be able to procure for the King as much money as he will need."

"I thought that you said just now that everyone here was poor," said the King, thinking that the man did not

[1] **palaver** (på·lăv′ẽr): a discussion.

know what he was talking about.

"Yes, that's true," replied the rector, "and the parson has no more than any of the others. But if the King would condescend to listen to me for a moment, I will explain how the pastor happens to have the power to help him."

"You may speak," said the King. "You seem to find it easier to get the words past your lips than your friends and neighbors out there, who never will be ready with what they have to tell me."

"It is not so easy to reply to the King! I'm afraid that, in the end, it will be the parson who must undertake this on behalf of the others."

The King crossed his legs, folded his arms, and let his head sink down upon his breast. "You may begin now," he said in the tone of one already asleep.

"Once upon a time there were five men from this parish who were out on a moose hunt," began the clergyman. "One of them was the parson of whom we are speaking. Two of the others were soldiers, named Olaf and Eric Svärd; the fourth man was the innkeeper in this settlement, and the fifth was a peasant named Israel Per Persson."

"Don't go to the trouble of mentioning so many names," muttered the King, letting his head droop to one side.

"Those men were good hunters," continued the parson, "who usually had luck with them, but that day they had wandered long and far without getting anything. Finally they gave up the hunt altogether and sat down on the ground to talk. They said there was not a spot in the whole forest fit for cultivation; all of it was only mountain and swampland. 'Our Lord has not done right by us in giving us such a poor land to live in,' said one. 'In other localities people can get riches for themselves in abun-

dance, but here, with all our toil and drudgery we can scarcely get our daily bread.' "

The pastor paused a moment, as if uncertain that the King heard him, but the latter moved his little finger to show that he was awake.

"Just as the hunters were discussing this matter, the parson saw something that glittered at the base of the mountain, where he had kicked away a moss tuft. 'This is a queer mountain,' he thought, as he kicked off another moss tuft. He picked up a sliver of stone that came with the moss and which shone exactly like the other. 'It can't be possible that this stuff is lead,' said he.

"Then the others sprang up and scraped away the turf with the butt ends of their rifles. When they did this, they saw plainly that a broad vein of ore followed the mountain.

" 'What do you think this might be?' asked the parson.

"The men chipped off bits of stone and bit into them. 'It must be lead, or zinc at least,' said they.

" 'And the whole mountain is full of it,' added the innkeeper."

When the parson had got thus far in his narrative, the King's head was seen to straighten up a little and one eye opened. "Do you know if any of these persons knew anything about ore and minerals?" he asked.

"They did not," replied the parson.

Then the King's head sank and both eyes closed.

"The clergyman and his companions were very happy," continued the speaker, without letting himself be disturbed by the King's indifference; "they fancied that now they had found that which would give them and their descendants wealth. 'I'll never have to do any more work,' said one. 'Now I can afford to do nothing at all the whole week through, and on Sundays I shall drive to church in a golden chariot!' They were otherwise sensible men, but the great find had gone to their heads, and they talked like children. Still they had enough presence of mind to put back the moss tufts and conceal the vein of ore. Then they carefully noted the place where it was, and went home. Before they parted company, they agreed that the parson should travel to Falun and ask the mining expert what kind of ore this was. He was to return as soon as possible, and until then they promised one another on oath not to reveal to a soul where the ore was to be found."

The King's head was raised again a trifle, but he did not interrupt the speaker with a word. It appeared as though he was beginning to believe that the man actually had something of importance he wished to say to him, since he didn't allow himself to be disturbed by his indifference.

"Then the parson departed with a few samples of ore in his pocket. He was just as happy in the thought of becoming rich as were the others. He was thinking of rebuilding the parsonage, which at present was no better than a peasant's cottage, and then he would marry a dean's daughter whom he liked. He had thought that he might have to wait for her many years. He was poor and obscure and knew that it would be a long while before he should get any post that would enable him to marry.

"The parson drove over to Falun in two days, and there he had to wait another whole day because the mining expert was away. Finally he ran across him and showed him the bits of ore. The mining expert took them in his hand. He looked at them first, then at the parson. The parson related how he had found them in a mountain at home in his parish, and wondered if it might not be lead.

"'No, it's not lead,' said the mining expert.

"'Perhaps it is zinc, then?' asked the parson.

"'Nor is it zinc,' said the mineralogist.

"The parson thought that all the hope within him sank. He had not been so depressed in many a long day.

"'Have you many stones like this in your parish?' asked the mineralogist.

"'We have a whole mountainful,' said the parson.

"Then the mineralogist came up closer, slapped the parson on the shoulder, and said, 'Let us see that you make such good use of this that it will prove a blessing both to yourselves and to the country, for this is silver.'

"'Indeed?' said the parson, feeling his way. 'So it is silver!'

"The mineralogist began telling him how he should go to work to get legal rights to the mine and gave him many valuable suggestions; but the parson stood there dazed and did not listen to what the mineralogist was saying. He was thinking how wonderful it was that at home in his poor parish stood a whole mountain of silver ore, waiting for him."

The King raised his head so suddenly that the parson stopped short in his narrative. "It turned out, of course, that when he got home and began working the mine, he saw that the mineralogist had only been fooling him," said the King.

"Oh, no, the mineralogist had not fooled him," said the parson.

"You may continue," said the King as he settled himself more comfortably in the chair to listen.

"When the parson was at home again and was driving through the parish," continued the clergyman, "he thought that first of all he should inform his partners of the value of their find. And as he drove alongside the innkeeper Sten Stensson's place, he intended to drive up to the house to tell him they had found silver. But when he stopped outside the gate, he noticed that a broad path of evergreen was strewn all the way up to the doorstep.

"'Who has died in this place?' asked the parson of a boy who stood leaning against the fence.

"'The innkeeper himself,' answered the boy. Then he let the clergyman know that the innkeeper had drunk himself full every day for a week. 'Oh, so much brandy, so much brandy, has been drunk here!'

"'How can that be?' asked the parson. 'The innkeeper used never to drink himself full.'

"'Oh,' said the boy, 'he drank because he said he had found a mine. He was very rich. He should never have to do anything now but drink, he said. Last night he drove off, full as he was,

and the wagon turned over and he was killed.'

"When the parson heard this, he drove homeward, distressed over what he had heard. He had come back so happy, rejoicing because he could tell the great news.

"When the parson had driven a few paces, he saw Israel Per Persson walking along. He looked about as usual, and the parson thought it was well that fortune had not gone to his head too. Him he would cheer at once with the good news that he was a rich man.

" 'Good day!' said Per Persson. 'Do you come from Falun now?'

" 'I do,' said the parson. 'And now I must tell you that it has turned out even better than we had imagined. The mineralogist said it was silver ore that we had found.'

"That instant Per Persson looked as though the ground had opened under him. 'What are you saying, what are you saying? Is it silver?'

" 'Yes,' answered the parson. 'We'll all be rich men now, all of us, and can live like gentlemen.'

" 'Oh, is it silver?' said Per Persson, looking more and more mournful.

" 'Why, of course it is silver,' replied the parson. 'You mustn't think that I want to deceive you. You mustn't be afraid to be happy.'

" 'Happy!' said Per Persson. 'Should I be happy? I believed it was only glitter that we had found, so I thought it would be better to take the certain for the uncertain; I have sold my share in the mine to Olaf Svärd for a hundred dollars.' He was desperate and, when the parson drove away from him, he stood on the highway and wept.

"When the clergyman got back to his home, he sent a servant to Olaf Svärd and his brother to tell them that it was silver they had found. He thought that he had had quite enough of driving around and spreading the good news.

"But in the evening, when the parson sat alone, his joy asserted itself again. He went out in the darkness and stood on a hillock upon which he contemplated building the new parsonage. It should be imposing, of course, as fine as a bishop's palace. He stood there long that night, nor did he content himself with rebuilding the parsonage! It occurred to him that, since there were such riches to be found in the parish, throngs of people would pour in and, finally, a whole city would be built around the mine. And then he would have to erect a new church in place of the old one. Toward this object a large portion of his wealth would probably go. And he was not content with this, either, but fancied that, when his church was ready, the King and many bishops would come to the dedication. Then the King would be pleased with the church; but he would remark that there was no place where a king might put up, and then he would have to erect a castle in the new city."

Just then one of the King's courtiers opened the door of the vestry and announced that the big royal coach was mended.

At the first moment the King was ready to withdraw, but on second thought he changed his mind. "You may tell your story to the end," he said to the parson. "But you can hurry it a bit. We know all about how the man thought and dreamed. We want to know about how he acted."

"But while the parson was still lost in his dreams," continued the clergyman, "word came to him that Israel Per Persson had made away with himself. He had not been able to bear the disappointment of having sold his share in the mine. He had thought, no doubt, that he could not endure to go about every day seeing another enjoying the wealth that might have been his."

The King straightened up a little. He kept both eyes open. "Upon my word," he said, "if I had been that parson, I should have had enough of the mine!"

"The King is a rich man," said the parson. "He has quite enough, at all events. It is not the same thing with a poor curate who possesses nothing. The unhappy wretch thought instead, when he saw that God's blessing was not with his enterprise, 'I will dream no more of bringing glory and profit to myself with these riches, but I can't let the silver lie buried in the earth! I must take it out, for the benefit of the poor and needy. I will work the mine, to put the whole parish on its feet.'

"So one day the parson went out to see Olaf Svärd, to ask him and his brother as to what should be done immediately with the silver mountain. When he came in the vicinity of the barracks he met a cart surrounded by

armed peasants, and in the cart sat a man with his hands tied behind him and a rope around his ankles.

"When the parson passed by, the cart stopped and he had time to regard the prisoner, whose head was tied up so it was not easy to see who he was. But the parson thought he recognized Olaf Svärd. He heard the prisoner beg those who guarded him to let him speak a few words with the parson.

"The parson drew nearer, and the prisoner turned toward him. 'You will soon be the only one who knows where the silver mine is,' said Olaf.

"'What are you saying, Olaf?' asked the parson.

"'Well, you see, parson, since we have learned that it was a silver mine we had found, my brother and I could no longer be as good friends as before. We were continually quarreling. Last night we got into a controversy over which one of us five it was who first discovered the mine. It ended in strife between us, and we came to blows. I have killed my brother and he has left me with a souvenir across the forehead to remember him by. I must hang now, and then you will be the only one who knows about the mine; therefore I wish to ask something of you.'

" 'Speak out!' said the parson. 'I'll do what I can for you.'

" 'You know that I am leaving several little children behind me,' began the soldier, but the parson interrupted him.

" 'As regards this, you can rest easy. That which comes to your share in the mine they shall have, exactly as if you yourself were living.'

" 'No,' said Olaf Svärd, 'it was another thing I wanted to ask of you. Don't let them have any portion of that which comes from the mine!'

"The parson staggered back a step. He stood there dumb and could not answer.

" 'If you do not promise me this, I cannot die in peace,' said the prisoner.

" 'Yes,' said the parson slowly and painfully. 'I promise you what you ask of me.'

"Thereupon the murderer was taken away, and the parson stood on the highway thinking how he should keep the promise he had given him. On the way home he thought of the wealth which he had been so happy over. What if it really were true that the people in this community could not stand riches? Already four were ruined who hitherto had been dignified and excellent men. He seemed to see the whole community before him, and he pictured to himself how this silver mine would destroy one after another. Was it befitting that he, who had been appointed to watch over these poor human beings' souls, should let loose upon them that which would be their destruction?"

All of a sudden the King sat bolt upright in his chair. "I declare!" said he, "you'll make me understand that a parson in this isolated settlement must be every inch a man."

"Nor was it enough with what had already happened," continued the parson, "for as soon as the news about the mine spread among the parishioners, they stopped working and went about in idleness, waiting for the time when great riches should pour in on them. All the ne'er-do-wells there were in this section streamed in, and drunkenness and fighting were what the parson heard talked of continually. A lot of people did nothing but tramp round in the forest searching for the mine, and the parson marked that as soon as he left the house people followed him stealthily to find out if he wasn't going to the silver mountain and to steal the secret from him.

"When matters were come to this pass, the parson called the peasants together to vote. To start with he reminded them of all the misfortunes which the discovery of the mountain had brought upon them, and he asked them if they were going to let themselves be ruined or if they would save themselves. Then he told them that they must not expect him, who was their spiritual adviser, to help on their destruction. Now he had declared not to reveal to anyone where the silver mine was, and never would he himself take riches from it. And then he asked the peasants how they would have it henceforth. If they wished to continue their search for the mine and wait upon riches, then he would go so far away that no word of their misery could reach him; but if they would give up thinking about the silver mine and be as heretofore, he would remain with them. 'Whichever way you may choose,' said the parson, 'remember this, that from me no one shall ever know anything about the silver mountain.' "

"Well," said the King, "how did they decide?"

"They did as their pastor wished," said the parson. "They understood that he meant well by them when he wanted to remain poor for their sakes. And they commissioned him to go to the forest and conceal the vein of ore with evergreen and stone, so that no one would be able to find it — neither they nor their posterity."

"And ever since the parson has been living here just as poor as the rest?"

"Yes," answered the curate, "he has lived here just as poor as the rest."

"He has married, of course, and built a new parsonage?" said the King.

"No, he couldn't afford to marry and he lives in the old cabin."

"It's a pretty story that you have told me," said the King. After a few seconds he resumed, "Was it of the silver mountain that you were thinking when you said that the parson here would be able to procure for me as much money as I need?"

"Yes," said the other.

"But I can't put the thumbscrews on him," said the King. "Or how would you advise that I get such a man to show me the mountain — a man who has renounced his sweetheart and the allurements of life?"

"Oh, that's a different matter," said the parson. "But if it's the Fatherland that is in need of the fortune, he will probably give in."

"Will you answer for that?" asked the King.

"Yes, that I will answer for," said the clergyman.

"Doesn't he care, then, what becomes of his parishioners?"

"That can rest in God's hands."

The King rose from his chair and walked over to the window. He stood for a moment and looked upon the group of people outside. The longer he looked, the clearer his large eyes shone; and his figure seemed to grow. "You may greet the pastor of this congregation and say that for Sweden's King there is no sight more beautiful than to see a people such as this!"

Then the King turned from the window and looked at the clergyman. He began to smile. "Is it true that the pastor of this parish is so poor that he removes his black clothes as soon as the service is over and dresses himself like a peasant?" asked the King.

"Yes, so poor is he," said the curate, and a crimson flush leaped into his roughhewn face.

The King went back to the window. One could see that he was in his best mood. All that was noble and great within him had been quickened into life. "You must let that mine lie in peace," said the King. "Inasmuch as you have labored and starved a lifetime to make this people such as you would have it, you may keep it as it is."

"But if the kingdom is in danger?" said the parson.

"The kingdom is better served with men than with money," remarked the King. When he had said this, he bade the clergyman farewell and went out from the vestry.

Without stood the group of people, as quiet and taciturn as they were when he went in. As the King came down the steps, a peasant stepped up to him.

"Have you had a talk with our pastor?" said the peasant.

"Yes," said the King. "I have."

"Then of course you have our answer?" said the peasant. "We asked you to go in and talk with our parson, that he might give you an answer from us."

"I have the answer," said the King.

THINKING IT OVER

1. Point out the boundaries of the inner story.

2. Was the parson right in persuading the people to make no use of the mine? How does this story differ from the Bible story of the gold talents?

3. The pastor tells the King that the villagers are good but that they would be no better than any others if they were subjected to temptation. How does the story he tells the King prove this?

4. In what ways did the parson show greatness? the King?

5. Compare the king in "The Lady or the Tiger?" with King Gustaf.

6. State the theme of this story in your own words.

INFERRING CHARACTER

1. What do you learn about the character of the King from the manner in which he treats his attendants in the earliest part of the story? Do later actions show these same character traits?

2. The King's actions, plus a remark to himself when he first views the villagers, show something else about him. What is this?

3. What do you learn of the parson's character from the first half dozen or so paragraphs of conversation between him and the King? Quote lines that prove your statements.

4. You learn something about the true stature of the King in the paragraph not far from the end which begins, "The King went back to the window." How do his deeds prove what the author has said about him?

5. Find and read several places in which the author interprets the thoughts of various characters. What is this interpretation called?

6. Find and read several passages in which description is used to help develop a character.

LOOKING AT THE FRAMEWORK STORY

"The Silver Mine" is an excellent example of the techniques found in the "story-within-a-story." The arrival of King Gustaf at the village church and his encounter with the parson constitute the first or "outer" story. The parson's narrative then becomes the second or "inner" story. In a painting, it is the picture on the canvas which is important, more than the frame which encloses it. The same holds true for framework stories. Almost always, the "inner" story has the larger importance, as it certainly does in "The Silver Mine"; the "outer" story is chiefly the device used by the author to establish the setting, characters, and opening situation of his tale. The famous *Canterbury Tales* of the fourteenth-century British author, Geoffrey Chaucer, is an early example of this technique.

ABOUT THE AUTHOR

Selma Lagerlöf [1] (1858–1940), a Swedish novelist, became the first woman to win the Nobel prize for literature, when this honor was accorded her in 1909. She had to fight against heavy odds during her life. At the age of three, she was crippled by infantile paralysis. The illness made it impossible for her to attend school, so she was educated at home. It was during this period that her grandmother told her many of the tales which later appeared in the many stories and books she went on to write. At her death, she was an internationally known figure. *The Wonderful Adventures of Nils* is a book by Selma Lagerlöf that you would enjoy.

[1] **Lagerlöf** (lä′gĕr·lûv).

As the Camera Sees It ➤

The illustration on the facing page is an example of how effectively photography can be used to capture the spirit and content of a story. The photograph is of the Swedish countryside and was taken, of course, in contemporary times. What feeling does the scene depicted convey to you? Point out some qualities in "The Silver Mine" which might be reflected in the photograph.

The Unicorn in the Garden

JAMES THURBER

This little story is a fable, and a fable, in case you have forgotten, is a story with a moral. Many fables involve animals in one way or another, and this one is no exception. Here, however, the animal is the unicorn. The unicorn, of course, exists only in myths and has never been seen by man or woman. But one morning —

ONCE upon a sunny morning a man who sat in a breakfast nook looked up from his scrambled eggs to see a white unicorn with a gold horn quietly cropping the roses in the garden. The man went up to the bedroom where his wife was still asleep and woke her. "There's a unicorn in the garden," he said. "Eating roses." She opened one unfriendly eye and looked at him. "The unicorn is a mythical beast," she said, and turned her back on him. The man walked slowly downstairs and out into the garden. The unicorn was still there; he was now browsing among the tulips. "Here, unicorn," said the man, and he pulled up a lily and gave it to him. The unicorn ate it gravely. With a high heart, because there was a unicorn in

his garden, the man went upstairs and roused his wife again. "The unicorn," he said, "ate a lily." His wife sat up in bed and looked at him coldly. "You are a booby," she said, "and I am going to have you put in the booby hatch." The man, who had never liked the words "booby" and "booby hatch," and who liked them even less on a shining morning when there was a unicorn in the garden, thought for a moment. "We'll see about that," he said. He walked over to the door. "He has a golden horn in the middle of his forehead," he told her. Then he went back to the garden to watch the unicorn, but the unicorn had gone away. The man sat down among the roses and went to sleep.

As soon as the husband had gone out of the house, the wife got up and dressed as fast as she could. She was very excited and there was a gloat in her eye. She telephoned the police and she telephoned a psychiatrist; she told them to hurry to her house and bring a strait jacket. When the police and the psychiatrist arrived, they sat down in chairs and looked at her with great interest. "My husband," she said, "saw a unicorn this morning." The police looked at the psychiatrist and the psychiatrist looked at the police. "He told me it ate a lily," she said. The psychiatrist looked at the police and the police looked at the psychiatrist. "He told me it had a golden horn in the middle of its forehead," she said. At a solemn signal from the psychiatrist, the police leaped from their chairs and seized the wife. They had a hard time subduing her, for she put up a terrific struggle, but they finally subdued her. Just as they got her into the strait jacket, the husband came back into the house.

"Did you tell your wife you saw a unicorn?" asked the police. "Of course not," said the husband. "The unicorn is a mythical beast." "That's all I wanted to know," said the psychiatrist. "Take her away. I'm sorry, sir, but your wife is as crazy as a jay bird." So they took her away, cursing and screaming, and shut her up in an institution. The husband lived happily ever after.

Moral: *Don't count your boobies until they are hatched.*

THINKING IT OVER

1. The moral of the story has a pun in it. What earlier sentences in the story form the basis for the pun?
2. The three main characters (if the unicorn really *was* in the garden, that is) are drawn very briefly by the author, yet each has a distinct personality. What sort of person was the husband? the wife? the unicorn? Find the descriptive phrases or words which helped to indicate their personalities to you.
3. Again with remarkable brevity, the author has also managed to establish the relationship between the husband and the wife. What details in the first four sentences suggest the nature of their relationship?
4. Do you know any old traditional fables that you could relate to the class?
5. The story may be extremely short, but the author has equipped it with a

fully developed plot. Check the definitions on pages 3–4 and explain the conflict in the story. Point out a crisis that occurs in the action. What is the climax? the resolution?

ABOUT THE AUTHOR

James Thurber (1894–1961) lost the sight of one eye because of a childhood accident. He ultimately became totally blind. In spite of his failing eyesight over the years, his contributions to both writing and cartooning made him one of America's best-loved humorists. He began writing at the age of ten, and drawing at fourteen. Born in Columbus, Ohio, he left Ohio State University in his senior year to work as a code clerk in Washington and then with the American Embassy in Paris. Eventually he wound up on the staff of the *New Yorker* Magazine, where his stories and drawings first brought him fame. At his death, E. B. White, the author, wrote of James Thurber: "In a lifelong act of generosity, he poured out his hundreds upon hundreds of drawings, stories, fables, memoirs, and essays — many of them among the funniest any writer or artist has ever produced . . . and by the end his work gave him a place in history as one of the great comic artists and one of the great American humorists." You will enjoy reading Thurber's *My Life and Hard Times*.

James Thurber

The Gift

RAY BRADBURY

Every word counts in a story! This is especially true of the *short-short* story, a form in which length must be kept to a minimum. Notice how economically Ray Bradbury creates his characters, plot, and setting, and how quickly all of the parts are tied together in this science-fiction tale.

Tomorrow would be Christmas, and even while the three of them rode to the rocket port the mother and father

were worried. It was the boy's first flight into space, his very first time in a rocket, and they wanted everything to be perfect. So when, at the customs table,[1] they were forced to leave behind his gift, which exceeded the weight limit by no more than a few ounces, and the little tree with the lovely white can-

[1] **customs table:** the center at an airport or pier where incoming or outgoing articles are inspected for clearance.

dles, they felt themselves deprived of the season and their love.

The boy was waiting for them in the Terminal room. Walking toward him, after their unsuccessful clash with the Interplanetary officials, the mother and father whispered to each other.

"What shall we do?"

"Nothing, nothing. What can we do?"

"Silly rules!"

"And he so wanted the tree!"

The siren gave a great howl and people pressed forward into the Mars Rocket. The mother and father walked at the very last, their small pale son between them, silent.

"I'll think of something," said the father.

"What . . . ?" asked the boy.

And the rocket took off and they were flung headlong into dark space.

The rocket moved and left fire behind and left Earth behind on which the date was December 24, 2052, heading out into a place where there was no time at all, no month, no year, no hour. They slept away the rest of the first "day." Near midnight, by their Earth-time New York watches, the boy awoke and said, "I want to go look out the porthole."

There was only one port, a "window" of immensely thick glass of some size, up on the next deck.

"Not quite yet," said the father. "I'll take you up later."

"I want to see where we are and where we're going."

"I want you to wait for a reason," said the father.

He had been lying awake, turning this way and that, thinking of the abandoned gift, the problem of the season, the lost tree and the white candles. And at last, sitting up, no more than five minutes ago, he believed he had found a plan. He need only carry it out and this journey would be fine and joyous indeed.

"Son," he said, "in exactly one half hour it will be Christmas."

"Oh," said the mother, dismayed that he had mentioned it. Somehow she had rather hoped that the boy would forget.

The boy's face grew feverish and his lips trembled. "I know, I know. Will I get a present, will I? Will I have a tree? You promised — "

"Yes, yes, all that, and more," said the father.

The mother started. "But — "

"I mean it," said the father. "I really mean it. All and more, much more. Excuse me, now. I'll be back."

He left them for about twenty minutes. When he came back, he was smiling. "Almost time."

"Can I hold your watch?" asked the boy, and the watch was handed over and he held it ticking in his fingers as the rest of the hour drifted by in fire and silence and unfelt motion.

"It's Christmas now! Christmas! Where's my present?"

"Here we go," said the father and took his boy by the shoulder and led him from the room, down the hall, up a rampway, his wife following.

"I don't understand," she kept saying.

"You will. Here we are," said the father.

They had stopped at the closed door of a large cabin. The father tapped three times and then twice in a code. The door opened and the light in the cabin went out and there was a whisper of voices.

"Go on in, Son," said the father.

"It's dark."

"I'll hold your hand. Come on, Mamma."

They stepped into the room and the door shut, and the room was very dark indeed. And before them loomed a great glass eye, the porthole, a window four feet high and six feet wide, from which they could look out into space.

The boy gasped.

Behind him, the father and the mother gasped with him, and then in the dark room some people began to sing.

"Merry Christmas, Son," said the father.

And the voices in the room sang the old, the familiar carols, and the boy moved forward slowly until his face was pressed against the cool glass of the port. And he stood there for a long, long time, just looking and looking out into space and the deep night at the burning and the burning of ten billion billion white and lovely candles. . . .

THINKING IT OVER

1. Find the very first clue which tells you that this is a science-fiction tale.

2. Is this to be the first space flight for every member of the family? What are your reasons for thinking as you do?

3. From the scanty description of the rocket port, what can you assume about space travel in general at the time of the story?

4. What was the gift? What arrangements had to be made to present it?

5. People in space are supposed to be weightless, yet the characters in this story walk around very casually. What does the author assume that you will guess about space travel a hundred years hence?

6. Perhaps you read with a question in mind: If Christmas means so much to the boy and his parents, and if space flight is so commonplace and regular, then why — ? You supply the rest of the question. In other words, can you suggest reasons why a family might leave earth and live on Mars?

LOOKING AT SCIENCE FICTION

This increasingly popular field of writing is by no means new or of recent origin. Jules Verne (1828–1905) is an important literary figure who has long been identified with it. You may be familiar with his *Journey to the Center of the Earth* and *Twenty Thousand Leagues Under the Sea* or have seen the films that were based on these novels. Another contributor to the field is H. G. Wells (1866–1946), represented by *The Invisible Man* and *The War of the Worlds,* among other novels. Sir Arthur Conan Doyle is another first-rate author who wrote some science-fiction stories. In addition to Bradbury, today's outstanding science-fiction authors include Robert Heinlein, Arthur Clarke, and Frederick Pohl. The discoveries of the space age have changed the subject matter and various technical aspects of this special kind of fiction, but its spirit has remained much the same.

ABOUT THE AUTHOR

Born in Waukegan, Illinois, Ray Bradbury (1920–   ) attended high school in Los Angeles and began writing science-fiction stories in his own magazine — it ran four issues — while still in school. Besides the hundreds of stories to his credit, he is also widely known for his radio and television plays. His stories have such a distinctive flavor critics have come to call it "the Bradbury touch."

REVIEWING THE SECTION

Think back briefly over all the stories in this section by reviewing the table of contents at the front of this book. Ready? Now nominate and vote for the:

1. Story with biggest surprise

2. Story with happiest ending

3. Story with unhappiest ending

4. Author you would most like to meet

5. Author you would least like to be shipwrecked with

6. Most admirable adult character in stories

7. Most admirable animal character (no fair nominating the fifty-first dragon!)

8. Juvenile character most likely to suceed in life

9. Story you most wish you had written

Short Stories

SUGGESTIONS FOR FURTHER READING

Annixter, Paul, *Pride of Lions* (Hill & Wang, 1960)
   Stories of adventure and the outdoors by a popular author for young people.
Carroll, Gordon, ed., *The Post Reader of Civil War Stories* (Doubleday, 1958)
   Nineteen stories of suspense and action from the *Saturday Evening Post*.
Certner, Simon, and George H. Henry, eds., *Short Stories for Our Times* (Houghton Mifflin, 1950)
   Nearly two dozen tip-top tales for hours of reading pleasure.
Chute, B. J., *Teen-Age Sports Parade* (Lantern, 1949)
   A rousing roundup of sports stories by the author of "Dive Right In."
Daly, Maureen, ed., *My Favorite Stories* (Dodd, Mead, 1948)
   Just what she says, by the author of *Seventeenth Summer*.
Dickens, Charles, *Christmas Stories* (World Publishing, 1946)
   Contains the famous "Christmas Carol" and other favorites.
Fenner, Phyllis R., ed., *The Price of Liberty* (Morrow, 1960)
   Here is the American Revolution in a dozen fine stories.
Ferris, Helen, ed., *The Brave and the Fair* (Holt, Rinehart & Winston, 1960)
   Stories of romance and courage in this country's growing-up period. Also of interest: *Girls, Girls, Girls* (Franklin Watts, 1956), and *Time of Discovering* (Franklin Watts, 1961). The latter is a collection for girls interested in careers.
Godden, Rumer, *Mooltiki* (Viking, 1958)
   For those who like "special flavors," here are some stories and poems set in far-off India.
Halliday, Brett, ed., *Big Time Mysteries* (Dodd, Mead, 1958)
   Suspense, excitement, and intrigue.
Harte, Bret, *The Best of Bret Harte* (Houghton Mifflin, 1947)
   A lively sampling of the writer who first made Western stories popular.
Hazeltine, Alice I., ed., *Red Man, White Man* (Lothrop, Lee & Shepard, 1957)
   A picture of America's Indians presented through stories, myths, and legends by topnotch authors.
Henry, O., *Best Short Stories of O. Henry* (Modern Library)
   The master is represented here by twenty-six of his colorful and unusual tales.
Heydrick, A., and B. J. Thompson, eds., *Americans All* (Harcourt, Brace & World, 1942)
   A cross section of Americans in all walks of life.
Hoke, Helen, *Alaska, Alaska, Alaska* (Franklin Watts, 1960)
   A true-to-life story collection that pictures our forty-ninth state from territorial days to the present.
Holman, Mabel, ed., *The Short Story Parade* (Harcourt, Brace & World, 1940)
   Twenty stories of special interest for young people.
Irving, Washington, *The Sketch Book*
   Includes "Rip Van Winkle" and "The Legend of Sleepy Hollow."
Ivens, Bryna, ed., *Nineteen from Seventeen* (Lippincott, 1952)
   Tales that were popular with the girl readers of the magazine *Seventeen*.
Sandoz, Mari, *Winter Thunder* (Westminster, 1954)
   Here's a long short story you won't forget.
Schaefer, Jack, ed., *Out West* (Houghton Mifflin, 1955)
   Three dozen five-star Westerns collected by the author of *Shane*. You might also like his own collected Westerns in *Kean Land* (Houghton Mifflin, 1959).
Tibbets, Albert B., ed., *Salute to the Brave* (Little, Brown, 1960)
   Rattling good tales of World War II. Boys should also like his *Youth, Youth, Youth* collection (Franklin Watts, 1955).
Wood, William R., and others, eds., *Just for Sport* (Lippincott, 1943)
   You pick the sport — here is a story about it!

FOR YOUR LISTENING

"The Tell-Tale Heart" is available on longplay record *Many Voices* 9A.

Nonfiction

The world of nonfiction is an exhilarating, informative world, and in recent years more and more readers have been turning to it for the rewards it holds. To the reader, nonfiction offers a view of real life, present and past, with all of its adventures and challenges.

In the first part of this section devoted to nonfiction, you will become acquainted with the stimulating mixture of facts and observations to be found in articles and essays. Articles, with their accounts of far-off places, scientific discoveries, and interesting events, bring the world close to the reader. The essay has a formal-sounding ring to its name, but in content it can range from the sublime to the ridiculous, as you will learn.

The second part of the nonfiction section, "Biography: People to Remember," will take you into the lives of a group of memorable people at a time when they were at an age close to yours. In common with all young people, these men and women had problems to overcome. Each person you will meet in these selections has a story about life and living that will enrich you. Very likely you will want to read more about these men and women.

And very likely you will find yourself wishing that the third and final part of this nonfiction section, "Man's Conquest of the Air," were longer. In the early years of our own century, man was earth-bound; today he stands at the threshold of interplanetary flight. Here in this section, a series of articles and biographical and autobiographical selections bring you the story of man and the sky.

Here, then, is a sampling of the world of nonfiction — the real world of people, ideas, and discoveries, both of the past and of the present.

◀ This jewel-encrusted gold cup was made by the matchless sixteenth-century goldsmith and sculptor, Benvenuto Cellini (1500–1571), for Prince Rospigliosi of Rome. Called the Rospigliosi Cup, it is a reminder of the beauty and art which are part of the world around us.

Articles and Essays: Facts and Observations

When the French author Montaigne put into writing his ideas on an assortment of subjects back in the 1500's, he created a new literary form called the essay. The very next time you write a composition on almost any topic at all, you will be writing an essay. Interestingly, one of the features Montaigne put into his essays will go into yours — a personal interpretation or viewpoint. This has become an identifying mark of the essay.

The typical essay can be long or short, although usually it does not have great length. It can be about people, places, the price of eggs, or the pleasure of traveling from Timbuktu to Oshkosh. The subject of an essay is not important; what distinguishes it is that it has a particular viewpoint: a personal interpretation of its subject matter.

Today, essays come to us in such assorted attire that we do not always recognize them. For example, newspaper columnists write essays, or they do when they develop an idea or viewpoint on a subject. Editorials are essays, too. And so are a great many of the articles that you read in a magazine.

As it has developed and grown, the article has taken on many of the characteristics of the essay. Today, an article may have a viewpoint — a personal interpretation by the author — and still be called an article. The essay and the article have become closely linked together; in style and content the two often follow a parallel line. The difference between the two is largely one of degree, perhaps. Certain articles simply present the reader with straight information — facts and figures, statistics that carry no personal comment from the author. But other articles can be intensely personal, with a strong sense of the author's viewpoint and ideas. Articles such as these have taken on the qualities of the essay.

Article or essay, there is no question about the tremendous vogue that this area of nonfiction enjoys among readers today. Articles are written, and avidly read, on almost any subject you can think of. Entire magazines are given over to articles about such specialized interests as stamp collecting, mountain climbing, and model trains. Essays — or articles with the personal flavor of essays — are collected in book form and run high on the best-seller lists month after month.

Here, now, is an opportunity to discover the reason for this popularity. The celebrated author James Michener will describe Hawaii in an article for you and make the islands as real as if you'd just returned from a visit. Essays by three famous humorists will invite you to be amused; another essay by a gifted nature writer will point out a fantastic, hidden world that is available to you. And there is an article which tells a real-life story about a piano that is as unusual as any fictional story.

Hawaii

JAMES MICHENER

Here is an article which is both descriptive and informative. Its purpose is to help you see what the author saw and share his reactions to it. The viewpoint is fresh and clear; the author is one of America's best-known writers. He wrote this, incidentally, just before the fiftieth star was added to the flag.

I DOUBT if anyone knows all the islands of Hawaii, but to know even a part of one — say Waikiki [1] Beach, which is about one millionth of the whole — is to enjoy at least something of a rare land. These islands are easy to visit; you board a plane in New York at midnight and reach Honolulu the next day. But after you have been here for weeks and even months, you will still fail to believe how one small portion of the world could be so crammed with wonders.

[1] **Waikiki** (wī′kĭ·kē′).

There are the mountains. They rise behind Honolulu in great purple heights, clothed forever in forest, with waterfalls drifting down, with clouds hanging above them. They are among the loveliest in the world, accessible, close to the sea, an intimate part of island life.

There is Pali, one of the many cliffs that stretch for miles along Oahu's [2] coast, green clad with deep serrated valleys as if massive fingers had shredded the mountains. To your left, in a wide-sweeping arc, the giant cliffs enclose a coastal valley of dazzling color. The earth is red, the fields are green, the sea beyond is blue, the rain clouds that sweep by are gray, and at rare spots the cliffs themselves expose enduring rock of sullen black. And the play of colors is forever changing. Now a swift fog invades the valleys, and the

[2] **Oahu's** (ō·ä′hōōz): Oahu is Hawaii's most populated island. Honolulu is located here.

Visualizing. Visualizing is made easy when an author with the word magic of James Michener sets out to describe his favorite part of the world. Try to *see* the word pictures he paints of the people, mountains, flowers, and waters of Hawaii.

cliffs move in and out of view like a ballet. Now the sun shines upon incoming rain clouds and builds enormous rainbows. On a rare cloudless day the sun will illuminate the hills and the shore and the sea with unhampered tropic light. At night there is the moon. And all of this is within a few miles of Honolulu, a city of almost a quarter million.

There are the flowers. You will see long roads lined with flowering trees ablaze with beautiful blossoms. I remember a hedge nearly a mile long composed of hibiscus flowers in at least twenty colors. One school is surrounded by a hedge of twisting night-blooming cereus, a climbing cactus which produces gigantic white flowers all summer and fall. There are many lath greenhouses in which bank clerks raise rare orchids, and open fields where professionals raise common orchids and sell them by the half ton. Wherever you go, there are flowers, more flowers than you have ever seen in one spot before.

There are the people — and they are the real glory of the islands. Hawaii has 465,000 people, about as many as Seattle. The principal groups are: Japanese, 189,000; part Hawaiian, 77,000; Caucasian, 69,000; Filipino, 63,000; Chinese, 32,000; pure Hawaiian, 13,000; Puerto Rican, 10,000; Korean, 7,000. All these peoples live together in reasonable harmony.

Most of these groups came to work in the sugar-cane fields, the chief exception being the Hawaiians, who were already here and who, like all sensible Polynesians,[1] saw no reason to work and refused to do so. Chinese were brought in, in 1852, but they were a grave disappointment. Instead of re-

maining peasants, they saved their money, studied, and became merchants and doctors. In 1878, Portuguese from the Azores were tried, but they, too, saved and went into business for themselves. The Japanese came next, in 1885, and they saved money faster than anyone else. Puerto Ricans, Koreans, Spaniards, and Filipinos were used in turn — the last as recently as 1946 — but as soon as they reached these islands, the air of freedom affected them and they started to act like Americans: they became businessmen and began sending their sons to college.

There is no simple definition of a Hawaiian. The islands are a part of the United States. The largest island in the group is also named Hawaii, but is usually referred to as the main island. The word Hawaiian sometimes means one of the handsome original Polynesians, sometimes a resident of the main island, sometimes anyone living in the territory. In general usage it means a Polynesian, but this leaves no general noun like Texan or Californian to denote the people who live in the islands. I call them islanders, but even this is not satisfactory, because some residents resent the term. They insist on "residents of the islands."

All the islanders use certain Polynesian words in their conversation, words so expressive that visitors pick them up with glee. Absolutely necessary are *haole*,[2] which once meant a foreigner but now means a white man, *kamaaina*,[3] a long-time resident, and *malihini*,[4] a newcomer. After a few days you will probably branch out with phrases like "a lot of *hoomalimali*" [5] —

[1] **Polynesians** (pŏl'ĭ·nē'shănz): the original settlers of Hawaii.

[2] *haole* (hä'ō·lā).
[3] *kamaaina* (kä'mä·ä'ē·nä).
[4] *malihini* (mä'lĭ·hē'nĭ).
[5] *hoomalimali* (hō·ō·mä'lē·mä'lē).

applesauce — "too much *pilikia*" [1] — trouble — and the delightfully compact *pau* [2] — which means finished or washed up. If words fail you, you will roll your eyes and cry "*Auwe! Auwe!*" [3] which means almost anything dire and doleful.

Hawaii is much more than a laboratory in human relations. It is also a sophisticated cultural center. Honolulu's Academy of Arts, with a fine collection of Italian primitives, [4] is probably not equaled in any mainland city of comparable size. There are also good libraries here, and the University of Hawaii is a first-rate institution. Broadway plays are popular, and the symphony orchestra has been solvent for fifty-two years and now has $10,000 in the bank. But pianists in Honolulu have one problem that seldom comes up on the mainland. Sometimes when they sit down to play, the piano falls apart. Reason: termites love the well-cured wood.

Hawaii is also extraordinarily hospitable. Partly because the islands are so far from the mainland, any visiting dignitary is apt to get the jillion-dollar treatment. If a traveler fails to have a good time in Hawaii, I would say there was no hope for him.

So bedazzling is his welcome that some visitors stay put on Oahu and never think of visiting the outer islands, which is regrettable. Some never leave the boundaries of Honolulu, which is shortsighted. A few rich people move only in the narrow confines of Waikiki and the plush hotels, and that seems downright cowardly.

As the earth goes, the Hawaiian Islands are very young land, all volcanic. The main island of Hawaii is geologically a child, possibly not more than ten million years old. It was built by five great volcanoes, two of which are still tremendously active. One is Mauna Loa, [5] one of the highest mountains on earth if we consider its sheer rise from ocean bed. It has erupted twenty-nine times in a hundred years, spewing forth more than three billion cubic yards of lava, much of which has rushed down to the sea, erasing forests and farms and villages, plunging at last into the ocean in a roar of steam.

The other is Kilauea, [6] smaller than Mauna Loa, but much more loved by the Hawaiians. Its pit is accessible by a fine macadam road which permits even the laziest traveler to drive right up to one of the world's rarest sights. According to island legend, the goddess Pele [7] wanders from one volcano to another across the world, setting them afire, but always comes back to her permanent home in Kilauea's fire pit. When this volcano erupts, it is a sign of good luck.

It is at night that Kilauea is incomparable. Above the crater hangs a great, glowing cloud of steam, while around the outside rim move hundreds of automobile headlights, spiraling down to the floor of the crater. Near the edge of the fire pit, perhaps a thousand people stare down at the writhing lava. You cannot see the sheer cliffs, nor the multicolored stone, nor the old deposits of lava, nor the faces of your friends. You see only the fiery lake, down far below you in the bottom of the pit. Its surface, which in the daytime looked like solid rock, now shows

[1] *pilikia* (pē'lĭ·kē'á).
[2] *pau* (pä'oo).
[3] *Auwe* (äu·wē').
[4] primitives (prĭm'ĭ·tĭvz): paintings from a much earlier period. Today, some self-taught artists are also called *primitives*.

[5] **Mauna Loa** (mou'nä lō'ä).
[6] **Kilauea** (kē'lou·ā'ä).
[7] **Pele** (pā'lå).

hundreds of fissures,[1] each glowing red in the darkness, twisting and crawling in intricate patterns of fire.

I had seen Hawaii from land, from mountaintops, from the sea and from the air, but by far the most spectacular view was still to come. I owe it to Carroll Corbaley, a thin, red-headed man with sharp brown eyes and piercing glance. Corbaley is a man dedicated to one thing, to deep-sea diving, and he speaks with admirable logic. I spent two days with him and never heard him fail to finish a sentence or complete a thought.

"They tell me you might be willing to go diving," he said when we met. "Got to warn you the divers from California make three criticisms of the way we dive. We go too deep, we catch too many fish, and we take too many chances. I don't agree. What we've done is invent a new way to explore coral caves under water. Idea consists of three parts: air compressor, long length of fool-proof hose, small face mask bringing fresh air to the nose and mouth. With this we can go down seventy-five feet. We catch four things: fish, lobsters, octopus, and eels. We also lasso big turtles and sometimes we find rare shells. Other day I took one hundred and eighty-six pounds of lobster by hand and speared about two hundred and fifty pounds of fish. Gave it all to friends.

"Got to warn you of four dangers. The big eels are six feet long and go well over twenty-five pounds. Terrific teeth slant backward. Secret is, if you're going to spear an eel, get him right in the mouth, then he can't wrap himself around your arm and bite you. Better still, avoid them. Coral cuts are

[1] **fissures** (físh′ĕrz): narrow breaks or openings in the rock.

poisonous. Avoid them too. Spiny sea urchins are very poisonous. Avoid them. Fourth is ear trouble. If you find you can't make your ears pop free at twenty feet, quit. A man can either pop his ears or he can't. If you can't, the pain will be unbearable.

"Three things you don't have to worry about. Sharks in these waters are harmless. Farther south they take a leg off. Here all they do is nuzzle you, especially if you carry bleeding fish. If one comes at you, push him away. Second, if you work your way into a deep cave, you can be sure the men in the boat won't pull you up suddenly and cut your air line on the coral edges. They won't pull you up unless you demand it. Third is most important. If you get real active, say chasing lobsters, you may get your mask knocked off and you'll think you're going to drown. Take it calm. Push the mask back on, press it tight, and the air will positively drive the water out so you can breathe again. If you feel you're drowning, don't get panicky.

"Well, you want to go down?"

I did. At dawn we climbed into a small boat and reached a spot some miles from shore. It was a gusty day and soon I was seasick, but Corb was in good spirits. "On a day like today," he said, "lobsters."

He plunged off the side to scout the bottom, which usually at fifty feet is nine tenths sandy desert and only one tenth coral formation where the fish stay. In five minutes he came back with four big fish, one a twenty-pounder. He dropped again and reappeared with two lobsters.

It was now my turn. First a lead belt, containing the valve that regulates the air pressure, was tied about my middle. Next flipper fins were tied to my feet, and finally the mask was fitted, a surprisingly small affair that merely covered my eyes, nose, and mouth. I ducked into the water and met a roaring sound as air whooshed past my mouth and out the escape valve. I was seasick, scared, and cold and would have quit, but Corb pushed me under with his foot.

Slowly, with enormous pressure on my unprotected ears, I drifted down forty feet to see, all about me, a coral fantasia: tall spires, deep caves, castles, ugly rubble heaps, valleys, and yawning gaps dropping away mysteriously for a hundred feet. Constantly I increased the air pressure so that the air forced its way into my lungs and I had to breathe only once or twice a minute. I was able to see clearly in the green-filtered sunlight, which crept down to the remotest cavern until my undersea world was like the hour when twilight starts. I wondered if this pale sun cast shadows, and when I looked at the ocean floor, I saw that it did.

The motionless green water, the caverns, the white floor of coral sand, the bubbles rising from my face were all new and strange. And the fish. I had asked Corbaley if, when I went down, I would see any, and he had replied, "A hundred thousand. All the time. All around you." He had not lied. As I stood among the coral caves, there were more than a hundred thousand — and they were not afraid of me. They seemed actually to crowd in upon me, yet whenever I put out my hand to touch them, they moved off, without apparent motion, and when I withdrew it, they just as mysteriously resumed their positions near me.

There were green fish and blue and gold and yellow and brown and rainbow. Some had ugly hammer heads and others graceful diaphanous [1] tails. Most

fantastic were the *kihikihi*,[2] striped in yellow and brown and jet, with an arched upper fin that trails far behind the body. Sometimes the fish moved with graceful purpose in vast formations, three or four thousand at a time, in and out of some dark coral cave, and it was like watching a materialized dream.

After I had been at forty feet for some time, my ears stopped hurting and I saw ahead of me a cavern leading far down to lower depths. One flip of one foot sent me swiftly toward it, and I started the descent. The pain in my ears came back sharper, but a slight movement upward always relieved it; so governed by my aching ears, I went alternately up and down until I touched bottom at fifty-six feet.

Now I was in a new world of big fish, the kind Corb caught. The light was dimmer and the caves more foreboding. I looked into one and stared right into the beady eyes of a lobster. In another nested an eel. I saw no octopus or shark, but I did see this wondrous thing, the surface of the ocean seen from beneath: gray-green and wispy and shot through with currents; iridescent with sunlight and rolling like a monster and fractured wherever a wave rose; and on it, bobbing like a forlorn leaf, was our boat. Here was beauty, a gem of many facets shifting constantly in a shimmer of new lights, and our boat so far above me seemed so trivial that involuntarily I thought of the old mariner's cry: "Oh, God! Thy sea is so vast and my boat so small."

Corb and I went hunting lobsters, and I learned what real fright is, for while I was struggling with one, it knocked my face mask off. Immediately the water, under heavy pressure, engulfed me, and I forgot that I shouldn't

[1] **diaphanous** (dī·ăf′*à*·nŭs): transparent.

[2] *kihikihi* (kē′hē·kē′hē).

panic. I started kicking violently toward the surface, but realized that with my heavy belt I couldn't make it. Then I recalled Corb's words and jammed the mask back on my face. In a twinkling the air had cleared it. I took three deep breaths and felt the air probing my lungs.

When I climbed back into the boat, Corb ran his finger under my nose, which was bleeding, and said, "Good sign. Means nothing broken inside," but it took two doctors three weeks to get my ears opened again. Even so, exploring those coral caves was the most exciting thing I have ever done in tropic seas.

It must be obvious by now that I like Hawaii.

As an islander put it when he thought with horror of my returning to the cold mainland next day — "When Hawaii calls, more better you listen."

THINKING IT OVER

1. What information about the state of Hawaii was new to you? List five facts the author supplies about the islands.

2. Why, according to Michener, is there no simple definition of a Hawaiian?

3. Discuss this statement: "The air of freedom affected them and they started to act like Americans."

4. Discuss the dangers a diver has to avoid. In Hawaiian waters, what problems does he *not* have to worry about?

5. Reading this article has almost certainly made you want to visit Hawaii. What features, as described in the article, would draw you to our fiftieth state?

LOOKING AT THE STRUCTURE OF AN ARTICLE

"Hawaii" is a good example of the article as a literary form. As such, the article uses much of the technique and structure of the essay. Read over the very first sentence of "Hawaii," in which James Michener quickly establishes his point of view toward the subject he is writing

about. This statement is termed an *opening generalization*. In the second paragraph the author describes the mountains that rise behind Honolulu. In effect, he is giving the reader an example of *why* he considers the islands "a rare land." He then goes on to give other examples. In an article, these examples are called *supporting ideas*. Usually, an article will contain several supporting ideas; together, they will make up the bulk of the article. Then, at the end, the author will make a final statement of his viewpoint, called a *conclusion*. Find other supporting ideas the author supplies to back up his viewpoint in "Hawaii." (There are at least ten.) Find the *conclusion*, where he states his viewpoint for the final time.

FOR YOUR VOCABULARY

From the new state of Hawaii have come new words to enrich the language of "stateside" Americans. The following exotic words are defined in the selection you have just finished. Test your memory at defining them, then check the text: *auwe; haole; hoomalimali; kamaaina; pau; pilikia.*

ABOUT THE AUTHOR

James Michener (1907–) was born in New York City and has been a distinguished teacher, author, and editor. He volunteered for service in World War II, served in the Pacific, and finished as a lieutenant-commander. His war-gathered *Tales of the South Pacific* won the 1947 Pulitzer prize and was made into one of the most successful modern musical plays.

Hawaii in Words and Pictures ➤

The photographs on the opposite page express graphically the word pictures created by James Michener in this selection. At upper left is Akaka Falls in Hawaii; at upper right is Lanua Beach, showing Diamond Head in the distance; below this is Kilauea Volcano in Hawaiian National Park; and the bottom photo offers a view of Nuuanu Pali Pass on Oahu. In a paragraph or two, describe any one of these scenes. Test your own ability as a word artist.

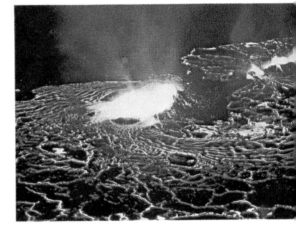

Every Dog Should Own a Man

COREY FORD

Essays offer ideas, and in this case it is a whimsical idea. Instead of people owning dogs, perhaps it is the other way around, suggests Corey Ford, the author of this essay. If so, fine! He has lots of helpful advice for dogs on how to train their masters.

Every dog should have a man of his own. There is nothing like a well-behaved person around the house to spread the dog's blanket for him, or bring him his supper when he comes home man-tired at night. Properly trained, a man can be a dog's best friend.

For example, I happen to belong to a medium-sized English setter, who acquired me when he was about six months old and has been training me quite successfully ever since. He has taught me to shake hands with him, and fetch his ball. I've learned not to tug at the leash when he takes me for a walk. I am completely housebroken, and I make him a devoted companion.

The secret of a dog's success in handling a man is patience. Some men are a little slow to respond, but a dog who makes allowances and tries to put himself in the man's place will be rewarded with a loyal pal. My setter has broken me so thoroughly that I have decided to set down a few basic rules of manhandling, as a guide for other dogs who happen to own friends of mine.

The first problem is to pick out the right man. A dog should exercise great care in making his choice, since he is apt to become quite attached to the man and will find it hard to get rid of him later if he proves to be unsatisfactory. Every dog wants to own a champion, but a gay and affectionate disposition is more important than an expensive pedigree.

I do not happen to be registered, for example, but my setter is just as fond of me as though I came from a long line of blue bloods.

The main things to look for in a man are sound teeth and gums, a good coat, and a self-confident manner. Remember that a dog is judged by the man he leads, so do not accept a specimen that is scrawny or a runt. Before acquiring a man, it is a good idea to walk him up and down a couple of times, in order to make sure that his action is free and he has springy hindquarters.

The next question to decide is whether the dog and man should share the house together. Some dogs prefer a kennel because it is more sanitary, but my setter decided at the start that he'd move right in the house with me. I can get into any of the chairs I want except the big overstuffed chair in the living room, which is his.

Training a man takes time, of course. A dog should realize that man does not possess a dog's instincts, and it is not his fault when he fails to understand what the dog desires. Men are apt to be high-strung and sensitive, and a dog who loses his temper will only break the man's spirit.

A friend of mine, who was owned by a cocker spaniel, was handled very badly when his dog first got him. When my friend failed to serve him his meal on time, for example, the dog snarled and nipped him in the calf. As a result my friend became dog-shy and would crawl under the sofa whenever he saw his dog coming. The spaniel finally had to give him away.

It is a great mistake to break a man by using force. Punishment should be meted out sparingly, and then only in cases of deliberate disobedience. More can be accomplished by a reproachful look than by flying off the handle. My setter has never raised a paw to me, but he has cured me almost entirely of the habit of running away. When he sees me start to pack my suitcase, he just lies down on the floor with his chin on his forepaws and gazes at me sadly. Usually I wind up by unpacking the suitcase and canceling my train reservations.

A lot of dogs make the added mistake of breaking a man too fast. A few minutes of yard work each afternoon are sufficient, and the pupil will look forward to the next day's session with enthusiasm. Make each lesson a game, and always reward a man when he has done particularly well. A man is anxious to please his dog, and he will respond gratefully to an occasional friendly gesture, such as wagging the tail.

The first thing to teach a man is to stay at heel. To accomplish this lesson, the dog should hook one end of a long leather leash to his collar and loop the other end around the man's wrist so he cannot get away.

Start down the street slowly, pausing at each telephone pole until the man realizes that he's under control. He may tug and yank at first, but this can be discouraged by slipping deftly between his legs and winding the leash around his ankles. If the man tries to run ahead of the dog, brace all four feet and halt suddenly, thus jerking the man flat on his back. After a few such experiences, the man will become leadbroken and follow his dog with docility. Remember, however, that all such efforts at discipline must be treated as sport, and after a man has sprawled on the sidewalk the dog should run over and lick his face to show him it was all in fun.

Another trick every man should learn is to retrieve a rubber ball. The way my setter taught me this trick was simple. He would lie in the center of the floor, while I carried the ball to the far side of the room and rolled it along the rug toward him, at the same time uttering the word "Fetch!" The setter would watch the ball carefully as it rolled past him and came to a halt under the sofa. I would then walk to the other side of the room, get the ball from under the sofa and roll it past him again, giving the same command, "Fetch!"

This lesson would be repeated until the setter was asleep. After I got so I would retrieve the ball every time I said "Fetch!" my dog substituted other articles for me to pick up, such as an old marrowbone or a piece of waxed paper he found in the wastebasket.

Not only did I learn to keep the house neat, but the frequent bending over was good for my waistline.

The matter of physical conditioning is important. A man whose carriage is faulty, and who slouches and droops his tail is a reflection on the dog who owns him. The best way to keep him in shape is to work him constantly, and never give him a chance to relax. Racing him up and down the street at the end of a leash, for example, is a great conditioner.

If he attempts to slump into an easy chair when he gets back, the dog should leap into it ahead of him and force him to sit in a straight-backed chair to improve his posture.

Be sure to get him up three or four times during the night and make him go out for a walk, particularly if it is raining.

Equally important is diet. The average man has a tendency to gobble everything in sight, and the dog should exercise a restraining influence on his appetite by eating all the leftovers in the house before the man gets a chance at them.

Last but not least, it is up to the dog to see that his man has the right companions. If he does not approve of a guest who has been invited to the house for dinner, he should express his dislike by removing a small section of the visitor's trouser leg as a gentle hint. Personally, I look forward to seeing the milkman these days, because he is practically the only person my dog will let in the house.

Not every dog who tries to bring up a man is as successful as my setter. The answer lies in understanding. The dog must be patient, and not work himself into a tantrum if his man cannot learn to chase rabbits or wriggle under fences as well as the dog does.

After all, as my setter says, it's hard to teach an old man new tricks.

THINKING IT OVER

1. Mr. Ford must have had fun writing this essay. What were the most amusing ideas, from your point of view?

2. Seriously, do you think the author understands dogs very well? What is your proof?

3. Name some of the "upside-down" ideas in this whimsical essay involving either familiar sayings or situations.

4. Can you cite an example in which a person or a family has had to adjust to a pet's way of doing things? What was the final outcome of the situation?

5. Note that the author did not simply state his idea in the title and let it go at that. What did he do to emphasize it?

6. Just for fun, what suggestions would you give to a cat who might "own" an old lady? Your suggestions ought to include such cat habits as upholstery scratching, drapery climbing, and nocturnal wandering.

WORD HISTORIES

1. The word *whimsical* was used in the introduction to this essay. *Whimsey* comes from the Old Norse *hvima* — whim — which meant "to wander with the eyes." Today it means mind wandering; a whim is a fancy, a surprising or unexpected turn of the mind, such as Mr. Ford takes in this essay.

2. Some familiar words associated with dogs used in the essay are *pedigree, kennel, spaniel,* and *leash.* All these words came into English from French words that trace back to earlier Latin forms. *Pedigree* in Latin meant "crane's foot" (*pes, pedis* — foot; *grus* — crane). This was a three-line mark like a crane's foot track which showed the line of descent. . . . *Kennel* was *chenil* in French and *canile* in Latin. . . . *Spaniels* — and what could be more reasonable? — trace their name to the Latin word for Spain, *Hispania.* . . . *Leash* originally came from the Latin *laxa,* meaning loose. A *leash* is a loosely held cord.

LOOKING AT THE ESSAY FORM

Many essayists deal with their topics in a very serious tone, and their writings are known as formal essays. Other writers, however, approach both their subjects and their readers in a friendly or informal manner; hence, their writings have been called "friendly" or "informal" essays. "Every Dog Should Own a Man" is an example of this latter kind of essay. Here, it is not the subject matter itself that is unusual or important. It is Corey Ford's amusing, turnabout point of view that makes this selection witty and entertaining. Often, in the informal essay, the author's point of view will be the springboard for the entire development of the composition. Note, too, that "Every Dog Should Own a Man" follows the same structure that was pointed out to you in "Hawaii." Can you state the *opening generalization* of Corey Ford's essay? What are some of the *supporting ideas?* The next two selections — "The Truth About Thunderstorms" and "A, B, and C — The Human Element in Mathematics" — will provide you with other examples of this literary form, in which can be found a rich share of entertainment and human commentary.

PEN AND PAPER

The longer we live with our possessions, the more they seem to take on living characteristics. Have you ever "begged" a wobbly bicycle wheel not to fall off? The family car is another example of an object which acquires a life and personality of its own. Select this, or some other familiar possession, as the subject for a short humorous essay. Write the essay from your subject's point of view, in which "it" describes life in your household. You might begin with an account of your arrival at the house and your reactions to the various members of the family. Then tell of the calamities that have since befallen you.

ABOUT THE AUTHOR

Corey Ford (1902–), born in New York City, is a bachelor who lives with at least one dog at Hanover, New Hampshire. He was graduated from Columbia University, has been a playwright, and served as an Air Force colonel in World War II. A frequent contributor to magazines, he has created a brand of humor that is distinctly his own.

The Truth
About
Thunderstorms

ROBERT BENCHLEY

When a writer captures a feeling or tells of an experience shared by nearly everyone, we say that what he has written has "universality." For instance, if thunderstorms did not strike a note of fear in many people, this essay would lose a great deal of its appeal, and our laughter at the author's confessions would not be so appreciative. As it is, he could be any one of us.

ONE OF THE advantages of growing older and putting on weight is that a man can admit to being afraid of certain things which, as a stripling, he had to face without blanching. I will come right out and say that I mean thunderstorms.

For years I have been concealing my nervousness during thunderstorms, or, at least, I have flattered myself that I was concealing it. I have scoffed at women who gave signs of being petrified, saying, "Come, come! What is there to be afraid of?" And all the time I *knew* what there was to be afraid of, and that it was a good, crashing sock on the head with a bolt of lightning. People *do* get it, and I have no particular reason for believing that I am immune. On the contrary.

Just where any of us in the human race get off to adopt the Big-Man attitude of "What is there to be afraid of?" toward lightning is more than I can figure out. You would think that we knew what lightning is. You would think that we knew how to stop it. You would think that no one but women and yellow dogs were ever hit by it and that no man in a turtle-neck sweater and a three days' beard on his chin would give it a second thought. I am

Noting an Author's Technique. Entertainment is the purpose of this essay. To achieve it, Robert Benchley uses techniques often employed by other humorists. He (1) pokes fun at himself; (2) relates (or invents) some comic incidents to illustrate his point; and (3) uses both overstatement and understatement to underscore his point. As you read, see whether you can recognize these techniques.

sick of all this bravado about lightning and am definitely abandoning it herewith.

Ever since I was a child old enough to have any pride in the matter, I have been wincing inwardly whenever 100,-000 volts of simon-pure electricity cut loose in the air. My nervous system has about six hundred ingrowing winces stored up inside it, and that is bad for any nervous system. From now on I am going to humor mine and give a shrill scream whenever I feel like it, and that will be whenever there is a good sharp flash of lightning. I will say this for myself: I will scream when the lightning flashes and not when the thunder sounds. I may be timid but I am no fool.

My nervousness begins when I see the black clouds in the distance. At the sound of the first rumble my digestive system lays off work, leaving whatever odds and ends of assimilation there may be until later in the day.

Of course, up until now I have never allowed myself to show trepidation.[1] If I happened to be out on the water or playing tennis when it was evident that a storm was coming, I have looked casually at my watch and said, "Ho-hum! What about going in and making a nice, cool drink?" Sometimes I even come right out and say, "It looks like a storm — we'd better get in"; but there is always some phlegmatic [2] guy who says, "Oh, we aren't going to get that — it's going around the mountain," and, by the time it is evident that we *are* going to get that and it isn't going around the mountain, it is too late.

It is remarkable how slow some people can be in taking down a tennis net or bringing a boat inshore when

there is a thunderstorm on the way. They must not only take the net down but they must fold it up, very carefully and neatly, or they must put things away all shipshape in the cabin and coil ropes. Anything to waste time.

My attempts to saunter toward the house on such occasions must have, at times, given away the dread I have of being the recipient of a bolt of lightning. I guess that I have done some of the fastest sauntering ever pulled off on a dry track. Especially if my arms are loaded down with cushions and beach umbrellas, I make a rather ungainly job of trying to walk as if I didn't care and yet make good time.

If possible, I usually suggest that someone run ahead and shut the windows in the house, and then immediately delegate myself to this job. I am not so crazy about shutting windows during a thunderstorm, but it is better than dawdling around outside.

I once got caught up in an airplane during an electrical storm. In fact, there were *two* storms, one on the right and one on the left, and we were heading right for the spot where they were coming together. We could see them quite a long time before they hit us, and I was full of good suggestions which the pilot didn't take. I wanted to put down right where we were. It was a rocky country, covered with scrub pines, but it seemed to be preferable to hanging around up in the air.

I was considerably reassured, however, by being told (or shouted to) that you are safer up in the air during a thunderstorm than you are on the earth, as lightning cannot strike unless the object is "grounded." It sounded logical to me, or as logical as anything connected with lightning ever could sound, and I sat back to enjoy my first electrical display in comfort. It really was

[1] **trepidation** (trĕp·ĭ·dā'shŭn): fear, state of alarm.
[2] **phlegmatic** (flĕg·măt'ĭk): sluggish, calm.

great, although I hate to admit it. You couldn't hear the thunder because of the motors and there were some very pretty flashes.

It was only several months after, on reading of a plane being struck by lightning three thousand feet up, that I began to get nervous. Perhaps you can't get hit unless you are "grounded" according to all the laws of nature, but it is always the exception that proves the rule, and it would be just my luck to be one of the exceptions.

Perhaps the worst part that a nervous man has to play during a crisis like this is reassuring the ladies. If I am alone, I can give in and go down cellar, but when there are women around, I have to be brave and joke and yell "Bang!" every time there is a crash. To make matters worse, I find that there are a great many women who are not frightened, and who want to sit out on the porch and play bridge through the whole thing.

This is a pretty tough spot for a man of my temperament. At best, I am an indifferent bridge player, even with the sun shining or a balmy summer night's breeze wafting around outside. I have to go very carefully with my bidding and listen to everything that is being said or I am in danger of getting a knife in my back from my partner when the game is over. But with a thunderstorm raging around my ears and trees crashing down in the yard by my elbow, I might just as well be playing "slapjack" for all the sense I make.

A good flash of lightning has been known to jolt a "Five spades" out of me, with an eight and queen of spades in my hand. Sometimes it would almost have been better if the bolt had hit me. (Only fooling, Lord! Just kidding!)

I would feel more ashamed of confessing all this if I weren't sure that I am in the right about it. I am not afraid of snakes or burglars or ghosts or even Mussolini,[1] but when it comes to lightning — boy, there's something to be afraid *of!* And anyone who says that he isn't, is either lying or an awful sap.

Of course, being nervous isn't going to keep you from getting hit, but when you are nervous, you don't lie around with water dripping on you and holding a copper plate in your mouth, and avoiding all this sort of thing certainly helps.

If I were running a thunderstorm, I would pick out some big man who goes around saying there is nothing to be afraid of and clip a cigar or two out from between his teeth just to show him. And any nice guy like me, who knows his place and tries to keep it, I would let go scot-free[2] and might even uproot a fine big pot of buried gold pieces for him.

The funny part about all this is that now that I am old enough to come out frankly and admit how I feel about thunderstorms, I seem to be getting too old to mind them so much. It has been a couple of years now since I had a really good scare (I am now knocking wood so hard that the man in the next room just yelled "Come in!"). Perhaps it is just that, when you get to be my age, it doesn't make so much difference. If it isn't lightning, it will be hardening of the arteries. I still would prefer hardening of the arteries, however.

---

[1] **Mussolini** (mōōs'ŏ·lē'nê): the dictator of Italy at the time this essay was written.
[2] **scot-free:** tax-free.

NOTING AN AUTHOR'S TECHNIQUE

1. What is the first comic incident the author relates as a technique of creating humor? He follows this by making a confession about himself. Do you think this

confession adds to the humor? Explain.

2. Explain the humor in the line in paragraph 3, ". . . no man in a turtle-neck sweater and a three days' beard on his chin . . ." Is the author poking fun at himself, or is his target wider? Explain.

3. Paragraph 5 contains an example of humorous overstatement. What is it? Can you find at least three other examples in the text where overstatement is used for humorous effect?

4. Paragraph 7 consists of three brief sentences. The author first makes another humorous overstatement, then in the next sentence adds to the comic effect by indulging in further exaggeration. How does the third and final sentence of the paragraph heighten the humor and provide a climax to it?

5. Another technique used by humorists is to start with a funny situation and add details that increase the comic aspects. Explain how paragraph 8 is an example of this technique.

THINKING IT OVER

1. In the first paragraph the author states that he can now admit a fear of lightning which, as a youth, he had to pretend not to feel. This is an example of why some psychologists say that growing up is often harder for boys than for girls. They say that boys feel obliged to prove their courage and that sometimes their efforts can be misdirected and lead them into trouble. Girls, on the other hand, can succeed more easily by conforming to the rules. Do you agree or disagree with this theory? Explain your answer. Give examples to prove your point.

2. Which of the first six paragraphs in this essay develops the idea stated in paragraph 1, that boys have to pretend not to be afraid of certain things? Quote lines. Is this idea carried further in later paragraphs?

3. Which of the last four paragraphs is definitely whimsical? Point out the whimsical ideas.

4. Discuss some other fears the author mentions — snakes, burglars, ghosts. What fears would you have mentioned if you had written this essay? Would you take a humorous or a serious attitude toward your subject? Why?

ABOUT THE AUTHOR

Robert Benchley (1889–1945) was born in Worcester, Massachusetts. After graduating from Harvard, he went to work in a New York advertising office. Beginning then, Benchley managed to create an astonishing variety of careers for himself. He did newspaper work, became a magazine editor, and also saw service as a drama critic. In this last capacity he was associated with the *New Yorker* Magazine. Benchley was also an actor, appearing first on Broadway, then in Hollywood films. As a film actor, he wrote, produced, and starred in a series of one-reel comedies which are still being shown on television today. Most of Benchley's humorous essays were centered on the character of a shy, rather fumbling little man constantly being defeated by the harsh realities of life. On the surface no one resembled this character more than Benchley himself — but he was something very much more than that: he was one of the finest writers of humor this country has ever produced. Perhaps his best-remembered book is *My Ten Years in a Quandary, and How They Grew.*

Robert Benchley

A, B, and C—
The Human
Element in
Mathematics

STEPHEN LEACOCK

Today's "thinking machines" can solve the most complicated mathematical equations, but one aspect of the science has not changed. The problems in mathematics books still feature that old familiar trio, A, B, and C. In this essay, a famous humorist takes a whimsical look at the trio and pretends that they are three real people, busily working out the problems in which they so often appear. The idea is original, the results highly amusing.

THE STUDENT of arithmetic who has mastered the first four rules of his art, and successfully striven with money sums and fractions, finds himself confronted by an unbroken expanse of questions known as problems. These are short stories of adventure and industry with the end omitted, and though betraying a strong family resemblance, are not without a certain element of romance.

The characters in the plot of a problem are three people called A, B, and C. The form of the question is generally of this sort:

"A, B, and C do a certain piece of work. A can do as much work in one hour as B in two, or C in four. Find how long they work at it."

Or thus:

"A, B, and C are employed to dig a ditch. A can dig as much in one hour as B can dig in two, and B can dig twice as fast as C. Find how long, etc., etc."

Or after this wise:

"A lays a wager that he can walk faster than B or C. A can walk half as fast again as B, and C is only an indifferent walker. Find how far, and so forth."

The occupations of A, B, and C are many and varied. In the older arithmetics they contented themselves with doing "a certain piece of work." This statement of the case, however, was found too sly and mysterious, or possibly lacking in romantic charm. It became the fashion to define the job more clearly and to set them at walking matches, ditch digging, regattas, and piling cordwood. At times, they became commercial and entered into partnership, having with their old mystery a "certain" capital. Above all they revel

"A, B, and C — The Human Element in Mathematics" by Stephen Leacock. Reprinted by permission of Dodd, Mead & Company from *Literary Lapses* by Stephen Leacock.

in motion. When they tire of walking matches — A rides on horseback, or borrows a bicycle and competes with his weaker-minded associates on foot. Now they race on locomotives; now they row; or again they become historical and engage stagecoaches; or at times they are aquatic and swim. If their occupation is actual work, they prefer to pump water into cisterns, two of which leak through holes in the bottom and one of which is watertight. A, of course, has the good one; he also takes the bicycle, and the best locomotive, and the right of swimming with the current. Whatever they do, they put money on it, being all three sports. A always wins.

In the early chapters of the arithmetic, their identity is concealed under the names John, William, and Henry, and they wrangle over the division of marbles. In algebra they are often called X, Y, Z. But these are only their Christian names, and they are really the same people.

Now to one who has followed the history of these men through countless pages of problems, watched them in their leisure hours dallying with cordwood, and seen their panting sides heave in the full frenzy of filling a cistern with a leak in it, they become something more than mere symbols. They appear as creatures of flesh and blood, living men with their own passions, ambitions, and aspirations like the rest of us. Let us view them in turn. A is a full-blooded blustering fellow, of energetic temperament, hotheaded and strong-willed. It is he who proposes everything, challenges B to work, makes the bets, and bends the others to his will. He is a man of great physical strength and phenomenal endurance. He has been known to walk forty-eight hours at a stretch, and to pump ninety-six. His life is arduous and full of peril.

A mistake in the working of a sum may keep him digging a fortnight without sleep. A repeating decimal in the answer might kill him.

B is a quiet, easygoing fellow, afraid of A and bullied by him, but very gentle and brotherly to little C, the weakling. He is quite in A's power, having lost all his money in bets.

Poor C is an undersized, frail man, with a plaintive face. Constant walking, digging, and pumping have broken his health and ruined his nervous system. His joyless life has driven him to drink and smoke more than is good for him, and his hand often shakes as he digs ditches. He has not the strength to work as the others can; in fact, as Hamlin Smith [1] has said, "A can do more work in one hour than C in four."

The first time that ever I saw these men was one evening after a regatta. They had all been rowing in it, and it had transpired that A could row as much in one hour as B in two, or C in four. B and C had come in dead fagged, and C was coughing badly. "Never mind, old fellow," I heard B say, "I'll fix you up on the sofa and get you some hot tea." Just then A came blustering in and shouted, "I say, you fellows, Hamlin Smith has shown me three cisterns in his garden, and he says we can pump them until tomorrow night. I bet I can beat you both. Come on. You can pump in your rowing things, you know. Your cistern leaks a little, I think, C." I heard B growl that it was a dirty shame and that C was used up now, but they went, and presently I could tell from the sound of the water that A was pumping four times as fast as C.

For years after that I used to see them constantly about town and always busy. I never heard of any of them eat-

[1] **Hamlin Smith**: author of mathematics textbooks.

ing or sleeping. Then owing to a long absence from home, I lost sight of them. On my return I was surprised to find A, B, and C no longer at their accustomed tasks; on inquiry I heard that work in this line was now done by N, M, and O, and that some people were employing for algebraical jobs four foreigners called Alpha, Beta, Gamma, and Delta.

Now it chanced one day that I stumbled upon old D, in the little garden in front of his cottage, hoeing in the sun. D is an aged laboring man who used occasionally to be called in to help A, B, and C. "Did I know 'em, sir?" he answered. "Why, I knowed 'em ever since they was little fellows in brackets. Master A, he were a fine lad, sir, though I always said, give me Master B for kindheartedness-like. Many's the job as we've been on together, sir, though I never did no racing nor aught of that, but just the plain labor, as you might say. I'm getting a bit too old and stiff for it nowadays, sir — just scratch about in the garden here and grow a bit of a logarithm, or raise a common denominator or two. But Mr. Euclid he use me still for them propositions, he do."

From the garrulous old man I learned the melancholy end of my former acquaintances. Soon after I left town, he told me, C had been taken ill. It seems that A and B had been rowing on the river for a wager, and C had been running on the bank and then sat in a draft. Of course the bank had refused the draft, and C was taken ill. A and B came home and found C lying helpless in bed. A shook him roughly and said, "Get up, C, we're going to pile wood." C looked so worn and pitiful that B said, "Look here, A, I won't stand this, he isn't fit to pile wood tonight." C smiled feebly and said, "Perhaps I might pile a little if I sat up in bed."

Then B, thoroughly alarmed, said, "See here, A, I'm going to fetch a doctor; he's dying." A flared up and answered, "You've no money to fetch a doctor." "I'll reduce him to his lowest terms," B said firmly, "that'll fetch him." C's life might even then have been saved, but they made a mistake about the medicine. It stood at the head of the bed on a bracket, and the nurse accidentally removed it from the bracket without changing the sign. After the fatal blunder, C seems to have sunk rapidly. On the evening of the next day, as the shadows deepened in the little room, it was clear to all that the end was near. I think that even A was affected at the last as he stood with bowed head, aimlessly offering to bet with the doctor on C's labored breathing. "A," whispered C, "I think I'm going fast." "How fast do you think you'll go, old man?" murmured A. "I don't know," said C, "but I'm going, at any rate."

The end came soon after that. C rallied for a moment and asked for a certain piece of work that he had left downstairs. A put it in his arms and he expired. As his soul sped heavenward, A watched its flight with melancholy admiration. B burst into a passionate flood of tears and sobbed, "Put away his little cistern and the rowing clothes he used to wear. I feel as if I could hardly ever dig again."

The funeral was plain and unostentatious. It differed in nothing from the ordinary, except that out of deference to sporting men and mathematicians, A engaged two hearses. Both vehicles started at the same time, B driving the one which bore the sable parallelepiped [1] containing the last remains of his ill-fated friend. A on the box of

[1] **sable parallelepiped** (sā′b'l păr′ă·lĕl′ê·pī′-pĕd): a black six-sided body with parallel surfaces — in other words, a coffin.

the empty hearse generously consented to a handicap of a hundred yards, but arrived first at the cemetery by driving four times as fast as B. (Find the distance to the cemetery.) As the sarcophagus was lowered, the grave was surrounded by the broken figures of the first book of Euclid.

It was noticed that after the death of C, A became a changed man. He lost interest in racing with B, and dug but languidly. He finally gave up his work and settled down to live on the interest of his bets.

B never recovered from the shock of C's death; his grief preyed upon his intellect, and it became deranged. He grew moody and spoke only in monosyllables. His disease became rapidly aggravated, and he presently spoke only in words whose spelling was regular and which presented no difficulty to the beginner. Realizing his precarious condition, he voluntarily submitted to be incarcerated in an asylum, where he abjured mathematics and devoted himself to writing the *History of the Swiss Family Robinson* in words of one syllable.

THINKING IT OVER

1. Give thumbnail character sketches of A, B, and C. Also, who was D, and how was he characterized?

2. What are the mathematical stumbling blocks you would encounter if you attempted to solve the three problems given at the beginning of this essay?

3. Aside from the manner in which poor old D speaks, what other touches of humor do you find in the paragraph devoted to his story? Point out a pun in the paragraph following it.

4. Who is the "Mr. Euclid" in whose propositions old D says he is still used? The last sentence of the third paragraph from the end mentions the broken figures of the first book of Euclid around C's grave. What figures are these?

5. Has this essay made you think of any other humorous aspects about mathematics? What?

FOR YOUR VOCABULARY: WORDS IN CONTEXT

On page 136, the system of using context clues — determining the meaning of a word by studying the words around it — was explained to you. Using this system results in better, more enjoyable reading and an enlarged vocabulary as well. To practice your skill at using context clues, read over the final three paragraphs of this selection, where you will find the following words:

> unostentatious
> deference
> sarcophagus
> incarcerated
> abjured

By studying the context in which each of these five words is used, see whether you can define the word or supply a synonym for it. Afterward, check a dictionary for complete definitions of the words.

ABOUT THE AUTHOR

Stephen B. Leacock (1869–1944) was born in England, and was educated both in Canada and the United States. For a number of years he was head of the Department of Political Economy at McGill University in Montreal. In 1907 and 1908 he toured the British Empire as a Cecil Rhodes Trust lecturer. All the while, he remained a busy, productive writer. He wrote many serious works, but it is as one of the most popular humorists of his time that he is best remembered. Creative writing — particularly the light, seemingly effortless essays for which he became celebrated — always struck Stephen Leacock as a most difficult task. He found it deeply rewarding, however. "To write something out of one's own mind," he once stated, ". . . is an arduous contrivance. Yet I would rather have written *Alice in Wonderland* than the whole of the *Encyclopaedia Britannica*."

The Piano That Wouldn't Die

ARTHUR CAVANAUGH

Every now and then a true story turns out to be stranger than fiction. This article, which reads like a mystery story, is a true account of an unusual piano that has had some very unusual adventures in the one hundred and fifty years since it was built. In 1961 this unique piano was the subject of a television program. Recordings featuring it have fascinated thousands of today's music lovers.

"Very well," sighed Avner Carmi to his three daughters who were waiting anxiously outside the bedroom door. He tucked his shirt into his trousers, reached for his shoes. "It is late at night, I am a tired soldier home on leave, but let us have another look at this ailing piano of yours."

Carmi was a piano tuner by trade — the leading piano expert in Tel Aviv.[1] Pianos were not only his business, they were his love. Except for this piano. No, he would not even call it a piano. It was a phantom, a nuisance, a disturber of sleep.

[1] **Tel Aviv** (tĕl á·vēv'): capital city of Israel, the country formerly known as Palestine.

Mrs. Carmi came into the hall tying the cords of her night robe. "Dragging your father into the street," she scolded the three girls, "to look at a piano he already knows is worthless."

"But, Mamma," Zmira,[2] the eldest daughter, protested. "Papa himself says a sick piano is like a sick man and should be treated the same. This poor piano has been cast into the gutter as well. Abandoned!"

"Your father already knows about it."

The family proceeded down the shadowy stairs. Carmi tried to rub the sleep out of his eyes. The year was 1945, World War II had not ended yet, and in another week Carmi would have to report back to Italy for duty with the Transport Corps of the British Eighth Army. War didn't leave much time for pianos, he reflected, as he trudged down the stairs. Probably there wouldn't be time to reopen his old piano workshop again, as he had hoped to do during his furlough. Only a week left, yet what was he doing now? Interrupting his sleep to attend to a worthless, abandoned —

[2] **Zmira** (z'mĭ'rá).

"I'll get the light," Ora, the second daughter, volunteered. She switched on the bulb in the downstairs hall and went to the door. "Oh, the poor piano, Papa. I knew you wouldn't just let it lie there."

A week ago, a junk dealer had thrown the piano into the gutter from his cart as he was passing the Carmi home. Carmi had gaped at the ruined instrument in amazement. Not only was it the strangest-looking piano he had ever set eyes on — an ancient, battered upright, encased from top to bottom in a hard, thick shell of plaster — but Carmi had encountered this same instrument once before. He remembered the earlier encounter vividly — 1943, the German retreat from El Alamein,[1] the desert strewn with discarded possessions . . .

Aviva,[2] the youngest Carmi daughter, held open the door to the street for her parents. She followed them onto the dark, deserted thoroughfare. "Yesterday, Papa, a gang of kids were hitting the piano with sticks. Imagine, a poor, sick — "

"Children, children," sighed Carmi. "You know quite well that this instrument is more than sick. It is deceased, *dead*. What did I explain after my first look at it? Inside the plaster there is nothing. No strings, no action,[3] no hammers. Only the sounding board — otherwise, nothing. Such a piano is beyond help."

Mrs. Carmi nodded in agreement. "Of course! Why else do you suppose no one has bothered to claim it?"

"But look," said Zmira slowly. Raising her arm, she pointed across the street.

"If no one would bother to claim it, then why — "

Carmi gave a low whistle of surprise — and as he did, another climax in a strange but true story was being reached. Carmi was the leading, real-life character in the story, though he didn't know it yet. And like the rest of the tale, this new climax was filled with a sense of the unexpected.

Carmi stared at the street across from him. The piano — the plaster piano which had lain there for days — was gone.

Perhaps it is incorrect to name Avner Carmi as the story's leading character. By rights, the piano itself must be the leading character. Nor can the story begin, really, in 1945 on the dark Tel Aviv street outside Carmi's home. The setting of the story moves across two continents, a desert, and half a dozen cities — and for its beginning, it is necessary to go back to Italy, to a time nearly a hundred years before Avner Carmi was born.

Turin, a city in northern Italy, is best known today for the fine automobiles and racing cars which are built there. Despite its modern, industrial appearance, Turin is a very old city, and a hundred and fifty years ago it had long been a bustling center of trade and commerce. Living at that time in Turin was a family named Marchesio.[4] Grandfather, father, and son, the family had been engaged for generations in the manufacture of musical instruments. On the day that this story has its beginning, the scene in the Marchesio household was one of stir and excitement. A Marchesio daughter, Rebecca, had just been married, and the family was busy preparing for the bride's departure. A long journey was ahead for Rebecca, for she

[1] **El Alamein** (ĕl ăl′*à*·măn′): Egyptian village where the Germans were defeated by the Allied armies in one of the decisive battles of World War II.

[2] **Aviva** (*à*·vēv′*à*).

[3] **action**: here, the mechanism in a piano by which sound is produced.

[4] **Marchesio** (mär·kā′zĕ·ō).

had married a young man from the town of Siena, many miles to the south of Turin. In the courtyard outside the Marchesio home, a bridal coach awaited the couple; behind this was a wagon packed with the bride's wedding gifts. In the house the wedding breakfast was reaching a merry conclusion, while in the courtyard workers loaded onto the wagon the family's most precious gift to Rebecca. It was a piano made in their workshop.

For the Marchesios as well as for the rest of the musical world — the time, remember, is the early 1800's — the piano was a relatively new invention, only just coming into general use. It had been derived from a much older keyboard instrument, the harpsichord. Small in size and elegant, the harpsichord produced a delicate, harplike music which had been greatly favored in the recital halls of Europe. The instrument had a limitation, however. The volume or tone of the playing could not be varied to any extent. But in 1709 an Italian harpsichord maker, Bartolommeo Cristofori,[1] had experimented with the problem. Previously the keys of the harpsichord had been wired directly to the strings. Thus, when a key was struck, the wire to which it was attached would pluck at the strings, producing a sound. Cristofori rejected this arrangement. He constructed a series of little hammers and wired them to the keys. When a key was struck, it now caused a hammer to strike at the strings. The result was a deeper, richer sound, which could be made soft or loud, according to the pressure of the player's fingers on the keys. In effect, Cristofori had evolved a totally different instrument, and he christened it a "pianoforte." The name was a combination of two Italian

words, *piano,* meaning "soft," and *forte,* which means "loud or strong." In modern times the name became shortened to simply "piano."

The piano that was being hoisted onto the wagon in the Marchesio courtyard was a large, gleaming upright. By the 1800's, Cristofori's invention had become one of the most popular musical instruments in Europe. Already, Johann Sebastian Bach and Wolfgang Amadeus Mozart [2] had written immortal compositions for this new, exciting instrument. In a few years would come Franz Liszt and Frederic Chopin [3] to add to the brilliant repertoire.[4] Soon their playing would make piano recitals the rage of the continent. No royal palace or noble household would consider itself complete without one or several pianos. Kings and emperors would compete in assembling magnificent piano collections, just as they competed in collecting paintings and jewels. Even the men who built the pianos would become celebrated — Frederici, Stein of Augsburg, Broadwood of England. But in all this swirl of activity, there would be only one piano which, alone and by itself, would achieve fame. The Marchesios' upright was this very instrument.

The piano was slowly edged onto the wagon.

"Careful!"

"Tilt it this way."

"Where are the ropes? We must strap it tightly; the roads to Siena are not smooth."

At last the piano was securely in place, lashed to the wagon by strong

[2] **Johann Sebastian Bach . . . Wolfgang Amadeus Mozart** (yô·hän bäk . . . ăm′a·dē′- ŭs mō′tsärt).

[3] **Franz Liszt . . . Frederic Chopin** (fränts lĭst . . . shô′păn′).

[4] **repertoire** (rĕp′ẽr·twär): list; in this context, the list of compositions written for the piano.

[1] **Bartolommeo Cristofori** (bär′tô·lôm·mâ′ô krês·tô′fô·rē).

ropes. It had taken two generations of Marchesios to build this upright, but the result, they felt, had been worth the effort. The family was agreed that never had they turned out a more beautiful instrument. To listen to the music of this piano made one weep! The tone was a marvel of purity and richness. It was almost as if there were hidden within the instrument a magic . . .

Into the courtyard came the Marchesio bride, dressed in her going-away clothes, surrounded by the gay, toasting wedding party. It is pleasant to envision the departure scene: the groom, Antonio Ferri, helping young Rebecca into the coach; the wedding party calling out blessings and waving good-by as the coach pulls away; behind the swaying coach, the wagon brimming with the bride's possessions — and, jutting up from the other gifts, with perhaps a faint tinkle of keys, the piano. One can picture the little caravan making its way southward to Siena, traveling along the dusty roads that wind through the soft hills of Tuscany.

Antonio Ferri and his bride reached Siena, lived there, and had a son, Nicodemo — that much is known about the next years. In terms of the piano, however, a lapse of time must now occur in the story. It will not be the last such lapse; at every step, the story is shot through with an air of mystery, raising questions ("But how did — ?") that cannot be entirely answered.

The next recorded historical fact about the piano is that in the year 1868 it was acquired by the township of Siena for a glittering purpose. Crown Prince Umberto [1] of Italy's Royal House of Savoy was to be married. A royal wedding called for royal gifts; for each town and province in Italy it was a mat-

[1] **Umberto** (ōͅom·bĕr′tô).

Siena, Italy.

ter of pride to bestow on the Prince the finest of all the gifts he might receive. But Siena had no qualms; it had made its choice: the town was to present to Umberto the piano once owned by Antonio and Rebecca Ferri. From this it can certainly be assumed that the piano's unique qualities had become famous in Siena. Legends — the story abounds in legends as well as time gaps — tell of passers-by halting outside the Ferris' home, caught by the enchanting piano music drifting from the windows, and of concerts held in Rebecca's drawing room, rapt silence spreading over the guests as she wove magic at the keyboard. No other piano had ever sounded like this instrument! Here was a piano which, as if by wizardry, was able to take on the color and the character of whatever music was played on it; a piano which could sound at times like a harp, and at other times like an organ, deep and sonorous. The clear, sweet sound of a lute could be drawn from this piano; the liquid, strumming tones of a guitar. What gift could Siena find that was worthy of a prince? Why, the Ferris' piano, of course.

So again the piano embarked on a journey — this time to the residence of Prince Umberto in Rome. The piano made the journey fitted out in a new case. The Ferris' son, Nicodemo, had grown up to become a sculptor. The piano had worked its spell on him, too, and he had made it a new case of rare, beautifully polished wood. Lavishly, he had covered the entire surface with carving: cherubs and garlands of flowers, urns, and clusters of fruit. Across the lid of the piano were carved cameos of five composers: Mozart, Handel, Cherubini, D'Arezzo,[1] and Gluck, each likeness rendered in finest detail. To Nicodemo Ferri, such a case was the least he could provide for the piano whose music had spilled like gold through his youth.

In 1868, then, the piano left Siena, resplendent in a new case, and traveled to its third home, the Quirinal [2] Palace in Rome — and once more there occurs a time lapse in the story.

The setting is still Rome, but several years have passed when the story picks up its thread again. It is evening. In the home of the Russian ambassador in Rome, a private concert is about to take place. A man in evening dress moves across the crowded music room, bows, and sits down at the piano. He is Matthew Yanowsky, a pianist and a new figure in the story. To the music lovers of mid-nineteenth-century Europe there was, of course, only one great pianist, and his name was Franz Liszt. By comparison, Matthew Yanowsky's success as a pianist had been modest, but he had given concerts in all the great capitals of Europe, before audiences which had often included royalty. Tonight at the ambassador's,

there was a king to play for. It was Umberto, no longer prince, but now the reigning monarch of Italy. The presence of royalty did little to lift Yanowsky's spirits, however; the man whose fingers sought to bring music from the ivory keys was old, tired, and discouraged. After the concert he was presented to the king and immediately apologized for the performance he had given. It had not gone well. If only, he told the king, he could have played on a certain piano he had once used in Russia. There was an instrument! Franz Liszt himself had performed on it.

"Ah," Umberto replied. "In my palace I have a piano also used by Liszt. Let me tell you, maestro,[3] there is no other piano its equal. Words cannot describe the music that comes from it. Liszt called it divine; he compared it in beauty to the harp of David." [4]

Umberto described the piano in detail. It was an upright built in Italy. Every inch of its case was carved with flowers and angels; on the lid were cameos of Mozart, Handel —

He paused, touched by the look of reverence on Yanowsky's face. He thought of how humbly the man had apologized for the evening's concert. "But why have I not thought of it," he said. "You must come to the palace one day and play the piano for yourself, maestro. Do you live here in Rome?"

Matthew Yanowsky answered, "I haven't a permanent home, your majesty. My wife is dead, and three of my children. I have only a son left, Abraham. My son and I — we're going to Palestine to live."

---

[1] **Cherubini, D'Arezzo** (kā′rōō·bē·nė, dä-rät′tsô).

[2] **Quirinal** (kwĭr′ĭ·nắl).

[3] **maestro** (mä·ĕ′strô): master; in music and other of the arts, the term is given as a title of honor to men of outstanding accomplishment.

[4] **harp of David**: the legendary instrument played by the Biblical shepherd boy who became king of Israel.

"Well, one day you will return to Rome. Don't forget to come to the Quirinal and perform on my piano."

Yanowsky looked up at the king. He reviewed the long years of his career, the failures and hardships, the occasional triumphs. An invitation from a king to play on a royal piano! How would it sound, this incredible piano which Liszt had compared to David's harp? The years suddenly were not so dark.

"I will come, your majesty," Yanowsky promised. "When I am back in Rome, I will come. Thank you. Thank you."

Shortly afterward, Matthew Yanowsky went to live in Palestine. The thought of the king's piano stayed with him. The years passed. Yanowsky's son Abraham married and presented grandchildren to the aging pianist. One of the children, a boy, displayed a gift for music, and came to live with Yanowsky in his house in Tel Aviv to study music. To play the royal piano had now become the old man's dream. King Umberto had died, killed by an assassin, but still Yanowsky dreamed of somehow visiting the palace in Rome. He told the story of the invitation to his grandson. It soon became the boy's favorite tale; for him, the piano in the palace in Rome loomed up as the most beautiful object on earth.

"Soon a trip can be arranged," Yanowsky would tell the boy. "I will take you with me. Umberto's son, Victor Emmanuel, is king now. We will visit the palace, the two of us together, and explain to him about the invitation. Soon. Soon we will go. . . ."

Sometimes, as he talked of the trip, the old man grew afraid that it would never take place. The years were racing by — already it was 1914. Life had dealt out many disappointments; perhaps this

Rome: Hadrian's Tomb.

trip was to be another. When he had such thoughts, Yanowsky would extract a promise from his grandson.

"If I cannot go to Rome," he would say, "you must go without me. Promise. If I cannot go, you must go in my place."

It was a newspaper headline which ultimately put an end to Yanowsky's dream. The trip to Rome exploded one morning in a splash of black printer's ink spread across a front page. EUROPE AT WAR, the headline read. Then in smaller type, *Austria Invades Serbia.*

The British sergeant mopped his brow and squinted up at the hot sun that glared down on Cairo. How many more years would the war last, he wondered. The Yanks had joined up, but there was still a long road ahead. The sergeant thought ruefully of the men in his village in England who had fought in World War I. "The war to end war," they'd called that one. Hadn't quite worked out. . . .

Cairo, Egypt.

How cool the word *England* sounded. The sergeant's glance took in the length of the salvage depot. Destruction — that was the word for war. The Germans had fled Africa weeks ago, yet each morning trucks still groaned into the depot weighed down with the mountains of objects the Jerries had left behind, half mangled or destroyed. Rifles and helmets, guns, canvas tents, pots and pans, desks, cupboards, stolen paintings, automobile parts, bits of statuary — each morning the parade continued. The sergeant studied the smoking rubbish pile at the opposite end of the depot. Smoke rising into the sky from ruins — that was war. And heat — scorching, blistering heat.

There was a noise at the entrance gate, the chug-chug of an approaching truck. Careening in through the gate, the vehicle wheeled to an ear-splitting stop, and out jumped a squat little fellow in the uniform of a British army private. In the rear of the truck was the most peculiar-looking object the sergeant had yet to see. It looked like — well, like nothing he had ever before observed. A tombstone, perhaps. A plas-

ter box, designed for what crazy purpose he could not imagine.

"Private Carmi," the vehicle's driver announced. This was Avner Carmi, the same Carmi who later would encounter the same plaster object abandoned in a Tel Aviv street. Words raced out of him, accompanied by excited gestures.

"It's a piano, sergeant — yes, believe it or not, a piano. That is to say, *inside* the plaster there is a piano. In very bad condition — oh, terrible condition. But to me a sick piano is like a sick man, and should be treated the — "

The sergeant eyed the object warily. "Mean to tell me that dirty chunk of plaster is a piano? Looks more like a booby trap."

The private rushed to the object's defense. "It has already been tested for mines. A detector crew found it in the desert near El Alamein. Evidently the Germans left it behind."

"The Jerries took along a piano when they cleared out? Whatever for?"

"I don't know, sergeant. It is a very old piano, of European make — Italian, I'd guess. Perhaps a German officer — perhaps Rommel[1] himself — stole it in Italy and brought it here. The poor instrument has been ruined. Nothing left inside but the soundboard. If I had not asked to inspect it, the detector crew would have blown it up. I am a piano tuner by trade, you see — in my home in Tel Aviv I have my own workshop, which of course I had to close when I enlisted in the corps — But that's aside from the point, isn't it? What I wondered about this piano — "

The sergeant thumped the dirty plaster case suspiciously. "Why not remove the plaster and see what the thing looks like?"

The private hopped onto the truck.

[1] **Rommel:** Nazi general, leader of the German campaign in Africa in World War II.

He struck at the plaster, kicked hard at it. "Impossible to loosen it, you see? And to smash it might ruin the instrument altogether. No, we cannot harm it further. It is weak and wounded, in need of surgery — "

The sergeant watched the little private stroke the plaster case, as if to offer it comfort and hope. "You're not planning to keep that box of junk?"

Private Carmi's face registered hurt. "I am an excellent piano tuner, sergeant. If anyone can repair this instrument, it is I, Avner Carmi. But I must clear it with you first."

The sergeant looked at the smoking rubbish dump at the other end of the depot. Then he looked at the ridiculous plaster box and the private standing alongside it protectingly. That pile of plaster was easily the most worthless item yet trucked into the depot.

"Your permission, sergeant?" the private asked.

The sergeant threw back his head and laughed. It felt good to laugh; it felt like a lovely breeze or a drink of cool water. "My permission, Private Carmi? Permission — granted!"

It took many days to repair the piano, to replace the missing strings, hammers, and keys. When the work was at last finished, everyone agreed that it gave out a nice bit of music, after all. The haunting tone it had! And what would it be like, perhaps, without all that plaster?

A group of entertainers, who had arrived in the area to perform for the troops, were in need of a piano. The plaster piano was offered them. Yes, they would accept it.

After all, they explained, anything was a good bit better than nothing.

And that seemed the end of it. But it was not. There was another chapter, perhaps the most incredible of all.

For its ending, the story returns to Tel Aviv, a week after the night Avner Carmi found the piano gone from the street outside his home. Since then, Carmi had been busy. Despite everything, he had managed to reopen his old workshop again. At the moment, however, the workshop was filled with shouting.

"I demand — my money — BACK," bellowed Mr. Noah, whacking at the object in the middle of the workship floor. "It is worthless. I demand my money this INSTANT."

The shouting made Carmi wince. Mr. Noah, he decided, had the loudest voice God had ever put inside a human. Like a tuba, it was — an off-key tuba.

"Do you hear? My money back!"

Carmi shook his head wearily. This much was certain: nothing more could go wrong on his furlough. What had happened as soon as he had reopened the workshop? Before the paint on the sign outside had even dried, who had appeared? Mr. Noah in a truck. And what had been in the truck? Carmi's old friend, the plaster piano, turning up again like a bad penny. Evidently Mr. Noah had spied it lying in the gutter that night and decided that it might have value. This, then, had been Carmi's first customer — Mr. Noah and the plaster piano.

"Yes, I can repair it for you," Carmi had assured the man, thinking that this wouldn't be the first time he had tackled the job. El Alamein, the desert . . .

"Here is the money in advance," Mr. Noah had said. "Don't try to remove the plaster — I plan to decorate it with flowers and such. I will have the most unusual piano in Tel Aviv."

But now Mr. Noah was singing a different tune. He whacked his great hand down on the plaster piano, while Mrs. Noah provided a choral accompaniment to his solo. "The instrument is EMPTY inside. It is NOT a piano, merely an EMPTY one. My money back this INSTANT, Carmi, you cheat."

"I told you I would replace the missing parts," Carmi explained. "If you will only trust me —"

"I won't PAY for EMPTY pianos!"

Carmi looked over at his daughters, who had retreated into a corner of the workshop, eyes wide with apprehension. The ridiculous scene must be ended. "Mr. Noah," he said, stepping forward, as the great hand gave the plaster another whack, "Mr. Noah, I will be happy to refund your money. Here, let me count it for you."

"Fifty pounds, it was." Mr. Noah took the bills, stuffed them into his pocket, and marched from the shop, followed by his wife. "Worthless. The thing was absolutely worthless."

Gratefully, Carmi closed the shop door on the tuba. Turning, he saw that his daughters had gone over to the piano and were staring at it.

"Look, Papa," cried Aviva. "Hurry, come look. Mr. Noah's thumping has dislodged some of the plaster. A piece of plaster has fallen off."

Carmi hurried to the piano. Aviva handed him the fragment of plaster from the floor.

"Oh, look what's underneath," she said. "Look what the plaster is hiding."

And, looking — already excitement was sweeping through him — Avner Carmi saw what the fallen plaster had exposed: the carved figure of an angel. It couldn't be possible! He tried frantically to push away the memory that had leaped into his mind. This couldn't be the piano of that memory. It simply wasn't possible.

"Look, Papa."

Carmi gazed in wonder, as other frag-

ments of the plaster fell from the piano. Forever after, it was to seem to Avner Carmi to have been nothing less than a miracle.

For as the chunks of plaster fell from the piano, a carved wooden surface was revealed underneath. The entire piano was carved. Cherubs were carved into the wood, and garlands of flowers, urns, and clusters of fruit. On the lid of the piano were carved five beautiful cameos. . . .

"Papa, what's wrong?" little Ora asked, seeing the look on her father's face.

Carmi could not answer. He was not standing in the workshop, surrounded by his children. In his mind's eye, he was a boy again, sitting in a room, listening to an old man tell the story of a fabled piano owned by a king. He heard again the promise the old man had asked of him.

"If I cannot go to Rome" — how deeply the words had fallen on his heart — "you must go without me . . . you must go in my place."

The old man had been Matthew Yanowsky. The old man had been Avner Carmi's grandfather.

The years spun dizzily around. Carmi saw himself, a young man setting out from Tel-Aviv for Europe. World War I had just ended. By then he had dropped his family name of Yanowsky. To honor the memory of his mother, who was dead, he had taken her name, Carmi, for his own. And he had sailed away, bound for Berlin to study music. But first he had stopped off in Rome and gone to the Quirinal Palace. If I cannot go . . . you must go in my place. For three days the palace guards had refused to admit him or listen to his story of the king and the piano. He had left the city, vowing to return. If I cannot go . . . you must go in my place.

Eight trips in all Carmi had made to Rome, and each trip had brought him no closer to the piano. He had traveled to Siena and found documents that proved the piano's existence. He had found in Siena old photographs of the piano, and records of the gift of the piano to the prince. He had held the documents in his hands and asked for reproductions of the photographs, which he had kept and treasured. He had studied the photographs, running his hands over them, holding them, as if they represented proof that the piano had really existed and was not simply a myth, a tale told by a king —

But no matter, thought Carmi. The search was over. A miracle had taken place. The piano still existed, it still lived. It had found its way to the one man on earth who could have identified it. It had reached safety at last. Its journey was over.

On the last count, Carmi was wrong.

Today, the piano built by the Marchesios more than a hundred and fifty years ago, the piano which traveled to Siena, to the Roman palace of a prince, and then across the Mediterranean to Africa and a war-torn desert, and from there to a gutter in Tel Aviv — still continues its journey. Avner Carmi is its custodian; famous concert halls are its home; the great pianists of the world have sat at its keyboard and made recordings of the unique sounds — soft and shimmering, like a guitar, deep and sonorous, like an organ — which once drifted from the windows of the Ferri home, enchanting the people of Siena as they passed by in the street.

Completely restored, still living, the piano has been given the name of that Tuscan town for its own name. It is called today "The Siena Pianoforte," and kings still listen to its magic.

THINKING IT OVER

1. When Avner Carmi first saw the piano abandoned in the street in Tel Aviv, why didn't he rescue it? Who prevailed upon him to salvage it? What did he then find out?

2. What are the known facts about the piano's origin? What was the first journey it made? the second?

3. What did you learn from this article about the background of our modern piano? What is the literal meaning of the word *pianoforte*?

4. What were the two wars that the piano survived? the two weddings in which it played a part? the two families that made or remade it?

5. Describe some of the reactions of the people in the article to the music of the piano. Tell the class about any similar experience of your own where music may have stirred you.

6. Discuss the remarkable coincidences which are involved in the story of the piano. What circumstances brought about Avner Carmi's final recognition of the piano? Where is the piano today?

PEN AND PAPER

Write a composition entitled "The Music I Like Best," giving the reasons why you prefer this kind of music. You may want to write about a particular musical instrument that you enjoy, or a composer — or perhaps a singer that you like especially.

ABOUT THE AUTHOR

Arthur Cavanaugh (1926–   ) was born in Woodhaven, New York. It was in high school, after working on the school magazine and newspaper, that he set his course on a writing career. He attended William and Mary College and served overseas with the USO during World War II. As a writer, he has been active as a dramatist and has had numerous original plays produced on television. He has also published short stories and articles, and has been an editor in a New York publishing house. He is the author of the book *My Own Back Yard.*

An Adventure in Viewpoint

EDWIN WAY TEALE

All essays present their author's viewpoints. In this selection, however, Edwin Way Teale, the famous nature writer, tries to get you to see life from the viewpoint of the animal and insect world that is as near to you as the nearest outdoors. All you need for your adventure is a new viewpoint — and a bit of imagination.

On the thirtieth day of January 1841, Henry Thoreau [1] set down in his journal this record of a small adventure among the snow-covered fields of Concord.

"Looking down the river," he wrote, "I saw a fox some sixty rods off, making across the fields to my left. As the snow lay five inches deep, he made but slow progress, but it was no impediment to me. So, yielding to the instinct of the chase, I tossed my head aloft and bounded away, snuffing the air like a foxhound, and spurning the world and human society at each bound. It seemed the woods rang with the hunter's horn

and Diana and all the satyrs [2] joined in the chase and cheered me on."

Thus, for a few exhilarating moments, Henry Thoreau entered another world than his own. They are all about us — these other worlds — the world of the fox, the squirrel, the beetle, the fish, the bird. We need only the keys of curiosity and imagination to reach their infinite variety. Adventures in viewpoint are within the grasp of all.

When, like Thoreau, we imagine ourselves part of another realm — whether it is the weedy water world of the perch, the grass jungles of the katydid, the mossy well of the frog, the hot, conical sand pit of the ant lion, the white foam castle of the tiny froghopper, the fungus forests of the beetle or the dark haunts of the earthworm and the mole — we are exploring as surely as though we were journeying across a tundra [3] or

[1] **Henry Thoreau** (thôr′ō): famous American writer, naturalist, philosopher.

[2] **Diana . . . satyrs** (săt′ẽrz): in Greek mythology, Diana was goddess of the hunt; satyrs were demigods of the woods, with a man's head and body, and the legs of a goat.

[3] **tundra** (tōͦn′drả): one of the level, treeless plains found in the northern arctic regions.

through the rain forest of some remote land.

To stop and wonder, to put ourselves for a passing moment in the place of the creatures around us— to visualize life from their standpoint — here, truly, is an adventure in exploring. Such journeys require neither ships nor trains nor rubber tires nor gasoline. They take only leisure moments from our time.

One of the most vivid memories of my childhood concerns just such an adventure of the mind.

Between the yellow flanks of the Indiana sand dunes and my grandfather's farm, a field of rye used to rise like a mane of hair above the brow of a low hill. Swallows tilted and skimmed over this grain field and when light breezes ran across its changing surface, the whole field seemed fluid, part of the running, invisible air. There, one hot and somnolent [1] afternoon when I was six or seven, I crawled deep into the gray-green luminous light that filtered down between the stalks in this sea of waving grain.

All around a vast jungle of slender stalks hedged me in. Overhead there was the sibilant [2] murmur of the moving rye. And at my feet the floor of the field, like the sandy bed of some shallow green bay, appeared as a strange world in itself to my young eyes.

I remember I hollowed out a tiny cave amid the grain and as the sultry afternoon wore on, I played that I, too, was an inhabitant of the narrow aisles between the stalks of rye. I became, like Tennyson's Ulysses,[3] a part of all I saw. I shared the toil of the ants, the varied labors of the multihued beetles, the ac-

tivity of the flies that descended and landed, took off and landed again and yet again. I even tried to picture the field as it must appear to little dust-colored toads that hopped, with incorruptibly solemn expressions, down the sandy aisles, and to the harmless, striped garter snake that slid leisurely along the floor of this forest of rye. The viewpoint, as I had it there, revealed a whole new, silent world of activity, a world unseen and unappreciated by the casual eye. Returning home that evening was like landing from a distant voyage of discovery.

That was long ago. But the emotion, after a lapse of more than a quarter of a century, remains more vivid than many events of a month ago. It may have played its part in a peculiar Odyssey of the mind which has added interest to ensuing years.

On city streets, my eyes have followed dusty sparrows flying, with trailing straws, to half-built nests on ledges high above the traffic. And I have walked on oblivious, except in a physical sort of way, to events around me. My mind has been visualizing life as it must be lived on that high ledge, life in storm and wind and rain and blistering heat, an existence in which the life preservers of wings play so large a part. Again, I have looked out of an upper window into the treetop world of a maple or spruce, watching a squirrel scurry along a limb with fits and starts or a spider spread its aerial net among the bluish needles of the evergreen. And in the moments that followed, my surroundings have fallen away and I have given myself up to the delights of picturing in vivid detail how life must appear from the standpoint of an arboreal [4] existence.

At one time or another there comes

[1] **somnolent** (sŏm′nṓ·lĕnt): drowsy.

[2] **sibilant** (sĭb′ĭ·lănt): hissing.

[3] **Ulysses** (û·lĭs′ēz): the Latinized name of Homer's Greek hero, Odysseus. See *The Odyssey*, page 525. The reference here is to a poem by Tennyson.

[4] **arboreal** (är·bō′rḗ·ăl): pertaining to trees.

to most of us a realization of how much will remain undone when the world ends for us. Even if we circle the globe, how many sights and sounds and smells we still shall miss! Even if we become acquainted with millions, how many possible friends we never shall know! Even if we devour whole libraries, how many volumes will remain unread! No matter how full, our lives inevitably must remain, in some respects, random and incomplete.

Of this vast undone, I think the part I will regret most of all will be missing, in so many phases, fascinating and infinitely varied forms of life — life as it is known to the ocean bird whose home is the open sea, to the mole that has forsaken the pleasures of sight, to the snake that "walks on its ribs," to the winter springtails [1] that skip by thousands across the fields of snow. How strong and how unattainable is the longing to know life on the tundra, in the treetops, in the hot mud of sulphur springs, in the jungle, on the sea wastes; life in all its color and forms and habits and activity; bird life, insect life, animal life, human life!

Such thoughts as these were passing through my mind this afternoon as I stood leaning back against the rough, honest bark of one of my apple trees. Out across the swamp, below my orchard hillside, red-winged blackbirds dropped into the waving masses of wind-blown cattails as though they were diving into the breakers of a green sea. Here and there, sunlight glinted on the wings of dragonflies. I fell to wondering how the swamp forest, the wide cattail islands with their thousands of waving sword leaves, must appear to the dragonfly, the blackbird, the ant,

living among the dense vegetation of this marshland jungle. I decided to find out. So, slipping on rubber boots, I started off on a fresh adventure in viewpoint.

With the "Okaleeee!" of the blackbirds ringing in my ears, I waded across Dragonfly Hollow and a hundred yards of sloshy marsh grass, made treacherous by the tunneling of muskrats. From my orchard hillside, masses of whitish blooms of the climbing boneset [2] stood out on the dense stand of cattails like splotches of foam on waves of dark green water. Their mahogany-colored creepers, I discovered as I neared the cattail island, laced together the upright vegetation of the outer wall into an almost solid barrier. Lowering my head and driving forward like a football halfback, I plowed into the interior until I came to a mud-stained log stranded by a freshet. [3] There I stopped and, as I had done so long before in the field of rye, tramped down a little cave amid the cattails.

On all sides rose the slender columns of the cattails, old and new, brown and green. Sunlight, slanting downward, was diffused into the soft illumination of the swamp bottom. Over the black and glistening mud ran ghostly white creepers, and decaying cattail leaves lay crisscrossed like the cane seat of a discolored chair. Midway up the cattails the weathered remnants of dead boneset creepers of other years hung in curls and masses. Loosened by winter gales, they were descending slowly toward the black, moist earth below, their ultimate destination.

When a quick gust struck the cattail island, a multitude of green swordlike blades waved against the sky above my

[1] springtails: small insects which leap with the aid of a springlike appendage that folds under their bodies and is suddenly released.

[2] boneset (bōn'sĕt'): a type of flowering herb.

[3] freshet: a stream of fresh water.

head. The stiff brown cattails nodded gravely amid the wild flutter of their leaves. The wind passed and the flutter ebbed away. In the hot, moist silence that followed, bits of fluff drifted down from the older stalks, dropping slowly and silently as though descending through water.

They reminded me of the tens of thousands of these floating seeds which can come from a single cattail. One earlier winter, my innate curiosity had led me to carry home an average-sized head and to begin counting the seeds at the ends of their parachutes of fluff. Dividing the cattail into half-inch sections, I set gaily to work. But my exuberance soon faded.

At the end of a whole evening's labor, I had accounted for hardly more than a redwing could pull out with one thrust of its beak. Night after night, the count went grimly on. I had a botanical bear by the tail and couldn't let go. Thousands, tens of thousands, of seeds were duly recorded in my one-man cattail-seed census. In bed, I counted seeds instead of sheep. Cattail fluff began to drift about the house. The side of the shoebox, on which I kept my tally, looked as though an endless game of ticktacktoe were in progress. Gradually I worked myself along one side, around the end, and down the other side. More than ten days went by before, to the great relief of the whole family, the tally was complete. It showed that the single head contained 147,265 close-packed seeds.

From outside my little cave in the swamp tangle came sounds, each bringing its mental picture. The creaking clatter of the long-billed marsh wren, for all the world like the noise of a miniature unoiled lawn mower, presented to the mind's eye the vision of its little body rising on vibrating wings a dozen feet into the air and then dropping back again in the manner of one of those tin helicopters we used to send aloft as boys. There were other noises: the far-carrying clang of metal, the yelp of a dog, the faint drone of a high-flying plane, the cry of a gull coasting across the little patch of sky above my cavern.

The air around me was filled with the faint sweetish perfume of the boneset blooms. In a cluster hardly more than an inch in diameter, I counted forty flowerets. Close beside me a wild bee alighted and, grasping a small clump of blooms with its forelegs as though holding a goblet, ran its long tongue into floweret after floweret. Brilliant little gold-banded flies walked up and down the green highways of the cattail leaves. On one dying leaf — brown along the edges, rich green beside the central rib, and yellow between — a fly with pinkish eyes, gold-white stripes down its face, and a tail tipped with red, basked in the sun. Below, on the floor of the cavern where an old cattail lay like a burst bomb, a gray fly with reddish eyes washed its face, kitten-wise, over and over again.

Single-file, three ants hurried across a boneset-creeper bridge and disappeared into a tangle of cattails beyond. A yellowish mass, dimly seen through the leaves, attracted my eye. A quick investigation revealed it was the abandoned nest of a long-billed marsh wren. This six-inch oval was formed of twisted cattail leaves lined with fluff. The doorway was almost entirely closed. I poked an investigating finger inside. Instantly, a stream of dark little ants poured from the interior. The nest was the penthouse home of an ant colony.

In their excitement, some of the insects, carrying white pupae [1] in their

[1] **pupae** (pū′pē): insects in a cocoonlike intermediate stage.

jaws, dropped fully three feet to the wet, glistening vegetation below. Five minutes later, when their fright had passed away, I saw these same ants, unhurt by their fall, toiling up the cattails again with the pupae still clutched in their jaws. The existence of this colony resembled, in some respects, that of the ancient Lake Dwellers [1] within their pile-supported homes. Water and mud lay below them and they were cut off from the solid land beyond the swamp by more water, standing among the marsh grass. Hunting and travel for these insects were made possible only by the endless crisscrossing and interlacing of narrow leaves. Their whole lives were spent in an unstable world of moving leaves; they rarely, if ever, came in contact with solid earth.

For a long time I stood watching the hurried labors of these semiaerial insects. Successive gusts swept across the island. Their progress was recorded by the cattails all bending first one way, then holding the position for a moment, and finally rising erect once more. Each time the upper leaves moved in the wind, now, their shadows ran swiftly up and down the stalks of their eastern neighbors. The sun was swinging lower in the west.

I stooped and pushed my way out of the opening I had made. Beyond, I could see the familiar trees and garden of my hillside. Straightening up once more was like closing a door behind me. But never again would that cattail island seem quite the same. I had seen it from a fresh viewpoint. I had, for part of a summer afternoon, lived in another world within its depths.

[1] **Lake Dwellers:** Stone Age and Early Bronze Age people who built their homes over marginal waters of lakes on platforms supported by piles. Remains of their villages have been found in many parts of the world.

THINKING IT OVER

1. Small children often play games of viewpoint or make-believe. They pretend to be animals, perhaps, or that their toys and dolls are real, or they identify themselves with the heroes and heroines of television and story books. What adventures like these have you observed in the games of young children? What "adventures in viewpoint" of your own have you had?

2. In paragraph 3 the author suggests that other worlds are all about us, and names a few of them. If these particular "worlds" are inconvenient for you to reach, what places near at hand might you consider suitable? Perhaps you can name a particular bird or animal whose world you would like to explore.

3. What careful observations have you made, perhaps, of birds, animals, or insects? Tell your experience and what you learned from your observation.

4. Discuss this statement of the author's: "No matter how full, our lives inevitably must remain, in some respects, random and incomplete." What does the author mean by this statement? What are some of the places in the world you would most want to visit during your life? Why?

ABOUT THE AUTHOR

Edwin Way Teale (1899–   ) is one of America's best-loved nature writers. In addition to being an author and naturalist, he is a lecturer and photographer. He has also been a newspaper columnist and a magazine writer on the staff of *Popular Science Monthly*. His career started, in large part, with his hobby of watching insects in the outdoor surroundings nearest him. If you like nature study, you will enjoy *Adventures in Nature*, the book from which this essay is taken, as well as others of his works.

As the Camera Sees It ➤

Point of view, as discussed in this selection, can also be expressed in photography. In this picture, the photographer brings us up close to a clump of cattails, so that we see them as they might appear to a small swamp creature.

Biography: People to Remember

People have always wanted to know about other people. As the world became smaller in terms of distance and larger in terms of complexity, this interest in other people has grown. Confronted by such a complex world, we look to the lives of others for guidance. What were the difficulties of others in the past, and how did they solve them? What values have helped the people of our own time to succeed, and what can be learned from their lives? Reading biography is a rewarding way to find the answers to these questions.

The word *biography* comes from two Greek words, *bios,* meaning "life," and *graphein,* which means "to write." Biography, then, means "to write a life"; it is the written history of a particular person's life. If the account is written by the person himself, it is called *autobiography,* which makes use of a third Greek word, *autos,* meaning "self." As a literary form, biography can be traced to the ancient times of the Romans and Greeks. Plutarch's *Lives* is still one of the most widely read of all collections of biographies.

Today, a variety of nonfiction writing can be grouped under the heading of biography. The field ranges from the formal, full-length history of a life to the casual recollections of the past that are listed so frequently among our best sellers. Biographical articles are a major feature of today's magazines. So popular have these articles become that a special word has been coined to identify them: "profiles." The interviews of prominent personalities carried in newspapers are a form of biography. An author who recounts his adventures as a traveler or explorer, or describes an experiment in living he made, is writing biography. Biography can be long or short, serious or light in tone, but its main essential is that it tells of an actual life, the story of a person of the past or the present. It might give an account of its subject's entire life or concentrate merely on an episode from it. The reward in reading these records of other lives, as presented to us in biography, is that we find something for our own lives.

In the following group of biographical selections, you will be introduced to seven outstanding men and women. Of the seven, four are contemporary and three belong to the past. But what all of these men and women have in common is that each of them was once young and confronted with all of the problems with which young people must deal. You will read about a beloved American President during his growing-up days on a frontier farm, and learn of the difficult boyhood of a great English novelist, a boyhood haunted by the grim shadow of a debtors' prison. You will sympathize with the efforts of a young boy facing the problem of blindness. Queen Elizabeth II, Mark Twain, and Katharine Cornell, the celebrated actress, are the other people you will read about. What in their stories will you find for your own lives?

Charles Dickens: The Boy of the London Streets

RUPERT SARGENT HOLLAND

Here is an account of the boyhood of the great novelist, Charles Dickens. Reading it will show you how deeply an author's own experiences can be later reflected in his work. Dickens' early life was anything but happy, yet all the while his mind was at work, storing up impressions of the people and places around him. Later on in this book, you will have a chance to read one of Dickens' best-loved novels, *Great Expectations.*

T HE LITTLE FELLOW who worked all day long in the tumble-down old house by the river Thames pasting oil-paper covers on boxes of blacking [1] fell ill one afternoon. One of the workmen, a big man named Bob Fagin, made him lie down on a pile of straw in the corner and placed blacking bottles filled with hot water beside him to keep him warm. There he lay until it was time for the men to stop work, and then his friend Fagin, looking down upon the small boy of twelve, asked if he felt able to go home. The boy got up looking so big-

[1] blacking: shoe polish.

eyed, white-cheeked, and thin that the man put his arm about his shoulder.

"Never mind, Bob; I think I'm all right now," said the boy. "Don't you wait for me; go on home."

"You ain't fit to go alone, Charley. I'm comin' along with you."

" 'Deed I am, Bob. I'm feelin' as spry as a cricket." The little fellow threw back his shoulders and headed for the stairs.

Fagin, however, insisted on keeping him company; and so the two, the shabbily dressed undersized youth and the big strapping man, came out into the murky London twilight and took their way over the Blackfriars Bridge.

"Been spendin' your money at the pastry shops, Charley, again? That's what was the matter with you, I take it."

The boy shook his head. "No, Bob. I'm trying to save. When I get my week's money, I put it away in a bureau drawer, wrapped in six little paper packages, with a day of the week on each one. Then I know just how much I've got to live on, and Sundays don't count. Sometimes I do get hungry, though; so hungry! Then I look in at the windows and play at being rich."

They crossed the bridge, the boy's big eyes seeming to take note of everything, the man, duller-witted, listening to his chatter. Several times the boy tried to say good night, but Fagin would not be shaken off. "I'm goin' to see you to your door, Charley lad," he said each time.

At last they came into a little street near the Southwark Bridge. The boy stopped by the steps of a house. "Here 't 's, Bob. Good night. It was good of you to take the trouble for me."

"Good night, Charley."

The boy ran up the steps, and, as he noticed that Fagin still stopped, he pulled the doorbell. Then the man went on down the street. When the door opened, the boy asked if Mr. Fagin lived there, and being told that he did not, said he must have made a mistake in the house. Turning about, he saw that his friend had disappeared around a corner. With a little smile of triumph, he made off in the other direction.

The door of the Marshalsea Prison stood open like a great black mouth. The boy, tired with his long tramp, was glad to reach it and to run in. Climbing several long flights of stairs, he entered a room on the top story where he found his family, his father, a tall pompous-looking man dressed in black, his mother, an amiable but extremely fragile woman, and a small brother and sister seated at a table eating supper. The room was very sparsely furnished; the only bright spot in it was a small fire in a rusty grate, flanked by two bricks to prevent burning too much fuel.

There was a vacant place at the table for Charles, and he sat down upon a stool and ate as ravenously as though he had not tasted food for months. Meanwhile the tall man at the head of the table talked solemnly to his wife at the other end, using strange long words which none of the children could understand.

Supper over, Mr. and Mrs. Dickens (for that was their name) and the two younger children sat before the tiny fire, and Mr. Dickens talked of how he might raise enough money to pay his debts, leave the prison, and start fresh in some new business. Charles had heard these same plans from his father's lips a thousand times before, and so he took from the cupboard an old book which he had bought at a little secondhand shop a few days before, a small tattered copy of *Don Quixote*,[1] and read it by the light of a tallow candle in the corner.

The lines soon blurred before the boy's tired eyes, his head nodded, and he was fast asleep. He was awakened by his father's deep voice. "Time to be leaving, Charles, my son. You have not forgotten that my pecuniary[2] situation prevents my choosing the hour at which I shall close the door of my house. Fortunately it is a predicament which I trust will soon be obviated[3] to our mutual satisfaction."

The small fellow stood up, shook hands solemnly with his father, kissed his mother, and took his way out of the great prison. Open doors on various landings gave him pictures of many peculiar households; sometimes he would stop as though to consider some unusually puzzling face or figure.

Into the night again he went, and wound through a dismal labyrinth of the dark and narrow streets of old Lon-

---

[1] *Don Quixote* (dŏn kwĭk'sŏt): a novel by the Spanish writer Cervantes, considered to be the finest literary work of that land.

[2] **pecuniary** (pē·kū'nĭ·ĕr'ĭ): relating to money.

[3] **obviated** (ŏb'vĭ·āt·ĕd): disposed of.

don. Sometimes a rough voice or an evil face would frighten him, and he would take to his heels and run as fast as he could. When he passed the house where he had asked for Mr. Fagin, he chuckled to himself; he would not have had his friend know for worlds that his family's home was the Marshalsea Prison.

Even that room in the prison, however, was more cheerful than the small back attic chamber where the boy fell asleep for the second time that night. He slept on a bed made up on the floor, but his slumber was no less deep on that account.

The noise of workmen in a timber yard under his window woke Charles when it seemed much too dark to be morning. It was, however, and he was quickly dressed and making his breakfast from the penny cottage loaf of bread, a section of cream cheese, and a small bottle of milk, which were all he could afford to buy from the man who rented him the room. Then he took the roll of paper marked with the name of the day from the drawer of his bureau and counted out the pennies into his pocket. They were not many; he had to live on seven shillings [1] a week, and he tucked them away very carefully in a pocket lest he lose them and have to do without his lunch.

He was not yet due at the blacking factory, but he hurried away from his room and joined the crowd of early morning people already on their way to work. He went down the embankment along the Thames until he came to a place where a bench was set in a corner of a wall. This was his favorite lounging place; London Bridge was just beyond, the river lay in front of him, and he was far enough away from people to be secure from interruption. As

London, 1872: from an engraving by the artist, Paul Gustave Doré.

[1] **shillings:** a British coin, the shilling was worth about 25¢ at the time.

he sat there watching the bridge and the Thames, a small girl came to join him. She was no bigger than he, perhaps a year or two older, but her face was already shrewd enough for that of a grown-up woman. She was the maid-of-all-work at a house in the neighborhood, and she had fallen into the habit of stopping to talk for a few moments with the boy on her way to work in the morning. She liked to listen to his stories. This was his hour for inventing them. He could spin wonderful tales about London Bridge, the Tower, and the wharves along the river. Sometimes he made up stories about the people who passed in front of them, and they were such astonishing stories that the girl remembered them all day as she worked in the house. He seemed to believe them himself; his eyes would grow far away and dreamy and his words would run on and on until a neighboring clock brought him suddenly back to his own position.

"You do know a heap o' things, don't you?" said the little girl, lost in admiration. "I'd rather have a shillin', though, than all the fairy tales in the world."

"I wouldn't," said Charles stoutly. "I'd rather read books than do anything else."

"You've got to eat, though," objected his companion; "and books won't make you food. 'T ain't common sense." She relented in an instant. "It's fun, though, Charley Dickens. Good-by till tomorrow."

Charles went on down to the old blacking factory by Hungerford Stairs, a ramshackle building almost hanging over the river, damp and overrun with rats. His place was in a recess of the counting room on the first floor, and as he covered the bottles with the oil-paper tops and tied them on with a string, he could look from time to time through a window at the slow coal barges swinging down the river.

There were very few boys about the place. At lunch time he would wander off by himself and, selecting his meal from a careful survey of several pastry cooks' windows, invest his money for the day in fancy cakes or a tart. He missed the company of friends his own age. Even Fanny, his oldest sister, he only saw on Sundays, when she came back to the Marshalsea from the place where she worked to spend the day with her family. It was only grown-up people that he saw most of the time, and they were too busy with their own affairs to take much interest in the small shabby boy who looked just like any one of a thousand other children of the streets. In all the men at the factory it was only the big clumsy fellow named Fagin who would stop to chat with the lad. So it was that Charles was forced to make friends with whomever he could, people of any age or condition; and was driven to spend much of his spare time roaming about the streets, lounging by the river, reading stray books by a candle in the prison or in the little attic where he slept. It was not a boyhood that seemed to promise much.

In time the boy left the factory and tried being a lawyer's clerk, then a reporter, and at last wrote a book of his own. The book was *Pickwick Papers*, and it was so original that people clamored for more. Then the young man took note of all the strange types of people among whom he had lived as a boy, and those days of poverty and drudgery were turned to wonderful account because he could write of such people and such scenes as he remembered them. The little maid-of-all-work became the "Marchioness" in the *Old Curiosity Shop*, Bob Fagin loaned his name to *Oliver Twist*, and in *David Copperfield* we read the story of the small boy who had to fight his way through London alone. Those days of his boyhood had given him a deep insight into human nature, into the humor and pathos [1] of other people's lives; and it was that rare insight that enabled him to become in time one of the greatest of all English writers, Charles Dickens, the beloved novelist of the Anglo-Saxon people.

[1] **pathos** (pā′thŏs): a quality that awakens pity.

THINKING IT OVER

1. This selection is organized into three parts: scenes of Dickens' early life, a paragraph outlining his later life, and a final paragraph describing his development as a writer. Summarize these parts, one at a time.

2. What characteristic is illustrated in Charles's attempt to keep Bob Fagin from finding out where he lived? In what way can this trait be useful instead of harmful? What did his spending money on pastry tarts indicate about Charles? Explain whether you think it is always wrong to buy extravagances you cannot afford or that are not of practical value.

3. Do you agree or disagree with the servant girl's statement, "I'd rather have a shillin', though, than all the fairy tales in the world"? Back up your opinion. Suggest a reason for Charles's statement "I'd rather read books than do anything else."

4. The selection tells us that some of the people in Dickens' childhood later served as models for characters in his novels. Do you think that a good novelist reproduces the people he has known for a book, or does he do something more creative than that?

5. The author states that after Dickens left the shoe-blacking factory, he worked as a lawyer's clerk and as a reporter. Do you think those two jobs would have value for a young person aspiring to be a novelist? Explain.

CONTINUING THE STORY

After finishing a work of fiction, readers sometimes play the game of guessing what might have happened after the ending. No guessing is needed with biography; when you read an episode of someone's life, the facts can usually be found to fill in more of the story. Do some further reading about Dickens and be ready to tell about other facts of his life that may have influenced his attitude as a writer.

PEN AND PAPER

1. Many distinguished people have come from humble backgrounds. Look up the life story of Marian Anderson, Thomas Edison, Dwight Eisenhower, or some well-known person of your own choice. In a short composition, describe your subject's early struggles, later life, and outstanding achievements.

2. What field of interest attracts you most as a possible future career? Pretend that you have won success in this field and that you have been asked to write about your achievements. Point out the factors that led to your choice of career and explain what early practices helped to train you for this career. Describe the obstacles you had to overcome and some mistakes you made. Conclude your composition by giving your advice to young people aiming for a similar career.

ABOUT THE AUTHOR

Rupert Sargent Holland (1878–1952) was only a lad of ten when he decided to be a writer and began "a history of English literature." Born in Louisville, Kentucky, Mr. Holland was the editor of three Harvard University publications — *Crimson, Lampoon,* and *Advocate.* He became a lawyer, settling in Philadelphia, but he always maintained his interest in writing. By a final count he wrote more than fifty books for young people, many of them seeing print first in the *St. Nicholas Magazine,* in which this article appeared. Among his books you might enjoy are *Wrecker's Reef* and *The Boy Who Lived on London Bridge.*

Queen Elizabeth II

MARION CRAWFORD

All young people have problems of one kind or another to face, and England's Queen Elizabeth II was no exception. In this selection you will meet her when she was fifteen, still called by her childhood name of "Lilibet." Her sister, Princess Margaret, was eleven, and the two young girls, like the rest of Britain's youth, were caught in the tide of World War II. Because the story is told by their ex-governess, Marion Crawford — "Crawfie" was their nickname for her — the picture of the two princesses, and their parents, is intimate and appealing. You will also see how the background of war helped to shape the character of a queen.

THE LONG slow months went by, and we remained incarcerated and cut off in Windsor Castle.[1] They were monoto-

[1] **Windsor Castle:** the official residence of the reigning British family.

nous days, but certain incidents stand out. All through one lovely early-summer day we could hear the sound of far-off shattering explosions and gunfire. Aircraft kept coming over. The little girls were bothered and anxious about their father and mother, and kept pausing in their play to ask anxiously:

"Crawfie, whatever is it?"

I was at least able to assure them that whatever was taking place, it was not in London; I knew it was too far for that; and I was right. It was at Dunkirk,[2] where the army was being taken off the beaches by the little boats. We had seen an Admiralty notice in the papers asking that anyone owning a small boat of any kind would take or send it to a rendezvous, but no one knew exactly what it was for. So the

[2] **Dunkirk:** a town on the northern French seacoast.

Drawing Conclusions. A book is incomplete unless it is read by someone — and an incomplete reader is the person who makes no contribution to what he reads. A good reader reflects on what he reads and draws conclusions about the characters and situations. In this selection, watch for the details which enable you to make conclusions about the British Royal Family.

news given out over the wireless came as a shock, mixed with thankfulness that most of our men had escaped. There had been vague rumors that the army was cut off, but most of them came from abroad, and no one knew what to believe.

We had a large map with flags on it which we moved from place to place, and I kept the little girls up to date as far as possible with what was happening.

It was with profound relief, I remember, that they both rushed to speak to their Mummie and Papa on the telephone that evening, and learned that they were still quite all right.

The King and Queen remained at Buckingham Palace [1] all through the London blitz. There were times when we felt extremely anxious about them. Unsuccessful efforts were made in official circles to get them away to a safer place. Accommodations had been arranged for them secretly that would not be so simple a landmark for the enemy as Buckingham Palace was, or even Windsor Castle. This, being on the Thames, was rather easy to locate from the sky.

There were evenings in that summer of 1941 when London was under fire that we all felt anxious. Windsor was near enough to London for what was going on there to be all too evident to us all. The castle is built on chalk, and vibrations were felt from great distances.

To divert the little girls' attention, we would play the piano, and they would sing their duets at the top of their voices. When I think back on it now, there was through all this war period an immense amount of laughter and fun in spite of it all, so that sometimes Lilibet,

[1] **Buckingham Palace:** the London residence of the Royal Family.

who was a very thoughtful little girl, would pause and say:

"Oh, Crawfie, *do* you think we are being too happy?"

I replied, "Mummie and Papa want you to be happy, and we shall not help anything or anyone if we sit in the corners and cry, shall we?"

The little girls lived for Friday nights, when their parents would come if it was at all possible. It was heartbreaking to see how all this was telling on Their Majesties. The Queen's charming and youthful face became pale and drawn, and the great strain she was undergoing showed in her eyes. The King began suddenly to look very much like his father.

But the royal discretion still held. Unpleasant or bothersome matters were never discussed. When they came down to Windsor, we took up the pleasant family life again for a little while and tried to live those three short days as if there were nothing else.

Then came Monday, or often even Sunday night, and they had to go.

Food grew scarce. Now we all looked forward greedily to our Sunday morning egg, the only one we got. We had it fried until fat became scarce.

Ration books and gas masks we all had had for some time. It was difficult to fit the little girls properly. After several efforts they were issued Mickey Mouse masks, horrible affairs with red and blue noses that never failed to put us in mind of the mandrill at the zoo.

We had to put these contraptions on every day and wear them for ten minutes to get used to them. This was a grim and at first rather frightening business, for a gas mask, until you get used to it, gives a nice imitation of slow suffocation.

We knitted, Lilibet making manful

efforts to improve her skill. Margaret and I collected acorns and beech huskings, painted them in gay colors, and made them into ornaments to be worn in buttonholes. We sold these for the war effort and made five pounds.[1] Sometimes I was able to visit my home in Scotland for a short time, but even on their holidays the girls made an effort to do something useful, as this letter shows:

Windsor Castle

Dear Crawfie:

Mummie thanks you for your letter and has asked me to write to you. Can you come back the beginning of next week, Tues. or Wed. 1st and 2nd of Oct.? We have had quite a long holiday, but poor Monty[2] has had very little. She has got a cold at the moment, so perhaps she will give it to us.

We have been collecting chestnuts every day for nearly a fortnight now. It is a very backbreaking work, but quite fun. We also get acorns. We pick damsons[3] for a jam factory, and we climb ladders to pick the fruit. There is so much that the branches are breaking.

Hoping you will be able to come.

Love from
Lilibet

In June 1944 the war took a sudden turn. One hot Sunday the Royal Family was as usual at church in St. George's Hall in Windsor Castle. News came through that the Guards' Chapel in Wellington Barracks, opposite Buckingham Palace, had had a direct hit by a strange new kind of pilotless aircraft. The place had been wrecked and a great many people killed, including the sister of the Queen's Treasurer.

I had not been to church that day. I had gone out to lunch. I returned to the castle to find everything in a state of chaos, the King and Queen anxiously awaiting further news. For the one and only time during the whole war, I saw the Queen really shaken. She seemed broken by the news. No one quite knew what this new weapon of frightfulness was, or what it could do. Appalling stories began to go round.

Various officials and war ministers came in for consultations. Vague threats had hung in the air for some time about a new and horrific weapon, and we could only suppose that this was it.

There had been something human about the old bombers. They were guided by living crews and, anyway, we had all grown accustomed to them. One would cock an ear and listen, and even the little girls would know and say either "Ours" or "Theirs" as the bombers went over. They knew the name of every English aircraft and had models of most of them.

This new abomination came zipping over the sky, making a frightful noise and with its tail on fire. As long as the engine went on running, the thing kept going. But there came an awful moment when the noise stopped, the engine cut out, and then it was a matter of seconds before the thing fell and exploded.[4]

We actually had our first sight of one when we were cooking sausages with the Girl Guides in Windsor Park. The Guide captain and I heard the thing coming and we made everyone lie down. I lay next Margaret and flung myself across her, and we waited and saw the thing go over us. Mercifully it kept on going. It cut out and dropped on the Windsor Race Course several

---

[1] **five pounds:** a little over $20 in 1941.

[2] **Monty:** Mrs. Montaudon-Smith, who taught French to the girls.

[3] **damsons** (dăm′zŭnz): A **damson** is a kind of plum.

[4] **This new abomination . . . exploded:** This refers to rocket bombs developed for use by the Germans at this stage of the war. They were known as V–1's and V–2's.

miles ahead, but we were all shaken by the explosion.

At this time I noticed the little girls showed signs of strain. Conversation would break off and I would know they were listening. Though there was admittedly something oddly fiendish about these things — they were so utterly inhuman — it was not long before we got used even to this. Our daily routine was in no way affected, except that we would, from time to time, take refuge under the table and retire into corners away from glass windows. But this, to the children, very soon became another kind of game.

Lilibet, in common with her parents and Mr. Churchill,[1] always wanted to watch an air raid. She wanted to look. "*Do* let me see what is happening," she would beg, her eyes very large. I often had to shout at her to come away from windows.

We carried on our Guiding all through the war, and had our headquarters at the mausoleum.[2] There is a tree sanctuary in the grounds of Windsor Castle, which was built by Queen Victoria in memory of the Prince Consort. Queen Victoria's summerhouse is close by, and we made use of that, also, for our Guide camp. When we were camping out, I slept in the summerhouse. I never cared much for sleeping under canvas, nor did Lilibet. She was immensely tactful about this, and never actually refused, but there always seemed to be some very good reason why she should not do so.

Sleeping out came to an end with the arrival of the doodlebugs, or buzz

bombs. The Queen felt it was too dangerous to have the responsibility of other people's children there at night. So the camp became a daytime institution only, and everyone came over early in the morning, but went to her own home at night. We had some deep slit trenches made near our camping ground, close to the mausoleum, and an air raid man was told to keep in touch with the wardens up at the castle, so that we would get plenty of warning if anything happened to be coming along our way. The warning they had arranged was a loud tooting on a car that was kept near the listening post. As soon as we heard it, we dropped whatever we were doing and bundled into the trench. It always seemed to happen at lunch time, when we were very hungry and the lunch smelled extra good. There we would have to crouch in our deep trench, watching the soup and other things gradually cool off in the distance.

I have often thought it was about this time that it began to dawn on Lilibet what her future might be, and that it was unlikely she would lead the carefree life of an ordinary English girl. She rarely spoke of what was uppermost in her mind and, like the rest of the Royal Family, said least of what she felt most deeply. But we had a talk together on the morning of her confirmation day. Eluding the boisterous Margaret for once, we went off together. When we were on our way home again, she slipped a small hand into mine for a moment.

"I'll have to try to be good, won't I, Crawfie?" she said, and I knew she wasn't thinking then of the ordinary schoolroom tasks and her home life.

One day Philip appeared on the scene. It was quite a time since we had

---

[1] **Mr. Churchill:** Sir Winston Churchill, then Prime Minister, who later was knighted by Elizabeth in 1953.

[2] **mausoleum** (mô'sô·lē'ŭm): a building housing a tomb, in this case the tombs of Victoria and her husband, Prince Albert.

seen him.[1] We were all involved in one of the pantomimes,[2] very excited just before our first performance, when Lilibet came to me looking rather pink. "Who *do* you think is coming to see us act, Crawfie? Philip."

He had been in the navy for some time, and I wondered what he would be like now that he was grown-up. He was, I knew, to sit in the front row, and I took a moment off to have a look at him. He was greatly changed. It was a grave and charming young man who sat there, with nothing of the rather bumptious boy I had first known. He looked more than ever, I thought, like a Viking, weather-beaten and strained, and his manners left nothing to be desired.

Lilibet registered, when she was sixteen, along with other girls of her own age group, at the Labor Exchange in Windsor.

From that moment she agitated to be allowed to join one of the women's services. "I ought to do as other girls of my age do," she said firmly. Many of her friends had already gone. Her cousin, Lady Mary Cambridge, was a VAD (Voluntary Aid Detachment), working not in some hospital for officers where her presence would have been more than welcomed, but in the poorest parts of blitzed London, where she did a wonderful job.

There was little doubt now that Lilibet was England's future Queen. No one ever spoke of this. But I think perhaps it was in the King's mind, more than anyone knew, and that it was because of this he was at first very reluc-tant to allow her to join up and face what could not help being a certain amount of danger and hazard. Finally he gave way. After some discussion with his advisers, it was decided the Princess would be allowed to join the Auxiliary Territorial Service as a subaltern.[3] So Commandant Wellesley arrived one morning, very brisk and hearty, and took Lilibet in hand. At the depot [4] a car jacked up, its wheels off, awaited her. In the following weeks she was put through the whole business of taking an engine to bits and putting it together again.

There was great excitement when her uniform came. She was very proud of it, and I think the King in his own heart was very proud of his daughter for having taken this stand. Margaret was much too young to join up, and as usual she was very cross at seeing Lilibet do something without her. But when she saw how very unbecoming khaki was, I think it made her feel much better.

Lilibet passed all her driving tests, and there came the triumphant autumn day when she drove all through the heavy wartime traffic of London, up the Great West Road, along Piccadilly and down the Mall in the blackout, into Buckingham Palace, to show her parents her achievement. The beaming policeman threw the gates open for her.

None of us ever owned how anxious were some of our moments when the sirens went off and we knew she was out, and awaited her return.

The experience taught her a great deal besides the driving and oiling of motorcars. From her days in the mess,[5]

---

[1] The Princesses had last seen Philip when he was a Royal Naval College student.

[2] **pantomimes:** musical plays, usually based on fairy tales, which are a traditional part of British theater. The Princesses produced private pantomimes to raise money for wartime causes.

[3] **subaltern** (sŭb·ôl′tern): an officer below the rank of captain.

[4] **depot** (U.S., dē′pō; in England, dĕp′ō): a supply center.

[5] **mess:** a group of people who eat together; most often used as a military term.

she caught a glimpse she would probably never have had of another side of
life.

One day she said to me, "Crawfie,
Aunt Mary is coming down on an in-
spection, and you've no idea what a
business it has been. Everyone working
so hard — spit and polish the whole day
long. Now I realize what must happen
when Papa and Mummie go anywhere.
That's something I shall never forget."

At that time I remember being afraid
that, surrounded as she had been by so
much that was tragic and depressing in
the most impressionable years of her
life, she would lose her brightness and
that love of fun all young people ought
to have.

And then, like the sudden blowing
away of a storm, the atmosphere lightened. It was as if quite suddenly the
sun had come out again after years of
gloom. Victory was in the air. We began to wait for the daily papers with
new hope and excitement. Things were
happening. Everyone rushed to his
room for the one o'clock news. Rocket
bombs falling in Windsor Park had
brought the war right to our doorstep
— and then, suddenly, it was all over.

The war actually ended on May
eighth. The palace was hemmed in by a
surging mob of excited people calling
for Their Majesties. There were the
usual balcony appearances, this time
joined by Mr. Churchill. At first he
stood back modestly, but the King and
Queen drew him forward, and he stood
there, beaming, while the crowds yelled
their approval.

No one not in England at that time
can realize the almost hysterical relief
that came with the lessening of the awful tension we had come through. No
more lying awake at night listening. No
more waking up to the early morning

Elizabeth in World War II.

sound of the sweeping up of broken
glass.

Now, at long last, the family could
take a real holiday, could sit back and
relax and for a short time let the world
go by without them. I rejoined them at
Balmoral [1] toward the end of September. There was an entirely new atmosphere in the castle. The King and
Queen were both like their old selves
again. They looked rested and years
younger, and the King had found great
amusement in having Lilibet taken out
deer stalking.

As usual the clothes question was
acute. There were no coupons to spare
for sporting garments, and in the end
Lilibet wore the plus-four trousers of
one of her father's suits.

Prince Philip was abroad. We did not
see him again that summer, but I knew
that Lilibet wrote to him and he to her,
and her parents were also aware of it,
and nothing was said. Then one day I
suddenly became aware that she had
his picture on her mantelpiece.

"Is that altogether wise? Your dress
fitters from Hartnell come and go," I
pointed out. "You know what that will

[1] **Balmoral** (băl·mŏr′ăl): a castle in Scotland, the summer home of the Royal Family.

lead to. People will begin all sorts of gossip about you."

She looked at the photograph for a moment thoughtfully. "Oh, dear, I suppose they will," she said, and she laughed rather ruefully.

The next time I went into her room the picture had disappeared. In its place there was another one. It was still of Philip, but this time completely ambushed behind the enormous fair beard he had managed to raise while he was at sea during the war.

"There you are, Crawfie. I defy anyone to recognize who that is," said Lilibet. "He's completely incognito in that one."

The disguise was a good one, but it was not good enough. Those oddly piercing, intent blue eyes were much too individual. In the end, what I had expected took place. The first early rumors began to get around outside the palace, the whispers and the stories began. Presently one paper came right out into the open and announced it was Prince Philip of Greece [1] whose photograph the Princess kept in her room.

Lilibet now attended Council meetings, went about with her mother, did more and more visiting and going about by herself, and discussed state affairs most days with her father. By now the important part she would one day have to play in the world was officially recognized. This became obvious when she got her own flag with her special coat of arms, her secretary, and her lady in waiting.

Mr. Churchill, his hands full enough already, often found opportunity when at the palace to discuss the general situation at length with this young girl. The advice and counsel he gave Lilibet

[1] Philip was the son of Alice Mountbatten, an English noblewoman, and Prince Andrew of Greece.

then from his vast wisdom and experience must have been of inestimable value to her.

One day Lilibet came to my room, her eyes very bright.

"Crawfie! Someone is coming tonight!" she said half shyly.

Prince Philip was back from abroad.

Lilibet, Margaret, and Philip had dinner together in Lilibet's sitting room. It is difficult, looking back on it, to remember the sequence of events. I noticed, suddenly, that Lilibet began to take more trouble with her appearance, that it seemed to matter more to her what she wore at an evening party. Then I would find that Philip had been there!

And I noticed that suddenly she began to play her phonograph more than usual, and that her favorite tune of the moment was "People Will Say We're in Love" from the musical show Oklahoma! They had been to that show together, and Lilibet would often ask the band at the various restaurants where they dined and danced to play this tune for her. She and Philip rarely danced together. They had to be so discreet. But one can picture the glances they exchanged as they passed on the dance floor, each with another partner.

Everyone in the household was by now aware of what was in the air. One could not see the young people together without realizing what they felt for each other. But what her father and mother, the King and Queen, thought about it we had not the slightest idea.

Now the newspapers began to speculate about the royal romance, and wherever they went, a thousand eyes watched them. It must have been torture to both of the young people. One day Lilibet came back rather excited from visiting a factory. I hurried to her room to see what was wrong.

"Crawfie, it was horrible," she said "They shouted at me, 'Where's Philip?'"

It was a coarse piece of thoughtlessness on the part of those who apparently had never paused to consider the feelings of a very young girl, sensitive and in love, but not as yet engaged. It spoiled for them both days that should have been carefree and happy. She began to dread the trips to factories and shops, deeply conscious now of the ever-watchful eye that so soon became the overvocal voice.

When it was known that Prince Philip was going to Balmoral that autumn, public excitement and speculation brimmed over. The papers carried whole columns of "inside information" and entirely unfounded stories. It must have been trying indeed for these two young people, between whom there had as yet been neither proposal nor acceptance.

The generally accepted idea was that this was for Prince Philip a trial trip. The King and Queen were commonly supposed to have invited Philip up to see whether he would be acceptable as a son-in-law, but this was mere surmise.

The silliness of all this is apparent when it is realized that they had both known him from his boyhood, and had seen a great deal of him just previous to this in London. He was asked up because he was a young man they all liked, who would make an amusing addition to the party. Perhaps also to give Lilibet a good long spell of his company, to see how she liked him in large doses. Perhaps to give older members of the household an opportunity of getting to know him against the family background.

Nothing of that sort was said. But Lilibet was well aware that there were two schools of thought. Some of the King's advisers did not think him good

enough for her. He was a prince without home or kingdom. Some of the papers played long and loud tunes on the string of Philip's foreign origin. There must have been for Lilibet in those autumn days, that should have been such happy ones for her, plenty of doubts, plenty of embarrassments, uncertainties, and heartaches. Her own mind never wavered for an instant. It was solidly made up.

It is good fun to be a princess in a palace. But not always. Not all the time.

One day that look of strain we had all been conscious of disappeared from Lilibet's eyes. She poked her head into my room looking absolutely radiant.

"Crawfie," she said, "something is going to happen at last!"

"It's about time," was all I could say, and there was a big lump in my throat.

"He's coming tonight," she said, and then she kissed me and danced away.

Next morning was Wednesday, July 9, 1947. Lilibet came to my room much earlier than usual. I have never seen her look lovelier than she did on that day, not even on her wedding morning. She wore a deep yellow frock, a shade that has always suited her very well. She closed the door behind her and held out her left hand.

Her engagement ring sparkled there. It was a large square diamond with smaller diamonds on either side. At that time it was too large for her, and it had to go back to be made smaller. It was a ring they had chosen together secretly, but of course she had been unable to go to try it on.

That was a happy day for all of us. The morning papers announced in a Court Circular that the King had been graciously pleased to give his assent to the betrothal of his beloved daughter to Lieutenant Philip Mountbatten. Philip's naturalization papers had come through, and he had dropped his title of Prince. He was a junior officer now in the British Royal Navy, and had taken the family name of his uncle, Lord Louis Mountbatten, who had been his guardian most of his life and had given him the only home he had ever known.

The romance did something wonderful to the palace. All of a sudden the gloomy corridors seemed lighter. Everyone was immensely excited and pleased, for the tall, rather unconventional young man who had been around for some time had made many friends for himself. He appeared presently, looking very handsome and happy. I congratulated him and said how very glad I was that everything had come right for them at last.

He looked at me and smiled. "I'm so proud of her, Crawfie."

"Sir, you have good reason to be. And who should know that better than I?" I replied.

THINKING IT OVER

1. Give at least five examples of the hardships the war brought to the two Princesses. What in your opinion was the most difficult hardship they had to endure?

2. "It does not help anything or anyone if we sit in the corners and cry." What do you think of this as a philosophy for a time of crisis?

3. The selection provides a good description of how the relationship between Elizabeth and Philip developed and progressed. List the stages of the relationship, beginning with "childhood meeting." What was the next stage? What event seemed to be the most important in terms of a possible marriage between the young people?

DRAWING CONCLUSIONS

1. What did the statement "The King and Queen remained at Buckingham Palace all through the London blitz" make

you conclude about Elizabeth's father and mother?

2. The author describes several activities the Princesses undertook to aid various patriotic causes. What conclusion about the two girls might be made from this?

3. What did you conclude about Elizabeth from her determination to join one of the women's wartime services? What facts about Margaret may have led you to conclude that she was different in personality? How was she different?

4. Based on the author's descriptions, what are your final conclusions about the life of royalty?

ABOUT THE AUTHOR

Marion Crawford (1909–) writes in the book from which this selection is taken, "I had always wanted to teach, but I had certainly never intended to become a governess." Nevertheless, fate brought this Scottish girl, who had hoped someday to specialize in child psychology, into the household of the Duke and Duchess of York, who were later to become King George VI and Queen Elizabeth. Their daughters were then five and one, respectively, and Miss Crawford supervised most phases of their education from 1930 to 1947, when she finally left the Royal Family to be married. *The Little Princesses* is the title of Marion Crawford's book about her royal charges.

The World of Elizabeth II ➤

On the opposite page are shown three stages in the life of Queen Elizabeth II: *upper left:* Elizabeth and Margaret in the gardens of Buckingham Palace; *portrait, upper right:* the young, newly crowned Queen in her coronation robes; *bottom photograph:* Elizabeth, Prince Philip, and their children at Balmoral. To continue the story suggested by these illustrations, do some research and try to uncover these facts about Elizabeth's adult life: the circumstances which led to her ascension to the throne; the date and place of her coronation; Prince Philip's other title; and the names of their three children.

A Pilot's Needs

MARK TWAIN

In this autobiographical selection, one of the greatest and best-loved of American writers, Mark Twain, gives his own account of a period in his youth. When Mark Twain was a boy living on the Mississippi, the steamboat era was at its height. Looking back on those adventurous days, he recalls the skills and feats of the pilots and tells of the lesson these men taught a young apprentice pilot — himself. You will enjoy the colorful comparisons he makes to illustrate a point and the anecdotes he tells of this difficult but glamorous way of life that has vanished from our land.

THERE is one faculty which a pilot must incessantly cultivate until he has brought it to absolute perfection. Nothing short of perfection will do. That faculty is memory. He cannot stop with merely thinking a thing is so and so; he must know it; for this is eminently one of the "exact" sciences. With what scorn a pilot was looked upon, in the old times, if he ever ventured to deal in that feeble phrase "I think" instead of the vigorous one "I know!"

One cannot easily realize what a tremendous thing it is to know every trivial detail of twelve hundred miles of river, and know it with absolute exactness. If you will take the longest street in New York and travel up and down it, conning [1] its features patiently until you know every house and window and lamppost and big and little sign by heart, and know them so accurately that you can instantly name the one you are abreast of when you are set down at random in that street in the middle of an inky-black night, you will then have a tolerable notion of the amount and the exactness of a pilot's knowledge who carries the Mississippi River in his head. And then, if you will go on until you know every street crossing, the character, size, and position of the crossing stones, and the varying depth of mud in each of these numberless places, you will have some idea of what the pilot must know in order to keep a Mississippi steamer out of trouble. Next, if you will take half of the signs in that long street and change their places once a month, and still manage to know their new positions

---

[1] **conning:** studying.

"A Pilot's Needs" from *Life on the Mississippi* by Mark Twain, reprinted by permission of Harper & Brothers.

accurately on dark nights, and keep up with those repeated changes without making any mistakes, you will understand what is required of a pilot's peerless memory by the fickle Mississippi.

I think a pilot's memory is about the most wonderful thing in the world. To know the Old and New Testaments by heart and be able to recite them glibly, forward and backward, or begin at random anywhere in the book and recite both ways and never trip or make a mistake, is no extravagant mass of knowledge, and no marvelous facility, compared to a pilot's massed knowledge of the Mississippi and his marvelous facility in the handling of it. I make this comparison deliberately, and believe I am not expanding the truth when I do it. Many will think my figure [1] too strong, but pilots will not.

And how easily and comfortably the pilot's memory does its work; how placidly effortless is its way; how unconsciously it lays up its vast stores, hour by hour, day by day, and never loses or mislays a single valuable package of them all!

Take an instance. Let a leadsman [2] cry "Half twain! [3] half twain! half twain! half twain! half twain! " until it becomes as monotonous as the ticking of a clock; let conversation be going on all the time, and the pilot be doing his share of the talking, and no longer consciously listening to the leadsman; and in the midst of this endless string of half twains let a single "quarter twain!" be interjected, without emphasis, and then the half twain cry go on again, just as before; two or three weeks later that pilot can describe with precision the boat's position in the river when that quarter twain was uttered, and give you such a lot of head-marks, stern-marks, and side-marks to guide you, that you ought to be able to take the boat there and put her in that same spot again yourself! The cry of "quarter twain" did not really take his mind from his talk, but his trained faculties instantly photographed the bearings, noted the change of depth, and laid up the important details for future reference without requiring any assistance from him in the matter. If you were walking and talking with a friend, and another friend at your side kept up a monotonous repetition of the vowel sound A for a couple of blocks, and then in the midst interjected an R, thus, A, A, A, A, A, R, A, A, A, etc., and gave the R no emphasis, you would not be able to state, two or three weeks afterward, that the R had been put in, nor be able to tell what objects you were passing at the moment it was done. But you could if your memory had been patiently and laboriously trained to do that sort of thing mechanically.

Give a man a tolerably fair memory to start with, and piloting will develop it into a very colossus [4] of capability. But only in the matters it is daily drilled in. A time would come when the man's faculties could not help noticing landmarks and soundings, and his memory could not help holding on to them with the grip of a vise; but if you asked that same man at noon what he had had for breakfast, it would be ten chances to one that he could not tell you. Astonishing things can be done with the human memory if you will devote it faithfully

---

[1] **figure:** the comparison between knowing the Bible and knowing the Mississippi.

[2] **leadsman** (lĕdz'măn): the man who measures the depth of the water.

[3] **half twain:** a water depth of one fathom, or six feet. Water depth is measured in fathoms. Two fathoms equal a twain, and the pilot's frequent cry of "mark twain" to the leadsman — "measure the depth" — gave Samuel Clemens the idea for his pen name.

[4] **colossus** (kô·lŏs'ŭs): anything huge.

to one particular line of business.

At the time that wages soared so high on the Missouri River, my chief, Mr. Bixby, went up there and learned more than a thousand miles of that stream with an ease and rapidity that were astonishing. When he had seen each division once in the daytime and once at night, his education was so nearly complete that he took out a "daylight" license; a few trips later he took out a full license, and went to piloting day and night — and he ranked A–1, too.

Mr. Bixby placed me as steersman for a while under a pilot whose feats of memory were a constant marvel to me. However, his memory was born in him, I think, not built. For instance, somebody would mention a name. Instantly Mr. Brown would break in:

"Oh, I knew him. Sallow-faced, red-headed fellow, with a little scar on the side of his throat, like a splinter under the flesh. He was only in the Southern trade six months. That was thirteen years ago. I made a trip with him. There was five feet in the upper river then; the *Henry Blake* grounded at the foot of Tower Island drawing four and a half; the *George Elliot* unshipped her rudder on the wreck of the *Sunflower* — "

"Why, the *Sunflower* didn't sink until — "

"I know when she sunk; it was three years before that, on the 2d of December; Asa Hardy was captain of her, and his brother John was first clerk; and it was his first trip in her, too; Tom Jones told me these things a week afterward in New Orleans; he was first mate of the *Sunflower*. Captain Hardy stuck a nail in his foot the 6th of July of the next year, and died of the lockjaw on the 15th. His brother John died two years after — 3d of March — erysipelas.[1] I

never saw either of the Hardys — they were Allegheny River men — but people who knew them told me all these things. And they said Captain Hardy wore yarn socks winter and summer just the same, and his first wife's name was Jane Shook — she was from New England — and his second one died in a lunatic asylum. It was in the blood. She was from Lexington, Kentucky. Name was Horton before she was married."

And so on, by the hour, the man's tongue would go. He could not forget anything. It was simply impossible. The most trivial details remained as distinct and luminous in his head, after they had lain there for years, as the most memorable events. His was not simply a pilot's memory; its grasp was universal. If he were talking about a trifling letter he had received seven years before, he was pretty sure to deliver you the entire screed[2] from memory. And then, without observing that he was departing from the true line of his talk, he was more than likely to hurl in a long-drawn parenthetical[3] biography of the writer of that letter; and you were lucky indeed if he did not take up that writer's relatives, one by one, and give you their biographies, too.

Such a memory as that is a great misfortune. To it, all occurrences are of the same size. Its possessor cannot distinguish an interesting circumstance from an uninteresting one. As a talker, he is bound to clog his narrative with tiresome details and make himself an insufferable bore. Moreover, he cannot stick to his subject. He picks up every little grain of memory he discerns in his way, and so is led aside. Mr. Brown would

[1] **erysipelas** (ĕr'ĭ·sĭp'ĕ·lăs): a skin disease.

[2] **screed** (skrēd): a long discourse — in this case, the letter's contents.
[3] **parenthetical** (păr'ĕn·thĕt'ĭ·kăl): set off, as if by parentheses, from the main topic.

start out with the honest intention of telling you a vastly funny anecdote about a dog. He would be "so full of laugh" that he could hardly begin; then his memory would start with the dog's breed and personal appearance; drift into a history of his owner; of his owner's family, with descriptions of weddings and burials that had occurred in it, together with recitals of congratulatory verses and obituary poetry provoked by the same; then his memory would recollect that one of these events occurred during the celebrated "hard winter" of such-and-such a year, and a minute description of that winter would follow, along with the names of people who were frozen to death, and statistics showing the high figures which pork and hay went up to. Pork and hay would suggest corn and fodder; corn and fodder would suggest cows and horses; cows and horses would suggest the circus and certain celebrated bareback riders; the transition from the circus to the menagerie was easy and natural; from the elephant to equatorial Africa was but a step; then of course the heathen savages would suggest religion; and at the end of three or four hours' tedious jaw, the watch would change, and Brown would go out of the pilothouse muttering extracts from sermons he had heard years before about the efficacy [1] of prayer as a means of grace. And the original first mention would be all you had learned about that dog, after all this waiting and hungering.

A pilot must have a memory; but there are two higher qualities which he must also have. He must have good and quick judgment and decision, and a cool, calm courage that no peril can shake. Give a man the merest trifle of pluck to start with, and by the time he has become a pilot, he cannot be unmanned by any danger a steamboat can get into; but one cannot quite say the same for judgment. Judgment is a matter of brains, and a man must start with a good stock of that article or he will never succeed as a pilot.

The growth of courage in the pilothouse is steady all the time, but it does not reach a high and satisfactory condition until some time after the young pilot has been "standing his own watch" alone and under the staggering weight of all the responsibilities connected with the position. When the apprentice has become pretty thoroughly acquainted with the river, he goes clattering along so fearlessly with his steamboat, night or day, that he presently begins to imagine that it is his courage that animates him; but the first time the pilot steps out and leaves him to his own devices, he finds out it was the other man's. He discovers that the article has been left out of his own cargo altogether. The whole river is bristling with exigencies [2] in a moment; he is not prepared for them; he does not know how to meet them; all his knowledge forsakes him; and within fifteen minutes he is as white as a sheet and scared almost to death. Therefore pilots wisely train these cubs by various strategic tricks to look danger in the face a little more calmly. A favorite way of theirs is to play a friendly swindle upon the candidate.

Mr. Bixby served me in this fashion once, and for years afterward I used to blush, even in my sleep, when I thought of it. I had become a good steersman; so good, indeed, that I had all the work to do on our watch, night and day. Mr. Bixby seldom made a suggestion to me; all he ever did was to take the wheel on particularly bad

---

[1] **efficacy** (ĕf'ĭ·kȧ·sĭ): the power to produce effects.

[2] **exigencies** (ĕk'sĭ·jĕn·sĭz): emergencies.

*This drawing of a pilothouse is from the
original edition of* Life on the Mississippi.

nights or in particularly bad crossings,
land the boat when she needed to be
landed, play gentleman of leisure nine
tenths of the watch, and collect the
wages. The lower river was about bank-
full, and if anybody had questioned my
ability to run any crossing between
Cairo and New Orleans without help
or instruction, I should have felt ir-
reparably hurt. The idea of being afraid
of any crossing in the lot, in the daytime, was a thing too preposterous for
contemplation. Well, one matchless
summer's day I was bowling down the
bend above Island 66, brimful of self-
conceit and carrying my nose as high
as a giraffe's, when Mr. Bixby said:

"I am going below awhile. I suppose
you know the next crossing?"

This was almost an affront. It was
about the plainest and simplest crossing
in the whole river. One couldn't come
to any harm, whether he ran it right
or not; and as for depth, there never
had been any bottom there. I knew all
this perfectly well.

"Know how to run it? Why, I can
run it with my eyes shut."

"How much water is there in it?"

"Well, that is an odd question. I
couldn't get bottom there with a church
steeple."

"You think so, do you?"

The very tone of the question shook
my confidence. That was what Mr. Bixby was expecting. He left without saying anything more. I began to imagine
all sorts of things. Mr. Bixby, unknown
to me, of course, sent somebody down
to the forecastle with some mysterious
instructions to the leadsmen, another
messenger was sent to whisper among
the officers, and then Mr. Bixby went
into hiding behind a smokestack where
he could observe results. Presently the
captain stepped out on the hurricane
deck; next the chief mate appeared;
then a clerk. Every moment or two a
straggler was added to my audience;
and before I got to the head of the
island I had fifteen or twenty people assembled down there under my nose. I
began to wonder what the trouble was.
As I started across, the captain glanced
aloft at me and said, with a sham uneasiness in his voice:

"Where is Mr. Bixby?"

"Gone below, sir."

But that did the business for me. My
imagination began to construct dangers
out of nothing, and they multiplied faster than I could keep the run of them.
All at once I imagined I saw shoal
water ahead! The wave of coward
agony that surged through me then
came near dislocating every joint in me.
All my confidence in that crossing vanished. I seized the bell rope; dropped
it, ashamed; seized again; dropped it
once more; clutched it tremblingly once
again, and pulled it so feebly that I
could hardly hear the stroke myself.
Captain and mate sang out instantly

and both together:

"Starboard lead there! And quick about it!"

This was another shock. I began to climb the wheel like a squirrel; but I would hardly get the boat started to port before I would see new dangers on that side, and away I would spin to the other; only to find perils accumulating to starboard, and be crazy to get to port again. Then came the leadsman's sepulchral[1] cry:

"D-e-e-p four!"

Deep four in a bottomless crossing! The terror of it took my breath away.

"M-a-r-k three! M-a-r-k three! Quarter-less-three! Half twain!"

This was frightful! I seized the bell ropes and stopped the engines.

"Quarter twain! Quarter twain! Mark twain!"

I was helpless. I did not know what in the world to do. I was quaking from head to foot, and I could have hung my hat on my eyes, they stuck out so far.

"Quarter - less - twain! Nine - and - a - half!"

We were drawing nine! My hands were in a nerveless flutter. I could not ring a bell intelligibly with them. I flew to the speaking tube and shouted to the engineer:

"Oh, Ben, if you love me, back her! Quick, Ben! Oh, back the immortal soul out of her!"

I heard the door close gently. I looked around, and there stood Mr. Bixby, smiling a bland, sweet smile. Then the audience on the hurricane deck sent up a thunder-gust of humiliating laughter. I saw it all now, and I felt meaner than the meanest man in human history. I laid in the lead, set the boat in her marks, came ahead on the engines, and said:

¹ sepulchral (sê·pŭl′krăl): funereal.

"It was a fine trick to play on an orphan, wasn't it? I suppose I'll never hear the last of how I was fool enough to heave the lead at the head of 66."

"Well, no, you won't, maybe. In fact I hope you won't; for I want you to learn something by that experience. Didn't you know there was no bottom in that crossing?"

"Yes, sir, I did."

"Very well, then. You shouldn't have allowed me or anybody else to shake your confidence in that knowledge. Try to remember that. And another thing: when you get into a dangerous place, don't turn coward. That isn't going to help matters any."

It was a good enough lesson, but pretty hardly learned. Yet about the hardest part of it was that for months I so often had to hear a phrase which I had conceived a particular distaste for. It was, "Oh, Ben, if you love me, back her!"

THINKING IT OVER

1. Mark Twain compares a pilot's knowledge of a river to memorizing every detail of a city street. What two factors does he say would be necessary to make the comparison really accurate?

2. How did Mr. Brown's memory differ from the kind of memory most needed by a pilot? What is Twain's opinion of the two kinds of memory?

3. Mr. Bixby was a real, not a fictitious person. Just to be exact: How long a stretch of the Missouri River did he learn, and how quickly did he learn it?

4. The river pilot no longer has to practice the skills described by Twain. What do you suppose accounts for this? What modern technical advances are now of help to pilots?

5. While memory was vital to a river pilot, Twain says that there are two higher qualities. What are they? How was he taught a lesson that involved both these qualities?

6. Mr. Bixby's final advice to a pilot in time of danger is important. What is it? How might this advice be useful to others? Give some examples.

7. In describing how Mr. Brown's memory affected the simplest joke he told, Twain piles up the unnecessary details until they become very funny. Can you find other examples in the selection which show some techniques he uses to create humor?

CONTINUING THE STORY

1. To learn more about river pilots and steamboats, you might want to read *Life on the Mississippi*, the book by Mark Twain from which this selection is taken.

2. The rest of Twain's life was just as interesting and varied as this early period. In addition to winning fame as an author, he became a popular lecturer. To continue the story of his life for yourself, do some research at the library and answer these questions about him: (a) What other early jobs did he have? (b) As a lecturer, what sort of program did he present to audiences? (c) What President did he help, and how?

PEN AND PAPER

1. In less than one page, write a composition titled either "The Value of Judgment" or "The Value of Courage." Tell your ideas on the subject or relate an incident that illustrates it.

2. Or, to test your own capacity to memorize, you might like to write a one-page composition in which you describe, without looking it over beforehand, a room in your house. List as many objects, colors, and details about the room as your memory can summon for you.

ABOUT THE AUTHOR

Mark Twain (1835–1910), whose real name was Samuel Langhorne Clemens, stands in the front rank of American authors. His novels of boyhood, *The Adventures of Tom Sawyer* and *The Adventures of Huckleberry Finn,* are known around the world, and are considered by many to be among the best stories of youth written in any language. Twain was a born traveler and observer, as this selection certainly indicates. From his beginnings in Hannibal, Missouri, he traveled out West, where his talents as a humorist were first recognized. He went on to tour the entire world, writing about much of what he saw and experienced. He made a fortune from his work and lost it through unwise business ventures. Bankrupt and in debt, he paid off his obligations by more lecturing and writing. At the time of his death he was probably the most famous American author in the world. His writing ranges from the personal reminiscences of *Life on the Mississippi* and the later *Roughing It* to the historical romance of *The Prince and the Pauper*. He wrote many humorous essays and sketches and travel journals, the best-known of which is *Innocents Abroad*.

The Great Days ➤

The painting on the facing page – the work of Hippolite Sebron, an American artist of the nineteenth century – depicts a scene typical of the great days of the Mississippi steamboat. The setting is a busy port on the river. Along the rough-planked wharves a cluster of steamboats — all side-wheelers — lie at anchor. From the landing deck of the boat in the foreground, workers are unloading bales of cotton. A few passengers stroll on the deck above; this was the main deck, reserved for passengers' cabins and lounge rooms. On the hurricane deck, farther above, can be seen the structure which contained quarters for the captain and officers. Atop this, occupying the highest point on the boat, is the pilothouse. Proud and majestic, its tall stacks curling smoke into the sky, the Mississippi steamboat was a romantic sight to behold. Even today the once familiar cry of "Steamboat round the bend!" summons for many Americans images of high adventure and excitement.

Girl with a Dream: Katharine Cornell

LATROBE CARROLL

The course steered by an aspiring young actor or actress is far different from that of a river pilot's, but it has equal problems. And if most stage careers begin with a dream, it takes something more to turn them into reality. This biographical article describes the beginning and the rise of one of this country's foremost actresses. You will learn why Katharine Cornell became interested in the theater, what influences helped her, what difficulties and disappointments she overcame, how much work is involved in the struggle for perfection, and what advice she has for young people with dreams like hers.

L ONG AGO, in a theater now dismantled, a little girl of eight stood in a box hiding her face in the thick, tasseled draperies at the rear. Below, on the stage, the curtain had slid up. Maude Adams' clear voice was filling the house.

She was playing her famous role of Peter Pan.

The child in the box — little Katharine Cornell — had pulled the draperies over her eyes, not because she took no interest, but because her interest was so intense that it was almost agony. For weeks she had looked forward to seeing *Peter Pan*. It had seemed as though the long-dreamed-of afternoon would never come. But when the curtain went up, nervous dread seized her — a dread that the play might fail to live up to her dreams.

Her mother gently loosened the grip of small fingers on the draperies. She coaxed little "Kit" to the front of the box, persuaded her to sit down. From that time until the end of the first act, Kit lived enchantment. As the shining minutes passed, a decision took form

Relating Details to the Main Idea. The main idea of this selection, as you will see, is to describe how one individual won success in the theater. To accomplish his purpose, the author gives many details that show Katharine Cornell's character and what she did to gain stardom. Pay attention to these details and "add them up," as it were; together, they explain the story of her success.

in her mind. She was going to be an actress.

Not long ago, that same little girl — a woman now, whom many consider the foremost actress of our stage — talked to me about those childhood days. "Seeing Maude Adams," she said, "was a turning point for me, though I can't remember a time when I wasn't interested in the theater. We were, in a way, a theater family. My grandfather, Douglas Cornell, was so disappointed that more professional plays didn't come to Buffalo, our home city, that he built a stage in his house, on the top floor, and used to invite friends — gifted amateur actors — to give performances. He himself was a talented actor. Some of my earliest memories are of the time when I sat and watched plays in his home.

"My father, too — Dr. Peter Cornell — was an excellent amateur actor. But though the theater pulled him strongly, he studied medicine, became a doctor. Doctoring held him for about eight years, then the tug of the stage grew too strong. He wanted to go into professional show business. Grandfather was sympathetic. He bought the Star Theater — that was where I saw *Peter Pan* — and put Father in as manager.

"So the stage was in my blood and bones. Long before Maude Adams captivated me, I used to take part in pantomimes, used to divide my interest in nearly equal portions between white mice, rabbits, roller skating, and the putting on, with my little friends, of plays we made up ourselves. If the hero had the best part, I wanted to be the hero. If the villain's role was the ripest and juiciest, that was the role for me. Nobody else got a look-in.

"After the closing of *Peter Pan* at the Star Theater, I went with the family, as usual, to our summer home in Cobourg,

Ontario. Even there, Father and his friends put on plays. And I gathered my little Cobourg friends around me, and we, too, went in for play producing. It was there that I got my first press notice in the first — and last — issue of *The Cobourg Sun*, a four-page publishing venture printed in pencil on copybook paper. It was a good notice, prominently displayed — and why not? As the chief feature writer I had written it myself, and as editor I had accepted it and given it an emphatic position. It had a headline, 'Acting Is Hard,' and under that caption it said: 'Katharine Cornell and Joe Pierce wrote an A-1 play called *The Hidden Treasure*. The editor played the part of the Duke. In the part where Katharine was on the stage and the curtain man was half asleep, she called out, "Curtain, curtain," which made the people laugh. We made over twenty cents on the whole thing.'

"That notice may seem rather cocky, but the nub of the matter is in the caption, 'Acting Is Hard.' The main reason why acting was hard for me — why it's still hard — can be summed up in one word: shyness. Always, before I step onto a stage, I have to conquer a terrible shyness.

"To go back to the days of Cobourg. I loved the place because I could swim and run across fields and poke around barns in disreputable clothes. There's always been a mental split in me — a split on the subject of clothes. Choosing stage costumes, my interest zooms. Choosing off-stage clothes, it nosedives.

"In Cobourg I could be casual about clothes most of the time — a tomboy. But when we went back to Buffalo, Mother would bring out dainty dresses and put them on me, to make me look like 'a little lady' — and that depressed me. The things that interested me were outdoor sports and the stage. Especially the stage. And here I was luckier than most children. While I was growing up, many of the famous actors and actresses of that day played in the new theater — the Majestic — that Father had taken over. I watched Sothern and Marlowe, Sarah Bernhardt, Maxine Elliott, Sir Henry Irving, Minnie Maddern Fiske.

"Then, too, there was Jessie Bonstelle — Bonnie, we called her — who ran a famous stock company which played in Buffalo and in Detroit. Early every summer she used to bring her company to the Majestic. She would let me sit in the wings, hour after hour, day after day, and watch rehearsals. Fascinating! One day she said to me, 'Hurry and grow up and play Jo in *Little Women* for me.' I was startled and thrilled, but I did not believe it would actually come true."

The years passed. Years of school, of outdoor sports at which Katharine did increasingly well. Years of amateur theatricals, of delighted playgoing. And through those years, always the hope that Maude Adams had wakened, always the dream.

When Katharine was fifteen, her parents sent her to the Oaksmere School in Mamaroneck, New York. She liked the life there, for the school put emphasis on her twin interests, sports and amateur theatricals. True, several of the more fashionable girls elevated sniffish noses at her casualness in dress, but she didn't care. She knew she could do well at the things she really loved. By this time she was amateur swimming champion of Buffalo, runner-up at one of Buffalo's city-wide tennis championships. She played golf so well that a certain professional, an instructor, urged her to devote her life to the game. And she could more than hold

her own on the stage in the school auditorium.

At the Oaksmere School, her feeling for perfection — she had had it all her life — grew stronger. That same feeling had made her hide her head, long ago, in the curtains of a box, because she was afraid *Peter Pan* might not be perfect. A golf stroke, a tennis stroke, a line spoken in a play — she wanted each and every one of them to be *right*.

During her last year at the school, one of the drama coaches was the leading director of a little theater group that was putting on its productions at the Comedy Theater.[1] His name was Edward Goodman. After he had coached Katharine in a comedy she herself had written, he said to her casually, "If you're thinking of going into the theater, let me know when you come to New York." Offhand words, but they made her heart leap.

When she went home, early in the summer, she told her parents, "I want to go to New York and go on the stage."

Her father had the skepticism of a manager who had seen many young hopes disappointed. "Don't do it, Kit," he said. But, in late summer, Katharine boarded a train for New York. Outwardly she was composed. Inside she felt hollow, "all gone." At least, though, she would not starve, since she was heir to a small trust fund.

"I took a room at a hotel," she told me, "and went to work at a job — the full-time job of hanging around the Comedy Theater, of camping on Eddie Goodman's doorstep. For weeks Eddie hardly noticed me. One day, though, he gave me a chance to try out for a part. In the theater he handed me a typewritten script, told me to study the

[1] **Comedy Theater:** the first home of the organization that became the Broadway producing firm, the Theatre Guild.

lines, and then get up on the stage and read them. My breath came fast. 'Here,' I told myself, 'is my chance at last.'

"But when, presently, I stood on the stage to read I was full of self-consciousness, of fear. I wanted — wanted tremendously — to render those lines perfectly. But I realized all too well that I couldn't come within miles of perfection. My throat tightened. I couldn't get out a single word. I stood silent for a few awful seconds, then ran off the stage.

"For the next few days I was miserable, but I asked Eddie if I might watch rehearsals. 'I won't bother anybody,' I promised.

"'All right,' he said.

"Day after day I stood in the wings, alert to what was said and done. At last, a girl who had a tiny part — that of a mother in a play called *Bushido* [1] — failed to show up at a rehearsal. Eddie Goodman told me I might step into the role temporarily. It was just four words, to be spoken in anguish, 'My son, my son!'

"I worked like a beaver over those four words, speaking them aloud to the walls and furniture of my little hotel room, varying the emphasis, the intensity, the tone. I played the part for a few days, then the girl I was replacing dropped out entirely. Eddie said to me, 'Okay, the role's yours; go get your costume.' Was I delighted! *Bushido* was just a playlet, the company was only semiprofessional, my part precisely four syllables, but I was walking on air.

"The actors and actresses got little or no pay. I worked all that season, and my earnings were zero. During one of the performances a young man sat watching. His name was Guthrie Mc-

Clintic; he was casting director for Winthrop Ames, the producer, and one of his jobs was scouting for new talent. I didn't know him, had no idea he was there.

"He told me, long afterward, that when the play ended and the lights went up, he scribbled on his program opposite my name, 'Interesting, monotonous, watch.' Just that, to sum me up. Later on I met him at the home of an acquaintance, but we spoke only a few words to each other."

Miss Cornell was with the Washington Square Players for a second season, too — and this time, for her winter's work, she got the princely sum of forty dollars. Toward the end of that season, without her knowledge, her old friend Jessie Bonstelle sat in the audience. She had come at the request of Dr. Cornell, who had asked her to tell him frankly whether or not his daughter had any talent. Miss Bonstelle felt certain he hoped she would declare flatly that Katharine was wasting her time trying to build a stage career.

But Jessie Bonstelle came to a sharply different conclusion. That evening, Bonnie wrote a letter to Dr. Cornell. She listed, with brief descriptions, the actors and actresses she had chosen for her company which was to play in his theater the following summer. She ended with these words, "I have also engaged one young girl of more promise than any I have seen in a long time. Her name is Katharine Cornell."

After Dr. Cornell read that letter, he sent off a question by wire, HAVE YOU GONE CRAZY? Bonnie flashed back a single word — NO — and got an answering telegram within a few hours, WELL FOR HEAVENS SAKE MAKE HER GET SOME CLOTHES.

But though Katharine, keenly pleased by the prospect of working with Bon-

---

[1] *Bushido* (bōō'shē·dō').

nie, was interested in helping to plan the costumes for her first part, she showed no inclination to buy a new off-stage outfit.

During the first weeks with the Bonstelle company, her old, agonizing shyness stood in her way. Coached and led along by Jessie Bonstelle, she learned to do her work in spite of her shyness. As the season progressed, Katharine had all sorts of parts. In one she was a brash, fourteen-year-old boy; in another a deaf, timid old lady; in still another a silly, gushing ingénue.[1] She played chambermaid roles, waitress roles, the role of an Italian matron bubbling with talk. She found Bonnie a woman after her own heart because, like herself, Bonnie was aiming at perfection. Sometimes, in a rehearsal, the older woman would make her repeat a line many times until she put just the right shade of meaning into it.

All this gave Katharine Cornell a firm foundation in stagecraft. She learned to be versatile, to be prompt, to discipline herself, to feel a sense of responsibility to audiences and to her fellow players.

At the end of that first summer season, she went to New York and laid siege to Broadway — climbing stairs, waiting patiently for interviews — and getting nowhere. Winter passed, but brought no job. She went back to the Bonstelle company.

As the group was ending its summer work, William Brady, producer of the successful play *The Man Who Came Back*, asked Miss Bonstelle to organize one of the road companies that were to take the play on tour. Bonnie picked Katharine for the role of Marcelle, a cabaret girl.

When Miss Cornell was walking

[1] **ingénue** (ăn′zhā′nü′): theatrical term for the role of a young girl.

through the lobby of the Brady offices, after settling some business details, a young man — the same Guthrie McClintic who had noted her work several years earlier — was standing there with a friend. When she had gone out, he said to his friend, "It's a strange thing, but I've just seen my future wife. We're practically strangers — but I know we're going to be married."

The Man Who Came Back was Katharine Cornell's biggest part so far. In spite of the hardships of the road, she loved the life.

After the tour ended, she again went back to Jessie Bonstelle. Late that summer Miss Bonstelle organized a company to put on *Little Women* in London. Still holding fast to her original idea, she chose Katharine for the role of Jo. The girl drew praise from London critics.

Allan Pollock, an English actor, saw the play and liked her work. Later, his admiration was to bring her her first New York success.

Jessie Bonstelle had to go back to Buffalo before *Little Women* ended its London run. When, late in the spring, Katharine crossed the Atlantic and arrived in Buffalo, Bonnie met her at the railroad station. The first thing Bonnie said to her was, "I've engaged a young director named McClintic for this summer."

Guthrie McClintic had fallen in love with Katharine without getting to know her. As soon as she got to know him, amid the grind of putting on ten plays a week, she also fell in love. Both put the stage above all else. Both were perfectionists. Early in the fall of 1920, she told him she would marry him, but it was not until September 8, 1921, that they were married.

That September was doubly momentous. Eighteen days after the wedding, a play called *A Bill of Divorcement* opened, with Katharine in the deeply moving young-girl role of Sydney. It had come about through Allan Pollock. The play had done well in London, and he had bought the rights to American production. He remembered Miss Cornell as Jo. He believed she would bring to Sydney the same fresh, honest, hoydenish [1] qualities she had put into Jo. She did not disappoint him; the play swept on to success.

The next ten years were a decade of even harder work for Katharine Cornell. Ten years after *A Bill of Divorcement*, a playbroker [2] brought her a drama which had been turned down by more than twenty managers. Called *The Barretts of Wimpole Street*, it had as its leading character Elizabeth Barrett, the ailing girl with whom Robert Browning fell in love. The playbroker told Miss Cornell that the reason so many managers had rejected *The Barretts* was that they thought the public would not stand for a sick heroine. For that same reason Katharine was inclined to say "No." But Guthrie McClintic said with assurance, "The answer is *yes.*"

To produce *The Barretts*, the two formed a company — the Cornell-McClintic Corporation. This meant that Miss Cornell would have the commanding position of actress-manager. She brought Elizabeth Barrett to intense and luminous life.

The first performance has stayed deep in her mind, for her father was in the house. After the play ended, he went backstage, took her in his arms. "You've done it, Kit," he told her. "Now you can take your place with the best of them."

¹ **hoydenish** (hoi'd'n-ish): tomboyish.
² **playbroker**: a person who handles the rights to plays on a commission basis.

The stage partnership that had made *The Barretts* outstanding proved an excellent working arrangement. Five Cornell-McClintic productions shone with special luster in the "post-Barrett" period: *Romeo and Juliet,* two revivals of Bernard Shaw's *Candida,* and productions of his *Saint Joan* and *The Doctor's Dilemma.*

As actress-manager, Miss Cornell found that her days overflowed with work. She needed a permanent summer home where she could rest — and found it on the island of Martha's Vineyard. There, on a stretch of beach, she and Guthrie McClintic built a rambling place that is ample and welcoming.

"One thing that kept working on my mind when I was on Martha's Vineyard," she told me, "was the painful thought that young people are groping and stumbling along today, just as I groped and stumbled — looking for the right road, the royal road, to stage success. If only there were a royal road! When girls come to me for advice and ask me, 'Shall I try to go on the stage?' I say something like this: 'Don't — unless you're willing to swim upstream through some very cold rivers of discouragement — and keep swimming when you're exhausted, wondering whether you'll sink. Take up some other line of work unless your mind and body and will, your faith in yourself, your urge toward acting, are strong enough to stand failing and failing.'

"Sometimes people ask me if stage success doesn't demand a narrowing of yourself, a shutting out of every interest but the theater, a Broadway-mindedness. I tell them, 'Just the reverse is true. If you're hoping for durable success — success with dignity and quality — you must broaden yourself. Study history. You may be called on to interpret roles drawn from the past.

Look hard and long at the best paintings, read and reread the best books. Learn languages, especially French. Read French aloud – it will educate your lips and your tongue. Listen to good actors and actresses in good plays, but listen with a background of broad knowledge. Understanding music can help, since roles are so much a matter of timing.'

"After all, what do we love and value most out of the past? The masterpieces. If we can't keep the arts alive, we might as well be dead ourselves."

THINKING IT OVER

1. What evidence is there that Katharine Cornell was a well-rounded young person — that she had more interests than "play acting"?

2. What was her father's advice about a stage career for her? Consider the picture given of her as a young girl in this selection. What reason might it suggest to you for her father's attitude?

3. What incidents illustrate her desire for perfection? How did this play a part in the way in which she "fluffed" her first opportunity? Point out what is significant about her reaction to this failure.

4. The element called "luck" often plays a part in a successful career. Give two instances where "luck" – in this case, chance meetings – figured in Miss Cornell's success.

5. Playing the ailing Elizabeth Barrett required Katharine Cornell to lie on a sofa for most of the play's action. Can you suggest some difficulties this would involve in terms of stage acting? Explain which you think would be more arduous – moving around on a stage, or remaining in one position?

6. What are the main points in Katharine Cornell's advice for young people with dreams like hers? What does she mean by "durable success"? Point out some examples of persons who have had durable and nondurable success in the theater world. Can you supply reasons to explain this?

RELATING DETAILS TO THE MAIN IDEA

1. What detail does the author supply about Katharine Cornell's family that indicates why her dream centered naturally on the theater?

2. The author states that Miss Cornell made up her mind to be an actress after what experience? What was the first active step she took in this direction? What does this suggest about her capabilities?

3. A detail the author supplies about Katharine Cornell is that she was a sports lover. How might this have aided her as an actress? What quality of character helpful to success is suggested by the fact that she won swimming and tennis competitions?

4. After Katharine Cornell became a star, she also became the co-producer of her own plays. What does this fact suggest about her qualities for success?

ABOUT THE AUTHOR

Latrobe Carroll (1894–   ) was born in Washington, D.C., but spent his childhood in such scattered places as Colorado, Kansas, Egypt, Switzerland, and Germany. He sold his first magazine story while he was a freshman at Harvard University. After graduation and service with the army in World War I, he continued his magazine work. He was an editor-writer for *Liberty* Magazine for nine years. He is the author of books for young readers, some of which have been illustrated by his artist wife Ruth.

More About Katharine Cornell →

The photograph on page 232 is of Katharine Cornell as Elizabeth Barrett, and depicted opposite are more of her stage roles. To continue her story beyond the period covered in this selection, do some research and supply this information about her: (1) another Shakespearean heroine, in addition to Juliet, that she has played; and (2) her outstanding contribution as an actress during World War II. Later on in this book, in the afterword to *Romeo and Juliet*, Miss Cornell herself writes about her work, especially in regard to performing Juliet.

Three Favorite Roles

Here is Katharine Cornell as she looked in three of her favorite roles: *upper left,* as Juliet; *bottom left,* as Bernard Shaw's Saint Joan. The painting, *right,* is by the American artist, Eugene Speicher, and shows Miss Cornell in the title role of another Shaw play, *Candida.*

The Thread That Runs So True

JESSE STUART

One special quality of biography and autobiography is that they allow us to compare the lives of actual persons — the differences and the similarities. The famous people you have already met in these selections all had widely different childhoods. Here is another well-known person, whose childhood was different in still another way. Today the name Jesse Stuart is familiar to hosts of readers. But when he was a young teacher, his name meant nothing to the pupils he faced in a rough mountain school in Kentucky. To one pupil, it was a name to hate, as you will discover in this autobiographical episode.

Monday morning when I started on my way to school, I had with me Don Conway, a pupil twenty years of age, who had never planned to enter school again. I was the new teacher here at Lonesome Valley, and I didn't know what kind of brains he had. He had left school when he was in the fourth grade. But I did know that he had two good fists and that he would be on my side. All day Sunday while I had worked at the schoolhouse, I was trying to think of a plan so I could stay at Lonesome

Valley School. I knew I had to stay. I knew if one had to go it would be Guy Hawkins. I might have to use my head a little but that was why I had it.

It had taken a lot of persuasion to get Don Conway to return to school. He had planned to get married after his tobacco crop was sold. But I explained the value of an education to him in dollars and cents. I told him I would teach him how to measure a field and figure the number of acres, how to figure the number of bushels in a wagon bed or cornbin, and how many cubic yards of dirt one would have to remove to dig a cellar or a well. Don Conway was interested in this type of knowledge. I told him no man should be married and live on a farm unless he knew these simple things, for he could easily be cheated the rest of his days. I was interested in his learning these things all right, but I was interested in something else.

Don, his two small brothers, his sister Vaida, and I went to school together. I congratulated John Conway for sending all his children but one. I told him he should set the example for other farmers on the creek. It would have been hard on John to try to worm and sucker [1] his ten acres of tobacco and care for his other crops if Flossie, his older daughter, had not volunteered to help him. And Bertha, his wife, assured him she would divide her time between the housework and work in the field.

Flossie, eighteen years old, who had left school six years ago, would gladly have started back to school if I had insisted. But I knew John and Bertha had to have someone left to help them. I insisted and almost begged Don to return to school when he and I were sitting on the porch late one Sunday afternoon and Ova Salyers and Guy Hawkins rode past on their horses. They glanced toward the porch for their first look at the new teacher, never spoke but rode silently down the road.

Don Conway looked at Guy Hawkins and Ova Salyers and then he looked at me. He didn't ask me how old I was. I didn't tell him in eighteen more days I would be seventeen. One had to be eighteen before he was old enough to teach school. Don Conway knew the fate of my sister when she was employed to teach the Lonesome Valley School. He knew how Guy Hawkins had blacked her eyes with his fists, had whipped her before the Lonesome Valley pupils. She was a fair-haired, beautiful, blue-eyed girl of nineteen when she had come to Lonesome Valley. She went home a nervous wreck, long before her school was finished. After I'd seen the way my sister was beaten up, I begged to go to Lonesome Valley. My parents would have none of it. They thought if I went hunting trouble I would get more than my share. . . . Then I had John Hampton, a rural teacher and friend, contact John Con-

[1] to worm and sucker: to free from worms and cut off shoots, or suckers.

way and get the school for me. Superintendent Staggers didn't want me to go to Lonesome Valley. But there wasn't anything he could do about it after John Conway, Lonesome Valley District School trustee, recommended me. That was why I was here to teach school.

When Don and I reached the schoolhouse, at least thirty-five pupils were there waiting outside. Guy Hawkins and Ova Salyers were standing together near the coal house with their torn and tattered first-grade books. They looked out of place with the other pupils. They were larger than either Don or me. They were older too. They looked at me when I said "Good morning" to them. Many of the pupils turned shyly away and did not speak. They were waiting for the schoolhouse to be unlocked so they could rush in and select their seats. Each had his dinner basket or bucket in his hand. The majority of them carried tattered-edged and backless books.

The girls wore pigtails down their backs tied with all colors of ribbons. They wore clean print dresses and they were barefooted. Not one pupil in my school, large or small, boy or girl, wore a pair of shoes. I'd never seen in my life so many barefooted people, young, middle-aged, and old, as I had seen in Lonesome Valley. Wearing gloves on their hands in summer was the same to them as wearing shoes on their feet. They just didn't do it.

"Well, I'm opening the door," I said, to break the silence of my pupils.

When I opened the door, they laughed, screamed, and raced for the schoolhouse. Their shyness was gone now. There was a mad scramble to get inside the schoolhouse for seats. Then there was some discussion among them as to who would sit by whom. Girls had selected their seatmates. There were a few controversies and a few hurt feelings. Often two pupils wanted to sit by the same person. No trouble with Guy and Ova. They walked inside reluctantly and sat down in a seat on the boys' side farthest from my desk.

"Now let me make an announcement to you before school starts," I said, after walking up to my desk. "There will not any longer be a girls' side and a boys' side. Sit anyplace you want to."

They looked strangely at one another. Not one boy would cross to the girls' side. Not one girl would cross to the boys' side. In Lonesome Valley it was hard to break a teaching tradition more than a century old. But after I had been to high school, where there were no such things as a girls' side and a boys' side in a schoolroom, I didn't see why it wouldn't work in Lonesome Valley. Little did I dream that what I had said here would make news in Lonesome Valley, that it would be talked about by everybody, and that many would criticize me and call my school "a courting school." Boys and girls sitting together? Who had ever heard tell of it?

When I walked down the broad center aisle and pulled on the bell rope, the soft tones sounded over the tobacco, corn, and cane fields and the lush green valley; with the ringing of this bell, my school had begun. I knew that not half the pupils in the school census were here. There were one hundred and four in the school census, of school age, for whom the state sent per capita [1] money to pay for their schooling. I had thirty-five pupils. I thought the soft tones of this school bell through the rising mists and over warm cultivated fields where parents and their children were trying to eke out a bare subsistence from the

¹ **per capita** (pēr kăp′ĭ·tá̇): by heads, or so much per person.

soil might bring back warm memories of happy school days. For I remembered the tones of the Plum Grove school bell, and how I had longed to be back in school after I had quit at the age of nine to work for twenty-five cents a day to help support my family. If I could have, I would have returned to school when I heard the Plum Grove bell. So I rang the bell and called the Lonesome Valley pupils back to school — back to books and play. For going to school had never been work to me. It had been recreation. And I hoped it would be the same for my pupils in Lonesome Valley.

When I dismissed my pupils for the first recess, a fifteen-minute period between the beginning of the school day and the noon hour, I was amazed to see them all jump up from their seats at the same time and try to be the first out of the house. Big pupils pushed past the little ones, and there was so much confusion and disorder I knew they would never leave the room like this again. Why were they running? I wondered. I had a few minutes' work to do before I could join them on the playground. Before I had finished this work, I heard the tenor of their uneven voices singing these familiar words:

> The needle's eye that does supply,
> The thread that runs so true,
> Many a beau have I let go,
> Because I wanted you.

> Many a dark and stormy night,
> When I went home with you,
> I stumped my toe and down I go,
> Because I wanted you.

I walked to the door and watched them. They had formed a circle, hand in hand, and around and around they walked and sang these words while two pupils held their locked hands high for the circle to pass under. Suddenly the two standing — one inside the circle and one outside — let their arms drop down to take a pupil from the line. Then the circle continued to march and sing while the two took the pupil aside and asked him whether he would rather be a train or an automobile. If the pupil said he'd rather be an automobile, he stood on one side; if a train, he stood on the other of the two that held hands. And when they had finished taking everybody from the circle, the two groups faced each other, lined up behind their captains. Each put his arms around the pupil in front of him and locked his hands. The first line to break apart or to be pulled forward lost the game.

Fifteen minutes were all too short for them to play "the needle's eye." I let recess extend five minutes so they could finish their second game. It had been a long time since I had played this game at Plum Grove. These words brought back pleasant memories. They fascinated me. And my Lonesome Valley pupils played this game with all the enthusiasm and spirit they had! They put themselves into it — every pupil in school. Not one stood by to watch. Because they were having the time of their lives, I hated to ring the bell for "books." I lined them up, smaller pupils in front and larger ones behind, and had them march back into the schoolroom.

Guy Hawkins and Ova Salyers were the last on the line. When they came inside the door, Guy asked permission to go with Ova after a bucket of water. We didn't have a well or a cistern at the schoolhouse. We had to get water from some home in the district. I told them they could go but not to be gone too long, for the pupils, after running and playing, were thirsty. The July sun beat down on the galvanized tin roof. This made the pine boards so hot inside they

oozed resin.[1] We raised all the windows, but still the place was hot as the room in which I slept at Conways'. My little room upstairs with a high unscreened window of only one sash didn't cool off until about midnight. Then I could go to sleep.

The first bucket of water Guy and Ova brought didn't last five minutes. The majority of the pupils were still thirsty. I sent Guy and Ova back for more, telling them to borrow another bucket. I sent them in a hurry. And I knew I had to do something about the dipper problem. At Plum Grove, too, we had all drunk from the same dipper, but when I went to Landsburgh High School I was taught something different.

So I made "an important announcement" to my pupils. I told them each had to bring his own drinking cup the next day. It could be a glass, teacup, gourd, dipper, just so it was his own and no one else drank from it. My pupils looked at one another and laughed as if my announcement was funny. But I had seen sweat run from their faces into the dipper, and the next in line put his mouth where the sweat had run or where the other pupil had put his lips. I noticed, too, several pupils had put the rim up near the handle to their mouths, so I knew they didn't like to drink after the others.

On Tuesday they brought their dippers, tin cups, and glasses. Only a few had forgotten, and I stopped with my busy schedule of classwork long enough to teach them how to make paper drinking cups. I showed them how to take a clean sheet of paper from a tablet and fold it to hold water. I gave them a lecture about drinking water. I told them never to drink from a stream. I told

[1] **resin** (rĕz′ĭn): a brownish, sticky substance found in pine wood.

them how I had gotten typhoid fever twice: once from drinking cool water from a little stream, and once from drinking in a river. I had my pupils use the dipper to dip water from the bucket into their cups. They accepted my suggestion gladly. I also borrowed another water bucket from Bertha Conway and brought it to school. The one bucket allowed me for thirty-five pupils (and there would be more as soon as the farmers were through with their summer plowing and worming and suckering tobacco, stripping their cane and boiling the juice to sirup) was not enough. They played hard at recess and noon and in the "time of books" sat in a schoolroom almost as hot as a stove oven.

Tuesday when I stood beside Guy Hawkins and showed him how to hold his book when he read, my pupils laughed until I had to stop them. I was trying to teach Guy to read as he stumbled over the simple words in the *First Grade Reader*. My pupils laughed because Guy was taller by two inches than I was and heavier. He had a bull-neck almost as large as his head, and a prominent jaw. His beard was so heavy that he had to shave every day.

Wouldn't Coach Wilson like to have him! I thought. He would make the best tackle Landsburgh High School ever had.

Guy had big hands. His right hand covered the back of his *First Reader*. And he had powerful arms. The muscles rippled under his clean blue-faded shirt. I measured him as I stood beside him. I knew that if I ever had to fight him, it would be a fight. And I knew that I wasn't going to fight him unless he forced me to fight. He was more powerful physically than I was. And the outcome of our fight might depend on the one who successfully landed the first haymaker to the other's jaw.

Then I looked down at Ova Salyers sitting on the recitation seat beside me. Another tackle for Coach Wilson, I thought. This pair would be a coach's dream. Pity some coach doesn't have 'em instead of me.

If it were not for these two young men, I wouldn't have had any trouble disciplining my school. All the other pupils played hard and they were obedient. They would have been good in their classwork if they had had the proper training. I had ten-year-old pupils just starting to school. Nineteen-year-olds in the first grade. Fourteen-year-olds in the second grade. I had one twelve-year-old girl in the eighth grade. They had not been promoted because they had never attended a full school term. They had taken the same grade over and over until they could stand and recite some of the beginning lessons from memory.

"Guy, how long have you been in the first grade?" I asked.

"Oh, about eight years," he laughed.

"You're not going to be in it any longer," I said.

"Why?" he asked.

"Because I'm going to promote you," I said. "Tomorrow you start in the second grade."

Then I had Ova Salyers read. He had also been in the first grade eight years. I promoted him.

When these young men sat down again I saw them look at each other and laugh as if they thought my promoting them was funny. I knew they accepted school as a joke, a place to come and see people. A place where they could join a circle of smaller children and play "the needle's eye." And I knew there wasn't much chance of reasoning with either one. But I had a feeling that time would come. I didn't believe they were coming to school for any good. I felt that Guy was waiting his chance for me. I was not going to take any chances; I was going to give him the full benefit of the doubt.

The following Monday I had stayed at the schoolhouse to do some work on my school records, and Don Conway had gone home with his sister and brothers. This was the first afternoon I had stayed at school after all my pupils had gone. The room was very silent, and I was busy working when I heard soft footsteps walking around the building. I looked through the window on my left and I saw Guy Hawkins' head. His uncombed, tousled hair was ruffled by the Lonesome Valley wind.

I wondered why he was coming back. I wondered if he had forgotten something.

Then I realized this was the first time he had been able to catch me by myself. And I remembered a few other incidents in Greenwood County's rural schools where a pupil had come back to the school when the teacher was there alone and had beaten the tar out of him. I could recall three or four such incidents. But I didn't have time to think about them. Not now. Guy came in the door with his cap in his hand. I didn't want him to see me looking up at him, but I did see him coming down the broad middle aisle, taking long steps and swinging his big arms. He looked madder than any man or animal I had ever seen. He walked up to my desk and stood silently before me.

"Did you forget something, Guy?" I asked.

"Naw, I've never forgot nothin'," he reminded me.

"Then what do you want?" I asked.

"Whip you," he said.

"Why do you want to whip me?" I asked him.

"I didn't like your sister," he said. "You know what I done to her."

"Yes, I know what you did to her," I said.

"I'm a-goin' to do the same thing to you," he threatened.

"Why do you want to fight me?" I asked him. I dropped my pencil and stood up facing him.

"I don't like you," he said. "I don't like teachers. I said never another person with your name would teach this school. Not as long as I'm here."

"It's too bad you don't like me or my name," I said, my temper rising.

"I won't be satisfied until I've whipped you," he said.

"Can you go to another school?" I asked him. "Sandy Valley School is not too far from where you live."

"Naw, naw," he shouted, "if anybody leaves, you'll leave. I was in Lonesome Valley first. And I ain't a-goin' to no other school because of you!"

"Then there's nothing left for us to do but fight," I said. "I've come to teach this school, and I'm going to teach it!"

"Maybe you will," he snarled. "I have you penned in this schoolhouse. I have you where I want you. You can't get away! You can't run! I aim to whip you right where you stand! It's the same place where I whipped your sister!"

I looked at his face. It was red as a sliced beet. Fire danced in his pale blue, elongated eyes. I knew Guy Hawkins meant every word he said. I knew I had to face him and to fight. There was no other way around. I had to think quickly. How would I fight him?

"Will you let me take my necktie off?" I said, remembering I'd been choked by a fellow pulling my necktie once in a fight.

"Yep, take off that purty tie," he said.

"You might get it dirty by the time I'm through with you."

I slowly took off my tie.

"Roll up the sleeves of your white shirt too," he said. "But they'll be dirty by the time I sweep this floor up with you."

"Sweep the floor up with me," I said.

He shot out his long arm but I ducked. I felt the wind from his thrust against my ear.

I mustn't let him clinch me, I thought.

Then he came back with another right and I ducked his second lick. I came around with my first lick — a right — and planted it on his jaw, not a good lick but just enough to jar him and make him madder. When he rushed at me, I sidestepped. He missed. By the time he had turned around, I caught him a haymaker on the chin that reeled him. Then I followed up with another lick as hard as I had ever hit a man. Yet I didn't bring him down. He came back for more. But he didn't reach me this time. He was right. I did get my shirt dirty. I dove through the air with a flying tackle. I hit him beneath the knees. I'd tackled like this in football. I'd tackled hard. And I never tackled anybody harder than Guy. His feet went from under him, and I scooted past on the pine floor. I'd tackled him so quickly when he had expected me to come back at him with my fists, that he went down so fast he couldn't catch with his hands. His face hit flat against the floor and his nose was flattened. The blood spurted as he started to get up.

I let him get to his feet. I wondered if I should. For I knew it was either him or me. One of us had to whip. When he did get to his feet after that terrible fall, I waded into him. I hit fast and I hit hard. He swung wild. His fingernail took a streak of hide from my neck and left a red mark that smarted, and the blood oozed through. I pounded his chin. I caught him on the beardy jaw. I reeled him back and followed up. I gave him a left to the short ribs while my right in a split second caught his mouth. Blood spurted again. Yet he was not through. But I knew I had him.

"Had enough?" I panted.

He didn't answer. I didn't ask him a second time. I hit him hard enough to knock two men down. I reeled him back against a seat. I followed up. I caught him with a haymaker under the chin and laid him across the desk. Then he rolled to the floor. He lay there with blood running from his nose and mouth. His eyes were rolled back. I was nearly out of breath. My hands ached. My heart pounded. If this is teaching school! I thought. If this goes with it! Then I remembered vaguely I had asked for it. I'd asked for this school. I would take no other.

Guy Hawkins lay there sprawled on the unswept floor. His blood was mingled with the yellow dirt carried into the schoolroom by seventy bare feet. I went back and got the water bucket. With a clean handkerchief, I washed blood from his mouth and nose. I couldn't wash it from his shirt. I put cool water to his forehead.

I worked over a pupil — trying to bring him back to his senses — whom only a few hours before I had stood beside and tried to teach how to pronounce words when he read. "Don't stumble over them like a horse stumbles over frozen ground," I told him, putting it in a language he would understand. I had promoted him. I'd sent Guy and Ova after water when other pupils had wanted to go. On their way to get water, I knew they chewed tobacco and thought they were putting something over on me. I had known I couldn't allow them to use tobacco at school. I had known the time would eventually come. But I wanted to put it off as long as I could. Now I had whipped him, and I wondered as I looked at him stretched on the floor how I'd done it. He was really knocked out for the count. I knew the place where we had fought would always be marked. It was difficult to remove bloodstains from pine wood. It would always be there, this reminder, as long as I taught school at Lonesome Valley.

When Guy Hawkins came to his senses, he looked up at me. I was applying the wet cool handkerchief to his head. When he started to get up, I helped him to his feet.

"Mr. Stuart, I really got it poured on me," he admitted. "You're some fighter."

This was the first time he had ever called me "Mr. Stuart." I had heard, but had pretended not to hear, him call me "Old Jess" every time my back was turned. He had never before, when he had spoken directly to me, called me anything.

"I'm not much of a fighter until I have to fight, Guy," I said. "You asked for it. There was no way around. I had to fight you."

"I know it," he said. "I've had in mind to whip you ever since I heard you's a-goin' to teach this school. But you win. You winned fair, too," he honestly admitted. "I didn't think you could hit like that."

Guy was still weak. His nose and mouth kept bleeding. He didn't have a handkerchief, and I gave him a clean one.

"Think you can make it home all right, Guy?"

"I think so," he said.

He walked slower from the schoolhouse than he had walked in. I was too upset to do any more work on my rec-

Kentucky: A country road.

ord book. I stood by the window and watched him walk across the schoolyard, then across the foot log and down the Lonesome Creek Road until he went around the bend and was out of sight. Something told me to watch for Ova Salyers. He might return to attack me. I waited several minutes, and Ova didn't come. Guy had come to do the job alone.

I felt better now that the fight was over, and I got the broom and swept the floor. I had quickly learned that the rural teacher was janitor as well, and that his janitor work was one of the important things in his school. I believed, after my brief experience, that the schoolhouse should be made a place of beauty, prettier and cleaner than any of the homes the pupils came from so they would love the house and the surroundings, and would think of it as a place of beauty and would want to keep it that way.

The floor was easy to sweep. But it was difficult to clean blood from the floor. I carried a coal bucket of sand and poured it on the blood and then shoveled up the sand and carried it out.

I had the blood from the floor. Then I scrubbed the place, but the stain was there. I could not get it from the oily, soft pine wood. I knew this was one day in my teaching career I would never forget.

I didn't expect Guy Hawkins to return to Lonesome Valley School. I thought his schooling was ended. But when he left the schoolhouse he didn't take his books. I wondered if he would come back to get them, and, if he came, would he bring his father or one of his married brothers with him? Would he start another fight? The same thoughts must have troubled John Conway. When I went to school on Tuesday morning, John went with me.

This was John Conway's first visit to the school, for his farm work had piled up on him since all of his children but Flossie were going to school. When we got there, big Guy Hawkins with his black eyes and swollen lips was in a circle with the other pupils, going around, and singing "The Needle's Eye." Guy greeted me: "Good morning, Mr. Stuart."

Then John Conway smiled and turned to go. I watched him cross the foot log and go into the little store. I joined in the game, "the needle's eye," with my pupils. Guy Hawkins and I were captains. I was the hard-boiled egg and he was the soft-boiled egg. When we took pupils from the line and asked them whether they would rather be a soft-boiled or a hard-boiled egg, the majority chose the soft-boiled egg. Guy Hawkins got three-fourths of the pupils. And when we formed our tug of war to pull against each other, his side toppled my side. They pulled us all over the yard, and everybody laughed, especially Guy Hawkins. It was great fun. And never did Guy Hawkins or a pupil ask me about the fight. If they talked about it,

I didn't know. I did notice them observing the bloodstain on the floor. If Guy Hawkins ever said anything against me to a fellow pupil again, I never heard of it. He had, for the first time, become a pupil like the rest. He had, for the first time, acted as if he was a part of our school.

[After his first year of teaching, Jesse Stuart finished high school himself. Later he completed his college work in three years and took a teaching job at another small rural school, Winston High School, where he had fourteen pupils and where he himself comprised the entire faculty. As at Lonesome Valley, Jesse lived with a neighborhood family, the Baylors, but as this part of his account begins, he prepares for a visit to his home at Landsburgh, to see the county superintendent.]

Nobody could keep me from starting home. I was determined to go. I needed more novels, books of short stories, books of poems and essays for my pupils to read. I wanted to see Superintendent Larry Anderson. When Lucretia Baylor learned I was determined to go, she prepared a quick hot lunch for me. She did this while I packed my clothes and got ready. For my teaching day ended at 3:30 P.M., and I had walked the three-fourths mile from the school to Baylors' in a hurry. It was early in the afternoon, but the dark December skies hung low over the valley, and there were six inches of snow on the ground. I had seventeen miles ahead of me. The only way I could get to my destination was to walk.

"If you were a boy of mine," Ottis Baylor said, "I wouldn't let you go. Not on a seventeen mile journey on a night like this! I advise you against going. I know the road to Landsburgh better than you do. I've walked it enough to know. It's a treacherous road when you leave the Tiber Valley Road and try the short cut around Laurel Ridge."

I knew that I wasn't listening to Ottis Baylor. I was going, anyway. I knew that I was fast on foot. I had walked thirty-five miles in a day. That hadn't even made my legs or feet sore. If I could walk this far on a short day, then I was as positive as death, by steady walking, I could cover a mile every twelve minutes. I thought: If I had luck, I could make the journey in three and a half hours. I allowed myself four hours and that was plenty of time. And I was leaving Baylors' at four.

The massive black cloud rested on the east and west walls of the valley like a roof. The east wall was the one I had to climb. When I reached the top, I would be on Laurel Ridge. By going this way, I could cut three miles from my walking distance. I knew the path to Laurel Ridge. I'd been over it many times before. Whether the snow was broken over this path or not, I did not know. I did not care. I said good-by to the Baylors, and I was on my way.

The December wind whistled in the barren shoe-make [1] tops, where the redbirds hopped from limb to limb and chirruped plaintive notes. Snowbirds stood by the clumps of dead ragweed the snow hadn't covered. They were searching for a scanty supper of the frozen seeds. Though time was early on this short winter day, I thought darkness might come soon. Going up the mountain, I made excellent time. I followed the path all right. I had to break the snow, for no one had traveled this path. I knew how to follow the path by the clumps of trees, rock cliffs, and fences. These were the landmarks to follow.

Before I reached a small opening near Laurel Ridge, I lost my path. I

[1] **shoe-make**: sumac (shoō′măk), a small tree or shrub.

walked into a forest of tough-butted white oaks. They grew close together, shutting out the diminishing winter light. I had never seen these trees before. I turned quickly, retracing my steps until I found the path. I knew I had been in too much of a hurry. I'd have to be more careful. But why should I worry now? I had at least reached Laurel Ridge, for there was a five-strand, rusty barbed-wire fence nailed to the trees. I knew this fence. It followed Laurel Ridge some distance before it turned back down the mountain. When I held my arm up to look at my watch, I couldn't see the figures on the dial. I didn't know what time it was, but I knew it was early. I knew I was in the snow cloud. For the big snowflakes were falling around me. I could see them dimly, these white flakes about the size of dimes, falling just in front of my eyes. I could feel them hitting my overcoat.

All I had to do was turn to my left after I reached Laurel Ridge. That was the right direction. I could follow the wire fence even if I had to follow it with my hand as I walked. I had one free hand. I carried my suitcase with my right hand. My left hand was free. But I didn't touch the fence. Not yet. I was following Laurel Ridge Road. I was following it with my feet. I had hunted much at night in my lifetime. Darkness had never bothered me too much. But now I couldn't see the woods and I knew it couldn't possibly be six o'clock. I was in a snowstorm. I could hear the snowflakes falling through the barren oak tops whose branches interlocked above the road.

Then I heard voices, and the sound was sweet to hear. I had barely time to side-step for two mule teams. I almost walked into a mule before I saw him. Yet there was a lighted lantern on the joltwagon the mules were pulling. When I recognized Eif Potters, he stopped his mule team in great surprise. He asked me where I was going on a night like this. Then I knew what he was talking about.

The fury of the storm almost blotted out the lantern light. It didn't give light more than six feet away. The snowflakes were larger than nickels. They were almost as large as quarters. I was in the cloud I'd seen before I left Baylors'.

I told Eif Potters and his son Zeke, who was sitting on the wagon beside him, I was on my way home. That snow wasn't falling down in Tiber Valley when I left, not more than two hours ago. He told me they hadn't been in the snowstorm until they reached the top of Raccoon Hill. Then he invited me to get on the wagon and go home with them, but I refused. When I refused, he said he would loan me his lantern, but that they couldn't get around Laurel Ridge without it. Said he had five more miles to go, that he had taken a load of tobacco to Landsburgh and was getting back the same day, that he and his mules were very tired to push through five more miles of darkness and storm.

On this lonely ridge, high up in a snow cloud, I said good night to Eif and Zeke and was on my way, for I had lost about five minutes talking to them. I hadn't walked but a few steps when I looked back. The mule teams, wagon, riders, and lantern had disappeared in the storm. Yet I heard the jingling of the mules' harness, and I heard the men's voices as they talked to each other. Then I plunged on, alone, taking in both sides of the road. I hunted for the fence with an outstretched hand in the darkness, but I couldn't find it.

Eif had warned me about one place.

He told me if I bore too far to my left I would go into a vast tract of timber that lay on the east wall of Tiber Valley. And for this reason, I bore to my right, feeling with my feet while the snow came down as I had never felt it fall before. One thing I had forgotten to ask Eif for was matches. He was a pipe smoker too. He had smoked his pipe all the time he sat on his wagon and talked to me. If only I had a match! I was stumbling over the road. Once I went in water to my knee. Then I knew I must be on the Laurel Ridge Road. This was a deep wagon-wheel rut, and Eif had driven over it and had broken the thin ice down to the water. My foot was wet. Water squashed in my shoe. One of my galoshes was filled with water.

Then I stepped into a hole of water with my dry foot. I went in to my knee. Both pant legs were wet to my knees. Again and again I stepped into water, but my feet were already wet and it didn't make any difference if I did get them wet again. I kept moving. I followed the road the best I could. I knew I was on the Laurel Ridge Road. That was the main thing. I would soon reach the turnpike at the top of Raccoon Hill. That was where the Laurel Ridge Road ended. And this distance was approximately three miles from where my path from Baylors' had gone through the barbed-wire fence onto the Laurel Ridge. If I could only see my watch! I had surely walked three more miles!

Time in the night, I thought, when one was walking alone, might seem longer than it actually was. I kept on going. I waded water, and I waded snow. The snow was almost as deep as my galoshes were high. I walked on and on and on. Then I knew I'd gone far enough to reach the turnpike on Raccoon Hill . . . the turnpike that would take me straight to Landsburgh. While I thought about the fast time I would be able to make on the turnpike when I reached it, I suddenly walked into a cornfield. I thought it was a cornfield. I thought I was standing beside a fodder shock. It stood like a white wigwam before me. I pushed my hand through the snow and felt the dry fodder stalks. I knew now that I was lost.

I couldn't even retrace my steps. I couldn't see them. If it had been light enough for me to see them, I couldn't have followed them far because they would have been snowed under. I was lost, that was all. I was in this cornfield and I would have to make the best of it. I stood beside the fodder shock — this tiny thing of security — while I screamed at the top of my voice. I knew that in this part of Greenwood County there was much wasteland. There were miles and miles where there wasn't a house. But I screamed, anyway. I thought somebody might hear me and come to my rescue. The only answer I got was the faraway barking of a fox. When I screamed, he mocked me with his barking.

When I had reached this fodder shock, my feet were still warm and my face was wet with perspiration. But in this open space where corn had grown on the mountaintop, there was an incessant sweep of wind. The wind carried the snow directly at me. I could measure the speed of the wind by the way the soft flakes hit my face. The soft flakes felt like grains of corn. I had to start walking to keep warm. I had to do something in a hurry. Then a thought came to me. If there was one fodder shock here, there were others. The cornfield must be fairly large to give the wind such great velocity. I was almost afraid to leave the fodder shock I had already found. Even when I did, I

held to my suitcase. I walked a few paces and found another fodder shock. I put my arm around the top of the shock and dragged it back to the first one. I carried eight fodder shocks to one place. The fodder shocks were not large. The shocks were not as tall as I was. I used one hand to carry them; I held to my suitcase with the other. I was afraid I'd lose it and that it would soon be snowed under. Besides, I had other ideas.

After I'd pulled these fodder shocks together, I laid the heavy ends of the fodder to the windward side of the mountain. I bedded three shocks down on the snow. Then I put a shock on each side of the floor I'd made. I stood two shocks up on the windward side, to pull down on me as soon as I was ready to lie down. The last shock I stood up, to use where the fodder would be thinnest above me. Then I stood on the fodder and pulled off my shoes. The wind-driven snow was cold to my wet feet and legs. I pulled off my overcoat and wet pants. I took a dry soiled shirt from my suitcase and dried the water from my feet and legs. I tied dry dirty shirts around my feet. I put on a pair of soiled trousers I was taking to have dry-cleaned. I bundled myself with all the clothes I had in my suitcase. I lay down and spread my overcoat over me. Now I reached up and pulled the fodder shocks down upon me. The fodder quilt was thick but not too heavy. I lay there and listened to the mice in the fodder around me and the ticking of my watch while over me the wind moaned and the snow fell.

I knew that I should not go to sleep. For if I did, the wind might blow the fodder from over me. I would freeze to death, and I would not be found in this cornfield until the farmer came to haul his fodder home. I must have been half asleep when I heard the hoot owls start calling to one another from the timber all around this cornfield. I didn't know exactly where they were. But I knew they frequented the less populated places. From their calls, coming from all directions, I knew this must be their meeting place. I no longer heard the wind nor felt it seeping through the fodder. I parted the fodder stalks to see what had happened. There were a million bright stars high in the clear blue sky, and in a short distance all around me — for there was not more than two acres of this cornfield — I could see the dark outlines of trees. Among these trees were the hoot owls. They were on every side. They cried jubilantly to each other, asking always the same: "Who, who are you?"

I pulled the fodder quilt back over me and lay there listening to the hoots of the owls, to the mice over me, around me and through the fodder, and to the ticking of my watch. I thought that I could stay awake until morning. Since the skies had cleared, I knew the weather before morning would be sub-zero on this mountaintop. I went to sleep dreaming that I would not go to sleep.

When I awoke, there were fewer stars in the sky. Daylight didn't come on these short December days until nearly eight. I tried to see what time it was, but I couldn't see the hands of my watch. The owls had flown away, and all was silent save for the ticking of my watch and the mice that had never slept the whole night through. I had slept warm on this cold night. I had warmed the fodder for the mice. The place was comfortable for all of us. But now I sat up and placed the fodder around me like a wigwam. I wanted the day to break so I could put on my clothes and be on my way. I had never been so hungry in my life.

Just as soon as it was light enough to see what I was doing, I started dressing. The legs of the pants I'd pulled off were frozen stiff and hard. My shoes had frozen so that I couldn't get them on. I didn't have a match to build a fire to thaw them. It was impossible to put them on. I wrapped a soiled shirt around each foot. I put my feet into my frozen galoshes. I put my frozen shoes and pants into my suitcase. It was light enough for me to see dim footprints in the snow. I could retrace myself. I wanted to see where I had made my mistake.

I followed my tracks, dim little prints in the crusted snow, for more than a mile. Then I came to Laurel Ridge. Far, far, down below, I could see Hinton Valley, now a great white silence except for the dark, leafless, sleeping trees. And to my right, if I had gone just fifty feet to my left, I would have found the turnpike on Raccoon Hill. I had borne too far to my right after Eif Potters had warned me about turning left. I had gone somewhere on the mountain between the headwaters of North Fork and Raccoon, where I had found the cornfield and slept in the fodder.

Though it was Saturday morning, when farmers would be on their way to Landsburgh, I was the first person on the turnpike. The white silence of snow that was even with the tops of my galoshes remained unbroken until I made a path. I walked down Raccoon Hill, and in the distance, somewhere far down the road, I heard voices. They were coming toward me. I was going toward them. Their shouts at their teams grew louder. I saw three teams hitched to a snowplow, and the county road-workers were breaking the road. I walked past them, and they looked at me. I hadn't noticed the fodder blades still hanging to my overcoat, and I brushed them off before I stopped at Gullet's gristmill.[1]

I knew Ephraim Gullet. When I went inside the gristmill, he asked me if I wasn't traveling early. I told him I had been lost and had slept on the mountain. He put more coal in the potbellied stove. He made a pot of coffee. I thawed my shoes and my pants legs while I drank hot coffee and warmed myself in front of the red-hot stove. Ephraim told me that his thermometer was twelve below at six that morning. He couldn't understand how I had stripped my clothes and dried the water from my legs and feet there on the mountaintop facing the great sweeps of snow-laden wind. He couldn't understand how I had managed to survive the rigor of the raw elements on the mountaintop when it was twelve below in the valley.

When Superintendent Larry Anderson unlocked his office door at nine that Saturday morning, I was there waiting for him. I had caught a ride in on a coal truck from Gullet's gristmill to Landsburgh.

"Well, well, how did you get here so early?" Superintendent Anderson asked. "You didn't come all the way from Winston this morning?"

"Just part of the way," I said.

He didn't ask me where I stayed. And I didn't tell him. I had something else I wanted to talk to him about.

"How are you getting along with your school out there?" he asked me.

"I think I'm getting along all right," I said. "What reports have you heard?"

"Good reports," he said.

"I'm glad to hear the reports about my teaching have been favorable," I said. "I am learning myself. My pupils are working me as hard as I am working them!"

[1] gristmill: a mill for grinding grain.

My superintendent thought I was joking. He started laughing. He laughed until he couldn't talk.

"I'm telling you the truth," I said. "I'm not telling you a joke. I've worked harder than I did in high school or in college!"

Superintendent Larry Anderson laughed harder than before. He laughed so loud anybody in the corridors of the courthouse could have heard him.

"You know there's not anything as good for a man as a good laugh early in the morning," he said.

I knew that he still thought I was joking.

"Superintendent Anderson," I said seriously, "I'm up against teaching those fourteen pupils. I've not got a slow one among them. I've got a couple of average pupils, and they can do every bit of work I give them. And," I explained, with a gesture of my hand for emphasis, "I've got one pupil that's a genius. He knows more facts than I do. He's only a freshman in high school. I tell you, Budge Waters is a genius! If he isn't, I'm terribly dumb. I've got six or seven A pupils and he's above them!"

Superintendent Larry Anderson sat silently looking at me for a minute. We were in his office alone. Then he spoke thoughtfully: "Well, what is your problem?"

"I haven't any," I said. "I've not had to discipline a pupil. They work hard. They play hard."

I knew he was wondering why I had come to his office.

"But there is one thing I'd like to do," I said. "That's why I've called on you this morning. I'd like to test my own judgment to see if I am wrong or right in my opinion of my pupils. I'd like to know how to go about entering them in the state scholastic contest. The contest is held each spring, isn't it?"

"Oh, yes," he said, "but there is an elimination process. Your pupils will have to take an examination against the pupils in Landsburgh High School! Then, if you are successful there," he explained, "they'll go to Auckland to enter the district contest. If they are successful there, they'll go on to the state contests!"

I knew that to get past Landsburgh, now a joint city-and-county high school, we'd have to compete with the best from nearly four hundred pupils. To get past the regional, we'd have to compete with the best, selected from thousands. Yet, it took only one brain to win a contest. I knew Budge Waters had that brain if it was properly trained. I thought he was capable of competing state-wide. I thought Billie Leonard could take the district in algebra. And I was willing to challenge big Landsburgh High School in all the five subjects I was teaching my pupils.

"If it's all right with you, Superintendent," I said, "you make arrangements and set a date for us to meet Landsburgh High School in algebra, Latin, English, plane geometry, and history!"

"I'll do it," he smiled. "Would sometime in January suit you?"

"Any time's all right with me," I said. "Make it convenient for the Landsburgh High School!"

"That's fair enough," he said.

"This is all I wanted to see you about," I said.

With these words, I left him alone in his office.

When I told my pupils about a scholastic contest with Landsburgh High School, I watched their expressions. They were willing and ready for the challenge. The competitive spirit was in them.

"We must review everything we have covered in our textbooks," I told them. "We must cover more territory in our textbooks too. Hold up your right hands if you are willing!"

Every pupil raised his hand.

Right then we started to work. In addition to regular assignments, my pupils began reviewing all of the old assignments we had covered.

Despite the challenge ahead and all the reviewing and study we planned to do, we never stopped play. The Tiber River was frozen over. The ring of skates and merry laughter broke the stillness of the winter nights. We skated on the white winding ribbon of ice beneath the high, cold winter moon. Often we'd skate until midnight. We'd hear the wind blow mournfully over the great white silence that surrounded us and sing lonesome songs without words in the barren branches of the bankside trees. And we'd hear the foxes' barking, high upon the walls of sheltering cliffs, mocking the music of our ringing skates.

On winter days when the snow had melted, leaving the dark earth a sea of sloppy mud, we designed floor games for our little one-room school. They were simple games, such as throwing bolts in small boxes. And we played darts. We also played a game called "fox and goose." We made our fox-and-goose boards, and we played with white, yellow, and red grains of corn. We had to make our own recreation. I never saw a distracted look on a pupil's face. I never heard one complain that the short, dark winter days were boresome because there wasn't anything to do. I think each pupil silently prayed for the days to be longer. We were a united little group. We were small, but we were powerful. We played hard, and we studied hard. We studied and played while the December days passed.

One day in early January, we dismissed school. This was the first time we had dismissed for anything. We had never lost an hour. I had actually taught more hours than was required. This was the big day for us. It was too bad that another blizzard had swept our rugged land and that a stinging wind was smiting the valleys and the hills. But this didn't stop the boys and me from going. Leona Maddox, my best Latin pupil, couldn't go along. Her father, Alex Maddox, wouldn't let her ride a mule seventeen miles to Landsburgh to compete in a contest on a day like this. I couldn't persuade him to let her go.

On that cold, blizzardy morning, Budge Waters rode his mule to school very early and built a fire in the potbellied stove. When the rest of us arrived on our mules at approximately seven o'clock, Budge had the schoolroom warm. We tied our mules to the fence, stood before the fire, and warmed ourselves before we started on our journey. Then we unhitched our mules from the fence and climbed into the saddles. Little clouds of frozen snow in powdery puffs arose from the mules' hoofs as six pupils and their teacher rode down the road.

Though the force of wind in the Tiber Valley was powerful, it was at our backs. The wind was strong enough to give our mules more momentum. We made good time until we left the valley and climbed the big hill. Here, we faced the wind. It was a whipping wind — stinging, biting wind on this mountain — that made the water run from our eyes and our mules' eyes, but for us there was no turning back. We were going to Landsburgh High School. That was that. We were determined to meet this big school; big to us, for they out-

A Kentucky farm in winter.

numbered us twenty-six to one. Soon we were down in Hinton Valley. Then we rode to the top of the Raccoon Hill, where we faced the stinging wind again.

"Mr. Stuart, I have been thinking," Budge Waters said, as we rode along together, "if you can sleep in a fodder shock when it's twelve degrees below zero, we can take this contest from Landsburgh High School! I've not forgotten how you walked seventeen miles to carry us books. All of your pupils remember. We'll never let you down!"

Budge Waters thought of this because we were riding down the mountain where I had slept that night. Then we rode down into the Raccoon Valley, and Billie Leonard, only thirteen years old, complained of numbness in his hands, feet, and lips. He said he felt as if he was going to sleep. I knew what he was talking about. I had had the same feeling the day Ottis Baylor had put my hands and feet in cold water. We stopped at a home, tied our mules to the fence, and went in and asked to warm. Bert Patton, a stranger to us, piled more wood on the open fire until we were as warm as when we had left the schoolhouse. We told him who we were and where we were going.

"On a day like this!" he said, shaking his head sadly.

We climbed into the saddles again. We were over halfway now. The second hitch would put us at Landsburgh High School. We had valley all the way to Landsburgh, with walls of rugged hills on each side for windbreaks.

At eleven o'clock we rode across the Landsburgh High School yard, and hitched our mules to the fence around the athletic field. There were faces against the windowpanes watching us. Then we walked inside the high school, where Principal Ernest Charters met and welcomed us. He told us that he was surprised we had come on a day like this and that we had been able to arrive so soon.

In the principal's office my pupils and I huddled around the gas stove while we heard much laughter in the high-school corridors. The Landsburgh High School pupils thought we were a strange-looking lot. Many came inside their principal's office to take a look at us. We were regarded with curiosity, strangeness, and wonder. Never before had these pupils seen seven mules hitched to their schoolyard fence. Never before had they competed scholastically with so few in number — competitors who had reached them by muleback. The Landsburgh High School principal didn't feel about the contest the way we felt. To him, this was just a "setup" to test his pupils for the district contest which would soon be held. He told me this when he went after the sealed envelopes that held the questions. We warmed before the gas stove while he made arrangements for the contest.

"These questions were made out by the state department of education," he said when he returned. "I don't know

how hard they are."

My pupils stood silently by the stove and looked at each other. We were asked to go to one of the largest classrooms. A Landsburgh High School teacher had charge of giving the tests. When the Landsburgh High School pupils came through the door to compete against my pupils, we knew why Principal Charters had selected this large classroom. My pupils looked at each other, then at their competitors.

I entered redheaded Jesse Jarvis to compete with ten of their plane-geometry pupils. I entered Billie Leonard against twenty-one of their selected algebra pupils.

"Budge, you'll have to represent us in grammar, English literature, and history," I said. "And I believe I'll put you in civil government. Is that all right?"

"Yes," he agreed. Budge had never had a course in civil government. All he knew about it was what he had read in connection with history.

"Robert Batson, you enter in history and grammar.

"Robin Baylor, you enter in algebra.

"Snookie Baylor, you enter in algebra and plane geometry.

"Sorry, Mr. Charters," I said, "we don't have anyone to enter in Latin. My best Latin pupil, Leona Maddox, couldn't make this trip."

After the contest had begun, I left the room. Miss Bertha Madden was in charge. I took our mules to Walter Scott's barn on the east end of Landsburgh, where I fed and watered them.

With the exception of an interval when the contestants ate a quick lunch, the contest lasted until 2:30 P.M. I had one pupil, Budge Waters, in four contests. I had planned to enter him in two. Just as soon as Budge finished with civil government, we started grading the papers. All the pupils were requested to leave the room.

We graded the papers with keys. Mr. Charters, Miss Madden, and two other teachers, and I did the grading. Mr. Charters read the answers on the keys, and we checked the answers. Once or twice we stopped long enough to discuss what stiff questions these were. We wondered how far we would have gotten if we — all of us college graduates — had taken the same test. One of the teachers asked me, while we graded these papers, if Budge Waters had ever seen these questions before.

When we were through grading the papers, Mr. Charters called the contestants into the classroom.

"I want to read you the scores of this contest," Principal Charters said. His voice was nervous.

"Budge Waters, winner in English literature.

"Budge Waters, winner in grammar.

"Budge Waters, winner in history with almost a perfect score.

"Budge Waters, winner in civil government.

"Why didn't you bring just this one boy?" Principal Charters asked me.

"Because I've got other good pupils," I quickly retorted.

"Billie Leonard, winner in algebra, with plenty of points to spare.

"Jesse Jarvis, second in plane geometry, lost by one point.

"Snookie Baylor and Robin Baylor tied for second place in algebra.

"Congratulations," said Principal Charters, "to your pupils and to you, on your success. It looks as though Winston High will represent this county in the district scholastic contest. I've never heard of such a remarkable thing."

When we left the Landsburgh High School, we heard defeated pupils crying because "a little mudhole in the road like Winston beat us."

In a few minutes our mule cavalcade passed the Landsburgh High School. Faces were against the windowpanes, and many pupils waved jubilantly to us as we rode by, our coattails riding the wind behind our saddles, and the ends of our scarfs bright banners on the wind. We rode victoriously down the main street of Landsburgh on our way home.

THINKING IT OVER

1. List the problems Jesse Stuart had to face as a beginning teacher at Lonesome Valley.

2. Contrast the young people of Lonesome Valley with yourself. What disadvantages did they have compared with your life? What advantages?

3. Jesse Stuart had some good reasons for trying to persuade Don Conway to return to school. What were several?

4. Did Guy Hawkins surprise you after the fight in the schoolroom — and if so, how? What characteristics of his came to light that you had not observed before?

5. Name the ways in which the Lonesome Valley school differs from your own. Are there schools somewhat like this one in our country today?

6. The number "seventeen" had significance three times in this selection. Explain.

7. Putting together all the incidents in the selection, what traits of character would you assign to Jesse Stuart? Back each statement by citing an incident, and give your opinion of how well you think he handled the situation.

CONTINUING THE STORY

The Thread That Runs So True is also the title of Jesse Stuart's book from which this selection was taken. The book gives a more complete account of his early life and has the same vigorous appeal as this selection. You will find it exciting to read. Other details about this author are given on page 104.

Abe Lincoln Grows Up

CARL SANDBURG

To bring a subject to life, a good biographer uses facts and incidents which combine to form a living picture of the subject. With proper research, used in an imaginative manner, an author can make the reader see and hear his subject and come to know his thoughts and feelings. Carl Sandburg, the author of this selection, spent years collecting the background material for his story of Lincoln's life. But what makes his biography great literature is the astonishingly real portrait he has drawn of "the man in the stovepipe hat." In this excerpt from the biography, you will truly have a chance to know the young farm boy destined to enrich our land.

ON THE Knob Creek farm the child Abraham Lincoln learned to talk, to form words with the tongue and the roof of the mouth and the force of the breath from lungs and throat. "Pappy" and "Mammy," the words of the people meaning "father" and "mother," were among the first syllables. He learned what the word *name* meant; his name was Abraham, the same as Abraham in the Bible, the same as his grandfather Abraham. It was "Abe" for short; if his mother called in the dark, "Is that you, Abe?" he answered, "Yes, Mammy, it's me." The name of the family he belonged to was "Lincoln" or "Linkun," though most people called it "Linkern" and it was sometimes spelled "Linkhorn."

The family lived there on Knob Creek farm, from the time Abe was three or so till he was past seven years of age. Here he was told "Kaintucky" meant the state he was living in; Knob Creek farm, the Rock Spring farm where he

Recognizing Important Details. In whatever you read, some details will have more importance than others. To an author, all details **are** important because together they will help produce the final effect toward which he is working. This is a good rule for readers, too. As you read this selection, pay attention to the many details Carl Sandburg includes to show you what influenced and shaped Lincoln's early life.

was born, Hodgenville, Elizabethtown, Muldraugh's Hill, these places he knew, the land he walked on, was all part of Kentucky.

Yet it was also part of something bigger. Men had been fighting, bleeding, and dying in war, for a country, "our country"; a man couldn't have more than one country any more than he could have more than one mother; the name of the mother country was the "United States"; and there was a piece of cloth with red and white stripes having a blue square in its corner filled with white stars; and this piece of cloth they called "a flag." The flag meant the "United States." One summer morning his father started the day by stepping out of the front door and shooting a long rifle into the sky; and his father explained it was the day to make a big noise because it was the "Fourth of July," the day the United States first called itself a "free and independent" nation.

His folks talked like other folks in the neighborhood. They called themselves "pore" people. A man learned in books was "eddicated." What was certain was "sartin." The syllables came through the nose; joints were "jints"; fruit "spiled" instead of spoiling; in corn-planting time they "drapped" the seeds. They went on errands and "brung" things back. Their dogs "follered" the coons. Flannel was "flannen," a bandanna a "bandanner," a chimney a "chimbly," a shadow a "shadder," and mosquitoes plain "skeeters." They "gethered" crops. A creek was a "crick," a cover a "kiver."

A man silent was a "say-nothin'." They asked, "Have ye et?" There were dialogues, "Kin ye?" "No, I caint." And if a woman had an idea of doing something she said, "I had a idy to." They made their own words. Those who

spoke otherwise didn't belong, were "puttin' on." This was their wilderness lingo; it had gnarled bones and gaunt hours of their lives in it.

Words like *independent* bothered the boy. He was hungry to understand the meanings of words. He would ask what *independent* meant, and when he was told the meaning he lay awake nights thinking about the meaning of the meaning of *independent*. Other words bothered him, such as *predestination*.[1] He asked the meaning of that and lay awake hours at night thinking about the meaning of the meaning.

Seven-year-old Abe walked four miles a day going to the Knob Creek school to learn to read and write. Zachariah [2] Riney and Caleb [3] Hazel were the teachers who brought him along from A B C to where he would write the name "A-b-r-a-h-a-m L-i-n-c-o-l-n" and count numbers beginning with *one, two, three,* and so on. He heard "twice two is four."

The schoolhouse was built of logs, with a dirt floor, no window, one door. The scholars learned their lessons by saying them to themselves out loud till it was time to recite; alphabets, multiplication tables, and the letters of spelled words were all in the air at once. It was a "blab school"; so they called it.

The Louisville and Nashville pike running past the Lincoln cabin had many different travelers. Covered wagons came with settlers moving south and west, or north to Ohio and Indiana; there were peddlers with knickknacks

---

[1] **predestination** (prḗ·dĕs'tĭ·nā'shŭn): the belief that all the events which are to take place in the world have already been determined by God.

[2] **Zachariah** (zăk'à·rī'à).

[3] **Caleb** (kā'lĕb).

to spread out and tell the prices of; Congressmen, members of the legislature meeting at Lexington, men who had visited Henry Clay at Ashland.

Coming back from a fishing trip, with one fish, Abe met a soldier who came from fighting in the Battle of New Orleans with General Jackson, and Abe, remembering his father and mother had told him to be good to soldiers, handed the soldier the one fish.

The Lincolns got well acquainted with Christopher Columbus Graham, a doctor, a scientist, who was beginning to study and write books about the rocks, flowers, plants, trees, and wild animals of Kentucky; Graham slept in the bed while the Lincolns slept on the floor of the cabin, more than once; he told in the evening talk about days camping with Daniel Boone, and running backward with Boone so as to make foot tracks pointing forward to mislead the Indians; he talked about stones, leaves, bones, snakeskins he was carrying in a sack back to Louisville; he mentioned a young storekeeper at Elizabethtown, named John James Audubon, who had marvelous ways with birds and might someday write a great book about birds. The boy Abe heard traveling preachers and his father talk about the times when they held church meetings in cabins, and every man had his rifle by his side, and there were other men with rifles outside the cabin door, ready for Indians who might try to interrupt their Sabbath worship. And the boy never liked it when the talkers slung around words like *independent* and *predestination,* because he lay awake thinking about those long words.

Abe was the chore boy of the Knob Creek farm as soon as he grew big enough to run errands; to hold a pine knot at night lighting his father at a job; or to carry water, fill the woodbox,

clean ashes from the fireplace, hoe weeds, pick berries, grapes, persimmons for beer-making. He hunted the timbers and came back with walnuts, hickory and hazel nuts. His hands knew the stinging blisters from using a hoe handle back and forth a summer afternoon, and in autumn the mash of walnut stain that wouldn't wash off with all the rinsing and scrubbing of Nancy Hanks's homemade soap. He went swimming with Austin Gollaher; they got their backs sunburned so the skin peeled off.

Wearing only a shirt — no hat nor pants — Abe rode a horse hitched to a "bull-tongue" plow of wood shod with iron. He helped his father with seed corn, beans, onions, potatoes. He ducked out of the way of the heels of the stallion and brood mares his father kept and paid taxes on.

The father would ride away to auctions, once coming home with dishes, plates, spoons, and a washbasin, another time with a heifer, and again with a wagon that had been knocked down to the highest bidder for eight and one-half cents.

Abe and his sister picked pails of currants and blueberries for Mother Nancy to spread in the sun to dry and put away for winter eating. There were wild grapes and pawpaws; there were bee trees with wild honey; there were wild crab apples and red haws. If it was a good corn year, the children helped shell the corn by hand and put it between two big flat stones, grinding it into corn meal. The creeks gave them fish to fry. Tom Lincoln took his gun and brought back prairie turkey, partridge, rabbit, sometimes a coon, a bear, or a deer; and the skins of these big animals were tanned, cut, and sewed into shirts, trousers, moccasins; the coonskins made caps.

There were lean times and fat, all

depending on the weather, the rains, or floods, how Tom Lincoln worked and what luck he had fishing and hunting. There were times when they lived on the fat of the land and said God was good; other times when they just scraped along and said they hoped the next world would be better than this one.

It was wilderness. Life dripped with fat and ease. Or it took hold with hunger and cold. All the older settlers remembered winter in the year 1795, when "cold Friday" came; Kentucky was "cold as Canada," and cows froze to death in the open fields. The wilderness is careless.

In the fall of the year 1816 Abe watched his father cut down trees, cut out logs, and fasten those logs into a flatboat on Knob Creek. Abe ran after tools his father called for, sometimes held a hammer, a saw, and a knife in his hands ready to give his father the next one called for. If his father said, "Fetch me a drink of water," the boy fetched; his legs belonged to his father. He helped carry chairs, tables, household goods, and carpenter's tools, loading them on to the flatboat. These, with four hundred gallons of whisky, "ten bar'ls," Tom had loaded on to the boat, made quite a cargo. Tom Lincoln, who was not much of a drinking man, had traded his farm for whisky, which was a kind of money in that day, and twenty dollars cash.

Nancy Hanks and Sarah and Abe stayed on the farm while the husband and father floated down Knob Creek to Salt River and into the Ohio River. Tom was out of luck when the flatboat turned over so that the tool chest, household goods, and four barrels of whisky slid out of the boat. Most of the whisky and some of the other goods

he managed to fish up from the river bottom. Then he crossed the Ohio River, landed on the Indiana side at Thompson's Ferry, and left his whisky and household goods at the house of a man called Posey.

He started off on foot into the big timbers of what was then Perry County, later divided into Spencer County. He decided to live and to farm on a quarter section [1] of land on Little Pigeon Creek; he notched the trees with his ax, cleared away brush and piled it, as the government land laws required. This was his "claim," later filed at the Land Office in Vincennes, Indiana, as the Southwest Quarter of Section Thirty-two, Town Four South, Range Five West, to be paid for at two dollars an acre. His Indiana homestead was now ready for a cabin and a family; he walked back to the Knob Creek home in Kentucky and told the family he reckoned they'd all put in the winter up in "Indianny."

They had fifty miles to go, in a straight line "as the crow flies," but about one hundred miles with all the zigzags and curves around hills, timbers, creeks, and rivers.

Pots, pans, kettles, blankets, the family Bible, and other things were put into bags and loaded on two horses. Nancy and Sarah climbed on one horse, Tom and Abe on the other. When it was hard going for the horses, the father and mother walked. Part of the way on that hundred-mile ride made little Abe's eyes open. They were going deeper into the wilderness. In Kentucky there were ten people to the square mile and in Indiana only three. As Abe sat on the horse plodding along, he saw miles and miles of beeches, oaks, elms, hard and soft maples, hung and run

[1] quarter section: one fourth of a square mile, or one hundred and sixty acres.

over with the scarlet streamers and the shifting gray hazes of autumn.

Then they came to the Ohio River. The Frenchmen years before named it "La Belle Riviere," meaning it was a sheen of water as good to look at as a beautiful woman. There she lay — the biggest stretch of shining water his eyes had ever seen. And Abe thought how different it was from Knob Creek, which he could walk across on a log — if he didn't let his feet slip from under. They crossed the river, and at the house of the man called Posey they got a wagon, loaded the barrels of whisky and the household goods, and drove sixteen miles to their "claim." The trail was so narrow that a few times Tom Lincoln got off the wagon with an ax and cut brush and trees so the wagon could pass through. It was a hired wagon and horses they came with, and the wagon and horse team were taken back to Posey.

Tom Lincoln, his wife, boy, and girl, had arrived on a claim at Little Pigeon Creek, without a horse or a cow, without a house, with a little piece of land under their feet and the wintry sky high over. Naked they had come into the world; almost naked they came to Little Pigeon Creek, Indiana.

The whole family pitched in and built a pole shed or "half-faced camp." On a slope of ground stood two trees about fourteen feet apart, east and west. These formed the two strong corner posts of a sort of cabin with three sides, the fourth side open, facing south. The sides and the roof were covered with poles, branches, brush, dried grass, mud; chinks were stuffed where the wind or rain was trying to come through. At the open side a log fire was kept burning night and day. In the two far corners inside the camp were beds of dry leaves on the ground. To these beds the sleepers brought their blankets and bearskins.

Here they lived a year. In the summertime and fair weather the pole shed was snug enough. When the rainstorms or wind and snow broke through and drenched the place, or when the south or southwest wind blew the fire smoke into the camp so those inside had to clear out, it was a rough life.

As Abe Lincoln, seven years old, going on eight, went to sleep on his bed of dry leaves in a corner of the pole shed there on Little Pigeon Creek, in Indiana, in the winter of 1816, he had his thoughts, his feelings, his impressions. He shut his eyes, and looking glasses began to work inside his head; he could see Kentucky and the Knob Creek farm again; he could see the Ohio River shining so far across that he couldn't begin to throw a stone from one side to the other.

And while his eyes were shut, he could see the inside of the pole shed, the floor of earth and grass, the frying pan, the cooking pot, the water pail he and his sister carried full of water from the spring a mile away, and the log fire always kept burning. And sometimes his imagination, his shut eyes, and their quick-changing looking glasses would bring the whole outdoor sky and land indoors, into the pole shed, into the big shifting looking glasses inside of his head. The mystery of imagination, of the faculty of reconstruction and piecing together today the things his eyes had seen yesterday — this took hold of him and he brooded over it.

One night he tried to sleep while his head was working on the meaning of the heavy and mysterious words standing dark on the pages of the family Bible; the stories his mother told him from those pages; all the people in the world drowned, the world covered with water, even Indiana and Kentucky, all people drowned except Noah and his family; the man Jonah swallowed by a whale and after days coming out of the belly of the whale; the Last Day to come, the stars dropping out of the sky, the world swallowed up in fire.

And one night this boy felt the south-west wind blowing the log-fire smoke into his nostrils. And there was a hoot owl crying, and a shaking of branches in the beeches and walnuts outside, so that he went to the south opening of the shed and looked out on a winter sky with a high quarter-moon and a white shine of thin frost on the long open spaces of the sky.

And an old wonder took a deeper hold on him, a wonder about the loneliness of life down there in the Indiana wilderness, and a wonder about what was happening in other places over the world, places he had heard people mention, cities, rivers, flags, wars, Jerusalem, Washington, Baltimore.

He might have asked the moon, "What do you see?" And the moon might have told him many things.

That year of 1816 the moon had seen sixteen thousand wagons come along one turnpike in Pennsylvania, heading west, with people hungry for new land, a new home, just like Tom Lincoln. Up the Mississippi River that year had come the first steamboat to curve into the Ohio River and land passengers at Louisville. The moon had seen the first steamboat leave Pittsburgh and tie up at New Orleans. New wheels, wagons, were coming, an iron horse snorting fire and smoke. Rolling mills, ingots, iron, steel, were the talk of Pennsylvania; a sheet-copper mill was starting in Massachusetts.

When Napoleon sold to Jefferson the Great Plains between the Mississippi River and the Rocky Mountains, the moon saw only a few Indians, buffalo hunters and drifters, living there. The price for the land was fifteen million dollars; Jefferson had to argue with people who said the price was too high. Such things the moon had seen. Also, out of war-taxed and war-crippled Europe the moon could see steady lines of ships taking people from that part of the round world across the water to America. Also, lines of ships sailing to Africa with whisky, calico, and silk, and coming back loaded with Negroes.

And as the wagons, by thousands a year, were slipping through the passes of the Allegheny Mountains, heading west for the two-dollar-an-acre government land, many steered clear of the South; they couldn't buy slaves; and they were suspicious of slavery; it was safer to go farming where white men did all the work. At first the stream of wagons and settlers moving west had kept close to the Ohio River. Then it began spreading in a fan shape up north and west.

The moon could see, along the pikes, roads, and trails heading west, broken wagon wheels with prairie grass growing up over the spokes and hubs. And near by, sometimes, a rusty skillet, empty moccasins, and the bones of horses and men.

In the hot dog days,[1] in the long rains, in the casual blizzards, they had stuck it out — and lost. There came a saying, a pithy, perhaps brutal folk proverb, "The cowards never started and the weak ones died by the way."

Such were a few of the many, many things the moon might have told little Abe Lincoln, nearly eight years old, on a winter night in 1816 on Little Pigeon

[1] **dog days:** hot, sultry summer days.

Creek, in the Buckhorn Valley, in southern Indiana — a high quarter-moon with a white shine of thin frost on the long open spaces of the sky.

He was of the blood and breath of many of these things, and would know them better in the years to come.

During the year 1817 little Abe Lincoln, eight years old, going on nine, had an ax put in his hands and helped his father cut down trees and notch logs for the corners of their new cabin, forty yards from the pole shed where the family was cooking, eating, and sleeping.

Wild turkey, ruffed grouse, partridge, coon, rabbit, were to be had for the shooting of them. Before each shot Tom Lincoln took a rifle ball out of a bag and held the ball in his left hand; then with his right hand holding the gunpowder horn, he pulled the stopper with his teeth, slipped the powder into the barrel, followed with the ball; then he rammed the charge down the barrel with a hickory ramrod held in both hands, looked to his trigger, flint, and feather in the touchhole — and he was ready to shoot, to kill for the home skillet.

Having loaded his rifle just that way several thousand times in his life, he could do it in the dark or with his eyes shut. Once Abe took the gun as a flock of wild turkeys came toward the new log cabin, and, standing inside, shot through a crack and killed one of the big birds; and after that, somehow, he never felt like pulling the trigger on game birds. A mile from the cabin was a salt lick where deer came; there the boy could have easily shot the animals, as they stood rubbing their tongues along the salty slabs or tasting a saltish ooze. His father did the shooting; the deer killed gave them meat for Nancy's skillet; and the skins were tanned, cut, and stitched into shirts, trousers, mitts, moccasins. They wore buckskin; their valley was called the Buckhorn Valley.

After months the cabin stood up, four walls fitted together with a roof, a one-room house eighteen feet square, for a family to live in. A stick chimney plastered with clay ran up outside. The floor was packed and smoothed dirt. A log fire lighted the inside; no windows were cut in the walls. For a door there was a hole cut to stoop through. Bedsteads were cleated to the corners of the cabin; pegs stuck in the side of a wall made a ladder for young Abe to climb up in a loft to sleep on a hump of dry leaves; rain and snow came through chinks of the room onto his bearskin cover. A table and three-legged stools had the top sides smoothed with an ax, and the bark side under, in the style called "puncheon."

A few days of this year in which the cabin was building, Nancy told Abe to wash his face and hands extra clean; she combed his hair, held his face between her two hands, smacked him a kiss on the mouth, and sent him to school — nine miles and back — Abe and Sally hand in hand hiking eighteen miles a day. Tom Lincoln used to say Abe was going to have "a real eddication," explaining, "You air a-goin' to larn readin', writin', and cipherin'."

He learned to spell words he didn't know the meaning of, spelling the words before he used them in sentences. In a list of "words of eight syllables accented upon the sixth," was the word *incomprehensibility*. He learned that first, and then such sentences as "Is he to go in?" and "Ann can spin flax."

Some neighbors said, "It's a pore make-out of a school," and Tom complained it was a waste of time to send the children nine miles just to sit with a lot of other children and read out loud all day in a "blab" school. But Nancy, as she cleaned Abe's ears in corners where he forgot to clean them, and as she combed out the tangles in his coarse, sandy black hair, used to say, "Abe, you go to school now, and larn all you kin." And he kissed her and said, "Yes, Mammy," and started with his sister on the nine-mile walk through timberland where bear, deer, coon, and wildcats ran wild.

Fall time came with its early frost and they were moved into the new cabin, when horses and a wagon came breaking into the clearing one day. It was Tom and Betsy Sparrow and their seventeen-year-old boy, Dennis Hanks, who had come from Hodgenville, Kentucky, to cook and sleep in the pole shed of the Lincoln family till they could locate land and settle. Hardly a year had passed, however, when both Tom and Betsy Sparrow were taken down with the "milk sick," beginning with a whitish coat on the tongue. Both died and were buried in October on a little hill in a clearing in the timbers near by.

Soon after, there came to Nancy Hanks Lincoln that white coating of the tongue; her vitals burned; the tongue turned brownish; her feet and hands grew cold and colder, her pulse slow and slower. She knew she was dying, called for her children, and spoke to them her last choking words. Sarah and Abe leaned over the bed. A bony hand of the struggling mother went out, putting its fingers into the boy's sandy black hair; her fluttering guttural words seemed to say he must grow up and be good to his sister and father.

So, on a bed of poles cleated to the corner of the cabin, the body of Nancy Hanks Lincoln lay, looking tired . . . tired . . . with a peace settling in the pinched corners of the sweet, weary mouth, silence slowly etching away the lines of pain and hunger drawn around the gray eyes where now the eyelids closed down in the fine pathos of unbroken rest, a sleep without interruption settling about the form of the stooped and wasted shoulder bones; looking to the children who tiptoed in, stood still, cried their tears of want and longing, whispered, "Mammy, Mammy," and heard only their own whispers answering; looking to these little ones of her brood as though new secrets had come to her in place of the old secrets given up with the breath of life.

And Tom Lincoln took a log left over from the building of the cabin, and he and Dennis Hanks whipsawed [1] the log into planks, planed the planks smooth, and made them of a measure for a box to bury the dead wife and mother in. Little Abe, with a jackknife, whittled pine-wood pegs. And then, while Dennis and Abe held the planks, Tom bored holes and stuck the whittled pegs through the bored holes. This was the coffin, and they carried it the next day to the same little timber clearing near by, where a few weeks before they had buried Tom and Betsy Sparrow. It was in the way of the deer-run leading to the saltish water; light feet and shy hoofs ran over those early winter graves.

So the woman, Nancy Hanks, died, thirty-six years old, a pioneer sacrifice, with memories of monotonous, endless, everyday chores, of mystic Bible verses read over and over for their promises, and with memories of blue wistful hills and a summer when the crab-apple blossoms flamed white and she carried a boy child into the world.

She had looked out on fields of blue-

---

[1] **whipsawed:** used a whipsaw.

blossoming flax and hummed "Hey, Betty Martin, tiptoe, tiptoe"; she had sung of bright kingdoms by and by and seen the early frost leaf its crystals on the stalks of buttonweed and redbud; she had sung:

You may bury me in the East,
You may bury me in the West,
And we'll all rise together in that morning.

Some weeks later, when David Elkin, elder of the Methodist church, was in that neighborhood, he was called on to speak over the grave of Nancy Hanks. He had been acquainted with her in Kentucky, and to the Lincoln family and a few neighbors he spoke of good things she had done, sweet ways she had of living her life in this Vale of Tears, and her faith in another life yonder past the River Jordan.

The "milk sick" took more people in that neighborhood the same year, and Tom Lincoln whipsawed planks for more coffins. One settler lost four milch cows [1] and eleven calves. The nearest doctor for people or cattle was thirty-five miles away. The wilderness is careless.

Lonesome and dark months came for Abe and Sarah. Worst of all were the weeks after their father went away, promising to come back.

Elizabethtown, Kentucky, was the place Tom Lincoln headed for. As he footed it through the woods and across the Ohio River, he was saying over to himself a speech — the words he would say to Sarah Bush Johnston, down in Elizabethtown. Her husband had died a few years before, and she was now in Tom's thoughts.

He went straight to the house where she was living in Elizabethtown, and, speaking to her as "Miss Johnston," he

¹ **milch** (mĭlch) **cows:** cows giving milk.

argued: "I have no wife and you no husband. I came a-purpose to marry you. I knowed you from a gal and you knowed me from a boy. I've no time to lose; and if you're willin', let it be done straight off."

Her answer was, "I got debts." She gave him a list of the debts; he paid them; a license was issued; and they were married on December 2, 1819.

He could write his name; she couldn't write hers. Trying to explain why the two of them took up with each other so quickly, Dennis Hanks at a later time said, "Tom had a kind o' way with women, an' maybe it was somethin' she took comfort in to have a man that didn't drink an' cuss none."

Little Abe and Sarah, living in the lonesome cabin on Little Pigeon Creek, Indiana, got a nice surprise one morning when four horses and a wagon came into their clearing, and their father jumped off; then Sarah Bush Lincoln, the new wife and mother; then John, Sarah, and Matilda Johnston, Sarah Bush's three children by her first husband. Next off the wagon came a feather mattress, feather pillows, a black-walnut bureau, a large clothes chest, a table, chairs, pots and skillets, knives, forks, spoons.

Abe ran his fingers over the slick wood of the bureau, pushed his fist into the feather pillows, sat in the new chairs, and wondered to himself, because this was the first time he had touched such fine things, such soft slick things.

"Here's your new mammy," his father told Abe as the boy looked up at a strong, large-boned, rosy woman, with a kindly face and eyes, with a steady voice, steady ways. The cheekbones of her face stood out and she had a strong jawbone; she was warm and friendly for Abe's little hands to touch, right

Where Lincoln lived: Knob Creek farm.

from the beginning. As one of her big hands held his head against her skirt, he felt like a cold chick warming under the soft feathers of a big wing. She took the cornhusks Abe had been sleeping on, piled them in the yard, and said they would be good for a pigpen later on; and Abe sunk his head and bones that night in a feather pillow and a feather mattress.

Ten years pass with that cabin on Little Pigeon Creek for a home, and that farm and neighborhood the soil for growth. There the boy Abe grows to be the young man, Abraham Lincoln.

Ten years pass and the roots of a tree spread out finding water to carry up to branches and leaves that are in the sun; the trunk thickens, the forked limbs shine wider in the sun; they pray with their leaves in the rain and the whining wind; the tree arrives, the mystery of its coming, spreading, growing, a secret not even known to the tree itself; it stands with its arms stretched to the corners the four winds come from, with its murmured testimony, "We are here, we arrived, our roots are in the earth of

these years," and beyond that short declaration, it speaks nothing of the decrees, fates, accidents, destinies, that made it an apparition of its particular moment.

Abe Lincoln grows up. His father talks about the waste of time in "eddication"; it is enough "to larn readin', writin', cipherin'"; but the stanch, yearning stepmother, Sarah Bush Lincoln, comes between the boy and the father. And the father listens to the stepmother and lets her have her way.

When he was eleven years old, Abe Lincoln's young body began to change. The juices and glands began to make a long, tall boy out of him. As the months and years went by, he noticed his lean wrists getting longer, his legs too, and he was now looking over the heads of other boys. Men said, "Land o' Goshen, that boy air a-growin'!"

As he took on more length, they said he was shooting up into the air like green corn in the summer of a good corn year. So he grew. When he reached seventeen years of age, and they measured him, he was six feet, nearly four inches, high, from the bottoms of his moccasins to the top of his skull.

These were years he was handling the ax. Excepting in spring-plowing time and the fall fodder-pulling, he was handling the ax nearly all the time. The insides of his hands took on callus thick as leather. He cleared openings in the timber, cut logs and puncheons, split firewood, built pigpens.

He learned how to measure with his eye the half-circle swing of the ax so as to nick out the deepest possible chip from off a tree trunk. The trick of swaying his body easily on the hips so as to throw the heaviest possible weight into the blow of the ax — he learned that.

On winter mornings he wiped the frost from the ax handle, sniffed sparkles of air into his lungs, and beat a steady cleaving of blows into a big tree — till it fell — and he sat on the main log and ate his noon dinner of corn bread and fried salt pork — and joked with the gray squirrels that frisked and peeped at him from high forks of nearby walnut trees.

He learned how to make his ax flash and bite into a sugar maple or a sycamore. The outside and the inside look of black walnut and black oak, hickory and jack oak, elm and white oak, sassafras, dogwood, grapevines, sumac — he came on their secrets. He could guess close to the time of the year, to the week of the month, by the way the leaves and branches of trees looked. He sniffed the seasons.

Often he worked alone in the timbers, all day long with only the sound of his own ax, or his own voice speaking to himself, or the crackling and swaying of branches in the wind, and the cries and whirs of animals; of brown and silver-gray squirrels; of partridges, hawks, crows, turkeys, sparrows, and the occasional wildcats.

The tricks and whimsies of the sky, how to read clear skies and cloudy weather: the creeping vines of ivy and wild grape; the recurrence of dogwood blossoms in spring; the ways of snow, rain, drizzle, sleet, the visitors of sky and weather coming and going hour by hour — he tried to read their secrets; he tried to be friendly with their mystery.

So he grew, to become hard, tough, wiry. The muscle on his bones and the cords, tendons, cross weaves of fiber, and nerve centers — these became instruments to obey his wishes. He found with other men he could lift his own end of a log — and more too. One of the neighbors said he was strong as three men. Another said, "He can sink an ax deeper into wood than any man I ever saw." And another, "If you heard him fellin' trees in a clearin', you would say there was three men at work by the way the trees fell."

He was more than a tough, long, raw-boned boy. He amazed men with his man's lifting power. He put his shoulders under a new-built corncrib one day and walked away with it to where the farmer wanted it. Four men, ready with poles to put under it and carry it, didn't need their poles. He played the same trick with a chicken house; at the new, growing town of Gentryville nearby, they said the chicken house weighed six hundred pounds, and only a big boy with a hard backbone could get under it and walk away with it.

A blacksmith shop, a grocery, and a store had started up on the crossroads of the Gentry farm. And one night after Abe had been helping thresh wheat on Dave Turnham's place, he went with Dennis Hanks, John Johnston, and some other boys to Gentryville, where the farm hands sat around with John Baldwin, the blacksmith, and Jones, the storekeeper, passed the whisky jug, told stories, and talked politics and religion and gossip. Going home late that night, they saw something in a mud puddle alongside the road. They stepped over to see whether it was a man or a hog. It was a man — drunk — snoring — sleeping off his drunk — on a frosty night outdoors in a cold wind.

They shook him by the shoulders, doubled his knees to his stomach; but he went on sleeping, snoring. The cold wind was getting colder. The other boys said they were going home; and they went away, leaving Abe alone with the snoring sleeper in the mud puddle. Abe stepped into the mud, reached arms around the man, slung him over his shoulders, carried him to Dennis Hanks's cabin, built a fire, rubbed him warm, and left him sleeping off the whisky.

And the man afterward said Abe saved his life. He told John Hanks, "It was mighty clever of Abe to tote me to a warm fire that night."

So he grew, living in that Pigeon Creek cabin for a home, sleeping in the loft, climbing up at night to a bed just under the roof, where sometimes the snow and the rain drove through the cracks, eating sometimes at a table where the family had only one thing to eat — potatoes. Once at the table, when there were only potatoes, his father spoke a blessing to the Lord for potatoes; the boy murmured, "Those are mighty poor blessings." And Abe made jokes once when company came and Sally Bush Lincoln brought out raw potatoes, gave the visitors a knife apiece, and they all peeled raw potatoes and talked about the crops, politics, religion, gossip.

Days when they had only potatoes to eat didn't come often. Other days in the year they had "yaller-legged chicken" with gravy, and corn dodgers with shortening, and berries and honey. They tasted of bear meat, deer, coon, quail, grouse, prairie turkey, catfish, bass, perch.

Abe knew the sleep that comes after long hours of work outdoors, the feeling of simple food changing into blood and muscle as he worked in those young years clearing timberland for pasture and corn crops, cutting loose the brush, piling it and burning it, splitting rails, pulling the crosscut saw and the whipsaw, driving the shovel plow, harrowing, planting, hoeing, pulling fodder, milking cows, churning butter, helping neighbors at house raisings, logrollings, cornhuskings.

He found he was fast, strong, and keen when he went against other boys in sports. On farms where he worked, he held his own at scuffling, knocking off hats, wrestling. The time came when around Gentryville and Spencer County he was known as the best "rassler" of all, the champion. In jumping, foot racing, throwing the maul,[1] pitching the crowbar, he carried away the decisions against the lads of his own age always, and usually won against those older than himself.

He earned his board, clothes, and lodgings, sometimes working for a neighbor farmer. He watched his father, while helping make cabinets, coffins, cupboards, window frames, doors. Hammers, saws, pegs, cleats, he understood firsthand, also the scythe and the cradle for cutting hay and grain, the corn-cutter's knife, the leather piece to protect the hand while shucking corn, and the horse, the dog, the cow, the ox, the hog. He could skin and cure the hides of coon and deer. He lifted the slippery two-hundred-pound hog carcass, head down, holding the hind

[1] **maul** (môl): a heavy, long-handled hammer used to drive wedges in splitting logs.

hocks up for others of the gang to hook, and swung the animal clear of the ground. He learned where to stick a hog in the underside of the neck so as to bleed it to death; how to split it in two and carve out the chops, the parts for sausage-grinding, for hams, for "cracklings."

Farmers called him to butcher for them at thirty-one cents a day — this when he was sixteen and seventeen years old. He could "knock a beef in the head," swing a maul and hit a cow between the eyes, skin the hide, halve and quarter it, carve out the tallow, the steaks, kidneys, liver.

And the hiding places of fresh spring water under the earth crust had to be in his thoughts; he helped at well digging; the wells Tom Lincoln dug went dry one year after another; neighbors said Tom was always digging a well and had his land "honeycombed"; and the boy Abe ran the errands and held the tools for the well digging.

When he was eighteen years old, he could take an ax at the end of the handle and hold it out in a straight horizontal line, easy and steady — he had strong shoulder muscles and steady wrists early in life. He walked thirty-four miles in one day, just on an errand, to please himself, to hear a lawyer make a speech. He could tell his body to do almost impossible things, and the body obeyed.

Growing from boy to man, he was alone a good deal of the time. Days came often when he was by himself all the time except at breakfast and supper hours in the cabin home. In some years more of his time was spent in loneliness than in the company of other people. It happened, too, that this loneliness he knew was not like that of people in cities who can look from a window on streets where faces pass and repass. It

was the wilderness loneliness he became acquainted with; solved; filtered through body, eye, and brain; held communion with in his ears, in the temples of his forehead, in the works of his beating heart.

He lived with trees; with the bush wet with shining raindrops; with the burning bush of autumn; with the lone wild duck riding a north wind and crying down on a line north to south, the faces of open sky and weather, the ax which is an individual one-man instrument — these he had for companions, books, friends, talkers, chums of his endless changing soliloquies.[1]

His moccasin feet in the wintertime knew the white spaces of snowdrifts piled in whimsical shapes against timber slopes or blown in levels across the fields of last year's cut cornstalks; in the summertime his bare feet toughened in the gravel of green streams while he laughed back to the chatter of bluejays in the red-haw trees or while he kept his eyes ready in the slough quack grass [2] for the cow snake, the rattler, the copperhead.

He rested between spells of work in the springtime when the upward push of the coming out of the new grass can be heard, and in autumn weeks when the rustle of a single falling leaf lets go a whisper that a listening ear can catch.

He found his life thrown in ways where there was a certain chance for a certain growth. And so he grew. Silence found him; he met silence. In the making of him as he was, the element of silence was immense.

It was a little country of families living in one-room cabins. Dennis Hanks said at a later time, "We lived the same

[1] **soliloquies** (sȯ·lĭl′ȯ·kwĭz): conversations with oneself.
[2] **slough** (slōō) **quack grass**: a tough, coarse grass growing in sloughs or swampy places.

Interior of Knob Creek farmhouse, reconstructed.

as the Indians, 'ceptin' we took an interest in politics and religion."

Cash was scarce; venison hams, bacon slabs, and barrels of whisky served as money; there were seasons when storekeepers asked customers, "What kind of money have you today?" because so many sorts of wildcat dollar bills [1] were passing around. In sections of timberland wild hogs were nosing out a fat living on hickory nuts, walnuts, acorns; it was said the country would be full of wild hogs if the wolves didn't find the litters of young pigs a few weeks old and kill them.

Farmers lost thirty and forty sheep in a single wolf raid. Toward the end of June came "fly time," when cows lost weight and gave less milk because they had to fight flies. For two or three months at the end of summer, horses weakened, unless covered with blankets, under the attacks of horseflies; where one lighted on a horse, a drop of

blood oozed; horses were hitched to branches of trees that gave loose rein to the animals, room to move and fight flies.

Men and women went barefoot except in the colder weather; women carried their shoes in their hands and put them on just before arrival at church meetings or at social parties.

Rains came, loosening the topsoil of the land where it was not held by grass roots; it was a yellow clay that softened to slush; in this yellow slush many a time Abe Lincoln walked ankle-deep; his bare feet were intimate with the clay dust of the hot dog days, with the clay mud of spring and fall rains; he was at home in clay. In the timbers with his ax, on the way to chop, his toes, heels, soles, the balls of his feet, climbed and slid in banks and sluices of clay. In the cornfields, plowing, hoeing, cutting, and shucking, again his bare feet spoke with the clay of the earth; it was in his toenails and stuck on the skin of his toe knuckles. The color of

[1] **wildcat dollar bills:** paper money without adequate security behind it.

clay was one of his own colors.

In the short and simple annals of the poor it seems there are people who breathe with the earth and take into their lungs and blood some of the hard and dark strength of its mystery. During six and seven months each year in the twelve fiercest formative years of his life, Abraham Lincoln had the pads of his foot soles bare against clay of the earth. It may be the earth told him in her own tough gypsy slang one or two knacks of living worth keeping. To be organic with running wildfire and quiet rain, both of the same moment, is to be the carrier of wave lines the earth gives up only on hard usage.

He took shape in a tall, long-armed cornhusker. When rain came in at the chinks of the cabin loft where he slept, soaking through the book Josiah Crawford lent him, he pulled fodder two days to pay for the book, made a clean sweep, till there wasn't a blade left on a cornstalk in the field of Josiah Crawford.

His father was saying the big boy looked as if he had been roughhewn with an ax and needed smoothing with a jack plane. "He was the ganglin'est, awkwardest feller that ever stepped over a ten-rail snake fence; he had t' duck to git through a door; he 'peared to be all j'ints."

His stepmother told him she didn't mind his bringing dirt into the house on his feet; she could scour the floor, but she asked him to keep his head washed or he'd be rubbing the dirt on her nice whitewashed rafters. He put barefoot boys to wading in a mud puddle near the horse trough, picked them up one by one, carried them to the house upside down, and walked their muddy feet across the ceiling. The mother came in, laughed an hour at the foot tracks,

told Abe he ought to be spanked — and he cleaned the ceiling so it looked new.

The mother said, "Abe never spoke a cross word to me in his life since we lived together." And she said Abe was truthful; when Tilda Johnston leaped onto Abe's back to give him a scare on a lonely timber path, she brought the big axman to the ground by pulling her hands against his shoulders and pressing her knee into his backbone. The ax blade cut her ankle, and strips from Abe's shirt and Tilda's dress had to be used to stop the blood. By then she was sobbing over what to tell her mother. On Abe's advice she told her mother the whole truth.

As time went by, the stepmother of Abe became one of the rich, silent forces in his life. Besides keeping the floors, pots, pans, kettles, and milk crocks spick-and-span, weaving, sewing, mending, and managing with sagacity and gumption, she had a massive, bony, human strength backed with an elemental faith that the foundations of the world were mortised by God with unspeakable goodness of heart toward the human family. Hard as life was, she was thankful to be alive.

Once she told Abe how her brother Isaac, back in Hardin County, had hot words with a cowardly young man who shot Isaac without warning. The doctors asked Isaac if they could tie him down while they cut his flesh and took out the bullet. He told them he didn't need to be tied down; he put two lead musket balls in between his teeth and ground his teeth on them while the doctors cut a slash nine inches long and one inch deep till they found the bullet and brought it out. Isaac never let out a moan or a whimper; he set his teeth into the musket balls, ground them into flat sheets, and spat them from his mouth when he thanked the doctors.

Sally Bush, the stepmother, was all of a good mother to Abe. If he broke out laughing when others saw nothing to laugh at, she let it pass as a sign of his thoughts working their own way. So far as she was concerned, he had a right to do unaccountable things; since he never lied to her, why not? So she justified him. When Abe's sister, Sarah, married Aaron Grigsby and a year after died with her newborn child, it was Sally Bush who spoke comfort to the eighteen-year-old boy of Nancy Hanks burying his sister and the wraith of a child.

A neighbor woman sized him up by saying, "He could work when he wanted to, but he was no hand to pitch in like killing snakes." John Romine made the remarks: "Abe Lincoln worked for me, but was always reading and thinking. I used to get mad at him for it. I say he was awful lazy. He would laugh and talk — crack his jokes and tell stories all the time; didn't love work half as much as his pay. He said to me one day that his father taught him to work, but he never taught him to love it."

A misunderstanding came up one time between Abe Lincoln and William Grigsby. It ended with Grigsby so mad he challenged Abe to a fight. Abe looked down at Grigsby, smiled, and said the fight ought to be with John Johnston, Abe's stepbrother. The day was set for the fight; each man was there with his seconds; the mauling began, with the two fighters stripped to the waist, beating and bruising each other with bare knuckles.

A crowd stood around, forming a ring, cheering, yelling, hissing, till after a while they saw Johnston getting the worst of it. Then the ring of people forming the crowd was broken as Abe Lincoln shouldered his way through, stepped out, took hold of Grigsby and threw that fighter out of the center of the fight ring.

Then Abe Lincoln called out, "I'm the big buck of this lick." And looking around so his eyes swept the circle of the crowd, he let loose the challenge, "If any of you want to try it, come on and whet your horns." A riot of wild fist fighting came then between the two gangs and for months around the Jones grocery store there was talk about which gang whipped the other.

After a fox chase with horses, Uncle Jimmy Larkin was telling how his horse won the race, was the best horse in the world, and never drew a long breath; Abe didn't listen; Uncle Jimmy told it again, and Abe said, "Why don't you tell us how many short breaths he drew?" It raised a laugh on Jimmy, who jumped around threatening to fight, till Abe said quietly, "Now, Larkin, if you don't shut up, I'll throw you in that water."

Asked by Farmer James Taylor if he could kill a hog, he answered, "If you will risk the hog, I'll risk myself."

He had the pride of youth that resents the slur, the snub, besides the riotous blood that has always led youth in reckless exploits. When he was cutting up didoes one day at the Crawford farmhouse, Mrs. Crawford asked, "What's going to become of you, Abe?" And with mockery of swagger, he answered, "Me? I'm going to be President of the United States."

Driving a horse at the mill, he was sending the whiplash over the nag and calling, "Git up, you old hussy; git up, you old hussy." The horse let fly a hind foot that knocked down the big boy just as he yelled "Git up." He lay bleeding, was taken home, washed, put to bed, and lay all night unconscious. As his eyewinkers opened the next day and he came to, his tongue struggled and blurted, "You old hussy," thus finishing what he started to say before the knock-down.

The farm boys in their evenings at Jones's store in Gentryville talked about how Abe Lincoln was always reading, digging into books, stretching out flat on his stomach in front of the fireplace, studying till midnight and past midnight, picking a piece of charcoal to write on the fire shovel, shaving off what he wrote, and then writing more — till midnight and past midnight. The next thing Abe would be reading books between the plow handles, it seemed to them. And once, trying to speak a last word, Dennis Hanks said, "There's suthin' peculiarsome about Abe."

He wanted to learn, to know, to live, to reach out; he wanted to satisfy hungers and thirsts he couldn't tell about, this big boy of the backwoods. And some of what he wanted so much, so deep down, seemed to be in the books. Maybe in books he would find the answers to dark questions pushing around in the pools of his thoughts and the drifts of his mind. He told Dennis and other people, "The things I want to know are in books; my best friend is the man who'll get me a book I ain't read." And sometimes friends answered, "Well, books ain't as plenty as wildcats in these parts o' Indianny."

This was one thing meant by Dennis when he said there was "suthin' peculiarsome" about Abe. It seemed that Abe made the books tell him more than they told other people. All the other farm boys had gone to school and read *The Kentucky Preceptor,* but Abe picked out questions from it, such as "Who has the most right to complain, the Indian or the Negro?" and Abe would talk about it, up one way and down the other, while they were in the cornfield pulling fodder for the winter. When Abe got

hold of a storybook and read about a boat that came near a magnetic rock, and how the magnets in the rock pulled all the nails out of the boat so it went to pieces and the people in the boat found themselves floundering in water, Abe thought it was funny and told it to other people. After Abe read poetry, especially Bobby Burns's poems, Abe began writing rhymes himself. When Abe sat with a girl, with their bare feet in the creek water, and she spoke of the moon rising, he explained to her it was the earth moving and not the moon — the moon only seemed to rise.

John Hanks, who worked in the fields barefooted with Abe, grubbing stumps, plowing, mowing, said, "When Abe and I came back to the house from work, he used to go to the cupboard, snatch a piece of corn bread, sit down, take a book, cock his legs up high as his head, and read. Whenever Abe had a chance in the field while at work, or at the house, he would stop and read." He liked to explain to other people what he was getting from books; explaining an idea to someone else made it clearer to him. The habit was growing on him of reading out loud; words came more real if picked from the silent page of the book and pronounced on the tongue; new balance and values of words stood out if spoken aloud. When writing letters for his father or the neighbors, he read the words out loud as they got written. Before writing a letter he asked questions, such as, "What do you want to say in the letter? How do you want to say it? Are you sure that's the best way to say it? Or do you think we can fix up a better way to say it?"

As he studied his books, his lower lip stuck out; Josiah Crawford noticed it was a habit and joked Abe about the "stuck-out lip." This habit, too, stayed with him.

He wrote in his sum book, or arithmetic, that compound division was "When several numbers of Divers [1] Denominations are given to be divided by 1 common divisor," and worked on the exercise in multiplication — "If 1 foot contain 12 inches, I demand how many there are in 126 feet." Thus the schoolboy.

What he got in the schools didn't satisfy him. He went to three different schools in Indiana, besides two in Kentucky — altogether about four months of school. He learned his A B C; how to spell, read, write. And he had been with the other barefoot boys in butternut jeans learning "manners" under the schoolteacher, Andrew Crawford, who had them open a door, walk in, and say, "Howdy do?" Yet what he tasted of books in school was only a beginning, only made him hungry and thirsty, shook him with a wanting and a wanting of more and more of what was hidden between the covers of books.

He kept on saying, "The things I want to know are in books; my best friend is the man who'll git me a book I ain't read." He said that to Pitcher, the lawyer over at Rockport, nearly twenty miles away, one fall afternoon, when he walked from Pigeon Creek to Rockport and borrowed a book from Pitcher. Then when fodder-pulling time came a few days later, he shucked corn from early daylight till sundown along with his father and Dennis Hanks and John Hanks; but after supper he read the book till midnight, and at noon he hardly knew the taste of his corn bread because he had the book in front of him. It was a hundred little things like these which made Dennis Hanks say there was "suthin' peculiarsome" about Abe.

Besides reading the family Bible and figuring his way all through the old

[1] **Divers** (dī'vērz): different.

arithmetic they had at home, he got hold of *Aesop's Fables, The Pilgrim's Progress, Robinson Crusoe,* and Weems's *The Life of Francis Marion.* The book of fables, written or collected thousands of years ago by the Greek slave known as Aesop, sank deep in his mind. As he read through the book a second and third time, he had a feeling there were fables all around him, that everything he touched and handled, everything he saw and learned had a fable wrapped in it somewhere. One fable was about a bundle of sticks and a farmer whose sons were quarreling and fighting.

There was a fable in two sentences which read: "A coachman, hearing one of the wheels of his coach make a great noise, and perceiving that it was the worst one of the four, asked how it came to take such a liberty. The wheel answered that from the beginning of time creaking had always been the privilege of the weak." And there were shrewd, brief incidents of foolery such as this: "A waggish, idle fellow in a country town, being desirous of playing a trick on the simplicity of his neighbors and at the same time putting a little money in his pocket at their cost, advertised that he would on a certain day show a wheel carriage that should be so contrived as to go without horses. By silly curiosity the rustics were taken in, and each succeeding group who came out from the show were ashamed to confess to their neighbors that they had seen nothing but a wheelbarrow."

The style of the Bible, of Aesop's fables, the hearts and minds back of those books, were much in his thoughts. His favorite pages in them he read over and over. Behind such proverbs as "Muzzle not the ox that treadeth out the corn" and "He that ruleth his own spirit is greater than he that taketh a city," there was a music of simple wisdom and a mystery of common everyday life that touched deep spots in him, while out of the fables of the ancient Greek slave he came to see that cats, rats, dogs, horses, plows, hammers, fingers, toes, people — all had fables connected with their lives, characters, places. There was, perhaps, an outside for each thing as it stood alone, while inside of it was its fable.

One book came, titled *The Life of George Washington,* "with Curious Anecdotes, Equally Honorable to Himself and Exemplary to His Young Countrymen. Embellished with Six Steel Engravings, by M. L. Weems, formerly Rector of Mt. Vernon Parish." It pictured men of passion and proud ignorance in the government of England driving their country into war on the American colonies. It quoted the far-visioned warning of Chatham to the British Parliament, "For God's sake, then, my lords, let the way be instantly opened for reconciliation. I say instantly; or it will be too late forever."

The book told of war, as at Saratoga. "Hoarse as a mastiff of true British breed, Lord Balcarras was heard from rank to rank, loud-animating his troops; while on the other hand, fierce as a hungry Bengal tiger, the impetuous Arnold precipitated heroes on the stubborn foe. Shrill and terrible, from rank to rank, resounds the clash of bayonets — frequent and sad the groans of the dying. Pairs on pairs, Britons and Americans, with each his bayonet at his brother's breast, fall forward together faint-shrieking in death, and mingle their smoking blood." Washington, the man, stood out, as when he wrote: "These things so harassed my heart with grief that I solemnly declared to God, if I know myself, I would gladly offer myself a sacrifice to the butchering enemy if I could thereby insure the safety of these my poor distressed countrymen."

The Weems book reached some deep spots in the boy. He asked himself what it meant that men should march, fight, bleed, go cold and hungry for the sake of what they called "freedom."

"Few great men are great in everything," said the book. And there was a cool sap in the passage: "His delight was in that of the manliest sort, which, by stringing the limbs and swelling the muscles, promotes the kindliest flow of blood and spirits. At jumping with a long pole, or heaving heavy weights, for his years he hardly had an equal."

Such book talk was a comfort against the same thing over again, day after day, so many mornings the same kind of water from the same spring, the same fried pork and corn meal to eat, the same drizzles of rain, spring plowing, summer weeds, fall fodder-pulling, each coming every year, with the same tired feeling at the end of the day, so many days alone in the woods or the fields or else the same people to talk with, people from whom he had learned all they could teach him. Yet there ran through his head the stories and sayings of other people, the stories and sayings of books, the learning his eyes had caught from books; they were a comfort; they were good to have because they were good by themselves; and they were still better to have because they broke the chill of the lonesome feeling.

He was thankful to the writer of Aesop's fables because that writer stood by him and walked with him, an invisible companion, when he pulled fodder or chopped wood. Books lighted lamps in the dark rooms of his gloomy hours. . . . Well — he would live on; maybe the time would come when he would be free from work for a few weeks, or a few months, with books, and then he would read. . . . Yes, then he would read. . . . Then he would go and get at the proud secrets of his books.

His father — would he be like his father when he grew up? He hoped not. Why should his father knock him off a fence rail when he was asking a neighbor, passing by, a question? Even if it was a smart question, too pert and too quick, it was no way to handle a boy in front of a neighbor. No, he was going to be a man different from his father. The books — his father hated the books. His father talked about "too much eddication"; after readin', writin', 'rithmetic, that was enough, his father said. He, Abe Lincoln, the boy, wanted to know more than the father, Tom Lincoln, wanted to know. Already Abe knew more than his father; he was writing letters for the neighbors; they hunted out the Lincoln farm to get young Abe to find his bottle of ink with blackberry-brier root and copperas [1] in it, and his pen made from a turkey-buzzard feather, and write letters. Abe had a suspicion sometimes his father was a little proud to have a boy that could write letters, and tell about things in books, and outrun and outwrestle and rough-and-tumble any boy or man in Spencer County. Yes, he would be different from his father; he was already so; it couldn't be helped.

[1] copperas (kŏp′ĕr·ăs): a chemical used in making ink.

THINKING IT OVER

1. To keep the sequence correct, which came first: the Knob Creek farm or the one on Little Pigeon Creek? Hodgenville or Gentryville?

2. The boy Abe was hungry to learn new words; two of the words he pondered over were "independent" and "predestination." What sort of character does his interest in these particular words suggest to you? Explain whether his later life reflected this quality in him.

3. Abe's boyhood was a mixture of back-breaking work and lively fun. What were some of the chores he performed and some of the ways he enjoyed himself?

4. Give your own opinion of Nancy Hanks Lincoln. What words would you use to describe her? Sandburg writes that as she lay dying she looked "as though new secrets had come to her in place of the old secrets given up with the breath of life." What might her old secrets have been? her new secrets?

5. Look up "milk sickness" in a dictionary, then tell what you think the author meant by calling Nancy Hanks Lincoln a "pioneer sacrifice."

RECOGNIZING IMPORTANT DETAILS

1. To sort out the various influences at work in Lincoln's early years, set up three columns on a sheet of paper and use these headings: *Persons, Incidents,* and *Other Facts.* Read over the selection; as you go along, list the details supplied by the author in the column where they belong. For *Other Facts,* you might list "studying nature" or "reading," among others.

2. Compare your lists of details. Which list is the longest? Which detail in each column does the class think influenced Lincoln most strongly? Explain your opinions.

3. Frontier life, as pictured in this selection by Carl Sandburg, was discouraging. What details does he give to bear this out?

4. Find the details which show that Abe's stepmother did the best she could, and that her best was pretty good.

5. What details prove that Abe was physically strong?

6. Abe had a consuming desire to learn. Point out the details that indicate this.

POETRY IN PROSE

1. In addition to being recognized as Lincoln's foremost biographer, Carl Sandburg is one of the country's best-known poets. This selection offers many examples of the poetic quality to be found in his prose writing. Point out several passages — page number, column, and paragraph — which illustrate his poet's use of vivid images and figures of speech.

2. Sandburg writes: "Books lighted lamps in the dark rooms of his gloomy

hours" (page 276). Explain this statement. Are there any books that have "lighted lamps" for you?

3. What does the author mean when he says about Abe that "looking glasses began to work inside his head" (page 262)?

4. Of all the descriptions of Lincoln in this selection, find the one which forms the sharpest picture for you. Explain why you think this description is so good. What, if any, are the poetic qualities in it?

CONTINUING THE STORY

Abraham Lincoln: The Prairie Years and *The War Years* is the title of the one-volume edition of Carl Sandburg's biography of Lincoln. Someday you will want to read this classic work. For the present, continue the story of Lincoln by supplying the answers to these questions: (1) What was the first elective office Lincoln held, and where did he live at the time? (2) What trade did he teach himself at this point in order to supplement his income? (3) What new act of legislation led to Lincoln's first debate with Stephen A. Douglas, an occasion which brought him his first national fame?

FOR YOUR VOCABULARY: WORD HISTORIES

The word *pike,* meaning "highway," is a shortened form of *turnpike.* Originally a turnpike (*turn + pike,* a long-handled weapon with a sharp point) was a turnstile entrance to a toll road. When the traveler paid his toll, the pike was turned to let him through. Today we have turnpikes and other toll roads, as well as roads much like turnpikes but that have no fee or toll. What are some of these? How did the fish named the pike get its name?

ABOUT THE AUTHOR

Carl Sandburg (1878–) was the son of poor Swedish immigrants who settled in Illinois. In many ways Sandburg's youth was similar to that of the man whose biographer he was to become. He had to leave school while still a boy and work at many hard jobs. He drove a milk wagon, portered in a barbershop, shifted scenery in a theater, worked in a brick kiln and in a pottery, washed dishes, and labored as a farm hand and painter. Eventually, he continued his education at Lombard College in Illinois. A popular lecturer, he has also appeared in concerts and on television, reciting his poems and singing American folk ballads to his own guitar accompaniment. Some of his poems are included in the poetry section of this book.

AN AUTHOR'S RESEARCH: THIRTY YEARS

In the preface to volume one of his biography of Lincoln, Carl Sandburg writes: "For thirty years and more I have planned to make a certain portrait of Abraham Lincoln . . . the country lawyer and prairie politician who was intimate with the settlers of the Knox County neighborhood where I grew up as a boy. . . ." The result of Sandburg's thirty years of research was an entire room in his house in Herbert, Michigan, filled with notes and material on Lincoln. Sandburg read everything that had ever been printed about Lincoln; he searched out old letters, legal papers, court documents, historical records; he combed through old newspapers and magazines; most valuable of all, he was able to find, in his own Illinois neighborhood, people who had actually known Lincoln and who could quote conversations they had had with him. The writing of the biography took Carl Sandburg fifteen years, one of the longest periods of time ever given by an author to a single work. The first two volumes of the biography were published in 1926 and won immediate acclaim. Originally Sandburg had planned to write only of Lincoln's early life, but he had become so fascinated by Lincoln's character that he wrote four more volumes, which appeared in 1939 under the title *The War Years.* In his book *Lincoln Collector,* Carl Sandburg writes about the many and unusual sources of material available about Lincoln.

The Rail Splitter ➤

Opposite is a painting of young Abe Lincoln by an unknown nineteenth-century artist. The painting originally appeared on a campaign banner that probably was carried in the torchlight parades in which Lincoln took part during his bid for the Presidency in 1860.

The World at My Finger Tips

KARSTEN OHNSTAD

What might life be like for a young person whose world is suddenly blacked out by blindness? How would he feel about it? What would he need to do to bring "light" back into his world? This is one person's story of how he faced just such a situation. Because the story is autobiographical, the reader is able to share the experience at first hand, exactly as it seemed to the author.

I took off my glasses, wiped them, started to hoe again. My hoe sank into the soft dirt between the rows of sprouting potato plants. The cool shadow of Dad's hospital stretched across the garden. My white leghorn pullets were scratching beneath the plum trees. I looked beyond them to our neighbor's house on the far corner of the block. I blinked. I looked again. The house was alive. The green paint along the corners was no longer straight and upright. It twisted over into the white of the wall; the white edged over into the green. I took my glasses off and looked again. The green and white still twisted, still faded and blurred. Black streaks that could not be rubbed away floated before my eyes. Getting more nearsighted, I told myself. I'd have Dad examine my eyes again and get stronger lenses.

That afternoon I spilled the parrot's sunflower seeds. Mother watched me scooping them together and dumping them back into the pail.

"Why don't you pick all of them up?" she said.

"I did," I protested.

"There are a lot more down there."

I bent down again and stared at the floor. "I can't see any."

"Right there in front of you," she replied. "Can't you see them?"

"No, I can't," I admitted.

I told my father about the tricks my eyes were playing. He took me into his office.

"Read those letters on that card," he said.

I read the first line and lost my way in the second. Dad took out his watch.

"We'll see a specialist right now," he said.

I followed Doctor A—— through the office into a dark room. A pane of crystallized glass lighted up on the opposite wall. A large red letter moved to the center of it.

"Read these letters as they appear."

The letters shrank and blurred.

Doctor A—— snapped out the light. "Your boy sees very poorly, Doctor," he said. "The left eye was pierced with a scissor when you were five? Do you see with it at all?"

That eye could barely distinguish sunlight.

"And when did you first notice something wrong with the vision of your right eye?"

I tried to remember.

The doctor tilted my head back and dropped some medicine into my better eye.

"I am putting in some atropine to dilate the pupil," he said. "Did anything ever happen to this eye?"

I remembered. In March a soccer ball had crashed into my right eye. I had a beautiful shiner.

Doctor A—— bent over me with his ophthalmoscope.[1] "The blow on the eye must have been the start of the trouble," he said. "The inflammation went from one eye to the other — sympathetic. We will have to get that inflammation stopped before it injures the interior of the eye."

Doctor A—— gave his instructions: atropine, hot compresses, pills. "Come back in a week," he said. "Don't do any reading and stay out of the sun. If you are in the light at all, wear dark glasses."

It was hard to obey that order.

We drove along the city streets, then stopped to let a parade go by. Drum corps from every city in the state marched before us. I listened to the drums, the blare of trumpets, the shrill whistles. Right before me men in gay uniforms were marching over the pavement, and I could not look. Temptation got the better of me. I lifted my dark glasses, took one quick look. Framed within the dark outlines of the car window, as if caught by the click of a camera, was a line of drummers in flashing scarlet coats, white breeches, shining black boots. Drumsticks poised in air, one black boot raised off the ground, like men in a painted picture they stood, moving but without motion. The picture was printed indelibly on my mind. It was the last parade I ever saw.

In June as I sat at the dinner table and looked across the room at the clock, I could not distinguish the numbers as I had before. Two steps nearer — the numbers came into focus. In August I could not see the numbers unless I stood immediately before the clock, less than a foot away.

As I sat at the table during mealtime, I could no longer tell what was on my plate. The meat and potatoes and corn were brown and white and yellow puddles of color, like a board on which a painter has slapped his brush.

When I awoke in the morning, matter had dried upon my lashes and sealed them together. I brooded over the fact that my classmates were going ahead in school while I sat at home doing nothing. I was being left behind. I noticed that the white house on the opposite corner of the block was no longer visible.

Dad and I drove to Bemidji.[2] Dr. G—— examined my eyes long and studiously. I saw the light of the ophthalmoscope, but I could not distinguish his face.

"I believe we should operate imme-

---

[1] **ophthalmoscope** (ŏf·thăl′mŏ·skōp): an instrument for viewing the interior of the eye.

[2] **Bemidji** (bĕ·mĭj′ĭ): a town in Minnesota.

diately," Doctor G—— said finally. "It is the only thing which will save the other eye. I believe it will begin to clear up right away."

I listened dully as the plans were being made. Be in the hospital before ten the next morning. I would be there only two days.

When I got out of the hospital, I felt sensitive about being seen with all those bandages on my head. I held tightly to my brother's arm as we walked leisurely through the crowded streets. Old acquaintances greeted him. I wanted to shrink behind him, to hide myself from every curious stare.

My sight was improving. Each day I looked eagerly for new indications of it. My brother spread a large sheet of orange-colored paper on the desk before me.

"Can you make this out?" he asked.

I scrutinized the paper from top to bottom — black lines ran in every direction at first over the orange paper. Then they began to take shape — a pointed hat, an eye, a crooked nose, a pointed chin.

"It's a witch, an old black witch riding on a broom!"

"That's right!" he exclaimed jubilantly. "It's Halloween."

But when I looked at the light of the window, black dots swam before my eyes. I turned my head rapidly from left to right, then looked straight ahead. The black dots, agitated by the movement, floated across my center of vision, twisting, turning, breaking up into small segments and reuniting.

Dad peered long into my eye.

"There is a small gray speck back in the lens," he said. "The aqueous humor [1] is no longer clear. A cataract might be forming."

[1] aqueous (ā'kwê·ŭs) humor: a fluid between the lens and the cornea of the eye.

A cataract! It meant that the lens was becoming opaque.

The light from the window shone on my father's face as he bent over me. For the first time in many weeks I saw him — white hair brushed back from his forehead; blue eyes steady, narrowed slightly as he peered; lips straight and firm, rarely giving indication of alarm. Father was stolid and deliberate. He spoke frankly, as if he were expressing his opinion to another doctor who had called him in on a puzzling case.

"Does that mean I will never see again?" I asked.

He sat down on the bed beside me.

"It does not mean that," he said at length. "The cataract can be removed. You remember Mother's friend who had cataracts. Now, with glasses, she sees well enough to do her own work. She even reads a newspaper."

I felt sick. The last hope that I might again see perfectly was gone.

"Are you sure it is a cataract?" I begged.

Another trip to Bemidji. The treatment of my cataract, Doctor G—— felt, was beyond his skill. It required the care of someone more specialized. He recommended Doctor B—— in St. Paul. Once more I packed my clothes. On a freezing stormy January morning, we drove to St. Paul.

"I think I can give you sight in that eye," Doctor B—— said when he finished the examination. A great wave of relief passed over me and left me weak and trembling. "I am going to keep you in the hospital a few weeks," he explained, putting his hand on my shoulder. "We are going to give you some shots, triple typhoids. You won't like it. They will give you a headache and backache, but we've got to break that inflammation."

The few weeks stretched into nine months. Finally the doctors came to a decision: an operation to remove the cataract.

I awoke from the anesthetic with a terrific pain in my head. My nose was filled with the stench of ether. The nurse kept swabbing my arm and sticking me with needles, but the pain did not lessen. Everything was black. I was sealed in. A wire mask like a pair of enormous goggles had been strapped over my eyes to keep my fingers away. Mother was at my bedside. The following day she told me of the operation. Only part of the cataract or lens had been removed. The adhesions binding it to the iris had made the operation more difficult than Doctor B—— had anticipated. When the liquid of the eye was clear again, perhaps —

Days dragged by. My head began to itch. I awoke in the night and found my fingers clawing the wire mask. One day Doctor B—— announced that the bandages were to be removed.

"Pull down the shades," he ordered. Then he untied the mask. He snipped the bandages, then lifted them layer by layer from my face.

"Now. Open your eyes . . . Can you see my fingers?"

I stared at the ceiling, a dim confusion of light and shadow. "No. I can't see them."

"Can you see them now?"

I stared, afraid to move my eyes. "No, I can just see light." I was not worried. Dad had explained cataract operations to me before. When only part of the lens was removed, it took time for the remainder to clear away.

Doctor B—— returned each day and blinked his light in my eye. He never said much. He looked with his ophthalmoscope, had me count his fingers, then left without comment. My eye, I knew, was not clearing up as he had hoped. Men with cataracts had come and gone. Doctor B—— came into my room a few days before I was to leave for home and handed me a card. On it were a lot of small bumps as if the point of a nail had been shoved almost through the paper. I was puzzled. I held it close to my eye, stared at it, touched it with my fingers. "What is it?"

"The Braille alphabet," Doctor B—— replied. "Hold it this way. Let me see how much of it you can memorize before I come back tomorrow."

Unless you come into the dark world suddenly, you feel it before you meet it. It is around you, but you cannot touch it; it talks, but you do not understand. It hides its contours and its language. Until you find a Rosetta stone.[1] Then you perceive suddenly that there is order and reason and communication within the vast darkness which had seemed only chaos.

That is one of the great moments of life. No Egyptologist,[2] no explorer, no astronomer ever felt a greater moment.

My Rosetta stone was a clothespole.

I hesitated a long time before venturing out of the house alone. Indoors I could smash into everything and no one would see me. Outside I would be pointed at, stared at. I trampled the rosebushes. I stumbled into the woodpile. I crashed into the young evergreen, sent the nesting robins flapping and squawking. When I didn't know where I was, I pretended that I had stopped to examine some object in my pocket or to tie my shoe.

[1] **Rosetta** (rô·zĕt′à) **stone:** a famous stone found near the mouth of the Nile in 1799, which gave the first clue to Egyptian inscriptions.

[2] **Egyptologist** (ē′jĭp·tŏl′ô·jĭst): a scientist specializing in Egyptian relics and ancient culture.

As my self-consciousness waned, I got in the habit of strolling around and around the house. I got along with only a few bumps. One day, as I was walking slowly past the steps where there was no walk, I stopped, drew back sharply. Something was ahead. I put out my hand. Two or three feet before me, directly in my path, was the clothespole. That was my imagination, perhaps. I walked around the house again. Approaching the vicinity of the post, I experienced the same sensation. I put out my hand, a little to the right — the post was there! Somehow, in some way, I could detect its presence. It was not my imagination. Excited, I walked around the house again and again. Without fail I found the post while it was still some distance away.

For eleven years I had seen that post daily. I had carved into it with my knife. I had covered it with white paint, I had driven nails into it, and chinned myself on the crossbar. But at that moment I discovered that it possessed another quality of whose existence I had been completely unaware.

I ran up the steps, bowled over a kitchen chair, careened down the hall, burst into the office.

"Dad, I can tell when I am coming to the clothespole!" I exclaimed. "I don't know how I do it. I can't see it, I can't hear it, I don't have to touch it, but I *know* it's there!"

The clothespole opened up the outside to me. If I could detect nearby objects without seeing them, I could get around safely by myself. I was the Columbus of the clothespole! The new world was mine!

The clothespole did more than that. It suggested to me that my remaining senses might serve me in ways I had little suspected. I found hearing to be my greatest aid when I was going through this process of revising and co-ordinating faculties. My rediscovery of the clothespole was no miracle: I heard a sound wave reflected from it. The experience is common among both men and animals; Albert Payson Terhune [1] tells of a blind collie which had such sharp hearing that it could run straight at a stone wall and stop inches from it. There has been a great deal of speculation about this "blind sense." In order to throw some light on the matter, a few years ago a laboratory was dotted with obstacles and blind persons asked to walk across the floor. When their ears were covered, they had many bumps; when their ears were uncovered, they struck far fewer obstacles. The conclusion seemed to be that the new "sense" was directly related to hearing.

One night I found out how to use echoes to locate myself. Every blind person, of course, hears of the fabulous accomplishments of Torger Lien [2] with echoes. A tap of his cane gives him the location of trees and buildings as he walks to work. A snap of his finger tells him the size of a room and whether it is furnished or empty. I had heard him talk to a high school assembly some years before, when it had not occurred to me that I might someday have to learn his skill. Then one night I tried out his plan when I lost the path in a silent snowfall.

I snapped my fingers and listened. Sure enough, I could locate houses for blocks around. The echoes followed the trees along the river and came back

[1] **Albert Payson Terhune** (1872–1942): a famous American author of dog stories.

[2] **Torger Lien** (tôr′gä lĭn): a faculty member of the Minnesota State School for the Blind, the school later attended by the author.

softened and diffused. Buildings threw back a sharp distinct click. The louder the snap, the more distant became the houses that I could locate. I walked toward a building, snapping my fingers every few steps. The speed of the echo increased. At a distance of several yards from the building, the snap and the echo merged into one simultaneous sound. A step closer and the impression of sound disappeared. The object seemed to be sensed rather than heard.

Until that night, echoes had been simply a source of amusement to me, something to throw back a halloo from a great distance. Now I had a broader world literally at my finger tips. I stood there snapping my fingers until the night watchman came along and wanted to know what was going on.

The one thing that does not throw back an echo is a drop-off. Stairways are a constant source of trouble. It would be a good thing, too, for someone to invent an appliance for the detection of low, overhanging awnings and open cellarways along the business section of the city. A street excavation with a sign over it, "Danger! Men at Work," doesn't convince the blind man. He drops right in for a personal investigation.

I came gradually to need less help. When venturing out alone over unfamiliar city streets, I kept a mental account of directions and blocks — three blocks from the bus depot, six blocks north, two blocks east. I reinforced my directions and blocks by recording landmarks along the way. A gasoline station was on the corner where I turned north; at the opposite end of the block a large mailbox flanked the wall; two blocks farther north a cement mixer chugged away at some construction job. Sometimes even the sweet odor of an apple tree in bloom, or the chattering of sparrows on an ivy-covered building, helped me to remember my location.

The sense of smell proved surprisingly useful. I soon found that every store had its characteristic odor — the corner pharmacy its fruity combination of drugs and perfumes; the mouth-watering whiff of steak and onions from the restaurant; the fresh ground coffee from the grocery; the smell of new cloth from the clothing store.

In winter it was more difficult to distinguish one store or shop from another. Closed doors shut off odors and noises from within. I had to depend on the footsteps of shoppers walking in and out to indicate the position of doors.

Busy street crossings remained a hazard. A solitary car rumbling by was more puzzling than a streetful of traffic. There might be other cars behind it, or there might be none. It was not safe for me to stop on what I thought was the middle of the street and let the cars whiz by on either side. Trucks and motorcycles made an auditory chaos of everything.

Wind was even worse than trucks and motorcycles. It uprooted all my auditory guideposts and danger signals, mixed them all together and swept the whole mess past my ears in one grand howling confusion.

Eventually, as my mother had prophesied, I swallowed my pride and used a white cane. I no longer cared if people saw that I was blind. It was to my advantage. The cane was a nuisance, clattering against everything and catching in my trouser cuffs as I twirled it idly about like a baton; but at street corners it proved its worth. Car drivers saw it and stopped. I held it out before me and walked across the pavement with an assurance that I had never felt before. I was a worker of miracles. I was the Moses of the metropolis. I held out my staff over that roaring, honking sea, and lo! the traffic parted, and I stepped up on the opposite curb sound as a dollar.

I looked forward to entering the Minnesota State School for the Blind at Faribault for two reasons especially. For one thing, it represented the longest step I had yet made by myself — the farthest reach toward learning to live in the world without my parents' protecting kindness. In the second place, it represented my first comprehensive view of this army of persons which I had joined when I lost my sight. The one hundred and thirty students at the school would be a good cross section of the two hundred thousand blind persons in the United States. What were they like? I wondered. What had been their experiences? How did they get around?

I arrived at early evening. Study hour was beginning in the Main building, I was told — second door to your right, next to the typing room. I stood in the doorway, confused by the chatter of the boys and girls pushing and crowding into the seats. A lady showed me to a desk and put a Braille alphabet card in my hand. A bell rang. The chatter ceased. Books were opened. I heard the rustle of pages and a rhythmic *scrape-scrape* as a boy sitting next to me drew his hand back and forth across the dots. I laid my Braille card on the desk and touched it with the tip of my point finger. *A* — one dot. *B* — two dots, one above the other. *C* — two dots, side by side.

I heard a continuous noise that seemed to come from all parts of the room, a rapid clicking like a flock of chickens pecking corn on a tin roof. I listened, wondering. Maybe it was some kind of knitting machine with steel needles. A bell rang. Books were slammed shut. Students scrambled from their seats. Someone took me by the arm and we marched along, listening to the shouting and calling as the boys scattered over the campus.

"What was that noise in there?" I asked.

"Noise? What noise?"

"That funny clicking sound. Were they making something?"

My companion chuckled. "That was the kids writing Braille. They have a steel slate and a wire stylus to punch into the paper. You'll get one of your own tomorrow."

The principal, a pleasant-voiced woman, asked me a few questions about myself, then began picking out the subjects I would take — geometry, history, physics. "How about Latin? Wouldn't you like to take that?"

I shuddered. "I tried it once before," I said, "and I didn't like it."

"I'll put you down for it anyway. And how about industrial work? You can have your choice — broommaking, woodwork, rug weaving, basketry, network, chair caning, piano tuning."

The industrial work did not appeal to me. I was afraid that by taking that work I was resigning myself to a life of unprofitable drudgery. I dreaded to think of myself sitting behind a loom all the rest of my life, making brooms, weaving baskets. It was an academic education that I wanted. My talents, my training, my hopes, all turned in that direction. I compromised on chair caning and piano tuning.

Gradually I found out how the school was run and what was studied. The students ranged in age from five to twenty-one. The school — primary grades and high school — was fully accredited. Its graduates could attend any college or university. With the exception of but one subject, chemistry, the curriculum was the same as that of any public school.

In addition to the regular academic subjects, all students were required to take industrial work. Music was everywhere. These subjects — industrial work, music, and also typing — were in addition to the sixteen academic credits required for graduation from high school. Every student there needed all the advantages he could get to help offset the disadvantage of blindness.

Class procedure was very much the same as that in public school. More emphasis, perhaps, was placed upon oral recitation. The slowness of reading Braille made it necessary to reduce slightly the amount of reading covered each year. Book reports were given orally for convenience. Themes were typewritten. Few if any of the sighted teachers could read Braille with facility. It was easier for the students to type their examinations, easier for the instructor to correct the papers. The class gathered in the typing room and tapped out the answers while the teacher walked from one to the other, reading the questions aloud.

Textbooks were the same as those used in public school. The sight-saving students, always under the supervision of an eye specialist, read enlarged print. Our Braille texts contained the same material. It happened that I had used one of our textbooks before I lost my sight. I remembered it as a thick blue volume containing many pictures. The Braille copy was eight thick volumes and not a picture from the first front to the last back.

Working mathematics with the Braille writing slate was extremely dif-

ficult. As a matter of fact, it was more of a problem than the mathematical problem itself. Because of the difficulties, many of the students had become proficient in mental arithmetic. They were human adding machines and Comptometers. They put the numbers together, pressed a mental lever, and the answer popped out before the other students, using a Braille slate and paper, had punched out the results of two times two.

For me, accustomed to working mathematics with pencil and paper, seeing the figures at a glance, it was difficult to visualize the problem. I saw the numerals clearly in my mind, but the moment I began multiplying or subtracting, they all had an irresistible tendency to migrate. I multiplied the numbers over and over again and strove manfully to hold them in place. Then, just as I was ready for the final addition, the whole colony popped out of place like rows of Mexican jumping beans, and I had to start the agonizing process over again.

It wasn't a sad atmosphere, I found, at the blind school. It was lighthearted. In such an easy atmosphere, it wasn't hard to get acquainted.

Midway in my course I realized that one of the longest steps I could take toward freedom would be to learn to type well. I signed up for typewriting. Mother had seen stenographers at the medical conventions taking down speeches on shorthand typewriters. There was money in that. A blind person could do the work as well as anyone else.

Each day, at noon and at night when classwork was over, I went up to the typewriter on the third floor of the dormitory to practice. To the incentive of preparing myself for a profession was added the necessity of writing my own letters. I still wrote with pencil and paper, using a system I had developed in the hospital, but it took too long. Speed was what I wanted. I was behind schedule, and I wanted to catch up quickly. I called one of the advanced students of typing into the room. He showed me the positions for each finger, the punctuation, the letters, the numbers. Within a week I had the keyboard memorized and was working for speed, more speed, and still more speed. I thought of words and sentences containing every letter in the alphabet and wrote them over and over again as rapidly as I could think, as fast as my fingers could travel. The room was like an oven. I pulled off my shirt and kept hammering away at the typewriter while the perspiration trickled down my arms and chest. And I was vastly proud when I heard the other beginners with their slow, tedious tapping. "R-a-t, r-a-t. C-a-t, c-a-t." By the time they completed one line of cats and rats, I had armies and nations of cats and rats running all over the page.

In those last weeks in the hospital I had given up certain things which I had expected to be important parts of my life: reading, writing, athletics, music, handwork, book education. Now, in three years, I had got them all back. As I approached my graduation, that great fact outweighed all the irritation I had felt, all the complaints I had uttered.

THINKING IT OVER

1. What is the significance of the title of this selection?

2. At the time the selection begins, what had already happened to handicap the author's vision?

3. The author was confined to the hospital for nine months before he was operated on for the cataract removal. He does not describe those months in detail, but what do you think they must have been like for a young person in his condition?

4. What was the author's first concession to his blindness on the walks he took? What hazards for the blind person does he mention that cannot be overcome by using the sense of hearing?

5. Why were music, hand skills, and typing important parts of the program at the School for the Blind? Why was chemistry not studied?

6. At one point, the author mentions the trouble he had in working mathematics problems without using Braille. Students acquainted with "mental math" processes may be able to demonstrate a few techniques to the rest of the class.

PEN AND PAPER

Sight is a gift seldom used to its fullest extent. A single flower, a solitary leaf, a small expanse of sky, all offer multiple beauty to the eye of the careful beholder. To appreciate the gift of sight more deeply, think for a few moments of a particular view that you enjoy. It might be your garden at home or a scene that you pass each day, a city or a country scene — something that is familiar to you. In a composition of 150 words or more, describe this scene. Try to set down all of the details that make the scene memorable to you.

ABOUT THE AUTHOR

Karsten Ohnstad (1912–   ) has had a vital and productive life, despite the handicap of blindness. After he left the Minnesota State School for the Blind, he went on to college and helped pay his expenses by tuning pianos. He found that his Braille shorthand notes were good enough to equip him to help other students prepare for examinations. He has been a librarian, a lecturer, a chairman of a college speech department, and a supervisor for veterans blinded in World War II. His lost eyesight has not prevented him from enjoying ice skating and roller skating, as well as swimming and skiing. *The World at My Finger Tips* is the title of his autobiographical book from which this selection was taken. The book originated as the material for Mr. Ohnstad's thesis for a master's degree in creative writing.

Man's Conquest of the Air

In this group of selections you will find articles, biography, and autobiography arranged together to present one of the most exciting of man's achievements — his conquest of the air. The selections were written by different authors at widely different times, but together they form a unified account of man's steps into the sky. This grouping together of selections may suggest a future pattern for your own reading of nonfiction. When a particular topic is of interest to you, you can read about it in different books and magazines and form a related story like this one.

Man has always dreamed of flight. Almost five hundred years ago a famous painter and sculptor, Leonardo da Vinci, drew detailed sketches of primitive machines designed to fly. But it was not until two Frenchmen made a balloon flight in 1783 that man first broke the bonds of gravity that had kept him to the earth.

In the one hundred and ten years between that historic balloon ascension and the day Orville and Wilbur Wright made four short flights in the first man-carrying airplane, there were many balloonists and a number of glider pioneers. Yet when that first powered flight was made, only two newspapers in the United States printed the story. Most sensible people had come to the conclusion that man was not intended to fly.

Today we are ready to believe that almost anything is possible in the fields of air travel and space exploration. Cross the continent in an hour? There will hardly be time, during the flight, to do much thinking about the long months it took our ancestors to travel just a part of the same distance in their covered wagons. Space stations between here and the moon? Why not! Make a trip of perhaps fifty million miles to Mars? Eventually — yes.

But first turn the calendar back to 1903.

Kitty Hawk

KATHERINE B. SHIPPEN

At some time or other, you may have watched a big four-engine passenger plane roll down a runway, take off, and tuck its wheels up into its body. If this was a DC-6, just one of its four side wheels — with its brake and tire — was heavier in weight than the entire first airplane flown by the Wright brothers. That plane, with its pilot, weighed only 750 pounds. It was only a big box kite with a tail, some movable surfaces for steering and height adjustment, and a motor. Weighing the importance of that plane is a different matter!

A LL NIGHT he could not sleep. Wilbur Wright lay on his hard cot in the shack at Kitty Hawk and did not close his eyes. He heard the pounding of the surf on the beach, and the showering of sand blown by the wind against the side of the shack. He saw the patch of moonlight on the floor. It changed its shape as the white moon moved across the sky. Beside him on the other cot his brother Orville slept, his breathing steady and deep.

But Wilbur lay awake. In his mechanic's brain, calculations were coming and going — figures from the tables of air pressures they had worked out in their wind tunnel, angles of glides they had made, straight planes, and curving winds. Tomorrow — tomorrow would be the final test. They were almost sure that the rudder would hold. They thought the propeller shaft was strong enough. . . . The hours passed, Wilbur lying there awake, Orville sleeping.

Tomorrow might mark the end of a long effort. It had started when they were still at school. One day they had been skating on the ice and someone had slipped, and Wilbur had been hit in the face with a shinny stick. It had not hurt him badly at all, but he had to remain in bed for a long time. Orville had tried to keep him from being bored by bringing him books to read from the public library. They used to read them together. They were nearly all books about "flying machines," a subject that everybody seemed to be interested in at the turn of the century, though most people thought then that the very idea of flying was nonsense.

One day Orville came in empty-handed from the library. "There isn't a single book there that we haven't read," he said. Somebody suggested then that they write to the Smithsonian Institution[1] in Washington for the names of books that they might buy. So after they had left school and gone to work, they continued to read and dream about flying.

It was through the Smithsonian later that they learned of the Frenchman Octave Chanute and his book *Progress in Flying Machines*. They read it, but he knew about the work of all the men who had ever dreamed of flying — Clément Ader, Langley, Alexander Graham Bell, Hiram Maxim — There were a host of them, and they all had failed, and still people kept on trying. "There has been no one like Lilienthal in Germany," he wrote them. "That man has wonderful gifts of patience and industry and scientific imagination."

But Lilienthal was killed when he tried to lift his machine from the ground. "I don't believe he calculated the air pressure on his wing surfaces

---

[1] **Smithsonian Institution:** an institution noted chiefly for its museum and art galleries; it also provides scientific information on studies conducted in the United States and abroad.

right," Orville said. And Wilbur said, "Could we go on where Lilienthal left off?"

Wilbur was getting well now. The brothers had left school and opened a bicycle-repair shop.

Repairing bicycles and renting bicycles made them a living, but it didn't take all their time. It was not very long before they had made a glider. "And we don't want to crash; we couldn't go on experimenting if we did."

But you couldn't use a glider very well in Dayton: there were too many houses and too many people around. "What we need," they said, "is a fairly level place where the wind is steady. If the place has soft sand to fall into, so much the better. And if the slopes are free from trees and shrubs, we'll run less risk."

They wrote the Weather Bureau in Washington. The Weather Bureau suggested Kitty Hawk, North Carolina.

Every year when they could take a little time from their bicycle business they went to Kitty Hawk. It was a tiny fishing village on an island off the coast. They built themselves a shack on the sand dunes, and fitted it up in what they called "royal luxury." They cooked their meals on a smoky oil stove, and washed their dishes with sand "by a patented process." And they watched the buzzards and chicken hawks flying, to try to find out how they kept their balance in a wind, and gathered bucketfuls of starfish to take home. And day after day they practiced gliding on the air currents. It was a wonderful sport. Once they made more than a hundred glides in a single day.

After a while they knew they had the secret of gliding — they had been going down to Kitty Hawk for about three years then, staying several months each time. When they thought they were ready to put a motor in their machine, they wrote to various companies, giving the specifications for the motor they wanted. But none of the companies would make it. So they made the motor themselves.

"But it's the design of the wings that's the important thing," they agreed. "That's the important thing — more important than engines or propellers, or even the rudder."

Once Wilbur said, "I don't believe anyone will fly in a thousand years." But then he said, "I think that we'll succeed."

He knew that they would succeed, that night when he lay awake in the shack at Kitty Hawk. He was sure that somehow the thing would fly. The hours passed. The patch of moonlight faded into a general grayness; the morning came — the morning of December 17, 1903.

There was a steady wind outside the shack that morning. It blew at the rate of about twenty miles an hour. Wilbur and Orville gulped down some coffee and went to get out their machine. But first they ran up a signal on the flagpole to let the men at the lifesaving station down the beach know that they expected to fly. Four men from the station came over to watch, and there was a boy from the village of Nag's Head. And two little boys and a black dog came, but they were frightened away by the noise when the motor started.

Wilbur and Orville tossed a coin to see which one of them should make the first try. It fell to Orville.

The machine was a curious-looking contraption — a biplane that looked a good deal like a box kite. Its wings were covered with cloth. They had stitched the seams on their sister's sewing machine at home. The motor was on one side, and Orville lay down flat on the

other side with his feet hanging out behind. The weight of his body balanced the motor.

After Orville had got into the right position, Wilbur slipped a rope, and the machine started down an inclined track, and Orville felt it rise a little. It was only a tiny lift — perhaps he was too busy with the rudder even to be sure of it. But the rudder was not properly adjusted, and the flying machine dived down to the ground, its underpinnings broken. One of the bystanders snapped a picture of it though, just as it left the track. And Wilbur, who ran along beside it with a stop watch in his hand, estimated that it was in the air about twelve seconds.

With the help of the bystanders, they brought it back to the shed and began a repair job: they had to work clumsily because their hands were so cold. Soon after eleven o'clock the repairs were finished. They were ready to try again.

This time it was Wilbur who lay down beside the engine, and Orville who held the stop watch. And again they slipped the rope, and again it started. Again the machine darted up and plunged down, but this time it went a little farther before it came to rest.

A third time they tried it, and a fourth. Now the controls worked better, and the darting up and down was subdued. That fourth time it stayed in the air fifty-nine seconds and traveled eight hundred and fifty-two feet. Then it hit a hummock and was stopped, and the rudder frame was badly broken up.

They took off the rudder, and carried the flying machine back to the side of the shack and set it down. But just then a gust of wind struck it. Everyone rushed to hold it, but it rolled over and over, for the wind was stronger than they.

It didn't matter. They had flown.

They had been first to drive a machine through the air with a motor. They had done what Langley had failed to do, what Lilienthal had lost his life in trying to do. All the work in aviation that followed was merely a matter of improving on what they had done.

But they behaved as anyone else would have behaved. They ate their lunch, and walked over to the Coast Guard Station to send a telegram to their father. It seems strange to think of them — thin, long-legged, walking along the cold hard beach, with the waves rolling in and the wind blowing and the sandpipers and the seagulls, and they knowing they could fly.

The telegram read,

SUCCESS FOUR FLIGHTS THURSDAY MORNING ALL AGAINST TWENTY-ONE-MILE WIND STARTED FROM LEVEL WITH ENGINE POWER ALONE AVERAGE SPEED THROUGH AIR THIRTY-ONE MILES, LONGEST 59 SECONDS INFORM PRESS HOME CHRISTMAS

ORVILLE WRIGHT

After they had sent the telegram, they packed up their things and started for home. Their father must have been happy when he received the telegram. He informed the press as Orville had requested. But he needn't have done it; the newspaper editors didn't want to bother with the story. Only two papers in the whole United States made any mention of the flight next day.

But Wilbur and Orville knew that they had done it. They had the photograph tacked up on the wall of their bicycle shop, with Orville lying there on the wing beside the engine, and Wilbur running alongside with the stop watch in his hand.

Six years passed after that, and Wilbur and Orville Wright kept on with their flying. They gave public exhibitions in Dayton and in Cleveland, and more and more people were convinced that it was possible for a man to fly in a machine that was powered by an engine. To be sure, no one had ever seen a plane fly very far. They simply crowded into some country field and stood gaping while the strange vehicle made of sticks and cloth cut awkward circles over their heads in the sky.

Was this all that could be done? Would it ever be possible to navigate an aerial craft on the currents of the sky? To fly from one city to another, say?

THINKING IT OVER

1. Thoroughness was one of the character traits which made the Wrights successful where others had failed. Point out examples of this painstaking carefulness.

2. Tell what you know about any of the unsuccessful flying machines. Perhaps your library has some books on the subject.

3. Describe the living conditions of the Wright brothers at Kitty Hawk.

4. Point out the qualities necessary for a pioneer in a new field of endeavor, as shown in this selection.

RECOGNIZING MAIN IDEAS

State briefly the main ideas that emerge from these parts of this selection:

1. Page 290, beginning with "Tomorrow might mark . . ." and ending with "Could we go on where Lilienthal left off?"

2. Page 291, beginning with "Repairing bicycles . . ." and ending with "I think that we'll succeed."

3. Page 292, beginning with "There was a steady wind . . ." and ending with ". . . knowing they could fly" on page 293.

ABOUT THE AUTHOR

Katherine B. Shippen (1892–) has had an active writing career dedicated, for the most part, to the interests of young people. She has been a teacher and a headmistress in private schools, and for nine years she served as curator and lecturer at the Brooklyn Children's Museum. In addition to her books for young people, she has written books on history and travel.

Lindbergh

HERMANN HAGEDORN

The 1920's and early 1930's were a period of competition against time and distance. There were popular six-day bicycle races, long-distance walking and running "derbies," and dance-hall marathons. Men had themselves locked inside automobiles and tried to see how many days they could keep driving without stopping. There were transcontinental auto races, speedway races, and airplane flights which spanned increasing distances at faster rates of speed. But no single achievement in aviation so captured the imagination of people all over the world as did one airplane flight in 1927. That was Charles Lindbergh's solo nonstop flight from New York to Paris in 1927. Here is the story, and the background, of that historic accomplishment.

For days the clouds make a gray canopy over Long Island, and as dusk creeps in on Thursday, May 19, 1927, rain is dripping on Curtiss Field and beating at intervals against the hangars before the fitful northeast wind. It is no weather for flying, but "Slim" Lindbergh gets a late weather report and gives up the idea of staying in New York at the theater that evening. The Weather Bureau is announcing a high-pressure area over the entire North Atlantic, with fogs receding from Nova Scotia and Newfoundland. If the weather should clear . . .

An hour short of midnight the rain is still falling. The young man goes to his hotel in Garden City to get a few hours' rest, but there are too many things still to do to permit of sleep. He is back at the field before daybreak.

A gray smudge is on the horizon. That's dawn. The rain? By George! the rain has stopped. He helps the mechanics run the silvery plane out of the hangar and lash her to a truck for the trip to Roosevelt Field adjoining. They set her at the field's extreme west end. The *Spirit of St. Louis.* She looks like a spirit in the gray morning light.

For a last time he inspects her, calmly, without haste or flurry.

"Well, let's go."

The mechanics begin to fill the big tanks of the plane; one hundred gallons, two hundred, three hundred, four hundred forty-eight.

"Lindbergh" from *Book of Courage* by Hermann Hagedorn. Reprinted by permission of the author.

"That's a hundred forty-five more than she's ever lifted before."

"She'll rise to it."

One of the young man's financial backers comes from somewhere with sandwiches. Lindbergh tucks three or four into his pockets. In addition he has army emergency rations in the plane, dried beef, dried eggs, chocolate, hardtack, and four quarts of water; also a fishing line if the worst comes to the worst.

"You're sure you'll have enough to eat and drink?" asks a friend.

"Sure," says the boy with a grin. "If I get to Paris, I won't need any more, and if I don't get there, I won't need any more either."

Someone hands him his fur-lined, one-piece flying suit. With a last searching look at the clouds, he steps into the closed cabin. He seems entirely calm and at ease and might be taking off merely to cross Long Island Sound. The thing is, he is prepared. There is nothing haphazard about this enterprise of his, this venture into the terrifying solitude between continent and continent, through the thin upper reaches of the atmosphere. He knows the dangers which confront him, and, so far as human being may, he has prepared for them, in his plane, in his equipment, in his own training and knowledge. For the rest, there is a spirit which some call Providence and some Fate; and there is an odd and unaccountable joker who hops in and out of situations and goes by the name of Luck. But first, there is courage and resolution and faith and patient work and the steady mind.

He is assured because he has studied the principles which rule his machine and the realm in which it lives.

It is full daylight, but a gray daylight, sunless and chilly. A crowd is on the field drawn together by excited rumors that someone is actually "taking off" on the great hop. They run this way and that across the field, with raincoats blowing in the wind.

A mechanic turns over the motor. The young man in the cockpit lets it idle, warming it up until it roars. "How is she?" he calls to one of his men.

"She sounds good to me."

"Well, then we might as well go."

The mechanics pull away the blocks from the wheels. The flier flips his hand at his friends. "So long." That is all.

Down the runway the silvery plane speeds. The field is wet and heavy. Will she rise? No plane of her size has ever lifted so great a weight. If she does not rise before she reaches the end of the field, she is gone and the man inside her is gone. Suppose she strikes a ditch, crumples up, bursts into flame? Those are heartbreaking seconds. Men and women in the crowd with straining eyes and dry throats seem to have forgotten how to breathe.

But suddenly they are breathing again. A joyous sigh marks the relaxation of relief. The plane is off the ground, rising, rising. Then there is a low groan; she settles once more. Barely she clears a tractor on the field. She seems to be diving straight into a web of telephone wires. She clears the wires but has to swerve to avoid a clump of tall trees. Then, at last, she is sweeping upward.

There is a broken cheer, a scurrying this way and that to get a better view.

For a few seconds the plane is outlined dimly against a gray cloud. Then she seems to melt into the cloud.

"Slim" Lindbergh is off for France.

Lindbergh. It was a new name to the American public. For months the newspapers had been talking of a nonstop flight across the Atlantic, but the names which had been mentioned in connection with the adventure had been Byrd and Chamberlin and the Frenchmen, Nungesser and Coli.[1] There had been columns about this man or that, but practically nothing about this fellow Lindbergh. He had come across the country from San Diego in a Ryan monoplane shining like Joan of Arc's armor; an airmail flier, backed by a group of men in St. Louis. That was all anyone seemed to know.

There was indeed not a great deal to tell about Charles Lindbergh. He was just twenty-five and hadn't had a chance to make much history. His father was of sturdy Swedish stock, a lawyer and progressive politician, a Congressman for a while, and candidate for governor of Minnesota on the Farmer Labor ticket when he died in 1924. His mother was partly Irish, partly English and French. Just then she taught school in Detroit.

It was in Detroit that on February 4, 1902, Charles Augustus Lindbergh was born; but he grew up here, there, and everywhere. In winter he was in Washington, in summer in Little Falls, Minnesota. He went to a dozen different schools from Washington to California but managed even so to get through high school at sixteen. Schoolmates spoke of him as "a peculiar guy." The fact was that he had jumped about so much that he hadn't had a chance to make the attachments natural to boys. Besides, he liked to be alone — alone with his boat, his rifle, or his dog.

[1] **Byrd and Chamberlin . . . Nungesser** (nùɴ′zhä·sâr′) **and Coli** (kô·lē′): pioneer aviators along with Lindbergh. Your library will have information about the famous Admiral Byrd, as well as about Clarence Chamberlin. The two French aviators died in attempting solo flights across the Atlantic, as you will learn later in this selection.

At eighteen he entered the University of Wisconsin to study engineering. He did not think much of the book work and got his relaxation tearing about the country on a motorcycle. But no motorcycle covered the ground fast enough for him. He became interested in aviation, and in the middle of his second year he left college and enrolled as a flying student with the Nebraska Aircraft Corporation. The instruction was sketchy, but the young aspirant learned the fundamentals and proved to a skeptical and hard-boiled instructor that he had an uncanny aptitude for flying, an instinctive touch, the thing known as "air sense."

He took to "barnstorming" with a companion, going from town to town and taking passengers for little spins at five dollars a head. It was not long before mere flying became commonplace. Lindbergh learned stunts. Wing-walking was one of them, jumping with a parachute was another. It was all highly entertaining for all concerned. Incidentally, he was accomplishing two things: getting experience and laying by funds to buy a plane of his own. The next spring, when the government was selling off some wingèd remnants of the war days at an abandoned airport in Georgia, Lindbergh bought a Curtiss Jennie [2] for five hundred dollars.

His first solo flight was as desperate an undertaking for him as it is for every young aviator. But it was not long before he became accustomed to sitting alone in the cockpit a thousand feet above the earth. He went "barnstorming" now on his own, up and down the Middle West. He was becoming a flier, but he knew well enough how superficial his knowledge was. In March, 1924, he enrolled in the army training

[2] **Jennie:** nickname for a military training plane.

school at Brooks Field outside San Antonio.

It was a stiff course, and at the end of six months three-fourths of his classmates had dropped by the wayside. Lindbergh with the remainder moved over to Kelly Field for another half year of training. When at last graduation came, only eighteen remained of the one hundred and four who had entered the school at Kelly Field with Lindbergh. But those eighteen were second lieutenants in the Air Service Reserve Corps.

When, in the spring of 1926, the Robertson Aircraft Corporation of St. Louis entered into a contract to carry mail, on the government's new air route between St. Louis and Chicago, Lindbergh became its chief flier. For a year through fair weather and foul, he kept his "appointed round." Twice he was lost in darkness and fog, and, when his fuel gave out, had to jump for his life. It was all a part of the game.

It was on these lonely journeys back and forth that Lindbergh began to ruminate [1] over the possibility of competing for the $25,000 prize which a wealthy New Yorker named Raymond Orteig was offering to the man who made the first nonstop flight between New York and Paris. The "hop" could be made, he was certain; and he told the head of the Robertson Corporation that, given the right plane, he could do it. That gentleman had been watching his chief pilot for a year with growing appreciation. "If anybody can jump the Atlantic and grab the Orteig prize," he said to himself, "Lindbergh can."

He talked the matter over with his friends. Six or eight agreed to contribute to a fund to build the ship. Lindbergh himself put in all his savings, a matter of two thousand dollars,

[1] ruminate (roo'mĭ-nāt): think over.

Lindbergh at work on the Spirit of St. Louis *before the flight.*

and looked for a suitable plane. At San Diego the Ryan Airlines Corporation agreed to build him what he wanted. He supervised the designing, he worked with the builders. Seven days in the week, all day and sometimes all night, he worked. Every part of the ship felt the touch of his hand. He knew it to the last square inch of canvas and steel.

And long before the ship was ready, he knew also the course he would follow, from San Diego to St. Louis, from St. Louis to New York, from New York to Paris. For months, in a corner of the Ryan shop, he labored over the charts and checked over the Atlantic route with the nautical tables. Should he take a navigator with him? A navigator, or thirty extra gallons of gasoline? He decided in favor of the gasoline and the three hundred additional miles of cruising range it would give him.

The great American public knew nothing of all these preparations. It had never heard of Charles Augustus Lindbergh. It began to hear of him on May 10 when he hopped off from San Diego; and took note of him with some interest on May 11, when he gently came to earth in St. Louis, fourteen hours later, having broken the record for a single long-distance flight. He made the hop to New York in seven hours and quietly informed anyone who might be entitled to know that he was about to take off for France.

That, in brief, is the history of the young man whom the raincoated little crowd at Roosevelt Field had watched disappear into the gray morning.

The young man himself is less excited than the spectators. The haze is clearing. He is over Connecticut, over Rhode Island, over Cape Cod, flying low. Then he is over open water. At noon, he is crossing Nova Scotia, noting patches of snow here and there. Beyond are ice cakes, then open water again, and fishing boats off the Newfoundland coast. He flies low over St. John's. The time is 7:15 P.M. He circles once over the most easterly tip of land on the American continent and sweeps forward into the gathering dusk.

The Weather Bureau has promised clear skies over the Atlantic. The forecast proves false. As night falls, a thin, low fog forms through which the icebergs loom, ghostly and clear. Minute by minute the fog thickens and increases in height.

There is no moon, and it is very dark and bitter cold. It is lonely over the open Atlantic. Against the body of the plane suddenly beats a gust of sharp crystals. Sleet! The next instant he is in the heart of the storm.

Sleet is nothing new to him, and he knows what it means. A plane in flight is kept aloft by the curvature of its wings. Once let these surfaces be flattened by a burden of sleet, and the plane will fall like a dead bird.

He can still turn back, make a landing at St. John's, and return to New York for a fresh start under better conditions. But turning back and starting over is not one of the traditions of the airmail. He swoops downward and emerges from the cloud bank scarcely two hundred feet above the black waters. Under the low white roof he speeds eastward, but as he flies he sees the roof press down upon the sea. Lower and lower he flies, and lower and lower presses the thick canopy of fog. The sleet drives down and sweeps over the wings with a gritty sound.

There is nothing timid, nothing hesitant in the boy whose hand is on these controls. He is filled with a calm confidence in himself, in his motor, and in something greater than both. He has flown beneath the fog bank to escape the sleet. Now that the fog has closed down upon him, his only hope is to soar upward to clear air above the fog, taking the chance that he can reach it before the weight of sleet forces him down to defeat.

He climbs upward for two miles and at last, dimly through the mist, he can discern the stars. But even at ten thousand feet elevation he is in a thick haze and now and again finds himself in an upjutting angle of the storm, swept around with sleet. Again and again the weight on his wings forces him to turn back into a clear air and find a way around the storm center. But at last the mists before him clear and the moon rises. At one o'clock New York time, dawn comes.

Slowly the fog bank descends, and he descends with it. For miles he is flying within a hundred feet of the surface of the water. But a hailstorm drives him upward and soon he is once more in impenetrable fog. He flies high, he flies low; nowhere can he pierce it. He sweeps forward, flying blindly through the white solitude.

Then once more the fog breaks. Patches of sky appear, patches of sea. Slowly the air absorbs the mists, and he is flying through a clear May day with a blue-green ocean beneath him rising to whitecaps.

It is time to be looking out for land. "Come, you Ireland!" He knows what it is going to look like. It will be green, it will be mountainous. He sees a shore line, cliffs, trees, high ridges, valleys. He studies his map. But even as he gazes at the pleasant sight, the vision fades. A mirage, a trick of his imagination. He is on a shoreless ocean again. On his course? Or where?

He comes upon a small fishing boat, then another, and flies low, circling the little vessel. A man's astonished face appears at a cabin window.

The boy closes the throttle and leans out of the cockpit. "Which way is Ireland?" he shouts.

The fisherman is too amazed to reply. The boy sweeps on.

Less than an hour later a rugged coast line appears on the east. Ireland, surely, this time! He swerves toward the nearest point of land to make sure, and consults the map. Dingle Bay — Cape Valentia! Europe! He is across!

He swerves back to his compass course to Paris. The time is twelve-thirty, Saturday afternoon. By three o'clock he is over southern England, noting English farms and English hedges. Then he is flying across the Channel.

At sunset he is over Cherbourg.[1] At ten in the evening (six o'clock, New York time) he sees the lights of Paris. A few minutes later he is circling the Eiffel Tower looking for the landing field at Le Bourget.[2] Yes, there are the lights. He spirals downward. He can make out the long line of hangars. Roundabout, the roads are jammed with cars. He wonders why. It has never occurred to him that his arrival might kick up any wide interest. He has expected, in fact, to feel a bit friendless in Paris, and has taken the precaution of arming himself with a few letters of introduction.

How can he, intent on the task, know that, for a day and a half, men all over the world have as it were been holding their breath? News! Lindbergh is over Cape Cod! News! Lindbergh is over Nova Scotia! Lindbergh has crossed St. John's! The silence, suspense!

"Is he still in the air? How far is he now? He's such a kid! And all alone! I bet he makes it! He's going to make it! The kid's going to win! But if anything goes wrong? All alone over the Atlantic!"

Hours, a night of silence. What is his mother thinking, waiting in Detroit? Millions are sharing her anxiety. Saturday comes, morning, noon . . .

News! Lindbergh is over Ireland. He's crossed the ocean. He wins! The kid wins! *Extra! Extra!* Lindbergh's safe and across!

Lindbergh is over Plymouth! Lindbergh is over northern France!

The American Embassy in Paris is in wild excitement. "Old man" Herrick, the ambassador, is more thrilled than anyone has seen him in years. He is at Le Bourget long before Lindbergh can possibly get there.

Suddenly above the murmur of the

[1] **Cherbourg** (shâr′bŏŏrg): a French seaport.

[2] **Le Bourget** (lĕ bŏŏr′zhā′): a town northeast of Paris.

The Spirit of St. Louis *soars over Paris.*

crowd, comes the far droning of a motor. *C'est lui!* [1] Out of the north, like a noiseless, celestial visitor, a great bird appears, silver gray in the rays of the beacon.

It flies low over the field once. Circles into the wind, and lands; then turns again and "taxis" back to the lights. To the youth in the cockpit, it seems that all the world is surging toward him like a tidal wave. He shouts to the first who reach him to hold the crowd back, but they do not understand and he turns off the motor to keep the propeller from slaughter in that excited mob. He attempts to organize an impromptu guard for his plane, but his words are lost in jubilant shouts of welcome.

---

[1] *C'est lui!* (sĕ l'wē′): It is he!

He opens the cockpit door and starts to descend. "Well, here we are," he says, with a shy, friendly smile, to the first face he encounters. "My name is Charles Lindbergh. We —"

His feet do not touch the ground; they do not touch it for half an hour. He is clutched by the exultant crowd and lifted high. As far as he can discern are faces and waving hands and a movement like the movement of the sea. All Paris is out at Le Bourget. Paris which, only this morning, was saying sharp things about war debts and Uncle Shylock, and complaining bitterly because the United States Weather Bureau issued a forecast which, everyone feels, is partially responsible for the loss of the French fliers, Nungesser and Coli — Paris has forgotten its grievances, Paris has forgotten national barriers and, seeing only a brave youth in splendid triumph, is going delirious with joy and pride. Pride? He is not one of theirs. Their fliers are lost in the cold solitudes of that wide ocean which this youth has defied and successfully crossed. And yet, he is their own. What are Frenchmen or Americans in an hour like this? Our kinship is closer than we thought. This youth is the young brother of all mankind.

The Ambassador claims him and spirits him away from the throng which is likely to kill him with its welcome. It is three o'clock in the morning before the crowd outside the embassy and the reporters within will let the young man make his way to a bed.

The world gives him eight hours of sleep, and then it claims him. A crowd is in the street, waiting for him. He appears on the Embassy balcony. There is wild cheering and clapping and waving of hats and handkerchiefs. He says nothing. He only bows and smiles. But the bows and the smiles have a shy boyishness in them which captivates the people in the street.

They captivate the bigwigs no less. Heroes, they will tell you, are not rare, but most of them know too well how heroic they are, and topple from their pedestals. This boy does not appear to be thinking about himself at all, or really to feel that the honors are for him. Self does not seem to interest him. "I" is scarcely heard in his talk; it is always "we" — himself plus the machine. He seems, moreover, to have no intention of capitalizing his sudden fame. He receives offers to write this or that, to appear in vaudeville at thousands a night, to enter the movies for fabulous sums. Of course, he will accept? Everybody does.

Lindbergh, it happens, doesn't.

France applauds. America, four thousand miles away, gasps and rejoices. In a world largely given, it seems, to grabbing hungrily and spending wildly, here is a young man who is *different*. And his people pronounce judgment on many things in their common life when they say, "Thank God!"

The fact is that Lindbergh is not half so interested in himself or his exploit as he is in aviation; and he tells everyone how much harder was the thing Nungesser and Coli failed in than the thing in which he succeeded.

The President of the French Republic pins a medal on him, the city of Paris, the French Senate, all the great men of France crowd about him, Joffre, Foch, Briand,[1] honor him, but it remains for Ambassador Herrick, tender and wise, to give him a larger significance than that of a young hero, and to make clear to the people of France that he is a symbol. The Ambassador has been having a terrible time over the war debt which France owes the United States. The tangle of misunderstanding and suspicion appears to be hopeless. The enthusiasm of the French crowd for Lindbergh gives him his cue. We are all akin, he points out. "The Americans love France, and this young man when he goes back to America will be able to tell Americans, as no other man could, that France really loves the people of the United States."

Lindbergh is no longer just a heroic young man. He is an "ambassador of good will." He fits himself into the role, glad for the opportunity it gives him to put the "hero business" in the background a bit. All Europe comes over-

[1] **Joffre** (zhô'fr'): French general in World War I; **Foch** (fôsh): French general, Commander in Chief of Allied Armies in France in World War I; **Briand** (brē'äɴ'): French foreign minister at the time, and several times prime minister of France.

night to realize that here is something other than just a gallant young flier. Here is a rare phenomenon — a man, a boy, who can have everything for himself that he wants, personal honors, riches; and he turns aside the honors and quietly rejects the riches, being more interested in a cause than in personal advancement.

It is that phenomenon that statesmen and kings turn out to greet. In Belgium and in England, kings and queens, dukes, princes, and common folk together pay tribute of admiration and affection. From every capital in Europe come invitations, but from his own country comes a more urgent call — and a warship to bring him home.

Could any dreams of boyhood equal the tooting of the whistles, as the *Memphis* steams up the Potomac, the ringing of the church bells, the screaming of the fire sirens? Batteries on the warship and batteries on shore exchange salutes; airships wheel overhead. At the Navy Yard, Cabinet officials, admirals, generals are waiting, and a schoolteacher from Detroit, invited by the President of the United States.

Through streets lined with cheering crowds, escorted by cavalrymen and marines, with bands playing and flags everywhere, "Slim" Lindbergh comes home.

The President of the United States, surrounded by the notables of the nation, is speaking. "This wholesome, earnest, fearless, courageous product of America." And how the crowd roars its approval and how delightedly the wife of the President applauds! "This young man has returned. He is here. He has brought his unsullied fame home. It is our great privilege to welcome back to his native land, on behalf of his own people, a Colonel of the United States Officers' Reserve Corps, an illustrious citizen of the Republic . . . a conqueror of the air and strengthener of the ties which bind us to our sister nations across the sea. . . ."

The President has spoken his name, "Charles A. Lindbergh." Out across the waving field of faces it floats, and from the slopes round about ten thousand voices roar their cheers.

After this, boys of tomorrow, dare to dream anything!

THINKING IT OVER

1. List the character traits of Lindbergh as shown in this selection. What characteristics impressed you most? Which characteristics were most vital to him during his preparation and flight? Explain the reasons for your answer.

2. What was Lindbergh's training as an aviator? Give three areas of flying experience which prepared him for the Atlantic flight.

3. List the different kinds of weather conditions encountered from take-off to landing. What weather conditions could have caused the plane to fall?

4. What was the "larger significance" that Ambassador Herrick gave to the flight? Explain the difference between the public reaction to this flight and the reaction to the first flight of the Wright brothers.

5. How did the Lindbergh flight "advance the cause of aviation"?

ABOUT THE AUTHOR

Hermann Hagedorn (1882–   ) was born in New York City. After graduating from Harvard University in 1907, he returned there two years later to teach. He was a founder and later the secretary and executive director of the Theodore Roosevelt Memorial Association. The author of some two dozen books, he is known as a biographer, novelist, and poet. You would enjoy reading some of the other chapters in his *Book of Courage*, from which this selection was taken.

Chuting for Fun

LOUDON WAINWRIGHT

Parachuting existed long before airplanes did — as far back as the time of George Washington, in fact. The first public parachute drop was made by a Frenchman from a balloon at a height of 2,000 feet. The year? 1792. In 1802, in England, the same man made a descent of about 8,000 feet. Parachutists, you can see, have been thrilling themselves and others for a good long while. This article will show you that chuting has now become a popular sport — at least for some people!

IF YOU are between the ages of 16 and 45 and are bored with motorcycling, skin diving, mountain climbing, and bullfighting, the chances are good that you could recapture some of the old zip by taking a parachute jump, preferably one involving a long free fall,[1] say for about 30 seconds from the time you leave the airplane until you pull the rip cord.

The view from the plane at 7,000 feet is marvelous. The fall itself, at a top

[1] **free fall:** a descent in which the jumper waits as long as possible before pulling his parachute cord.

speed of 125 mph, is exciting without being taxing. The time is passed pleasantly in barrel rolls and loops as the patchwork of the ground slowly expands before your eyes and the actual opening — if the man back in the rigging shed has done his job conscientiously — is gentle. The final swinging descent takes place in blessed silence as you deftly manipulate your 28-foot-diameter, stocking-thin nylon for a dead-center landing on the target. Of course, it is perfectly permissible to shout in jubilation on the way down, and you are almost sure to be wearing a silly expression when, after a one-and-a-half-mile drop, you land with the delicate shock of a man who has jumped from a four-foot wall.

Most parachutists, whether novices or veterans, wear the same expression: the cheeks are flushed, the eyes are shining, the mouth trembles. It is a look compounded of joy, satisfaction, and, for the novice, enormous relief, and it plainly states that you are a jumper and you are alive and it's all a whale of a kick.

Most people, whose fear of heights

A practice session before take-off.

and falling probably dates back to their first infant plunge to the floor of the nursery, understandably feel that a parachute is a horrifying emergency device used to get from up to down only when there is no other way out. The thesis, therefore, that parachuting is a restorative and fun besides amounts to apparent insanity.

Yet there is a growing, if still exclusive, coterie [1] of serious-minded and responsible young men in the U.S. who devoutly believe in the manifold [2] physical and spiritual benefits of parachuting. Not only that, they believe that it is utterly safe — though they would deem a leap like the one described above inadvisable without considerable practice and training. These men, when they are not falling out of airplanes themselves, are busily spreading their exhilarating gospel, which is that practically everybody can and should jump.

Astonishingly enough, their message appears to be having some effect, indicating that there are more relaxed people around than one might suppose.

[1] **coterie** (kō′tĕ·rĭ): a group.
[2] **manifold**: many and varied.

While it is still possible to jump almost anywhere without falling into another chutist, the sport is definitely on the increase around the country. There are week-end parachuting clubs in Seattle, Cincinnati, San Francisco, New Orleans, and 70 other U.S. localities. Several colleges have clubs that compete against one another. Military paratroopers whose daily business is jumping have formed free-time chuting groups at posts in North Carolina, Kentucky, and California. At all of these places the membership is rising — or rather floating downward — in evergreater numbers. It is estimated that whereas in 1958 there were only 1,500 organized jumpers in the U.S., a year later there were as many as 3,000 — a slightly larger number than the French total, but still well below the estimated figure of 6,000 sport jumpers in the Soviet Union.

The new leapers are generally not the sort of thrill-seekers for whom a long fall is the only thing left. Business executives, doctors, lawyers, lady librarians, and teachers are some of the more respectable types who are parachuting these heady days, and in Philadelphia there is an honor-roll college student with the odd distinction of never having gone up in a plane that he has not left in mid-air.

The jumping center of the nation is a country airport ringed by green hills in Orange, Massachusetts. On a clear day with light winds there is rarely a moment when the sky above Orange is not dotted with the blossoms of brightly colored chutes gently lowering their enthusiastic cargoes to the ground. In the three months since the Sport Parachuting Center there first opened, more than 700 jumpers, 175 of them initiates, have taken advantage of its unique facilities. The worst injury to a parachutist in that period has been a slight ankle sprain, although there was an awful moment one gusty Saturday in June when a tiny lady in an oversized chute appeared actually to be climbing for a while immediately after she left the plane, soaring like Dorothy in the opening cyclone in *The Wizard of Oz*. Normal time of descent after opening is about two minutes. Four minutes elapsed before this lady arrived harmlessly in the woods.

Small planes carrying prospective jumpers drop in to Orange from Boston, New York, and as far away as Kansas City. Young men who arrive in their own cars are continually walking into the center's office and inquiring, somewhat shamefacedly, "Is this the place where people jump?" Others come with their families. It is a startling commonplace at Orange to see mothers and fathers calmly munching hot dogs while they wait for Junior to come plunging out of that airplane high above them.

The proprietor of the Orange facility is a 30-year-old French-born American named Jacques André Istel.[1] An ex-Marine officer whose heavy neck and sloping shoulders give the impression of great physical strength, Istel has made 383 jumps, but he considers this a measly total. "The most inexperienced man on the Russian team we faced in competition in 1958 had more than 1,000 jumps," Istel says. "To be a great parachutist, you have to keep jumping. Of course there's a limit to it. Not long ago someone jumped 124 times in a single day, but this did not prove much except that he had an awfully good airplane."

Although the word is not normally associated with long falls from high places, safety is the watchword at

Orange. As they do at all reputable parachuting clubs, jumpers at Orange wear two chutes, a main chute which is slung on the back and a reserve chute strapped to the front of the harness to be used in case the first malfunctions.

New candidates must pass a physical exam, the instructors are all expert jumpers, weather conditions must be within strict minimums, and the equipment is kept in perfect condition. Before a beginner can take a free fall by himself, he must make five supervised jumps using a strap hooked to the inside of the plane which pulls the chute open after only a four-second fall.

In spite of the speed with which the Istel-led crusade is progressing, it seems safe to assume that some aspects of the sport still require explanation. For instance, the idea behind the whole thing is not just to traverse safely the yawning gap between plane and ground, though this basic facility is helpful to those planning a long jumping career. One requirement is accuracy: the jumper tries to land in the center of a target. He achieves this in two ways — by leaving the plane at the proper point in the sky and by steering his chute through the air. In modern sport jumping this is accomplished with the help of "open gores." A chute with an open gore is simply one with a pie-shaped section of the canopy[2] removed. Such chutes are easily steered by experienced jumpers. They drop even more slowly than the old-style canopies without holes.

Although accuracy in landing is a key requirement of sport jumping, it must be obvious that everything depends on what seems the ultimate madness: leaving the plane in the first place. By this it is not intended to conjure up

[1] Istel (ĭs·tĕl′).

[2] **canopy**: the umbrella-like top of the parachute.

images of reluctant jumpers losing their nerve, fighting off their jumpmasters, and demanding to be taken back to earth the way the Wright brothers intended — by plane. Actually this almost never happens, although every novice is afraid that it will. However reluctant he may be at the last moment, the jumper has already made his decision before he leaves the ground. Though he is frightened and often wonders what wild combination of stupidity and bravado got him into this dreadful spot, he goes when he is told to go. His pride demands it. One first jumper who was asked how he felt as he was about to climb into the plane summed up the dilemma of a man caught between sober contemplation and pride: "It all seems very unlikely."

When the most unlikely moment of all arrives, it is not enough just to fling oneself out of the plane. At the jumpmaster's command to stand by, the chutist must swing his feet out of the open side of the plane (it is usually a high-wing monoplane) and place them carefully on a step which extends about 18 inches out from the cabin. When the instructor says "Go," the jumper rises to his feet on this step and reaches outside for the strut which supports the wing. This maneuver completed, he is standing entirely outside the cabin, facing the direction in which the plane is going. In goggles and helmet, with the wind whipping at his coveralls and the chute packs around his body, he looks in his crouched stance like a throwback to the golden days of cinematic wing-walking. Though he is often a fearful man wondering how he is possibly going to do what he has to do next, he looks unmistakably like a movie hero waiting for just the proper time to drop off and fall straight into the cockpit of the enemy plane beneath him.

At this biggest of all possible moments, the jumper is supposed to leave immediately. This is not an attractive time. Although the plane has slowed for his departure, the wind is still tearing at him at about 80 mph, and there are very large quantities of open space beneath him. "When I got out there," said one novice, "I forgot absolutely everything. But it seemed a poor time for further questions, so I just let go."

Letting go is one way to do it, but the best take-off requires a more concentrated effort. The jumper should lean forward against the strut, then kick vigorously back and up with his feet and push off with his hands. If he does all this properly, he finds himself in mid-air, parallel to earth, back arched, head thrown back, and arms flung wide in the swan dive to end all swan dives.

This mid-air, spread-eagle stance, curiously known in the trade as the "stable position," is crucial for a smooth, relatively uneventful flight. If the novice does not maintain it until his opening chute pulls him into an upright position, he is very likely to start an uncontrolled tumbling and looping called "disorderly fall."

Such inadvertent [1] acrobatics can be distressingly uncomfortable. It is entirely possible that a man in the midst of a long delay before opening could be spun into unconsciousness if his fall got sufficiently disorderly.

When a beginner makes his first safety jumps on the "static line," which opens the chute automatically, he does not really have time to get into serious trouble. But there is plenty of time for the nervous novice to think he is in trouble.

---

[1] **inadvertent** (ĭn'ăd·vûr'tĕnt): unplanned.

It would seem that virtually nothing could call for more sheer resolve than just bailing out and letting the static line take care of the opening. Yet experienced jumpers scorn it for themselves. They tend to look on the novice's jumping altitude of 2,400 feet as a sort of kiddie pool in the sky. Parachuting to them means long free falls from high altitudes. During these falls, they perform truly astonishing gyrations and, although they are only wingless bodies ultimately powerless against gravity, they actually fly. This is sky diving, without question the world's most exacting and exciting sport.

A first-rate sky diver — there are probably only 50 of them in the U.S., including Istel and his three instructors at Orange — is in most cases a man who has made 100 or more jumps, the great majority of them free falls with delays of up to 60 seconds before opening the chute. To bring off a 60-second "delay" successfully, the jumper has to bail out at 12,500 feet; when he finally pulls the rip cord a minute later, he is 2,000 feet from the ground.

If the sheer span of time and distance covered in these falls stirs wonderment in the breasts of groundlocked laymen, it is really what takes place on the way down that counts. The free-falling parachutist can perform a wide variety

Safe landing.

of controlled acrobatics through subtle movements of his arms, legs, and even hands. A good jumper can do flat horizontal turns, loops, and barrel rolls under perfect control. His greatest danger is not that he will whirl into unconsciousness, but that he will simply get carried away by the fun of it all.

Such bemusement is dangerous for a simple but startling reason: there is very little feeling in falling. When he first leaves the airplane, a man drops like a stone and picks up speed rapidly, but around 10 or 12 seconds after he has jumped he is traveling between 120 and 125 mph and never goes any faster. Lew Sanborn, an instructor at Orange, says, "It's like floating in an ocean of air." Another instructor, Nate Pond, comments, "You can get over on your back and stabilize there and it's just like being in a great big featherbed with all of your arms and legs and body resting against the air." Losing track of time and altitude in such comfortable surroundings can be fatal: the feathers reach only to the ground.

There are safeguards against this. Most experienced jumpers wear both stop watches and altimeters to keep track of both seconds and feet so that they can pull their cords in ample time.

French jumpers have devised a buzzer, like a kitchen timer, that sounds inside their helmets at the right moment. But it is all too easy to forget to look at the instruments.

Aside from not jumping at all, the best way to eliminate dangers is by training and experience. Istel's group, like other parachuting clubs around the country, takes great pains to insure a jumper's readiness before allowing him to sample the heady magic of free fall. At Orange the novice gets a brief lecture on parachuting theory, and he is shown the proper way to exit from the plane and to steer his open canopy. Then he is put through a rigorous course on the right way to make a tumbling fall when he finally hits the ground. Only after this does the student go up for his first static line jump.

Beginners are accompanied by a jumpmaster, who sees to it that the static line is properly hooked up, gauges the wind, and directs the pilot to the proper jump point. The jumpmaster studies the novice carefully as he leaves the plane. His written reports on the poorer exits, given later to the student, make enlightening reading. "Thrashed," "Tumbled," "Very weak exit, flopped on the wheel before clearing," "Eyes shut," and "Remained on the step too long" are some of the candid comments. They indicate not only the jumper's performance but something of the extraordinary tension most first leapers experience when it is really time to go.

Parachuting is mostly an individual performance, but at times it becomes positively congenial. There are five-man drops in international competition, and a particularly companionable form of jumping takes place when two parachutists make their delayed falls together, swooping, rolling, diving in close to each other and then pulling apart again. This sight makes it clear that the human body, in the midst of its inevitable plunge to earth, is able to fly. Even without artificial wings, which most parachutists deplore as dangerous, the body is a primitive airfoil.[1] Slight movements can affect its attitude, direction, and even its rate of fall.

The single most astonishing act performed by two parachutists is the baton pass, which is rather like the engineer of one train trying to pass a flag to the engineer of another train as they go by in opposite directions at high speed. At Orange it was attempted by Instructor Lew Sanborn and Bradford Straus, a 22-year-old Harvard graduate. The men were to leave the airplane at 7,000 feet. Straus, who was going first, would be carrying a foot-long wooden baton. Sanborn would follow about a second later. His job was to overtake Straus in the air and get the baton. A small group of watchers, some with binoculars, others shielding their eyes against the afternoon glare, looked on from the ground.

Straus leaped, a tiny black figure against the washed-out blue of the sky. He fell spread-eagled, stomach to earth, the baton in his outstretched hand. Sanborn followed almost immediately. He kept his head down, arms against his sides, streamlining his body as much as possible in an effort to overtake Straus in the sky. He began to catch up with Straus, who, after four seconds of free fall, was more than 50 feet ahead.

In 12 seconds, after both jumpers had reached top speed, it was possible to see that Sanborn had reached Straus's level. They were now about 5,000 feet

[1] **airfoil:** a curved surface, such as an airplane's wing, which enables an object to make use of the air to remain aloft; man can use the curves of his body to obtain a measure of flight.

above the ground and almost half their margin of time was gone. Horizontally, the two chutists were about 60 feet apart.

Suddenly, at what appeared to be great speed, they veered in toward one another. From the ground it seemed certain that they would collide. The two black figures merged and then broke apart again. One of the watchers, who had been following the whole jump with binoculars, groaned. "They missed," he said. "Too fast." Twenty seconds had passed since the chutists had left the plane. Very little time was left.

Wide apart again, Sanborn and Straus renewed their approach, more cautiously this time. The tense crowd on the ground watched silently now. The men were only 3,000 feet up; they had five seconds left. With what seemed agonizing slowness, they drew close to each other. They were almost together, and then Sanborn veered and passed over Straus's body. It was possible to see that they had made contact: both bodies seemed to tumble for an instant. And as the man with binoculars cheered "He got it!" the two jumpers drifted apart, and from their packs the two parachutes, one red, the other red, white, and blue, bloomed simultaneously in the bright afternoon sky. Sanborn landed standing up, collapsed his chute, and waved happily to his partner with the baton he had seized in mid-air.

Such work can be particularly hazardous. Men working together can get even more preoccupied than on an individual jump. There are two people cluttering up a relatively small patch of sky, and quite often baton-passers bump each other hard.

Working with another jumper not long ago, Nate Pond, correctly reading the altimeter and stop watch placed on top of his chest reserve chute, opened at the proper place. The other man delayed a bit longer. As he pulled and his chute began to trail out above him, he plunged directly through Pond's canopy near the outer edge and dragged his still unopened chute right through the three-foot hole he had made. His canopy opened directly underneath the startled Pond. No one was hurt, though Pond thoughtfully broke open his reserve chute to compensate for the extra gap in his main canopy.

The question remains: Why do people jump? Why, in a culture whose proudest ornament is the moderate,[1] with his feet planted firmly on the ground, does anybody feel obliged to strap on a parachute and take his chances with half a mile or more of literal space? Why bother?

There are many first jumpers who go because it seems the most dangerous thing they could possibly do with any reasonable degree of safety. They go because the thought of it scares them to death but also because they know the chances of survival are really very good. In jumping, they are proving at a minimal[2] cost that they can face fear. But this does not mean that the strain on these jumpers is minimal. As they ride up to bail-out altitude beside the yawning open door, their gaze becomes fixed, their faces sweat, they only nod numbly in response to the cheerful chatter of the jumpmaster. "These people do not usually intend to become parachutists," Istel says. "And neither do the others who come up to have something entertaining to talk about at cocktail parties." Representatives of both groups, the fearful self-provers and the

frivolous prestige-seekers, rarely return for a second jump.

But the great majority of first jumpers seem to be those who for some reason genuinely want the experience: the leap, the fall, the opening, the gentle, lonely ride back to earth under the full canopy of the extended parachute.

These people, though almost invariably nervous, listen carefully to Istel and other instructors and take their jump rides with a look of calm anticipation on their faces. These are the jumpers most likely to go on with the sport.

THINKING IT OVER

1. What are the pleasures of parachuting that are described in this article?

2. Judging from the article, what is the author's attitude toward chuting? Is he enthusiastic, amused, or strictly impartial about it? Prove your answer with references to the text.

3. List some of the features of a jumping center such as the one at Orange, Massachusetts.

4. A variety of people have taken up this new, exciting sport. Point out the different types and tell why these people want to become jumpers.

5. What care has to be exerted in "letting go"? Why?

6. What free-fall danger has to be guarded against? How is this done?

ABOUT THE AUTHOR

Loudon Wainwright (1924–) has been interested in aviation for as long as he can remember. He was born in New York City, grew up on Long Island, and began writing stories and articles while he was an undergraduate at the University of North Carolina. Before this, his schooling had been interrupted by service in the Pacific with the Marine Corps in World War II. Since 1949, he has been on the staff of *Life* Magazine and has written numerous articles on aviation and space.

[1] **moderate:** a person who follows a restrained course of action.
[2] **minimal** (mĭn′ĭ·măl): least.

Destination: Space

Who was the first man to think about flying not just miles, but hundreds of miles, into the sky in order to reach outer space? Exactly when did this dream first seem to have even a small chance of coming true? No one, of course, can answer these questions. Amazingly, however, the dream has come true; man now finds it possible to soar into outer space and to return safely. This achievement grew out of the hard work, the momentary failures, and the successes of the Wright brothers, of Lindbergh, and of many persons in different countries. Here you can read about some of the events in our own country that have gone into this most recent chapter in man's conquest of the air.

As with so many great achievements, this one began in failure, in a series of failures. But as one author points out in the first part of this success story, men learn from failure — if they have enough courage and wisdom to accept it as a teacher.

Canaveral —
From the Cape to the Stars

WOLFGANG LANGEWIESCHE

The first man to land on the moon will have reached there by a new form of a very old Chinese invention. Rockets are at least two thousand years old. As far back as seven hundred years ago, the Chinese used them as weapons. Even earlier they had been used for signals and messages. In more recent centuries they carried explosives — the rockets mentioned in "The Star-Spangled Banner" were flying bombs, for example. But the development of the rocket that has taken place in recent times was undreamed of in those earlier ages. In this selection, written in 1959, a stage in the spectacular development of the rocket is described for you.

Cape Canaveral, Fla., where the space age is starting, is much like Kitty Hawk, N.C., where the air age started. Both are on the narrow "barrier beach" that — separated from the mainland by bays, lagoons, and tidal marshes — forms most of the U.S. Atlantic Coast.

To reach the Cape from the mainland, you drive on causeways across a lagoon, an island, another lagoon, for about a mile.

Long before you get there you see a dozen or so steel-structured towers. Through the sea haze it looks as if a bunch of lighthouses were standing around having an interminable talk. These are the "gantries" which raise the big rockets up to a standing position and surround them with scaffolding so men can work on them.

Here live machines of awesome possibilities. One thinks of the rocket mostly as a sort of long-distance artillery, but essentially the same machine can work as a satellite, a space probe, a moon ship, a space platform, a mail transporter, and even, in the far-distant future, as a super-high-speed airliner.

The Cape is the focal point of the American effort to make this new machine work; to make it work better than the Russians' machine. Canaveral is not where missiles are designed or built. That is done in the aircraft factories, mostly on the West Coast, or in the Army's arsenals in Alabama. Canaveral is where they bring the rockets to test-fly them over the range.

The "Atlantic Missile Range" extends from here 5,000 miles southeastward to Ascension Island in the South Atlantic, halfway to Africa. Arching over open seas, high above altitudes at which airplanes travel, the flyway goes past a whole string of islands and countries; from these, U.S. radar observatories, mostly on foreign soil, look slantwise

up at the flying missile and measure its exact course. There are also a dozen radar ships. The observatories are tied together by radio into one gigantic observation tool of great precision. All these activities are directed from the Cape and all the observations flood back there.

The missile range is civilian-operated, but is under Air Force supervision. Pan American World Airways, as contractor, runs the stations, hires and fires the men, owns and runs the ships, fuels the rockets, runs the liquid-oxygen plant, and with RCA as subcontractor runs the radar and communications system. It is a very large operation. Merely to operate one of those distant radar observatories takes about 200 men, with skills ranging from electronics to cooking.

Canaveral is not a town. There is no post office by that name. Nobody lives on the Cape except a lighthouse keeper. People only work there — perhaps 5,000 of them.

Some twenty miles away from Canaveral, also on the beach, is Patrick Air Force Base. This is administrative headquarters for Canaveral and it does have a sort of town attached to it, composed of the usual dreary government-personnel housing and, strung out along the beach highway, a line of glamorous, high-priced motels with names like "The Satellite" and "The Vanguard."

The unofficial community center is the Starlite Motel. In its bar, underneath murals of moon scenes and space flight, you hear the special jargon of the missilemen. "Lox" is liquid oxygen. A missile is a "bird," a launching is a "shoot." The "beat-beat" and "azuza" are radarlike devices for tracking the missile. "Joe went down-range to try and recover the data can." "Down-range" is the blue island world toward the southeast. A "data can" is a small container, heavily insulated and crash-proofed, which rides in the nose cone of the missile and brings home additional information. "We had to destruct." If a missile goes out of control and heads for inhabited land, the safety officer pushes a button and the missile blows itself up.

For all the juicy talk, however, you get no information — because you're not supposed to. Security is strict; and, more than that, few people at Canaveral are really in the know. The rocket art is already far beyond the understanding of most people, even the engineers. Most are supporters of supporters of the effort. But I did get some answers to questions that bother people.

Why are there so many failures? Our missiles never seem to go right. They blow up right on the launching pad. They go astray and have to be "destructed." They burn up in the air. They fall short of their supposed range. There's a whole new class of humor — Canaveral jokes — the point of which is that the thing won't go. Some of them are quite funny but they miss the real point.

The real point is that this is a test operation. Canaveral's product is not rockets, not even successful rocket flights, but simply information. They don't care whether the rocket goes or blows up. They want to know exactly how it blows up.

The failure rate is bound to be terrific for these reasons:

1. Once a missile works okay, they no longer fly at Canaveral — they give it to the troops. Or, more probably, it is becoming obsolete by that time and they start testing a new design, again full of bugs.

2. Testing missiles is different from testing airplanes. With an airplane, you can bring the machine back and fix some trouble. With a missile, every test run ends in destruction, and every slight trouble makes a faulty run. You may know what the trouble was, but to fix it, you have to work on a new machine; and on the new machine some other part, something that worked okay on the first one, may give trouble. Result? Another batch of Canaveral jokes.

3. The complications of a big rocket are monstrous. Inside its deceptively simple shape it is full of the fiercest machinery yet devised by man. To get the lox and the fuel into the combustion chambers, for example, it has fuel pumps of fantastic capacity; they could empty a standard gas truck in five seconds. The flame that drives the rocket is hot enough to melt any ordinary metal. The little gyros of the rocket's guidance system spin at 40,000 rpm; the electrical system has perhaps 100,000 soldered connections, and so on. To get a good flight, all this has to work perfectly at the same time. It is almost a mathematical certainty that the first flight will go wrong.

Why don't they do more testing on the ground? They can't. The "environment" in which the missile must work cannot be duplicated on earth — the emptiness of space, the intense cold, the weightlessness of free flight, the terrific acceleration while the rocket is blasting. For example, the flame that spews out of the rocket's tail-nozzle takes one shape when you run the rocket motor on the test stand, a different shape when the rocket flies fast through air, still another shape in empty space. Will it burn part of the rocket? There is literally no way on earth to find out. You have to shoot it off and see what happens.

Cape Canaveral, March 1960: A Thor Able rocket ready for launching.

The same goes for vibrations caused by the rocket's internal machinery. You can run vibration tests on the ground; but then the clamps that hold the rocket down also damp [1] the vibrations. So does the thick air that surrounds it. To find out what the vibrations will be in free flight in empty space, there is only one way: free flight in empty space.

The Germans saw more than 3,000 of the V-2's [2] go wrong before they ever got one to go right. Compared to that, we are economical. Now our failures are down from the thousands to the dozens.

To the Canaveral mind, these failures are not failures. They are discoveries. The way some people talk there, a successful flight would bore them. You learn nothing from that. It's the unex-

pected that's interesting! Sometimes this sounds like "double-think": "Failure is success."

I looked into this and found much truth in it. A flight of only a few seconds can produce valuable information. The missile is not only observed from the ground, by radar, beat-beat, azuza, etc.; it also reports, by radio, its own internal condition. This is a new art — telemetry, or measurement-at-a-distance.

The famous beeps of the Sputnik are an example. Each beep probably contained hundreds of separate messages, each message a figure. When a missile takes off from Cape Canaveral, it carries perhaps 200 instruments which measure a temperature, a pressure, an angle, an rpm, a weight, a voltage. From each, a reading is transmitted several times per second back to the ground and is recorded on magnetic tape. The principal product of Canav-

[1] **damp:** check.
[2] **V-2's:** rockets used by the Germans in World War II. See page 216.

eral really is miles and miles of tape.

Sometimes, when something has gone wrong, the engineers make a "quick-look analysis" of the tape and find the trouble right then and there. More normally the tape goes back to the missile's home factory, and a minute of flight may supply the grist for months of engineering analysis: Just what went wrong? It's from the failures that the new art learns.

For example, one of the first Atlas missiles went out of control in full sight of everybody. It slued around to the right, then fishtailed to the left, flying crosswise through the air. Then it burned up in full view of most of the Florida east coast.

The failure was spectacular. It was also productive. The Atlas is of daring design. To keep the dead weight small, the superstructure is built of light sheet metal, held in shape by its own internal pressures, not by heavy framing. The mighty-looking shape is little more than a blimp! The fact that this Atlas nevertheless held together while flying crosswise showed it was still stronger than necessary, hence heavier. So Convair shaved several hundred more pounds off the Atlas. The effect was the same as if they had increased the rocket thrust by many thousands of pounds! "Success from failure."

All my time at Canaveral I was in a negative mood. Missiles are interesting, but you can't gloss over the dirty reality. They are machines for possible large-scale killing. I thought: Leadership of the world will go to the people with the most idea power and here we are engaged in a contest of killing power.

The space-travel possibilities are more appealing, of course, but as it has been said, "Why go to outer space when so much inner space remains to be explored?" I thought: People all over the world want America to show them how to be rich, how to be free, how to keep children from dying — matters which we understand very well. Instead, we are determined to show them the back side of the moon.

But one can change one's mind. I was on the Cape the night the first moon ship went up. It never made it. It fell back to earth after 33 hours and burned up in the air. But that didn't matter. I thought: Someone has said that the leading obsession [1] of our Western civilization has been the idea of infinity, the conquest of infinity. What goes on here at the Cape is right along the main line of a thousand years of Western effort. We've been across the oceans and the poles. The air is conquered. Now for space.

Only VIP's get to see the launching from the "blockhouse." This is a concrete bunker, shaped like a turtle, a thousand feet or so from the launching site. It is blast-proof, in case the rocket blows up, and looks out on the missile only through periscopes, or by TV. During the last few minutes of the countdown, the firing crew ducks into the blockhouse. It is inside the control room here that the last valves are turned and the firing button pushed. The room is full of instruments; in them, the experts read the action. The action is real, yet abstract [2] — as in the cockpit of an airplane flying blind.

Ordinary people are better off. The closest that outsiders get is a grandstand for the press about three miles from the launching pad. At that distance the rocket looks very small in

[1] **obsession** (ŏb·sĕsh'ŭn): a very persistent idea.
[2] **abstract:** separate; unconnected to any specific object.

size and shape — about like the Washington Monument seen from 20 miles away. But you can see it for real, with the naked eye. Floodlit, it is a white pillar in the night. The gantry has been rolled away on tracks, leaving the rocket standing alone, upright, destined for the stars. Nearby, a red light flashes once a second; it is a warning light for aircraft. It also shows time ticking away as the countdown proceeds.

The countdown is really a check list and timetable of all operations which have to be performed before the rocket can go. For this shot it has been in progress for 48 hours — not only here at the firing site, but all over the Atlantic Missile Range, perhaps all over the continent. Special airplanes fly far patrols to see that it is safe to shoot — no ships or aircraft will be hit. Other planes fly a high patrol to listen for possible radio interference. Circuits are tested, men alerted, radar warmed up, generators and stand-by power plants started.

Some of these tasks must be performed days ahead; others can be performed only in the last hours and minutes. The liquid oxygen, for example, starts boiling away as soon as it goes into the rocket tanks.

The press stand has a loud-speaker, and it keeps you informed of the progress of the countdown:

"T minus 38 minutes and counting."

"T minus 20 minutes, a short technical hold."

"We are resuming the count at T minus 20."

In the last seconds, the people on the press stand count out loud in a chorus, led by the red flasher. Just before the deadline, at T minus five seconds, a puff of smoke appears at the foot of the rocket and blanks out everything.

Then — 5-4-3-2-1 — nothing! You think it didn't go. It's burning up right on the launching pad.

But then, slowly, it pokes its head above the smoke. Slowly it rises — spectacularly slowly. The rocket is so burdened with fuel that it just hangs there, spewing flame. You think, "It's not making it — it will fall back!" You also think, "Why doesn't it fall over?" It is astounding how the autopilot keeps it standing straight up in the air during the first few seconds. Its sword-shaped flame flutters violently. It struggles.

But gradually the spaceship gathers speed. It is burning fuel at the rate of perhaps 1,000 pounds per second, and getting lighter every instant. Ten seconds after the first flash, it definitely gets going. The searchlight beams follow it, keep it white.

Now, after 15 seconds, comes the sound: an amazing voice, half distress, half defiance, as from a living thing. The flame that drives the rocket is intensely bright. At 1,000 feet it lights up the sea and the beaches for miles around, and also the underside of the clouds. You expect in another few seconds the rocket will be swallowed by the clouds and the show will be over. Far from it. The rocket goes through the clouds, now lights up the cloud deck from above. Then the sound fades and the flame gradually becomes just points of light and goes out.

As I watched, I thought of what a Canaveral engineer said, one jubilant night, when his rocket had gone farther away from earth than any man-made thing had ever been before. He didn't mention Russia, or killing power, or national prestige, or rivalries between the Army and the Air Force.

He said, "We've gained a little on infinity."

The men and women working at Canaveral — and at the laboratories, testing grounds, offices, and factories that supported the project — continued the slow, painstaking process of "creeping up on infinity." Then came success. . . .

FROM *Newsweek*, May 15, 1961.

At 9:34 Eastern standard time, Friday morning, May 5, 1961, a 37-year-old test pilot named Alan B. Shepard lay atop a white, pillar-like rocket. His destination was space, his vehicle, a wingless, blunt-nose, 2,800-pound ship shaped like the Liberty Bell and called "Freedom 7." One second later he was launched on a journey that took him 115 miles high and 302 miles out into the Atlantic.

Test No. 108 had originally been scheduled for Tuesday, May 2, but squally weather forced an indefinite postponement. During the days of delay the astronaut kept busy in his secluded quarters on the cape. Like a quarterback before the big game, he went over and over his assignments.

At 5:20 A.M. he snaked into the snug, black-painted Freedom 7 capsule. Launching time had been set for 7:00 A.M., but a hold for a weather check, a momentary computer failure at Central Control, and a faulty pressure regulator caused T-time (launching time) to be pushed back one, two, then four hours.

Then suddenly the minutes which had dragged by dwindled away too fast. The last ten seconds to the command "ignition" were counted off, and observers all over the cape fell silent.

Lift-off. The white rocket rose majestically through the warm morning air, its tail of fire pale in the bright southern sun. For eight seconds, silence; then the deep roar of the rocket engine rolled across the scrubby landscape.

A Mercury Redstone rocket.

Test No. 108

ALAN B. SHEPARD, JR.

America's first manned spacecraft was a 69-foot Redstone rocket with a Mercury capsule attached to its nose. Tons of liquid oxygen propelled this capsule and its human cargo on a cannonball-like flight 115 miles high and 302 miles in distance, reaching a maximum speed of 5,160 miles per hour — a far different flight from the one of 59 seconds and 852 feet made by the Wright brothers in 1903. Yet this rocket, with all the world watching the outcome, was still as far away from final spacecraft form as the Wrights' plane is different from today's superjet airliners.

Here the man who was in the Mercury capsule recounts the story of this first American flight into space and describes what it was like for him.

IT WAS time to go. Shortly after five in the morning, I left the transfer van where I'd been waiting and started toward the gantry elevator that would take me up 65 feet to the capsule. I already had on my pressure suit and didn't really need to go out that early, but I wanted a little extra time on top with the capsule. And I wanted to stop below and take a good long look at the Redstone booster that would push me into space.

It was a lovely sight. I always enjoy the sight of a bird that's getting ready to go. The Redstone with the Mercury capsule on top is a particularly good-looking combination, long and slender, and this one had a decided air of expectancy about it. It stood there, frost all over the sides. Liquid oxygen was being vented out in great white clouds, and the searchlights turned the whole scene a brilliant white. This was probably the last time I'd see this Redstone. I stood there for a few moments and studied it. Then I got into the elevator. The crew standing around the base of the rocket applauded as we started up the gantry.

Topside, in the green plastic penthouse that covered the capsule, preparations were almost completed. I walked around a bit, chatted briefly with Gus Grissom and John Glenn. I wanted especially to thank John for all the work he'd done as my backup.[1] He'd just completed his final check in the cockpit. Some of the crew looked a little tense up there, but none of the astronauts showed it.

It was 5:20, time to get into the capsule. There, inside where no one but the pilot could see it, I found a prelaunch joke. Attached to the instrument panel was a little notice that read: NO

[1] **backup:** alternate.

HANDBALL PLAYING IN THIS AREA. When he saw me laugh behind the visor, John Glenn grinned, reached in, and pulled down the sign.

The countdown proceeded. My straps were all checked, the final connections were made into my suit. Different heads and hands kept popping through the opening to make last-minute adjustments. Then at 6:10 the hatch was closed and I was alone.

This was a very big moment, and one I had thought about a lot. The butterflies were pretty active. I said to myself, "O.K., Buster, you volunteered for this thing. Now it's up to you to do it." I had anticipated this moment of apprehension and had made plans to get busy right away. As soon as the door was sealed, I got right to work.

I went through all the checkoff lists, tested the radio systems and the gyro switches. The tension slacked off immediately. As I worked, I could look out through the periscope viewer in the center of the instrument panel and see the crew working around the outside of the capsule.

When the gantry rolled back at 6:34, the view through the periscope was fascinating. I could see clouds in the sky and people working far below me on the ground. The rising sun came right up into the scope, getting so bright that I had to crank in some filters to cut down the glare.

With the count at T-15, we had a delay because of clouds in the Cape area. Then, while we were still holding for weather, there was trouble with a small electrical component in the booster, and the gantry was rolled back around me so the crew could replace it. During this delay, which lasted a total of 86 minutes, I continued to feel fine.

With the electrical problem solved, the gantry rolled away, the cherry-picker crane [1] came back near the capsule, and the countdown went on. We had another hold at T-2 minutes 40 seconds, and here I got a little impatient. I'd been in the capsule more than three hours now, and I was ready to go. Hearing the deliberate, careful voices discussing this new problem, which involved one of the computers, I was strongly tempted to get into the act myself and urge everybody along. But I decided that their caution might benefit me in the long run and I kept quiet. The count picked up again.

At T-2 I got my final transmissions from the blockhouse, set the control valves for the suit and the cabin temperatures, and began talking to Deke Slayton in the control center.

At T-35 seconds I watched through the periscope as the connection which had fed power and air into the capsule was pulled out and fell away. Now the capsule was on its own power. The top of the periscope retracted, the covering door closed, and the good view I'd had all morning was temporarily gone. I wouldn't be able to see anything again until I was in space. I reported "periscope in" and the fact that the voltage and current readings for the batteries which now ran the capsule systems were both in GO condition. I heard Deke say "Roger" and then listened to his count run down from 10 seconds. My right hand was up to start a stop watch exactly at liftoff, and my left hand was on the abort handle,[2] which I was ready to throw if there was trouble on the launch.

The count reached zero.

I must admit that I braced myself

[1] **cherry-picker crane:** a high jointed crane which could lift the astronaut from the capsule in emergency.

[2] **abort handle** (*á·bôrt'*): in rocket language, the lever that would cancel the rest of the flight.

too much for that marvelous liftoff. I had tensed myself against the vibration and shock and I'd even turned up the volume on my headphones near full power so that I could hear transmissions through the noise. When the bird lighted, I could hear a rumble beneath me and feel the vibration, but both were at a much lower level than I expected. There was no question about the fact that I was going. That was certain. I could see it on the instruments, hear it on the headphones, feel it all around me. My trip had finally started, but it had started in an astonishingly pleasant way.

For the first minute the ride continued smooth, and my main job was to keep the people on the ground as relaxed and informed as I could. I reported that everything was functioning perfectly, that all the systems were working, that the Gs [1] were mounting slightly as predicted. The long hours of rehearsal had helped. It was almost as if I had been there before. It was enormously strange and exciting, but my earlier practice gave the whole thing a comfortable air of familiarity. Deke's clear transmissions in my headphones reassured me still more.

One minute after liftoff the bird rode a little rough. At this point in the flight the booster and capsule passed from subsonic to supersonic speed and then immediately went through the zone of maximum dynamic pressure, where the forces of air density and speed combine at their peak. There was a good bit of vibration and buffeting.

We had known that this was going to happen, but it was a little heavier than I had thought it would be. I never con-

[1] **Gs:** A "G" stands for the normal pull of gravity. As the speed of the capsule increased, Shepard's weight increased to several times the normal pull of gravity, or several "Gs."

sidered getting out. I tried to focus on the cabin pressure reading. I thought briefly about reporting the buffeting but then decided against it. A garbled transmission about vibration at that point might have sent everybody on the ground into a state of shock. I didn't want to leave or have anyone make any quick decision that I should leave. My mind had probably been made up in advance to handle things alone if I could and to call for help only if I couldn't. The vibration stopped and we were through in one piece. I called to Deke: "O.K. It is a lot smoother now. A lot smoother."

At two minutes after launch, at an altitude of about 25 miles, the Gs were building as I climbed at a speed of about 2,700 mph. The ride was now fine, just exactly as we had planned. I made my last radio transmission before the booster engine cut off: "All systems are GO."

The cutoff occurred right on schedule. Nothing abrupt happened. As the fuel burned out in the chamber, there was a gradual drop in the level of forward thrust, all very smooth. Then I heard a roaring noise when the escape tower, now no longer needed, was blown off. Separation of the capsule from the booster, a point I'd thought quite a lot about in the past, was coming. I heard the noise of the separation rockets as they fired and saw the verifying light flash green on the panel. I don't recall thinking anything in particular at separation, but there's good medical evidence that I was concerned about it at the time. My pulse rate reached its peak here, 132, and started down afterward.

Right after separation, the capsule and I went weightless. I could feel the capsule begin its slow, lazy turnaround as the autopilot pivoted it 180 degrees

Man in a capsule: Commander Shepard.

so that the blunt end faced forward. The periscope came out but, though I was aware of land and clouds and movement in the viewer, I didn't really look. I still had a most important function before I could stop to enjoy the view. We wanted to see if the pilot could control the capsule in space, and this was the time to begin.

Up to that point the free and weightless capsule, traveling at 4,500 miles per hour, had been flown by the autopilot. Now using my three-axis control stick,[1] I switched over to manual control, one axis at a time. First I tried controlling the pitch axis and found I could easily raise or lower the blunt end of the capsule. The instruments recorded the movements. Each time I moved the stick, little jets of hydrogen peroxide popped off on the outside of the capsule and pushed it the way I wanted it to go. Then I fed in the yaw axis to my

[1] **three-axis control stick:** This controlled three types of motion – pitch, meaning up or down slant; yaw, meaning right or left sideways forward movement; and roll.

hand controller and it worked too. Finally I took over control of the roll motion of the capsule and was flying Freedom 7 on my own. This was a big moment for me and for everybody who had worked so hard on Project Mercury.

Now was the time to go to the periscope. I'd been well briefed; I knew what to expect in the way of land masses, cloud cover, and color. But no one could be briefed well enough not to be astonished at the view I got from 100 miles up. It was breath-taking.

To the south I could see that the cloud cover stopped around Fort Lauderdale and that the weather was clear all the way down past the Florida Keys. To the north I could see up the coast of the Carolinas to where Cape Hatteras was obscured by clouds. Across Florida to the west I saw Tampa Bay and Pensacola and easily spotted Lake Okeechobee. Because there were now scattered clouds far beneath me, I was not able to see some of the Bahama Islands I had been briefed to look for, so I shifted my view to an open area and found that I could identify Andros Island and Bimini.[2] The colors around the ocean islands below were brilliantly clear, and the variations were sharp between the blue of deep water and the light green of the shoal areas around the reefs.

For a while then, using Cape Canaveral as a heading, I flew the capsule by looking through the periscope instead of at the instruments and found that this was not at all difficult. Even if the instruments and autopilot should fail on a later flight, we now know we can handle the capsule another way.

All through this period the capsule and I were weightless. The condition

[2] **Bahama . . . Andros . . . Bimini** (bȧ-hä′mȧ; ăn′drŏs; bĭm′ĭ·nĭ).

was just as we expected, pleasant and relaxing, and it had absolutely no effects on my movements or efficiency. In fact I didn't even notice the condition until I realized that someone would surely question me about it. I was completely comfortable, and it was something of a relief to feel no pressure against the couch. The ends of my straps floated a bit and there was a little dust drifting around the cockpit, but these were just unimportant peripheral [1] indications of being at Zero G.

Near the apogee [2] of my flight, at about 115 miles of altitude, I began to hear Deke's countdown for the firing of the retro-rockets. In an orbital flight these braking rockets would be necessary to begin the return to earth, but here we were just testing them and my reactions to their firing. No matter what happened now on this flight, I'd drop back down on a regular ballistic trajectory.[3]

Still using the hand controller, I tilted the blunt end of the capsule up to an angle of 34 degrees above the horizon, and at five minutes and 11 seconds after launch, the first of the three retro-rockets fired. There was just a small upsetting motion as our speed was slowed and I was pushed back into the couch a bit. But, as the rockets fired in sequence, each time pushing the capsule somewhat off its proper angle, I brought it back. Perhaps the most encouraging product of the trip was the way I was able to stay on top of the flight by using manual controls.

We were on the way down now and I got set for the jettisoning [4] of the used

retros which were attached to the blunt end of the capsule. The retro package blew off right on time. I could feel it go, and through the periscope I could see part of the strapping fall away. But the jettison light did not change to green on the panel. This was our only circuit failure in the whole flight, and when I pushed an override button that acts as a backup, the light turned green as it was supposed to do.

Now I brought the capsule into its re-entry attitude, front end pointing downward, and switched over to the autopilot. The flight was more than half over and I hadn't yet had a chance to look out the porthole for the planets I had hoped to spot. But it was now too late in the morning for me to see them. Still, the view through the port was spectacular. The sky was very dark blue and the clouds a brilliant white. Between me and the clouds was something that looked like haze; it was the refraction of the sun's light on the various layers of the atmosphere.

In that long plunge back to earth I was pushed back into the couch with a force about ten times the pull of gravity. I was able to report the G level with normal voice procedure and I never reached the point, as I often had in the centrifuge, where I had to use the maximum amount of effort to speak or even to breathe.

All the way down, through mile after mile of descent, I grunted out "O.K., O.K., O.K.," just to show how I was doing. Throughout this period of descent the capsule rolled very slowly in a counterclockwise direction. This had no noticeable effect on me, and neither did the heat which, though it built up to 1,500 degrees on the outside wall, only climbed to 102 in the cabin and 78 in the suit. The life support system — oxygen, water coolers, ventilators, the suit

[1] **peripheral** (pĕ-rĭf′ĕr-ŭl): external.
[2] **apogee** (ăp′ô-jē): point of greatest distance from the earth.
[3] **ballistic trajectory** (trȧ-jĕk′tô-rĭ): a missile's course.
[4] **jettisoning** (jĕt′ĭ-sŭn-ĭng): throwing overboard.

itself — all worked without a hitch. At worst it was like being in a closed car on a warm summer day. As the G forces dropped and we reached about 80,000 feet, I switched back to the auto-pilot.

By the time I reached 30,000 feet, the capsule had slowed to about 300 mph. I had known all along from talking to Deke that my trajectory was good and that Freedom 7 was going to hit right in the center of the recovery area. But a lot of things had to happen before I could stretch out and take it easy. I began to concentrate quite heavily on the parachutes.

A small stabilizing chute called a drogue [1] is supposed to come out of the capsule at 21,000 feet. Right about this time the periscope, which had been retracted during re-entry, came out again too. Sure enough, the first thing I saw against the sky in my viewer was this little drogue, streaming out white about the size of a silver dollar in the top of the scope. So far, so good. At 15,000 feet a ventilation valve opened on schedule and cool fresh air came into the capsule. The main chute was yet to come.

This invaluable aid to the weary space traveler is supposed to make its appearance at 10,000 feet. If it fails to show, the pilot can break out the reserve chute by pulling a ring on the instrument panel. I must admit my finger was right on the ring as we passed through 10,000 feet. But I didn't need to pull. Through the periscope I could watch a whole beautiful sequence start taking place.

I saw a small canister become released from the top of the capsule and get pulled away by the drogue chute. Then the canister in its turn pulled out

[1] **drogue** (drōg).

the bag that held the main chute. The bag slipped off and all of a sudden there it was, the main chute stretched out long and thin and not yet opened against the sky. Four seconds later the brilliant orange and white canopy bloomed above me. It looked wonderful. I stared at it through the periscope for signs of trouble. It was drawing perfectly. A glance at my rate-of-descent indicator on the instrument panel proved that I had a good chute. This was a moment of high relief for me. In fact I felt great.

The water landing was still ahead and I started getting ready for it. I opened the face plate in the helmet and disconnected the hose that keeps the visor sealed when the suit is pressurized. I took off my knee straps and released the strap that went across my chest. During the descent, the capsule swung gently back and forth under the chute. At about 1,000 feet, I looked out the port and saw we were getting close to the water. I didn't see the pickup helicopters but assumed they were nearby and braced myself for the impact.

The landing was abrupt but no more upsetting than we'd expected. The capsule dug into the water and went over on its right side to an angle of about 60 or 70 degrees. I was pushed down into the couch and then over to the right. The right porthole went under water immediately and stayed there. I hit the switch that was supposed to kick out the reserve chute. This would take some weight off the top of the capsule and eventually help it right itself. The same switch would start the sequence to deploy [2] a high-frequency radio antenna. Other recovery aids — dye markers, a sonar depth bomb — were working. I

[2] **deploy** (dē·ploi'): extend.

sat back and watched things happen.

I knew that in about a minute the capsule should swing back into an upright position. If not, there could be a little difficulty. There seemed to be no water coming in anywhere, but there were all kinds of gurgling sounds and there might, for all I knew then, have been small leaks. But there was clearly nothing big.

I remember feeling, "Well, O.K., you're in good shape now. If you have to get out that side door there, underwater, you've done it before in practice and you know you can do it now." But I was pleased to see that the capsule was slowly swinging to its proper position. As soon as I knew the radio antenna was well clear of the water, I sent a message that I was on the water and all right.

I took off my lap belt and loosened my helmet so that I could take it off when I went out the door. Leaving the capsule for the helicopter had been the plan all the way. I was getting ready to take a final reading on all the capsule instruments when the pilot called and said that he was right above me, getting ready to hook on. A second helicopter, the first sign I'd seen of people since leaving the pad, appeared on the periscope screen.

I heard the hook catch hold in the top of the capsule. "O.K.," the pilot radioed, "you've got two minutes to come out." This was a fine capsule and I was grateful. I opened the door and came out, headfirst, reaching for the sling that would haul me up those last 25 feet.

On the way back to the carrier, I felt relieved and happy. The Mercury systems were good and I'd had a fine and effective ride. We'd brought off a good one, right out in the open where the whole world could watch us take our

chances. I was feeling very chipper and was just about to start talking with the pilot on the intercom when we came over the port side of the carrier. I looked down and saw a great press of people covering the afterpart of the deck, jammed in among the planes and packed all over the island.[1] As we came in to set the capsule down on the cleared part of the deck, I saw that all these people were being held back by the master-at-arms force and by ropes, that they were all looking up and yelling. I remember thinking well, here are all these people yelling for me, and I thought of a lot of other men who deserved to share that moment with me. I had a great sense of gladness and humility.

[1] island: here, the control tower of the carrier.

THINKING IT OVER

Canaveral — From the Cape to the Stars.
1. Give some facts about the Atlantic Missile Range and its operation, as revealed in the selection.
2. The author asks and answers some questions. What does he say were some of the chief reasons for many rocket failures at the time this article was written?
3. What did you learn about the scientific attitude toward rocket failures? Give an illustration from the text of one spectacular failure that led to an important development.
4. What are the "down-range" preparations for a shoot?
5. Suppose you are in a blockhouse for VIP's. Describe a launching. How does it seem different when seen from the press grandstand about three miles away?
6. Discuss the concluding sentence of the article. Give your opinion about Western civilization's "leading obsession," the phrase used by the author earlier in the text (page 315).

Test No. 108. 1. Point out some differences between the ordinary rocket "shoot," as described in the Canaveral article, and "Test No. 108," Shepard's flight. What similarities did you note?

2. Because of failures in rocket launchings, what measures were taken to insure Shepard's safety in Test No. 108? How had these safety measures also been a factor in the physical preparation or training of the astronauts? in the weather report system? the preparation for leaving the capsule? the constant communication?

3. On the Tuesday flight that was canceled, Shepard had to wait for 3 hours in the capsule. On flight day he waited for 4 hours and 14 minutes. What do you conclude about his emotional control?

4. Shepard had anticipated feeling nervous and apprehensive when left alone in the capsule. How had he planned to combat these feelings? In your opinion, would this plan be worthwhile in moments of stress for all of us?

5. Recount some of the activities Shepard had to perform during the flight. What temperatures were recorded?

6. Shepard's achievement was followed by the successful flight of Virgil Grissom and the three-orbit flight of John Glenn. Based on your own knowledge of these later flights, or on independent research, decide what these three astronauts had in common. What about the characters of the three men and their approach to the project? What differences do you find between them and the early pioneers of aviation as discussed in this air unit?

FOR YOUR VOCABULARY: WORD HISTORIES

1. Just as rockets are very ancient, many of the words of the space age are older than you think. Perhaps one of the oddest, *gantry,* is the best illustration. It traces its origin to the Greek word, *kanthēlios,* which meant a pack-carrying donkey. Today, a *gantry* means a raised frame structure which spans over something. Railroad signals, for example, are carried on *gantries.* . . . *Satellite* comes from a Latin word, *satelles,* meaning "an attendant." . . . The word *gyroscope* has two Greek words in its make-up: *gyros,* "a circle made by a moving object"; and *skopein,* "to view."

Today *-scope* usually means an instrument of some kind. A new word which has become a part of the space age is *radar.* Referring to the navigation equipment first developed during World War II, the word is formed from the letters in *radio detecting and ranging.*

2. Consult a dictionary and look up the origins of these related words: *telemetry, periscope, pilot.*

PEN AND PAPER

Write a report of no fewer than 250 words on the achievements in space exploration since Shepard's flight. Describe the progress that has been made; the more recent improvements in fuels, engines, and equipment; and the new frontiers that have been reached.

ABOUT THE AUTHORS

Wolfgang Langewiesche (1907–) is a native of Austria, but he has resided in America since his arrival here in 1930. He studied at Columbia University and also became an aviation enthusiast. After taking up flying as a hobby, he became a research pilot, a college professor, and an author specializing in aviation. Included in the extensive writing he has done on the subject is a pilot's manual, as well as several books. Of the latter, you might enjoy *I'll Take the High Road* and *A Flier's World.*

Alan B. Shepard, Jr. (1923–) hails from East Derry, New Hampshire, where his father is a retired army colonel. America's first astronaut graduated from the U.S. Naval Academy in 1944, where he was a member of the rowing crew, and then served on a destroyer in World War II. Flying next occupied his attention, and he logged 3,600 flight hours on high-altitude research missions. In 1958, when the search was begun for pilots to serve with Project Mercury, hundreds of men were screened and thirty-two candidates selected. For these men there followed grueling aptitude and psychological tests, including a week-long physical examination. Finally seven pilots were chosen as America's first astronauts. Alan Shepard, of course, was one of the seven.

So You're Going to Mars

ARTHUR C. CLARKE

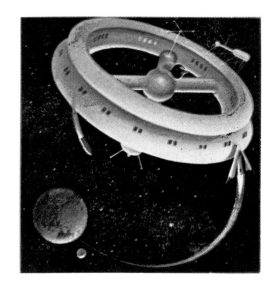

The small boats of the Vikings, the sailing ships, the covered wagons – with these, men explored the surface of the earth. On a strip of North Carolina beach, a strange-looking contraption, resembling a box kite with wings, took off from the ground and began our exploration of the sky. Now man is stretching for the step into space that will take him to the moon. The author of this selection, a member of the Royal Astronomical Society, goes another step and writes as if travel to Mars were already a reality. Here is his advice to someone about to make the journey.

So YOU'RE GOING to Mars? That's still quite an adventure, though I suppose that in another ten years no one will think twice about it. Sometimes it's hard to remember that the first ships reached Mars scarcely more than half a century ago, and that our colony on the planet is less than thirty years old. (By the way, don't use that word when you get there. Base, settlement, or whatever you like – but not colony, unless you want to hear the ice tinkling all around you.)

I suppose you've read all the forms and tourist literature they gave you at the Department of Extraterrestrial [1] Affairs. But there's a lot you won't learn just by reading, so here are some pointers and background information that may make your trip more enjoyable. I won't say it's right up to date – things change so rapidly and it's a year since I got back from Mars myself – but on the whole you'll find it pretty reliable.

Presumably you're going just for curiosity and excitement – because you

[1] **Extraterrestrial** (ĕks′trȧ·tĕ·rĕs′trĭ·ăl): beyond the earth.

"So You're Going to Mars" from *The Challenge of the Space Ship* by Arthur C. Clarke. Copyright © 1953 by The Curtis Publishing Company. Reprinted by permission of Harper & Brothers.

want to see what life is like out on the new frontier. It's only fair, therefore, to point out that most of your fellow passengers will be engineers, scientists, or administrators traveling to Mars — some of them not for the first time — because they've got a job of work to do. So whatever your achievements here on Earth, it's advisable not to talk too much about them, as you'll be among people who've had to tackle much tougher propositions. I won't say that you'll find them boastful: it's simply that they've got a lot to be proud of, and they don't mind who knows it.

If you haven't booked your passage yet, remember that the cost of the ticket varies considerably according to the relative positions of Mars and Earth. That's a complication we don't have to worry about when we're traveling from country to country on our own globe, but Mars can be six times further away at one time than at another. Oddly enough, the shortest trips are the most expensive, since they involve the greatest changes of speed as you hop from one orbit to the other. And in space, speed, not distance, is what costs money.

Incidentally, I'd like to know how you've managed it. I believe the cheapest round trip comes to about $30,000, and unless the firm is backing you or you've got a very elastic expense account — Oh, all right, if you don't want to talk about it . . .

I take it you're O.K. on the medical side. That examination isn't for fun, nor is it intended to scare anyone off. The physical strain involved in space flight is negligible — but you'll be spending at least two months on the trip, and it would be a pity if your teeth or your appendix started to misbehave. See what I mean?

You're probably wondering how you can possibly manage on the weight allowance you've got. Well, it can be done. The first thing to remember is that you don't need to take any suits. There's no weather inside a spaceship — the temperature never varies more than a couple of degrees over the whole trip, and it's held at a fairly high value so that all you'll want is an ultra-light-weight tropical kit. When you get to Mars you'll buy what you need there, and dump it when you return. The great thing to remember is — only carry the stuff you actually need on the trip. I strongly advise you to buy one of the complete travel kits — most of the big stores can supply the approved outfits. They're expensive, but will save you money on excess baggage charges.

Take a camera, by all means — there's a chance of some unforgettable shots as you leave Earth and when you approach Mars. But there's nothing to photograph on the voyage itself, and I'd advise you to take all your pictures on the outward trip. You can sell a good camera on Mars for five times its price here — and save yourself the cost of freighting it home. They don't mention that in the official handouts.

Now that we've brought up the subject of money, I'd better remind you that the Martian economy is quite different from anything you'll meet on Earth. Down here, it doesn't cost you anything to breathe, even though you've got to pay to eat. But on Mars the very air has to be synthesized [1] — they break down the oxides [2] in the ground to do this — so every time you fill your lungs, someone has to foot the bill. Food production is planned in the same way — each of the cities, remem-

[1] **synthesized** (sĭn'thė-sīz'd): artificially created.
[2] **oxides** (ŏk'sīdz): compounds containing oxygen.

ber, is a carefully balanced ecological [1] system, like a well-organized aquarium. No parasites can be allowed, so everyone has to pay a basic tax which entitles him to air, food, and the shelter of the domes. The tax varies from city to city, but averages about ten dollars a day. Since everyone earns at least ten times as much as this, they can all afford to go on breathing.

You'll have to pay this tax, of course — and you'll find it rather hard to spend much more money than this. Once the basic needs for life are taken care of, there aren't many luxuries on Mars. When they've got used to the idea of having tourists, you'll find that most reasonable requests won't cost you anything. However, I should make arrangements to transfer a substantial credit balance to the Bank of Mars — if you've still got anything left. You can do that by radio, of course, before you leave Earth.

So much for the preliminaries; now some points about the trip itself. The ferry rocket will probably leave from the New Guinea field, which is about two miles above sea level on the top of the Orange Range. People sometimes wonder why they chose such an out-of-the-way spot. That's simple: it's on the equator, so a ship gets the full thousand-mile-an-hour boost of the Earth's spin as it takes off — and there's the whole width of the Pacific for jettisoned fuel tanks to fall into. And if you've ever heard a spaceship taking off, you'll understand why the launching sites have to be a few hundred miles from civilization. . . .

Don't be alarmed by anything you've been told about the strain of blast-off. There's really nothing to it, if you're

[1] ecological (ĕk'ô·lŏj'ĭ·kăl): pertaining to ecology, the relations between living organisms and their environment.

in good health — and you won't be allowed inside a spaceship unless you are. You just lie down on the acceleration couch, put in your earplugs, and relax. It takes over a minute for the full thrust to build up, and by that time you're quite accustomed to it. You'll have some difficulty in breathing, perhaps — it's never bothered me — but if you don't attempt to move, you'll hardly feel the increase of weight. What you will notice is the noise, which is slightly unbelievable. Still, it only lasts five minutes, and by the end of that time, you'll be up in the orbit and the motors will cut out. Don't worry about your hearing; it will get back to normal in a couple of hours.

You won't see a great deal until you get aboard the space station, because there are no viewing ports on the ferry rockets and passengers aren't encouraged to wander around. It usually takes about thirty minutes to make the necessary steering corrections and to match speed with the station; you'll know when that's happened from the rather alarming "clang" as the air locks make contact. Then you can undo your safety belt, and of course you'll want to see what it's like being weightless.

Now, take your time — and do exactly what you're told. Hang on to the guide rope through the air lock and don't try to go flying around like a bird. There'll be plenty of time for that later: there's not enough room in the ferry and if you attempt any of the usual tricks, you'll not only injure yourself but may damage the equipment as well.

Space Station One — which is where the ferries and the liners meet to transfer their cargoes — takes just two hours to make one circuit of the Earth. You'll spend all your time in the observation lounge; everyone does, no matter how many times they've been out into space.

An artist's conception of a space station on Mars.

I won't attempt to describe that incredible view; I'll merely remind you that in the hundred and twenty minutes it takes the station to complete its orbit you'll see the Earth wax [1] from a thin crescent to a gigantic, multicolored disk — and then shrink again to a black shield eclipsing the stars. As you pass over the night side you'll see the lights of cities down there in the darkness, like patches of phosphorescence. And the stars! You'll realize that you've never really seen them before in your life.

But enough of these purple passages; let's stick to business. You'll probably remain on Space Station One for about twelve hours, which will give you plenty of opportunity to see how you like weightlessness. It doesn't take long to learn how to move around; the main secret is to avoid all violent motions — otherwise you may crack your head on the ceiling. Except, of course, that there isn't a ceiling, since there's no up or down any more. At first you'll find that confusing: you'll have to stop and

[1] **wax:** increase in size.

decide which direction you want to move in, and then adjust your personal reference system to fit. After a few days in space, it will be second nature to you.

Don't forget that the station is your last link with Earth. If you want to make any final purchases or leave something to be sent home — do it then. You won't have another chance for a good many million miles. But beware of buying items that the station shop assures you are "just the thing on Mars."

You'll go aboard the liner when you've had your final medical check, and the steward will show you to the little cabin that will be your home for the next few months. Don't be upset because you can touch all the walls without moving from one spot. You'll only have to sleep there, after all, and you've got the rest of the ship to stretch your legs in.

If you're on one of the larger liners, there'll be about a hundred other passengers and a crew of perhaps twenty. You'll get to know them all by the end of the voyage. There's nothing on Earth quite like the atmosphere in a spaceship. You're a little, self-contained community floating in vacuum millions of miles from anywhere, kept alive in a bubble of plastic and metal. If you're a good mixer, you'll find the experience very stimulating. But it has its disadvantages. The one great danger of space flight is that some prize bore may get on the passenger list — and short of pushing him out of the air lock, there's nothing anyone can do about it.

It won't take you long to find your way around the ship and to get used to its gadgets. Handling liquids is the main skill you'll have to acquire: your first attempts at drinking are apt to be messy. Oddly enough, taking a shower is quite simple. You do it in a sort of plastic cocoon, and a circulating air current carries the water out at the bottom.

At first the absence of gravity may make sleeping difficult — you'll miss your accustomed weight. That's why the sheets over the bunks have spring tensioning. They'll prevent you drifting out while you sleep, and their pressure will give you a spurious [1] sensation of weight.

But learning to live under zero gravity is something one can't be taught in advance: you have to find out by experience and practical demonstration. I believe you'll enjoy it, and when the novelty's worn off, you'll take it completely for granted. Then the problem will be getting used to gravity again when you reach Mars!

Unlike the take-off of the ferry rocket from Earth, the breakaway of the liner from its satellite orbit is so gentle and protracted that it lacks all drama. When the loading and instrument checks have been completed, the ship will uncouple

from the space station and drift a few miles away. You'll hardly notice it when the atomic drive goes on — there will be the faintest of vibrations and a feeble sensation of weight. The ship's acceleration is so small, in fact, that you'll weigh only a few ounces, which will scarcely interfere with your freedom of movement at all. Its only effect will be to make things drift slowly to one end of the cabin if they're left lying around.

Although the liner's acceleration is so small that it will take hours to break away from Earth and head out into space, after a week of continuous drive the ship will have built up a colossal speed. Then the motors will be cut out and you'll carry on under your own momentum until you reach the orbit of Mars and have to start thinking about slowing down.

Whether your weeks in space are boring or not depends very much on you and your fellow passengers. Quite a number of entertainments get organized on the voyage, and a good deal of money is liable to change hands before the end of the trip. (It's a curious fact, but the crew usually seems to come out on top.) You'll have plenty of time for reading, and the ship will have a good library of microbooks. [2] There will be radio and TV contact with Earth and Mars for the whole voyage, so you'll be able to keep in touch with things — if you want to.

On my first trip, I spent a lot of my time learning my way around the stars and looking at clusters and nebulae [3] through a small telescope I borrowed from the navigation officer. Even if you've never felt the slightest interest in astronomy before, you'll probably be

[1] spurious (spū'rĭ·ŭs): false.

[2] microbooks (mī'krō·bŏoks): books in very small print.
[3] nebulae (nĕb'ū·lē): strung-together structures.

a keen observer before the end of the voyage. Having the stars all around you — and not merely overhead — is an experience you'll never forget.

As far as outside events are concerned, you realize of course that absolutely nothing can happen during the voyage. Once the drive has cut out, you'll seem to be hanging motionless in space: you'll be no more conscious of your speed than you are of the Earth's seventy thousand miles an hour round the Sun right now. The only evidence of your velocity will be the slow movement of the nearer planets against the background of the stars — and you'll have to watch carefully for a good many hours before you can detect even this.

By the way, I hope you aren't one of those foolish people who are still frightened about meteors. They see that enormous chunk of nickel-steel in New York's American Museum of Natural History and imagine that's the sort of thing you'll run smack into as soon as you leave the atmosphere — forgetting that there's rather a lot of room in space and that even the biggest ship is a mighty small target. You'd have to sit out there and wait a good many centuries before a meteor big enough to puncture the hull came along — it hasn't happened to a spaceship yet.

One of the big moments of the trip will come when you realize that Mars has begun to show a visible disk. The first feature you'll be able to see with the naked eye will be one of the polar caps, glittering like a tiny star on the edge of the planet. A few days later the dark areas — the so-called seas — will begin to appear, and presently you'll glimpse the prominent triangle of the Syrtis Major.[1] In the week before land-

ing, as the planet swims nearer and nearer, you'll get to know its geography pretty thoroughly.

The braking period doesn't last very long, as the ship has lost a good deal of its speed in the climb outward from the Sun. When it's over, you'll be dropping down onto Phobos,[2] the inner moon of Mars — which acts as a natural space station about four thousand miles above the surface of the planet. Though Phobos is only a jagged lump of rock not much bigger than some terrestrial mountains, it's reassuring to be in contact with something solid again after so many weeks in space.

When the ship has settled down into the landing cradle, the air lock will be coupled up and you'll go through a connecting tube into the port. Since Phobos is much too small to have an appreciable gravity, you'll still be effectively weightless. While the ship's being unloaded, the immigration officials will check your papers. I don't know the point of this; I've never heard of anyone being sent all the way back to Earth after having got this far!

There are two things you mustn't miss at Port Phobos. The restaurant there is quite good; it's very small, and only goes into action when a liner docks, but it does its best to give you a fine welcome to Mars. And after a couple of months, you'll have got rather tired of the shipboard menu.

The other item is the centrifuge;[3] I believe that's compulsory now. You go inside and it will spin you up to half a gravity, or rather more than the weight Mars will give you when you land. It's simply a little cabin on a rotating arm, and there's room to walk around inside so that you can practice

[1] **Syrtis Major** (sûr′tĭs mā′jēr): a region of Mars, greenish-blue in color.

[2] **Phobos** (fō′bŏs).

[3] **centrifuge** (sĕn′trĭ·fūj): a whirling or rotating device.

using your legs again. You probably won't like the feeling; life in a spaceship can make you lazy.

The ferry rockets that will take you down to Mars will be waiting when the ship docks. If you're unlucky, you'll hang around at the port for some hours, because they can't carry more than twenty passengers and there are only two ferries in service. The actual descent to the planet takes about three hours – and it's the only time on the whole trip when you'll get any impression of speed. Those ferries enter the atmosphere at over five thousand miles an hour, and go halfway round Mars before they lose enough speed through air resistance to land like ordinary aircraft.

You'll land, of course, at Port Lowell: besides being the largest settlement on Mars, it's still the only place that has the facilities for handling spaceships. From the air the plastic pressure domes look like a cluster of bubbles – a very pretty sight when the Sun catches them. Don't be alarmed if one of them is deflated. That doesn't mean that there's been an accident. The domes are let down at fairly frequent intervals so that the envelopes can be checked for leaks. If you're lucky, you may see one being pumped up – it's quite impressive.

After two months in a spaceship, even Port Lowell will seem a mighty metropolis. (Actually, I believe its population is now well over twenty thousand.) You'll find the people energetic, inquisitive, forthright – and very friendly, unless they think you're trying to be superior.

It's a good working rule never to criticize anything you see on Mars. As I said before, they're very proud of their achievements – and after all, you are a guest, even if a paying one.

Port Lowell has practically everything you'll find in a city on Earth, though of course on a smaller scale. You'll come across many reminders of "home." For example, the main street in the city is Fifth Avenue – but surprisingly enough you'll find Piccadilly Circus where it crosses Broadway.

The port, like all the major settlements, lies in the dark belt of vegetation that roughly follows the Equator and occupies about half the southern hemisphere. The northern hemisphere is almost all desert – the red oxides that give the planet its ruddy color. Some of these desert regions are very beautiful; they're far older than anything on the surface of our Earth, because there's been little weathering on Mars to wear down the rocks – at least since the seas dried up, more than five hundred million years ago.

You shouldn't attempt to leave the city until you've become quite accustomed to living in an oxygen-rich, low-pressure atmosphere. You'll have grown fairly well acclimatized on the trip, because the air in the spaceship will have been slowly adjusted to conditions on Mars. Outside the domes, the pressure of the natural Martian atmosphere is about equal to that on the top of Mount Everest – and it contains practically no oxygen. So when you go out, you'll have to wear a helmet or travel in one of those pressurized jeeps they call "sand fleas."

Wearing a helmet, by the way, is nothing like the nuisance you'd expect it to be. The equipment is very light and compact, and as long as you don't do anything silly it is quite foolproof. As it's most unlikely that you'll ever go out without an experienced guide, you'll have no need to worry. Thanks to the low gravity, enough oxygen for twelve hours' normal working can be carried quite easily — and you'll never be away from shelter as long as that.

Don't attempt to imitate any of the locals you may see walking around without oxygen gear. They're second-generation colonists and are used to the low pressure. They can't breathe the Martian atmosphere any more than you can, but like the old-time native pearl divers, they can make one lungful last for several minutes when necessary. Even so, it's a silly sort of trick and they're not supposed to do it.

As you know, the other great obstacle to life on Mars is the low temperature. The highest thermometer reading ever recorded is somewhere in the eighties, but that's quite exceptional. In the long winters, and during the night in summer or winter, it never rises above freezing. And I believe the record low is minus one hundred and ninety!

Well, you won't be outdoors at night, and for the sort of excursions you'll be doing, all that's needed is a simple thermosuit. It's very light and traps the body heat so effectively that no other source of warmth is needed.

No doubt you'll want to see as much of Mars as you can during your stay. There are only two methods of transport outside the cities — sand fleas for short ranges and aircraft for longer distances. Don't misunderstand me when I say "short ranges" — a sand flea with a full charge of power cells is good for a couple of thousand miles, and it can do eighty miles an hour over good ground. Mars could never have been explored without them — you can survey a planet from space, but in the end someone with a pick and shovel has to do the dirty work filling in the map.

One thing that few visitors realize is just how big Mars is. Although it seems small beside the Earth, its land area is almost as great because so much of our planet is covered with oceans. So it's hardly surprising that there are vast regions that have never been properly explored — particularly around the poles. Those stubborn people who still believe that there was once an indigenous [1] Martian civilization pin their hopes on these great blanks. Every so often you hear rumors of some wonderful archaeological discovery in the wastelands — but nothing ever comes of it.

Personally, I don't believe there ever were any Martians — but the planet is interesting enough for its own sake. You'll be fascinated by the plant life and the queer animals that manage to live without oxygen, migrating each year from hemisphere to hemisphere across the ancient sea beds to avoid the ferocious winter. The fight for survival on Mars has been fierce, and evolution has produced some pretty odd results. Don't go investigating any Martian life forms unless you have a guide, or you may get some unpleasant surprises.

Well, that's all I've got to say, except to wish you a pleasant trip. Oh, there is one other thing. My boy collects stamps, and I rather let him down when I was on Mars. If you could drop me a few letters while you're there — there's no need to put anything in them if you're too busy — I'd be much obliged. He's trying to collect a set of space-mail covers postmarked from each of the principal Martian cities, and if you could help — thanks a lot!

[1] **indigenous** (ĭn·dĭj′ĕ·nŭs): native.

THINKING IT OVER

1. When does the voyage that is described in this selection take place? The first paragraph gives you a partial clue:

fifty years plus the time you estimate it will take for the first spaceship to reach Mars.

2. From the names of the streets and the Martian port city and the take-off place, what nation or nations are implied as being in control of the Martian settlements?

3. The author does not say, but what kinds of work do you think are carried on by the residents of the Martian colonies? What clues are there that Earth is still the dominant or controlling factor in any Martian plans? Why do you suppose this would be the case?

4. Why would a person with claustrophobia (the fear of narrow spaces) make a poor passenger on a Mars liner?

5. Why is the trip from Earth to Space Station One more difficult than the millions of miles between it and Mars? What is the second space station?

6. Compare life on earth as you know it with that on the Mars of this selection. Why would anyone choose to live permanently on the latter?

RELATING DETAILS TO THE MAIN IDEA

1. What are the details of preparation for the trip?

2. List some of the physical details — those connected with day-to-day living — of life on Mars.

3. What are the important details of the trip from the New Guinea launching pad to Space Station One?

4. Fill in the chief details of the trip from Space Station One to Phobos, and from there to Port Lowell.

5. Fill in the details for one of these subjects covered in the selection: forms of life on Mars; daily living on Mars; characteristics of the people; climate, seasons, and atmosphere.

PEN AND PAPER

1. You have just arrived on Mars and are sitting down to write a descriptive letter about it — the spaceship, the discomforts and pleasures, the sights, the other passengers on the journey — to a friend or relative back home.

2. Or, you have just finished your first week on Mars and are going to tell that same person about life on Mars — the people, places, sights, and sounds. Remember, your letter will be microfilmed, and you will be allowed as much as 300 words — if you are neat.

ABOUT THE AUTHOR

Arthur C. Clarke (1917–) was born in the seaside town of Minehead in England and spent his youth there and at his parents' nearby farm. An early interest in both science and literature eventually led him into the science-fiction field as a writer. The first of his many stories in this vein was sold while he was a pilot in the Royal Air Force during World War II. A graduate of King's College in London, he is also a lecturer on science and space and has written plays as well. Two of his best-known books are *Island in the Sky* and *Expedition to Earth.*

FOR THE FUTURE:
VARIATIONS ON A THEME

In the introduction to *Man's Conquest of the Air,* the practice of consulting different sources in reading about a particular topic was pointed out to you. It was suggested, too, that you might enjoy applying this idea to a subject in which you are especially interested. Within the area of your choice, however, you will need to make certain decisions. To read all that has been written about nearly any topic would be impossible; you will want, therefore, to choose a phase or area of your subject, moving on afterward to other phases of the same subject. The following are a few topics that might appeal to you, along with suggested aspects of the topic to read about:

ARCHAEOLOGY: Restoring Pompeii; discovering the lost city of Troy.

AUTOMOBILES: Racing cars; early American automobiles.

BASEBALL: American baseball in the early days; great baseball pitchers.

MOUNTAIN CLIMBING: Mount Everest and the men who tried to climb it; mountain climbing in America.

MOVIES: The silent screen; great movie directors; movie techniques.

MUSIC: American folk music; famous opera singers; the lives of great composers.

THEATER: Stage design in America; the great comedians of the theater; the Shakespearean theater in America.

Nonfiction

SUGGESTIONS FOR FURTHER READING

GENERAL

Adamson, Joy, *Born Free* (Pantheon, 1960)
Unusual story — with excellent photos — of the captive lioness Elsa who was trained by a Kenya game warden and his author wife for a return to jungle life. The sequel, *Living Free* (Harcourt, Brace & World, 1961), traces Elsa's experiences in the jungle.
Bannister, Roger, *The Four-Minute Mile* (Dodd, Mead, 1955)
Runners, here's how!
Baumann, Hans, *The Caves of the Great Hunters* (Pantheon, 1954)
Four boys discover France's most important Ice-Age cave.
Bothwell, Jean, *The Animal World of India* (Franklin Watts, 1961)
Everything from birds to bulls and snakes to elephants, with monkeys and leopards to boot. Fine illustrations.
Court, Alfred, *My Life with the Big Cats* (Simon & Schuster, 1955)
A world-famous animal trainer tells about tigers, lions, and panthers.
Crile, Jane and Barney, *Treasure-Diving Holidays* (Viking, 1954)
An unusual family follows an unusual interest. Fine photographs.
Dooley, Thomas A., *The Night They Burned the Mountain* (Farrar, Straus & Cudahy, 1960)
More about this American doctor's struggle against disease and Communism in his beloved Laos.
Fitch, John, with William F. Nolan, *Adventure on Wheels* (Putnam, 1959)
An ex-fighter pilot takes up road racing — with championship results.
Frazee, Steve, *First Through the Grand Canyon* (Holt, Rinehart & Winston, 1960)
Action-packed account of the first boat expedition down the Green and Colorado Rivers in 1869.
Graham, Frank, *The New York Yankees* (Putnam, rev. 1958)
Yankee fans can't miss this one.
Heyerdahl, Thor, *Kon-Tiki* (Rand McNally, 1950)
Six men on a raft. First-rate adventure.

Hoke, Helen, ed., *Nurses, Nurses, Nurses* (Franklin Watts, 1960)
Girls with an interest in nursing should give this a careful reading.
Johnson, Martin E., *Safari* (Grosset & Dunlap)
Adventures in Africa.
Lagus, Charles, *Operation Noah* (Coward-McCann, 1960)
Animal rescue teams at work in Africa to save animals trapped by water.
MacDonald, Betty, *Onions in the Stew* (Lippincott, 1955)
Ever want to live on an island?
Papashvily, George and Helen, *Dogs and People* (Lippincott, 1954)
These two popular writers really like dogs. Try also *Thanks to Noah* (Harper, 1946)
Poole, Lynne, *Today's Science and You* (McGraw-Hill, 1952)
Informative, with many drawings.
White, Anne Terry, *Lost Worlds* (Random House, 1941)
About the civilizations that have long since disappeared and the people who study them.

BIOGRAPHY

Andrews, Roy Chapman, *Beyond Adventure* (Duell, Sloan & Pearce, 1954)
Meet three famous American explorers — Robert Peary, Carl Akeley, and Mr. Andrews himself.
Brown, John Mason, *Daniel Boone* (Random House, 1952)
Rousing and readable, with good pictures.
Busoni, Rafaello, *The Man Who Was Don Quixote* (Prentice-Hall, 1958)
Fascinating life story of Miguel Cervantes, whose career was as unusual as that of his fictional hero. Illustrated.
Crawford, Marion, *The Little Princesses* (Harcourt, Brace & World, 1950)
You will like this book from which "Queen Elizabeth II" was taken.
Dolan, Edward F., Jr., *Green Universe* (Dodd, Mead, 1959)
Exciting biography of the adventurous scientist, Alexander von Humboldt.
Forsee, Aylesa, *Louis Agassiz: The Pied Piper of Science* (Viking, 1958)

A great American naturalist and teacher who began life as a humble Swiss village boy.

Frank, Anne, *Anne Frank: The Diary of a Young Girl* ° (Modern Library)
The autobiography of a young Jewish girl who died in a Nazi concentration camp. A modern classic.

Kendall, Lace, *Houdini: Master of Escape* (Macrae Smith, 1960)
Fascinating account of the master escape artist.

Kenney, Gen. George C., *Dick Bong: Ace of Aces* (Duell, Sloan & Pearce, 1960)
Air fighting with America's top flying ace in World War II.

Kugelmass, J. Alvin, *Roald Amundsen* (Messner, 1955)
The story of the great polar explorer.

Levinger, Elma Ehrlich, *Albert Einstein* (Messner, 1949)
Another highly readable biography by the same author: *Leonardo da Vinci* (Messner, 1954).

McGiffin, Lee, *Swords, Stars, and Bars* (Dutton, 1958)
Exciting studies of Confederate cavalry generals in sudden action.

Moody, Ralph, *Little Britches* (Norton, 1950)
A fine father-son tale of ranch life in Colorado about fifty years ago.

Noble, Iris, *The Courage of Doctor Lister* (Messner, 1960)
A famous doctor's career and the part played by his devoted wife.

Putnam, Peter, *Keep Your Head Up, Mr. Putnam!* (Harper, 1952)
Autobiographical account of a hunting accident, blindness, and a Seeing-eye dog.

Stafford, Marie Peary, *Discoverer of the North Pole* (Morrow, 1959)
The famous admiral's daughter provides an interesting account of her father's life.

Steffens, Lincoln, *Boy on Horseback* (Harcourt, Brace & World, 1931)
An autobiography that has become a modern classic.

Stuart, Jesse, *The Thread That Runs So True* (Scribner, 1949)
The complete book from which the ex-

° Available in *Four Adventures in Courage,* Fuller and Thompson, eds. (Harcourt, Brace & World, 1962).

cerpt in the nonfiction section was taken.

Sutton, Felix, *Big Game Hunter* (Messner, 1960)
Good story of Carl Akeley.

Waite, Helen Elmira, *Valiant Companions* (Macrae Smith, 1959)
The heart-warming story of Helen Keller and her teacher, Anne Sullivan Macy.

MAN'S CONQUEST OF THE SKY

Bridgeman, William, and Jacqueline Hazard, *The Lonely Sky* (Holt, Rinehart & Winston, 1955)
A test pilot's view of his exciting work.

Caidin, Martin, *War for the Moon* (Dutton, 1959)
Good explanation and background of the race to reach the moon. Illustrated.

de Leeuw, Hendrik, *Conquest of the Air* (Vantage, 1960)
Excellent coverage on everything from balloons to rockets.

Gubitz, Myron B., *Rocketship X–15* (Messner, 1960)
Just about all there is to know about the famous experimental sound barrier breaker.

Lindbergh, Charles A., *The Spirit of St. Louis* (Scribner, 1953)
Don't miss this grand book!

Reynolds, Quentin, *The Wright Brothers, Pioneers of American Aviation* (Random House, 1950)
Colorful and highly readable.

Shippen, Katherine B., *A Bridle for Pegasus* (Viking, 1951)
Famous "flying firsts" by the author of "Kitty Hawk."

Simons, David G., with Don A. Schanche, *Man High* (Doubleday, 1960)
Story of the balloon flight on which Lieutenant Colonel Simons stayed at 102,000 feet for 32 hours.

Wainwright, Loudon, ed., *The Astronauts, Pioneers in Space* (Golden Press, 1961)
Excitingly illustrated, this account of the work of Project Mercury is told by the seven astronauts themselves.

FOR YOUR LISTENING

"Fantasy on Greensleeves," as recorded on the Siena pianoforte — the instrument described in "The Piano That Wouldn't Die" — is included on longplay record *Many Voices* 9A.

Poetry

Poetry is a difficult word to define. But then, so is *music*. What a time you'd have trying to define *music!*

It is far easier to say what music does than what it is.

How might you begin?

"There are many kinds of music: gay, serious, thoughtful, to match a person's moods. There is music for dancing, music to stir us to action, to cheer us up, music to make us daydream . . ."

Isn't this equally true of poetry?

And aren't there some particular things poetry can do that no other type of writing can do quite so well?

Let's see.

Poetry can surprise us into seeing commonplace objects in a new light. For instance, a poet named Charles Malam looked at a huge, ungainly machine, and in a way that is akin to magic, his words turned it into a prehistoric monster. . . .

Steam Shovel

The dinosaurs are not all dead.
I saw one raise its iron head
To watch me walking down the road
Beyond our house today.
Its jaws were dripping with a load
Of earth and grass that it had cropped.
It must have heard me where I stopped,
Snorted white steam my way,
And stretched its long neck out to see,
And chewed, and grinned quite amiably.[1]

[1] From *Upper Pasture* by Charles Malam. Copyright, 1930, by Charles Malam. Copyright renewed 1958 by Charles Malam. Reprinted by permission of Holt, Rinehart and Winston, Inc.

◄ Shimmering in its shifting patterns of motion, this gold-wire mobile construction by Richard Lippold (1915–) is called "The Sun." It is an unusual example of the striking forms used by an artist — sculptor, painter, or poet — to interpret what he sees and feels.

Poetry can put striking ideas into very few words.

This is what a poet named Emily Dickinson did in four quick lines and seventeen words. Instead of writing a long prose sentence to say that in the world of nature, animals and insects do not concern themselves with titles, family backgrounds, or royal estates, she made a sharp little poem . . .

Pedigree

The pedigree of honey
   Does not concern the bee;
A clover, any time, to him
   Is aristocracy.[1]

When we are moved to rejoice and be thankful, we discover in poetry strong, soaring words like these from the Bible . . .

Psalm One Hundred

Make a joyful noise unto the Lord, all ye lands.
Serve the Lord with gladness:
Come before his presence with singing.
Know ye that the Lord he is God:
It is he that hath made us, and not we ourselves;
We are his people, and the sheep of his pasture.
Enter into his gates with thanksgiving,
And into his courts with praise:
Be thankful unto him, and bless his name.
For the Lord is good; his mercy is everlasting;
And his truth endureth to all generations.[2]

What other things can poetry do, perhaps with greater dramatic force than the sentences of prose writing?

For one thing, poetry can capture almost every imaginable mood.

For another, a poem can transport one *instantly* anywhere in this world — or out of it — by whatever means fancy dictates.

[1] From *Poems* by Emily Dickinson, edited by Martha Dickinson Bianchi and Alfred Leete Hampson. Reprinted by permission of Little, Brown & Co.
[2] From *The Bible, Designed to Be Read as Living Literature* by Ernest Sutherland Bates, editor. Copyright 1936 by Simon and Schuster, Inc., New York. By permission of Simon and Schuster, Inc., New York.

Here is a poem by John Masefield to strike a responsive chord in the shyest stay-at-home . . .

Sea Fever

I must go down to the seas again, to the lonely sea and the sky,
And all I ask is a tall ship and a star to steer her by,
And the wheel's kick and the wind's song and the white sail's shaking,
And a gray mist on the sea's face and a gray dawn breaking.

I must go down to the seas again, for the call of the running tide
Is a wild call and a clear call that may not be denied;
And all I ask is a windy day with the white clouds flying,
And the flung spray and the blown spume, and the sea gulls crying.

I must go down to the seas again, to the vagrant gypsy life,
To the gull's way and the whale's way where the wind's like a whetted knife;
And all I ask is a merry yarn from a laughing fellow rover,
And quiet sleep and a sweet dream when the long trick's over.[1]

[1] From *Collected Poems* by John Masefield. Copyright, 1912, by The Macmillan Company, renewed 1940 by John Masefield, and reprinted by permission of The Macmillan Company.

"All's Well": oil painting by the American Artist Winslow Homer (1836–1910).

Now and again a poem speaks directly to us, like a sympathetic friend, to help strengthen us in moments when we are discouraged, as Hamlin Garland does in these lines.

Do You Fear the Force of the Wind?

Do you fear the force of the wind,
The slash of the rain?
Go face them and fight them,
Be savage again.
Go hungry and cold like the wolf,
Go wade like the crane:
The palms of your hands will thicken,
The skin of your cheek will tan,
You'll grow ragged and weary and swarthy,
But you'll walk like a man! [1]

[1] Used by permission of Constance Garland Doyle and Isabel Garland Lord.

Poetry can be full of humor. Many a poem as light as a bubble will blow up and burst into laughter or a happy smile. Ogden Nash, the poet, looked at an octopus and asked . . .

The Octopus

Tell me, O Octopus, I begs,
Is those things arms, or is they legs?
I marvel at thee, Octopus;
If I were thou, I'd call me Us.[1]

When one tries to say exactly what poetry *is,* the definition is still elusive, still a little beyond easy reach.

We could say, "Poetry is a matter of selecting the right words and putting them together in the right way so that they have a beat and a rhythm — like music, or marching."

But that's not the whole story, is it?

We might add: "Sometimes the words in a poem make patterns — patterns of sounds and rhymes."

However, we are forgetting an essential point: A poem is a way of using well-chosen words to express ideas as carefully and as precisely as possible.

Robert Frost, the poet, must have meant this when he declared that a complete poem is one in which "an emotion has found the thought and the thought has found the words."

And yet we have not actually begun to mention all that poetry can do.

We have not said that a poem can tell a story. We have not said that through poems we share the thoughts and feelings of people, whether they live now or were alive thousands of years ago, so that we grow in our understanding of others.

Some poems have no more rhyme or reason for being than a song does — because they *are* songs! Poetry gives voice to foolish moods or trivial hopes with the same grace that it grants us insights into nature's world.

[1] From *Verses from 1929 On.* Copyright 1942 by Ogden Nash. Reprinted by permission of Little, Brown & Co.

The territory of poetry is vaster than the earth's, because its boundaries are limitless. Indeed, its concern is with anything that touches man's life now, or in the past, or even in the mysterious future that lies ahead.

Poetry offers to us as much as we consent to find in it — and more.

We could end by saying that poetry is a challenge to the adventurous.

But that is not an ending. There is no end to challenges, any more than there is to adventure.

Adventure and challenges are forever beginning anew.

. . . And so are poems.

ABOUT THE POETS

Behind every poem stands a poet. If this Introduction has presented to you an old friend or a fresh new personality whose work you would like to explore, it has served its purpose. You will meet some of these poets again in this section; Emily Dickinson is represented by a special group of poems, and another of the beautiful Psalms of David awaits your reading.

You may already know the name of John Masefield, author of "Sea Fever." Born in 1876, Masefield became well acquainted with the seafaring life during his early years of voyaging around the world. He has the title of Poet Laureate of England, an honor which is bestowed by the reigning monarch.

The author of "Do You Fear the Force of the Wind?" is Hamlin Garland (1860–1940). He was born in Wisconsin and wrote many novels and short stories with the Middle West as their background. One of his books received a Pulitzer prize.

Charles Malam (1906–   ), whose "Steam Shovel" you read, is also an American poet, and so is Ogden Nash (1902–   ), author of "The Octopus." Reading one Nash poem is like eating one peanut — you want more! Fortunately, his books of verse are many.

In the pages ahead, poets from many ages and lands will spread out their treasures for you. The treasures are varied and contrasting, the pleasures of sampling them quite limitless.

Storytelling Poems

Long before books were commonplace and television, motion pictures, and record players were invented, where could a person find entertainment? Stories and music did exist, of course, but how did they reach the people in castle and cottage?

If you had lived during the Middle Ages, a wandering minstrel might have visited your town. Invited to the simplest home or the great hall of the castle, he would please the townspeople with poetic tales of adventure, glorious deeds, and romance. He might accompany himself on a lute, a type of small harp. Although the names of these minstrels have been forgotten, a number of their story-songs endure today. These are called *traditional ballads.* Ballads have one clear distinguishing feature: the ballad refrain, a group of words repeated at the end of each line. Modern authors continue to use the ballad style, and many of our popular songs are in ballad form. The first poem in the following group is a ballad. However, it is called a *literary ballad,* because it was written by a known poet centuries after the days of the traditional ballad.

Not all the poems in this group are ballads, but they all have stories to tell.

If you want to work out readings in which each member of the class can take part, these poems are excellent for that purpose. And you will be reminded of a simple truth that is often overlooked: *poetry is meant to be heard.*

Allen-a-Dale

SIR WALTER SCOTT

This ballad tells an old story and contains a "riddle" that you might try to answer.

> Allen-a-Dale has no faggot for burning,
> Allen-a-Dale has no furrow for turning,
> Allen-a-Dale has no fleece for the spinning,
> Yet Allen-a-Dale has red gold for the winning.
> Come, read me my riddle! come, hearken my tale!   5
> And tell me the craft of bold Allen-a-Dale.
>
> The Baron of Ravensworth prances in pride,
> And he views his domains upon Arkindale side,

The mere° for his net, and the land for his game,
The chase for the wild, and the park for the tame;   10
Yet the fish of the lake, and the deer of the vale,
Are less free to Lord Dacre than Allen-a-Dale!

Allen-a-Dale was ne'er belted a knight,°
Though his spur be as spark, and his blade be as bright;
Allen-a-Dale is no baron or lord,   15
Yet twenty tall yeomen will draw at his word;
And the best of our nobles his bonnet will vail,°
Who at Rere-Cross on Stanmore meets Allen-a-Dale.

Allen-a-Dale to his wooing is come;
The mother, she asked of his household and home: 20
"Though the castle of Richmond stand fair on the hill,
My hall," quoth bold Allen, "shows gallanter still;
'Tis the blue vault of heaven, with its crescent so pale,
And with all its bright spangles!" said Allen-a-Dale.

9. **mere** (mẹr): a lake or pool. 13. **belted a knight:** In the ceremony of being knighted, a young man was given a sword and belt. 17. **vail** (vāl): to take off, as a sign of reverence or submission.

The father was steel and the mother was stone;   25
They lifted the latch, and they bade him begone;
But loud, on the morrow, their wail and their cry!
He had laughed on the lass with his bonny black eye,
And she fled to the forest to hear a love-tale,
And the youth it was told by was Allen-a-Dale!   30

HOW WELL DID YOU READ?

1. Although neither a knight nor a nobleman, Allen-a-Dale commanded the respect of everyone. Which lines in stanza three show this? What is the meaning of *bonnet*, line 17?

2. To what was Allen-a-Dale referring in lines 23 and 24 when he described his "hall"?

3. What is your answer to the "riddle" proposed in stanza one?

A CLASS READING

Why not try a class reading of this poem? You might have individuals read the first four lines of each stanza and the class, as a chorus, read the last two lines of each stanza.

ABOUT THE POET

Sir Walter Scott (1771–1832) learned early in life to love the tales of the border country of his homeland — Scotland. Although educated to be a lawyer, he devoted his life to writing — chiefly long narrative poems and historical novels. Since he had been a childhood victim of infantile paralysis, he was lame, and he also suffered from ill health all his life. His best-known works include the novels *Ivanhoe*, *Kenilworth*, and *The Talisman*. *The Lady of the Lake* and *Marmion* are among his better-known poems.

Napoleonic battle scene: engraving by the French artist, Gerard.

Incident of the French Camp

ROBERT BROWNING

This poem by one of England's greatest storytellers strikes a note of high courage. Browning created many fine dramatic poems in which the story is told in the first person. The incident in this poem, many authorities believe, really did take place during Napoleon's Austrian campaign in 1809. Some say that it was a man rather than a boy who performed the act of bravery. Which theory do you favor?

> You know, we French stormed Ratisbon.°
>   A mile or so away,
> On a little mound, Napoleon
>   Stood on our storming-day;
> With neck outthrust, you fancy how,   5
>   Legs wide, arms locked behind,
> As if to balance the prone brow
>   Oppressive with its mind.
>
> Just as perhaps he mused "My plans
>   That soar, to earth may fall,   10
> Let once my army-leader Lannes°
>   Waver at yonder wall" —

1. **Ratisbon** (rătʹĭs·bŏn), now Regensburg (rāʹgĕns·bo͝ork): a city in eastern Bavaria, Germany. 11. **Lannes** (län′): Marshal Lannes was one of Napoleon's most trusted commanders.

Out 'twixt the battery smokes there flew
    A rider, bound on bound
Full-galloping; nor bridle drew   15
    Until he reached the mound.

Then off there flung in smiling joy,
    And held himself erect
By just his horse's mane, a boy:
    You hardly could suspect —   20
(So tight he kept his lips compressed,
    Scarce any blood came through)
You looked twice ere you saw his breast
    Was all but shot in two.

"Well," cried he, "Emperor, by God's grace   25
    We've got you Ratisbon!
The Marshal's in the market-place,
    And you'll be there anon
To see your flag-bird flap his vans°
    Where I, to heart's desire,   30
Perched him!" The chief's eye flashed; his plans
    Soared up again like fire.

The chief's eye flashed; but presently
    Softened itself, as sheathes
A film the mother-eagle's eye   35
    When her bruised eaglet breathes;
"You're wounded!" "Nay," the soldier's pride
    Touched to the quick, he said:
"I'm killed, Sire!" And, his chief beside,
    Smiling, the boy fell dead.   40

29. **vans:** wings (on the emblem on Napoleon's banner).

HOW WELL DID YOU READ?

1. Compare the description given by the poet in lines 5–8 with a picture of Napoleon. Is the description accurate?

2. The battle for Ratisbon was a critical one for the French. Marshal Lannes stormed the fortified city in a daring feat of arms. What part did the boy himself play in the siege, according to lines 27–31?

3. Someone familiar with bird life should be able to explain the film that "sheathes . . . the mother-eagle's eye," lines 34 and 35. Probably he can tell how this so-called "third lid" functions. Why is this figure of speech appropriate in this stanza?

4. Have you a story of personal heroism that compares in some way with the bravery of Browning's young hero? Perhaps you can relate it to the class, explaining how it compares with the bravery Browning described.

ABOUT THE POET

Robert Browning (1812–1889), one of England's most scholarly poets, achieved fame for his dramatic writings in poetic form. He married Elizabeth Barrett, also a well-known British poet, and they spent fifteen happy years together in Italy before she died.

The Fool's Prayer

EDWARD R. SILL

There are many kinds of courage. In this famous poem by a nineteenth-century American poet, a humble man gives evidence of a kind of courage that is more than a match for his master's willful pride.

The royal feast was done; the king
    Sought some new sport to banish care,
And to his jester cried: "Sir Fool,
    Kneel now, and make for us a prayer!"

The jester doffed his cap and bells,   5
    And stood the mocking court before;
They could not see the bitter smile
    Behind the painted grin he wore.

He bowed his head, and bent his knee
    Upon the monarch's silken stool;   10
His pleading voice arose: "O Lord,
    Be merciful to me, a fool!

"No pity, Lord, could change the heart
    From red with wrong to white as wool;
The rod must heal the sin: but, Lord,   15
    Be merciful to me, a fool!

" 'Tis not by guilt the onward sweep
    Of truth and right, O Lord, we stay;
'Tis by our follies that so long
    We hold the earth from heaven away.   20

"These clumsy feet, still in the mire,
    Go crushing blossoms without end;
These hard, well-meaning hands we thrust
    Among the heartstrings of a friend.

"The ill-timed truth we might have kept —   25
    Who knows how sharp it pierced and stung?
The word we had not sense to say —
    Who knows how grandly it had rung?

"The Fool's Prayer" from *Poems* by Edward R. Sill. Reprinted by permission of and arrangement with Houghton Mifflin Company, the authorized publishers.

◀ *"Clown 1912": oil painting by the French artist, Georges Rouault (1871–1958).*

"Our faults no tenderness should ask,
   The chastening° stripes must cleanse them all;   30
But for our blunders — oh, in shame
   Before the eyes of heaven we fall.

"Earth bears no balsam° for mistakes;
   Men crown the knave, and scourge the tool
That did his will; but Thou, O Lord,   35
   Be merciful to me, a fool!"

The room was hushed; in silence rose
   The king, and sought his gardens cool,
And walked apart, and murmured low,
   "Be merciful to me, a fool!"   40

30. **chastening** (chās″n·ĭng): correcting by punishment. 33. **balsam** (bôl′săm): balm or healing ointment.

HOW WELL DID YOU READ?

1. In what spirit does the king give his order to the jester (line 4)?
2. What particular lines spoken by the jester may have made the deepest impression on the king? Express the meaning of these lines in your own words.
3. Why does the king rise and go alone into his gardens?
4. Why may the jester be called a courageous man? What else does the poem reveal about his character?

THE TOOLS OF THE POET: ALLITERATION

A poet uses "sound effects" to make a poem pleasing to the ear. One means of creating sound effects — one of the "tools" of the poet — is *alliteration*. This is the use, in a line or sentence, of two or more words which begin with the same sound. Some examples are: "Between the *d*ark and the *d*aylight"; "What early tongue *so sweet saluteth* me?" A good example in this poem is in line 2. Point out other examples of alliteration in the poem.

A Dutch Picture

HENRY WADSWORTH LONGFELLOW

"Pirates!" There's a word to chill an honest seaman's blood! This Longfellow poem tells the story of an old pirate lost in dreams of the past. To make the story glow, Longfellow uses words as rich in color as the paintings of the artist Rembrandt, mentioned in stanza seven.

Simon Danz has come home again,
   From cruising about with his buccaneers;
He has singed the beard of the King of Spain,
And carried away the Dean of Jaen°
   And sold him in Algiers.   5

4. **Dean of Jaen** (hä·än′): a high-ranking church official of a city in southern Spain.

In his house by the Maese,° with its roof of tiles,
  And weathercocks flying aloft in air,
There are silver tankards of antique styles,
Plunder of convent and castle, and piles
  Of carpets rich and rare.   10

In his tulip garden there by the town,
  Overlooking the sluggish stream,
With his Moorish cap and dressing gown,
The old sea captain, hale and brown,
  Walks in a waking dream.   15

A smile in his gray mustachio lurks
  Whenever he thinks of the King of Spain;
And the listed° tulips look like Turks,
And the silent gardener as he works
  Is changed to the Dean of Jaen.   20

The windmills on the outermost
  Verge° of the landscape in the haze,
To him are towers on the Spanish coast,
With whiskered sentinels at their post,
  Though this is the river Maese.   25

But when the winter rains begin,
  He sits and smokes by the blazing brands,
And old seafaring men come in,
Goat-bearded, gray, and with double chin,
  And rings upon their hands.   30

They sit there in the shadow and shine
  Of the flickering fire of the winter night;
Figures in color and design
Like those by Rembrandt° of the Rhine,
  Half darkness and half light.   35

And they talk of ventures lost or won,
  And their talk is ever and ever the same,
While they drink the red wine of Tarragon,°
From the cellars of some Spanish Don,°
  Or convent set on flame.   40

Restless at times with heavy strides
  He paces his parlor to and fro;

6. **Maese** (māz): the Meuse (mūz) River. 18. **listed** (lĭst′ĕd): formed into a straight border or line. 22. **Verge** (vûrj): edge. 34. **Rembrandt** (rĕm′brănt): a great Dutch painter. 38. **Tarragon**: a province in northeastern Spain. 39. **Don**: the title of a Spanish nobleman.

He is like a ship that at anchor rides,
And swings with the rising and falling tides
  And tugs at her anchor tow.   45

Voices mysterious far and near,
  Sound of the wind and sound of the sea,
Are calling and whispering in his ear,
"Simon Danz! Why stayest thou here?
  Come forth and follow me!"   50

So he thinks he shall take to the sea again
  For one more cruise with his buccaneers,
To singe the beard of the King of Spain,
And capture another Dean of Jaen
  And sell him in Algiers.   55

HOW WELL DID YOU READ?

1. Did Simon Danz really "singe the beard" of the King of Spain? What is the literal meaning of this expression?

2. Tell briefly what is revealed of the old buccaneer's past. Do you know what period in history is referred to?

3. Is the old man entirely happy with his memories? Explain.

THE TOOLS OF THE POET: SIMILE AND METAPHOR

Just as the artist relies on certain principles of light, line, and perspective to create a picture, so a poet has techniques and "tools" with which to work. *Figures of speech* are the means often used to express ideas in unusual ways. A *simile* is a figure of speech which makes a comparison between two seemingly unlike objects. Look at line 18 in "A Dutch Picture." Longfellow has used two poetic devices here: (1) alliteration (the *l*isted *t*ulips look *l*ike *T*urks), and (2) simile — the comparison of flowers to men.

The *metaphor* is another figure of speech you will want to recognize. In lines 21, 22, and 23 of "A Dutch Picture" Longfellow says that to Simon Danz the windmills are towers. The poet is making a comparison, just as he did with the tulips in the simile in line 18, except that he makes this comparison in the form of a direct statement without using *like* or *as:* the windmills *are* towers.

We unconsciously depend on figures of speech such as the metaphor and the simile to enliven our conversation and our writing. We say, "He's as cross as a bear when he's tired," using the simile. "He's a bear when he is tired" is the metaphor. Be alert for these devices in poetry.

To show your own skill, try inventing three similes and three metaphors. Take about three minutes to do so. Perhaps you can then read some aloud. Identify each as a metaphor or simile.

ABOUT THE POET

Henry Wadsworth Longfellow (1807–1882) was born and educated in Maine. He was a professor of modern languages, first at Bowdoin College in Brunswick, Maine, from which he had been graduated, and later at Harvard University. He became one of America's best-loved poets and was widely known abroad. He traveled and studied extensively in Europe, and he helped to bring the culture of Europe to America by his translations of the works of European poets. Among his most noted works are his long poems based on American legends — "The Song of Hiawatha," "Evangeline," and "The Courtship of Miles Standish."

"Old Man with the Red Cap," the painting opposite, ▶
is by the magnificent Dutch artist, Rembrandt van Rijn (1606–1669).

Of Nature's People

The art of the poet is to put into words certain feelings and insights that most of us cannot express readily or with quite such grace. In reading some of the poems in this group, perhaps you will say, "That's just the way *I* feel." Even the "narrow fellow" slithering through the grass may give you the same shock of surprise that Emily Dickinson's poem conveys.

These poems do not attempt to tell stories. Rather, they present snapshot glimpses of animals, some tame, some as wild and free as their natural homes. Each "picture" has a distinctive quality, reflecting the poet's individual way of looking at his subject. His own mood colors the object he describes, and your enjoyment grows if you share the mood with him.

A Narrow Fellow in the Grass

EMILY DICKINSON

Poets are keen observers. In her observations about nature, Emily Dickinson is brief and thrifty with words. Her poems always deserve more than one reading, however. Later in this section you will learn more about this woman who became one of our most famous American poets.

> A narrow fellow in the grass
> Occasionally rides;
> You may have met him — did you not?
> His notice sudden is.
>
> The grass divides as with a comb,   5
> A spotted shaft is seen;
> And then it closes at your feet
> And opens further on.
>
> He likes a boggy acre,
> A floor too cool for corn.   10
> Yet when a child, and barefoot,
> I more than once, at morn,

"A Narrow Fellow in the Grass" from *Poems* by Emily Dickinson, edited by Martha Dickinson Bianchi and Alfred Leete Hampson. Reprinted by permission of Little, Brown & Co.

Have passed, I thought, a whip-lash
Unbraiding in the sun —
When, stooping to secure it,   15
It wrinkled, and was gone.

Several of nature's people
I know, and they know me;
I feel for them a transport°
Of cordiality;   20

But never met this fellow,
Attended or alone,
Without a tighter breathing,
And zero at the bone.

19. **transport** (trăns′pōrt): strong feeling.

HOW WELL DID YOU READ?

To see how keenly this poet observes nature, check on these points:

1. In what sense does a snake "ride" in the grass (line 2)?

2. Line 4 comments, "His notice sudden is." Does this refer to the snake's notice of you, or yours of him? Why?

3. What habits of this type of snake are accurately described in the second and third stanzas? Do they apply to all snakes?

4. Why is the word *wrinkled,* line 16, especially appropriate?

5. What is your interpretation of the sixth stanza?

6. What is there about the way the poem as a whole is constructed that makes the final two lines a dramatic surprise?

Three Poems About Cats

People usually have strong feelings about cats; they either like them very much or not at all. Which of these three poems reflects your feelings?

Poem

WILLIAM CARLOS WILLIAMS

As the cat
climbed over
the top of

the jamcloset
first the right   5
forefoot

carefully
then the hind
stepped down

into the pit of   10
the empty
flower pot

Contented Kitten

ARTHUR GUITERMAN

A ball of silky fur
Inhabited by purr.

Macavity: the Mystery Cat

T. S. ELIOT

Macavity's a Mystery Cat: he's called the Hidden Paw —
For he's the master criminal who can defy the Law.
He's the bafflement of Scotland Yard, the Flying Squad's despair:
For when they reach the scene of crime — *Macavity's not there!*

Macavity, Macavity, there's no one like Macavity,   5
He's broken every human law, he breaks the law of gravity.
His powers of levitation° would make a fakir° stare,
And when you reach the scene of crime — *Macavity's not there!*
You may seek him in the basement, you may look up in the air —
But I tell you once and once again, *Macavity's not there!*   10

Macavity's a ginger cat, he's very tall and thin;
You would know him if you saw him, for his eyes are sunken in.
His brow is deeply lined with thought, his head is highly domed;
His coat is dusty from neglect, his whiskers are uncombed.
He sways his head from side to side, with movements like a snake;   15
And when you think he's half asleep, he's always wide awake.

Macavity, Macavity, there's no one like Macavity,
For he's a fiend in feline shape, a monster of depravity.°
You may meet him in a by-street, you may see him in the square —
But when a crime's discovered, then *Macavity's not there!*   20

7. **levitation** (lĕv′ĭ·tā′shŭn): the illusion of rising and moving freely through the air; **fakir** (fȧ·kēr′): an East Indian wonder-worker. 18. **depravity** (dē·prăv′ĭ·tĭ): evil.

He's outwardly respectable. (They say he cheats at cards.)
And his footprints are not found in any file of Scotland Yard's.
And when the larder's looted, or the jewel case is rifled,
Or when the milk is missing, or another Peke's been stifled,
Or the greenhouse glass is broken, and the trellis past repair — 25
Aye, there's the wonder of the thing! *Macavity's not there!*

And when the Foreign Office find a Treaty's gone astray,
Or the Admiralty lose some plans and drawings by the way,
There may be a scrap of paper in the hall or on the stair —
But it's useless to investigate — *Macavity's not there!* 30
And when the loss has been disclosed, the Secret Service say:
"It *must* have been Macavity!" — but he's a mile away.
You'll be sure to find him resting, or a-licking of his thumbs,
Or engaged in doing complicated long division sums.

Macavity, Macavity, there's no one like Macavity, 35
There never was a Cat of such deceitfulness and suavity.°
He always has an alibi, and one or two to spare:
At whatever time the deed took place — MACAVITY WASN'T THERE!
And they say that all the Cats whose wicked deeds are widely known
(I might mention Mungojerrie, I might mention Griddlebone) 40
Are nothing more than agents for the Cat who all the time
Just controls their operations: the Napoleon of Crime!

36. **suavity** (swăv′ĭ·tĭ): polite smoothness.

HOW WELL DID YOU READ?

Poem 1. This poem has something in common, in its form, with "A Narrow Fellow." What? What unusual details do you observe about its form? Why is there no punctuation of any kind?

2. The cat is a graceful animal. In what way does the poet make this point without once mentioning it?

Contented Kitten 1. Seriously: what made you smile?

2. Can you think up as good a definition of a kitten at play, in two lines of not more than ten words altogether?

Macavity: the Mystery Cat 1. What is your first clue to the fact that this is a humorous poem?

2. What characteristics make Macavity look like a criminal?

3. What does he do to earn the title "the Napoleon of Crime"? In what sense is the word *Napoleon* used?

4. Mungojerrie and Griddlebone, mentioned in line 40, are other cat characters in poems by this author in a book called *Old Possum's Book of Practical Cats.* If Macavity interests you, you ought to look up his friends.

ABOUT THE POETS

William Carlos Williams (1883–) is a modern American poet whose work is usually very serious in tone. *Arthur Guiterman* (1871–1943), another modern American poet, is best known for the light verse he wrote. *T. S. Eliot* (1888–) was born in America but became a British subject after long residence abroad. He became one of today's most illustrious and serious poets. Would you say that all three of these poets knew cats and liked them? Explain.

At Woodward's Gardens

ROBERT FROST

This poem discusses monkeyshines. But is that all it does? Woodward's Gardens was a large privately owned estate that used to be an old San Francisco showplace. Sight-seers would visit its lakes, its seal tank, and its zoo. Robert Frost, who is another poet you will learn more about later in this section, lived in California until he was ten. He must have liked that zoo. Perhaps the experience he describes here actually happened, and later on he thought about it, as poets do.

A boy, presuming on his intellect,
Once showed two little monkeys in a cage
A burning glass they could not understand
And never could be made to understand.
Words are no good: to say it was a lens   5
For gathering solar rays would not have helped.
But let him show them how the weapon worked.
He made the sun a pin point on the nose
Of first one then the other till it brought
A look of puzzled dimness to their eyes   10
That blinking could not seem to blink away.
They stood arms laced together at the bars,
And exchanged troubled glances over life.
One put a thoughtful hand up to his nose
As if reminded — or as if perhaps   15
Within a million years of an idea.
He got his purple little knuckles stung.
The already known had once more been confirmed
By psychological experiment,
And that were all the finding to announce   20
Had the boy not presumed too close and long.
There was a sudden flash of arm, a snatch,
And the glass was the monkeys', not the boy's.
Precipitately° they retired back cage
And instituted an investigation   25
On their part, though without the needed insight.
They bit the glass and listened for the flavor.
They broke the handle and the binding off it.
Then none the wiser, frankly gave it up,
And having hid it in their bedding straw   30
Against the day of prisoners' ennui,°

24. **Precipitately:** hurriedly. 31. **ennui** (än'wē): boredom.

Came dryly forward to the bars again
To answer for themselves: Who said it mattered
What monkeys did or didn't understand?
They might not understand a burning glass. 35
They might not understand the sun itself.
It's knowing what to do with things that counts.

HOW WELL DID YOU READ?

1. The poet whimsically shows the monkeys hiding the glass in order to be able to study it later in case they become bored. Do you think that Robert Frost is serious in giving their actions this interpretation?

2. This poet is famous for his salty and wise comments about people and their relationships to the world of nature. The closing five lines are characteristic. To whom does his comment apply? Can you give some examples of the wisdom of this remark?

Three Things to Remember

WILLIAM BLAKE

This poem presents a point of view in an unusual manner — and also gives you something to think about.

A Robin Redbreast in a cage
Puts all Heaven in a rage.

A skylark wounded on the wing
Doth make a cherub cease to sing.

He who shall hurt the little wren
Shall never be beloved by men.

HOW WELL DID YOU READ?

1. In your own words, state the three things the poet is warning against.

2. Extend the thought of the third stanza by explaining why this person "Shall never be beloved." What other actions might such a person be likely to perform?

The Flower-fed Buffaloes

VACHEL LINDSAY

Here is a backward look at a vanished American scene and at one of nature's people that is seldom seen today.

The flower-fed buffaloes of the spring
In the days of long ago,
Ranged where the locomotives sing
And the prairie flowers lie low;
The tossing, blooming, perfumed grass   5
Is swept away by the wheat,
Wheels and wheels and wheels spin by
In the spring that still is sweet.
But the flower-fed buffaloes of the spring
Left us long ago.   10
They gore no more, they bellow no more,
They trundle around the hills no more —
With the Blackfeet lying low,
With the Pawnees lying low,
Lying low.   15

HOW WELL DID YOU READ?

1. What changes does Vachel Lindsay say have taken place since the buffaloes ranged the prairies?

2. Lines 13 and 14 are capable of being interpreted as meaning more than that the Indians are "hiding." What other meanings can you discover?

3. Thinking over the message of this poem, try to develop two or three effective slogans for the wise protection of our wild animals. Word each statement as though you were to use it on a poster about wildlife conservation.

ABOUT THE POETS

William Blake (1757–1827) was an artist and an engraver as well as a poet. He engraved the text and illustrations for all his poems on copper plates, making his publications works of art. His intensely vivid imagination so brilliantly colored his poems and drawings that the effect was often mystical. Another of his poems that you will enjoy is "The Tiger."

Vachel Lindsay (1879–1931) traveled as a vagabond around the United States, reciting his dramatic verse in return for food. On his travels he used to hand out copies of a leaflet called "Rhymes to Be Traded for Bread." He was born in Springfield, Illinois, Lincoln's early home. He wrote about American heroes in such poems as "Abraham Lincoln Walks at Midnight." The poetry of Vachel Lindsay often has the exciting beat and rhythm of American jazz. An artist as well as a poet, he wrote essays on his "gospel of beauty," lectured on art, and depended for his livelihood on his dramas as well as on his poems.

A *detail from "The Last of the Buffalo," a painting* ▶
by the American artist, Albert Bierstadt (1830–1902).

The Fawn

EDNA ST. VINCENT MILLAY

You will discover as you read more of her poems later in this section that
Edna St. Vincent Millay was a poet whose observant eyes found beauty in
wild forests and big cities alike. In "The Fawn" she makes us her companions in a sudden meeting with a small creature of the woods.

There it was I saw what I shall never forget
And never retrieve.
Monstrous and beautiful to human eyes, hard to believe,
He lay, yet there he lay,
Asleep on the moss, his head on his polished cleft small ebony hooves,   5
The child of the doe, the dappled child of the deer.

Surely his mother had never said, "Lie here
Till I return," so spotty and plain to see
On the green moss lay he.
His eyes had opened; he considered me.   10

I would have given more than I care to say
To thrifty ears, might I have had him for my friend
One moment only of that forest day:

Might I have had the acceptance, not the love
Of those clear eyes;   15
Might I have been for him the bough above
Or the root beneath his forest bed,
A part of the forest, seen without surprise.

Was it alarm, or was it the wind of my fear lest he depart
That jerked him to his jointy knees   20
And sent him crashing off, leaping and stumbling
On his new legs, between the stems of the white trees?

HOW WELL DID YOU READ?

1. The word *Monstrous*, line 3, is a surprising one to appear along with *beautiful*. One of its meanings is "unnatural in
form or structure"; another, "enormous"
or "huge." Still a third is "fabulous" or
"mythical." Consider which of these best
applies to the word as it is used here.

Try to explain how this sleeping fawn
gave this impression to the poet.

2. Compare the mood of this poem
with that of "Four Little Foxes" on page
366. What is similar about the moods?

3. What particular words — adjectives
and verbs — in the final stanza help to
make this description almost unforget-
tably vivid?

THE TOOLS OF THE POET: LYRIC POETRY

A lyric poem such as "The Fawn" may be defined as "emotional verse of songlike form." The word *lyric* has quite a history. Among the ancient Greeks a lyre was the stringed instrument which the young man of good education learned to play, just as he learned to read, write, sing, and participate in sports. Originally, a lyric was a poem that was sung or recited to the accompaniment of the lyre.

By a lyric today we mean a poem or song that expresses strong emotion. Lyric poems have many different forms. The poet's intense personal feeling about his subject is the most marked feature of the lyric poem rather than any particular pattern of line or stanza. Watch for other examples of lyric poetry in this section.

Four Little Foxes

LEW SARETT

The creatures of nature cannot speak for themselves. Yet poets have a way of knowing how to speak for them, as the modern Middle Western poet Lew Sarett does here.

> Speak gently, Spring, and make no sudden sound;
> For in my windy valley, yesterday I found
> Newborn foxes squirming on the ground —
>   Speak gently.

> Walk softly, March, forbear the bitter blow;   5
> Her feet within a trap, her blood upon the snow,
> The four little foxes saw their mother go —
>   Walk softly.

> Go lightly, Spring, oh, give them no alarm;
> When I covered them with boughs to shelter them from harm   10
> The thin blue foxes suckled at my arm —
>   Go lightly.

> Step softly, March, with your rampant hurricane;
> Nuzzling one another, and whimpering with pain,
> The new little foxes are shivering in the rain —   15
>   Step softly.

HOW WELL DID YOU READ?

1. Why is March, the month in which spring arrives, asked to "forbear the bitter blow"? What two things can be meant by the word *blow?*

2. There is a variety of fox called "blue." Do you think that the poet was referring only to this in the third stanza? Why?

3. What happened to the mother fox? How recently had it happened?

FOR YOUR VOCABULARY:
WORD HISTORIES

Rampant (răm'pănt), in line 13 of "Four Little Foxes," is a rewarding word on which to use your detective talents.

You will find that it comes down to us from medieval heraldry, the science of recording family origins in symbols on armor and flags. You have seen pictures of lions *rampant*, or horses *rampant*, on bright banners and decorations. They are shown rearing up, with their forelegs or paws extended. The word is from the French. It also means "threatening," "unchecked," "extravagant." Observe how the poet has made it apply to the "hurricane" of March. What figure of speech is he using with this phrase? Why is it very apt, or appropriate, in relation to the month of March? Can you now explain the meaning of such a statement as this: "Ignorance and superstition ran *rampant* among the natives"?

"Four Little Foxes" from *Covenant with Earth* by Lew Sarett. Edited and copyrighted, 1956, by Alma Johnson Sarett. Gainesville: University of Florida Press, 1956. Reprinted by permission of Mrs. Sarett.

All But Blind

WALTER DE LA MARE

All the poems of this modern British writer reflect a sensitive, imaginative insight into life's creatures and their surroundings. The strong appeal of this poem will unfold with thoughtful reading.

> All but blind
> In his chambered hole
> Gropes for worms
> The four-clawed Mole.
>
> All but blind   5
> In the evening sky,
> The hooded Bat
> Twirls softly by.
>
> All but blind
> In the burning day   10
> The Barn-Owl blunders
> On her way.
>
> And blind as are
> These three to me,
> So, blind to Someone   15
> I must be.

HOW WELL DID YOU READ?

1. Remembering that the mole is a burrowing animal, what is the meaning of *chambered*, line 2?

2. Is there a bat expert in class? Can he explain what is meant by a "hooded" bat? (An encyclopedia will yield information about a species of bat whose long ears are actually joined across the forehead. Does this help?)

3. Why is "twirls" a very accurate verb to describe a bat's flight?

4. Why do you think the poet capitalizes the words Mole, Bat, and Barn-Owl?

5. Why does he capitalize Someone? How do you interpret the meaning of the last stanza?

ABOUT THE POET

Walter de la Mare (1873–1956) was born and educated in England. His poems for and about children brought him lasting fame, and equally memorable are his poems about nature. *Peacock Pie* is the title of his best-known book of poetry. Later on in this section he is represented by one of his most enduring poems, "Silver."

Poems That Never Grow Old

In your conversation and your writing, there is always the moment when you wish to illustrate a point or to express a certain mood in a way that will make your meaning vivid and clear. Frequently you cannot summon words of your own that will convey this meaning, and so you find yourself quoting a few lines of verse which express perfectly what you wish to say. Poetry, like music, has the power to linger in one's mind long after one has come upon it. Probably you can still recall many of the jingles that you learned and chanted in your childhood. As your familiarity with poetry grows, you will discover poems that not only stay with you, but that you will want to commit to memory so that you can make them your own in a special way.

Here are some poems that have been known and cherished for many years, in some instances for hundreds of years. They are ageless because they concern themselves with thoughts and ideas that are meaningful to people regardless of the land they live in, or, thanks to the work of translators, the language they speak.

The Twenty-third Psalm

The Twenty-third Psalm was composed by David, a young shepherd boy in Biblical times, who grew up to become king of his people. David, a gifted singer and harpist, wrote many of the Psalms, of which this is probably the best known and loved.

The Lord is my shepherd; I shall not want.
He maketh me to lie down in green pastures:
He leadeth me beside the still waters.
He restoreth my soul:
He leadeth me in the paths of righteousness for his name's sake.   5
Yea, though I walk through the valley of the shadow of death,
I will fear no evil: for thou art with me;
Thy rod and thy staff they comfort me.
Thou preparest a table before me in the presence of mine enemies:
Thou anointest my head with oil; my cup runneth over.   10
Surely goodness and mercy shall follow me all the days of my life:
And I will dwell in the house of the Lord forever.

"The Twenty-third Psalm" reprinted by permission from *The Bible, Designed to Be Read as Living Literature,* edited by Ernest Sutherland Bates. Copyright, 1936, by Simon and Schuster, Inc.

David with Harp: illustration from tenth-century Byzantine psalm book.

HOW WELL DID YOU READ?

1. Lines 2 and 3 give a picture of peace and contentment. Lines 6–8 present a contrasting scene of fear and evil. What might arouse such feelings in a shepherd as he watched his flocks?

2. What would a shepherd mean by *rod* and *staff* in line 8?

3. Compare this poem with Psalm One Hundred on page 340. What have the two in common?

HOW DOES POETRY DIFFER FROM PROSE?

To a child, poetry means rhyme, and, of course, much fine poetry does contain lines that rhyme. We might add that all poetry has a certain beat or rhythm. But does it follow that all poetry must have a rhyme scheme and a definite rhythmic pattern? Some students leap to this conclusion, which is incorrect. Not all poetry contains lines that rhyme, and no law says that poetry must have a clearly marked rhythmic beat.

Here are a few points that you should remember about poetry: A poet works with language to express thoughts *concisely* as he creates scenes and captures moods. Because he observes intently, and also because he draws freely upon imagination, the language of a poem will be *natural but never ordinary*. The idea of a poem may be simple but never commonplace.

And yet even a free-verse poem, which has no special rhythmic pattern and perhaps no rhyme at all, usually has a "plan" to it which the reader can sense: a free flow rather like the irregular break of waves on the shore. "This," says the reader of the poem, "is about something I know. I've felt this. I've seen it, but I could not have expressed it so well nor so exactly. Despite its lack of rhyme or regularity of rhythm, this is a poem."

Walt Whitman is one of America's greatest poets. He once said, ". . . the narrowest hinge in my hand puts to scorn all machinery." Had he been writing prose, how would he have said this? The difference between your prose statement of his words and the line as he wrote it will illustrate rather well the difference between prose and poetry.

The Donkey

G. K. CHESTERTON

A donkey is often the target of jokes and ridicule. In this poem, a donkey reminds us that however much he and his kind may be laughed at, all donkeys can look back to a moment of high honor — when one of them was chosen for a triumphant entrance into a famous city.

When fishes flew and forests walked
   And figs grew upon thorn,
Some moment when the moon was blood
   Then surely I was born;

With monstrous head and sickening cry   5
   And ears like errant wings,
The devil's walking parody
   Of all four-footed things.

The tattered outlaw of the earth,
   Of ancient crooked will;   10
Starve, scourge, deride me: I am dumb,
   I keep my secret still.

Fools! For I also had my hour;
   One far fierce hour and sweet:
There was a shout about my ears,   15
   And palms before my feet.

HOW WELL DID YOU READ?

1. In stanza 1, what is this donkey admitting about donkeys in general?
2. Parody is writing that pokes fun at the language or style of an author. Explain what this word means as it is used in lines 7 and 8 in this poem.
3. The last stanza refers to the moment of triumph all donkeys can share to make up for the humiliation they otherwise endure. What event is referred to, and in what book is it recorded?
4. Describe the picture of donkeys that this poem may have created for you. What has the poet made you feel about this animal?
5. Can you relate other stories or poems in which the donkey is treated sympathetically?

THE TOOLS OF THE POET: UNUSUAL SENTENCE PATTERNS

In poetry, the word order of sentences is often different from that in everyday speech. Unless you understand the purpose of the special word order used by the poet, you may be impatient with him.

In "The Donkey," the stanzas consist of a sentence each. To create interest and suspense, Chesterton does not reveal the main thought of each sentence until the last line of the stanza. For example, instead of stating "Surely I was born when fishes flew and forests walked," in stanza 1, he reverses the order of the sentence and gains a dramatic effect. To appreciate this, make direct statements of the other stanzas, then compare these with the poet's handling of them.

"The Donkey" from the book *The Wild Knight and Other Poems* by G. K. Chesterton. Published by E. P. Dutton & Co., Inc., and reprinted with their permission.

An Old Song

SOLOMON BLOOMGARDEN

Translated by Marie Syrkin

The source of this poem is a very old
Japanese song. Solomon Bloomgarden, a
modern American poet, wrote it in Yid-
dish, which is a modified German dialect
with Hebrew letter characteristics. Its
English translation keeps a light, musical
touch.

In the blossom-land Japan
Somewhere thus an old song ran.
Said a warrior to a smith,
"Hammer me a sword forthwith.
Make the blade   5
Light as wind on water laid.
Make it long
As the wheat at harvest song.
Supple, swift
As a snake, without rift,   10
Full of lightnings, thousand-eyed!
Smooth as silken cloth and thin
As the web that spiders spin.
And merciless as pain, and cold."

"On the hilt what shall be told?"   15

"On the sword's hilt, my good man,"
Said the warrior of Japan,
"Trace for me
A running lake, a flock of sheep,   19
And one who sings her child to sleep."

HOW WELL DID YOU READ?

1. Explain why the warrior uses such
contrasting scenes to describe the blade
he wishes made.
2. Why does the warrior have such a
peaceful scene traced on the hilt of his
sword?

"An Old Song" by Solomon Bloomgarden, translated by Marie Syrkin. Reprinted by permission of the translator.

When Icicles Hang by the Wall

WILLIAM SHAKESPEARE

Shakespeare is best known to you as a writer of plays, but he was also a writer of songs. Some of these were sung in his plays, as was "Hark, Hark, the Lark," from *Cymbeline*, and "Under the Greenwood Tree" in *As You Like It*. This little song, with its lively picture of a winter scene, is from *Love's Labor's Lost*.

When icicles hang by the wall,
   And Dick the shepherd blows his nail,
And Tom bears logs into the hall,
   And milk comes frozen home in pail,
When blood is nipped, and ways be foul,   5
Then nightly sings the staring owl,
        To-whit!
To-who! — a merry note,
While greasy Joan doth keel° the pot.

When all aloud the wind doth blow,   10
   And coughing drowns the parson's saw,°
And birds sit brooding in the snow,
   And Marian's nose looks red and raw,
When roasted crabs° hiss in the bowl,
Then nightly sings the staring owl,   15
        To-whit!
To-who! — a merry note,
While greasy Joan doth keel the pot.

9. **keel:** stir. 11. **saw:** wise saying. 14. **crabs:** crab apples.

HOW WELL DID YOU READ?

1. What does one do when he "blows his nail," line 2? Have you ever done that on a frosty day?

2. In stanza 2 the poet has deftly described three different settings. Name each of them.

3. This poem has many scenes of activity and work. What kinds of work and play are going on?

Fable

RALPH WALDO EMERSON

The purpose of a fable, of course, is to point out a moral. (Remember *Aesop's Fables*?) If the little story is told with humor, we enjoy the lesson all the more. You may know some people who have "big heads," or too high opinions of themselves. Is there a lesson for them in this poem?

The mountain and the squirrel
Had a quarrel,
And the former called the latter "Little Prig";
Bun° replied,
"You are doubtless very big;   5
But all sorts of things and weather
Must be taken in together,
To make up a year
And a sphere.
And I think it no disgrace   10
To occupy my place.
If I'm not so large as you,
You are not so small as I,
And not half so spry.
I'll not deny you make   15
A very pretty squirrel track;
Talents differ; all is well and wisely put;
If I cannot carry forests on my back,
Neither can you crack a nut."

4. **Bun:** the squirrel.

HOW WELL DID YOU READ?

1. What line or lines state the main idea of this fable?

2. A handicapped person often makes up for his handicap by becoming skilled in other ways. A blind person, for instance, is usually more sensitive to sounds and touch than the seeing person is. The squirrel is aware that in size he is no match for the mountain. In what way does he make up for his small size?

PEN AND PAPER

Here is a poem with a moral which has significance for almost everyone. A discussion of the poem and its moral should prove stimulating and rewarding. Perhaps the following topics, all suggested by the poem, would make interesting composition material. Choose a topic and take up your pen! Try: "A Talent I Wish I Had"; "Biggest Doesn't Mean Best"; "The Advantage of Being My Size."

An Old Woman of the Roads

PADRAIC COLUM

A homeless old woman is not a common sight in our country, today at least. But years ago in rural Ireland, it was not unusual to see, wandering from village to village, a very old woman who had outlived her friends and family. The photograph opposite reflects the spirit of one "old woman of the roads" as captured in this poem by Padraic Colum (pôth'rĭg kŏl'ŭm).

O to have a little house!
To own the hearth and stool and all!
The heaped-up sods upon the fire,
The pile of turf against the wall!

To have a clock with weights and chains   5
And pendulum, swinging up and down!
A dresser filled with shining delph,°
Speckled and white and blue and brown!

I could be busy all the day
Clearing and sweeping hearth and floor,   10
And fixing on their shelf again
My white and blue and speckled store!

I could be quiet there at night
Beside the fire and by myself,
Sure of a bed and loth to leave   15
The ticking clock and the shining delph!

Och! but I'm weary of mist and dark,
And roads where there's never a house nor bush,
And tired I am of bog and road
And the crying wind and the lonesome hush!   20

And I am praying to God on high,
And I am praying Him night and day,
For a little house — a house of my own —
Out of the wind's and the rain's way.

7. **delph**: glazed pottery.

HOW WELL DID YOU READ?

1. What are some of the possessions that the old woman yearns for? What do these hopes tell you about her as a person? What do they tell you about the Irish countryside of that day?

2. What does stanza 5 tell you about the old woman's personal experiences?

"An Old Woman of the Roads" from *Collected Poems* by Padraic Colum, published by the Devin-Adair Co., New York. Reprinted by permission of the author.

Invictus

WILLIAM ERNEST HENLEY

The triumph of a courageous spirit over personal misfortune is the theme of this poem. Its author, a British poet, waged a constant battle against ill health. The impact of these strong lines makes the poem a favorite with many people.

Out of the night that covers me,
   Black as the Pit from pole to pole,
I thank whatever gods may be
   For my unconquerable soul.

In the fell° clutch of circumstance   5
   I have not winced nor cried aloud.
Under the bludgeonings of chance
   My head is bloody, but unbowed.

Beyond this place of wrath and tears
   Looms but the horror of the shade,
And yet the menace of the years   11
   Finds, and shall find, me unafraid.

It matters not how strait° the gate,
   How charged with punishments the
      scroll,
I am the master of my fate;   15
   I am the captain of my soul.

     5. **fell:** cruel; deadly. 13. **strait:** narrow.

HOW WELL DID YOU READ?

   1. To what extent, if any, do you agree with the idea in lines 15–16?
   2. This poem has been set to music. If you were an artist and were asked to draw a cover design for the song, what sort of picture would you draw?
   3. There are other poems about courage in this section, and perhaps you know still others. If you have a favorite among them, which is it? Why?

The Goat Paths

JAMES STEPHENS

It must have been on a quiet, sunny day that James Stephens, an Irish poet, came upon the scene he describes in "The Goat Paths." A sunny, quiet mood must have prompted his writing this poem.

The crooked paths go every way
   Upon the hill — they wind about
   Through the heather in and out
Of the quiet sunniness.
And there the goats, day after day,   5
   Stray in sunny quietness,
Cropping here and cropping there,
   As they pause and turn and pass,
Now a bit of heather spray
   Now a mouthful of the grass.   10

In the deeper sunniness,
   In the place where nothing stirs,
Quietly in quietness,
   In the quiet of the furze,°
For a time they come and lie   15
Staring on the roving sky.

If you approach, they run away,
   They leap and stare, away they
      bound,
   With a sudden angry sound,
To the sunny quietude;   20
   Crouching down where nothing stirs
   In the silence of the furze,
Crouching down again to brood
In the sunny solitude.

If I were as wise as they,   25
   I would stray apart and brood,
I would beat a hidden way
Through the quiet heather spray
   To a sunny solitude;

     14. **furze** (fûrz): a flowering green shrub.

"Invictus" by William Ernest Henley. Reprinted by permission of Charles Scribner's Sons.
"The Goat Paths" from *Collected Poems* by James Stephens. Copyright 1915 by The Macmillan Company and renewed in 1943 by James Stephens. Used with permission of The Macmillan Company.

And should you come, I'd run away,   30
    I would make an angry sound,
    I would stare and turn and bound
To the deeper quietude,
    To the place where nothing stirs
    In the silence of the furze.   35

In that airy quietness
    I would think as long as they;

Through the quiet sunniness
    I would stray away to brood
By a hidden beaten way   40
    In a sunny solitude.

I would think until I found
    Something I can never find,
Something lying on the ground,
    In the bottom of my mind.   45

HOW WELL DID YOU READ?

1. What sort of setting does the poem have?

2. The use of repetition is one way to gain a desired effect. The poet has used this device with unusual effectiveness here. Point out the repeated words that convey a sense of quietness and sunniness. What are some variations of these words?

3. There is a paradox in the last stanza of this poem — that is, a statement which seems contrary to common sense but really is not. Try to put the poet's idea into your own words to show that what he says is not so puzzling as it may seem but actually makes good sense.

Travel

ROBERT LOUIS STEVENSON

Who does not daydream about faraway places? Where would you go — to the South Seas, the jungles of Africa, or to the ancient ruins in Egypt or Greece? But you may be thinking of space travel! Whatever your imaginary destination, you will surely sympathize with this author's mood.

I should like to rise and go
Where the golden apples grow;
Where below another sky
Parrot islands anchored lie,
And, watched by cockatoos and goats,
Lonely Crusoes building boats;⠀⠀⠀⠀6
Where in sunshine reaching out
Eastern cities, miles about,
Are with mosque and minaret
Among sandy gardens set,⠀⠀⠀⠀10
And the rich goods from near and far
Hang for sale in the bazaar;
Where the Great Wall round China
⠀⠀goes,
And on one side the desert blows,
And with bell and voice and drum,⠀⠀15
Cities on the other hum;
Where are forests, hot as fire,
Wide as England, tall as a spire,
Full of apes and coconuts
And the Negro hunters' huts;⠀⠀⠀⠀20
Where the knotty crocodile
Lies and blinks in the Nile,
And the red flamingo flies
Hunting fish before his eyes;
Where in jungles, near and far,⠀⠀⠀⠀25
Man-devouring tigers are,
Lying close and giving ear
Lest the hunt be drawing near,
Or a comer-by be seen
Swinging in a palanquin;°⠀⠀⠀⠀30
Where among the desert sands

Some deserted city stands,
All its children, sweep° and prince,
Grown to manhood ages since,
Not a foot in street or house,⠀⠀⠀⠀35
Not a stir of child or mouse,
And when kindly falls the night,
In all the town no spark of light.
There I'll come when I'm a man
With a camel caravan;⠀⠀⠀⠀40
Light a fire in the gloom
Of some dusty dining room;
See the pictures on the walls,
Heroes, fights, and festivals;
And in a corner find the toys⠀⠀⠀⠀45
Of the old Egyptian boys.

30. **palanquin** (păl'ăn·kēn'): an enclosed litter or chair borne on the shoulders of men by means of projecting poles. It is used in India and China.

33. **sweep:** a chimney sweeper.

HOW WELL DID YOU READ?

1. Does this poem make you want to travel, too? If somebody were to give you a plane ticket or a steamship ticket for your coming birthday, what destination would you choose?

2. Can you name places which this poem describes but does not name? Point them out on a world map.

3. Deserted cities are mentioned in lines 31–46. Where might they be? In parts of America there are old ghost towns, especially in forsaken mining areas. Have you ever visited one?

PEN AND PAPER

Travel, imaginary or real, makes a good composition topic. Why not write a composition — or a poem — expressing your own "travel dream"?

◄ "*Street in Tahiti*," *by the French artist, Paul Gauguin* (1848–1903).

Night Clouds

AMY LOWELL

Have you ever stood at night and watched the fantastic shapes made by
clouds moving across the dark skies? Poet Amy Lowell finds a story in
such a scene.

> The white mares of the moon rush along the sky
> Beating their golden hoofs upon the glass Heavens;
> The white mares of the moon are all standing on their hind legs
> Pawing at the green porcelain doors of the remote Heavens.
> Fly, mares!
> Strain your utmost,
> Scatter the milky dust of stars,
> Or the tiger sun will leap upon you and destroy you
> With one lick of his vermilion tongue.

5

HOW WELL DID YOU READ?

1. What figures of speech are used in
this poem?
2. Which words present the most intense colors? Which lines have the most
unusual images?
3. What is the "milky dust of stars"?
4. Why do you think the poet calls the
doors of the Heavens green?

"Night Clouds" from *What's O'Clock* by Amy Lowell. Published by Houghton Mifflin Company.

The Lorelei

HEINRICH HEINE

Translated by Louis Untermeyer

Long ago, sailors on ships traveling the
Rhine River in Germany dreaded a steep
cliff. At its base were violent rapids. This
cliff, known as the Lorelei, became famous
in legends as the place where a beautiful
woman sat, singing songs to lure sailors to
their doom, much as did the Greek sirens.

I cannot tell why this imagined
   Sorrow has fallen on me;
The ghost of an unburied legend
   That will not let me be.

The air is cool, and twilight   5
   Flows down the quiet Rhine;
A mountain alone in the high light
   Catches the faltering shine.

One rosy peak half gleaming
   Reveals, enthroned in air,   10
A goddess, lost in dreaming,
   Who combs her golden hair.

With a golden comb she is combing
   Her hair, as she sings a song;
Heard and reheard through the gloam-
     ing,   15
   It hurries the night along.

The boatman has heard what has bound
   him
   In throes of a strange, wild love.
He is blind to the reefs that surround
   him
   Who sees but the vision above.   20

And lo, the wild waters are springing —
   The boat and the boatman are
     gone . . .
Then silence. And this with her singing,
   The Lorelei has done.

HOW WELL DID YOU READ?

1. Who do you think is telling this
story?

2. If you have read about Odysseus'
experiences with the sirens in the *Odyssey*
(page 537), compare the two stories.

3. "Die Lorelei" is the name of the
famous German song made from this
poem. If a recording of it can be obtained,
perhaps you would enjoy listening to the
original German words set to music.

"The Lorelei" from *Heinrich Heine: Paradox and Poet, The Poems* by Louis Untermeyer, copyright, 1937, by
Harcourt, Brace & World, Inc.

Silver

WALTER DE LA MARE

If there is a better word to describe moonlight than the word "silver," whatever could it be?

> Slowly, silently, now the moon
> Walks the night in her silver shoon;°
> This way, and that, she peers, and sees
> Silver fruit upon silver trees;
> One by one the casements catch   5
> Her beams beneath the silvery thatch;
> Couched in his kennel, like a log,
> With paws of silver sleeps the dog;
> From their shadowy cote° the white breasts peep
> Of doves in a silver-feathered sleep;   10
> A harvest mouse goes scampering by,
> With silver claws and a silver eye;
> And moveless fish in the water gleam,
> By silver reeds in a silver stream.

2. **shoon**: shoes.   9. **cote** (kōt): coop.

HOW WELL DID YOU READ?

1. What objects or animals are silvered by the moon's glow?

2. Point out at least four examples of alliteration in this poem (see page 352).

3. Can you recall a night when a full moon seemed to change the appearance of familiar objects? If so, describe the change that took place.

FOR YOUR VOCABULARY: SYNONYMS AND ANTONYMS

Walter de la Mare uses the word *silver* nine times in this poem, but there is a good reason why it never occurs at the end of a line. Can you guess why? Curiously enough, there is no exact rhyme for it in our language! In such an instance the poet may use words that are similar in meaning and for which there are rhymes. Doing this, he is turning to synonyms (sĭn'ó·nĭmz). A *synonym* is a word whose meaning is similar to that of another, closely related word. The opposite of a synonym is an *antonym* (ăn'tó·nĭm), a word of opposite meaning. Most dictionaries show them clearly, usually as the last item under the definitions.

Both prose and poetry draw upon synonyms and antonyms. And whenever you look up an unfamiliar word, check on its synonyms and antonyms whenever they are given. The meaning of the unfamiliar word is clearer; you will remember it better, and in the process you may add another word or two to your expanding vocabulary. Test this for yourself: look up the synonyms for *lethargy* and *heed;* now check on the antonyms for *insolent, mysterious,* and *mythical.*

*Detail from "Moonlit Landscape" by the early American artist, ▶
Washington Allston (1779–1843).*

The Last of the Books

ALFRED NOYES

Science-fiction writers like to imagine life on other planets and what the
distant future holds in store for us. Although this poem was written dec-
ades before the first man-made satellite went into orbit, it is as up to
date as the latest science-fiction tale — and suggests something about
books that you may not have thought of.

Is it too strange to think
   That, when all life at last from earth is gone,
And round the sun's pale blink
   Our desolate planet wheels its ice and stone,
Housed among storm-proof walls there yet may abide,   5
   Defying long the venoms of decay,
A still dark throng of books, dumb books of song
   And tenderest fancies born of youth and May?

A quiet remembering host,
   Outliving the poor dust that gave them birth,   10
Unvisited by even a wandering ghost,
   But treasuring still the music of our earth,
In little fading hieroglyphs they shall bear
   Through death and night, the legend of our spring,
And how the lilac scented the bright air   15
   When hearts throbbed warm, and lips could kiss and sing.

And, ere that record fail,
   Strange voyagers from a mightier planet come
On wingèd ships that through the void can sail
   And gently alight upon our ancient home;   20
Strange voices echo, and strange flares explore,
   Strange hands, with curious weapons, burst these bars,
Lift the brown volumes to the light once more,
   And bear their stranger secrets through the stars.

HOW WELL DID YOU READ?

1. Explain lines 3 and 4. What physical
condition of earth is the poet referring to?
2. What is the significance of *hieroglyphs*, line 13?
3. "Time capsules" are often put in the
foundations of new buildings. The capsules usually contain examples of our modern music, newspapers, magazines, photographs, and books. If you were on a committee to select certain objects for future
scientists to study, what would you vote
to include? Your limit is three objects.
4. What are some of the special qualities of books that make them particularly
valuable as records of what our life on
earth is really like?

"The Last of the Books" from *Dick Turpin's Ride* by Alfred Noyes. Copyright 1927–1955 by Alfred Noyes. Published by J. B. Lippincott Company.

USING WORDS IN UNUSUAL WAYS

A quite ordinary word used in an extraordinary way suddenly takes on new life. *Blink* and *venoms* are two examples found in stanza 1 of "The Last of the Books." We *blink* our eyes several times a minute, but this obviously is not the meaning of the word as used in this poem. Look up the word in a dictionary and see which meaning makes sense in this context. What other meanings for the word are given? Did you know that this common word had so many meanings?

Venom is ordinarily thought of as the poison released by a snake's fangs when it bites, but it can mean any poison. When the poet combines *venoms* with the word *decay*, he achieves a phrase that multiplies the meanings of both words.

ABOUT THE POETS

Gilbert Keith Chesterton (1874–1936) was an English journalist and poet. His work includes biographies, essays, histories, novels, and a series of popular detective stories which feature an unusual sleuth: a priest called Father Brown.

Ralph Waldo Emerson (1803–1882) was one of America's most important and influential writers of the nineteenth century. He was born in Boston and educated at Harvard. After college he was ordained as a Unitarian minister. He also became one of the most distinguished lecturers of his time. Today he is best known, perhaps, for his essays, ideas from which are still being quoted and discussed. In his *Journal*, which he called his "Savings Bank," he recorded his thoughts on many subjects, including New England life and people. He considered himself primarily a poet, however, so it is right that in this book you meet him, possibly for the first time, as a poet.

Padraic Colum (1881–) has written many appealing poems about his native Ireland, its people, and its folklore. Besides being a poet, he has been a teacher, a literary critic, and a playwright. He has also retold great stories from many lands for young readers. Colum now resides in the United States, where he has lived for many years.

James Stephens (1882–1950), another Irish writer, retold Irish legends in some of his books and wrote fine short stories as well as poetry. Unlike Padraic Colum, however, James Stephens continued to live in Ireland until his death.

Robert Louis Stevenson (1850–1894) was born in Scotland but lived much of his life in other parts of the world. Despite almost constant ill health, he traveled with the spirit of a vagabond, and finally made his home on the South Pacific Island of Samoa. His novels *Treasure Island* and *Kidnapped* show his love of adventure and fantasies; his stories, journals, and poems show how many-sided were his talents.

Amy Lawrence Lowell (1874–1925) broke away from traditional poetic forms to write "free verse." She came from the distinguished New England family which has also produced two other poets, James Russell Lowell and Robert Lowell, as well as statesmen and scholars. Amy Lowell's place as a leader in new poetic forms is firmly established.

Heinrich Heine (hīn′rĭk hī′nĕ) (1797–1856) was born in Dusseldorf, Germany, and as a student at Bonn University became interested in literature. He worked for a newspaper in Berlin and there published his first poems, which were an immediate success. A restless, searching person, Heine left Germany to settle in Paris — the place where he was happiest. He spent the last eight years of his life confined to bed with a crippling spinal disease, but these were also the years when he wrote some of his finest poems. He died in Paris and is buried there.

Alfred Noyes Great fame came to Alfred Noyes (1880–1958) as the result of a single poem, "The Highwayman." He wrote many ballads related to English history and also other poems, all holding to the traditional patterns of rhythm and rhyme. He was born in England and educated at Oxford University; his first book of poems was published while he was a student. He appeared as a lecturer at many universities in the United States. One of his books, *No Other Man*, was made into a film.

Just for Fun

No one has said that poetry must be serious and difficult to understand, but that is the opinion of some. Where's the proof? There are poems written simply to amuse you, and poems that might even make you laugh. You've met a few such poems already in this section; here is a special group of them.

Down through the years, light verse — as this kind of poetry is called — has remained a cheerful, and often wise, ally of serious poetry. Light verse can sparkle with wit and at the same time offer wisdom. It can add up to nothing more than lighthearted — even lightheaded — nonsense. It can practice the artful, entertaining, but serious type of criticism we call *satire*, and poke fun or fire outright insults at almost anything, including social customs, politics, and people.

The variety and range of light verse, as you see, are impressive. But all it asks, really, is to be enjoyed.

Prepare for a surprise in the first of these two examples of light verse. An initial glance at the second poem might make you think the printer is playing a joke — or is it the author?

To the Yearners

FRANKLIN P. ADAMS

Do you feel the call of the sudden Spring?
  Do you long for the Open Road?
Do you crave to fly with an eager wing
  To a beautiful antipode?°

Do you long for the waves and the Open Sea?   5
  And yearn for the Varying Shore?
Do you burn to be free, be free, be free
  Where your soul may soar and soar?

Do you ache for the Land of a Fairer Day?
  Are you sick of the Beaten Track?   10
Do you hark to the call of the Far Away?
  Well, don't let me keep you back.

4. **antipode** (ăn′tĭ·pōd): a place which is exactly opposite another place on the globe.

Llyric of the Llama

BURGES JOHNSON

Puzzling as it may seem at first, do not decide that you have develloped
eye troubllle whille tackllling this lllyric. Nonsensicalll as it is, it makes
excellllllent nonsense.

Behold how from her lair the youthful llama
   Llopes and llightly scans the llandscape o'er.
With llusty heart she llooks upon llife's drama,
   Relying on her llate-llearnt worldly llore.

But llo! Some llad, armed with a yoke *infama*   5
   Soon llures her into llowly llabor's cause;
Her wool is llopped to weave into pajama,
   And llanguidly she llearns her Gees and Haws.

My children, heed this llesson from all llanguishing young lllamas,
If you would lllive with lllatitude, avoid each llluring lllay;°   10
And do not llllightly lllleave, I beg, your llllonesome, llllloving mammas,
And lllllast of allll, don't spellll your name in such a silllllly way.

10. **lay:** song.

PLAYING WITH WORDS

1. The rhymes children chant at play
and the humorous jingle songs that become hits are evidence that playing with
words is a popular pastime. Poets enjoy
it, too. In line 5, Burges Johnson uses the
word *infama* to rhyme with *pajama*. You
will not find *infama* in any English dictionary. In the poem the word *infama* has
been put in italic type to suggest that it is
a foreign word, but it cannot be found in
a dictionary of any other language. Indeed, it is no true member of any language; yet its meaning is clear because it
is so close to the English word *infamous*.
Word detectives will realize that this word
comes from the Latin word *fama*, meaning
fame or *renown*. Added to it is the prefix
in, also from the Latin, which means *not*
(*insane*, *insecure*, etc.). By changing the
suffix *–ous* in *infamous* to *a*, the poet has
made it sound like a real foreign word.
The fun that peeks out of this clever poem
is more enjoyable as we watch this nonsense word appear in the procession of lines
and swing neatly into the rhyme scheme.

2. What other words do you know that
are coined, or invented, words? *Discom-
bobulate* is in fairly wide use, but, if you
found it at all in a dictionary, it would be
listed as slang.

3. Incidentally, can you explain the
words *Gees* and *Haws* in line 8? Someone
might do some research and find out how
these words came to be used.

"Llyric of the Llama" from *Bashful Ballads* by Burges Johnson, published by Harper & Brothers. Reprinted here by permission of the author.

The Embarrassing Episode of Little Miss Muffet

GUY WETMORE CARRYL

Guy Wetmore Carryl, a popular American poet of the 1890's, wrote lines of poetry that seem to march smartly along, inviting the reader to get in step and see where the words are going. Part of the success of this poem is due to its surprising rhymes and its crisp, clearly marked rhythm. Notice how the rhythm of each line makes you emphasize the words and phrases the author wants stressed.

Little Miss Muffet discovered a tuffet
   (Which never occurred to the rest of us),
And, as 'twas a June day, and just about noonday,
   She wanted to eat — like the best of us:
Her diet was whey, and I hasten to say   5
   It is wholesome and people grow fat on it.
The spot being lonely, the lady not only
   Discovered the tuffet, but sat on it.

A rivulet gabbled beside her and babbled,
   As rivulets always are thought to do,   10
And dragonflies sported around and cavorted,
   As poets say dragonflies ought to do;
When, glancing aside for a moment, she spied
   A horrible sight that brought fear to her,
A hideous spider was sitting beside her,   15
   And most unavoidably near to her!

Albeit° unsightly, this creature politely
   Said: "Madam, I earnestly vow to you,
I'm penitent that I did not bring my hat. I
   Should otherwise certainly bow to you."   20
Though anxious to please, he was so ill at ease
   That he lost all his sense of propriety,
And grew so inept that he clumsily stept
   In her plate — which is barred in Society.

This curious error completed her terror;   25
   She shuddered, and growing much paler, not
Only left tuffet, but dealt him a buffet
   Which doubled him up in a sailor-knot.
It should be explained that at this he was pained:
   He cried: " I have vexed you, no doubt of it!   30
Your fist's like a truncheon." " You're still in my luncheon,"
   Was all that she answered. " Get out of it! "

And *The Moral* is this: Be it madam or miss
   To whom you have something to say,
You are only absurd when you get in the curd   35
   But you're rude when you get in the whey!

      17. **Albeit** (ôl·bē′ĭt): Even though.

A Hot-Weather Song

DON MARQUIS

I feel so exceedingly lazy,
    I neglect what I oughtn't to should!
My notion of work is so hazy
    That I couldn't to toil if I would!

I feel so exceedingly silly   5
    That I say all I shouldn't to ought!
And my mind is as frail as a lily;
    It would break with the weight of a thought!

Habits of the Hippopotamus

ARTHUR GUITERMAN

The llama is not the only animal in our comedy act. Enter now a hippopotamus! Shall we, in consideration thereof, call this a hippopoem?

The hippopotamus is strong
    And huge of head and broad of bustle;
The limbs on which he rolls along
    Are big with hippopotomuscle.

He does not greatly care for sweets   5
    Like ice cream, apple pie, or custard,
But takes to flavor what he eats
    A little hippopotomustard.

The hippopotamus is true
    To all his principles, and just;   10
He always tries his best to do
    The things one hippopotomust.

He never rides in trucks or trams,°
    In taxicabs or omnibuses,
And so keeps out of traffic jams   15
    And other hippopotomusses.

13. **trams:** streetcars (British).

Some poems turn cartwheels and kick up their heels in fun. Here is one that stands on its head. Turn it upside down, and this adventure in light verse will still refuse to right itself. Start at the bottom and see what happens.

Till here I am, at last, on top!
With dizzy speed, with haste, chop-chop,
Line over line, word over word,   20
As swift as any soaring bird,
And therefore up and up I go,
Where writers do. Well, now I know,
(How slowly, too) had they begun
Imagine what they would have done   15
Who built the ancient pyramid.
Start at the bottom? So men did
Used up in writing prose and rhyme.
The precious months and years of time
To think I might have cut in half   10
And laugh a bitter little laugh
Not having thought of this before,
And famous now, I but deplore
Is where men started who are rich
I started at the bottom, which   5
And with my eyes upon my goal,
And so, with all my heart and soul,
Should give this new technique a try,
In need of time, I thought that I

fastest way is to start from the bottom of the paper and work up. — *News item.*
his goal — the top of the page. According to the pen company's research, the
time in half. The company theorizes that a person can work faster if he sees
A pen company reports that studies have shown a new way to cut writing

RICHARD ARMOUR

New Technique

"New Technique" by Richard Armour, first appeared in the August 15, 1959, issue of *Saturday Review*. Reprinted by permission of the author and *Saturday Review*.

Phaëthon

MORRIS BISHOP

If you are acquainted with Greek myths,
you may recognize Phaëthon (fā′ĕ·thŏn) as
a son of the god Apollo. One day this
young fellow — But surely his request
could have nothing in common with today's youth! Or could it?

Apollo through the heavens rode
  In glinting gold attire;
His car was bright with chrysolite,°
  His horses snorted fire.
He held them to their frantic course 5
  Across the blazing sky.
His darling son was Phaëthon,
  Who begged to have a try.

"The chargers are ambrosia-fed,
  They barely brook control; 10
On high beware the Crab, the Bear,
  The Serpent round the Pole;
Against the Archer and the Bull°
  Thy form is all unsteeled!"
But Phaëthon could lay it on; 15
  Apollo had to yield.

3. **chrysolite** (krĭs′ô·līt): a semiprecious
gem. 11–13. **the Crab, the Bear, the Serpent
. . . the Archer and the Bull:** constellations
of stars. Do you know their mythical names?

Out of the purple doors of dawn
  Phaëthon drove the horses;
They felt his hand could not command,
  They left their wonted courses. 20
And from the chariot Phaëthon
  Plunged like a falling star —
And so, my boy, no, no, my boy,
  You cannot take the car.

FOR YOUR VOCABULARY

Mention is made in line 9 of this poem
of Apollo's "ambrosia-fed" steeds. Ambrosia was the mythical food of the Olympian gods, whose drink was nectar. Here
is another pair of words that have come
into our everyday language from a distant
past. In what sense is the word *nectar* used
today? Can you think of a sentence with
the word *ambrosia* used in its modern
meaning?

Four Limericks

The limerick is a form of light verse that is five lines long — and several smiles wide. While nobody guarantees to refund your money if these verses do not produce grins, you'll miss something by turning the page too fast.

A girl who weighs many an oz.
Used language I will not pronoz.
   Her brother one day
   Pulled her chair right away.
He wanted to see if she'd boz.
               Anonymous

When you think of the hosts without No.
Who are slain by the deadly cuco.
   It's quite a mistake
   Of such food to partake;
It results in a permanent slo.
               Anonymous

There was a young fellow of Perth,
Who was born on the day of his birth;
   He was married, they say,
   On his wife's wedding day,
And he died when he quitted the earth.
               Anonymous

As a beauty I'm not a great star,
There are others more handsome by far,
   But my face I don't mind it,
   Because I'm behind it —
'Tis the folks in the front that I jar.
             Anthony Euwer

PEN AND PAPER

It might be entertaining to try some limerick writing of your own. To get started, you might use something like this:

A girl named Jo Ann was quite sweet.
Her sunshiny smile was a treat,
   But she'd cloud up and rain,
   Calling homework a strain,
. . . . !

Or this:

There was a young student named Finch
Who confused a square mile with an inch.
   His math teacher wept
   To see how Finch slept
. . . . !

Or perhaps you would like to compose a limerick of your own. Follow the pattern of making the fifth line rhyme with the first two, and give it no more than three marked beats.

HOW WELL DID YOU READ?

1. A glance backward at these humorous verses will disclose that several varieties of humor are represented. Funny misspellings, tricky rhymes, and surprise, O. Henry-like endings account for some of the humor. What other varieties are represented?

2. Much of the humor in this group of poems comes from the author's point of view; that is, the unusual or unexpected view taken by the poet of his subject. Burges Johnson's viewing of the word *llama*, for instance, is the basis for the poem he wrote. Can you think of some subjects which, regarded with a different or original point of view, would make good material for humor? How many ideas can you supply?

Young Ideas

Does the word *poet* suggest to you someone old and gray, with a lifetime of experience and wisdom? Then it is time you met some authors who wrote fine poems while in high school. These four talented young writers had a broad and varied range of ideas. They had imagination. They had skill and a concern for exactness of expression that is the mark of the careful worker with words.

Wisdom

WILLIAM KIMBALL FLACCUS

Do not ask me of dynasties and wars;
Ask me the way a meadow looks in the spring,
Ask me to conjure up the mystical stars
And the white moon glimmering.

Wild bees tasting the honey of sweet wild clover,   5
Murmur of tall grass that is ready to mow,
The gay lark's song, and hawthorn bursting over
The hills like a drift of snow;

Beautiful ships beating home from far places,
The vast, deep-throated thunder of pounding seas,   10
Abasing beauty and sadness in women's faces;
Ask me of these.

When beauty leaps to the heart like a great cry
Not to be stilled today or ever after,
The voices of dead men out of history   15
Are only an echo of laughter.

Men's Work

ROBERT BURNS BEGG, JR.

The white chips burst:
And distant ax blows
Cut across the air
Like thawing ice.
The swish of falling trees   5
And ringing thuds resound . . .
As solid cords are piled!
Pine knots strew the ground,
Like ant-picked, desert bones . . .
The horses' eyes are wild;   10
Their nostrils twitch
At brush fire smoke.
Men's work's afoot!
The hemlock hills
Against the denim sky,   15
Reverberate . . . and every root
Is shaken by the cry
Of dying trees!

THE TOOLS OF THE POET: ONOMATOPOEIA

1. Such a word as *swish* or *blow* or *burst* suggests what it means by its very sound. When a writer uses a word whose sound suggests its meaning, he is using the device called onomatopoeia (ŏn′ô·măt′ô·pē′-yà). "Men's Work" does this well. Those quick, explosive *b* sounds in lines 1 and 2 give force to the lines. The effect is to make you "hear" the men at work in the poem.

2. Many writers — not poets only — depend on onomatopoeia to enliven their work. Wouldn't a Western yarn be unthinkable without "neighing" horses, "yapping" dogs, and the "crackle" of gunfire? For that matter, a baby's first efforts to talk are fine examples of onomatopoeia. What does a baby call a train? a cat?

3. Why not memorize an example or two to help you remember the word *onomatopoeia*? A bee *buzzes*. A boiling kettle *hisses* or perhaps *whistles*. Whenever you are doing some descriptive writing, remind yourself to search for words whose sounds fit the ideas, thoughts, or scenes you are trying to capture.

HOW WELL DID YOU READ?

Wisdom 1. *Dynasties*, line 1, means successions of rulers, all descended from the same family line. The first stanza makes clear the author's wish to talk of matters not in history books. In your own words, what concerns him?

2. Account for the sudden change of subject and mood in line 11.

Men's Work 1. Robert Begg's economical use of words produces a razor-sharp impression of sound, motion, and color. Pick out the verbs that do the main job. Strong nouns and adjectives shoulder their share of work. Pick out the "sound" words and then the "color" words.

2. "The denim sky," line 15, is not only a colorful expression but an appropriate one. Why?

Penelope, to an Absent Ulysses

MARGARET DEMOREST

Should you come back to me, in this my room,
And push aside the frosty, green brocade,
Hearing the sleepy snarling of the loom
Whereon a silver-threaded hunt is laid,
Perhaps, because the pattern tired my eyes,   5
I should look up and see you, standing so,
Smiling assuredly, Ulysses-wise,
Your brownness strange against the portico.
Oh, I would drop my shuttle, rise, and take
Your battered, golden head between my hands,   10
And I'd not tell you how you cannot wake
A love in me for your dim "other lands."
So I would hold you, yet how far apart
Your life-crowned head, and my cool-shadowed heart!

Wind-Wolves

WILLIAM D. SARGENT

Do you hear the cry as the pack goes by,
The wind-wolves hunting across the sky?
Hear them tongue it, keen and clear,
Hot on the flanks of the flying deer!

Across the forest, mere, and plain,   5
Their hunting howl goes up again!
All night they'll follow the ghostly trail,
All night we'll hear their phantom wail,

For tonight the wind-wolf pack holds sway
From Pegasus Square to the Milky Way,   10
And the frightened bands of cloud deer flee
In scattered groups of two and three.

HOW WELL DID YOU READ?

Penelope, to an Absent Ulysses 1. In form, this poem is a sonnet. Sonnets may vary in their patterns of rhyme. A common form of the sonnet consists of exactly fourteen lines divided into two parts. The first part has eight, the second part six lines. Reread the poem to see what the division enables the poet to do in the first eight and the second six lines.

2. Explain the following words: *brocade, loom, portico, shuttle.*

Wind-Wolves 1. Pegasus is the great winged horse of mythology. A constellation is named after him. Instead of simply referring to the constellation, why did the writer use the expression "Pegasus Square"?

2. Compare this reference to the constellation with the ones in "Phaëthon," page 392. How does the mood of "Wind-Wolves" differ from that of the other poem?

3. What is your explanation of "the flying deer," line 4?

American Songs and Portraits

Much of America's history shines forth in the songs and poems of her people. The poems that follow strike as many different notes as do the voices of Americans themselves. Some of the poems in the group may afford you a new insight into people and places that you have known or read about in history books. There will be glimpses, also, of unfamiliar scenes. And you will find poems that may lead you to new discoveries — about yourself and your fellow-Americans.

Conestoga Wagons

JESSAMYN WEST

Because they were first manufactured in Conestoga (kŏn′ĕs·tō′gȧ), a Pennsylvania town, covered wagons were often called "Conestogas." This poem is a reminder that the sturdy wagons of the pioneers had their own part in shaping our country's history.

> Listen to the rumble on the Reading° Road:
> Great Conestogas heavy with a load
> Of bedsteads, cradles, firing irons, and brooms,
> French harps, fluting irons,° daguerreotypes,° and looms,
> Crockery, Bibles, tankards, and seeds,   5
> Handmade pillow shams and old family deeds,
> All moving westward, flowing like a stream,
> Conestoga wagons moving toward a dream.
> Great Conestogas, white against the sky:
> Listen to the rumble as the East goes by,   10
> Listen to the sound of a nation turning West,
> Mothers, children, babes still at the breast;
> Young men, mounted, singing on their way,
> Old men, mounted, but twice as quick to pray.
> Westward with their wagons, dying, giving birth,   15
> The great Conestogas measure off the Earth.

1. **Reading** (rĕd′ĭng): a city in Pennsylvania. 4. **fluting irons**: irons used for pressing flutes (ruffles or pleats) in ladies' dresses; **daguerreotypes** (dȧ·gĕr′ŏ·tĩps): old-fashioned photographs, printed on metal plates.

Detail from "Emigrant Train" by the American artist Samuel Colman (1832–1920).

HOW WELL DID YOU READ?

1. The wagon trains that left for the wilderness used to follow a route known as the Reading Road, which began at Philadelphia. What sort of journey faced the people who were heading westward?

2. Lines 13 and 14 tell us that while the young men sang, the old men were twice as quick to pray. Why?

3. Why would a housewife carry along her fluting iron? Mention of the various articles carried in the wagons tells much about the hopes and expectations of their owners. Explain briefly what you can infer about the people from the household articles they are transporting.

Whoopee Ti Yi Yo, Git Along, Little Dogies

Dogies (with a long *o*) is the name cattlemen give to the motherless calves in a range herd. Here is an authentic old song about them.

As I walked out one morning for pleasure,
I spied a cowpuncher a-ridin' alone;
His hat was throwed back and his spurs was a-janglin',
As he approached me a-singin' this song,

    Whoopee ti yi yo, git along, little dogies,   5
    It's your misfortune, and none of my own.
    Whoopee ti yi yo, git along, little dogies,
    For you know Wyoming will be your new home.

Early in the spring we round up the dogies,
Mark 'em and brand 'em and bob off their tails;   10
Round up our horses, load up the chuck wagon,
Then throw the dogies upon the old trail.

It's whooping and yelling and driving the dogies;
Oh, how I wish you would go on!
It's whooping and punching and "Go on, little dogies,   15
For you know Wyoming will be your new home."

Your mother she was raised way down in Texas,
Where the jimson weed and sandburs grow;
Now we'll fill you up on prickly pear and cholla°
Till you are ready for the trail to Idaho.   20

Oh, you'll be soup for Uncle Sam's Injuns;
"It's beef, heap beef," I hear them cry.
Git along, git along, git along, little dogies,
You're going to be beef steers by and by.

    Whoopee ti yi yo, git along, little dogies,   25
    It's your misfortune, and none of my own.
    Whoopee ti yi yo, git along, little dogies,
    For you know Wyoming will be your new home.

19. **cholla** (chōl'yä): cactus.

HOW WELL DID YOU READ?

1. From the cowboy's own words, what can you tell about where his herd has traveled? Is it on the move at present? What will be done before the animals reach the end of the trail? Explain your answer.

2. Describe the duties of a cowpuncher, as related in the poem. What do lines 6 and 26 indicate about a cowpuncher's attitude toward his work?

"Whoopee Ti Yi Yo, Git Along, Little Dogies." Collected, Adapted & Arranged by John A. & Alan Lomax. Copyright 1938 by John A. & Alan Lomax in the book *Cowboy Songs and Other Frontier Ballads.* Copyright assigned 1958 to Ludlow Music, Inc., New York, N.Y. Used by permission.

Go Down Moses

Negro spirituals are songs that expressed the deep religious nature of a people. These spirituals have been described as the most original, the most truly American, music that we have. Many recordings of this song have been made by famous singers.

1. When Is-rael was in E-gypt's land,
2. "Thus saith the Lord", bold Mo-ses said,
3. No more in bon-dage shall they toil,

Let my peo-ple go! "If not, I'll smite your first-born dead"
Op-pressed so hard they could not stand
Let them come out with E-gypt's spoil

Let my peo-ple go! Go down Mo-ses, Way down in

E-gypt's land, Tell old Pha-raoh, "Let my peo-ple go!"

"Go Down Moses" from *American Negro Songs and Spirituals* edited by John W. Works, published by Crown Publishers.

FROM *The Kallyope Yell*

VACHEL LINDSAY

The circus may not visit the little towns and the big cities nearly so often as in the past. But when it does come, there's bound to be a marvelous steam organ in its parade. You probably call it the "kǎ·lī′ȯ·pė," and you're right. But once it was better known as the "kǎl′ī·ōp." As a poem for reading aloud, this one seems made to order. The sound effects are built in: just look at the printing, decide where to speed up and slow down, and try a class reading as you . . . let . . . off . . . steam!

1

Proud men
Eternally
Go about
Slander me,
Call me the "Calliope,"   5
Sizz . . .
Fizz . . .

2

I am the Gutter Dream,
Tune-maker, born of steam,
Tooting joy, tooting hope.   10
I am the Kallyope,
Car called the Kallyope.
Willy willy willy wah HOO!
See the flags: snow-white tent,
See the bear and elephant,   15
See the monkey jump the rope,
Listen to the Kallyope, Kallyope,
    Kallyope!
Soul of the rhinoceros
And the hippopotamus
(Listen to the lion roar!)   20
Jaguar, cockatoot,
Loons, owls,
Hoot, hoot.
Listen to the lion roar,
Listen to the lion *roar*,   25
Listen to the lion R–O–A–R!
Hear the leopard cry for gore,

Willy willy willy wah HOO!
Hail the bloody Indian band,
Hail, all hail the popcorn stand,   30
Hail to Barnum's picture there,
People's idol everywhere,
Whoop whoop whoop WHOOP!
Music of the mob am I,
Circus day's tremendous cry:—   35
I am the Kallyope, Kallyope, Kallyope!
Hoot toot, hoot toot, hoot toot, hoot
    toot,
Willy willy willy willy wah HOO!
Sizz . . .
Fizz . . .   40

FOR YOUR VOCABULARY: WORD HISTORIES

Words have histories, like families or nations. The word *calliope* has a strange and unexpected history. Any good desk dictionary will inform you that this word was the name of a Greek Muse, the one in charge of oratory and heroic poetry. You will find that you are headed for an adventure in word discoveries if you follow this lead a little farther. Who were the Muses? How many of them gave their names to words we use at the present time? What words are they? In getting this information, be sure not to forget that the word *Muse* has led a long and extremely useful life. How much information about it can your detective work uncover?

Two Poems About Washington

A man of twenty-one, trim and vigorous from frontier life as a surveyor, is the Washington whose portrait is presented in the first of these poems. His knowledge of the wilderness was useful when, in 1753, he rode on a mission for the Governor of Virginia. With him went a message of warning to the French, then taking possession of the Ohio River. The land was considered British crown property. Commissioned a major, Washington knew well the difficulties ahead, as the French and Indian wars were not over.

The second poem is a "portrait" in a different sense. It is a "portrait" that formed in a poet's mind as he looked up at the monument and recalled the Washington whose strength of character is still an inspiration to his countrymen today. Also, one aspect of the poem makes it unlike any other you have ever read. Carl Sandburg, its author, is a poet you will learn more about later in this section.

Young Washington

The Embassy to the French Forts, 1753

ARTHUR GUITERMAN

Tie the moccasin, bind the pack,
Sling your rifle across your back.
Up! and follow the mountain track,
  Tread the Indian Trail.
North and west is the road we fare   5
Toward the forts of the Frenchmen, where
"Peace or War!" is the word we bear,
  Life and Death in the scale.

The leaves of October are dry on the ground,
The sheaves of Virginia are gathered and bound,   10
Her fallows° are glad with the cry of the hound,

11. **fallows** (făl'ōz): land usually used for crops, but which is unplanted during one growing season.

"Young Washington" from the book *I Sing the Pioneer* by Arthur Guiterman. Copyright, 1926, by E. P. Dutton & Co., Inc. Renewal, 1954, by Mrs. Vida Linda Guiterman. Reprinted by permission of the publishers.

The partridges whirr in the fern;
But deep are the forests and keen are the foes
Where Monongahela° in wilderness flows;
We've labors and perils and torrents and snows   15
    To conquer before we return.

Hall and council-room, farm and chase,
Coat of scarlet and frill of lace
All are excellent things in place;
    Joy in these if ye can.   20
Mine be hunting shirt, knife and gun,
Camp aglow on the sheltered run,
Friend and foe in the checkered sun;
    That's the life for a man!

14. **Monongahela** (mô·nŏn′gȧ·hē′lȧ). River in West Virginia which unites with the Allegheny
River at Pittsburgh, Pennsylvania, to form the Ohio River.

Washington Monument by Night

CARL SANDBURG

1

The stone goes straight.
A lean swimmer dives into night sky,
Into half-moon mist.

2

Two trees are coal black.
This is a great white ghost between.   5
It is cool to look at.
Strong men, strong women, come here.

3

Eight years is a long time
To be fighting all the time.

4

The republic is a dream.   10
Nothing happens unless first a dream.

5

The wind bit hard at Valley Forge one Christmas.
Soldiers tied rags on their feet.
Red footprints wrote on the snow . . .
. . . and stone shoots into stars here   15
. . . into half-moon mist tonight.

6

Tongues wrangled dark at a man.
He buttoned his overcoat and stood alone.
In a snowstorm, red hollyberries, thoughts,
  he stood alone.   20

7

Women said: He is lonely
. . . fighting . . . fighting . . . eight years . . .

8

The name of an iron man goes over the world.
It takes a long time to forget an iron man.

9

. . . .
. . . .

INTERPRETING AND RESPONDING TO THE LANGUAGE

Would it be possible for any writer to hurl a more startling challenge to his reader than Carl Sandburg does in "Washington Monument by Night"? What a thing to do — to present one "stanza" of a poem that lacks any words at all! After your first surprise, if you're a reader who responds to a challenge, you probably gave this stanza some thought. A good procedure would be to go back over the earlier stanzas and let the mood of the poem come through to you more strongly. A courteous reader would pay Mr. Sandburg the compliment of rereading this poem closely, allowing the powerful word pictures and figurative language to make deeper impressions on him. For a reader to blame a poem and not himself when he has made no effort to respond to the poem is very unfair. Of course, if you are so unfamiliar with our nation's history that the words "Red footprints wrote on the snow" are for you empty and meaningless, that is one thing; if you too hurriedly decided that you didn't "get" the meaning, that's quite another. Consider other vivid word pictures contained in this poem. ". . . stone shoots into stars here" — in just five simple words a stunning picture is created. What picture do the first two lines of stanza 2 form for you?

Never be afraid to make your own interpretations of this or any other poem. It is the reader's privilege; you are fully capable of it. The fact is that once you do permit yourself to interpret and to respond to a poet's words, you may discover meanings in the lines that, shared with the class, might be a real contribution to everyone's understanding and enjoyment of the poem.

PEN AND PAPER

"Washington Monument by Night" is a free-verse poem; that is, there are no rhymed words, and its lines have no set or regular length. For his poetic effects, the poet relies on images and figures of speech. To try out this technique for yourself, select a subject that appeals to you and write a "free-verse" description of it. Include as many images and figures of speech as possible in your description. You will want to choose a subject that will lend itself to description. For example, you might like to try a free-verse description of a great jet plane soaring from an airfield, a flight of birds winging out to sea at sunset, or have you a particular topic of your own you are anxious to try?

HOW WELL DID YOU READ?

Young Washington 1. Since there were unfriendly Indians in the territory Washington was about to enter, why should he take to "the Indian Trail," line 4?

2. What "labors and perils," line 15, are ahead for him? Use a map, if possible, to point out regions of "torrents and snows" which are mentioned along with the labors and perils.

3. Explain what the poem tells us about the life young Major Washington is leaving as he heads into the wilderness. What is the meaning of "Coat of scarlet," line 18? What is its more usual description?

Washington Monument by Night 1. What are the most unusual features of this poem?

2. How would you describe its mood? Compare it with that of "Young Washington."

3. Stanzas 5 and 6 recall events during Washington's years as Commander-in-Chief. To be exact, what events are mentioned?

4. What is your interpretation of line 17?

5. Line 19 is open to several interpretations, since it gives *impressions* rather than a clearly phrased statement. How do you explain its possible meanings?

6. Bearing in mind that this poem requires one to gather and interpret *impressions*, what is your explanation of stanza 9? What impression does the whole poem make?

Two Poems About Lincoln

Abe Lincoln's mother died when he was a boy of nine. We know from what he wrote and said that he loved Nancy Hanks and kept her in his memory. In this first poem about Lincoln, the poet imagines what the mother's memories were like.

"A Farmer Remembers Lincoln," the second poem, is a picture by Witter Bynner, the modern American poet, of the great man as seen by a farmer who knew him.

Both of the poems might be called dramatic monologues — the spoken words of a person telling a dramatic happening. After you have studied the two poems, some good, dramatic readers might read them aloud for the class.

Nancy Hanks
1784–1818

FROM *A Book of Americans* BY

ROSEMARY AND STEPHEN VINCENT BENÉT

If Nancy Hanks
Came back as a ghost,
Seeking news
Of what she loved most,
She'd ask first   5
"Where's my son?
What's happened to Abe?
What's he done?

"Poor little Abe,
Left all alone   10
Except for Tom,
Who's a rolling stone;
He was only nine
The year I died.
I remember still   15
How hard he cried.

"Scraping along
In a little shack
With hardly a shirt
To cover his back,   20
And a prairie wind
To blow him down,
Or pinching times
If he went to town.

"You wouldn't know   25
About my son?
Did he grow tall?
Did he have fun?
Did he learn to read?
Did he get to town?   30
Do you know his name?
Did he get on?"

A Farmer Remembers Lincoln

WITTER BYNNER

"Lincoln? —
Well, I was in the old Second Maine,
The first regiment in Washington from the Pine Tree State.
Of course I didn't get the butt of the clip;°
We was there for guardin' Washington —   5
We was all green.

"I ain't never ben to but one theater in my life —
I didn't know how to behave.
I ain't never ben since.
I can see as plain as my hat the box where he sat in   10
When he was shot.
I can tell you, sir, that was a panic
When we found our President was in the shape he was in!
Never saw a soldier in the world but what liked him.

"Yes, sir. His looks was kind o' hard to forget.   15
He was a spare man,
An old farmer.
Everything was all right, you know,
But he wa'n't a smooth-appearin' man at all —
Not in no ways;   20
Thin-faced, long-necked,
And a swellin' kind of a thick lip like.

"And he was a jolly old fellow — always cheerful;
He wa'n't so high but the boys could talk to him their own ways.
While I was servin' at the hospital   25
He'd come in and say, 'You look nice in here,'
Praise us up, you know.
And he'd bend over and talk to the boys —
And he'd talk so good to 'em — so close —
That's why I call him a farmer.   30
I don't mean that everything about him wa'n't all right, you understand,
It's just — well, I was a farmer —
And he was my neighbor, anybody's neighbor.

"I guess even you young folks would 'a' liked him."

4. **butt of the clip:** the heavy end of the blow; that is, the farmer didn't get into the main action of the war.

"A Farmer Remembers Lincoln," reprinted from *Grenstone Poems* by Witter Bynner. Reprinted by permission of Alfred A. Knopf, Inc.

Lincoln visiting the Union troops, 1863: photograph by Mathew Brady.

HOW WELL DID YOU READ?

Nancy Hanks 1. Suppose that you knew very little, or nothing, about Lincoln's early life. How much could you learn from this poem? Point out the lines which give us quite exact information.

2. How is his later life summed up in the last two lines? Do you think these lines are adequate? Why?

3. "Tom," mentioned in line 11, was Thomas Lincoln, Abe's father. Can you explain the description of him as "a rolling stone"?

A Farmer Remembers Lincoln 1. In a dramatic monologue, one person speaks as if he were talking to someone else. How does line 1 of the poem achieve this?

2. Point out the lines showing that the farmer wants his listener to be sure that he is not criticizing Lincoln.

3. The speaker's awkward phrases show him to be a man who finds it hard to express himself in words. Why is his description of Lincoln as a farmer a term of praise?

4. What qualities in Lincoln's personality and character is the speaker trying to sum up? Why are these important qualities for anyone to have?

ABOUT THE POETS

Stephen Vincent (1898–1943) and *Rosemary Benét* (bĕ·nā′), his wife, wrote many noteworthy poems together. Stephen began writing poetry in his boyhood, won poetry prizes when he was twelve, and published his first book of poems at seventeen, as a freshman at Yale. After he married Rosemary Carr, much of his work was done in collaboration with her. Other members of the Benét family have had distinguished literary careers. Stephen's sister Laura and his late brother William both won recognition as poets and critics. *John Brown's Body*, a book-length poem about the War Between the States, is probably Stephen Benét's most famous work. His story "The Devil and Daniel Webster" has appeared as a radio play, a television play, a film, and an opera.

Witter Bynner (1881–   ) combined the writing of poetry with work as a magazine editor and as a teacher at the University of California. An enthusiastic student of Oriental art and literature, he collaborated with a Chinese scholar in the fine translations of poetry of the T'ang dynasty which were published in *The Jade Mountain*.

Deepening Friendships . . .
Getting Better Acquainted
with Four American Poets

"I have several good friends," you say. How did you build these friendships? You must have found shared tastes and interests and had frequent meetings, if only by letter.

You have already been introduced to a number of poets in this section. Here you will have a chance to deepen your acquaintance with four of them by reading groups of their poems and by learning something about their lives. The four authors — Emily Dickinson, Carl Sandburg, Edna St. Vincent Millay, and Robert Frost — are among the finest and most popular of all American poets. Yet their fame is not what should concern you most. It is pleasant to have a famous friend, of course, but what is important is that you have a *friend* offering you the warm rewards of good friendship.

Try to discover, then enjoy, the tastes and interests you have in common with each of these poets. What subjects appeal to them and to you? A friend is a person who can understand you and be sympathetic. If that is true, here are four people who are fine candidates for your friendship.

Emily Dickinson

Sometimes Emily Dickinson gave her newest poem to a neighbor as a little gift, carrying it with a plate of cookies across the street of the New England village where she lived. Or some flowers would go with the poem. She used to write her poems on little scraps of paper. The village was Amherst, Massachusetts, where she had been born in 1830 and where she remained until her death in 1886. Only a few of her poems were published before she died; the rest have been discovered, collected, and published during the last sixty years. Emily Dickinson lived quietly and apart from the world, but her poems now belong to the world.

The second of those that follow was written to accompany a cocoon she had saved as a present for a small nephew she loved.

You, too, will find this poem a delightful gift if you give it more than one or two readings. This seems not too much to ask, especially if you have the feeling Emily Dickinson must have had: that our world of everyday living is made up of small miracles, if only we take time enough to let ourselves become aware of them.

The Mountains Grow Unnoticed

The mountains grow unnoticed,
Their purple figures rise
Without attempt, exhaustion,
Assistance, or applause.

In their eternal faces   5
The sun with broad delight
Looks long — and last — and golden,
For fellowship at night.

Drab Habitation of Whom?

Drab habitation of whom?
Tabernacle or tomb,
Or dome of worm,
Or porch of gnome,
Or some elf's catacomb?   5

I Took My Power in My Hand

I took my power in my hand
And went against the world;
'Twas not so much as David had,
But I was twice as bold.

I aimed my pebble, but myself   5
Was all the one that fell.
Was it Goliath was too large,
Or only I too small?

FROM A Bird Came down the Walk

A bird came down the walk:
He did not know I saw;
He bit an angle-worm in halves
And ate the fellow, raw.

And then he drank a dew   5
From a convenient grass,
And then hopped sidewise to the wall
To let a beetle pass.

Emily Dickinson's home in Amherst, Massachusetts.

HOW WELL DID YOU READ?

The Mountains Grow Unnoticed. 1. Just 33 words make up the two stanzas of this poem. However, it is like a large landscape painting. What particular words give the impression of spaciousness and height?

2. In what way does the sun look "For fellowship at night"? What is the poet describing in stanza 2?

3. How do you explain the title? In what way do the mountains grow?

Drab Habitation of Whom? 1. The word *Tabernacle*, line 2, is rich with many meanings. The poet wanted those manifold meanings to enrich the reader's interpretation. Tabernacle can be used to denote a tent or temporary house; the body as the dwelling-place of the soul; a place of worship; a temple. In line 2, which meaning or meanings best suggest the poet's thought?

2. A *catacomb*, line 5, is of course an underground burial place. Have you observed by now that this poem is made up of a series of contrasting items? Point out what each contrast is. Some are playful. Which ones? Some are playful but with serious undertones. Which are they?

I Took My Power in My Hand
1. Tell the story of David and Goliath.

2. The meaning of stanza 2 will be more apparent if you understand that in lines 5 and 6 the poet is saying, "but I myself was the *only* one to fall." Now can you put the question of this stanza into your own words? Why is this a good question for anyone to ask himself?

FROM *A Bird Came down the Walk*
1. In which lines does Emily Dickinson show that she has a sense of humor?

2. Compare this poem with "I Took My Power in My Hand." How do they differ in mood?

DISCUSSING THE POET

1. What have you learned about Emily Dickinson as a person — her likes and dislikes, for example? Do you think you would want her for a friend?

2. What have you learned about her as a poet? List some literary characteristics you would assign to her.

3. What have you learned from her poems about the subject matter of poetry, the kinds of things that poets write about?

Carl Sandburg

Born in 1878, Carl Sandburg went to work at all sorts of jobs when he finished grade school at thirteen. He left his home in Galesburg, Illinois, when he was very young. Since then he has traveled widely. He knows the far reaches of America — the small towns and farms, the huge industrial cities of his age. He has written realistically and vigorously about our land, especially about the Middle West, its farmers and mill hands, and about the smoke and steel of the great cities like Chicago. He is often called "the Chicago poet," since that is the city with which his life and his poetry are most closely identified. He is the author of a distinguished biography of Abraham Lincoln, a selection from which you may already have read on page 258. On page 406 is his poem "Washington Monument by Night." With the poems that follow, you have the opportunity to deepen your acquaintance with this celebrated American writer.

© *Arnold Newman*

Primer Lesson

Look out how you use proud words.
When you let proud words go, it is not easy to call them back.
They wear long boots, hard boots; they walk off proud; they can't hear you
    calling —
Look out how you use proud words.

Paper I

Paper is two kinds: to write on, to wrap with.
If you like to write, you write.
If you like to wrap, you wrap.
Some papers like writers, some like wrappers.
Are you a writer or a wrapper?   5

See the Trees

See the trees lean to the wind's way of learning.
See the dirt of the hills shape to the water's way of learning.
See the lift of it all go the way the biggest wind and the strongest water want it.

Wind Song

Long ago I learned how to sleep,
In an old apple orchard where the wind swept by counting its money and throw-
    ing it away,
In a wind-gaunt orchard where the limbs forked out and listened or never listened
    at all,
In a passel° of trees where the branches trapped the wind into whistling, "Who,
    who are you?"
I slept with my head in an elbow on a summer afternoon and there I took a sleep
    lesson.   5
There I went away saying: I know why they sleep, I know how they trap the
    tricky winds.
Long ago I learned how to listen to the singing wind and how to forget and how
    to hear the deep whine,
Slapping and lapsing under the day blue and the night stars:
                Who, who are you?

                Who can ever forget   10
                listening to the wind go by
                counting its money
                and throwing it away?

    4. **passel** (păs′l): a dialect word for *parcel*. Sandburg is using it in the sense that ranchers
speak of "a *passel* of cattle."

HOW WELL DID YOU READ?

Primer Lesson 1. The child learning to read starts with a primer. Why is this title appropriate?
2. Whom do you visualize as the speaker, a man or a woman? What section of America would make a suitable setting? Explain how you imagine the advice is given: in anger, in stern warning, or simply as a bit of wise counsel. Why?

Paper I 1. What is the poet's mood?
2. What is your interpretation of line 4?
3. What is *your* answer to line 5?

See the Trees 1. In what way do the shapes of trees and the contours of soil actually take form?
2. This poem could be described as an allegory — a story or account with a hidden meaning. What meaning has it? To what extent does this hidden meaning apply to persons?

Wind Song 1. Carl Sandburg frequently selects one unusual figure of speech and uses it as the central idea of a poem. What figure of speech is used in "Wind Song"?
2. Explain how the wind might seem to be "counting its money." (Think what happens to trees in the fall.)
3. Sandburg makes skillful use of onomatopoeia and alliteration in this poem. Pick out two examples of each.
4. What particular sounds and words are used to give a "sleepy" feeling to the lines?

DISCUSSING THE POET

1. What have you learned about Carl Sandburg as a person? Do you think that you would enjoy him as a friend or companion? Why?
2. In what ways do you find Sandburg's poetry about nature different from Emily Dickinson's poems on the same subject? Might the differences in their lives explain the differences in how they wrote about life? Explain your opinions.

Edna St. Vincent Millay

Slender and slight, Edna St. Vincent Millay had red hair that fell to her shoulders. She lived in cities, but much of her time was spent on the coast of Maine, where she was born. The sounds of the Maine woods and the traffic noises of the city are in many of her poems.

She was born in 1892 and early in life achieved a popularity which has continued since her death in 1950. As a student at Vassar College she won the Intercollegiate Poetry Contest. In 1923 Miss Millay was awarded the Pulitzer prize for poetry. Besides many books of poems, she wrote the libretto for an opera and verse plays for stage and radio.

For more than two generations, young people have been drawn to her poems. Underlying all of them is an expression of wonder at the beauty of the world and its creatures that youth itself is especially quick to recognize.

Travel

The railroad track is miles away,
   And the day is loud with voices speaking,
Yet there isn't a train goes by all day
   But I hear its whistle shrieking.

All night there isn't a train goes by,   5
   Though the night is still for sleep and dreaming,
But I see its cinders red on the sky,
   And hear its engine steaming.

My heart is warm with the friends I make,
   And better friends I'll not be knowing,   10
Yet there isn't a train I wouldn't take,
   No matter where it's going.

Winter Night

Pile high the hickory and the light
Log of chestnut struck by the blight.
Welcome-in the winter night.

The day has gone in hewing and felling,
Sawing and drawing wood to the dwelling   5
For the night of talk and storytelling.

These are the hours that give the edge
To the blunted ax and the bent wedge,
Straighten the saw and lighten the sledge.

Here are question and reply,   10
And the fire reflected in the thinking eye.
So peace, and let the bobcat cry.

City Trees

The trees along this city street,
    Save for the traffic and the trains,
Would make a sound as thin and sweet
    As trees in country lanes.

And people standing in their shade   5
    Out of a shower, undoubtedly
Would hear such music as is made
    Upon a country tree.

Oh, little leaves that are so dumb
    Against the shrieking city air,   10
I watch you when the wind has come —
    I know what sound is there.

The Courage
That My Mother Had

The courage that my mother had
Went with her, and is with her still:
Rock from New England quarried;
Now granite in a granite hill.

The golden brooch my mother wore 5
She left behind for me to wear;
I have no thing I treasure more:
Yet, it is something I could spare.

Oh, if instead she'd left to me
The thing she took into the grave! — 10
That courage like a rock, which she
Has no more need of, and I have.

FOR YOUR VOCABULARY: WORD ORIGINS

In "The Courage That My Mother Had" the poet speaks of a keepsake which she treasures. When used as a noun, the word *treasure,* as you well know, refers to a hoard of money or jewels. It comes into English from an Old French word, *tresor,* which can be traced back to the Latin word *thesaurus* and before that to the Greek *thesauros.* In each language it meant a collection of valuable things.

How appropriate it is that we use the word *thesaurus* as the name for that special type of dictionary which lists synonyms and antonyms. A thesaurus is a treasury which one can use to replenish his own word storehouse. Have you discovered its riches for yourself? And have you ever looked up the origins of the words *encyclopedia* and *anthology?*

HOW WELL DID YOU READ?

Travel 1. The locomotive is not so prominent a part of the American scene as it used to be, but its whistle on lonely prairies or in busy suburbs still commands respect. How do you account for the poet's statements in the last stanza, since they seem so contradictory?

2. Compare this poem with Robert Louis Stevenson's "Travel" on page 379. How do the two poets differ in their discussion of the same subject? What sort of person do you imagine is speaking the words of "Travel" by Miss Millay? Compare or contrast this person with your impression of the speaker in the Stevenson poem. Which of the two would you choose as a traveling companion for a trip around the world?

Winter Night 1. The poet tells us that this evening leisure follows a day of hard work. What is your interpretation of the work this group of friends has been doing? What is the basis for your answer?

2. Lines 7, 8, and 9 will be clear if you follow the statements of the first two stanzas. Can you explain how the quiet hours spent with friends can do what stanza 3 says they do?

3. Why might the poem be called a true lyric? Which lines would you select to justify your answer?

City Trees 1. This poem, like "Wind Song," is noteworthy for its alliteration. Which lines make almost insistent use of alliterative words?

2. In line 10 "the shrieking city air" is a strange phrase; air itself does not shriek. Explain why this figurative language is effective.

The Courage That My Mother Had 1. With what does the author compare courage?

2. Is there a contradiction in stanza 2? Explain your answer.

3. In what respect is the main idea of this poem utterly different from that of "Invictus," page 376?

DISCUSSING THE POET

1. From the evidence found in these poems, do you think that Edna St. Vincent Millay would have been content to live the secluded life of Emily Dickinson? Explain your answer. Toward which of the two poets do you feel more friendly? Give the reasons for your preference.

2. Try to describe in a word or two the difference between Edna St. Vincent Millay's poem "Travel" and any of the poems that you have read by Emily Dickinson.

Robert Frost

Though California was his birthplace in 1874, Frost has spent most of his life in various parts of New England. Still, his poetry does not confine itself to any special regions or subjects. His curiosity about human nature, animal nature, and, one could add, about Mother Nature herself has given depth and dimension to his poems.

During his lifetime he has worked as a cobbler, a mill hand, and an editor, but chiefly as a farmer, teacher, and university professor. The Pulitzer prize for poetry has been awarded him four times. In recent years his television appearances have made Americans everywhere better acquainted with the man whose poems have been so much admired and so widely honored.

The Secret Sits

We dance round in a ring and suppose.
But the Secret sits in the middle and knows.

The Birthplace

Here further up the mountain slope
Than there was ever any hope,
My father built, enclosed a spring,
Strung chains of wall round everything,
Subdued the growth of earth to grass,   5
And brought our various lives to pass.
A dozen girls and boys we were.
The mountain seemed to like the stir,
And made of us a little while —
With always something in her smile.   10
Today she wouldn't know our name.
(No girl's, of course, has stayed the same.)
The mountain pushed us off her knees.
And now her lap is full of trees.

Sand Dunes

Sea waves are green and wet,
But up from where they die,
Rise others vaster yet,
And those are brown and dry.

They are the sea made land   5
To come at the fisher town,
And bury in solid sand
The men she could not drown.

She may know cove and cape,
But she does not know mankind   10
If by any change of shape,
She hopes to cut off mind.

Men left her a ship to sink:
They can leave her a hut as well;
And be but more free to think   15
For the one more cast-off shell.

Desert Places

Snow falling and night falling fast, oh, fast
In a field I looked into going past,
And the ground almost covered smooth in snow,
But a few weeds and stubble showing last.

The woods around it have it — it is theirs.   5
All animals are smothered in their lairs.
I am too absent-spirited to count;
The loneliness includes me unawares.

And lonely as it is that loneliness
Will be more lonely ere it will be less —   10
A blanker whiteness of benighted° snow
With no expression, nothing to express.

They cannot scare me with their empty spaces
Between stars — on stars where no human race is.
I have it in me so much nearer home   15
To scare myself with my own desert places.

11. **benighted:** overtaken by the night or by darkness.

Tree at My Window

Tree at my window, window tree,
My sash is lowered when night comes on;
But let there never be curtain drawn
Between you and me.

Vague dream-head lifted out of the ground,   5
And thing next most diffuse° to cloud,
Not all your light tongues talking aloud
Could be profound.

But tree, I have seen you taken and tossed,
And if you have seen me when I slept,   10
You have seen me when I was taken and swept
And all but lost.

That day she put our heads together,
Fate had her imagination about her,
Your head so much concerned with outer,   15
Mine with inner, weather.

6. **diffuse** (dĭ·fūs'): spread in all directions.

FOR YOUR VOCABULARY: WORDS IN CONTEXT

The expression *of course*, in line 12 of Robert Frost's "The Birthplace," is one we use every day. The word *course* comes to us by way of the French language, which borrowed it from the Latin *cursus:* a place of running, such as the bed of a stream or the orbit of a star. In its most exact sense, *of course* means "in the usual running place" — or "naturally," "as is to be expected."

Some related words are *concourse, discourse, recourse.* From their use in the following sentences, explain what each of them means:

1. All passengers for jet flight Number 12 were sent to *Concourse* Three.

2. The *discourse* between the nuclear scientist and the electronics engineer was hard for the average listener to understand.

3. The final *recourse* for the condemned prisoner was the United States Supreme Court.

HOW WELL DID YOU READ?

The Secret Sits 1. This is a riddle. What do you think would be a good explanation of it?

2. Why is the word *Secret* capitalized?

The Birthplace 1. Lines 1–3 show that the poet's father did a quite remarkable job. What was it?

2. He adds that his father "Subdued the growth of earth to grass." How does a farmer do this?

3. Why did no girl's name stay "the same," line 12?

4. It is interesting to compare this poem with "The Mountains Grow Unnoticed," page 413. Which poem would you say shows that the writer draws upon the experience of living in mountain country? Which is more of an allegory than a bit of personal history?

Sand Dunes 1. Stanza 1 is really a "capsule" statement of a fact of natural science. How would a science book state it?

2. Stanza 3 declares that the sea does not know mankind, and says why. What is the reason?

3. How do you interpret the "one more cast-off shell" of line 16?

Desert Places 1. The lyric qualities of this poem are probably the first thing you recognized. What lines are clues to the fact that this is an intensely personal expression of a man's mood and feelings?

2. Who or what might be the "They" in line 13?

3. How can a person have "desert places" within himself?

4. Does the final stanza call to mind any poem you have read in this book? Which one?

Tree at My Window 1. What are the "light tongues" in line 7?

2. In speaking of "outer" and "inner" weather, lines 15 and 16, what is the poet referring to?

3. In what way is the theme of this poem similar to that of "Desert Places"?

4. Look back at "City Trees," page 419. Both poems are lyrics. Both refer to the feelings of the poets, and both are about trees. Which one might be called an allegory? Can you express the central thought of "City Trees" in one sentence? And can you put the central thought of "Tree at My Window" in a sentence of your own? In spite of their titles, are these poems about trees only, or do they discuss matters more personal to the poets? Explain your answer.

DISCUSSING THE POET

1. Compare Frost's poems about nature with those of any, or all, of the poets you have studied in this group. Do you find anything special about his viewpoint? If so, what? Remember that Emily Dickinson also wrote about New England.

2. Robert Frost and Carl Sandburg have much in common and much that is different, both as poets and as men. Judging from the poems of theirs which you have read in this group, specify what you think these differences and similarities are.

3. Which of the four poets you have met in the group do you like best? Why?

PEN AND PAPER

As with anything of value, words should not be squandered or used wastefully. Robert Frost and all the other authors in this poetry section demonstrate the truth of this, and the striking power that words alone can achieve. To understand this for yourself, plan and write a composition of no fewer than 125 or more than 150 words. Describe a personal experience, an emotion you have felt, or a scene that impressed you strongly. Your composition can be serious or humorous in tone, but try to make as good use of your words as poets do.

Poetry

SUGGESTIONS FOR FURTHER READING

Adshead, Gladys L., and Annis Duff, eds., *Inheritance of Poetry* (Houghton Mifflin, 1948)
    Poems to sample or to treasure. Many moods, subjects, and types are represented.
Aiken, Conrad, ed., *A Comprehensive Anthology of American Poetry* (Random House, 1944)
    Short and long poems, old and new, to whet many appetites.
Auslander, Joseph, and Frank Ernest Hill,

eds., *The Winged Horse Anthology* (Doubleday, 1949)
    A wide range of poems, each selected because of its appeal to youth.
Benét, Rosemary and Stephen Vincent, *A Book of Americans* (Holt, Rinehart & Winston, 1952)
    Many famous personalities appear, and humor abounds in this little book.
Cole, William, ed., *The Fireside Book of Humorous Poetry* (Simon and Schuster, 1959)
    A delightful collection of 450 poems by British and American poets. *Story*

Poems New and Old (World Publishing, 1957) is a collection of narrative poems from four centuries.

De la Mare, Walter, *Peacock Pie* (Knopf, 1961)

A book of rhymes, fun to read. *Collected Poems* (Holt, Rinehart & Winston, 1941) contains a wider variety of the author's work. *Come Hither* (Knopf, 1957), first published in 1923, is still a favorite with many people.

Ferris, Helen, *Favorite Poems, Old and New* (Doubleday, 1957)

Hundreds of poems to suit every taste.

Friedman, Albert B., ed., *The Viking Book of Folk Ballads of the English-Speaking World* (Viking, 1956)

Ballads of all sorts, with an interesting introduction explaining the ballad, its history, and form.

Frost, Robert, *You Come Too* (Holt, Rinehart & Winston, 1959)

Many of Frost's favorites and students' favorites.

Johnson, James Weldon, ed., *American Negro Poetry* (Harcourt, Brace & World, 1931)

A fine collection.

Johnson, Thomas H., ed., *Complete Poems of Emily Dickinson* (Little, Brown, 1960)

Poems to read and reread. Many have only recently been published.

Kipling, Rudyard, *Verse* (Doubleday, 1940)

Ballads and story poems of lasting appeal.

Longfellow, Henry W., *Tales of a Wayside Inn*

An old tavern in Massachusetts is the background for the telling of these verse stories.

Love, Katherine, *A Little Laughter* (Thomas Y. Crowell, 1957)

These limericks and nonsense verses are amusingly illustrated.

McGinley, Phyllis, *Times Three* (Viking, 1960)

Some serious and some light verse, touching on every imaginable subject.

Millay, Edna St. Vincent, *Mine the Harvest; A Collection of New Poems* (Harper, 1954)

A group of poems with which to deepen your friendship with Edna Millay.

Nash, Ogden, *Parents Keep Out: Elderly Poems for Youngerly Readers* (Little, Brown, 1951)

Rib-ticklers by the poet who just won't rhyme in the usual way.

Noyes, Alfred, *Two Worlds for Memory* (Lippincott, 1953)

Poems that you will enjoy by the author of "The Last of the Books."

Parker, Elinor, *One Hundred More Story Poems* (Thomas Y. Crowell, 1960)

Both well-known and little-known poets are represented.

Plotz, Helen, *Imagination's Other Place: Poems of Science and Mathematics* (Thomas Y. Crowell, 1955)

A remarkable collection about science and scientists.

Read, Herbert, *This Way, Delight* (Pantheon, 1956)

Poems to add to life's enjoyment.

Sandburg, Carl, ed., *The American Songbag* (Harcourt, Brace & World, 1936)

Words and music: a real treat to browse through or sing to! *The Sandburg Range* (Harcourt, Brace & World, 1957) has a representative selection from Sandburg's entire works.

Untermeyer, Louis, ed., *The Magic Circle* (Harcourt, Brace & World, 1952)

Story poems that can't fail to keep you reading for sheer enjoyment.

Van Doren, Mark, ed., *Anthology of World Poetry* (Harcourt, Brace & World, 1936)

For students who want to broaden their poetry horizons. *Selected Poems* (Holt, Rinehart & Winston, 1954) contains selections from nine volumes published over the past thirty years.

FOR YOUR LISTENING

The following poems from this section can be heard on the longplay record *Many Voices* 9A: "The Fool's Prayer," "Poem," "Four Little Foxes," "All But Blind," "The Twenty-third Psalm," "Night Clouds," "The Lorelei," "The Last of the Books," "Whoopee Ti Yi Yo, Git Along, Little Dogies," "Travel," "Winter Night," "City Trees," and "The Courage That My Mother Had."

Drama

As a citizen of the twentieth century, you have at your command certain powers that would awe a person from a primitive society. With the flick of a switch you command music to play for you. With the turn of a dial you bring before your eyes a play you would like to see: a comedy, a mystery, or perhaps a famous tragedy performed by noted actors. Twentieth-century playgoers do not necessarily have to go to a theater. The theater comes into their homes. In no century before ours have there been so many kinds of dramatic entertainment. First films, then radio, and most recently television have brought about this modern miracle.

If we look backward a moment, we discover that as far into the past of civilized man as we can see, people seem to have hungered for dramatic spectacles. Before there was such a thing as a theater — either a building or an outdoor viewing-place — there were plays. The earliest were processions or pageants arranged to honor the gods. Later, in Greece and Rome, playwrights wrote out their plays. Trained actors learned their parts and acted them. During the Middle Ages, new and different dramatic forms developed out of the religious dramas that were based on Bible stories.

Still, it is our own century that has seen the truly startling changes. Moving pictures and television have created special forms of drama. School and community theater groups produce plays that are both old and new. Among the reading public are many people who like to read the printed version of a play, whether or not they have seen it acted. So we can grant drama an important place in our lives, as a medium of mass entertainment and as literature to be read for enjoyment.

In many ways drama is strikingly different from other types of litera-

◀ Leonardo da Vinci (1452–1519), the superb Renaissance artist, created the dramatic design from which this bronze sixteenth-century sculpture, "Rearing Horse," was made.

ture. A short story, an essay, or a biography is meant specifically to be read. So it is with a novel too: the printed page is complete in itself. Poetry shares some similarity with drama in that a poem is meant not only to be read but to be heard. A play, however, is written to be *seen* as well as to be heard. The ideal audience for a play does not consist of people sitting in their armchairs at home turning the pages of the text. A play is designed for a group audience gathered together to watch a company of actors bring to life, by means of physical action and spoken word, the play written by the author. The audience is seated, the curtain rises, and, except for intermissions, the audience remains until the play is ended.

For these reasons you need to take an approach to the reading of a play that is different from your approach to other types of literature. A good reader always tries to visualize what he is reading. With a play the reader must try to visualize not only the settings indicated by the author; he must go a step farther and attempt to visualize the settings as they would look on a stage. The reader of a play must strive to "hear" the playwright's words, as if actors were speaking those words. The author, in the text of the play, will usually indicate or briefly describe whatever physical action takes place. The reader must visualize this action as completely as possible and visualize it in terms of actors moving about on a stage — or, as in a television play, before a camera. As you read the plays in this section, pretend that you are seated in an imaginary theater viewing what you read as if it were being performed on a stage. Then a play becomes fully satisfying as a reading experience.

In "The Dancers," the realistic problems of a teen-age boy and girl who are like people you know are presented in the form of a comedy, but you will share the emotions of the leading characters in the play's more serious moments. In "The Valiant" you will be puzzled by the secret of a man who goes to death bravely silent rather than betray his own ideals. When you read Shakespeare's *Romeo and Juliet*, included in this section, you will come to appreciate why, for more than four hundred years, people have been so touched and stirred by this story.

In this section you have at your finger tips a series of adventures in the drama. Some will come from the reading of plays typical of today. Others will be unforgettable experiences gained from your study of a noble play of the past.

The Dancers

A TELEVISION PLAY

HORTON FOOTE

If $1 + 1 = 2$, does it follow that 1 shy boy + 1 shy girl = 2 shy people? In the case of Horace, a young man who finds it difficult to please everyone all the time, $1 + 1 = be$ *yourself*. Several of the young people in this television play will seem like old friends to you from the instant you meet them.

Cast

HERMAN	WAITRESS
INEZ	MARY CATHERINE
HORACE	VELMA
ELIZABETH	MR. DAVIS
EMILY	MRS. DAVIS

Act I

The living room of Inez and Herman Stanley. It has been cleaned and straightened with obvious care. The time is early summer. HERMAN STANLEY *and his brother-in-law* HORACE *come in the front door.* HERMAN *is carrying Horace's suitcase.* HERMAN *is a man in his middle thirties, and* HORACE *is in his middle teens, a thin, sensitive, likable boy.*

Following the Plot. A play minus problems and conflict would be lifeless and dull, for without conflict there is no drama. The plot of a play deals with problems; the solution must be reached through the decisions and actions of its characters. Many incidents are combined to make up the main story-thread. Through such incidents the action of the play moves forward and the audience learns important facts about the characters.

In this play we soon become aware of the main character's problem. Our first insight is gained during the conversation he has with his sister in Act I. How Horace will work out the problem will be our concern throughout the play. Notice how every little incident, no matter how trifling, contributes its share to the final working out of the plot.

HERMAN. Inez. Inez. We're here.

[*He puts the bag down in the living room.* INEZ *comes flying out of the kitchen.*]

INEZ. You're early.

HERMAN. The bus was five minutes ahead of time.

INEZ. Is that so? Why, I never heard of that. (*She kisses her brother.*) Hello, honey.

HORACE. Hello, Sis.

INEZ. You look fine.

HORACE. Thank you.

INEZ. You haven't put on a bit of weight, though.

HORACE. Haven't I?

INEZ. Not a bit. I'm just going to stuff food down you and put some weight on you while you're here. How's your appetite?

HORACE. Oh, it's good. I eat all the time.

INEZ. Then why don't you put on some weight?

HORACE. I don't know. I guess I'm just the skinny type.

INEZ. How are the folks?

HORACE. Fine.

INEZ. Mother over her cold?

HORACE. Yes, she is.

INEZ. Dad's fine?

HORACE. Just fine.

INEZ. Oh, Herman, did you ask him?

HERMAN. Ask him what?

INEZ. Ask him what? About his tux.

HERMAN. No, I didn't . . .

INEZ. Honestly, Herman. Here we have a date for him with the prettiest and most popular girl in Harrison, and Herman says ask him what. You did bring it, didn't you, Bubber?

HORACE. Bring what?

INEZ. Your tux.

HORACE. Oh, sure.

INEZ. Well, guess who I've got you a date with. Aren't you curious?

HORACE. Uh-huh.

INEZ. Well, guess.

[*A pause. He thinks.*]

HORACE. I don't know.

INEZ. Well, just try guessing . . .

HORACE. Well . . . uh . . . uh . . . (*He is a little embarrassed. He stands trying to think. No names come to him.*) I don't know.

INEZ. Emily Crews! Now, isn't she a pretty girl?

HORACE. Yes. She is.

INEZ. And the most popular girl in this town. You know her mother is a very close friend of mine, and she called me day before yesterday, and she said, "I hear Horace is coming to town," and I said yes, you were, and she said that the boy Emily is going with is in summer school and couldn't get away this week end, and Emily said she wouldn't go to the dance at all, but her mother said that she had insisted and wondered if you'd take her . . .

HORACE. Her *mother* said. Does Emily want me to take her?

INEZ. That isn't the point, Bubber. The point is that her mother doesn't approve of the boy Emily is in love with, and she likes you.

HORACE. Who likes me?

INEZ. Emily's mother. And she thinks you would make a very nice couple.

HORACE. Oh. (*A pause*) But what does Emily think?

INEZ. Emily doesn't know what to think, honey. I'm trying to explain that to you. She's in love.

HORACE. Where am I supposed to take her?

INEZ. The dance.

HORACE. But, Inez, I don't dance well enough . . . I don't like to go to dances . . . yet.

INEZ. Oh, Horace! Mother wrote me you were learning.

HORACE. Well . . . I am learning. But I don't dance well enough yet.

INEZ. Horace, you just make me sick. The trouble with you is that you have no confidence in yourself. I bet you can dance.

HORACE. No, I can't.

INEZ. Now let's see. (INEZ *goes to the radio and turns it on. She comes back to him.*) Now, come on. Show me what you've learned.

HORACE. Aw, Sis . . .

HERMAN. Inez, why don't you let the boy alone?

INEZ. Now you keep out of this, Herman Stanley. He's my brother, and he's a stick. He's missing all the fun in life, and I'm not going to have him a stick. I've sat up nights thinking of social engagements to keep him busy every minute of these next two weeks — I've got three dances scheduled for him. So he *has* to dance. Now come on, dance with me.

[*He takes her by the arm awkwardly and begins to lead her around room.*]

INEZ. Now, that's fine. That's just fine. Isn't that fine, Herman?

HERMAN. Uh-huh.

INEZ. You see all you need is confidence. And I want you to promise me you'll talk plenty when you're with the girl, not just sit there in silence and only answer when you're asked a question. Now promise me!

HORACE. I promise.

INEZ. Fine. Why, I think he dances very well. Don't you, Herman?

HERMAN. Yes, I do. Just fine, Inez.

INEZ. Just a lovely dancer. All he needs is confidence. He is very light on his feet, and he has a fine sense of rhythm. Why, brother, you're a born dancer —

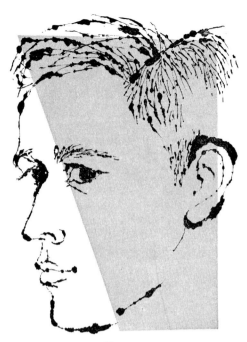

Horace.

HORACE *is smiling over the compliments, half wanting to believe what they say, but then not so sure. He is dancing with her around the room as we dissolve* [1] *to the living room of Elizabeth Crews.* EMILY *is in the living room. She has on her dressing gown. She is crying.* ELIZABETH *comes in.*

ELIZABETH. Emily.

EMILY. Yes, ma'am.

ELIZABETH. Do you know what time it is?

EMILY. Yes, ma'am.

ELIZABETH. Then why in the world aren't you dressed?

EMILY. Because I don't feel good.

ELIZABETH. Emily . . .

EMILY. I don't feel good . . . (*She begins to cry.*) Oh, Mother. I don't want to go to the dance tonight. Please, ma'am, don't make me. I'll do anything in this world for you if you promise me . . .

[1] **dissolve:** a camera term used in television meaning to dim out on one scene while bringing another scene into camera focus.

ELIZABETH. Emily, this is all settled. You are going to that dance. Do you understand me? You are going to that dance. That sweet nice brother of Inez Stanley will be here any minute.

EMILY. Sweet nice brother! He's a goon, that's what he is. A regular goon. A bore and a goon . . .

ELIZABETH. Emily . . .

EMILY. That's all he is. Just sits and doesn't talk. Can't dance. I'm not going to any dance or anyplace else with him, and that's final. (*She runs out of the room and up the stairs.*)

ELIZABETH. Emily . . . Emily . . . You get ready this minute.

[*The doorbell rings.*]

ELIZABETH (*yelling*). Emily! Emily . . . Horace is here. I want you down those stairs in five minutes . . . dressed.

[*She goes to the front door.* HORACE *is*

Emily.

there all dressed up. He has a corsage box in his hand.]

ELIZABETH. Hello, Horace.

HORACE. Good evening.

ELIZABETH. Sit down, won't you, Horace? Emily is a little late getting dressed. You know how girls are.

HORACE. Yes, ma'am. (*He sits down. He seems a little awkward and shy.*)

ELIZABETH. Can I get you something to drink, Horace?

HORACE. No, ma'am.

[*A pause.* ELIZABETH *is obviously very nervous about whether* EMILY *will behave or not.*]

ELIZABETH. Are you sure I can't get you a Coca-Cola or something?

HORACE. No, thank you.

ELIZABETH. How's your family?

HORACE. Just fine, thank you.

ELIZABETH. I bet your sister was glad to see you.

HORACE. Yes, she was.

ELIZABETH. How's your family? Oh, I guess I asked you that, didn't I?

HORACE. Yes, you did.

[ELIZABETH *keeps glancing up the stairs, praying that* EMILY *will put in an appearance.*]

ELIZABETH. I understand you've become quite an accomplished dancer.

HORACE. Oh . . . well . . . I . . .

ELIZABETH. Inez tells me you do all the new steps.

HORACE. Well — I . . .

ELIZABETH. Excuse me. Let me see what is keeping that girl.

[*She goes running up the stairs.* HORACE *gets up. He seems very nervous. He begins to practice his dancing. He seems more unsure of himself and awkward . . . We can hear* ELIZABETH *upstairs knocking on Emily's door. At first* HORACE *isn't conscious of the knocking or the ensuing conversation and goes on practicing his dancing. When he first becomes aware of what's to follow he tries to pay no attention. Then gradually he moves to the bottom of the stairs. The first thing we hear from above is* ELIZABETH's *light tapping at Emily's door. Then she begins to call: softly at first, then louder and louder.*]

ELIZABETH. Emily. Emily. Emily Crews. *Emily Carter Crews . . .*

[*The pounding is getting louder and louder.*]

Emily. I can hear you in there. Now, open that door.

EMILY (*screaming back*). I won't. I told you I won't.

ELIZABETH. Emily Carter Crews. You open that door immediately!

EMILY. I won't.

ELIZABETH. I'm calling your father from downtown if you don't open that door right this very minute.

EMILY. I don't care. I won't come out . . .

ELIZABETH Then I'll call him.

[*She comes running down the stairs.* HORACE *quickly gets back to his chair and sits.*]

ELIZABETH. Excuse me, Horace.

[*She crosses through the room and out the door.* HORACE *seems very ill at ease. He looks at the box of flowers. He is very warm. He begins to fan himself.* ELIZABETH *comes back in the room. She is very nervous, but she tries to hide her nervousness in an overly social manner.* ELIZABETH *has decided to tell a fib.*]

ELIZABETH. Horace, I am so sorry to have to ruin your evening, but my little girl isn't feeling well. She has a headache and a slight temperature, and

I've just called the doctor and he says he thinks it's very advisable that she stay in this evening. She's upstairs insisting she go, but I do feel that under the circumstances I had just better keep her in. I hope you understand.

HORACE. Oh, yes, ma'am. I do understand.

ELIZABETH. How long do you plan to visit us, Horace?

HORACE. Two weeks.

ELIZABETH. That's nice. Please call Emily tomorrow and ask her out again. She'll just be heartbroken if you don't.

HORACE. Yes, ma'am. Good night.

ELIZABETH. Good night, Horace.

[HORACE *goes out the door.* ELIZABETH *turns on the porch light for him. She calls out after him.*]

ELIZABETH. Can you see, Horace?

[*In the distance we hear* HORACE.]

HORACE. Yes, ma'am.

ELIZABETH. Now, you be sure and call us tomorrow. You hear?

[*She stands waiting for a moment. Then she shuts the door, turns off the light, and starts to scream at the top of her voice.*]

ELIZABETH. Emily Carter Crews. You have mortified me. You have mortified me to death. For your information, I have called your father, and he is interrupting his work and is coming home this very minute, and he says to tell you that you are not to be allowed to leave this house again for two solid weeks. Is that perfectly clear?

She is screaming as she climbs the stairs. Dissolve to a drugstore about half an hour later. HORACE *comes in. He seats himself at the counter. He still has the box of flowers. The drugstore is deserted. A* WAITRESS *is up near the cash regis-*

ter with her arms on the counter. She keeps glancing at a clock. HORACE *is examining a menu.*

HORACE. May I have a chicken salad sandwich?

WAITRESS. We're all out of that.

HORACE. Oh. (*He goes back to reading the menu.*)

WAITRESS. If it's all the same to you, I'd rather not make a sandwich. I'm closing my doors in ten minutes.

HORACE. Oh. Well, what would you like to make?

WAITRESS. Any kind of ice cream or soft drinks. (*She looks up at the ice-cream menu.*) Coffee is all gone.

HORACE. How about a chocolate ice-cream soda?

WAITRESS. O.K. Coming up. (*She starts to mix the soda. She talks as she works.*) Going to the dance?

HORACE. No.

WAITRESS. The way you're all dressed up, I thought for sure you were going.

HORACE. No. I was, but I changed my mind.

[MARY CATHERINE DAVIS *comes into the drugstore. Somehow in her young head she has got the idea that she is a plain girl, and in defiance of the pain of that fact, she does everything she can to make herself look plainer.*]

WAITRESS. Hello, Mary Catherine. Been to the movies?

MARY CATHERINE. Yes, I have.

[*The* WAITRESS *puts the drink down in front of* HORACE. *He begins to drink.*]

WAITRESS. What'll you have, Mary Catherine?

MARY CATHERINE. Vanilla ice cream.

WAITRESS. O.K. (*She gets the ice cream. She talks as she does so.*) There weren't many at the picture show tonight, I bet. I can always tell by whether we have a crowd in here or not after

the first show. I guess everybody is at the dance.

MARY CATHERINE. I could have gone, but I didn't want to. I didn't want to miss the picture show. Emily Crews didn't go. Leo couldn't get home from summer school, and she said she was refusing to go. Her mother made a date for her with some bore from out of town without consulting her, and she was furious about it. I talked to her this afternoon. She said she didn't know yet how she would get out of it, but she would. She said she had some rights. Her mother doesn't approve of Leo, and that's a shame, because they are practically engaged.

WAITRESS. I think Emily is a very cute girl, don't you?

MARY CATHERINE. Oh, yes. I think she's darling.

[HORACE *has finished his drink and is embarrassed by their talk. He is trying to get the* WAITRESS's *attention but doesn't quite know how. He finally calls to the* WAITRESS.]

HORACE. Miss . . .

WAITRESS. Yes?

HORACE. How much do I owe you?

WAITRESS. Twenty cents.

HORACE. Thank you. (*He reaches in his pocket for the money.*)

WAITRESS. Emily has beautiful clothes, doesn't she?

MARY CATHERINE. Oh, yes. She does. She has the prettiest things. But she's not a bit stuck up.

[HORACE *holds the money out to the* WAITRESS.]

HORACE. Here you are.

WAITRESS. Thank you.

[*She takes the money and rings it up on the cash register.* HORACE *goes out. The* WAITRESS *shakes her head as he goes.*]

WAITRESS. There's a goofy nut if I ever saw one. He's got flowers under his arm. He's wearing a tux, and yet he's not going to the dance. Who is he?

MARY CATHERINE. I don't know. I never saw him before.

[*The* WAITRESS *goes to the door and looks out. She comes back shaking her head. She sits on the stool beside* MARY CATHERINE.]

WAITRESS (*while laughing and shaking her head*). I ought to call the sheriff and have him locked up. Do you know what he's doing?

MARY CATHERINE. No. What?

WAITRESS. Standing on the corner, dancing back and forth. He's holding his arm up as though he's got a girl and everything. Wouldn't it kill you? (MARY CATHERINE *goes to the front and looks out.*) See him?

MARY CATHERINE. No. He's stopped.

WAITRESS. What's he doing?

MARY CATHERINE. Just standing there, looking kind of lost.

[MARY CATHERINE *comes back to the counter. She starts eating her ice cream again.*]

WAITRESS. Well — it takes all kinds.

MARY CATHERINE. I guess so.

[*She goes back to eating her ice cream. She is eating as there is music for the fade-out.*[1]]

[1] **fade-out**: dimming out on a scene until the picture screen is blank.

Act II

The living room of the Stanleys. INEZ *is reading a book.* HERMAN *comes in.*

HERMAN. Hi, hon.

INEZ. Hello . . .

HERMAN. What's the matter with you? You look down in the dumps.

INEZ. No. I'm just disgusted.

HERMAN. What are you disgusted about?

INEZ. Horace. I had everything planned so beautifully for him, and then that silly Emily had to go and hurt his feelings.

HERMAN. Well, honey, that was pretty raw, the trick she pulled.

INEZ. I know. But he's a fool to let that get him down. He should have just gone to the dance by himself and proved her wrong. Why, as I told him, show her up. Rush a different girl every night. Be charming. Make yourself popular. But it's like trying to talk to a stone wall. He refused to go out any more. He says he's going home tomorrow.

HERMAN. Where is he now?

INEZ. Gone to the movies.

HERMAN. Well, honey, I hate to say it, but in a way it serves you right. I've told you a thousand times if I've told you once: leave the boy alone. He'll be all right. Only don't push him. You and your mother have pushed the boy and pushed him and pushed him.

INEZ. And I'm going to keep on pushing him. I let him off tonight because his feelings were hurt, but tomorrow I'm going to have a long talk with him.

HERMAN. Inez. Leave the boy alone.

INEZ. I won't leave him alone. He is my brother and I'm going to see that he learns to have a good time.

HERMAN. Inez . . .

INEZ. Now you just let me handle this, Herman. He's starting to college next year, and it's a most important time in his life. He had no fun in high school.

HERMAN. Now, he must have had some fun . . .

INEZ. Not like other people. And he's not going through four years of college like a hermit with his nose stuck in some old book. (*She jumps up.*) I'll never forgive Elizabeth for letting Emily behave this way. And I told her so. I said, "Elizabeth Crews, I am very upset and I want you to know that I am very upset . . ."

She is angrily walking up and down as we dissolve to the drugstore. The WAITRESS *is there alone.* MARY CATHERINE *comes in.*

WAITRESS. Did you go to the movies again tonight?

MARY CATHERINE. Uh-huh. Lila, do you remember when I was telling you about Emily's date and how she wouldn't go out with him because he was such a bore?

WAITRESS. Uh . . .

MARY CATHERINE. Oh. I just feel awful. That was the boy sitting in here.

WAITRESS. Last night?

MARY CATHERINE. Yes. I went riding with Emily and some of the girls this afternoon, and we passed by his sister's house, and there sat the boy.

WAITRESS. Sh . . . sh!

[*She has seen* HORACE *come in the door. He comes to the counter. He seems very silent. He picks up a menu.*]

WAITRESS. Back again tonight?

HORACE. Uh-huh.

WAITRESS. What'll you have?

HORACE. A cup of coffee.

WAITRESS. All out. We don't serve coffee after eight unless we happen to have some left over from suppertime.

HORACE. Thanks. (*He gets up.*)

WAITRESS. Nothing else?

HORACE. No, thanks.

[*He goes over to the magazine rack. He picks up a magazine and starts looking through it.* EMILY CREWS *comes in. She doesn't see* HORACE *and goes right over to* MARY CATHERINE.]

EMILY. Leora and I were riding around the square, and we saw you sitting in here.

[MARY CATHERINE *points to* HORACE. *She turns around and sees him.* EMILY *looks a little embarrassed. He happens to glance up and sees her.*]

HORACE. Hello, Emily.

EMILY. Hello, Horace . . . Do you know Mary Catherine Davis?

HORACE. No. How do you do?

MARY CATHERINE. How do you do?

EMILY. I feel awfully bad about last night, Horace. My mother says that you know I wasn't really sick. I just wanted to tell you that it had nothing to do with you, Horace. It was a battle between me and my mother. Mary Catherine can tell you. I promised the boy I go with not to go with any other boys.

HORACE. Oh, that's all right. I understand.

EMILY. You see, we've gone steady for two years. All the other boys in town understand it, and their feelings are not a bit hurt if I turn them down. Are they, Mary Catherine?

MARY CATHERINE. No.

EMILY. Mary Catherine is my best friend, and she can tell you I'm not stuck up. And I would have gone, anyway, except that I was so mad at my mother . . .

MARY CATHERINE. Emily is not stuck up a bit. Emily used to date all the boys before she began going with Leo steadily. She even had a date with Gus Meredith. All the other girls wouldn't go with him because they thought he was so fat and unattractive, but Emily said she wouldn't have hurt his feelings for the world, and she went with him. Didn't you, Emily?

EMILY. Uh-huh. How long are you going to be here, Horace?

HORACE. Well, I haven't decided, Emily.

EMILY. Well, I hope you're not still hurt with me.

HORACE. No, I'm not, Emily.

EMILY. Well, I'm glad of that. Mary Catherine, can you come with us?

MARY CATHERINE. No, I can't, Emily. Velma came in after the first show started, and I promised to wait here for her, and we'd walk home together.

EMILY. Come on. We can ride around and watch for her.

MARY CATHERINE. No. I don't dare. You know how sensitive Velma is. If she looked in here and saw I wasn't sitting at this counter, she'd go right home and not speak to me again for two or three months. I don't want to go through that again.

EMILY. Velma's too sensitive. You shouldn't indulge her in it.

MARY CATHERINE. I'm willing to grant you that. But you all are going off to college next year, and Velma and I are the only ones that are going to be left here, and I can't afford to get her mad at me.

EMILY. O.K. I'll watch out for you, and if we're still riding around when Velma gets out, we'll pick you up.

MARY CATHERINE. Fine . . .

EMILY. 'By . . .

MARY CATHERINE. 'By . . .

EMILY. 'By, Horace.

HORACE. Good-by, Emily.

[*She goes out.*]

Mary Catherine.

MARY CATHERINE. She's a lovely girl. She was my closest friend until this year. Now we're still good friends, but we're not as close as we were. We had a long talk about it last week. I told her I understood. She and Eloise Dayton just naturally have a little more in common now. They're both going steady, and they're going to the same college. (*A pause*) They're going to Sophie Newcomb. Are you going to college?

HORACE. Uh-huh.

MARY CATHERINE. You are? What college?

HORACE. The University.

MARY CATHERINE. Oh. I know lots of people there. (*A pause*) I had a long talk with Emily about my not getting to go. She said she thought it was wonderful that I wasn't showing any bitterness about it. (*A pause*) I'm getting a job next week so I can save up enough money to go into Houston to business school. I'll probably work in Houston someday — if I don't get too lonely. Velma Morrison's oldest sister went into Houston and got herself a job, but she almost died of loneliness. She's back here now, working at the courthouse. Oh, well, I don't think I'll get lonely. I think a change of scenery would be good for me.

[VELMA MORRISON *comes in. She is about the same age as* MARY CATHERINE. *She is filled with excitement.*]

VELMA. Mary Catherine, you're going to be furious with me, but Stanley Sewell came in right after you left, and he said he'd never forgive me if I didn't go riding with him . . . I said I had to ask you first, as I had asked you particularly to wait for me and that I knew you were very sensitive.

MARY CATHERINE. *I'm* very sensitive! *You're* very sensitive . . . I have never in my life stopped speaking to you over anything.

[*A car horn is heard.*]

VELMA. Will you forgive me if I go?
MARY CATHERINE. Oh, sure.

[VELMA *goes running out.*]

VELMA. Thank you. (*She disappears out the door.*)

MARY CATHERINE. I'm not nearly as close to Velma as I am to Emily. I think Emily's beautiful, don't you?
HORACE. Yes. She's very pretty.
MARY CATHERINE. Well, Lila's going to kill us if we don't stop holding her up. Which way do you go?
HORACE. Home.
MARY CATHERINE. I go that way, too. We can walk together.
HORACE. O.K.
MARY CATHERINE. Good night, Lila.
WAITRESS. Good night.

[*They go out.*]

As we dissolve to the living room of the Crews' house, ELIZABETH CREWS *is there crying.* EMILY *comes in.*

EMILY. Mother, what is it? Has something happened to Daddy?
ELIZABETH. No. He's in bed asleep.
EMILY. Then what is it?
ELIZABETH. Inez has blessed me out and stopped speaking to me over last night. She says we've ruined the boy's whole vacation. You've broken his heart, given him all kinds of complexes, and he's going home tomorrow.
EMILY. But I saw him at the drugstore tonight, and I had a long talk with him, and he said he understood.
ELIZABETH. But Inez doesn't understand. She says she'll never forgive either of us again. (*She starts to cry.*)
EMILY. Oh, Mother. I'm sorry . . .
ELIZABETH. Emily, if you'll do me one favor, I promise you I'll never ask another thing of you again as long as I live. And I will never nag you about going out with Leo again as long as I live.
EMILY. What is the favor, Mother?
ELIZABETH. Let that boy take you to the dance day after tomorrow.
EMILY. Now, Mother . . .
ELIZABETH. Emily, I get down on my knees to you. Do this one favor for me. (*A pause*) Emily . . . Emily . . . (*She is crying again.*)
EMILY. Now, Mother, please. Don't cry. I'll think about it. I'll call Leo and see what he says. But please don't cry like this . . . Mother . . . Mother!

She is trying to console her as . . . we dissolve to the cottage and yard of Mary Catherine's parents. It is a small yard and a very small, unpretentious cottage. There is a light on in the living room. MARY CATHERINE *and* HORACE *come walking in on the pathway in front of the yard. In the distance can be heard music from a barbecue café.*

MARY CATHERINE. Well, this is where I live.

HORACE. In that house there?

MARY CATHERINE. Uh-huh.

[*A pause*]

HORACE. Where is that music coming from?

MARY CATHERINE. The Flats.

HORACE. What's the Flats?

MARY CATHERINE. I don't know what it is. That's just what they call it. It's nothing but a bunch of barbecue restaurants and beer joints down there, and they call it the Flats. There used to be a creek running down there that they called Willow Creek, but it's all dry now. My father says when he was a boy, every time the river flooded, Willow Creek would fill up. The river doesn't overflow any more since they took the raft [1] out of it. I like to come out here at night and listen to the music. Do you like to dance?

HORACE. Well . . . I . . .

MARY CATHERINE. I love to dance.

HORACE. Well . . . I don't dance too well.

MARY CATHERINE. There's nothing to it but confidence.

HORACE. That's what my sister says.

MARY CATHERINE. I didn't learn for the longest kind of time for lack of confidence, and then Emily gave me a long lecture about it, and I got confidence and went ahead and learned. Would you like to come in for a while?

HORACE. Well, if it's all right with you.

MARY CATHERINE. I'd be glad to have you.

HORACE. Thank you.

[*They go into the house.* MARY CATHERINE's *father is there.*]

MARY CATHERINE. Hello, Daddy.

MR. DAVIS. Hello, baby.

[1] **raft:** a collection of driftwood blocking a river.

MARY CATHERINE. Daddy, this is Horace.

MR. DAVIS. Hello, son.

HORACE. Howdy do, sir.

[*They shake hands.*]

MARY CATHERINE. Horace is Mrs. Inez Stanley's brother. He's here on a visit.

MR. DAVIS. That's nice. Where's your home, son?

HORACE. Flatonia.

MR. DAVIS. Oh, I see. Well, are you young people going to visit for a while?

MARY CATHERINE. Yes, sir.

MR. DAVIS. Well, I'll leave you then. Good night.

MARY CATHERINE. Good night, Daddy.

HORACE. Good night, sir.

[MR. DAVIS *goes out.*]

What does your father do?

MARY CATHERINE. He works in a garage. He's a mechanic. What does your father do?

HORACE. He's a judge.

MARY CATHERINE. My father worries so because he can't afford to send me to college. My mother told him that was all foolishness, and that I'd rather go to business school anyway.

HORACE. Would you rather go to business school?

MARY CATHERINE. I don't know. (*A pause*) Not really. But I'd never tell him that. When I was in the seventh grade, I thought I would die if I couldn't get there, but then when I was in the ninth, Mother talked to me one day and told me Daddy wasn't sleeping at nights for fear I'd be disappointed if he couldn't send me, so I told him the next night I had decided I'd rather go to business school. He seemed very relieved.

[*A pause*]

HORACE. Mary Catherine. I . . . uh . . . heard you say a while ago that you didn't dance because you lacked confidence and, uh . . . then I heard you say you talked it over with Emily and she told you what was wrong, and you got the confidence and you went ahead.

MARY CATHERINE. That's right.

HORACE. Well, it may sound silly and all to you . . . seeing I'm about to start my first year at college . . . but I'd like to ask you a question.

MARY CATHERINE. What is it, Horace?

HORACE. How do you get confidence?

MARY CATHERINE. Well, you just get it. Someone points out to you that you lack it, and then you get it.

HORACE. Oh, is that how it's done?

MARY CATHERINE. That's how I did it.

HORACE. You see, I lack confidence. And I . . . sure would like to get it . . .

MARY CATHERINE. In what way do you lack confidence, Horace?

HORACE. Oh, in all kinds of ways. (A pause) I'm not much of a mixer.

MARY CATHERINE. I think you're just mixing fine tonight.

HORACE. I know. That's what's giving me a little encouragement. You're the first girl I've ever really been able to talk to. I mean this way . . .

MARY CATHERINE. Am I, Horace?

HORACE. Yes.

MARY CATHERINE. Well, I feel in some way that's quite a compliment.

HORACE. Well, you should feel that way. (A pause) Mary Catherine . . .

MARY CATHERINE. Yes, Horace?

HORACE. I had about decided to go back home tomorrow or the next day, but I understand there's another dance at the end of the week.

MARY CATHERINE. Uh-huh. Day after tomorrow.

HORACE. Well . . . I . . . don't know if you have a date or not . . . but if you don't have . . . I feel if I could take you . . . I would gain the confidence to go . . . I mean . . .

MARY CATHERINE. Well, Horace, you see . . .

HORACE. I know I'd gain the confidence. My sister is a swell dancer, and she'll let me practice with her every living minute until it's time for the dance. Of course, I don't know if I could learn to jitterbug by then or rumba or do anything fancy, you understand, but I know I could learn the fox trot, and I can waltz a little now.

MARY CATHERINE. I'm sure you could.

HORACE. Well, will you go with me?

MARY CATHERINE. Yes, Horace. I'd love to.

HORACE. Oh, thank you, Mary Catherine. I'll just practice night and day. I can't tell you how grateful Inez is going to be to you. Mary Catherine, if we played the radio softly, could we dance now?

MARY CATHERINE. Why, certainly, Horace.

HORACE. You understand, I'll make mistakes.

MARY CATHERINE. I understand. (She turns the radio on very softly.)

HORACE. All right.

MARY CATHERINE. Yes . . .

[He approaches her very cautiously and takes her in his arms. He begins awkwardly to dance. MARY CATHERINE is very pleased and happy.]

Why, you're doing fine, Horace, just fine.

HORACE. Thank you, Mary Catherine. Thank you.

[They continue dancing. HORACE is very pleased with himself, although he is still dancing quite awkwardly as there is music for the fade-out.]

Act III

Early the next morning. INEZ *is in the living room straightening up.* HORACE *comes in whistling. He seems brimming over with happiness.*

INEZ. What are you so happy about?

HORACE. I'm just happy.

INEZ. Wait until you hear my news, and you'll be happier.

HORACE. Is that so?

INEZ. Miss Emily has seen the light.

HORACE. What?

INEZ. She has succumbed.[1]

HORACE. What do you mean?

INEZ. She has crawled on her knees.

HORACE. She's crawled on her knees? I don't get it.

INEZ. She has eaten dirt.

HORACE. Sister, what's this all about?

INEZ. Last night around ten o'clock she called in the meekest kind of voice possible and said, "Inez, I've called up to apologize to you. I have apologized to Horace in the drugstore." Did she?

HORACE. Uh-huh.

INEZ. "And now I want to apologize

[1] **succumbed** (sŭ·kŭmd′): given in, yielded.

to you and to tell you how sorry I am I behaved so badly."

HORACE. Well. Isn't that nice of her, Inez.

INEZ. Wait a minute. You haven't heard the whole thing. And then her highness added, "Tell Horace if he would like to invite me to the dance to call me and I'd be glad to accept." And furthermore, Elizabeth called this morning and said they were leaving for Houston to buy her the most expensive evening dress in sight, just to impress you.

HORACE. Oh. (*He sits down on a chair.*)

INEZ. Brother, what is the matter with you? Now are you going to start worrying about this dancing business all over again? You are the biggest fool sometimes! We've got today and tomorrow to practice.

HORACE. Inez —

INEZ. Yes?

HORACE. I already have a date with someone tomorrow.

INEZ. You do?

HORACE. Yes. I met a girl last night at the drugstore and I asked her . . .

INEZ. What girl did you ask?

HORACE. Mary Catherine Davis.

INEZ. Well, you've got to get right out of it. You've got to call her up and explain just what happened.

HORACE. But, Inez . . .

INEZ. You've got to do it, Horace. They told me they are spending all kinds of money for that dress. I practically had to threaten Elizabeth with never speaking to her again to bring this all about. Why, she will never forgive me now if I turn around and tell her you can't go . . . Horace! Don't look that way. I can't help it. For my sake, for your sister's sake, you've got to get out of this date with Mary Catherine Davis. Tell her . . . tell her . . . anything, but just get out of it.

HORACE. O.K. (*A pause. He starts out.*) What can I say?

INEZ. I don't know, Horace. (*A pause*) Say . . . well, just tell her the truth. That's the best thing. Tell her that Emily's mother is your sister's best friend and that Emily's mother has taken her into Houston to buy her a very expensive dress.

HORACE. What if Mary Catherine has bought a dress?

INEZ. Well, she can't have bought an expensive dress.

HORACE. Why not?

INEZ. Because her people can't afford it. Honey, you'll be the envy of every young man in Harrison bringing Emily Crews to the dance . . . Why, everybody will wonder just what it is you have.

HORACE. I'm not going to do it.

INEZ. Horace . . .

HORACE. I don't want to take Emily. I want to take Mary Catherine, and that's just what I'm going to do.

INEZ. Horace . . .

HORACE. My mind is made up. Once and for all.

INEZ. Then what am I going to do? (*She starts to cry.*) Who's going to speak to Elizabeth? She'll bless me out putting her to all this trouble, making her spend all this money and time. (*She is crying loudly now.*) Horace, you just can't do this to me. You just simply can't.

HORACE. I can't help it. I'm not taking Emily Crews.

INEZ. Horace . . .

HORACE. *I am not taking Emily Crews.*

[*He is firm. She is crying as we dissolve to Mary Catherine's house. Her father is seated there reading his paper. In the distance the dance music can be heard.* MRS. DAVIS *comes in.*]

MRS. DAVIS. Mary Catherine's date will be here any minute.

MR. DAVIS. What time is it?

MRS. DAVIS. Nine o'clock.

MR. DAVIS. The dance has already started. I can hear the music from here.

MRS. DAVIS. I know. But you know young people — they'd die before they'd be the first to a dance.

MR. DAVIS. O.K.

MRS. DAVIS. As soon as her date arrives, we'll go.

MR. DAVIS. O.K.

[MARY CATHERINE *comes in. She has on an evening dress and she looks very pretty.*]

MRS. DAVIS. Why, Mary Catherine, you look lovely! Doesn't she look lovely, Tom?

MR. DAVIS. Yes, she does.

MRS. DAVIS. Turn around, honey, and let me see you from the back.

[MARY CATHERINE *does so.*]

MRS. DAVIS. Just as pretty as you can be, Mary Catherine.

MARY CATHERINE. Thank you.

[*The doorbell rings.*]

That's Horace.

[*She goes to the door and lets him in. He is in his tux and has a box with a corsage.*]

MARY CATHERINE. Hello, Horace.

HORACE. Hello, Mary Catherine.

MARY CATHERINE. You've met my mother and father?

HORACE. Yes, I have. I met your father the other night and your mother yesterday afternoon.

MRS. DAVIS. Hello, Horace.

MR. DAVIS. Hello, son.

MRS. DAVIS. Well, we were just going. You all have a good time tonight.

HORACE. Thank you.

MRS. DAVIS. Come on, Tom.

MR. DAVIS. All right. Good night, and have a nice time.

MARY CATHERINE. Thank you, Daddy.

[*They go out.* HORACE *hands her the corsage box. She takes it and opens it.*]

Oh, thank you, Horace. Thank you so much. (*She takes the flowers out.*) They're just lovely. Will you pin them on for me?

HORACE. I'll try. (*He takes the corsage and the pin. He begins to pin it on.*) Will about here be all right?

MARY CATHERINE. Just fine. (*He pins the corsage on.*) Emily told me about the mix-up between your sister and her mother. I appreciate your going ahead and taking me anyway. If you had wanted to get out of it, I would have understood. Emily and I are very good friends . . . and . . .

HORACE. I didn't want to get out of it, Mary Catherine. I wanted to take you.

MARY CATHERINE. I'm glad you didn't want to get out of it. Emily offered to let me wear her new dress. But I had

already bought one of my own.

HORACE. It's very pretty, Mary Catherine.

MARY CATHERINE. Thank you. (*A pause*) Well, the dance has started. I can hear the music. Can't you?

HORACE. Yes.

MARY CATHERINE. Well, we'd better get going.

HORACE. All right. (*They start out.*) Mary Catherine. I hope you don't think this is silly, but could we practice just once more?

MARY CATHERINE. Certainly we could . . .

[*They start to dance.* HORACE *has improved, although he is no Fred Astaire. They are dancing around, and suddenly* HORACE *breaks away.*]

HORACE. Mary Catherine, I'm not good enough yet. I can't go. I'm sorry. Please, let's just stay here.

MARY CATHERINE. No, Horace. We have to go.

HORACE. Please, Mary Catherine . . .

MARY CATHERINE. I know just how you feel, Horace, but we have to go. (*A pause*) I haven't told you the whole truth, Horace. This is my first dance, too.

HORACE. It is?

MARY CATHERINE. Yes. I've been afraid to go, afraid I wouldn't be popular. The last two dances I was asked to go, and I said no.

HORACE. Then why did you accept when I asked you?

MARY CATHERINE. I don't know. I asked myself that afterward. I guess because you gave me a kind of confidence.

[*A pause. They dance again.*]

You gave me confidence, and I gave you confidence. What's the sense of getting confidence, Horace, if you're not going to use it?

[*A pause. They continue dancing.*]

HORACE. That's a pretty piece.

MARY CATHERINE. Yes, it is.

[*A pause. They dance again.* HORACE *stops.*]

HORACE. I'm ready to go if you are, Mary Catherine.

MARY CATHERINE. I'm ready.

[*They start out.*]

Scared?

HORACE. A little.

MARY CATHERINE. So am I. But let's go!

HORACE. O.K.

[*They continue out the room. The music from the dance is playing as there is music for the final fade-out.*]

[THE END]

THINKING IT OVER

1. Why is Horace's sister so eager to get a date for him with Emily? What is her motive? How would you defend it?

2. Emily and Mary Catherine are two very different types of girls. Compare them. What do we learn about each one: as a daughter, as a friend, and as a "date"?

3. What qualities in Mary Catherine inspire confidence in Horace? In what ways does the personality of Emily add to his shyness? Select two or three of her most marked characteristics to illustrate the point.

4. Does this play remind you of any experience you have had when it seemed to you that older people were "pushing" you into something you disliked doing? What was the outcome? Was it a better one than you had anticipated, or was your first feeling about it justified by what followed?

5. The subject of self-confidence may be worth a class panel discussion. Base your talks not on personalities, but on the "causes and cures" you can suggest for a

lack of confidence in a teen-ager like Horace. Here are some questions to consider: To what extent do you think it wise and helpful for adults to "arrange" invitations and dates for teen-agers? Are most teen-agers capable of thinking for themselves without the help of their parents?

FOLLOWING THE PLOT

1. Explain how each of the following incidents in Act I adds suspense and interest to the plot: (a) Horace overhears Emily refuse to go to the dance. (b) The waitress asks Mary Catherine why she did not go to the dance. (c) Horace hears Mary Catherine tell the waitress Emily's real reason for staying home.

2. Mention two incidents which add to the complications of the plot in Act II.

3. In Act III, point out two new incidents and tell how they help to bring the action of the plot to a satisfying conclusion.

ABOUT THE AUTHOR

Horton Foote (1916–   ), one of the pioneer playwrights of television, was born in Wharton, Texas. His first full-length play, *Texas Town*, was completed in 1941. He has since become a television playwright of first importance. His television play *A Trip to Bountiful* won such acclaim that it was produced on Broadway.

Visualizing a Television Play →

Shown on the opposite page are three scenes from the NBC television production of "The Dancers." Identify each scene and the characters involved in it. Do the actors shown satisfy your visual concept of the characters they are portraying? Pictured on the bottom half of the page is a behind-the-scenes view of a telecast of the play *On Borrowed Time*. Keeping in mind the way a television production looks to its audience, tell why you think three cameras, instead of one, are being used here to photograph the action.

The Valiant

HOLWORTHY HALL and ROBERT MIDDLEMASS

A man faces death by hanging. Curiously enough, those near him during his final hours are more distressed than he is by his impending fate. The decision that he is to die is not — fortunately — up to you; but this famous play will challenge you to think about the reasons for his puzzling behavior.

Characters

WARDEN HOLT, *about 60*
FATHER DALY, *the prison chaplain*
JAMES DYKE, *the prisoner*
JOSEPHINE PARIS, *the girl, about 18*
DAN, *a jailer*
AN ATTENDANT

SCENE. *The Warden's office in the State's Prison at Wethersfield, Connecticut.*

TIME. *About half-past eleven on a rainy night.*

The curtain rises upon the Warden's office in the State's Prison at Wethersfield, Connecticut. It is a large, cold, unfriendly apartment, with bare floors and staring, whitewashed walls; it is furnished only with the Warden's flat-topped desk and swivel chair, with a few straight-backed chairs, one beside the desk and others against the walls, with a water cooler and an eight-day

Recognizing Significant Details. At any point in a short story or novel, the author can break in to tell the reader what his characters are thinking about or what feelings they have. On the other hand, the playwright must depend on the actors' interpretation of his written directions. To the actors falls the responsibility of projecting by their acting skill the thoughts and impulses of the characters. An audience, therefore, must be alert to interpret small details correctly. Tones of voice, gestures, a sudden pause or a tense silence — such details count heavily. As a play reader you want to be careful to note the directions given each actor, so that you will not misunderstand or overlook important details. "The Valiant" has a surprising number of significant details you will not want to miss.

clock. On the Warden's desk are a tele-phone instrument, a row of electric push buttons, and a bundle of forty or fifty letters. At the back of the room are two large windows, crossed with heavy bars; at the left there is a door to an anteroom, and at the right there are two doors, of which the more distant leads to the office of the deputy [1] *war-den, and the nearer is seldom used.*

WARDEN HOLT, *dressed in a dark brown sack suit, is seated at his desk, reflectively smoking a long, thin cigar. He is verging on sixty, and his responsi-bilities have printed themselves upon his countenance. His brown hair and bushy eyebrows are heavily shot with gray; there are deep wrinkles at the corners of his mouth and innumerable fine lines about his eyes. He is no senti-mentalist, but he believes that in each of us there is a constant oscillation* [2] *of good and evil; and that all evil should be justly punished in this world, and that all good should be generously rewarded — in the next.*

Behind the WARDEN, *the prison chap-lain stands at one of the barred win-dows, gazing steadily out into the night.* FATHER DALY *is a slender, white-haired priest of somewhat more than middle age; he is dressed in slightly shabby clerical clothes. His face is calm, intel-lectual, and inspiring; but just at this moment it gives evidence of a peculiar depression.*

The WARDEN *blows a cloud of smoke to the ceiling, inspects the cigar criti-cally, drums on the desk, and finally peers over his shoulder at the chap-lain. He clears his throat and speaks brusquely.*

---

[1] **deputy** (dĕp′ů·tĭ): substitute or assistant.
[2] **oscillation** (ŏs′ĭ·lā′shŭn): swinging back and forth.

THE WARDEN. Has it started to rain?

FATHER DALY (*answers without turn-ing*). Yes, it has.

THE WARDEN (*glaring at his cigar and impatiently tossing it aside*). It would rain tonight. (*His tone is vaguely re-sentful, as though the weather had add-ed a needless fraction to his impa-tience.*)

FATHER DALY (*glances at a big silver watch*). It's past eleven o'clock. (*He draws a deep breath and comes slowly to the center of the room.*) We haven't much longer to wait.

THE WARDEN. No, thank God! (*He gets up and goes to the water cooler; with the glass halfway to his lips he pauses.*) Was he quiet when you left him?

FATHER DALY (*a trifle abstractedly*). Yes, yes, he was perfectly calm, and I believe he'll stay so to the very end.

THE WARDEN (*finishes his drink, comes back to his desk, and lights a fresh cigar*). You've got to hand it to him, Father; I never saw such nerve in all my life. It isn't bluff, and it isn't a trance, either, like some of 'em have — it's plain nerve. You've certainly got to hand it to him. (*He shakes his head in frank admiration.*)

FATHER DALY (*sorrowfully*). That's the pity of it — that a man with all his courage hasn't a better use for it. Even now, it's very difficult for me to recon-cile his character, as I see it, with what we know he's done.

THE WARDEN (*continues to shake his head*). He's got my goat, all right.

FATHER DALY. Yes, and he's got mine, too.

THE WARDEN. When he sent for you tonight, I hoped he was going to talk.

FATHER DALY. He did talk, very freely.

THE WARDEN. What about?

FATHER DALY (*smiles faintly and sits beside the desk*). Most everything.

THE WARDEN (*looks up quickly*). Himself?

FATHER DALY. No. That seems to be the only subject he isn't interested in.

THE WARDEN (*sits up to his desk and leans upon it with both elbows*). He still won't give you any hint about who he really is?

FATHER DALY. Not the slightest. He doesn't intend to, either. He intends to die as a man of mystery to us. Sometimes I wonder if he isn't just as much of a mystery to himself.

THE WARDEN. Oh, he's trying to shield somebody, that's all. James Dyke isn't his right name — we know that; and we know all the rest of his story is a fake, too. Well, where's his motive? I'll tell you where it is. It's to keep his family and his friends, wherever they are, from knowing what's happened to him. Lots of 'em have the same idea, but I never knew one to carry it as far as this before. You've certainly got to hand it to him. All we know is that we've got a man under sentence; and we don't know who he is, or where he comes from, or anything else about him, any more than we did four months ago.

FATHER DALY. It takes moral courage for a man to shut himself away from his family and his friends like that. They would have comforted him.

THE WARDEN. Not necessarily. What time is it?

FATHER DALY. Half-past eleven.

THE WARDEN (*rises and walks over to peer out of one of the barred windows*). I guess I'm getting too old for this sort of thing. A necktie party didn't use to bother me so much; but every time one comes along nowadays, I've got the blue devils beforehand and afterward. And this one is just about the limit.

FATHER DALY. It certainly isn't a pleasant duty even with the worst of them.

THE WARDEN (*wheels back abruptly*). But what gets *me* is why I should hate this one more than any of the others. The boy is guilty.

FATHER DALY. Yes, he killed a man, "willfully, feloniously,[1] and with malice aforethought."

THE WARDEN. And he pleaded guilty. So he deserves just what he's going to get.

FATHER DALY. That is the law. But has it ever occurred to you, Warden, that every now and then when a criminal behaves in a rather gentlemanly fashion to us, we instinctively think of him as just a little less of a criminal?

THE WARDEN. Yes, it has. But, all the same, this front of his makes me as nervous as the devil. He pleaded guilty, all right, but he don't *act* guilty. I feel just as if tonight I was going to do something every bit as criminal as he did. I can't help it. And when I get to feeling like that, why, I guess it's pretty nearly time I sent in my resignation.

FATHER DALY (*reflectively*). His whole attitude has been very remarkable. Why, only a few minutes ago I found myself comparing it with the fortitude that the Christian martyrs carried to their death, and yet —

THE WARDEN. He's no martyr.

FATHER DALY. I know it. And he's anything in the world but a Christian. That was just what I was going to say.

THE WARDEN. Has he got any religious streak in him at all?

FATHER DALY. I'm afraid he hasn't. He listens to me very attentively, but — (*He shrugs his shoulders.*) It's only because I offer him companionship. Anybody else would do quite as well — and any other topic would suit him better.

THE WARDEN. Well, if he wants to face God as a heathen, *we* can't force him to change his mind.

[1] **feloniously** (fĕ·lō′nĭ·ŭs·lĭ): criminally.

FATHER DALY (*with gentle reproach*). No, but we can never give up trying to save his immortal soul. And his soul tonight seems as dark and foreboding to me as a haunted house would seem to the small boys down in Wethersfield. But I haven't given up hope.

THE WARDEN. No — you wouldn't.

FATHER DALY. Are you going to talk with him again yourself?

THE WARDEN (*opens a drawer of his desk and brings out a large envelope*). I'll have to. I've still got some government bonds that belong to him. (*He gazes at the envelope and smiles grimly.*) That was a funny thing — when the newspaper syndicate offered him twenty-five hundred for his autobiography, he jumped at it so quick I was sure he wanted the money for something or other. (*He slaps the envelope on the desk.*) But now the bonds are here, waiting for him, he won't say what to do with 'em. Know why? (FATHER DALY *shakes his head.*) Why, of course you do! Because the story he wrote was pure bunk from start to finish and the only reason he jumped at the chance of writing it was so's he could pull the wool over everybody's head a little farther. He don't want the bonds, but I've got to do *something* with 'em. (*He pushes a button on the desk.*) And besides, I want to make one more try at finding out who he is.

FATHER DALY. Shall I go with you to see him or do you want to see him alone?

THE WARDEN (*sits deliberating, with one hand at his forehead and the other hand tapping the desk*). Father, you gave me a thought — I believe I'm going to do something tonight that's never been done before in this prison — that is to say — not in all the twenty-eight years that *I've* been warden.

FATHER DALY. What's that?

THE WARDEN (*who has evidently come to an important decision, raps the desk more forcibly with his knuckles*). Instead of our going to see him, I'll have that boy brought into this office and let him sit here with you and me until the time comes for us all to walk through that door to the execution room.

FATHER DALY (*startled*). What on earth is your idea in doing a thing like that?

THE WARDEN. Because maybe if he sits here awhile with just you and me, and we go at him right, he'll loosen up and tell us about himself. It'll be different from being in his cell; it'll be sort of free and easy, and maybe he'll weaken. And then, besides, if we take him to the scaffold through this passageway, maybe I can keep the others quiet. If they don't know when the job's being done, they may behave 'emselves. I don't want any such yelling and screeching tonight as we had with that Greek. (*A* JAILER *in blue uniform enters from the deputy's room and stands waiting.*) Dan, I want you to get Dyke and bring him to me here. (*The* JAILER *stares blankly at him, and the* WARDEN'S *voice takes on an added note of authority.*) Get Dyke and bring him here to me.

THE JAILER. Yes, sir. (*He starts to obey the order but halts in the doorway and turns as the* WARDEN *speaks again. It is apparent that the* WARDEN *is a strict disciplinarian of the prison staff.*)

THE WARDEN. Oh, Dan!

THE JAILER. Yes, sir?

THE WARDEN. How nearly ready are they?

THE JAILER. They'll be all set in ten or fifteen minutes, sir. Twenty minutes at the outside.

THE WARDEN (*very sharp and magis-*

terial [1]). Now, I don't want any hitch or delay in this thing tonight. If there is, somebody's going to get in awful Dutch with me. Pass that along.

THE JAILER. There won't be none, sir.

THE WARDEN. When everything's ready — not a second before — you let me know.

THE JAILER. Yes, sir.

THE WARDEN. I'll be right here with Dyke and Father Daly.

THE JAILER (*eyes widening*). Here?

THE WARDEN (*peremptorily* [2]). Yes, here!

THE JAILER (*crushes down his astonishment*). Yes, sir.

THE WARDEN. When everything and everybody is ready, you come from the execution room through the passage — (*He gestures toward the nearer door on the right.*) open that door quietly, and stand there.

THE JAILER. Yes, sir.

THE WARDEN. You don't have to say anything, and I don't *want* you to say anything. Just stand there. That all clear?

THE JAILER. Yes, sir.

THE WARDEN. That'll be the signal for us to start — understand?

THE JAILER. Yes, sir.

THE WARDEN (*draws a deep breath*). All right. Now bring Dyke to me.

THE JAILER. Yes, sir. (*He goes out dazedly.*)

FATHER DALY. What about the witnesses and the reporters?

THE WARDEN. They're having their sandwiches and coffee now — the deputy'll have 'em seated in another ten or fifteen minutes. Let 'em wait. (*His voice becomes savage.*) I'd like to poison the lot of 'em. Reporters! Witnesses!

(*The telephone bell rings.*) Hello — yes — yes — what's that? — Yes, yes, right here — who wants him? (*To* FATHER DALY) Father, it's the Governor! (*His expression is tense.*)

FATHER DALY (*his voice also gives evidence of incredulity* [3] *and hope*). What! (*He walks swiftly over to the desk.*) Is it about Dyke?

THE WARDEN. Ssh. (*He turns to the telephone.*) Yes, this is Warden Holt speaking. Hello — oh, hello, Governor Fuller, how are you? Oh, I'm between grass and hay, thanks. Well, this isn't my idea of a picnic exactly — yes — yes — Oh, I should say in about half an hour or so — everything's just about ready. (*His expression gradually relaxes, and* FATHER DALY, *with a little sigh and shake of the head, turns away.*) Oh, no, there won't be any slip-up — Yes, we made the regular tests, one this afternoon and another at nine o'clock tonight — Oh, no, Governor, nothing can go wrong — Well, according to the law I've got to get it done as soon as possible after midnight, but you're the Governor of the state — How long? — Certainly, Governor, I can hold it off as long as you want me to — What say? — A *girl!* — You're going to send her to me? — You *have* sent her! — She ought to be here by this time? — All right, Governor, I'll ring you up when it's over. Good-by. (*He hangs up the receiver, mops his forehead with his handkerchief, and turns to* FATHER DALY *in great excitement.*) Did you get *that?* Some girl thinks Dyke's her long-lost brother, and she's persuaded the old man to let her come out here tonight — he wants me to hold up the job until she's had a chance to see him. She's due here any minute, he says — in his own car — escorted by his own

<hr>

[1] **magisterial** (măj'ĭs·tẹr'ĭ·ǎl): in such a way as to show his authority.

[2] **peremptorily** (pẹr·ĕmp'tô·rĭ·lĭ): positively; in a manner admitting no argument or refusal.

[3] **incredulity** (ĭn'krẻ·dū'lĭ·tĭ): inability to believe.

private secretary! Can you beat it?

FATHER DALY (*downcast*). Poor girl!

THE WARDEN (*blots his forehead vigorously*). For a minute there I thought it was going to be a reprieve at the very least. Whew!

FATHER DALY. So did I.

[*The door from the deputy's room is opened, and* DYKE *comes in, followed immediately by the* JAILER. DYKE *halts just inside the door and waits passively to be told what to do next. He has a lean, pale face, with a high forehead, good eyes, and a strong chin; his mouth is ruled in a firm straight line. His wavy hair is prematurely gray. His figure has the elasticity of youth, but he might pass among strangers either as a man of forty or as a man of twenty-five, depending upon the mobility of his features at a given moment. He is dressed in a dark shirt open at the throat, dark trousers without belt or suspenders, and soft slippers. The* JAILER *receives a nod from the* WARDEN *and goes out promptly, closing the door behind him.*]

THE WARDEN (*swings halfway around in his swivel chair*). Sit down, Dyke. (*He points to the chair at the right of his desk.*)

DYKE. Thanks. (*He goes directly to the chair and sits down.*)

THE WARDEN (*leans back and surveys him thoughtfully.* FATHER DALY *remains in the background*). Dyke, you've been here under my charge for nearly four months, and I want to tell you that from first to last you've behaved yourself like a gentleman.

DYKE (*vaguely cynical without being in the least impertinent*). Why should I make you any trouble?

THE WARDEN. Well, you *haven't* made me any trouble, and I've tried to show

what I think about it. I've made you every bit as comfortable as the law would let me.

DYKE. You've been very kind to me. (*He glances over his shoulder at the chaplain.*) And you, too, Father.

THE WARDEN. I've had you brought in here to stay from now on. (DYKE *looks inquiringly at him.*) No, you won't have to go back to your cell again. You're to stay right here with Father Daly and me.

DYKE (*carelessly*). All right.

THE WARDEN (*annoyed by this cool reception of the distinguished favor*). You don't seem to understand that I'm doing something a long way out of the ordinary for you.

DYKE. Oh, yes, I do, but maybe *you* don't understand why it doesn't give me much of a thrill.

FATHER DALY (*comes forward*). My son, the warden is only trying to do you one more kindness.

DYKE. I know he is, Father, but the warden isn't taking very much of a gamble. From now on, one place is about the same as another.

THE WARDEN. What do you mean?

DYKE (*his voice very faintly sarcastic*). Why, I mean that I'm just as much a condemned prisoner here as when I was in my cell. That door (*He points to it.*) leads right *back* to my cell. Outside those windows are armed guards every few feet. You yourself can't get through the iron door in that anteroom (*He indicates the door to the left.*) until somebody on the outside unlocks it; and I know as well as you do where *that* door (*He points to the nearer door on the right.*) leads to.

THE WARDEN (*stiffly*). Would you rather wait in your cell?

DYKE. Oh, no, this is a little pleasanter. Except —

THE WARDEN. Except what?

DYKE. In my cell, I could smoke.

THE WARDEN (*shrugs his shoulders*). What do you want — cigar or cigarette?

DYKE. A cigarette, if it's all the same.

[*The* WARDEN *opens a drawer of his desk, takes out a box of cigarettes, removes one, and hands it to* DYKE. *The* WARDEN, *striking a match, lights* DYKE's *cigarette and then carefully puts out the match.*]

DYKE (*smiles faintly*). Thanks. You're a good host.

THE WARDEN. Dyke, before it's too late I wish you'd think over what Father Daly and I've said to you so many times.

DYKE. I've thought of nothing else.

THE WARDEN. Then — as man to man — and this is your last chance — who are you?

DYKE (*inspects his cigarette*). Who am I? James Dyke — a murderer.

THE WARDEN. That isn't your real name and we know it.

DYKE. You're not going to execute a name — you're going to execute a *man*. What difference does it make whether you call me Dyke or something else?

THE WARDEN. You had another name once. What was it?

DYKE. If I had, I've forgotten it.

FATHER DALY. Your mind is made up, my son?

DYKE. Yes, Father, it is.

THE WARDEN. Dyke.

DYKE. Yes, sir?

THE WARDEN. Do you see this pile of letters? (*He places his hand over it.*)

DYKE. Yes, sir.

THE WARDEN (*fingers them*). Every one of these letters is about the same thing, and all put together we've got maybe four thousand of 'em. These here are just a few samples.

DYKE. What about them?

THE WARDEN. We've had letters from every state in the Union and every province in Canada. We've had fifteen or twenty from England, four or five from France, two from Australia, and one from Russia.

DYKE. Well?

THE WARDEN (*inclines toward him*). Do you know what every one of those letters says — what four thousand different people are writing to me about?

DYKE. No, sir.

THE WARDEN (*speaks slowly and impressively*). Who *are* you — and are you the missing son — or brother — or husband — or sweetheart?

DYKE (*flicks his cigarette ashes to the floor*). Have you answered them?

THE WARDEN. No, I couldn't. I want you to.

DYKE. How's that?

THE WARDEN. I want you to tell me who you are. (DYKE *shakes his head.*) Can't you see you *ought* to do it?

DYKE. No, sir, I can't exactly see that. Suppose you explain it to me.

THE WARDEN (*suddenly*). You're trying to shield somebody, aren't you?

DYKE. Yes — no, I'm not!

THE WARDEN (*glances at* FATHER DALY *and nods with elation*). Who is it? Your family?

DYKE. I said I'm not.

THE WARDEN. But first, you said you were.

DYKE. That was a slip of the tongue.

THE WARDEN (*has grown persuasive*). Dyke, just listen to me a minute. Don't be narrow, look at this thing in a big, broad way. Suppose you should tell me your real name, and I publish it, it'll bring an awful lot of sorrow, let's say, to *one* family, *one* home, and that's your own. That's probably what you're thinking about. Am I right? You want to spare your family, and I don't blame you. On the surface, it sure would look like a mighty fine thing for you to do. But look at it *this* way: suppose you came out with the truth, flat-footed, why, you might put all that sorrow into *one* home — your own — but at the same time you'd be putting an immense amount of relief in four thousand others. Don't you get that? Don't you figure you owe something to all these other people?

DYKE. Not a thing.

FATHER DALY (*has been fidgeting*). My boy, the warden is absolutely right. You do owe something to the other people — you owe them peace of mind — and for the sake of all those thousands of poor, distressed women, who imagine God knows what, I beg of you to tell us who you are.

DYKE. Father, I simply can't do it.

FATHER DALY. Think carefully, my boy, think very carefully. We're not asking out of idle curiosity.

DYKE. I know that, but please don't let's talk about it any more. (*To the* WARDEN) You can answer those letters whenever you want to, and you can say I'm not the man they're looking for. That'll be the truth, too. Because I haven't any mother — or father — or sister — or wife — or sweetheart. That's fair enough, isn't it?

FATHER DALY (*sighs wearily*). As you will, my son.

THE WARDEN. Dyke, there's one more thing.

DYKE. Yes?

THE WARDEN. Here are the government bonds (*He takes up the large envelope from his desk.*) that belong to you. Twenty-five hundred dollars in real money.

DYKE (*removes the bonds and examines them*). Good-looking, aren't they?

THE WARDEN (*casually*). What do you want me to do with them?

DYKE. Well, I can't very well take them with me, so, under the circumstances, I'd like to put them where they'll do the most good.

THE WARDEN (*more casually yet*). Who do you want me to send 'em to?

DYKE (*laughs quietly*). Now, Warden Holt, you didn't think you were going to catch me that way, did you?

THE WARDEN (*scowls*). Who'll I send 'em to? I can't keep 'em here, and I can't destroy 'em. What do you want to do with 'em?

DYKE (*ponders diligently and tosses the envelopes to the desk*). I don't know. I'll think of something to do with them. I'll tell you in just a minute. Is there anything else?

THE WARDEN. Not unless you want to make some sort of statement.

DYKE. No, I guess I've said everything. I killed a man and I'm not sorry for it — that is, I'm not sorry I killed that particular person. I —

FATHER DALY (*raises his hand*). Repentance —

DYKE (*raises his own hand in turn*). I've heard that repentance, Father, is the sickbed of the soul — and mine is very well and flourishing. The man deserved to be killed; he wasn't fit to live. It was my duty to kill him, and I did it. I'd never struck a man in anger in all my life, but when I knew what that fellow had done, I knew I had to kill him, and I did it deliberately and intentionally — and carefully. I knew what I was doing, and I haven't any excuse — that is, I haven't any excuse that satisfies the law. Now, I learned pretty early in life that whatever you do in this world you have to pay for in one way or another. If you kill a man, the price you have to pay is this (*He makes a gesture which sweeps the entire room.*) and that (*He points to the nearer door on the right.*) and I'm going to pay it. That's all there is to that. And an hour from now, while my body is lying in there, if a couple of angel policemen grab my soul and haul it up before God —

FATHER DALY (*profoundly shocked*). My boy, my boy, please —

DYKE. I beg your pardon, Father. I don't mean to trample on anything that's sacred to you, but what I do mean to say is this: If I've got to be judged by God Almighty for the crime of murder, I'm not afraid, because the other fellow will certainly be there, too, won't he? And when God hears the whole story and both sides of it, which *you* never heard and never will — and they never heard it in the courtroom, either — why, then, if He's any kind of a God at all, I'm willing to take my chances with the other fellow. That's how concerned I am about the hereafter. And, if it'll make you feel any better, Father, why I *do* rather think there's going to be a hereafter. I read a book once that said a milligram [1] of musk will give out perfume for seven thousand years, and a milligram of radium will give out light for *seventy* thousand. Why shouldn't a soul — mine, for instance — live more than twenty-seven? But if there *isn't* any hereafter — if we just die and are dead and that's all — why, I'm still not sorry and I'm not afraid, because I'm quits with the other fellow — the law is quits with me, and it's all balanced on the books. And that's all there is to that.

[*An* ATTENDANT *enters from the anteroom.*]

THE WARDEN. Well? What is it?

THE ATTENDANT. Visitor to see you, sir. With a note from Governor Fuller. (*He presents it.*)

THE WARDEN (*barely glances at the envelope*). Oh! A young woman?

THE ATTENDANT. Yes, sir.

[1] **milligram** (mĭl'ĭ-grăm): a thousandth of a gram.

THE WARDEN. Is Mrs. Case there?

THE ATTENDANT. Yes, sir.

THE WARDEN. Have the girl searched, and then take her into the anteroom and wait till I call you.

THE ATTENDANT. Yes, sir. (*He goes out.*)

THE WARDEN. Dyke, a young woman has just come to see you. Do you want to see her?

DYKE. I don't think so. What does she want?

THE WARDEN. She thinks maybe she's your sister, and she's come a thousand miles to find out.

DYKE. She's wrong. I haven't any sister.

THE WARDEN (*hesitates*). Will I tell her that, or do you want to tell it to her yourself?

DYKE. Oh, you tell her.

THE WARDEN. All right. (*He starts to rise but resumes his seat as* DYKE *speaks.*)

DYKE. Just a second — she's come a thousand miles to see me, did you say?

THE WARDEN. Yes, and she's got special permission from the Governor to talk to you — that is, with my O.K.

DYKE. A year ago, nobody'd have crossed the street to look at me, and now they come a thousand miles!

FATHER DALY. This is one of your debts to humanity, my boy. It wouldn't take you two minutes to see her, and, if you don't, after she's made that long journey in hope and dread and suffering —

DYKE. Where can I talk with her — here?

THE WARDEN. Yes.

DYKE. Alone? (*The* WARDEN *is doubtful.*) Why, you don't need to be afraid. I haven't the faintest idea who the girl is, but if she happens to be some poor misguided sentimental fool, with a gun or a pocketful of cyanide of potassium,[1] she's wasting her time. I wouldn't cheat the sovereign state of Connecticut for anything in the world — not even to please a young lady.

THE WARDEN. Dyke, there's something about you that gets everybody.

DYKE. How about the jury?

THE WARDEN. You've got a sort of way with you —

DYKE. How about that spread-eagle[2] district attorney?

THE WARDEN. I'm going to let you talk with that girl in here — alone.

DYKE. Thanks.

THE WARDEN. It's a sort of thing that's never been done before, but if I put you on your honor —

DYKE (*cynically*). My honor! Thank you so much.

FATHER DALY. Warden, are you sure it's wise?

DYKE. Father, I'm disappointed in you. Do you imagine I'd do anything that could reflect on Warden Holt — or you — or the young lady — or *me?*

THE WARDEN. Father, will you take Dyke into the deputy's room? I want to speak to the young lady first.

---

[1] cyanide of potassium (sī′á·nīd, pŏ·tăs′ĭ-ŭm): a kind of poison.

[2] spread-eagle: a colloquial expression referring here to someone who makes highly emotional speeches.

FATHER DALY. Certainly. Come, my boy. (FATHER DALY *and* DYKE *start toward the deputy's room.*)

THE WARDEN. I'll call you in just a couple of minutes.

DYKE. We promise not to run away. (*They go out together.*)

THE WARDEN (*calls*). Wilson! (*The* ATTENDANT *enters from the left.*)

THE ATTENDANT. Yes, sir.

THE WARDEN. Is the girl there?

THE ATTENDANT. Yes, sir.

THE WARDEN. Frisked?[3]

THE ATTENDANT. Yes, sir.

THE WARDEN. Everything all right?

THE ATTENDANT. Yes, sir.

THE WARDEN (*throws away his cigar*). Bring her in.

THE ATTENDANT. Yes, sir. (*He speaks through the door at the left.*) Step this way, Miss. This here's the warden.

[*A young* GIRL *appears on the threshold and looks about in mingled curiosity and apprehension. She is fresh and wholesome, and rather pretty. She wears a blue tailored suit with deep white cuffs and a starched white collar, and a small blue hat which fits snugly over her fluffy hair. Her costume is not quite conservative enough to be literally old-fashioned, but it hints at the taste and repression of an old-fashioned home. She is neither timid nor aggressive; she is unself-conscious. She looks at the* WARDEN *squarely, but not in boldness, and yet not in feminine appeal; she has rather the fearlessness of a girl who has lost none of her illusions about men in general. Her expression is essentially serious; it conveys, however, the idea that her seriousness is due to her present mission, and that ordinarily she takes an active joy in the mere pleasure of existence.*]

[3] frisked: searched.

THE WARDEN (*having expected a very different type of visitor, he is somewhat taken aback*). All right, Wilson.

THE ATTENDANT. Yes, sir. (*He goes out.*)

THE WARDEN (*with grave deference, half rises*). Will you sit down?

THE GIRL. Why — thank you very much. (*She sits in the chair beside the desk and regards him trustfully.*)

THE WARDEN (*affected by her youth and innocence, and not quite sure how best to proceed, but eventually making an awkward beginning*). You've had an interview with the Governor, I understand?

THE GIRL. Yes, sir. I was with him almost an hour.

THE WARDEN. And you want to see Dyke, do you?

THE GIRL. Yes, sir. I *hope* I'm not — too late.

THE WARDEN. No, you're not too late. (*He is appraising her carefully.*) But I want to ask you a few questions beforehand. (*Her reaction of uncertainty induces him to soften his tone.*) There isn't anything to get upset about. I just want to make it easier for you, not harder. Where do you live?

THE GIRL. In Ohio.

THE WARDEN (*very kindly*). What place?

THE GIRL. In Pennington, sir. It's a little town not far from Columbus.

THE WARDEN. And you live out there with your father and mother?

THE GIRL. No, sir — just my mother and I. My father died when I was a little baby.

THE WARDEN. Why didn't your mother come here herself, instead of sending you?

THE GIRL. She couldn't. She's sick.

THE WARDEN. I see. Have you any brothers or sisters?

THE GIRL (*slightly more at ease*). Just one brother, sir — this one. He and I were the only children. We were very fond of each other.

THE WARDEN. He was considerably older than you?

THE GIRL. Oh, yes. He's ten years older.

THE WARDEN. Why did he leave home?

THE GIRL. I don't really know, sir, except he just wanted to be in the city. Pennington's pretty small.

THE WARDEN. How long is it since you've seen him?

THE GIRL. It's eight years.

THE WARDEN (*voice almost paternal*). As long as that? Hm! And how old are you now?

THE GIRL. I'm almost eighteen.

THE WARDEN (*repeats slowly*). Almost eighteen. Hm! And are you sure after all this time you'd recognize your brother if you saw him?

THE GIRL. Well — (*She looks down, as if embarrassed to make the admission.*) of course I *think* so, but maybe I couldn't. You see, I was only a little girl when he went away — he wasn't a bad boy, sir, I don't think he could ever be really bad — but if this *is* my brother, why, he's been in a great deal of trouble, and you know that trouble makes people look different.

THE WARDEN. Yes, it does. But what makes you think this man Dyke may be your brother — and why didn't you think of it sooner? The case has been in the papers for the last six months.

THE GIRL. Why, it wasn't until last Tuesday that Mother saw a piece in the *Journal* — that's the Columbus paper — that he'd written all about himself, and there was one little part of it that sounded so like Joe — like the funny way he used to say things — and then there was a picture that looked the least little *bit* like him — well, Mother just wanted me to come East and find out for sure.

THE WARDEN. It's too bad she couldn't come herself. She'd probably know him whether he'd changed or not.

THE GIRL. Yes, sir. But I'll do the best I can.

THE WARDEN. When was the last time you heard from him, and where was he, and what was he doing?

THE GIRL. Why, it's about five or six years since we had a letter from Joe. He was in Seattle, Washington.

THE WARDEN. What doing?

THE GIRL. I don't remember. At home, though, he worked in the stationery store. He liked books.

THE WARDEN (*suspiciously*). Why do you suppose he didn't write home?

THE GIRL. I — couldn't say. He was just — thoughtless.

THE WARDEN. Wasn't in trouble of any kind?

THE GIRL. Oh, *no!* Never. That is — unless — he's here now.

THE WARDEN (*deliberates*). How are you going to tell him?

THE GIRL. I don't know what you mean.

THE WARDEN. Why, you say maybe you wouldn't know him even if you saw him — and I'll guarantee this man Dyke won't help you out very much. How do you think you're going to tell? Suppose he don't want to be recognized by you or anybody else? Suppose he's so ashamed of himself he —

THE GIRL. I'd thought of that. I'm just going to talk to him — ask him questions — about things he and I used to do together — I'll watch his face, and if he's my brother, I'm sure I can tell.

THE WARDEN (*with tolerant doubt*). What did you and your brother ever use to do that would help you out now?

THE GIRL. He used to play games with me when I was a little girl, and tell me stories — that's what I'm counting on mostly — the stories.

THE WARDEN. I'm afraid —

THE GIRL. Especially Shakespeare stories.

THE WARDEN. Shakespeare!

THE GIRL. Why, yes. He used to get the plots of the plays — all the Shakespeare plays — out of a book by a man named Lamb, and then he'd tell me the stories in his own words. It was wonderful!

THE WARDEN. I'm certainly afraid he —

THE GIRL. But best of all, he'd learn some of the speeches from the plays themselves. He liked to do it — he was sure he was going to be an actor or something — he was in all the high school plays, always. And then he'd teach some of the speeches to me, and we'd say them to each other. And one thing — every night he'd sit by the side of my bed, and when I got sleepy there were two speeches we'd always say to each other, like good night — two speeches out of *Romeo and Juliet*, and then I'd go to sleep. I can see it all. (*The* WARDEN *shakes his head.*) Why do you do that?

THE WARDEN. This boy isn't your brother.

THE GIRL. Do you think he isn't?

THE WARDEN. I *know* he isn't.

THE GIRL. How do you know?

THE WARDEN. This boy never heard of Shakespeare — much less learned him. (*He presses a button on his desk.*) Oh, I'll let you see him for yourself, only you might as well be prepared. (*The* ATTENDANT *enters from the anteroom.*) Tell Dyke and Father Daly to come in here — they're in the deputy's room.

THE ATTENDANT. Yes, sir. (*He crosses behind the* WARDEN *and goes off to the right.*)

THE WARDEN. If he turns out to be your brother — which he won't — you can have, say, an hour with him. If he don't, you'll oblige me by cutting it as short as you can.

THE GIRL. You see, I've got to tell Mother something perfectly definite. She's worried so long about him, and — and *now* the suspense is perfectly terrible for her.

THE WARDEN. I can understand that. You're a brave girl.

THE GIRL. Of course, it would be awful for us if this *is* Joe, but even that would be better for Mother than just to stay awake nights, and wonder and wonder, and never *know* what became of him.

[*The* ATTENDANT *opens the door of the deputy's room, and when* DYKE *and* FATHER DALY *have come in, he crosses again behind the* WARDEN *and is going out at the left when the* WARDEN *signs to him and he stops.*]

THE WARDEN (*gets to his feet*). Dyke, this is the young lady that's come all the way from Pennington, Ohio, to see you.

DYKE (*who has been talking in an undertone to* FATHER DALY, *raises his head quickly*). Yes, sir?

THE WARDEN. I've decided you can talk with her here — alone.

[*The* GIRL *has risen, breathless, and stands fixed;* DYKE *inspects her coldly from head to foot.*]

DYKE. Thank you. It won't take long.

THE WARDEN (*has been scanning the girl's expression; now, as he sees that she has neither recognized* DYKE *nor failed to recognize him, he makes a little grimace in confirmation of his own judgment*). Father Daly and I'll stay in the deputy's office. We'll leave the door open. Wilson, you stand in the anteroom with the door open.

DYKE (*bitterly*). My honor!

THE WARDEN. What say?

DYKE. I didn't say anything.

THE WARDEN (*to the* GIRL). Will you please remember what I told you about the time?

THE GIRL. Oh, yes, sir.

THE WARDEN. Come, Father. (*They go off into the deputy's room, and the* ATTENDANT, *at a nod from the* WARDEN, *goes off at the left.*)

[DYKE *and the* GIRL *are now facing each other;* DYKE *is well poised and gives the impression of complete indifference to the moment. The* GIRL, *on the other hand, is deeply agitated and her agitation is gradually increased by* DYKE'S *own attitude.*]

THE GIRL (*after several efforts to speak*). Mother sent me to see you.

DYKE (*politely callous*). Yes?

THE GIRL (*compelled to drop her eyes*). You see, we haven't seen or heard of my brother Joe for ever so long, and Mother thought — after what we read in the papers —

DYKE. That I might be your brother Joe?

THE GIRL (*obviously relieved*). Yes, that's it.

DYKE. Well, you can easily see that I'm not your brother, can't you?

THE GIRL (*stares at him again*). I'm not sure. You look a little like him, just as the picture in the paper did, but then again, it's so long — (*She shakes her head dubiously.*) and I'd thought of Joe so differently —

DYKE (*his manner somewhat indulgent, as though to a child*). As a matter of fact, I couldn't be *your* brother, or anybody else's brother, because I never had a sister. So that rather settles it.

THE GIRL. Honestly?

DYKE. Honestly.

THE GIRL (*unconvinced, becomes*

more appealing). What's your real name?

DYKE. Dyke — James Dyke.

THE GIRL. That's sure enough your name?

DYKE. Sure enough. You don't think I'd tell a lie at this stage of the game, do you?

THE GIRL (*musing*). No, I don't believe you would. Where do you come from — I mean where were you born?

DYKE. In Canada, but I've lived all over.

THE GIRL. Didn't you ever live in Ohio?

DYKE. No. Never.

THE GIRL. What kind of work did you do — what was your business?

DYKE. Oh, I'm sort of Jack-of-all-trades. I've been everything a man *could* be — except a success.

THE GIRL. Do you like books?

DYKE. Books?

THE GIRL. Yes — books to read.

DYKE. I don't read when there's anything better to do. I've read a lot here.

THE GIRL. Did you ever sell books — for a living, I mean?

DYKE. Oh, no.

THE GIRL (*growing confused*). I hope you don't mind my asking so many questions. But I —

DYKE. No — go ahead, if it'll relieve your mind any.

THE GIRL. You went to school somewhere, of course — high school?

DYKE. No, I never got that far.

THE GIRL. Did you ever want to be an actor? Or *were* you ever?

DYKE. No, just a convict.

THE GIRL (*helplessly*). Do you know any poetry?

DYKE. Not to speak of.

THE GIRL (*delays a moment, and then, watching him very earnestly, she recites just above her breath*).

Thou knowest the mask of night is on my face
Else would a maiden blush bepaint my cheek
For that which —

(*Realizing that* DYKE's *expression is one of utter vacuity* [1] *she falters, and breaks off the quotation, but she continues to watch him unwaveringly.*) Don't you know what that is?

DYKE. No, but to tell you the truth, it sounds sort of silly to *me*. Doesn't it to you?

THE GIRL (*her intonation becoming slightly forlorn, but gathering courage, and putting him to one more test*).

Good night, good night, parting is such sweet sorrow
That I shall say good night till it be morrow.

DYKE (*his mouth twitching in amusement*). Eh?

THE GIRL. What comes next?

DYKE. Good Lord, *I* don't know.

THE GIRL (*gazes intently, almost imploringly, at him as though she is making a struggle to read his mind; then relaxes and holds out her hand*). Goodby. You — you're *not* Joe, are you? I — had to come and find out, though. I hope I've not made you too unhappy.

DYKE (*ignores her hand*). You're not going now?

THE GIRL (*spiritless*). Yes. I promised the — is he the warden? — that man in there? — I said I'd go right away if you weren't my brother. And you aren't, so —

DYKE. You're going back to your mother?

THE GIRL. Yes.

DYKE. I'm surprised that she sent a girl like you on a sorry errand like this, instead of —

---

[1] **vacuity** (vă·kū′ĭ·tĭ): emptiness of mind.

THE GIRL. She's very sick.

DYKE. Oh, that's too bad.

THE GIRL (*twisting her handkerchief*). No, she's not well at all. And most of it's from worrying about Joe.

DYKE. Still, when you tell her that her son isn't a murderer — at least, that he isn't *this* one — that'll comfort her a good deal, won't it?

THE GIRL (*reluctantly*). Yes, I think maybe it will, only —

DYKE. Only what?

THE GIRL. I don't think Mother'll ever be *really* well again until she finds out for certain where Joe is and what's become of him.

DYKE (*shakes his head compassionately*). Mothers ought not to be treated like that. I wish I'd treated *mine* better. By the way, you didn't tell me what your name is.

THE GIRL. Josephine Paris.

DYKE (*suddenly attentive*). Paris? That's an unusual name. I've heard it somewhere, too.

THE GIRL. Just like the name of the city — in France.

DYKE (*knitting his brows*). And your brother's name was Joseph?

THE GIRL. Yes — they used to call us Joe and Josie — that's funny, isn't it?

DYKE (*thoughtfully*). No, I don't think it's so very funny. I rather like it. (*He passes his hand over his forehead as if trying to force his memory.*)

THE GIRL. What's the matter?

DYKE (*frowning*). I was thinking of something — now, what on earth was that boy's name! Wait a minute, don't tell me — wait a minute — I've got it! (*He punctuates his triumph with one fist in the palm of the other hand.*) Joseph Anthony Paris!

THE GIRL (*amazed*). Why, that's his name! That's Joe! How did you ever —

DYKE (*manner very forcible and convincing*). Wait! Now listen carefully to what I say, and don't interrupt me, because we've only got a minute, and I want you to get this all straight, so you can tell your mother. When the war came along I enlisted, and I was overseas with the Canadians. Early one morning we'd staged a big raid, and there was an officer who'd been wounded coming back, and was lying out there in a shell hole under fire. The Jerries were getting ready for a raid of their own, so they were putting down a box barrage [1] with light guns and howitzers [2] and a few heavies. This officer was lying right in the middle of it. Well, all of a sudden a young fellow dashed out not far from where I was, and went for the officer. He had to go through a curtain of shells and, more than that, they opened on him with rifles and machine guns. The chances were just about a million to one against him, and he must have known it, but he went out just the same. He got the officer in his arms and started back, but he'd only gone a few yards when a five point nine landed right on top of the two of them. Afterward, we got what was left — the identification tag was still there — and that was the name — Joseph Anthony Paris!

THE GIRL (*carries both hands to her breast*). Oh!

DYKE. If that was your brother's name, then you can tell your mother that he died like a brave man and a soldier, three years ago, in France.

THE GIRL. Joe — my brother Joe — is dead?

DYKE. On the field of battle. It was one of the wonderful, heroic things that went almost unnoticed, as so many of them did. If an officer had seen it,

[1] **box barrage** (bȧ·räzh′): concentrated gunfire on three sides of a given area to prevent escape or reinforcement.

[2] **howitzers** (hou′ĭt·sẽrz): light cannon.

there'd have been a decoration for your mother to keep and remember him by.

THE GIRL. And you were there — and saw it?

DYKE. I was there and saw it. It was three years ago. That's why you and your mother haven't heard from him. And if you don't believe what I've said, why, you just write up to Ottawa and get the official record. Of course (*He shrugs his shoulders contemptuously.*) those records are in terribly poor shape, but at least they can tell you what battalion he fought with when he went overseas. Only you mustn't be surprised no matter whether they say he was killed in action, or died of wounds, or is missing, or even went through the whole war with his outfit, and was honorably discharged. They really don't know what happened to half the men. But I've told you the truth. And it certainly ought to make your mother happy when she knows that her boy died as a soldier, and not as a criminal.

THE GIRL (*transfigured* [1]). Yes, yes, it will!

DYKE. And does that make you happy, too?

THE GIRL (*nods repeatedly*). Yes. So happy — after what we were both afraid of — I can't even cry — yet. (*She brushes her eyes with her handkerchief.*) I can hardly wait to take it to her.

DYKE (*struck by a sudden inspiration*). I want to give you something else to take to her. (*He picks up from the desk the envelope containing the government bonds and seals it.*) I want you to give this to your mother from me. Tell her it's from a man who saw your brother die, so it's a sort of memorial for him. (*He touches her arm as she absently begins to tear open the envelope.*) No, don't you open it — let *her* do it.

¹ **transfigured** (trăns·fĭg'ûrd): made bright.

THE GIRL. What is it? Can't I know?

DYKE. Never mind now, but give it to her. It's all I've got in the world and it's too late now for me to do anything else with it. And have your mother buy a little gold star to wear for her son — and you get one, too, and wear it — here — (*He touches his heart.*) Will you?

THE GIRL. Yes — I will. And yet somehow I'll almost feel that I'm wearing it for you, too.

DYKE (*shakes his head soberly*). Oh, no! You mustn't ever do that. I'm not fit to be mentioned in the same breath with a boy like your brother, and now I'm afraid it *is* time for you to go. I'm sorry, but — you'd better. I'm glad you came before it was too late, though.

THE GIRL (*gives him her hand*). Goodby, and thank you. You've done more for me — and Mother — than I could possibly tell you. And — and I'm so sorry for you— so *truly sorry* — I wish I could only do something to make you a tiny bit happier, too. Is there anything I could do?

DYKE (*stares at her and by degrees he becomes wistful*). Why — yes, there is. Only I — (*He leaves the sentence uncompleted.*)

THE GIRL. What is it?

DYKE (*looks away*). I can't tell you. I never should have let myself think of it.

THE GIRL. Please tell me. I want you to. For — for Joe's sake, tell me what I can do.

DYKE (*voice low and desolate*). Well — in all the months I've been in this hideous place, you're the first girl I've seen. I didn't ever expect to see one again. I'd forgotten how much like angels women look. I've been terribly lonesome tonight, especially, and if you really do want to do something for me — for your brother's sake — you see, you're going to leave me in just a minute and — and

I haven't any sister of my own, or anybody else, to say good-by to me — so, if you could — *really* say good-by — (*She gazes at him for a moment, understands, flushes, and then slowly moves into his outstretched arms. He holds her close to him, touches his lips to her forehead twice, and releases her.*)

DYKE (*thickly*). Good-by, my dear.

THE GIRL. Good night. (*She endeavors to smile, but her voice catches in her throat.*) Good-by.

DYKE (*impulsively*). What is it?

THE GIRL (*shakes her head*). N-nothing.

DYKE. Nothing?

THE GIRL (*clutches her handkerchief tight in her palm*). I was thinking — I was thinking what I used to say to my brother — for good night. (*She very nearly breaks down.*) If I *only* could have — have said it to him just once more — for good-by.

DYKE. What was it?

THE GIRL. I — I told it to you once, and you said it was silly.

DYKE (*softly*). Say it again.

THE GIRL (*cannot quite control her voice*).

Good night, good night, parting is such
   sweet sorrow
That I shall say good night till it be morrow.

[*She goes uncertainly toward the anteroom, hesitates, almost turns back, and then with a choking sob she hurries through the door and closes it behind her. For several seconds DYKE stands rigidly intent upon that door; until at length, without changing his attitude or his expression, he speaks very tenderly and reminiscently.*]

Sleep dwell upon thine eyes, peace in thy
   breast;
Would *I* were sleep and peace, so sweet to
   rest.

[*The* WARDEN *and* FATHER DALY *come in quietly from the deputy's room; and as they behold* DYKE, *how rapt and unconscious of them he is, they look at each other questioningly. The* WARDEN *glances at the clock and makes as though to interrupt* DYKE's *solitary reflections, but* FATHER DALY *quietly restrains him. The* CHAPLAIN *sits down in one of the chairs at the back wall; the* WARDEN *crosses on tiptoe and sits at his desk; he is excessively nervous and he continually refers to the clock.* DYKE *turns, as though unwillingly, from the door; there are depths in his eyes, and his thoughts are evidently far away. He sits in the chair to the right of the Warden's desk and leans outward, his right hand on his knee. He puts his left hand to his throat as though to protect it from a sudden pain. He gazes straight ahead into the unknown and speaks in reverie.*]

Of all the wonders that I yet have heard,
It seems to me most strange that men
   should fear;
Seeing that death, a necessary end,
Will come when it will come.

[*He stops and muses for a time, while the* WARDEN *glances perplexedly at*

FATHER DALY *to discover if the priest can interpret what* DYKE *is saying.* FATHER DALY *shakes his head. Abruptly* DYKE'S *face is illumined by a new and welcome recollection; and again he speaks, while the* WARDEN *tries in vain to comprehend him.*]

Cowards die many times before their death;
The valiant never taste of death but once.

[*He stops again and shudders a trifle; his head droops and he repeats, barely above a whisper.*]

The valiant never taste of death but once.

[*The nearer door on the right is opened noiselessly, and the* JAILER, *in obedience to his instructions, steps just inside the room and stands there mute.* FATHER DALY *and the* WARDEN *glance at the* JAILER, *and with significance at each other, and both rise, tardily. The* WARDEN'S *hand, as it rests on his desk, is seen to tremble. There is a moment of dead silence; presently* DYKE *lifts his head and catches sight of the motionless* ATTENDANT *at the open door. With a quick intake of his breath, he starts half out of his seat and stares, fascinated; he sinks back slowly, and turns his head to gaze first at* FATHER DALY *and then at the* WARDEN. *The* WARDEN *averts his eyes, but* FATHER DALY'S *expression is of supreme pity and encouragement. Involuntarily,* DYKE'S *hand again goes creeping upward toward his throat, but he arrests it. He grasps the arms of his chair and braces himself; he rises then and stands very erect, in almost the position of a soldier at attention.*]

THE WARDEN (*swallows hard*). Dyke!
FATHER DALY (*brushes past the* WARDEN, *his right hand lifted as though in benediction*). My son!

DYKE (*regards them fixedly; his voice is low and steady*). All right, let's go.

[*He faces about, and with his head held proud and high, and his shoulders squared to the world, he moves slowly toward the open door.* FATHER DALY, *with the light of his calling in his eyes, steps in line just ahead of* DYKE. *The* WARDEN, *his mouth set hard, falls in behind. When they have all gone forward a pace or two,* FATHER DALY *begins to speak, and* DYKE *to reply.* FATHER DALY'S *voice is strong and sweet; and* DYKE *speaks just after him not mechanically, but in brave and unfaltering response.*]

FATHER DALY. "I will lift up mine eyes unto the hills — "
DYKE. "The valiant never taste of death but once."
FATHER DALY. "From whence cometh my help."
DYKE. "The valiant never taste of death but once."
FATHER DALY (*has almost reached the door; his voice rises a semitone, and gains in emotion*). "My help cometh from the Lord, which made Heaven and earth."
DYKE. "The valiant never taste of death — but once."

[*When the* WARDEN, *whose hands are tightly clenched, has passed the threshold, the* JAILER *follows and closes the door behind him. There is a very brief pause and then*

[CURTAIN]

THINKING IT OVER

1. In the opening scene, several clues are given to establish some facts about Dyke's character and personality. What are they? What do they establish about him as a person?

2. What proof is given that Warden Holt has not become hardened by his years of service at the State's Prison? Both he and Father Daly are anxious to have Dyke reveal his identity. Why?

3. Father Daly grants that Dyke has "moral courage." What is Dyke's interpretation of courage? What is the difference between moral and physical courage? What do you think is the chaplain's opinion of Dyke's course of action?

4. What is your guess as to the nature and circumstances of Dyke's crime? How does he defend his action? Was the law just in imposing the death sentence?

5. Read again those lines that give such comfort to the prisoner, ending with "The valiant never taste of death but once." They are from Shakespeare's *Julius Caesar*. What is your interpretation of them?

6. Describe the changing emotions of Josephine Paris (a) upon arriving at the prison, (b) upon talking with Dyke, and (c) upon leaving. Has she become persuaded that this man is not her brother? What evidence have you?

7. Discuss the significance of Josephine's statement to the Warden, ". . . if this *is* my brother, why, he's been in a great deal of trouble, and you know that trouble makes people look different." To whom is she really speaking?

8. Many people oppose the death penalty for crimes of any sort. The question is earnestly debated on moral and religious grounds. Have you an opinion? Can you support it with facts, not just statements of strong feeling, in a classroom discussion? It may be well to talk over the subject with your family, teachers, or with other informed adults, to explore the legal, social, and moral aspects of the problem. See what information the library can yield. The topic is one to consider for a written or oral composition. The preparation you make for writing it can also provide material for use in a discussion or debate with other class members.

RECOGNIZING SIGNIFICANT DETAILS

Many of the stage directions in "The Valiant" tell us far more than the actual words spoken by the characters. Explain what each of the following details reveals about the people and events of the play:

1. Why does the jailer react with astonishment to the Warden's order to have the prisoner brought to his office?

2. Why is Warden Holt's voice "tense" and Father Daly's "hopeful" when the Governor telephones?

3. Why does the prisoner look "blank" when the girl recites poetry?

4. Why does James Dyke's mouth "twitch in amusement" as the girl waits for him to finish the lines from *Romeo and Juliet*?

5. Why does he stand "rigidly intent" after Josephine leaves?

6. As James Dyke starts to rise from his seat in the final moment of the play, why does the Warden "avert his eyes" from him?

7. In the closing paragraph, why are the Warden's hands "tightly clenched"?

FOR YOUR VOCABULARY: WORD FAMILIES

The title word *valiant* can refer to one person or to many. It has its roots in an old French word, *vailant*, "having worth," and the Latin verb *valere*, "to be strong." Thus a *valiant* person is both worthy and brave. James Dyke is *valiant* in the sense of being brave. Is anyone in the play valiant in both senses of this word? To whom could the title refer? Explain why.

Some related words are *valid*, *value*, and *validate*. Your dictionary will show a busy and thriving family of words, all related to the French word *vailant* and the Latin *valere*. With dictionary help, rewrite the following sentences to explain the italicized words, then find three other *val—* words from which to make sentences of your own:

1. He had a *valid* excuse for being late.

2. The *value* of the rare ancient coin cannot be measured in dollars.

3. The state registrar could not *validate* all the election returns until the absentee votes were received.

ABOUT THE AUTHORS

Holworthy Hall was the pen name used by the well-known writer Harold Everett Porter (1877–1936). He collaborated in the writing of "The Valiant" with **Robert Middlemass** (1883–   ), who has written a number of plays that are popular with amateurs and high school dramatic groups.

ROMEO AND JULIET

by *William Shakespeare*

Introducing the Play

Two young people meet one night at a party, as young people do. From the instant that they look at each other their lives are forever changed. The meeting is both surprising — they were not meant to meet — and joyous: they fall in love. But it is a fateful meeting. Their families are enemies. The hatred separating them is of such long standing that the peace of their city has been broken again and again by ugly quarreling.

The story of *Romeo and Juliet* was not original with Shakespeare. Other authors before him had written different versions of the story. A plot like it can be traced back to an ancient Greek writer.

But the story has its finest expression in the words of Shakespeare, the greatest dramatist of the English-speaking world. He wrote the play when he was young and earning his living as an actor in London. Into it went his deep understanding of human ambitions and disappointments and much of his delight in humor. Shakespeare was a master playwright, an experienced actor, and beyond that, a poet. This wealth of talents he brought to the telling of *Romeo and Juliet*.

Of all Shakespeare's plays, few can have the appeal of this one for young readers. Romeo and Juliet were determined to pit their love against cruel mistrust and tragically bad luck. It never seems to matter how familiar we are with the story or how frequently we read it; Shakespeare tells it with such compelling force that we find ourselves hoping against hope, hoping against our knowledge of the outcome, that *this time* the ending will be a happy one.

Historically Speaking:
Verona of the Fourteenth Century

The background of *Romeo and Juliet* is the city of Verona, Italy, during the fourteenth century — about two hundred years in the past, as Shakespeare looked back in time. Italian towns were starting to benefit from good trade and busy commerce. With these developments had come a surge of enthusiasm for art, literature, and architecture; the period known as the Renaissance had begun.

By imagining yourself a witness to the events of the play, you will enjoy it fully. Suppose, for instance, that you are a citizen of Verona. You are standing in the shade of an arched doorway, perhaps, or strolling on the cobblestones of a side street. The brightly uniformed servants of two noble families are picking a quarrel in the town square. Sword blades glitter. Someone yells. Steel clatters on steel. You are at once tense with alarm. This feuding can mean an outbreak of the warfare that has brought violence to Verona at intervals for two centuries.

Its causes go so far back that you find them confusingly hard to understand. You do know that for generations, two powerful and high-born families have been at odds. Long ago the fighting involved all Italy. It had set the most influential political forces against each other, involving even the heads of Church and the Emperor. Of recent years there has been less warfare, yet here in Verona the old resentments still smolder between your city's two leading families.

You do not think of yourself as an Italian, because Italy is not a unified country. You are a citizen of Verona, which is now more like an independent state, really, than a city; and you take pride in its handsome public buildings, its churches and rich private mansions. The ruler of your city is a prince, a just and fair man who has tried to enforce the peace.

What you cannot guess is that the fight you are watching has already set in motion a series of shocking events. Their unfolding makes up the action of the play *Romeo and Juliet.*

The Theater of Shakespeare's Day

Shakespeare lived during the rule of Queen Elizabeth I, a time of prosperity and achievement in England. The successful playwright was an important man. Everybody from the Queen to the poorest young apprentice loved to go to plays. London had several theaters, all well patronized. People went to be entertained, but in the plays they saw they learned much about their own history and the history of other countries. Popular actors presented the shows in a setting we would consider informal, to say the least. The theater of Shakespeare's day resembled the open courtyard of an inn. Most members of the audience stood to watch the afternoon performance; few could afford to buy seats. Actors appeared on a platform without benefit of a curtain or stage settings, and they had to command the attention of a crowd that expected to eat, drink refreshing

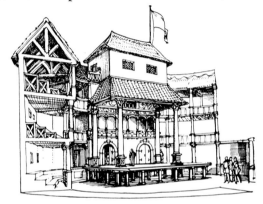

The Globe Theater.

beverages, and howl its pleasure or dissatisfaction whenever it liked. A trumpet sounded to announce the start of the play. People who might be pushing and elbowing for a place to stand in the open air — and these were known as "groundlings" — demanded to be amused and thrilled. The more well-to-do customers, sitting in the covered galleries around the stage, were equally exacting.

Theater-going was so popular that one year special laws were passed to provide penalties for young apprentices who sneaked away from their jobs to go to the Rose or the Swan or another of the London theaters. Audiences demanded action and excitement above all else. Shakespeare knew how to satisfy them. The great majority of people could not read. The dramatist whose play could make them feel the emotions of his characters and visualize the settings his lines suggested was the man to win their applause. No curtain descended to end an act or a scene. Actors simply left the stage. If a killing had occurred on stage, the body had to be removed as logically as possible, in full view of the audience — and Elizabethan audiences liked their action gory. Every good actor trained to become an expert swordsman. Because it was held to be improper for women to appear on the stage, boys took women's parts. It fell to the dramatist to write convincingly enough that the audience would be pleased.

The best playwrights were those who could persuade the audience that they were watching scenes from life. Why did they write in poetry? The lines themselves added dignity and grandeur to the acting. These audiences used their ears as critically as their eyes. They loved the music of good language; they liked puns and word games. The lines of poetry had to be so well composed that the members of the audience could believe that they were standing not in the hot afternoon sun or a sudden drenching shower, but in Juliet's moonlit garden in Verona. It was the genius of Shakespeare to accomplish such a feat. His gift for creating characters and his poet's way with words have won the hearts of men for better than three hundred years.

Shakespeare's plays moved swiftly, in answer to the demand for action made by the audiences of his day. A reader approaching one of the plays for the first time cannot expect to follow the text at so fast a pace, however. To help you appreciate the rapid and continuous action of *Romeo and Juliet*, brief narrative passages have been provided for the play as it appears here. These passages serve the purpose of bridging certain portions of the play, and they will enable you to visualize the action of the characters and grasp the full meaning of the events of the play as they occur.

ROMEO AND JULIET

Dramatis Personae

THE MONTAGUES

LORD MONTAGUE

LADY MONTAGUE

ROMEO, *son of Montague*

BENVOLIO, *nephew of Montague and friend of Romeo*

BALTHASAR, *servant of Romeo*

THE CAPULETS

LORD CAPULET

LADY CAPULET

JULIET, *daughter of Capulet*

TYBALT, *nephew of Lady Capulet*

NURSE *to Juliet*

SERVANT *of Lord Capulet*

PRINCE ESCALUS, *ruler of Verona*

MERCUTIO, *friend of Romeo*

FRIAR LAURENCE, *a Franciscan priest*

FRIAR JOHN, *of the same Order*

COUNT PARIS, *a young nobleman who wishes to marry Juliet*

APOTHECARY

PAGE *to Paris*

CHIEF WATCHMAN

Kinsmen of both houses, dancers, guards, watchmen, and attendants

THE TIME: the fourteenth century

THE PLACE: Verona, Italy

Verona: A public square.

Prologue

[*Enter the* chorus, *an actor who reads the Prologue, to introduce the story of* Romeo Montague *and* Juliet Capulet. *He stands before the curtain and speaks directly to the audience.*]

chorus. Two households, both alike in dignity,
    In fair Verona, where we lay our scene,
    From ancient grudge break to new mutiny,°
    Where civil blood makes civil hands unclean.
    From forth the fatal loins of these two foes   5
    A pair of star-crossed° lovers take their life,
    Whose misadventured piteous overthrows
    Do with their death bury their parents' strife.
    The fearful passage of their death-marked love,
    And the continuance of their parents' rage,   10
    Which, but their children's end, naught could remove,
    Is now the two hours' traffic° of our stage;
    The which if you with patient ears attend,
    What here shall miss, our toil shall strive to mend.°

[*The* chorus *exits, the curtain rises, and the play begins.*]

3. **From ... mutiny:** break into new fighting because of an old quarrel.   6. **star-crossed:** born under the wrong stars; ill-fated.   12. **traffic:** business, or concern.   14. **strive to mend:** in other words, what is not clear from this brief Prologue, our play will try to make clear.

Act I

SCENE 1. *A public square in Verona, Italy. Sunday afternoon.*

In the glare of the hot midsummer sun a street fight between two groups of men shatters the quiet of the town square. Fists fly, swords clash, the men leap at each other. These men are servants of the Montagues (mŏn'tà·gūz) and Capulets (kăp'ù·lĕts), two rich, powerful families of Verona. For years there has been a bitter feud between the families. Street fighting like this has been forbidden by Prince Escalus (ĕs'kà·lŭs), the ruler of Verona, under threat of harsh punishment.

[*As the fight rages,* BENVOLIO (bĕn·vō'lĭ·ō), *a young Montague nobleman, enters the square. Mindful of the Prince's order, he hastens toward the brawling servants.*]

BENVOLIO. Part, fools! (*He tries to beat down their swords.*)
  Put up your swords. You know not what you do.

[*Enter* TYBALT (tĭb'ălt), *a Capulet. He is hot-tempered and more impulsive than peace-loving Benvolio.* TYBALT *draws his sword.*]

TYBALT. Turn thee, Benvolio, look upon thy death.
BENVOLIO. I do but keep the peace. Put up thy sword,
  Or manage it to part these men with me.°   5
TYBALT. What, drawn and talk of peace! I hate the word
  As I hate Hell, all Montagues, and thee.
  Have at thee, coward!

  [BENVOLIO *is forced to draw his own sword. The two men fight.*]

  [*Enter* LORD CAPULET, *followed by* LADY CAPULET *and* SERVANTS.]

CAPULET. What noise is this? Give me my long sword, ho!
LADY CAPULET. A crutch,° a crutch! Why call you for a sword?   10
CAPULET. My sword, I say! Old Montague is come
  And flourishes his blade in spite of me.°

  [*Enter* LORD MONTAGUE, LADY MONTAGUE, *and* SERVANTS.]

MONTAGUE. Thou villain° Capulet! (*To his wife*) Hold me not, let me go.
LADY MONTAGUE. Thou shalt not stir one foot to seek a foe.

[*Like Lady Capulet, she is holding back her husband. Drawn by the shouts and clanking swords, townspeople now stream noisily into the square, some armed*

---

5. **to part . . . me:** to help me part these men.   10. **A crutch:** Lady Capulet is remind-
ing her husband of his age.   12. **in spite of me:** to spite or defy me.   13. **villain:** In
Elizabethan usage the meaning of this word is more often *peasant,* used scornfully, as it is here,
than *evildoer.* Lord Montague is using the word as a taunt.

with clubs and sticks to join the fray. The city's guards march in, crying for order. As the fight swells in size and fury, a blare of trumpets announces the entrance of PRINCE ESCALUS. *His face and voice show his anger.*]

TOWNSPEOPLE. Down with the Capulets! Down with the Montagues!　　　　15

[*The* PRINCE'S VOICE *rises above the uproar.*]

PRINCE. Rebellious subjects, enemies to peace —
　　Will they not hear? What ho, you men, you beasts!

[*The fighting stops. The* CROWD *grows silent.*]

　　Throw your mistempered weapons° to the ground,
　　And hear the sentence of your movèd° prince.
　　Three civil brawls bred of an airy word　　　　　　　　　20
　　By thee, old Capulet and Montague,
　　Have thrice disturbed the quiet of our streets.
　　If ever you disturb our streets again,
　　Your lives shall pay the forfeit of the peace.

[*Exeunt* ° *all but* MONTAGUE, LADY MONTAGUE, *and* BENVOLIO.]

[*In the now quiet square, the* MONTAGUES *tell* BENVOLIO *that they are deeply worried about their son Romeo. He has been keeping too much to himself, as if something were troubling him. Benvolio, Romeo's closest friend, has noticed his behavior, too. Now, as* ROMEO *himself approaches,* BENVOLIO *urges the* MONTAGUES *to leave, so that he can question him alone and try to discover what troubles him.*]

[*Exeunt* MONTAGUE *and* LADY MONTAGUE. *Enter* ROMEO.]

BENVOLIO. Good morrow, Cousin.
ROMEO.　　　　　　　　　　　　　Is the day so young?　　　　25
　　Aye me, sad hours seem long!
BENVOLIO. What sadness lengthens Romeo's hours?
ROMEO. Not having that which, having, makes them short.
BENVOLIO. In love?
ROMEO. Out —　　　　　　　　　　　　　　　　　　　　30
BENVOLIO. Of love? Tell me, who is that you love?
ROMEO. In sadness, Cousin, I do love a woman.
　　She hath forsworn to love,° and in that vow
　　Do I live dead, that live to tell it now.
BENVOLIO. Be ruled by me,° forget to think of her.　　　　35
　　Examine other beauties.

18. **mistempered weapons:** a figure of speech. The men, not their weapons, are ill-tempered. 19. **movèd:** angered.　° **Exeunt** (ĕk'sĕ·ŭnt): "They leave," the Latin plural for *exit; exit* and *exeunt* are used in plays to show that an actor or actors leave the stage.　33. **forsworn to love:** sworn not to love. He is speaking of Rosaline, a young lady of Verona.　35. **Be . . . me:** Take my advice. Notice that though Benvolio is sympathetic, he wants Romeo to stop dreaming about a girl who is not interested in him.

ROMEO. He that is stricken blind cannot forget.
　　　Farewell. Thou canst not teach me to forget.

　　　　　　[He starts to leave, but BENVOLIO *runs after him.]*

BENVOLIO. I'll pay that doctrine, or else die in debt.°

　　　　　　　　[Exeunt.]

　　　　　　SCENE 2. *The same. Later that afternoon.*

[The sun is beginning to fade as LORD CAPULET, PARIS (*a wealthy young kinsman
　of Prince Escalus*), *and a* SERVANT *enter the square.]*

CAPULET. But Montague is bound as well as I
　　　In penalty alike°; and 'tis not hard, I think,
　　　For men so old as we to keep the peace.
PARIS. Of honorable reckoning° are you both,
　　　And pity 'tis you lived at odds so long.
　　　But now, my lord, what say you to my suit?　　　　　　　　　5
CAPULET. By saying o'er what I have said before:
　　　My child is yet a stranger in the world —
　　　She hath not seen the change of fourteen years.
　　　Let two more summers wither in their pride°　　　　　　　　10
　　　Ere we may think her ripe to be a bride.
　　　Earth hath swallowed all my hopes but she,
　　　She is the hopeful lady of my earth.
　　　But woo her, gentle Paris, get her heart.
　　　My will to her consent is but a part.°　　　　　　　　　　15
　　　This night I hold an old accustomed feast,
　　　Whereto I have invited many a guest
　　　Such as I love; and you among the store,°
　　　One more, most welcome, makes my number more.

　　　　　　[To SERVANT, *giving him a list of guests invited to the ball.]*

　　　Go, sirrah,° find those persons out　　　　　　　　　　　20
　　　Whose names are written there, and to them say,
　　　My house and welcome on their pleasure stay.°

　　39. I'll pay . . . debt: As we might say, "I will convince you that you are wrong, or die
trying."　　2. In penalty alike: Both families are pledged to obey the Prince's order to keep
peace.　　4. honorable reckoning: good reputation.　　10. wither in their pride: pass.
15. My will . . . a part: My wish in the matter is of less importance than Juliet's own decision.　　18. store: group.　　20. sirrah (sĭr′ā): a term used to address servants and people
of low rank.　　22. stay: wait.

[*Exeunt* CAPULET *and* PARIS. *The* SERVANT *stares blankly at the list. He cannot read.*]

SERVANT. I am sent to find those persons whose names are here writ, and can never find what names the writing person hath here writ. I must to the learned. In good time.°   25

[*Enter* BENVOLIO *and* ROMEO.]

ROMEO. God-den,° good fellow.
SERVANT. God gi' god-den.° I pray, sir, can you read?
ROMEO. Aye, mine own fortune in my misery.
SERVANT. Perhaps you have learned it without book. But I pray, can you read anything you see?   30
ROMEO. Aye, if I know the letters and the language.
SERVANT (*about to leave*). Ye say honestly! Rest you merry!°
ROMEO (*kindly*). Stay, fellow; I can read.

[*He reads aloud the names on the list and hands it back.*]

A fair assembly. Whither should they come?
SERVANT. To supper — to our house.   35
ROMEO. Whose house?
SERVANT. My master's.
ROMEO. Indeed, I should have asked you that before.
SERVANT. Now I'll tell you without asking. My master is the great rich Capulet, and if you be not of the house of Montagues, I pray come and crush° a   40
cup of wine. Rest you merry!

[*Exit* SERVANT. BENVOLIO *appeals to* ROMEO *with enthusiasm. A party will lift his friend's spirits!*]

BENVOLIO. At this same ancient° feast of Capulet's
Sups the fair Rosaline whom thou so lovest.
Go thither,
Compare her face with some that I shall show.   45
ROMEO (*protesting*). One fairer than my love!
I'll go along, no such sight to be shown,
But to rejoice in splendor of mine own.

[*Exeunt.*]

<hr>

25. **In good time:** What a lucky chance — the arrival of two educated gentlemen; probably they can read.   26. **God-den:** Good evening, a greeting used in the afternoon.   27. **God gi' god-den:** God give you a good evening, the polite reply.   32. **Rest you merry:** God keep you merry (or happy).   40. **crush:** drink.   42. **ancient:** customary, in the same sense that Lord Capulet called it "an old accustomed feast."

SCENE 3. *Verona. A room in Capulet's mansion. Sunday evening.*

[*Enter* LADY CAPULET *and Juliet's* NURSE. *The talkative, foolish, good-hearted Nurse has loved and cared for Juliet since the girl was born.*]

LADY CAPULET. Nurse, where's my daughter? Call her forth to me.
NURSE. Where's this girl? What, Juliet!

[*Enter* JULIET.]

JULIET. Who calls?
NURSE. Your mother.
JULIET. Madam, I am here. What is your will?   5
LADY CAPULET. This is the matter — Nurse, give leave awhile,
    We must talk in secret.

[*Exit* NURSE.]

    Tell me, daughter Juliet,
    How stands your disposition to be married?
JULIET. It is an honor that I dream not of.   10
LADY CAPULET. Well, think of marriage now. Younger than you,
    Here in Verona, ladies of esteem
    Are made already mothers. By my count,
    I was your mother much upon these years
    That you are now a maid.° Thus then in brief —   15
    The valiant Paris seeks you for his love.
    Speak briefly. Can you like of Paris' love?
JULIET. I'll look to like, if looking liking move.°
    But no more deep will I endart mine eye
    Than your consent gives strength to make it fly.   20

[*Enter* SERVANT.]

SERVANT. Madam, the guests are come, supper served up.

[*Exeunt* JULIET *and* LADY CAPULET *for the ball.*]

SCENE 4. *Verona. A hall in the Capulet mansion. Sunday evening.*

    The great hall has been lavishly decorated for the masked ball, which is just starting. Musicians wait to play, clusters of candles glow brilliantly, uniformed servants move about in attendance. Two doors at opposite ends lead into this hall. Through one door, the guests are entering: richly gowned ladies, men in elaborate costumes, all with faces masked.

[*Enter, through one door,* ROMEO, BENVOLIO, *and* MERCUTIO (mûr·kū′shǐ·ō), *another friend.*]

    14–15. **much upon . . . maid:** about the same age as you now are.   18. **I'll . . . move:** I'll look at him if that will make me love him.

[*Enter, through the other door,* CAPULET, LADY CAPULET, *her nephew* TYBALT, JULIET, *and* NURSE. CAPULET *strides across the room to greet the guests.*]

CAPULET. Welcome, gentlemen! I have seen the day
    That I have worn a visor° and could tell
    A whispering tale in a fair lady's ear
    Such as would please. 'Tis gone, 'tis gone, 'tis gone.
    You are welcome, gentlemen. Come, musicians, play.   5

[*The music plays and the masked* DANCERS *glide across the polished floor.* ROMEO *moves among them. Suddenly he halts, his eyes intent on one of the dancers.*]

ROMEO (*to a* SERVANT, *obviously not a permanent member of the Capulet household*). What lady's that which doth enrich the hand
    Of yonder knight?
SERVANT. I know not, sir.
ROMEO. Oh, she doth teach the torches to burn bright!
    It seems she hangs upon the cheek of night   10
    Like a rich jewel in an Ethiop's° ear —
    Beauty too rich for use, for earth too dear!
    So shows a snowy dove trooping with crows
    As yonder lady o'er her fellows shows.
    The measure done, I'll watch her place of stand,°   15
    And, touching hers, make blessèd my rude hand.
    Did my heart love till now? Forswear it, sight!°
    For I ne'er saw true beauty till this night.

[*From among the dancers* TYBALT *steps forward and advances toward* ROMEO.]

TYBALT. This, by his voice, should be a Montague.
    Fetch me my rapier,° boy. What, dares the slave   20
    Come hither, covered with an antic face,°
    To fleer° and scorn at our solemnity?
    Now, by the stock and honor of my kin,
    To strike him dead I hold it not a sin.
CAPULET. Young Romeo, is it?
TYBALT.   'Tis he, that villain Romeo.   25
CAPULET. Content thee, gentle Coz,° let him alone.
    He bears him like a portly gentleman;
    And, to say truth, Verona brags of him
    To be a virtuous and well-governed youth.
    I would not for the wealth of all this town   30
    Here in my house do him disparagement.°

---

    2. **worn a visor:** worn a mask — and danced.   11. **Ethiop's:** Ethiopian's.   15. **The measure . . . stand:** When this dance ends, I'll find out where she is standing.   17. **Forswear it, sight:** Deny it, my eyes.   20. **rapier** (rā′pĭ·ēr): a two-edged sword with a narrow blade. Note that when Lord Capulet threatened to join in the street fight, he called for his long sword, a much heavier weapon. The rapier was just coming into fashion as a dueling sword. 21. **antic face:** fantastic mask.   22. **fleer:** sneer.   26. **Coz:** short for cousin, often meaning a kinsman. Tybalt, of course, is Lady Capulet's nephew.   31. **disparagement** (dĭs·păr′-ĭj·mĕnt): discourtesy, harm.

A hall at the Capulets'.

Therefore be patient, take no note of him.
It is my will, the which if thou respect,
Show a fair presence and put off these frowns.

TYBALT. I'll not endure him. (*Hand on sword, he starts toward* ROMEO.)

CAPULET (*stopping him*).   He shall be endured.   35
  What, goodman° boy! I say he shall! Go to,°
  Am I the master here or you? Go to!
  You'll not endure him? God shall mend my soul!

TYBALT. Why, uncle, 'tis a shame —

CAPULET.   Go to, go to!
  You are a saucy° boy. Be quiet   40
  Or — (*He breaks off and orders* SERVANTS *to light more candles.*)
      More light, more light! (*To* TYBALT) For shame!
  I'll make you quiet. (*To his* GUESTS, *some of whom have noticed Tybalt's
      outburst*)
                    What, cheerly,° my hearts!

TYBALT. I will withdraw, but this intrusion shall,
  Now seeming sweet, convert to bitt'rest gall.°

[*Exit* TYBALT. *The sight of Juliet draws* ROMEO *across the room to her. He places
  the palm of his hand against hers, comparing their joined hands to a holy shrine
  at which he is a pilgrim.*]

36. **goodman:** mister; **Go to:** Come, now! Lord Capulet is being sarcastic; he will not tolerate
rudeness to any guest.   40. **saucy:** insolent.   42. **cheerly:** cheerfully.   43–44. **I . . .
gall:** Tybalt means that he will obey his uncle, but he intends to make Romeo pay bitterly for
daring to come to the ball.

ROMEO. If I profane with my unworthiest hand 45
    This holy shrine, the gentle fine is this:
    My lips two blushing pilgrims ready stand
    To smooth that rough touch with a tender kiss.
JULIET. Good pilgrim, you do wrong your hand too much,
    Which mannerly devotion° shows in this: 50
    For saints have hands that pilgrims' hands do touch,
    And palm to palm is holy palmers' kiss.°
ROMEO. Have not saints lips, and holy palmers too?
JULIET. Aye, pilgrim, lips that they must use in prayer.
ROMEO. Oh, then, dear saint, let lips do what hands do! 55
    They pray. Grant thou, lest faith turn to despair.
JULIET. Saints do not move, though grant for prayers' sake.
ROMEO. Then move not while my prayer's effect I take.
    Thus from my lips, by thine, my sin is purged.° (*He kisses her.*)
JULIET. Then have my lips the sin that they have took. 60
ROMEO. Sin from my lips? Oh, trespass sweetly urged.
    Give me my sin again. (*And again he kisses her.*)
JULIET.   You kiss by the book.°
NURSE (*interrupting*). Madam, your mother craves a word with you.

[JULIET *goes. The* NURSE *starts to follow, but* ROMEO *detains her.*]

ROMEO. What is her mother?
NURSE.   Marry,° bachelor,
    Her mother is the lady of the house, 65
    And a good lady, and a wise and virtuous.
    I nursed her daughter that you talked withal.°
    I tell you, he that can lay hold of her
    Shall have the chinks.°
ROMEO.   Is she a Capulet?
    Oh, dear account! My life is my foe's debt.° 70

[BENVOLIO *appears.*]

BENVOLIO. Away, be gone; the sport is at the best.
ROMEO. Aye, so I fear; the more is my unrest.

[*He turns to leave, followed by* BENVOLIO. LORD CAPULET *goes to them.*]

50. **devotion**: a vow made by a pilgrim. Without hesitation Juliet has fallen into the spirit of
the word game.   52. **palmers' kiss**: The word game delights them both and grows more
fanciful. By *palmer* Juliet means a pilgrim who carries a palm leaf, as did those who visited the
Holy Land. Shakespeare's audiences enjoyed these plays on words, or puns, which are frequent
in all his plays.   59. **purged**: removed.   62. **by the book**: according to a rule book; not
from the heart.   64. **Marry**: Indeed.   67. **withal**: with.   69. **chinks**: money. Compare
our slang expression: "To be in the chips."   70. **Oh, dear . . . debt**: The shock of learning
that Juliet is a Capulet makes Romeo see that he owes his life to the enemy. It is a *dear* account in two senses of the word: it is costly, and he owes it to love.

CAPULET. Nay, gentlemen, prepare not to be gone;
     We have a trifling foolish banquet toward.° (*He sees that other guests are leaving.*)
     Is it e'en so? Why, then, I thank you all.   75
     I thank you, honest gentlemen. Good night.
     More torches here! Come on, then, let's to bed.
     Ah, sirrah, by my fay,° it waxes late.
     I'll to my rest.

     [*Slowly and in groups, all but* JULIET *and* NURSE *leave the ballroom.*]

JULIET (*indicating* BENVOLIO). Come hither, Nurse. What is yond gentleman?   80
NURSE. The son and heir of old Tiberio.
JULIET (*indicating* ROMEO). What's he that follows there, that would not dance?
NURSE. I know not.
JULIET. Go ask his name. (*To herself*) If he be marrièd,
     My grave is like to be my wedding bed.   85

     [NURSE *goes to find out the stranger's name, and returns.*]

NURSE. His name is Romeo, and a Montague,
     The only son of your great enemy.
JULIET. My only love sprung from my only hate!
     Too early seen unknown, and known too late!
NURSE. Come, let's away; the strangers all are gone.   90

     [*Exeunt.*]

74. **trifling . . . toward**: a modest way of saying, "We have a little supper coming."
78. **fay**: faith.

FOLLOWING THE PLOT

1. What happens as a result of the street fight between the Capulets and the Montagues in Act I, Scene 1?

2. Explain why Romeo's parents have been worried about him. How does Benvolio try to help him?

3. Several dramatic incidents take place while Romeo is at the Capulet ball. Briefly, what are they? In your opinion, which of these happenings is the most important? Explain your answer.

GETTING TO KNOW THE CHARACTERS

1. Shakespeare tells us that Juliet is not quite fourteen. About what age do you think Romeo is? How old is Paris?

2. Lady Capulet became Juliet's mother when she was not much older than Juliet

is now. About what age is Lady Capulet? Explain why both she and her husband, as well as Lord and Lady Montague, are considered "old." Would the attitude toward their ages be different today? If so, explain the difference.

3. The character of Lord Capulet is well rounded. What evidence have we that he is a considerate father? Quote the lines that illustrate this quality.

4. Describe Lord Capulet as a host. Sum up the outstanding personality traits of this man as we have observed them. Take into account the way he conducts himself when he is talking with members of his family, with servants, and with friends.

5. Do you consider Romeo fickle, or do you have the impression that he has fallen seriously in love with Juliet? Explain your answer.

Act II

SCENE 1. *Verona. The Capulets' walled orchard. Before dawn, Monday morning.*

The garden is bordered by a high wall. On one side of the garden, a balcony of the Capulet mansion overlooks flowering trees and shrubs. On the street side of the wall runs a narrow lane.

[*Enter* ROMEO *in the lane.*]

ROMEO. Can I go forward when my heart is here?
    Turn back, dull earth, and find thy center out.°

[*He climbs the wall into the garden and disappears from view. Romeo's friends,*
    BENVOLIO *and* MERCUTIO, *come along the lane.*]

BENVOLIO. Romeo!
MERCUTIO.   He is wise,
    And, on my life, hath stolen him home to bed.
BENVOLIO. He ran this way and leaped this orchard wall.   5
    Call, good Mercutio.
MERCUTIO. Romeo!
BENVOLIO. Come, he hath hid himself among these trees.
MERCUTIO. Romeo, good night. I'll to my truckle bed;°
    This field bed is too cold for me to sleep.   10
    Come, shall we go?

[*Exeunt* BENVOLIO *and* MERCUTIO. *Not even for his good friend will Mercutio spend the night on the cold ground!*]

SCENE 2. *The same. Moments later.*

[ROMEO *moves out of the darker shadows of the wall and approaches the house. He has heard the faithful Benvolio and Mercutio depart; he wants to avoid their lighthearted company now.*]

ROMEO. He jests° at scars that never felt a wound.

[ROMEO *stops as* JULIET *appears on the balcony of her room on the second floor.*]

    But, soft,° what light through yonder window breaks?
    It is the east, and Juliet is the sun.

---

    2. Turn back . . . out: By *earth*, Romeo means his body; by *center* he means the center of his universe — that is, his love, Juliet. He is trying to decide whether to stay or to leave the Capulet grounds. His decision is to stay.   **9. truckle bed:** a trundle bed, usually for a servant. It was kept on casters and was made to be rolled under a stationary bed.   **1. jests:** jokes, laughs.   **2. soft:** stop.

The Capulets' garden.

Arise, fair sun, and kill the envious moon,
Who is already sick and pale with grief 5
That thou her maid art far more fair than she.
Her eye discourses;° I will answer it.
I am too bold, 'tis not to me she speaks.
See how she leans her cheek upon her hand.
Oh, that I were a glove upon that hand, 10
That I might touch that cheek!

JULIET.   Aye me!
ROMEO.   She speaks.
Oh, speak again, bright angel! For thou art
As glorious to this night, being o'er my head,
As is a wingèd messenger of heaven
Unto the white-upturned wondering eyes 15
Of mortals that fall back to gaze on him.

JULIET (*not knowing that* ROMEO *is near and can hear her*). O Romeo, Romeo,
    wherefore° art thou Romeo?
Deny thy father and refuse thy name,
Or, if thou wilt not, be but sworn my love
And I'll no longer be a Capulet. 20

ROMEO (*still to himself*). Shall I hear more, or shall I speak at this?

JULIET. 'Tis but thy name that is my enemy.
Oh, be some other name.
What's in a name? That which we call a rose
By any other name would smell as sweet. 25
Romeo, doff° thy name
And for thy name which is no part of thee,
Take all myself.

ROMEO (*from the shadows*). I take thee at thy word.
Call me but love, and I'll be new baptized;
Henceforth I never will be Romeo. 30

7. **discourses:** speaks.   17. **wherefore:** why; for what reason.   26. **doff:** put aside.

JULIET (*startled*). What man art thou, that thus bescreened in night
　　So stumblest on my counsel?°
ROMEO.　　　　　　　　　　　　By a name
　　I know not how to tell thee who I am.
　　My name, dear saint, is hateful to myself
　　Because it is an enemy to thee.　　　　　　　　　　　　　　　35
　　Had I it written, I would tear the word.
JULIET. My ears have not yet drunk a hundred words
　　Of thy tongue's uttering, yet I know the sound.
　　Art thou not Romeo, and a Montague?
ROMEO (*comes forward so that she can see him*). Neither, fair saint, if either
　　thee dislike.　　　　　　　　　　　　　　　　　　　　　　　40
JULIET. How camest thou hither, tell me, and wherefore?
　　The orchard walls are high and hard to climb,
　　And the place death, considering who thou art,
　　If any of my kinsmen find thee here.
ROMEO. With love's light wings did I o'erperch° these walls;　　　　45
　　For stony limits cannot hold love out,
　　And what love can do, that dares love attempt.
　　Therefore thy kinsmen are no stop to me.
JULIET. If they do see thee, they will murder thee.
ROMEO. Alack, there lies more peril in thine eye　　　　　　　　　50
　　Than twenty of their swords.° Look thou but sweet,
　　And I am proof against their enmity.°
JULIET. I would not for the world they saw thee here.
ROMEO. I have night's cloak to hide me from their eyes,
　　And but° thou love me, let them find me here.　　　　　　　　55
　　My life were better ended by their hate
　　Than death prorogued,° wanting of thy love.
JULIET. By whose direction found'st thou out this place?
ROMEO. By love, that first did prompt me to inquire.
JULIET. Thou know'st the mask of night is on my face,　　　　　　60
　　Else would a maiden blush bepaint my cheek
　　For that which thou hast heard me speak tonight.
　　Fain° would I dwell on form, fain, fain deny
　　What I have spoke. But farewell compliment!°
　　Dost thou love me? I know thou wilt say "Aye,"　　　　　　　65
　　And I will take thy word. O gentle Romeo,
　　If thou dost love, pronounce it faithfully.
　　Or if thou think'st I am too quickly won,

---

32. **counsel:** secret thoughts.　　45. **o'erperch:** fly over.　　50–51. **Alack . . . swords:**
Alas, the love in Juliet's eye, which he is powerless to resist, holds more danger for Romeo
than her kinsmen's swords.　　52. **enmity:** hatred.　　55. **And but:** if only.　　57. **prorogued**
(prō·rōgd'): postponed.　　63. **Fain:** gladly.　　64. **farewell compliment:** good-by to polite
pretending. Juliet is saying that if Romeo had not overheard her confession of love for him, she
would gladly deny it, because it seems too sudden; she would flirt and show only mild interest,
as girls customarily do. But there is no use pretending!

I'll frown and be perverse° and say thee nay,
So thou wilt woo; but else, not for the world.   70
In truth, fair Montague, I am too fond,°
And therefore thou mayst think my 'havior light.
But trust me, gentleman, I'll prove more true
Than those that have more cunning to be strange.°
I should have been more strange, I must confess,   75
But that thou overheard'st, ere I was ware,
My true love's passion. Therefore pardon me,
And not impute° this yielding to light love,
Which the dark night hath so discovered.
ROMEO. Lady, by yonder blessèd moon I swear,   80
    That tips with silver all these fruit-tree tops —
JULIET. Oh, swear not by the moon, the inconstant moon,
    That monthly changes in her circled orb,°
    Lest that thy love prove likewise variable.
ROMEO. What shall I swear by?
JULIET.   Do not swear at all.   85
    Or, if thou wilt, swear by thy gracious self.
ROMEO. If my heart's dear love —
JULIET. Well, do not swear. Although I joy in thee,
    I have no joy of this contract° tonight.
    It is too rash, too unadvised, too sudden,   90
    Too like the lightning, which doth cease to be
    Ere one can say, "It lightens." Sweet, good night!
    This bud of love by summer's ripening breath
    May prove a beauteous flower when next we meet.
    Good night, good night! As sweet repose and rest   95
    Come to thy heart as that within my breast!
ROMEO. Oh, wilt thou leave me so unsatisfied?
JULIET. What satisfaction canst thou have tonight?
ROMEO. The exchange of thy love's faithful vow for mine.
JULIET. I gave thee mine before thou didst request it.   100

[NURSE *calls from inside.*]

I hear some noise within; dear love, adieu.°

[*She calls to the* NURSE, *then turns back to* ROMEO.]

Anon,° good Nurse! Sweet Montague, be true.
Stay but a little, I will come again.

[*She exits into the house.*]

69. **perverse:** stubborn or contrary.   71. **fond:** In Elizabethan usage, this means "foolish."
74. **Than those . . . strange:** Than those who have the cleverness to appear indifferent.
78. **impute:** credit. Juliet is afraid that Romeo may think she cannot love deeply or sincerely,
since she loved him almost at once.   83. **orb:** orbit.   89. **contract:** betrothal or engagement.   101. **adieu** (*à·dū′*): F., good-by; farewell.   102. **Anon** (*à·nŏn′*): in a moment;
very soon.

ROMEO. Oh, blessèd, blessèd night! I am afeard,
    Being in night, all this is but a dream,   105
    Too flattering-sweet to be substantial.

[JULIET *reappears.*]

JULIET. Three words, dear Romeo, and good night indeed.
    If that thy bent° of love be honorable,
    Thy purpose marriage, send me word tomorrow
    By one that I'll procure° to come to thee,   110
    Where and what time thou wilt perform the rite,
    And all my fortunes at thy foot I'll lay
    And follow thee my lord throughout the world.
ROMEO. So thrive my soul° —
JULIET. A thousand times good night!   115

[JULIET *exits; but in a moment she returns.*]

Good night, good night. Parting is such sweet sorrow
That I shall say good night till it be morrow.

[*She exits from the balcony.*]

ROMEO. Sleep dwell upon thine eyes, peace in thy breast.
    Would I were sleep and peace, so sweet to rest.

[*Exit* ROMEO *from the garden.*]

SCENE 3. *Verona. Friar Laurence's cell, a bare room with a simple cot,*
    table, and chair. It is early Monday morning.

[*Enter* FRIAR LAURENCE *with a basket of herbs he has been gathering in the*
    monastery garden. The herbs are used by the monks for making medicines.]

FRIAR LAURENCE. Oh, mickle° is the powerful grace that lies
    In plants, herbs, stones, and their true qualities.
    Within the infant rind of this small flower
    Poison hath residence, and medicine power:
    In man as well as herbs — grace and rude will;°   5
    And where the worser is predominant,
    Full soon the canker° death eats up that plant.

[*Enter* ROMEO.]

---

108. **bent:** intention.   110. **procure:** get.   114. **So . . . soul:** Romeo speaks almost in
a whisper, as if praying that his soul will find strength to help Juliet's plans come true.
1. **mickle** (mĭk'l): great.   5. **grace and rude will:** good and evil.   7. **canker** (kăng'-
kĕr): a destructive worm.

ROMEO. Good morrow, father.

FRIAR LAURENCE.   *Benedicite!*°
　　What early tongue so sweet saluteth me?
　　Therefore thy earliness doth me assure   10
　　Thou art uproused by some distemperature.°

ROMEO. Then plainly know my heart's dear love is set
　　On the fair daughter of rich Capulet.
　　As mine on hers, so hers is set on mine,
　　And all combined, save what thou must combine   15
　　By holy marriage. When, and where, and how
　　We met, we wooed and made exchange of vow
　　I'll tell thee as we pass. But this I pray,
　　That thou consent to marry us today.

FRIAR LAURENCE. And art thou changed? Pronounce this sentence then —   20
　　Women may fall when there's no strength in men.

ROMEO. Thou chid'st° me oft for loving Rosaline.

FRIAR LAURENCE. For doting,° not for loving, pupil mine.

ROMEO. And bad'st° me bury love.

FRIAR LAURENCE.   Not in a grave,
　　To lay one in, another out to have.°   25

ROMEO. I pray thee, chide not. She whom I love now
　　Doth grace for grace and love for love allow.
　　The other did not so.

FRIAR LAURENCE.   Oh, she knew well
　　Thy love did read by rote° that could not spell.
　　But come, young waverer, come, go with me,   30
　　In one respect I'll thy assistant be;
　　For this alliance may so happy prove,
　　To turn your households' rancor° to pure love.

ROMEO. Oh, let us hence. I stand on sudden haste.°

FRIAR LAURENCE. Wisely and slow. They stumble that run fast.   35

[*But* ROMEO *cannot slow his steps. He hastens to the market place where, at nine
o'clock, Juliet's messenger is to appear. At last the* MESSENGER *comes — Juliet's
old* NURSE. *She listens to Romeo's instructions: Juliet is to go that afternoon to
the cell of Friar Laurence, as if to make her confession. There the marriage will
take place. In no particular hurry, although Juliet waits anxiously for her, the*
NURSE *starts homeward. In the Capulet garden, with much complaining of her
aches and pains, she tells Juliet of the wedding plans. Radiant with happiness,*
JULIET *makes her way to the friar's cell.*]

---

　　8. **Benedicite** (bĕn′ē·dĭs′ĭ·tē): Bless you! (Latin.)　　11. **distemperature:** illness.
22. **chid'st** (chĭd'st): from the verb *chide,* meaning "scold."　　23. **doting:** being fond of,
but not actually loving.　　24. **bad'st** (băd'st): from *bid:* "You urged."　　25. **To lay . . .
have:** Friar Laurence is saying that he did not urge Romeo simply to exchange one sweetheart for another.　　29. **by rote:** by heart. In other words, with Rosaline ("The other,"
line 28) you talked about love mechanically, not from sincere feeling.　　33. **rancor:** hatred.
34. **Oh, . . . haste:** Let us hurry away from here. I am impatient.

SCENE 4. *Friar Laurence's cell. That afternoon.*

[ROMEO *eagerly awaits Juliet's coming. The friar cannot calm the young man's excitement, although he points out that by loving Juliet, Romeo is risking death at the hands of her kinsmen.*]

FRIAR LAURENCE. So smile the Heavens upon this holy act
    That afterhours with sorrow chide us not!
ROMEO. Amen, amen!
    Do thou but close our hands with holy words,
    Then love-devouring death do what he dare,   5
    It is enough I may but call her mine.
FRIAR LAURENCE. Here comes the lady. Oh, so light a foot
    Will ne'er wear out the everlasting flint.°

[*Enter* JULIET.]

JULIET. Good even to my ghostly° confessor.
FRIAR LAURENCE. Romeo shall thank thee, daughter, for us both.   10
JULIET. As much to him, else is his thanks too much.°
ROMEO. Ah, Juliet, if the measure of thy joy
    Be heaped like mine, and that thy skill be more
    To blazon° it, then sweeten with thy breath
    This neighbor air.°   15
FRIAR LAURENCE. Come, come with me, and we will make short work.
    For, by your leaves, you shall not stay alone
    Till Holy Church incorporate two in one.

[*Smiling, he leads the two lovers to the chapel and there performs the marriage ceremony.*]

8. **flint**: the stones of the cell floor.   9. **ghostly**: spiritual.   11. **As much . . . too much**: May the evening be good for him, too, or he has no reason to give thanks.   14. **blazon**: describe.   14–15. **sweeten . . . air**: If your happiness matches mine and you can express it, do speak of it.

FOLLOWING THE PLOT

1. Why is Romeo eager to slip away from Benvolio and Mercutio? What accidental happening causes him to declare his love for Juliet?

2. After acknowledging her love for him, what does Juliet require of Romeo? What is his response to this requirement?

3. Explain what takes place from the time Romeo leaves the garden until he next meets Juliet in Friar Laurence's cell.

THE CHARACTERS DEVELOP

1. In this act Romeo climbs the wall and enters the Capulet garden at dawn. From what you had learned of Romeo in Act I, did you find this action to be "in character"? Why?

2. Do you believe that Romeo was ready to propose marriage to Juliet when he entered the garden? What more do they now know about each other than when they first met? What is the effect of their further conversation upon Romeo? Select the lines that show that a significant change has taken place in their relationship.

3. Why does Friar Laurence assume the risk of marrying the young couple and thus angering their families? What do his words and actions tell you about his character?

Act III

SCENE 1. *Verona. The public square. Later that afternoon.*

[*Enter* MERCUTIO, BENVOLIO, PAGE, *and* SERVANTS.]

BENVOLIO. I pray thee, good Mercutio, let's retire.°
    The day is hot, the Capulets abroad,
    And if we meet, we shall not 'scape a brawl;
    For now these hot days is the mad blood stirring.
    By my head,° here come the Capulets.   5
MERCUTIO. By my heel, I care not.

[*Enter* TYBALT *and other* CAPULETS.]

TYBALT (*insultingly*). Gentlemen, a word with one of you.
MERCUTIO (*picking up the taunt*). And but one word with one of us? Couple it
    with something — make it a word and a blow.
TYBALT. You shall find me apt enough to that, sir, an° you will give me occa-
    sion.   11
MERCUTIO. Could you not take some occasion without giving?
TYBALT. Mercutio, thou consort'st with Romeo —
MERCUTIO. Consort!° What, dost thou make us minstrels? An thou make min-
    strels of us, look to hear nothing but discords. (*Puts his hand on his
    sword hilt.*) Here's my fiddlestick, here's that shall make you dance.
    'Zounds,° consort!   17
BENVOLIO. We talk here in the public haunt of men.
    Either withdraw unto some private place,
    Or reason coldly° of your grievances,   20
    Or else depart. Here all eyes gaze on us.
MERCUTIO. Men's eyes were made to look, and let them gaze.
    I will not budge for no man's pleasure, I.

[*Enter* ROMEO. *He has just been secretly married to Juliet — Tybalt's cousin.*]

TYBALT. Well, peace be with you, sir. Here comes my man.
    Romeo, the hate I bear thee can afford   25
    No better term than this — thou art a villain.
ROMEO. Tybalt, the reason that I have to love thee
    Doth much excuse the appertaining rage°

---

1. **retire:** go inside.   5. **By my head:** a mild oath.   10. **an:** if.   14. **Consort:** a company of musicians. Tybalt's use of "consortest" means "you are a companion of," but the fiery Mercutio chooses to make a pun — and return taunt for taunt.   17. **'Zounds:** By God's wounds, a common oath of the time.   20. **reason coldly:** talk calmly. Benvolio is always the man of peaceful ways.   28. **appertaining rage:** the anger with which you greet me.

To such a greeting. Villain am I none.
Therefore farewell. I see thou knowest me not.° 30
TYBALT. Boy, this shall not excuse the injuries
That thou hast done me. Therefore turn and draw.
ROMEO. I do protest I never injured thee,
But love thee better than thou canst devise°
Till thou shalt know the reason of my love. 35
And so, good Capulet — which name I tender
As dearly as mine own — be satisfied.

[BENVOLIO *is surprised at Romeo's apparent cowardice, but* MERCUTIO *is horrified.*]

MERCUTIO. O calm, dishonorable, vile submission!

[*Draws his sword, determined not to let these insults pass. Now he seeks to pro-voke* TYBALT *to fight.*]

Tybalt, you rat-catcher,° will you walk?
TYBALT. What wouldst thou have with me? 40
MERCUTIO. Good King of Cats, nothing but one of your nine lives, that I mean
to make bold withal, and, as you shall use me hereafter, dry-beat° the
rest of the eight. Will you pluck your sword out by the ears? Make haste,
lest mine be about your ears ere it be out.
TYBALT. I am for you. (*He draws his sword.*) 45
ROMEO. Gentle Mercutio, put thy rapier up.

[MERCUTIO *and* TYBALT *fight.* ROMEO *turns desperately to* BENVOLIO, *who, unlike Romeo, is wearing a long sword.*]

Draw, Benvolio; beat down their weapons.
Gentlemen, for shame, forbear this outrage!
Tybalt, Mercutio, the Prince expressly hath
Forbid this bandying° in Verona streets. 50
Hold, Tybalt! Good Mercutio!

[*He holds back* MERCUTIO's *sword arm; instantly,* TYBALT *thrusts his rapier into the now defenseless* MERCUTIO. *Then he turns and runs with the other* CAPU-LETS.]

MERCUTIO (*falls*). I am hurt.
A plague on both your houses! I am sped.°
Is he gone, and hath nothing?
BENVOLIO (*amazed*). What, art thou hurt?
MERCUTIO. Aye, aye, a scratch, a scratch — marry, 'tis enough.
Where is my page? Go, villain, fetch a surgeon. 55

[*Exit* PAGE.]

29–30. **Villain . . . not:** Romeo declares that Tybalt is incorrect; Romeo is a gentleman, not a peasant. Therefore Tybalt must not really know him. Romeo is trying to avoid a fight, though he dare not reveal his reason.   34. **devise:** imagine.   39. **rat-catcher:** "Tybalt" is the name of a cat in the old fable of Reynard the Fox.   42. **dry-beat:** to bruise without drawing blood.   50. **bandying:** quarreling.   52. **sped:** done for.

ROMEO. Courage, man, the hurt cannot be much.

MERCUTIO (*gasping for breath*). No, 'tis not so deep as a well, nor so wide as a
   church door, but 'tis enough, 'twill serve. Ask for me tomorrow and you   58
   shall find me a grave° man. I am peppered,° I warrant, for this world. A
   plague on both your houses! 'Zounds, a dog, a rat, a mouse, a cat, to scratch
   a man to death! A braggart, a rogue, a villain, that fights by the book of
   arithmetic!° (*To* ROMEO) Why the devil came you between us? I was hurt
   under your arm.

ROMEO (*numbly*). I thought all for the best.

MERCUTIO. Help me into some house, Benvolio,   65
   Or I shall faint. A plague on both your houses!
   They have made worms' meat of me. I have it,°
   And soundly, too — your houses!

[*He exits, supported by* BENVOLIO *and* SERVANTS *as* ROMEO *stands in a daze, looking after them.*]

ROMEO. This gentleman, the Prince's near ally,
   My very friend, hath got this mortal hurt   70
   In my behalf; my reputation stained
   With Tybalt's slander — Tybalt, that an hour
   Hath been my kinsman.

[*Re-enter* BENVOLIO. *He walks slowly to the grieving* ROMEO *and clasps his friend's
arm for a moment before he can speak.*]

BENVOLIO. O Romeo, Romeo, brave Mercutio's dead.
   That gallant spirit hath aspired° the clouds,   75
   Which too untimely° here did scorn the earth.

ROMEO. This day's black fate on more days doth depend;
   This but begins the woe others must end.

[*Re-enter* TYBALT.]

BENVOLIO. Here comes the furious Tybalt back again.

[ROMEO *wheels, at last gripping his sword.*]

ROMEO. Alive, in triumph! And Mercutio slain!   80
   Now, Tybalt, take the "villain" back again
   That late thou gavest me; for Mercutio's soul
   Is but a little way above our heads,
   Staying for thine to keep him company.
   Either thou, or I, or both, must go with him.   85

TYBALT. Thou, wretched boy, that didst consort him here,
   Shalt with him hence.°

---

59. **grave:** Even dying, the witty Mercutio continues to make puns; **peppered:** made very
hot, like a plate of food salted and peppered; that is, *finished*.   61–62. **book of arithmetic:**
Tybalt fought according to the exactly numbered rules of books about sword play.   67. **I
have it:** I've had it — a fatal wound.   75. **aspired:** gone above to.   76. **untimely:** early.
87. **Shalt . . . hence:** Shall go with him in death.

[ROMEO *raises his sword decisively.*]

ROMEO.   This shall determine that.

[*There is a brief, violent duel;* TYBALT *falls, killed by* ROMEO.]

BENVOLIO (*in alarm*). Romeo, away, be gone!
    The citizens are up, and Tybalt slain.
    Stand not amazed. The Prince will doom thee death   90
    If thou art taken. Hence, be gone, away!
ROMEO. Oh, I am fortune's fool!°

[*Exit* ROMEO.]

[*The street fills with cries and running feet as the townspeople of Verona pour
into the market place, drawn by reports of new outbursts of fighting.* LORD *and*
LADY MONTAGUE, LORD *and* LADY CAPULET *are among the crowd who see Tybalt's
body. Into the square run the soldiers and guards of Prince Escalus, announcing
his arrival. The ruler demands to know what has happened, and it is* BENVOLIO
who makes the explanation. LADY CAPULET, *weeping for her nephew, angrily
demands Romeo's death.* PRINCE ESCALUS *replies thoughtfully.*]

PRINCE ESCALUS. Romeo slew him, he slew Mercutio.
    Who now the price of his dear blood doth owe?
LORD MONTAGUE. Not Romeo, Prince, he was Mercutio's friend.   95
    His fault concludes but what the law should end,
    The life of Tybalt.
PRINCE ESCALUS.   And for that offense
    Immediately we do exile him hence.
    I will be deaf to pleading and excuses,
    Nor tears nor prayers shall purchase out° abuses.   100
    Let Romeo hence in haste,
    Else, when he's found, that hour is his last.

[*Exeunt* PRINCE *and* ATTENDANTS.]

SCENE 2. *Verona. Capulet's garden. Late Monday afternoon,
after the duels. Evening is approaching.*

[*Enter* JULIET. *She knows nothing of the deaths of Tybalt and Mercutio.*]

JULIET. Come, night, come, Romeo; come, thou day in night,
    For thou wilt lie upon the wings of night
    Whiter than new snow upon a raven's back.
    Come, gentle night, come, loving, black-browed night;
    Give me my Romeo, and when he shall die,   5
    Take him and cut him out in little stars,
    And he will make the face of heaven so fine

92. **Oh, . . . fool:** I am tricked by an evil fate!   100. **purchase out:** pay for.

That all the world will be in love with night
And pay no worship to the garish° sun.

[*Enter* NURSE.]

Aye, me, what news? Why dost thou wring thy hands?   10
NURSE. Ah, welladay!° He's dead, he's dead, he's dead.
We are undone, lady, we are undone.
Alack the day! He's gone, he's killed, he's dead.

[*To the frightened* JULIET, *the "he" can mean only Romeo. She cries out.*]

JULIET. What devil art thou, that dost torment me thus?
This torture should be roared in dismal hell.   15
If he be slain, say aye, or if not, no.
Brief sounds determine of my weal° or woe.
NURSE. I saw the wound, I saw it with mine eyes —
JULIET. Oh, break, my heart! Poor bankrupt,° break at once.
NURSE. O Tybalt, Tybalt, the best friend I had.   20
O courteous Tybalt, honest gentleman!
That ever I should live to see thee dead!
JULIET. What storm is this that blows so contrary?
Is Romeo slaughtered, and is Tybalt dead?
NURSE. Tybalt is gone, and Romeo banishèd.   25
Romeo that killed him, he is banishèd.
JULIET. Oh, God, did Romeo's hand shed Tybalt's blood?
NURSE. It did, it did. Alas the day, it did!
JULIET. Oh, serpent heart, hid with a flowering face!
O damnèd saint, an honorable villain!   30
Was ever book containing such vile matter
So fairly bound? Oh, that deceit should dwell
In such a gorgeous palace.
NURSE.   There's no trust,
No faith, no honesty in men — all perjured,
All forsworn, all naught, all dissemblers.°   35
Shame come to Romeo!
JULIET.   Blistered be thy tongue
For such a wish! He was not born to shame.°
My husband lives, that Tybalt would have slain,
And Tybalt's dead, that would have slain my husband.
Romeo is banishèd.   40
There is no end, no limit, measure, bound
In that word's death; no words can that woe sound.°
Where is my father and my mother, Nurse?

---

9. **garish:** gaudy; showy.   11. **welladay:** an exclamation of sorrow.   17. **weal:** well-being.
19. **bankrupt:** person without resources.   35. **dissemblers:** pretenders.   36–37. **Blistered
. . . shame:** Notice how strongly Juliet comes to her husband's defense when the Nurse speaks
against him.   42. **sound:** tell.

NURSE. Weeping and wailing over Tybalt's corse.°

Will you go to them? I will bring you thither. 45

JULIET. Wash they his wounds with tears. Mine shall be spent,

When theirs are dry, for Romeo's banishment.°

NURSE. Hark ye, your Romeo will be here at night.

I'll to him — he is hid at Laurence' cell.°

JULIET. Oh, find him! Give this ring to my true knight 50

And bid him come to take his last farewell.

[*Exeunt.*]

SCENE 3. *Verona. Friar Laurence's cell. Later Monday evening.*

[*As the* FRIAR *enters, his cell is apparently empty. He notices the movement of a curtain.*]

FRIAR LAURENCE. Romeo, come forth, come forth, thou fearful man.

[ROMEO *steps from behind a curtain.*]

ROMEO. Father, what news? What is the Prince's doom?°

FRIAR LAURENCE. Not body's death, but body's banishment.

ROMEO (*bitterly*). Ha, banishment! Be merciful, say "death."

Heaven is here, where Juliet lives.° 5

Oh, friar, how hast thou the heart

To mangle me with that word "banishèd"?

[*There is a knocking at the cell door.*]

FRIAR LAURENCE. Arise, one° knocks. Good Romeo, hide thyself.

ROMEO. Not I.

FRIAR LAURENCE. Thou wilt be taken. —

[*The knocking continues, more loudly. The* FRIAR *hurries from the cell.*]

God's will, I come, I come! 10

[*He returns with the* NURSE.]

NURSE. O holy friar, oh, tell me, holy friar,

Where is my lady's lord, where's Romeo?

ROMEO. Nurse —

NURSE. Ah, sir, ah, sir! Well, death's the end of all.

ROMEO. Spakest thou of Juliet? How is it with her? 15

Doth she not think me an old° murderer,

---

44. **corse:** corpse.   46–47. **Wash they . . . banishment:** Let them shed tears for Tybalt, declares Juliet; her tears will be for the forced exile of Romeo.   48–49. **Hark ye . . . cell:** The Nurse realizes that she has angered Juliet by speaking against Romeo and so tries to make amends to her dear mistress.   2. **doom:** sentence.   4–5. **Ha . . . lives:** Romeo would prefer death to the exile which means separation from Juliet.   8. **one:** someone.   16. **old:** actual.

[ACT III, SCENE 3]   **ROMEO AND JULIET**   **493**

Friar Laurence's cell.

Now I have stained the childhood of our joy
With blood removed but little from her own?°
NURSE. Oh, she says nothing, sir, but weeps and weeps
And now falls on her bed, and then starts up   20
And Tybalt calls, and then on Romeo cries,
And then down falls again.
ROMEO.   As if that name,
Shot from the deadly level of a gun,
Did murder her, as that name's cursèd hand
Murdered her kinsman. Oh, tell me, friar, tell me,   25
In what vile part of this anatomy
Doth my name lodge? Tell me, that I may sack
The hateful mansion.°

[*He draws his dagger and is about to plunge it into his heart.*]

FRIAR LAURENCE (*stopping him*). Hold thy desperate hand.
Art thou a man? By my holy order,
I thought thy disposition better-tempered.   30
Hast thou slain Tybalt? Wilt thou slay thyself?
And slay thy lady too that lives in thee,
By doing damnèd hate upon thyself°?
What, rouse thee, man! Thy Juliet is alive.
Go, get thee to thy love as was decreed,°   35
Ascend° her chamber — hence and comfort her.

18. **With blood . . . own:** that is, with the blood of a relative.   27–28. **sack . . . mansion:** destroy myself. In this figure of speech, Romeo is declaring that if his name were a part of his body, he would search it out and destroy that part.   33. **damnèd hate . . . thyself:** Self-destruction was forbidden by Romeo's religion.   35. **decreed:** decided.   36. **Ascend:** climb up to the balcony.

But look thou stay not till the watch be set,
For then thou canst not pass to Mantua,°
Where thou shalt live till we can find a time
To blaze° your marriage, reconcile your friends,   40
Beg pardon of the Prince, and call thee back.
NURSE. My lord, I'll tell my lady you will come.
ROMEO. Do so, and bid my sweet prepare to chide.°
NURSE. Here, sir, a ring she bid me give you, sir.
Hie you,° make haste, for it grows very late.   45

[*Exit* NURSE. ROMEO *looks lovingly at the ring, the token of Juliet's unchanging
love.*]

FRIAR LAURENCE. Go hence. Give me thy hand, 'tis late. Farewell, good night.

[ROMEO *clasps the hand of his loyal counselor, then hastens from the cell.*]

SCENE 4. *Verona. A hall in Capulet's house. Late Monday night.*

[*Enter* CAPULET, LADY CAPULET, *and* PARIS, *who has come to offer his sympathy to
the sorrowing aunt and uncle of* TYBALT.]

CAPULET. Things have fall'n out,° sir, so unluckily,
That we have had no time to move° our daughter.
Look you, she loved her kinsman Tybalt dearly.
PARIS (*sadly*). These times of woe afford no time to woo.
Madam, good night. Commend me to your daughter.   5
LADY CAPULET. I will, and know her mind early tomorrow;
Tonight she's mewed up to her heaviness.°
CAPULET. Sir Paris, I will make a desperate tender°
Of my child's love. I think she will be ruled
In all respects by me — nay, more, I doubt it not.   10
But soft, what day is this?
PARIS.   Monday, my lord.
CAPULET (*to his wife*). Monday? Well, Wednesday is too soon.
On Thursday let it be, on Thursday, tell her,
She shall be married to this noble earl.
PARIS. My lord, I would that Thursday were tomorrow.   15

[*Exeunt.*]

38. **Mantua** (măn′tŭ·ȧ): a city some twenty-five miles southwest of Verona. Friar Laurence's plan calls for Romeo to hide himself in Mantua until the feeling against him in Verona has died down. Friar Laurence will keep in touch with Romeo's servant during his banishment. Recall that the Friar promised, too, that he would do his best to get Prince Escalus to pardon Romeo. 40. **blaze:** make public. The Friar's outline of a possible plan of action gives Romeo fresh hope. 43. **chide:** scold; Romeo is admitting that Juliet has reason to blame him for being the cause of so much trouble.   45. **Hie you:** hurry.   1. **fall'n out:** happened.   2. **move:** persuade her (to marry you).   7. **mewed up . . . heaviness:** confined (like a caged bird) by grief. 8. **desperate tender:** bold offer.

SCENE 5. *Verona. Juliet's chamber opening onto the balcony.*
Before dawn, Tuesday morning.

[ROMEO *and* JULIET *stand before the open windows of the balcony.*]

JULIET. Wilt thou be gone? It is not yet near day.
    It was the nightingale, and not the lark,
    That pierced the fearful hollow of thine ear;
    Nightly she sings on yond pomegranate tree.
    Believe me, love, it was the nightingale.°   5
ROMEO. It was the lark, the herald of the morn,
    No nightingale. Look, love, what envious streaks
    Do lace the severing clouds in yonder east.
    Night's candles are burnt out, and jocund° day
    Stands tiptoe on the misty mountaintops.   10
    I must be gone and live, or stay and die.
JULIET. Yond light is not daylight, I know it, I.
    It is some meteor that the sun exhales,°
    To be to thee this night a torchbearer
    And light thee on thy way to Mantua.   15
    Therefore stay yet — thou need'st not to be gone.
ROMEO. Let me be ta'en, let me be put to death,
    I am content, so thou wilt have it so.
    I have more care° to stay than will to go.
    Come, death, and welcome! Juliet wills it so.   20
    How is't, my soul? Let's talk. It is not day.
JULIET (*decisively, as they move out onto the balcony*). It is, it is. Hie hence, be
    gone, away!
    Oh, now be gone; more light and light it grows.
ROMEO. More light and light; more dark and dark our woes!
    Farewell, farewell. One kiss, and I'll descend.   25

[*They embrace.* ROMEO *climbs down from the balcony and leaves.*]

JULIET (*returning from the balcony*). O fortune, fortune, all men call thee fickle.
    If thou art fickle, what dost thou with him
    That is renowned for faith? Be fickle, fortune,
    For then I hope thou wilt not keep him long,
    But send him back.   30
LADY CAPULET (*from inside the house*). Ho, daughter, are you up?
JULIET. Who is't that calls? It is my lady mother.
    What unaccustomed cause procures° her hither?

[*Enter* LADY CAPULET.]

---

    5. Believe me . . . nightingale: If Juliet can convince Romeo that he has heard the night-
ingale, which sings at night, he will not have to talk of leaving. As in the earlier balcony scene,
she is aware that he must soon leave and that every moment he stays, he endangers his life.
9. jocund (jŏk′ŭnd): cheerful.   **13. exhales:** draws out.   **19. care:** desire.   **33. pro-
cures:** sends.

LADY CAPULET. Why, how now, Juliet?

JULIET.   Madam, I am not well.

LADY CAPULET. Evermore weeping for your cousin's death?   35
    What, wilt thou wash him from his grave with tears?
    And, if thou couldst, thou couldst not make him live,
    Therefore have done. Some grief shows much of love,
    But much of grief shows still some want of wit.°

JULIET. Yet let me weep for such a feeling loss.   40

LADY CAPULET. So shall you feel the loss, but not the friend
    Which you weep for.

JULIET.   Feeling so the loss,
    I cannot choose but ever weep the friend.

LADY CAPULET. But now I'll tell thee joyful tidings, girl.

JULIET. And joy comes well in such a needy time.   45
    What are they, I beseech your ladyship?

LADY CAPULET. Marry,° my child, early next Thursday morn,
    The gallant, young, and noble gentleman,
    The County° Paris, at Saint Peter's Church,
    Shall happily make thee there a joyful bride.   50

JULIET. Now, by Saint Peter's Church, and Peter too,
    He shall not make me there a joyful bride.°
    I wonder at this haste, that I must wed
    Ere he that should be husband comes to woo.

LADY CAPULET. Here comes your father, tell him so yourself   55
    And see how he will take it at your hands.

[*Enter* CAPULET *and* NURSE. LORD CAPULET *is already a bit out of patience with what he, like his wife, thinks to be Juliet's sorrow over Tybalt's death.*]

CAPULET. What, still in tears?
    Evermore showering? How now, wife,
    Have you delivered to her our decree?

LADY CAPULET. Aye, sir, but she will none, she gives you thanks. 60
    I would the fool were married to her grave.

CAPULET (*with rising anger*). Soft! Take me with you,° take me with you, wife.
    How? Will she none? Doth she not give us thanks?
    Is she not proud? Doth she not count her blest,
    Unworthy as she is, that we have wrought   65
    So worthy a gentleman to be her bridegroom?

JULIET. Not proud you have, but thankful that you have.
    Proud can I never be of what I hate,
    But thankful even for hate that is meant love.

---

    39. **But much . . . of wit:** Lady Capulet naturally assumes that Juliet is grieving over Tybalt; she warns her daughter that too much grief shows a lack of common sense.   47. **Marry:** Indeed.   49. **County:** Count.   52. **joyful bride:** Juliet emphasizes *joyful* but knows she will not be a bride at all, since she is already married. Her words have one meaning for herself; for her mother, quite another.   62. **Take me with you:** Let me understand you.

CAPULET. How, how! How, how! Chop-logic!° What is this?   70
     "Proud," and "I thank you," and "I thank you not,"
     And yet "not proud" — Mistress minion,° you
     Thank me no thankings, nor proud me no prouds,
     But fettle° your fine joints 'gainst Thursday next,
     To go with Paris to Saint Peter's Church   75
     Or I will drag thee on a hurdle° thither.
JULIET (*kneeling*). Good Father, I beseech you on my knees,
     Hear me with patience but to speak a word.
CAPULET. Hang thee, young baggage! Disobedient wretch!
     I tell thee what. Get thee to church on Thursday   80
     Or never after look me in the face.
NURSE. You are to blame, my lord, to rate° her so.
CAPULET. Peace, you mumbling fool!
LADY CAPULET. You are too angry.
CAPULET. God's bread!° It makes me mad.   85
     Day, night, hour, tide, time, work, play,
     Alone, in company, still my care hath been
     To have her matched. And having now provided
     A gentleman of noble parentage,
     And then to have a wretched puling° fool,   90
     A whining mammet, in her fortune's tender,°
     To answer "I'll not wed, I cannot love,
     I am too young, I pray you, pardon me" —
     But an you will not wed, I'll pardon you.
     Graze where you will, you shall not house with me.   95
     Look to 't, think on 't, I do not use to jest.°
     Thursday is near. Lay hand on heart, advise.
     An you be not, hang, beg, starve, die in the streets,
     For by my soul, I'll ne'er acknowledge thee.°

                    [*He strides out.*]

JULIET (*brokenly*). Is there no pity sitting in the clouds   100
     That sees into the bottom of my grief?

---

     70. **Chop-logic:** one who splits hairs in an argument.   72. **Mistress minion:** saucy miss.
74. **fettle:** prepare.   76. **hurdle:** a cart used to take prisoners to execution. Lord Capulet,
who feels that Juliet is most ungrateful for his fatherly interest in seeing that she marries happily, is rising to new heights of anger.   82. **rate:** berate, or scold.   85. **God's bread:** the
bread of Holy Communion, an oath.   90. **puling:** whimpering.   91. **mammet . . . tender:** Lord Capulet's meaning is that it is the height of ingratitude to have his daughter act like
a whining puppet when she has been given such a fortunate offer (tender) of marriage.
96. **I . . . jest:** It is not my habit to joke.   97–99. **Lay hand . . . acknowledge thee:** Take
my advice and marry the Count, or if you don't, you can die before I'll take you back in my
house.

O sweet my mother,° cast me not away.
Delay this marriage for a month, a week,
Or if you do not, make the bridal bed
In that dim monument° where Tybalt lies.   105

[LADY CAPULET *supports her husband's decision, although the extent of his anger
has alarmed even her.*]

LADY CAPULET. Talk not to me, for I'll not speak a word.
    Do as thou wilt, for I have done with thee.

[*Exit* LADY CAPULET.]

JULIET. O God! O Nurse, how shall this be prevented?
    My husband is on earth, my faith in heaven.
    I'll to the friar to know his remedy.°   110
    If all else fail, myself have power to die.°

[*Exit* JULIET.]

102. **sweet my mother:** my dear mother.   105. **monument:** the Capulet burial vault.
110. **I'll . . . remedy:** I'll go to the Friar to find out whether he can help me.   111. **If
all . . . die:** If everything fails, I can kill myself.

FOLLOWING THE PLOT

1. What is the first incident in Scene 1 that threatens the peace? Who is responsible for the first act of violence? As a consequence of this, Romeo becomes involved in a series of unfortunate events. Explain them.

2. Describe how matters stand for Romeo by the end of Scene 1. How is Juliet affected by the situation?

3. What new action of Lord Capulet's presents a further threat to the future of Romeo and Juliet? What is Juliet's response to this?

CONTRAST IN CHARACTER AND LANGUAGE

1. Which lines in Act III show that Benvolio and Tybalt are almost opposite in temperament? What three adjectives would describe Tybalt? What three would describe Benvolio?

2. Shakespeare's use of names is often an important clue to character. The name *Tybalt* is derived from *Theobald; Mercutio* comes from *Mercury,* and *Benvolio* combines the Latin words *bene* and *volo.* With the help of an unabridged dictionary, explain why these names suit the personalities of the characters.

3. What are some of the different kinds of contrast shown in the scene between Juliet and her nurse? (The difference in their ages is one. Consider also their social position, and look for other contrasts.)

4. Discuss the scenes in Act III where Shakespeare makes dramatic contrast between life and death, night and day, impulsiveness and reasonableness, love and hate. What effect does this use of contrast have upon an audience?

Act IV

SCENE 1. *Verona. Friar Laurence's cell. Tuesday morning.*

[*Enter* FRIAR LAURENCE *and* PARIS. PARIS *is telling the* FRIAR *that Lord Capulet has set his daughter's marriage date two days from now. So confident of the event is Paris that he already thinks of Lord Capulet as his father-in-law.*]

FRIAR LAURENCE. On Thursday, sir? The time is very short.
PARIS. My father Capulet will have it so,
    And I am nothing slow to slack his haste.
FRIAR LAURENCE. You say you do not know the lady's mind.
    Uneven is the course,° I like it not.   5
PARIS. Immoderately she weeps for Tybalt's death,
    And therefore have I little talked of love,
    For Venus° smiles not in a house of tears.
    Now, sir, her father counts it dangerous
    That she do give her sorrow so much sway,   10
    And in his wisdom hastes our marriage,
    To stop the inundation° of her tears.
FRIAR LAURENCE (*to himself*). I would I knew not why it should be slowed.°
    Look, sir, here comes the lady toward my cell.

[*Enter* JULIET.]

PARIS (*joyously*). Happily met, my lady and my wife!   15
JULIET. That may be, sir, when I may be a wife.
PARIS. That may be must be, love, on Thursday next.
JULIET. What must be shall be.
FRIAR LAURENCE.   That's a certain text.°
PARIS. Come you to make confession to this father?
JULIET. To answer that, I should confess to you.   20
PARIS. Do not deny to him that you love me.
JULIET (*to* FRIAR LAURENCE). I will confess to you that I love him.°
PARIS. So will ye, I am sure, that you love me.
JULIET. Are you at leisure, holy father, now,
    Or shall I come to you at evening Mass?   25
FRIAR LAURENCE. My leisure serves me, pensive daughter, now.
    My lord, we must entreat the time alone.°

---

5. **course:** the course of events. Friar Laurence is hinting that it is unusual to plan on a marriage before Juliet's consent has been asked.   8. **Venus:** the goddess of love.   12. **inundation** (ĭn'ŭn·dā'shŭn): flooding.   13. **I would . . . slowed:** Friar Laurence wishes he had no knowledge of his having married Romeo and Juliet.   18. **certain text:** a true saying. 22. **I love him:** Juliet is, of course, speaking of Romeo, but Paris thinks she is being extremely modest. Once again, her words have a double meaning, as Friar Laurence understands. 27. **My lord . . . alone:** The Friar is courteously requesting Paris to leave them; he is at leisure to see Juliet alone.

PARIS. God shield° I should disturb devotion!
     Juliet, on Thursday early will I rouse ye.
     Till then, adieu, and keep this holy kiss.   30

          [*Exit* PARIS. JULIET *turns despairingly to her confessor.*]

JULIET. Oh, shut the door, and when thou hast done so,
     Come weep with me — past hope, past cure, past help.
FRIAR LAURENCE. Ah, Juliet, I already know thy grief.
     It strains me past the compass of my wits.°
     I hear thou must, and nothing may prorogue° it,   35
     On Thursday next be married to this County.
JULIET. Tell me not, friar, that thou hear'st of this,
     Unless thou tell me how I may prevent it.
     If in thy wisdom thou canst give no help,
     Do thou but call my resolution wise,   40
     (*Takes out a knife.*) And with this knife I'll help it° presently.
     God joined my heart and Romeo's, thou our hands,
     And ere this hand, by thee to Romeo's sealed,
     Shall be the label to another deed,
     Or my true heart with treacherous revolt   45
     Turn to another, this shall slay them both.
     Be not so long to speak; I long to die
     If what thou speak'st speak not of remedy.

          [FRIAR LAURENCE *seizes her wrist lest she try to kill herself.*]

FRIAR LAURENCE. Hold, daughter, I do spy a kind of hope,
     Which craves° as desperate an execution   50
     As that is desperate which we would prevent.
     If rather than to marry County Paris
     Thou hast the strength of will to slay thyself,
     Then is it likely thou wilt undertake
     A thing like death to chide° away this shame,   55
     And if thou darest, I'll give thee remedy.
JULIET. Oh, bid me leap, rather than marry Paris,
     From off the battlements of yonder tower,
     And I will do it without fear or doubt,
     To live an unstained wife to my sweet love.   60
FRIAR LAURENCE. Hold then, go home, be merry, give consent
     To marry Paris. Wednesday is tomorrow.
     Tomorrow night look that thou lie alone.
     Let not thy nurse lie with thee in thy chamber.
     Take thou this vial,° being then in bed,   65
     And this distillèd liquor drink thou off;

28. **shield:** forbid.   34. **past the compass . . . wits:** we would say "at my wit's end."
The Friar is gravely troubled by the turn of events.   35. **prorogue:** postpone.   41. **I'll
help it:** I'll help keep my resolution not to go through with this marriage.   50. **craves:** requires.   55. **chide:** drive.   65. **vial** (vī′ăl): a small bottle.

When presently through all thy veins shall run
A cold and drowsy humor;° for no pulse
Shall keep his native progress, but surcease;
No warmth, no breath, shall testify thou livest.°   70

[JULIET *listens intently to this description of the effects of the liquid, which will
cause the appearance of death. The* FRIAR, *seeing that she gathers hope from
his words, continues:*]

Each part, deprived of supple government,°
Shall, stiff and stark and cold, appear like death.
And in this borrowed likeness of shrunk death
Thou shalt continue two and forty hours,
And then awake as from a pleasant sleep.   75
Now, when the bridegroom in the morning comes
To rouse thee from thy bed, there art thou dead.
Then, as the manner of our country is,
In thy best robes uncovered on the bier,°
Thou shalt be borne to that same ancient vault   80
Where all the kindred of the Capulets lie.
In the meantime, against° thou shalt awake,
Shall Romeo by my letters know our drift,°
And hither shall he come, and he and I
Will watch thy waking, and that very night   85
Shall Romeo bear thee hence to Mantua.
And this shall free thee from this present shame,
If no inconstant toy° nor womanish fear
Abate thy valor° in the acting it.

JULIET. Give me, give me! Oh, tell not me of fear! (*She seizes the vial.*)   90
FRIAR LAURENCE. Hold! Get you gone, be strong and prosperous
In this resolve. I'll send a friar with speed
To Mantua, with my letters to thy lord.
JULIET. Love give me strength! And strength shall help afford.
Farewell, dear father.   95

[*She embraces* FRIAR LAURENCE *and runs from the cell.*]

SCENE 2. *Verona, a hall in Capulet's house. Tuesday afternoon.*

[LORD CAPULET, *pacing up and down, is questioning the* NURSE.]

CAPULET. What, is my daughter gone to Friar Laurence?

[*Enter* JULIET, *smiling and apparently lighthearted.*]

68. **humor:** fluid.   68–70. **for no pulse . . . livest:** your pulse and breathing will stop
and you will seem to be dead.   71. **supple government:** movement.   79. **bier** (bĕr): the
coffin and the stand on which it is borne to the grave. The Italian custom was to dress the body
in rich clothing and carry it to the grave with the face uncovered.   82. **against:** lest.
83. **drift:** intention.   88. **inconstant toy:** changeable whim.   89. **Abate thy valor:** lessen
your courage.

NURSE. See where she comes from shrift° with merry look.

CAPULET. How now, my headstrong! Where have you been gadding?

JULIET. Where I have learned me to repent the sin
Of disobedient opposition   5
To you and your behests,° and am enjoined
By holy Laurence to fall prostrate here
And beg your pardon. (*She kneels.*) Pardon, I beseech you!
Henceforward I am ever ruled by you.

CAPULET (*pleased and happy*). Send for the County, go tell him of this.   10
I'll have this knot knit up tomorrow morning.°

JULIET. I met the youthful lord at Laurence' cell.
And gave him what becomèd love I might,
Not stepping o'er the bounds of modesty.°

CAPULET. Why, I am glad on 't; this is well. Stand up.   15
This is as 't should be. Let me see the County.
Go, Nurse, go with her. We'll to church tomorrow.

[*Exeunt* JULIET *and* NURSE.]

My heart is wondrous light,
Since this same wayward girl is so reclaimed.

[*Exit.*]

SCENE 3. *Verona. Juliet's chamber. Tuesday evening.*

[JULIET *stands at her curtained bed.* LADY CAPULET *and* NURSE *are at the doorway.*]

LADY CAPULET. Good night.
Get thee to bed and rest, for thou hast need.

2. **shrift:** confession.   6. **behests:** commands.   11. **this knot . . . morning:** I'll have the marriage performed tomorrow morning. Lord Capulet is now changing the date of the ceremony from Thursday to Wednesday; Juliet, acting the part of the obedient daughter, is unable to protest. This change will, of course, shorten the length of time the Friar needs to send Romeo word of their plan.   13–14. **what becomèd . . . modesty:** I as much as told him I loved him without being immodest.

Juliet's chamber.

JULIET (*to herself*). Farewell. God knows when we shall meet again.
I have a faint cold fear thrills through my veins
That almost freezes up the heat of life.   5
I'll call them back again to comfort me.
Nurse! — (JULIET *starts toward the door; then turns back.*)
    What should she do here?
My dismal scene I needs must act alone.
Come, vial. (*She sits on the bed.*)
What if this mixture do not work at all?   10
Shall I be married then tomorrow morning?
No, no, this shall forbid it. Lie thou there. (*She places a dagger beside her
    on the bed.*)
What if it be a poison which the friar
Subtly hath ministered to have me dead,
Lest in this marriage he should be dishonored   15
Because he married me before to Romeo?
I fear it is. And yet methinks it should not,
For he hath still been tried a holy man.°
How if, when I am laid into the tomb,
I wake before the time that Romeo   20
Come to redeem me? There's a fearful point.
Shall I not then be stifled in the vault,
To whose foul mouth° no healthsome air breathes in,
And there die strangled ere my Romeo comes?
Or if I live, is it not very like,   25
The horrible conceit° of death and night,
Together with the terror of the place —
Oh, if I wake, shall I not be distraught,
Environèd with all these hideous fears,
And madly play with my forefathers' joints,   30
And pluck the mangled Tybalt from his shroud,°
And in this rage, with some great kinsman's bone,
As with a club, dash out my desperate brains?
(*She seems now to see a horrible vision.*) Oh, look! Methinks I see my
    cousin's ghost
Seeking out Romeo that did spit° his body   35
Upon a rapier's point. Stay, Tybalt, stay!
Romeo, I come! This do I drink to thee.

[*She takes the vial, drinks its contents, and falls unconscious on the bed.*]

13–18. **What if . . . holy man:** What if the liquid, or potion, is really a poison which will
kill her? No; the good Friar is too devout to trick her in order to protect himself. Juliet's distress of mind causes her to doubt her only helper.   23. **mouth:** entrance.   26. **conceit:**
idea.   31. **shroud:** burial garment. In this scene Juliet imagines the horror of wakening alone
in the Capulet tomb. She might go mad with terror.   35. **spit:** pierce.

SCENE 4. *Verona. Juliet's chamber. Early Wednesday morning.*

[NURSE *enters, to help Juliet dress in her wedding finery. She calls to* JULIET *to waken her.*]

NURSE. Mistress! What, mistress! Juliet! Fast,° I warrant her, she. (*She chuckles at Juliet's lack of response on such an important day.*)
    Why, lamb! Why, lady! Fie, you slugabed!
    Why, love, I say! Madam! Sweetheart! Why, bride!
    I must needs wake her.

[*She goes to the bed and looks closely at* JULIET. JULIET *lies motionless.* NURSE *screams.*]

                         Lady, lady, lady!
    Alas, alas! Help, help! My lady's dead!   5

            [LADY CAPULET *runs in, alarmed.*]

LADY CAPULET. What noise is here?
NURSE.   Oh, lamentable day!
LADY CAPULET. What is the matter?
NURSE.   Look, look! Oh, heavy day!
LADY CAPULET (*going to* JULIET). Oh, me, Oh, me! My child, my only life.
    Revive, look up, or I will die with thee.
    Help, help! Call help.   10

              [*Enter* CAPULET.]

CAPULET (*sternly*). For shame, bring Juliet forth; her lord is come.
LADY CAPULET. Alack the day, she's dead, she's dead, she's dead!
CAPULET. Ha! Let me see her. Out, alas! She's cold.
    Her blood is settled and her joints are stiff.
    Life and these lips have long been separated.   15
    Death lies on her like an untimely frost
    Upon the sweetest flower of all the field.
    Death, that hath ta'en her hence to make me wail,
    Ties up my tongue and will not let me speak.

        [*Enter* FRIAR LAURENCE *and* PARIS.]

FRIAR LAURENCE. Come, is the bride ready to go to church?   20
CAPULET. Ready to go, but never to return.°
    Oh, son, the night before thy wedding day
    Hath Death lain with thy wife. There she lies.
PARIS (*with violent grief*). Beguiled,° divorced, wronged, spited, slain!
    Most detestable Death, by thee beguiled,   25
    By cruel, cruel thee quite overthrown!
    Oh, love, Oh, life! Not life, but love in death.

---

   1. **Fast**: fast asleep.   21. **Ready . . . return**: Juliet is to go to the church for her funeral, not for the planned wedding.   24. **Beguiled** (bē·gīld′): cheated.

CAPULET. Dead art thou! Alack, my child is dead,
And with my child my joys are burièd!

[FRIAR LAURENCE *now tries to help the grief-stricken family accept what has happened and find some measure of consolation.*]

FRIAR LAURENCE. Peace ho, for shame! Confusion's cure lives not   30
In these confusions. Heaven and yourself
Had part in this fair maid, now heaven hath all,
And all the better is it for the maid.
Your part in her you could not keep from death,
But Heaven keeps his part in eternal life.   35
CAPULET. All things that we ordainèd festival
Turn from their office to black funeral,
Our instruments to melancholy bells,°
Our wedding cheer to a sad burial feast.
FRIAR LAURENCE. Sir, go you in, and, madam, go with him.   40
And go, Sir Paris, everyone prepare
To follow this fair corse unto her grave.
The heavens do lour° upon you for some ill;
Move them no more by crossing their high will.

[*Exeunt.*]

36–38. **All things . . . melancholy bells:** Lord Capulet's order is that all the festivities planned to celebrate the wedding shall now be changed to funeral observances. The musicians who were to play at the feasting will now use their instruments to play songs of mourning. 43. **lour:** frown threateningly.

FOLLOWING THE PLOT

1. Explain the plan which is drawn up by Friar Laurence and Juliet. Within what limit of time must their plan be completed? How is Romeo to be informed of his part in it?

2. Juliet proves herself to be a convincing actress in Scenes 1 and 2 of Act IV. For what reason is she "acting" in each of these scenes?

3. Before she swallows the sleeping potion, Juliet experiences terrible fears. Why, then, does she finally drink it? What happens after the Nurse fails to waken Juliet?

RECOGNIZING THE NATURE OF THE CONFLICT

Several kinds of conflict are felt by the leading character or characters in any drama. Some of these conflicts might be called "external"; that is, they come from sources or causes outside the characters themselves. Other conflicts might be called "internal," because they have to do with the problems or decisions that cause a struggle in the minds of the characters. They must cope with these internal conflicts by making their own choices.

1. Explain what conflict Juliet has in relation to Romeo. What is her conflict as far as Paris is concerned?

2. Surely you sense that Juliet feels other kinds of conflict about things that people want her to do. Tell how each one of the following people creates a problem, or conflict, for her: her father, her mother, the Nurse.

3. When the time comes for her to take the sleeping potion, what are Juliet's doubts and fears about Friar Laurence and about the tomb? What other course of action is open to her? Why is this an impossible choice?

4. Looking back at Questions 1, 2, and 3, tell which of the conflicts discussed may be called "external" and which "internal."

A street in Mantua.

Act V

SCENE 1. *A street in Mantua. Thursday afternoon.*

[*Enter* ROMEO. *Impatient for news of Juliet, he has sent his servant Balthasar to Verona to inquire about her. Now as he awaits Balthasar's return,* ROMEO's *hopes run high.*]

ROMEO. If I may trust the flattering truth of sleep,
    My dreams presage° some joyful news at hand;
    My bosom's lord° sits lightly in his throne,
    And all this day an unaccustomed spirit
    Lifts me above the ground with cheerful thoughts.   5
    I dreamed my lady came and found me dead
    And breathed such life with kisses in my lips
    That I revived and was an emperor.

        [BALTHASAR *enters.* ROMEO *greets him happily.*]

    News from Verona! How now, Balthasar!
    Dost thou not bring me letters from the friar?   10
    How doth my lady? Is my father well?

    2. **presage** (prė·sāj′): foretell.   3. **My bosom's lord:** my heart.

How fares my Juliet? That I ask again,
For nothing can be ill if she be well.
BALTHASAR (*speaking with difficulty*). Then she is well and nothing can be ill.
    Her body sleeps in Capel's° monument,   15
    And her immortal part with angels lives.
    I saw her laid low in her kindred's vault,
    And presently took post° to tell it you.
ROMEO (*looks up at the heavens; he has been "star-crossed" by an evil fate*). Is it
    even so? Then I defy you, stars!
    (*To* BALTHASAR) Thou knowest my lodging. Get me ink and paper,   20
    And hire post horses.° I will hence tonight.
BALTHASAR. I do beseech you, sir, have patience.
    Your looks are pale and wild, and do import
    Some misadventure.°

[ROMEO *ignores his servant's concern and questions him again.*]

ROMEO. Hast thou no letters to me from the friar?   25
BALTHASAR. No, my good lord.
ROMEO.   No matter. Get thee gone,
    And hire those horses. I'll be with thee straight.°

[*Exit* BALTHASAR.]

Well, Juliet, I will lie° with thee tonight.
Let's see for means.° O mischief, thou art swift
To enter in the thoughts of desperate men.   30

[*He looks around at the many small shops on this street and begins to walk.*]

I do remember an apothecary° —
And hereabouts he dwells — which late I noted
In tattered weeds,° with overwhelming brows.
Noting this penury,° to myself I said,
"An if a man did need a poison now,   35
Whose sale is present death in Mantua,
Here lives a caitiff° wretch would sell it him."
As I remember, this should be the house.
Being holiday, the beggar's shop is shut.
What ho! Apothecary!
APOTHECARY (*coming out of his shop*). Who calls so loud?   40
ROMEO. Come hither, man. I see that thou art poor.

---

15. **Capel's:** Capulet's.   18. **took post:** rode swiftly.   21. **post horses:** special fast saddle horses. In that day they could be rented by travelers wishing to make a fast journey. More often they were used by official messengers who carried letters, and they were dispatched by the "post master."   23–24. **do import . . . some misadventure:** indicate some rash action. 27. **straight:** immediately; at once.   28. **will lie:** will lie in the grave.   29. **Let's . . . means:** What way can I find to kill myself?   31. **apothecary** (*à·pŏth'ê·kĕr'ĭ*): seller of drugs and medicines.   33. **weeds:** garments.   34. **penury** (*pĕn'ū·rĭ*): poverty.   37. **caitiff** (*kā'tĭf*): miserable.

Hold, there is forty ducats.° Let me have
A dram of poison, such soon-speeding gear°
As will disperse itself through all the veins,
That the life-weary taker may fall dead.   45
APOTHECARY. Such mortal drugs I have, but Mantua's law
    Is death to any he that utters them.°
ROMEO. Art thou so bare and full of wretchedness,
    And fear'st to die? Famine is in thy cheeks,
    Need and oppression starveth in thy eyes.   50
    The world affords no law to make thee rich,
    Then be not poor, but break it and take this.

> [ROMEO *holds up a gold coin. The man eyes it greedily.*]

APOTHECARY. My poverty, but not my will, consents.

> [*He enters his shop.*]

ROMEO. I pay thy poverty and not thy will.

> [*The* APOTHECARY *comes back and hands a small vial to* ROMEO.]

APOTHECARY. Put this in any liquid thing you will   55
    And drink it off, and if you had the strength
    Of twenty men, it would dispatch° you straight.

> [ROMEO *tosses a bag heavy with gold to the frightened* APOTHECARY.]

ROMEO. There is thy gold, worse poison to men's souls,
    Doing more murder in this loathsome world
    Than these poor compounds that thou mayst not sell. 60
    I sell thee poison, thou hast sold me none.
    Come, cordial° and not poison, go with me
    To Juliet's grave, for there must I use thee.

> [*Exeunt.*]

SCENE 2. *Verona. Friar Laurence's cell. Thursday evening.*

> [FRIAR LAURENCE *hears someone calling from outside his cell.*]

FRIAR JOHN (*outside*). Holy Franciscan friar! Brother, ho!
FRIAR LAURENCE. This same should be the voice of Friar John.

> [FRIAR JOHN *comes in hurriedly.*]

Welcome from Mantua. What says Romeo?
    Or if his mind be writ, give me his letter.
FRIAR JOHN. Going to find a barefoot brother out,   5
    One of our order, to associate° me,

42. **ducats** (dŭk′ăts): gold coins, worth about $2.25 each.   43. **gear:** stuff.   47. **utters them:** sells them illegally.   57. **dispatch:** kill.   62. **cordial:** a sweet drink.   6. **associate:** accompany.

Here in this city° visiting the sick,
And finding him, the searchers of the town,
Suspecting that we both were in a house
Where the infectious pestilence° did reign,   10
Sealed up the doors and would not let us forth,
So that my speed to Mantua there was stayed.
FRIAR LAURENCE. Who bare° my letter, then, to Romeo?
FRIAR JOHN (*taking letter from his robes*). I could not send it — here it is again —
Nor get a messenger to bring it thee,   15
So fearful were they of infection.
FRIAR LAURENCE. Unhappy fortune! Friar John, go hence.
Get me an iron crow° and bring it straight
Unto my cell.

                [*Exit* FRIAR JOHN.]

Now must I to the monument alone;   20
Within this three hours will fair Juliet wake.
But I will write again to Mantua,
And keep her at my cell till Romeo come —
Poor living corse, closed in a dead man's tomb.

                [*Exit* FRIAR LAURENCE.]

SCENE 3. *Verona. A churchyard; the tomb of the Capulets.*
Late at night, Thursday.

[*The churchyard is silent and dark. Great stone burial vaults, as large as houses,
rise up from the ground like huge shadows. Their stone doors are sealed; within
the vaults lie the bodies of families whose names are carved above the entrance-
ways. A single torch suddenly lights the gloomy scene as* PARIS *and his* PAGE
enter.]

PARIS. Give me thy torch, boy. Hence, and stand aloof.°
    Yet put it out, for I would not be seen.

[*The* PAGE *puts out the torch and hands it to* PARIS. *The* PAGE *leaves.* PARIS *stands
looking toward the Capulet monument where* JULIET *lies.*]

Sweet flower, with flowers thy bridal bed I strew.
Oh, woe! Thy canopy° is dust and stones.
The obsequies° that I for thee will keep   5
Nightly shall be to strew thy grave and weep.

[*The* PAGE's *whistle warns that someone is coming.* PARIS *thinks that grave robbers
must be entering the churchyard.*]

7. **this city**: that is, Verona; Friar John reveals that he was not able even to start for Mantua.
10. **pestilence**: an epidemic disease.   13. **bare**: bore; carried.   18. **crow**: crowbar.
1. **aloof**: at a distance.   4. **canopy**: an overhead covering.   5. **obsequies** (ŏb'sĕ·kwĭz):
burial ceremonies.

The boy gives warning something doth approach.
What cursèd foot wanders this way tonight,
To cross my obsequies and true love's rite?
What, with a torch! Muffle me, night, awhile.   10

[PARIS *hides as* ROMEO *and* BALTHASAR *enter with a torch and tools.*]

ROMEO. Give me that mattock and the wrenching iron.°
    Hold, take this letter. Early in the morning
    See thou deliver it to my lord and father.
    Give me the light. Upon thy life, I charge thee,
    Whate'er thou hear'st or seest, stand all aloof,   15
    And do not interrupt me in my course.
    Why I descend into this bed of death
    Is partly to behold my lady's face,
    But chiefly to take thence from her dead finger
    A precious ring, a ring that I must use   20
    In dear employment.° Therefore hence, be gone.
    But if thou, jealous,° dost return to pry,
    By Heaven, I will tear thee joint by joint
    And strew this hungry churchyard with thy limbs.
BALTHASAR. I will be gone, sir, and not trouble you.   25
ROMEO. So shalt thou show me friendship. Take thou that.

[*He gives* BALTHASAR *some money.*]

Live and be prosperous, and farewell, good fellow.

[*Exit* BALTHASAR.]

Thou detestable maw,° thou womb of death,
Gorged with the dearest morsel of the earth,
Thus I enforce thy rotten jaws to open,   30
And in despite I'll cram thee with more food.

[*With the tools* ROMEO *pries open the entrance to the Capulet tomb.* PARIS *watches him from the darkness of his hiding place.*]

PARIS. This is that banished haughty Montague
    That murdered my love's cousin, with which grief
    It is supposèd the fair creature died,
    And here is come to do some villainous shame   35
    To the dead bodies. I will apprehend° him. (*He steps forward out of the shadows.*)
    Stop thy unhallowed toil, vile Montague!
    Can vengeance be pursued further than death?

[*It is too dark for* ROMEO *to identify his challenger.* PARIS *steps closer to him.*]

---

11. **mattock . . . wrenching iron:** a tool similar to a pickax, used for digging, and a crowbar.
21. **In dear employment:** to wear in her memory.   22. **jealous:** curious.   28. **maw:** stomach.   36. **apprehend:** seize.

Condemnèd villain, I do apprehend thee.
Obey, and go with me, for thou must die.   40
ROMEO. I must indeed, and therefore came I hither.
Good gentle youth, tempt not a desperate man.
Fly hence and leave me. Oh, be gone!
By Heaven, I love thee better than myself,
For I come hither armed against myself.   45
Stay not, be gone. Live, and hereafter say
A madman's mercy bid thee run away.
PARIS. I do defy thy conjurations°
And apprehend thee for a felon° here.
ROMEO. Wilt thou provoke me? Then have at thee, boy!   50

[They draw their swords and fight.]

PAGE. Oh, Lord, they fight! I will go call the watch.°

[He runs off.]

PARIS (*staggers and falls*). Oh, I am slain! If thou be merciful,
Open the tomb, lay me with Juliet. (PARIS *dies.*)
ROMEO (*holds up his torch*). In faith, I will. Let me peruse° this face.
Mercutio's kinsman, noble County Paris!   55
What said my man,° when my betossèd soul
Did not attend him as we rode? I think
He told me Paris should have married Juliet.
Said he not so? Or did I dream it so?
Or am I mad, hearing him talk of Juliet,   60
To think it was so? Oh, give me thy hand,
One writ with me in sour misfortune's book!°
I'll bury thee in a triumphant grave —
A grave? Oh, no, a lantern,° slaughtered youth.
For here lies Juliet, and her beauty makes   65
This vault a feasting presence° full of light.
Death, lie thou there, by a dead man interred.°

*[ROMEO gently carries the body of PARIS into the vault. Now at last he looks upon
the face of Juliet.]*

O my love, my wife!
Death, that hath sucked the honey of thy breath,
Hath had no power yet upon thy beauty.   70

---

48. **conjurations** (kŏn′joo·rā′shŭnz): solemn appeals. Paris suspects that Romeo intends to do
harm to the dead bodies: perhaps to attempt to communicate with the spirits by means of
black magic. His use of the word *conjurations* can thus have two meanings: he resists Romeo's
appeal and his efforts to practice magic. 49. **felon:** criminal.   51. **watch:** the sentries.
54. **peruse** (pě·rooz′): inspect carefully.   56. **my man:** Balthasar, who told Romeo about
Paris as they rode back to Verona.   62. **One . . . book:** You and I have both met with evil
fates.   64. **lantern:** an open structure, with windows, set in the roof of a hall to give additional light.   66. **presence:** the "Presence Chamber" was the great hall where the Queen held
court.   67. **interred** (ĭn·tùrd′): buried.

Thou art not conquered; beauty's ensign° yet
Is crimson in thy lips and in thy cheeks,
And death's pale flag is not advancèd there.
Ah, dear Juliet,
Why art thou yet so fair?   75
Here, here will I remain,
With worms that are thy chambermaids. Oh, here
Will I set up my everlasting rest,
And shake the yoke of inauspicious° stars
From this world-wearied flesh. Eyes, look your last!   80
Arms, take your last embrace! And lips, oh, you
The doors of breath, seal with a righteous kiss
A dateless bargain to engrossing death.°
Here's to my love! (*He takes out the poison and drinks it.*) O true apothe-
cary!
Thy drugs are quick. Thus with a kiss I die. (*He dies.*)   85

[*In the churchyard outside the tomb,* FRIAR LAURENCE *appears with a lantern,*
crowbar, and spade.]

FRIAR LAUPENCE. Saint Francis be my speed! How oft tonight
Have my old feet stumbled at graves! Who's there?

[*A figure appears; it is* BALTHASAR, *who has disobeyed his master Romeo and*
stayed close by in case he should be needed.]

BALTHASAR. Here's one, a friend, and one that knows you well.
FRIAR LAURENCE. Go with me to the vault.
BALTHASAR.   I dare not, sir.
FRIAR LAURENCE. Stay, then; I'll go alone. Fear comes upon me —   90
Oh, much I fear some ill unlucky thing.
(*He starts into the tomb and calls.*) Romeo!
Alack, alack, what blood is this which stains
The stony entrance of this sepulcher?° (*Now inside the tomb, he sees the*
bodies of Romeo and Paris.)
Romeo! Oh, pale! Who else? What, Paris too?   95
And steeped in blood? Ah, what an unkind hour
Is guilty of this lamentable chance!
The lady stirs.
                          [JULIET *wakes.*]

JULIET. O comfortable° friar, where is my lord?
I do remember well where I should be,   100
And there I am. Where is my Romeo?

[*They hear shouts of the approaching guards, who have been summoned by the*
PAGE.]

71. **ensign** (ĕn′sĭn): banner.   79. **inauspicious** (in′ôs·pĭsh′ŭs): unlucky.   83. **A dateless . . . death:** an eternal agreement with death, who wins everything.   94. **sepulcher**
(sĕp′ŭl·kẽr): tomb.   99. **comfortable:** comforting.

FRIAR LAURENCE. I hear some noise. Lady, come from that nest
    Of death, contagion, and unnatural sleep.
    A greater power than we can contradict
    Hath thwarted our intents.° Come, come away.   105
    Thy husband in thy bosom there lies dead,
    And Paris too. Come, I'll dispose of thee
    Among a sisterhood of holy nuns.
    Stay not to question, for the watch is coming.
    Come, go, good Juliet, I dare no longer stay.   110
JULIET. Go, get thee hence, for I will not away.

       [FRIAR LAURENCE *hurries from the tomb.* JULIET *looks at* ROMEO.]

    What's here? A cup, closed in my true love's hand?
    Poison, I see, hath been his timeless° end.
    Oh, churl!° Drunk all, and left no friendly drop
    To help me after?° I will kiss thy lips —   115
    Haply some poison yet doth hang on them
    To make me die with a restorative.° (*She bends down and kisses* ROMEO.)
    Thy lips are warm. (*She hears voices nearby.*)
CHIEF WATCHMAN. Lead, boy. Which way?
JULIET. Yea, noise? Then I'll be brief. O happy dagger! (*She snatches Romeo's*
    dagger.)   120
    This is thy sheath. There rust, and let me die.

[*She plunges the dagger into her heart. As she falls dead on Romeo's body, the*
   CHIEF WATCHMAN *enters the tomb. With him is the* PAGE.]

PAGE. This is the place — there, where the torch doth burn.
CHIEF WATCHMAN. The ground is bloody. Search about the churchyard. (*He shouts*
    orders to other guards outside the tomb.)
    Go, some of you, whoe'er you find attach.° (*He gazes in horror at the*
    scene.)
    Go tell the Prince. Run to the Capulets,   125
    Raise up the Montagues.

[*The tomb echoes with the sound of hurrying footsteps. Outside, the graveyard*
air rings with orders and commands. BALTHASAR *and* FRIAR LAURENCE *are found*
by the guards and led back to the tomb. Word of the tragedy spreads through
the town with astonishing speed; the graveyard is soon crowded with onlookers.
Summoned from their homes, LORD *and* LADY CAPULET *and* LORD MONTAGUE *are*
brought to the tomb. (Grief over the exile of her son has caused the death of
Lady Montague.) PRINCE ESCALUS *himself arrives and enters the tomb. From*
FRIAR LAURENCE *he and the others learn of the events that led to the deaths of*
Paris, Romeo, and Juliet. FRIAR LAURENCE *now tells of the secret marriage of*

---

    105. thwarted our intents: ruined our plans.   **113. timeless:** untimely; early.   **114. churl:**
rude, ill-bred fellow.   **115. after:** follow after.   **116–17. Haply . . . restorative:** Perhaps
some poison left on them will kill me — though a kiss from the living Romeo would return me
to life.   **124. whoe'er . . . attach:** arrest anyone you may find near here.

Romeo and Juliet; of how she drank a liquid that made her appear dead so that she might escape a marriage to Paris. It is Romeo's servant, BALTHASAR, *who reveals that he has a letter for Romeo's father. The* PRINCE *reads this letter, which discloses Romeo's plan to poison himself. The fatal duel between Romeo and Paris is told by the* PAGE, *who was an eyewitness.* PRINCE ESCALUS *turns sadly to* LORD *and* LADY CAPULET *and to* LORD MONTAGUE. *What has happened here tonight is now fully understood; but the* PRINCE *points to the cause behind these events.*]

PRINCE ESCALUS. Capulet! Montague!
    See what a scourge° is laid upon your hate
    That Heaven finds means to kill your joys with love!
    And I, for winking at your discords° too,   130
    Have lost a brace° of kinsmen. All are punished.

[*But now there are no protests or shouts for vengeance from the two families or their servants. Tragedy has stifled their anger and ended their bitterness. In the mutual loss of their children, they are no longer enemies. All of them are punished, as Prince Escalus has said.* LORD CAPULET, *his steps slowed by grief, approaches* LORD MONTAGUE.]

LORD CAPULET. O Brother Montague, give me thy hand.
    This is my daughter's jointure,° for no more
    Can I demand.

            [*They clasp hands.*]

LORD MONTAGUE.   But I can give thee more.
    For I will raise her statue in pure gold,   135
    That whiles Verona by that name is known
    There shall no figure at such rate° be set
    As that of true and faithful Juliet.

      [*The first light of sunrise filters into the tomb.*]

PRINCE ESCALUS. A glooming° peace this morning with it brings,
    The sun for sorrow will not show his head.   140
    Go hence, to have more talk of these sad things.
    Some shall be pardoned and some punishèd.
    For never was a story of more woe
    Than this of Juliet and her Romeo.

         [*Exeunt.*]

      [*The curtain falls.*]

128. **scourge** (skûrj): punishment.   130. **for winking . . . discords:** for not taking seriously and soon enough your quarrels with each other.   131. **brace:** a pair. Mercutio, as well as Paris, was a relative of the Prince.   133. **jointure:** dowry, the gift of goods or money a woman customarily gave her husband at marriage.   137. **at such rate:** of such value. 139. **glooming:** dark.

DRAWING TOGETHER THE THREADS OF THE PLOT

1. Why is Friar Laurence's message to Romeo not delivered?

2. What news does Romeo receive from Balthasar? What plan does he then make?

3. Why does Balthasar disobey the orders given him in the Verona churchyard?

4. For what reasons do Romeo and Paris happen to meet in the churchyard? Why does Romeo at first fail to recognize Paris?

5. Why does Juliet refuse to escape from the tomb with Friar Laurence?

THINKING IT OVER

1. There are several scenes in the play in which Shakespeare's characters speak in prose — ordinary conversation — rather than verse. This is done frequently in comedy scenes, often involving servants. For example, in Act I, the servant who cannot read speaks in prose. Why does Balthasar not speak in prose at the beginning of Act V?

2. What changes have taken place in the character of Juliet by the end of Act IV? Compare her with the Juliet of Act I.

3. The Romeo of Act I is one kind of young man. Contrast that Romeo with the Romeo of Act V.

4. Accidental happenings and coincidence as well as personal decisions influence the chain of events, or plot, of *Romeo and Juliet*. Explain which of the following is the result of choices made deliberately by Romeo or Juliet, or the result of accident or coincidence:

a. Romeo's attendance at the masked ball
b. Romeo's overhearing Juliet's declaration of love for him
c. the death of Mercutio; of Tybalt
d. Romeo's failure to receive Friar Laurence's message
e. the death of Paris
f. Romeo's death; Juliet's death

5. When we first see Friar Laurence, he is comparing plants to men. What theme of the play do we discover in his speech at that time (Act II, Scene 3, lines 1–7)? How is the theme stated at the end of

Act II, and how is it brought out again by the conclusion of the play?

6. *Dramatic irony* is the term used to describe a situation in which the audience is informed of facts that the characters do not know. Shakespeare often uses dramatic irony to heighten suspense or to create humor. One situation involving dramatic irony occurs when Mercutio does not understand Romeo's refusal to fight Tybalt. Pick out three other situations in which dramatic irony is found. Can you select one involving Romeo, one involving Juliet, and one involving Paris?

ABOUT THE AUTHOR

William Shakespeare (1564–1616) was born in Stratford, a village located on the Avon River, in Warwickshire, England. Because records were kept so informally, we lack a great many facts about the life of Shakespeare. But reason can be found to believe that young Will attended a good high school in Stratford, studying Latin and Greek and the English Bible, like other schoolboys of his time. Formal schooling seems to have ended for him when he was fourteen, and for a while he may have served as a schoolmaster. At eighteen he married Anne Hathaway, and three children were born to them. By 1590 Will Shakespeare had moved to London, where he entered the world of the theater. Most likely he served an apprenticeship, acting in minor roles and doing the odd jobs required of a man preparing for an actor's life. His first plays were *The Comedy of Errors* and *Love's Labor's Lost*. Shakespeare's career as an actor was eventually outstripped by his success as a playwright, although he continued to appear on the stage for many years in his own plays.

Romeo and Juliet was written and produced early in his career. From about 1590 until well after he retired in 1610, Shakespeare wrote as many as two plays a year. From the testimony of his friends and fellow playwrights it is clear that he was always a modest man; he was often called "gentle Will Shakespeare."

At his death he was buried in the parish church of his home town, Stratford, where he had retired.

AFTERWORD:

PERFORMING *Romeo and Juliet*

by *Guthrie McClintic and Katharine Cornell*

In "Girl with a Dream: Katharine Cornell" on page 232, an account is given of Katharine Cornell's acting career. Among the many famous roles she has played is that of
Juliet. The production — one of the most successful ever presented on Broadway — was
staged by her husband, the celebrated director, Guthrie McClintic. Prior to his death in
1961, Guthrie McClintic wrote, as a special feature for this edition of *Romeo and Juliet,*
his suggestions about performing the play, either as classroom scenes or as a school production. Katharine Cornell follows with her comments about playing Juliet.

Guthrie McClintic: The Play

The production of *Romeo and Juliet* that I directed on Broadway had many
sets, a ton of lighting equipment, and trunkloads of props and costumes. But now
look, if you will, at the photograph on this page. It shows the single setting devised
for *Romeo and Juliet* by the New York Shakespeare Festival for production in a
number of high schools. You will notice how simple the setting is: a platform,
benches, a railing, some chairs, and a curtained screen. Yet, by rearranging these
simple furnishings, it was possible to represent all of the scenes in *Romeo and
Juliet* — the town square of Verona, the ballroom of the Capulets, the garden (the
railing, placed on the platform, became Juliet's balcony), the cell of Friar Laurence, a street in Mantua, and the Capulet tomb. If you were to decide to present
Romeo and Juliet as a school play, a similar setting would serve you very well.

But perhaps it is your plan to present only a scene or two from this great drama, to be performed in the classroom. Whether you do the complete play or merely excerpts from it, my recommendations would be the same.

Do not, first of all, approach the play solemnly. *Romeo and Juliet* is an action-packed story of two young people facing terrible odds. It is an exhilarating play to perform. Forget that it is a tragedy. Enjoy the play for the exciting drama that it is; let the tragedy take care of itself.

Listen to the words of the play. Listen carefully to them, for therein lies your chief task in performing Shakespeare: attention to the words that he wrote so magnificently. Shakespeare chose to arrange his words in verse form, and perhaps the thought of trying to speak poetry has filled you with misgivings. I would heartily recommend that you forget, at the start, that it is poetry you will be speaking. Study the words for their *meaning*. If you do that, the poetry will gradually take care of itself.

For the first few rehearsals you will probably concentrate on simply reading Shakespeare's lines for meaning and pronunciation. Then — if it is a full production you are doing — your director will want to start rehearsing the physical action in the play. *Romeo and Juliet* is a drama of violent and almost continuous action. It contains fights and street brawls, duels; the action continues at reckless speed to the very end. All of this action must be planned as carefully as your school football team would map out its plays for Saturday's big game. The boys in the cast will have to learn something about fencing; perhaps the school athletic coach or the director of your local recreation center could serve as instructor. The same care must be used in planning the ballroom sequence: the dance at the Capulets' must be plotted and rehearsed with as much care as you would prepare a school dance recital.

What I have been urging, in these remarks, can be briefly summed up. If you plan to perform *Romeo and Juliet* — the whole play or simply a scene from it — be willing to give it time and attention to detail. Do not be solemn about it; it is a play of youth and action. Give foremost attention to the words of Shakespeare; speak them as he intended, not self-consciously as poetry, but as words that convey the passion, happiness, and heartbreak of life.

G. McC.

Katharine Cornell: Playing Juliet

Our production of *Romeo and Juliet* opened on Broadway on a frosty night in December. The day of a New York opening is a nerve-racking time. Usually I try to rest, but the prospect of playing Juliet was too exciting for me. On the afternoon of the opening, I went out for a walk and wound up at the theater instead. Suddenly fright overcame me. This time you've bitten off more than you can chew, I thought. My mind went back over the months of work which had preceded this day. I tried to follow again the course I had charted for my portrayal of Juliet. The steps are still fresh in my mind, and perhaps they will be of help to all the Juliets who have just read this beautiful play and might perhaps perform in it at school.

The key to Juliet is that she is young — not quite fourteen. Other actresses have played her as eighteen. But to me it seemed as if that extra four years would have made Juliet a far different character. Juliet, a few weeks short of her fourteenth birthday, has all the innocence and confusion of that age — and the impulsiveness which sometimes finds her taking action before really thinking a problem through. Young, very young, and impulsive — that is Juliet. Would she have eloped with Romeo, drunk Friar Laurence's potion, stabbed herself in the tomb — would she have done any of these things had she been older or wiser in the ways of life?

Her age, then, was my starting point for my portrayal of the role. I was over thirty at that time, but you who read this will be nearer Juliet's age. Bringing the point of view of youth to the role will require no work for you. For you the challenge will be to portray a young girl of fourteenth-century Italy, the daughter of a wealthy noble family. Juliet cannot behave as a young girl of today would behave. She must be more formal in manner, reflecting the customs and etiquette of the period in which she lived. To get a "feeling" of this period, it might help to visit a museum or the art section of your library; study the paintings, costumes, and architecture of the period. Imagine yourself placed in that splendid, different world. How would you have walked? spoken? behaved at a ball? Play some recordings of early Italian music. As you listen, imagine Juliet dancing to the music. A picture of her will come to you; use it as the basis for your portrayal. Use your imagination — I suppose that's what I'm trying to say. With the picture of a young girl of six hundred years ago clear in your mind, move on to the next step — the incomparable words Shakespeare has given Juliet to speak. You cannot spend too much time working on these words. Know the meaning of every syllable of every line. In a notebook, write out Juliet's speeches (writing out a speech is a good way to memorize it), and below each line write out the meaning as you understand it. The fact that you will be speaking poetry should not trouble you — not if you give thought to what you are saying, rather than the fact that it is written in the form of verse.

At the beginning of the play, Juliet is a young girl whom life has not touched yet. At the end she is a tragic woman who chooses to die with Romeo rather than live without him. To portray the growth and maturing of Juliet during the course of the play is the most difficult challenge that confronts any actress who attempts the role. But it will help you to realize that you are playing, in effect, two roles: a young girl and a woman.

Above everything, consider the words of the play. Use your imagination to form a picture of Juliet and then try to re-create that picture.

K. C.

Drama

SUGGESTIONS FOR FURTHER READING

PLAYS

Alexander, Ronald, *Time Out for Ginger* (Dramatists Play Service, 1953)
  A girl's father encourages her to join the high school football team, as a bid for equality for women.
Barrie, Sir James Matthew, *The Admirable Crichton*
  A British lord and his butler change places when their party is shipwrecked on an island. Don't forget *Peter Pan* and *What Every Woman Knows*, two other Barrie favorites.
Chodorov, Jerome, and Joseph Fields, *Junior Miss* (Dramatists Play Service, 1941)
  A little girl plays Miss-Fix-It with her family.
Galbraith, Esther E., ed., *Plays Without Footlights* (Harcourt, Brace & World, 1945)
  Short plays for teen-age readers.
Hackett, Walter, *Radio Plays for Young People* (Plays, Inc., 1950)
  Famous stories adapted for radio. Royalty-free.
Hart, Moss, and George S. Kaufman, *Six Plays by Kaufman and Hart* (Random House, 1942)
  Entertaining comedies, including *You Can't Take It with You.*
Lindsay, Howard, and Russel Crouse, *Life with Father* and *Life with Mother* (Knopf, 1950)
  Two plays based on Clarence Day's famous recollections of his parents.
Mayorga, Margaret, ed., *Best One-Act Plays* (Dodd, Mead, publ. annually since 1937)
  Short plays, each volume comprising that year's "best."
Miller, Helen Louise, *On Stage for Teenagers* (Plays, Inc., 1948)
  Twenty-two one-act comedies. Royalty-free.
Rodgers, Richard, and Oscar Hammerstein II, *Six Plays* (Random House, 1955)
  Included are the great Rodgers and Hammerstein musical hits.

GENERAL

Berk, Barbara, *How to Have a Show* (Franklin Watts, 1957)
  The do's and don'ts of preparing a show.
Cornberg, Sol, and Emanuel L. Gebauer, *A Stage Crew Handbook* (Harper, 1957)
  Helpful ideas for building stage sets.
Ommanney, Katharine Anne, *The Stage and the School* (McGraw-Hill, 1960)
  For students interested in theater, both in school and as a career.

SHAKESPEARE

Chute, Marchette, *Stories from Shakespeare* (New American Library, 1956)
  Thirty-six plays told simply and clearly in prose. *Wonderful Winter* (Dutton, 1954). A boy runs away from home and joins Shakespeare's acting troupe. *Shakespeare of London* ° (Dutton, 1949). A superior biography of the great writer.
Lamb, Charles and Mary, *Tales from Shakespeare* (Dutton, 1958)
  Twenty plays told as short stories, illustrated by Arthur Rockham.
Norman, Charles, *Playmaker of Avon* (McKay, 1949)
  A Shakespeare biography for teen-agers.
Shakespeare, William, *As You Like It*
  Mistaken identities make for fun in this play about young people. *A Midsummer Night's Dream*. Another good introduction to Shakespeare's comedies.
Van Doren, Mark, *Shakespeare* (Doubleday, 1953)
  A view of Shakespeare by a noted literary critic.
Webster, Margaret, *Shakespeare Without Tears* (World Publishing, 1955)
  The problems and pleasures of producing Shakespeare.

FOR YOUR LISTENING

  Scenes from *Romeo and Juliet* can be heard on longplay record *Many Voices* 9B.

° Included in *Four English Biographies*, Priestley and Davis, eds. (Harcourt, Brace & World, 1961).

The Epic Tale

The *Iliad* and the *Odyssey* have been called the world's first great adventure stories. The author of both of these stories in verse is the Greek poet Homer. In the *Iliad* the long struggle of the Greeks to capture the walled fortress city of Troy is told in exciting, often blood-curdling detail.

The *Odyssey* is the story of one of the Greek chiefs, a crafty and bold warrior king by the name of Odysseus. It was he who thought up the idea of having a wooden horse built in order to trick the Trojans into believing that their enemy had retreated and was giving up the ten-year battle for Troy. It was Odysseus who, though longing for his family and home on the island of Ithaca, was destined to wander the seas for another ten years because he had offended certain gods who favored the Trojans during the bitter war.

What a tale of adventure this *Odyssey* tells! Until the gods took pity on him and finally let him return to his island kingdom, Odysseus had to suffer many hardships. Nothing, however, could make him forget his wish to get home.

The *Odyssey*, like the *Iliad*, is an epic, a long narrative poem about one heroic man told in a particular poetic rhythm. Epics are found in the literature of nearly every country. In ancient Greece the tellers of such tales wandered from the court of one great king to another, sometimes carrying messages but always singing or chanting poems about a marvelous, godlike hero who faced many adventures. Each adventure, or story, was called an "epos"; together the stories made up the poem,

◀ The original of this bronze statue of the Greek mythological god Zeus was found in the sea off the Grecian coast, undamaged despite its age. It dates back to the fifth century B.C. Shown here is the proud head of Zeus, a symbol of Greek art which, like the *Odyssey*, has survived the centuries and continued to inspire man.

which eventually came to be called an epic. And it often happened that the hero of these tales bore a remarkable resemblance to an ancestor of the king at whose court the epic was being sung!

Not only kings but commoners could find something of themselves in the poems which praised the bravery or loyalty or daring of a great hero. And so the tales were sung and handed down through the generations, long before writing came into general use. It made people proud that someone of their kingdom or nation had dared such valiant deeds.

As you join Odysseus now, he is relating part of his story to a king to whose country he has come after being shipwrecked in a heavy storm. Ragged and worn, Odysseus still makes a vivid impression on his rescuers. As you read his words, you too will be struck by the skill he shows in coping with danger.

Be watchful of this man: he is sometimes conceited but always courageous; he is understanding of other men and their motives; he is quick-witted in emergencies— But you will want to discover for yourself the many other qualities which he possesses.

The journey of Odysseus.

The Odyssey

by HOMER

[Odysseus * is in the banquet hall of Alcinoüs,* king of Phæacia,* who helps him on his way after all his comrades have been killed and his last vessel destroyed. Odysseus tells the story of his adventures thus far.]

I am
Odysseus, great Laërtes'° son,
For cunning plans of every kind
Known among men; and even to heaven
Has spread my fame. My native land   5
Is Ithaca,° a sun-bright island
Low of shore which lies far out
To sea and toward the west. Rugged
It is, this land of mine, yet breeds
A sturdy youth, and I can find   10
No land more sweet to me than this,
My native Ithaca.
                    But come,
For I will tell the many sorrows
Zeus° sent upon me as I traveled
Homeward from hapless Troy.   15

THE LAND OF THE LOTUS-EATERS

Great Zeus, who guides the clouds, sent
    forth
Against our ships a wild north wind,
A raging tempest, and enshrouded
In dark clouds land and sea. Deep night
Came rolling from on high. Our ships

Drove headlong, while their sails were
    riven   21
Asunder by that gale; but these
We stored beneath the decks, still toil-
    ing
In dread of death, and striving ever,
Rowed on and reached the land   25
Where dwell the Lotus-eaters, men
Whose food is flowers. And we all
Here went ashore and drew us water,
And by the sides of their swift ships
My men prepared their meal. And now
When we at last had had our fill   31
Of meat and drink, I sent forth men
To learn what manner of mankind
That live by bread might dwell here.
    Two
I chose to go and sent with them   35
A third, a herald. And these quickly
Went forth into that land and mingled
Among the Lotus-eaters. Never
Did these men, eaters of the lotus,
Plan evil to my men, and yet   40
They gave them of the lotus flower
And bade them eat of it, and lo,
Whatever man of them but tasted
That blossom strange and honey-sweet,
Naught cared he then to hasten back
With tidings to the ships, or ever   46
Turn homeward any more, but longed
To dwell there with the Lotus-eaters,
And pluck and eat the lotus blossoms
And think no more of home.
                    But these   50
I brought back to the ships by force,

* **Odysseus** (ō·dĭs'ūs); **Alcinoüs** (ăl·sĭn'ō-ŭs); **Phæacia** (fē·ā'shá). 2. **Laërtes** (lå·ûr'tēz). 6. **Ithaca** (ĭth'å·ká): an island off the west coast of Greece. 14. **Zeus** (zūs): chief of the gods, ruler of the elements; the thunderbolt is his sign.

Selections from *The Odyssey of Homer*, translated by Herbert Bates. Copyright, 1929, by McGraw-Hill Book Company, Inc. Reprinted by permission of the publishers.

Though they lamented, and I dragged
  them
Aboard the hollow ships and bound
  them
Beneath the benches. Then I bade
The rest, my true companions, hasten
Aboard the ships, lest one of them   56
Taste of the lotus, too, and lose
All memory of home. So straightway
They came aboard and sat them down
In order on the thwarts° and smote   60
The foaming sea with oars.

THE CYCLOPS

                              So thence
We sailed upon our way sad-hearted.
And now we came unto the land
Where dwell the Cyclopes° — those
  proud
And lawless beings, who, with trust
In the undying gods, plow not   66
Nor plant with hands a single plant.
Yet crops spring up for them unsown
On fields untended — wheat and barley
And vines that bear full-clustered
  grapes   70
To make them wine. The rain of Zeus
Still brings increase in all. These men
Have neither meeting place for council
Nor settled laws. They live apart
On lofty mountain ridges, dwelling 75
In hollow caverns. Each makes laws
For wife and child, and gives no heed
To any save himself.
                      Thither we sailed
Seeking the land. Surely it was
Some god that gave us guidance thither
Through the dense night, for we could
  see   81
Nothing before our eyes: the mist
Shut close about the ships; no moon
Showed forth in heaven, for clouds en-
  closed it.
So no man with his eyes beheld   85

60. **thwarts** (thôrts): the rowers' seats in a
boat. 64. **Cyclopes** (sī·klō′pēz): plural form
of Cyclops (sī′klŏps).

That isle or saw the long seas rolling
Against the land till we had beached
Our well-benched ships.
                          Now we looked
And saw not far away the mainland
Where dwelt the Cyclopes. We saw   90
Smoke rise, and heard the speech of
  men
And bleat of sheep and goats. Then
  came
The setting of the sun and darkness; 93
And there we slept beside the breakers.
But when the earliest dawn appeared
Rose-fingered, then I called together
My men and spoke to all:
                          "Rest here,
Dear comrades, while with my own ship
And my own men I go to learn
What men these are — if wild and cruel
And ignorant of right, or kind   101
To every stranger and with hearts
That fear the gods."

                        Now when we reached
That land that lay hard by, we saw
Upon its utmost point a cave   105
Close to the sea: high-roofed it was,
With laurel overhung, and many
The flocks of sheep and goats that there
Found shelter in the night. Around it
A courtyard lay, high-walled with
  stones   110
Set deep in earth, with lofty pines
And high-leaved oaks.
                        Within this lair
A man was wont° to sleep, a monster
Who grazed his sheep far off, alone,
Nor ever mingled with his kind,   115
But lonely dwelt — lawless and evil.
And marvelously was he shapen —
This monstrous being, not like mortals
That live by bread, but like a peak
That rising rough with woods stands
  forth   120

113. **wont** (wŭnt): accustomed or used.

Apart from other hills.
                          And I
Now bade my trusty men to bide
Close by the ship and guard the ship,
But twelve I chose, the best of all,
And we set forth.
                          I bore with me   125
A goatskin filled with dark sweet wine,
Sweet and unmixed, a drink for gods.
Who drank that red wine, honey-sweet,
He took one cup, no more, and served it
Mingled with water twenty times   130
The measure of the wine, and yet
Up from the mixing bowl there rose
Rare scent and sweetness, till no man
Could find it easy to refrain
From drinking of that wine. I filled   135
A great skin with this, and I bore it
As I set forth, and bore besides
Food in a leathern sack. For now
My fearless heart foresaw a meeting
With a strange man of monstrous
    might —   140
A savage, scornful of the gods
And of man's law.
                          Straightway we reached
His cave and entered, but we found not
The man within. For far away
He herded, while they grazed at pas-
    ture,   145
His goodly flock. So on we passed
Far into that great cave and marveled
At all we saw within. Here stood
Crates heaped with cheese and here
    were pens
Crowded with lambs and kids.
                          My men
Besought me eagerly to carry   151
The cheeses thence, and come again
And loose the kids and lambs and drive
    them
In haste to our swift ship, then sail
Away o'er the salt sea. But this   155
I would not grant, though better far
Had I but done so! For I hoped
To look upon this man — he might
Give gifts of friendship. But, alas,

When he appeared, he was to bring
My poor men little joy!
                          So there   161
We kindled fire and of that cheese
We made an offering, and ate
Ourselves thereof, and sat and waited
Until at last he entered, driving   165
His flock before him.
                          He bore in
Dry wood to cook his meal, a load
Of wondrous weight, and down he flung
    it
Within the cave, with such a crash
We cowered back with fear and
    crouched   170
In the cave's corner. Then he drove
Into that spacious cave the sheep
That he must milk, and left the others —
The rams and goats — without, to roam
The high-walled court.
                          Then in its place   175
He set the massive rock that closed
The doorway of the cave: he raised it
Lightly aloft, a weight so vast
That never two and twenty wagons,
Four-wheeled and firmly built, might
    stir it   180
From where it lay on earth — so great
That towering crag was that he set
To close his door.
                          Now sat he down
And milked his sheep and bleating
    goats
That he might sup thereon. And now,
When he had labored busily   186
And finished every task, he stayed
And kindled up the fire and saw us
And asked us:
                          "Strangers, who are you,
And whence do you come sailing hither
Over the sea's wet ways? What er-
    rand   191
Can bring you hither? Or perchance
You wander purposeless, like robbers
Who rove the seas and venture life
To bring to strangers in far lands   195
An evil fortune."

So he spoke,
And at his words our hearts within us
Were crushed and broken, for we
    feared
The man's deep voice and monstrous
    body.   199
Yet I spoke up and answered, saying:
"We are Achæans° come from Troy;
We wander blown by every wind
Over the sea's great gulf, still striving
To reach our homes, yet ever go
On alien ways, by paths we never   205
Have willed to travel — so it pleases
Zeus to decree.
                    Now we come
Hither before your knees to pray you
Give welcome to your guests and grant
    us
Such gifts as guests should have. Re-
    spect,   210
O mighty one, the gods, for we
Are suppliants,° and Zeus avenges
The suppliant and stranger: he
Is god of strangers, watching over
Each worthy wanderer."
                    So I spoke,   215
And pitiless of heart, he answered:
"Stranger, you either are a fool
Or come from a far land, to bid me
Fear the gods! We Cyclopes
Fear not your ægis-wielding° Zeus   220
Nor any god above. For we
Are mightier far than they. I would not
Show mercy to your men or you
To shun the wrath of Zeus, nay, never
Unless my own heart bade. But
    come,   225
Tell me, where left you your good ship
When you came hither? Was it near
Or at the land's far end? Nay, tell me,
For I would know."
                    So asked he, striving

To trap the truth from me, but caught
    not   230
My tried mind unaware. So thus
With crafty words I spoke:
                    "The god
Who shakes the earth, Poseidon,° broke
My ship asunder, for he drove her
Upon the cliffs that line your land   235
And dashed her on the rocks. A tempest
Had blown us in from sea, and I
And these my comrades here but barely
Escaped sheer death."
                    So I replied.
He, cruel-hearted, made no answer,   240
But springing up, reached forth his
    hands
And seized my comrades. Two at once
He snatched up in his grasp and dashed
    them
To earth like helpless puppies. Forth
The brains flowed, moistening the
    ground.   245
Then limb from limb he tore their bod-
    ies
And made his meal, devouring them
Savagely as a lion bred
Among the mountains. Naught of them
He left uneaten — flesh or entrails   250
Or marrowy bones. And we cried out
In lamentation and uplifted
Our hands to Zeus, to see a deed
So horrible. Numb terror laid
Hold on our hearts.
                    And now the Cyclops,   255
When he had filled that monstrous belly
With flesh of men, and followed this
With draughts of unmixed milk, lay
    stretched
Full length upon the cavern floor
Among his flock.
                    And now I formed   260
This plan within my daring heart —
To venture nearer and to draw
My keen sword from my thigh and
    thrust it

201. **Achæans** (*à·kē'ănz*): term used for nearly all Greeks. 212. **suppliants** (*sŭp'lĭ-ănts*): those who earnestly beg or ask a favor. 220. **ægis-wielding** (*ē'jĭs-wēld'ĭng*): shield-bearing.

233. **Poseidon** (*pō·sī'dŏn*): god of the sea; the Romans called him Neptune.

Deep in his breast, straight to the spot
Where lay his liver, feeling first   265
To seek the place; and yet a thought
Withheld me, for we all, each man,
Must then have met sheer death; for
   never
Could our strength stir from that high
   door
The massive stone he set there. So   270
Lamenting there we sat and waited
The sacred dawn.
            And when the dawn
Came, rosy-fingered, then once more
He kindled fire and milked his flock
Of wondrous sheep, in order due,   275
Setting her young by each; and now
When he had labored busily
And finished every task, he seized
Once more upon two men and made
His morning meal. And after this,   280
His breakfast done, he drove away
His goodly flock, moving with ease
The mighty door-stone thence, then set
   it
In place as lightly as a man
Would set the lid upon a quiver.   285

And now I pondered how I best
Might find revenge, if but Athene°
Would hear my prayer. And this plan
   seemed
Best to my mind at last:
               There lay
Close by the pens, a mighty staff   290
Cut by the Cyclops. Olive wood
It was, still green, for he had cut it
To use when it had dried: it seemed,
As we stood gazing, the great mast
Of some broad ship of twenty oars,
Laden with cargo, a black ship   296
That sails the great gulf of the sea,
So long and thick it seemed. So there
I took my stand by it and cut
A fathom's length away, and this   300
I gave my men and bade them shape it.

287. **Athene** (*a·thē′nē*): also Athena, the
goddess of wisdom.

They made it smooth, while I stood by
And brought it to a point and charred it
In glowing fire; and then I took it
And hid it in the dung that lay   305
In heaps about the cave.
                            I bade then
My company cast lots to see
Which men of them would dare to join
    me
And lift that stake and bore it deep
Into his eye when gentle slumber   310
Should come upon him. And the lot
Fell on the four I should have chosen,
And I myself became the fifth
To share the venture.
                            And now came
The Cyclops home at evening, herding
His well-fleeced flocks. Straightway he
    drove   316
Into that cavern, one and all,
His goodly flocks, nor left he any
In the wide court without.° He felt,
Perhaps, some sense of coming evil;
Perhaps some god had warned him.
    Next   321
He set in place the massive door-stone,
Lifting it lightly, then once again
He seized on two of my companions
And made his evening meal.
                            And now   325
I stood before him, and thus spoke,
The while I held forth in my hands
An ivy bowl, filled with dark wine:
"Here, Cyclops, take this wine, and
    drink
After your feast of human flesh,   330
And learn how good a drink we kept
Hidden within our ship. I brought it
An offering to you, in hope
You might have pity on my sorrows
And help me home. But you, alas,   335
In rage exceed all patience! Madman!
How shall there ever come hereafter
Another stranger here to seek you
From any land on earth, if you
Thus scorn all human laws!"

                319. **without:** outside.

So said I.   340
He took the wine and drank it. Vastly
That sweet drink pleased him. And again
He begged of me:
                    "In goodness give me
Yet more, I pray. And tell me now
Your name, and quickly! I will give you
A gift to make your heart rejoice."   346
So thrice I bore that glowing wine
And gave it him, and thrice in folly
He drained it off. Then when the wine
Had stolen round his wits, I spoke   350
And said in honeyed words:
                            "O Cyclops,
You ask my far-famed name, and this
I now will tell. My name is Noman."
And he with cruel heart replied:
"Noman, of all his company,   355
I shall eat last. This shall be
My gift to you — my guest."
Then down he sank and on his back
Lay flat, his thick neck bent aside,
And from his throat there poured forth
    wine   360
And fragments of men's flesh.

                                    And now
Deep under heaped-up coals I thrust
That stake till it grew hot, and stirred
The courage of my men with speech
Lest one of them should shrink with
    fear   365
And fail my need.
                    And now that stake
Of olive wood, green as it was,
Was ready to burst forth in flame,
All glowing with fierce heat. I drew it
Forth from the fire, while round about
    me   370
My men stood ready. Then — for surely
Some god had breathed into our hearts
High courage — they laid hold upon
That sharpened olive stake and thrust it
Deep in his eye, the while above them
I leaned upon its top and turned it
As one who with an auger bores   377
A great ship timber. Those below him

Twist it by thongs on either side,
And still it ever turns unceasing.   380
So holding that huge stake of wood
Deep in his eye, we kept it turning.
Round that hot brand, forth poured the
   blood;
And round it all his brows and lashes
Were singed off by the blast that came
Out of that burning eye. Its roots   386
Seethed in the fire. As when a smith
Dips a great ax or adz° in water
To temper it, and loud it hisses —   389
For so steel gets its strength — even so
His eye hissed round that olive stake.
And loud his cry and terrible
Till the rocks echoed and we fled
Away in fear. Then from his eye
He wrenched away that stake, thick
   clotted   395
With his own blood and raging hurled
   it
Out of his hands. Then loud he shouted
To all the Cyclopes who dwelt
In caves upon the windy heights.

They heard his shout and straggling
   gathered,   400
One here, one there, from every side,
And standing all about his cave
They asked what grieved him.
                    "What can ail you,
O Polyphemus,° that so loudly
You cry out in the heavenly night   405
And keep us sleepless? Is some man,
Some mortal, driving off your flocks
Against your will; or is some man
Now slaying you by force or cunning?"
And thus in answer from his cave   410
Spoke mighty Polyphemus:
                    "Friends,
Noman is slaying me by cunning,
Nor uses force at all!"
                    And they

With winged words thus replied:
                    "Since no man
Now does you violence, while you   415
Are there alone, this illness sent
By mighty Zeus, no man may shun
In any way. But pray you now
To your great father, Lord Poseidon."

So said they and then went their way.
And in my heart I laughed to think   421
How with that name and my shrewd
   plan
I had deceived them.
                    But the Cyclops,
Groaning in agony and anguish,
Went groping with his hands, and lifted
The great rock from the door and
   there   426
He sat athwart° the doorway, stretch-
   ing
His hands, to catch, if it might be,
Any who sought to pass the door
Among the sheep; for in his heart   430
He hoped that I might prove so foolish
As thus to venture. But I still
Sat planning how to bring this peril
To a good end and win us all —   434
My men and me — escape. Full many
The plan and trick I fashioned, striving
For life itself, for great the peril
And close at hand. And at the last
This, as I deemed, was of them all
The wisest plan.
                    There in the cave   440
Were well-grown rams of thickest wool,
Fair beasts and great, and dark of
   fleece.
These silently I bound together
With twisted willow withes,° whereon
The Cyclops slept, that savage monster
Who knew no law nor right. I bound
   them   446
By threes together and the midmost
Bore under him a man; the others,

388. adz: a tool like an ax, but with a
curved blade set across the end of the handle.
404. Polyphemus (pŏl'ĭ·fē'mŭs): the name
of the Cyclops who has imprisoned Odysseus.

427. athwart (à·thwôrt'): across. 444. withes
(wĭths): slender twigs or branches, especially
those used as bands or ropes.

One on each side, were to conceal
And save my comrades: so there went
A man to each three sheep. And I,   451
Myself, now seized upon a ram,
The best of all that flock, and grasped
His back from underneath, and lay
Beneath his shaggy belly; there   455
Twisting my fingers deep within
That wondrous fleece, I hung, face up-
    ward,
With steadfast heart. And so, lament-
    ing,
We waited sacred dawn.
                                 And now,
When earliest dawn came rosy-fingered,
Then forth the rams went to the pas-
    ture,   461
But all the unmilked ewes went bleat-
    ing
About their pens with swollen udders.
Their lord, though torn by cruel pain,
Yet, ere each ram passed, made him
    stand   465
And felt along his back. He guessed not
In his dull mind that there beneath
Those fleecy breasts were bound my
    men.

Now to the door, last of them all,
The great ram slowly came, weighed
    down   470

With heavy fleece and with the burden
Of me and my shrewd plans. Upon him
The mighty Polyphemus then
Laid searching hands, and said:

     "Dear ram, 474
Why do you cross the cave so slowly,
Last of the flock? Till now, you never
Lagged thus, but ever first of all
Sped forth with mighty strides to crop
The soft bloom of the grass, and ever
Were first to reach the running wa-
 ters,   480
And first, when evening came, to long
To turn back home. And yet you now
Come last of all. Surely you sorrow
Over your lord's lost eye! A villain
Has quenched its sight — he and his
 crew   485
Of wretched fellows, mastering
My wits with wine, this fellow Noman!
Not yet, I say, has he escaped
The death that waits him. Would but
 you
Could know my thought and had the
 power   490
To speak in words and let me know
Where he is skulking from my wrath!
For I should smite him down and dash
His brains about the cave — here, there,
Aye, on the ground! By such a deed
My heart might find some ease from
 all   496
The evils that this worthless Noman
Has brought upon me."

     So he spoke,
And sent the ram forth through the
 doorway.

And now, when we were safe outside
That cavern and its yard, I loosed 501
My grip upon the great ram's fleece
And then unbound my men in turn,
Setting them free. And then in haste
We drove that flock before us —
 sheep   505
Most rich in fat, most long of stride —
And yet we often turned our heads

To glance behind us ere we came
Safe to our ship. Welcome indeed
We were to our dear comrades,
 snatched   510
From death itself; and yet they wept,
Lamenting those we lost. But this
I would not suffer, but forbade,
With lifted brows, all lamentation,
And bade them quickly bear aboard
Into the ship those many sheep 516
So fine of fleece, and sail away
Across the salt sea waves. And they
Went then aboard and took their seats
Each in his place, and smote with oars
The whitening sea.   521

THINKING IT OVER

1. What is the chief emotion expressed by Odysseus in the first 15 lines of the poem? The ancient Greeks, as they listened to these lines, probably would have experienced a strong reaction. Describe what that reaction most likely would have been.

2. The word *lotus* usually brings to mind the picture of a beautiful water lily. In Homer's story, however, the Lotus-eaters were people who ate the delicious flowerlike fruit of a tree that bore this name. What magic property was the fruit of the lotus supposed to have? What do we mean today by speaking of someone as a lotus-eater?

3. List the many tricks Odysseus uses to outwit the Cyclops. What does he gain by calling himself "Noman"?

4. Compare the way of life of the Cyclopes with that of the more civilized Odysseus and his crew. Take into account what Odysseus says of their farming, their religion, and their laws. Remember that ancient Greek laws of hospitality required that any stranger who came in peace to a man's home and was in need of help should be shown courtesy and be given the help he needed. Explain in what ways the reception accorded Odysseus and his men broke this honored tradition.

5. Use your dictionary to look up the origin of the word *Cyclops*. What other English words do you now recognize as "branches" of these roots?

[After this Odysseus lost more men and ships to some savage giants, and then came the year-long visit with the goddess Circe.° Following his adventure here, Odysseus made a journey into the Land of the Dead to find out, from the spirit of a famous prophet, just what things he must do in order to reach his native land. Before going onward, the men returned briefly to Circe's island, and here the goddess gave Odysseus some good advice.]

CIRCE'S WARNINGS

Then mighty Circe   521
Spoke thus, and said:
      "Now all these things
Are past and ended. Listen well
To what I have to tell. May heaven
Help you to heed it. You will first   525
Come to the Sirens, to those women
Who weave a magic spell that masters
All men who hear their song. For he
Who turns him from his way in folly
To hear the Sirens' song — no more   530
Shall he behold his wife and children
Coming to greet him, glad of heart
That he is home again. They sit,
These Sirens, in a grassy meadow,
And here they sing their clear, sweet song   535
And weave their spell. And all about them
Lie heaps of gleaming bones; and bodies
Shriveled, with shreds of skin.
      Row swiftly   538
And drive your ship till safely past.
But first mold honeyed wax and stop
Your comrades' ears, that none of them
May hear that song. Yet if you long

  ° Circe (sûr′sē).

With your own ears to hear it, bid them
First bind you hand and foot and lash you   544
Upright in your swift ship, your back
Against the mast, with ropes cast round you.
So you may listen with delight
And hear the Sirens' song. Yet first
Command your men that if you beg them
To set you free, they then must bind you   550
In faster lashings.
      When your men
Have urged your ship past these — what road
You next must take, I shall not tell you.
Take counsel with your heart, and choose.
I will make both ways plain. On one
Great rocks o'erhang the sea: against them   556
Roll in and break the mighty waves
Of dark-eyed Amphitrite.° Thence
No ship of man escapes, if once
She turn her thither. There together
Forevermore the planks of ships   561
And bodies of slain men go tossing
At will of rolling waves, and swept
By tempests of dread fire.
      There rise
Beside the other way two crags,   565
And one of these soars high to heaven
With pointed peak. About the summit
A cloud hangs ever, dark and sullen,
Nor ever passes thence. Nor ever
Does the clear light of heaven touch

  558. **Amphitrite** (ăm′fĭ·trī′tē): wife of Poseidon and goddess of the sea.

That peak, in summer or in harvest. 571
No mortal man might climb it — nay,
Nor find him foothold, though he had
A score of hands and feet, that rock
Rises so smooth, like polished stone
On every side. Midmost the front 576
Of this great crag, and deep in shadow
There lies a cave. Westward it looks
And toward the land of Death. And
    thither,
You must, illustrious Odysseus, 580
Steer with your ship.

               Within this cave
Dwells Scylla,° ever uttering
Her dreadful yelping cry, her voice
Shrill as a new-born whelp's. There
    dwells she,
A monstrous shape of evil. No one 585
Can see that sight unshaken, nay,
Not though a god should face her.
    Twelve
Her hanging feet are, and six necks
She stretches forth, on each a head
Hideous to see, and in each head 590
Teeth in three rows, close-set and bris-
    tling,
Filled with black death. And there she
    sits,
Sunk to her middle in that cave,
And stretches forth from that dread
    gulf 594
Her fearful heads, and fishes, groping
About the crag for sharks or dolphins
Or whatso greater beast her fortune
May make her prey — for many such
The deep-voiced sea-nymph Amphi-
    trite 599
Has in her pastures. Not one seaman
Can boast his ship has passed her by
Without some hurt. From each dark
    ship
She ever snatches, with each head,
One man away to death.

                   And now,
Odysseus, you shall see, close by, 605
The second crag. Lower it lies

     582. **Scylla** (sĭl′á).

Yet near the other: one could shoot
A shaft° across to it. Upon it
There stands a fig tree, great and tall
And all in leaf. And under this 610
The dread Charybdis° swallows in
The dark sea-water. Thrice each day
She sends it up and thrice again
She sucks it down, and terrible
That sight to see. I pray that you 615
May not be there when she is suck-
    ing
The water in, for no one then
Could save you from that evil — nay,
Not he that shakes the earth. So turn
Your ship to Scylla's crag and drive her
Swiftly upon her way. Far better 621
Lose six men from your ship than all
Should die together."

                  So she spoke,
And answering her I said:

                     "Nay, goddess,
Tell but this, and truly: may not 625
I find me out some way to shun
This dire Charybdis and yet fight
That other from my ship when she
Would make my men her prey?"

                     So spoke I,
And thus at once the goddess an-
    swered,
"Rash you are ever, with a heart 631
Set upon war and deeds of danger.
Can you not yield, when this must be,
To the immortal gods! This monster
Is not a mortal, but a thing 635
Of living evil none may slay,
Dread, fierce, unconquerable: no man
May fight against it. Courage here
Avails you nothing. This alone
Is best — to flee from her! What though
You linger by her rock and arm you,
I fear lest then she once again 642
Stretch forth those fearful heads and
    snatch
As many more. Nay, rather drive
Upon your way.

     608. **shaft:** arrow. 611. **Charybdis** (ká·rĭb′-
dĭs).

And now you reach 645
The island of Thrinacia.° Here
Are pastured all the Sungod's cattle
And his fat flocks. For seven herds
Of cattle graze here, seven flocks
Of goodly sheep, and there are fifty
In every flock. They bear no young 651
Nor do they ever die. If these
You leave unharmed and fix your hearts
Upon the homeward way, you yet
May come, though suffering sore perils,
To Ithaca. But if you harm them, 656
Then naught can I foresee but ruin
For you and ship and men. Nay, though
Yourself, you yet escape, then late,
In evil plight you shall come home,
With loss of all your men."
                          So said she, 661
And straightway came the dawn, rose-
    fingered,
And thence the goddess passed away
Up through the island. Then I turned
Back to the ship, and bade my men 665
Embark and loose the cables.

THE SONG OF THE SIRENS

                          Quickly
They went aboard and took their seats,
Each man in his own place, and smote
The whitened sea with oars. And now
There came, behind our dark-prowed
    ship, 670
A favoring wind to fill our sail,
A welcome comrade, sent by Circe,
That fair-tressed goddess of dread
    power,
Who speaks with mortals. So we
    trimmed
Our good ship's tackle right, and then
Sat at our ease, while wind and helms-
    man 676
Held her course true.
                    And now I said,
Sad-hearted, to my men:

646. **Thrinacia** (thrĭn-ā′shá).

                          "Unfitting
It is, friends, that but one or two
Should hear the sacred prophecies 680
Of that dread goddess, Circe. These
I now shall tell you, for then either
We die foreknowing what shall fall,
Or we escape and shun the death
And doom that wait us.
                    This she first 685
Bids us: — to shun the wondrous Sirens,
With their sweet voices and their mead-
    ows
Abloom with flowers. For she bade
That I alone should hear their song.
So bind me fast in bonds — aye, lash
    me 690
Upright against the mast, that thence
I may not stir, and cast strong ropes
About me, too. If I entreat you
And bid you set me free, then bind me
Yet tighter than before."
                          And so 695
I told them all she said. And ever
Our good ship sailed on swiftly, nearing
The Sirens' island, for the wind
Blew fair and drove her on. And now
The wind ceased suddenly; there came

A calm without a breath: some god
Laid all the sea to sleep. So now   702
My men rose, furled the sail, and
  stowed it
Within the hollow ship, and sitting
In order on the thwarts, they smote
With polished oars the whitening sea.
But I, with my keen blade, now cut   707
A great round lump of wax, and knead-
  ed
The fragments with my hands, till
  swiftly
The wax was softened. With this, I
  stopped   710
The ears of all my crew, in turn;
Then fast they bound me, hand and
  foot
Upright in my swift ship, my back
Against the mast, with ropes cast round
  me.
Then once again they sat and smote
The foaming sea with oars.
                      And now   716
When we were but so far away
As a man's cry may reach, and lightly
Went driving on, our ship's swift flight,
As close to land she sped, escaped not
The Sirens' sight, and they upraised   721
At once their clear, sweet song:
                  "Come hither,
O famed Odysseus, mighty glory
Of the Achæans. Turn your ship
But hither to the shore and hearken
The song we sing, for no man ever   726
Has steered his black ship hence till he
Has heard the honey-sweet delight
Of music from our lips; then forth
He went upon his way with joy   730
And fuller wisdom. For we know
All that the Argives° and the Trojans°
Endured on Troy's wide plains; we
  know
All that befalls mankind on earth,
The nourisher of all."

732. **Argives** (är'jĭvz): as used by Homer, almost any Greeks; **Trojans** (trō'jănz): men of Troy.

So sang they,   735
Uttering their sweet song. My heart
Yearned to hear further, and I bade
My men to loose me, and I frowned
My bidding with my brows, but they
Bent busier to their oars, and two,   740
Eurylochus° and Perimedes,°
Arose and bound me ever faster
With double lashings. But at last,
When we had passed them and no more
Might hear the song those Sirens sang
And their sweet voices, then my men
Took quickly from their ears the wax
Wherewith I stopped them, and they
  loosed   748
The bonds that bound me.

741. **Eurylochus** (û·rĭl'ô·kŭs); **Perimedes** (pĕr'ĭ·mē'dēz).

THINKING IT OVER

1. Of what dangers does Circe warn Odysseus? Explain what each of them is.

2. What precautions does Circe urge Odysseus to take in order to win over the first danger?

3. What effect does exposure to this first danger have on Odysseus? What action is taken as a result?

4. Identify Scylla and Charybdis. Circe explained them *figuratively;* make your explanation *factual.*

5. Explain what is meant when a person says he is "between Scylla and Charybdis."

6. Odysseus' men obey without question or hesitation the orders he gives as they approach the Sirens' island. In lines 695–96 he states that he has told them "all" that Circe predicted. Strictly speaking, is this accurate? What has he *not* told them? What qualities of leadership does Odysseus display by not giving every detail of the coming adventures?

7. Odysseus is an altogether interesting person with many sides to his character. What would you describe as his weaknesses? Explain.

[Odysseus has many other adventures. Finally a terrible storm wrecks his ship, and only Odysseus is saved. He is brought at last by friendly sailors to his native island of Ithaca. He does not recognize his homeland, but the goddess Athene, his protector, appears to warn him against going directly home lest he be murdered. Odysseus has been gone for twenty years, and in his absence, so Athene warns, powerful suitors have come to seek the hand of his wife Penelope and have stayed to feast in Odysseus' halls at his expense. They even plot to do away with his son Telemachus,* who is just reaching manhood. Athene further tells Odysseus that Telemachus has gone to Sparta to seek news of his father. Odysseus follows Athene's advice. He seeks shelter with faithful Eumæus,† his swineherd, who has looked out for his master's interest for twenty years. Eumæus does not recognize Odysseus, but he kindly shelters the stranger who brings the glad news that his master still lives.]

THE MEETING OF ODYSSEUS
AND TELEMACHUS

And now Athene went her way   750
To Lacedæmon,° for she sought
Noble Odysseus' son, to bid him
Return to his own home. And there
She found him, and drew near to him,
And said:

    "It is no longer wise,   755
Telemachus, to wander here
So far from home, leaving your
  house
And all the wealth there in the power
Of the proud wooers.° Now I warn
you,

And heed my words: Their leaders lie
Already watching at the straits   761
And plan to slay you ere you come
To your own land. So steer your ship
Outside the islands, and sail swiftly
By day and night. The god who watches
And keeps you safe will send a wind
To help you on your way.

    You   767
Shall seek the farm where dwells the
  swineherd
Who keeps your herds of swine, whose
  heart
Is ever faithful."

    At her words   770
Telemachus aroused his comrades
And bade them make his good ship
  ready
And loose the cables. And Athene
Sent a fair wind across the sea.

Odysseus and the goodly swineherd
Together in the hut at dawn   776
Prepared their breakfast, kindling
  fire,
When they had sent the men away
To drive the swine afield. And now
Telemachus drew near. The dogs,   780
Though wont to bark, now wagged
  their tails
Nor barked at all; and great Odysseus
Saw how they wagged their tails, and
  heard
The sound of footsteps, and spoke
  quickly
With winged words to Eumæus:

    "Surely,   785
Eumæus, there comes hither now
A friend or one you know!"

    And scarcely
Had he thus said, when his dear son
Stood in the doorway. Then the swine-
  herd
Sprang up, surprised, and from his
  hands   790
Let fall the bowl with which he la-
bored.

So in now stepped Telemachus
Over the sill of stone. His father
Rose from his seat to give him place,
But this he would not have, and stayed
    him,   795
And said:
            "Nay, stranger, sit. For we,
Here on this farm of ours, with ease
Shall find a seat, and this man here
Will soon provide one."
                        So he spoke.
Back to his seat then turned Odysseus,
And the good swineherd heaped fresh
    bushes   801
And spread a fleecy skin upon them
And here now sat Telemachus,
Odysseus' own dear son. . . .

                            And now,
When food and drink had stayed their
    hunger,   805
He said to the good swineherd:
                            "Whence,
Good father, comes this stranger?" . . .
                            Then,
Swineherd Eumæus, thus you° an-
    swered:
"From Crete, he told me, but through
    many
A city of mankind he passed   810
In wandering hither. . . . He has come
To my own house, and to your charge
I give him now. Do with him, then,
Whate'er you will. He is, he says,
Your suppliant."
            Then thus replied 815
Prudent Telemachus:
                    "Eumæus,
Your words pierce to my heart. How
    can I
Receive a guest at home? . . . But go
Quickly, my good old friend — go tell
Prudent Penelope° that I   820

808. **Eumæus, thus you:** this direct form
of address is used by Homer to show an especially warm feeling toward the old servant.
820. **Penelope** (pĕ·nĕl'ō·pė).

Am safe here, come from Pylos."° . . .
                                        So
Then spoke Telemachus, and sent
The swineherd on his way. And yet
He did not go his way unseen
By great Athene, for she came,   825
In form a woman, fair and tall,
And skilled in dainty crafts, and stood
Close by the door. Odysseus saw her;
His son beheld her not, though stand-
    ing
Before his face, nor knew her presence,
For not to all men do the gods   831
Appear in open sight. Odysseus
Saw, and the dogs saw too; they barked
    not,
But whimpering slunk off in fear
Across the farmland. With her brows
She signed° to him. Odysseus saw 836
And understood, and forth he came
By the great courtyard wall and there
He stood before her. Then to him
Thus spoke Athene:
                "Shrewd Odysseus, 840
Laërtes' son, now you shall tell
Your son your secret; now no longer
Need you keep silence. And you twain°
Shall plan together death and doom
For the proud wooers."
                    Upon his body 845
She put a fresh new cloak and tunic,
And mightier she made him seem
And fairer, and the deeper hue
Of youth came back.
                    And now Odysseus
Entered the lodge, and his son mar-
    veled   850
Beholding him, and turned his eyes
Away in awe, lest this might be
A god before him, and he spoke
In winged words:
                "You are changed, O stranger,
From what you seemed but now. Your
    garments   855

821. **Pylos** (pī'lŏs): a seaport southwest of
Sparta. 836. **signed:** signaled. 843. **twain:**
two.

At your own father, when at last   875
He stands before you! No Odysseus
But me will ever come! For I
It is, I that you see before you,
Who have borne perils and have wan-
    dered
In many lands, and now at last   880
Come, after twenty years, again
To my own native land."

                So said he,
And sat him down. Then round his
    neck
His son cast both his arms and sobbed
And poured forth tears.

            At last thus spoke   885
Noble Odysseus:

               . . . "Hither now
I come at counsel of Athene,
That you and I may plan the slaying
Of all our enemies."

[Odysseus and Telemachus talk over their
plan to rid themselves of the suitors. Telemachus promises to keep his father's identity
and the news of his return a secret from everyone, including Eumæus and even Penelope. Soon after Telemachus leaves, Odysseus
and Eumæus follow. In the courtyard of his
own home, Odysseus is seen by one of the idle
suitors, who fails to recognize him and hurls
taunting insults at the "beggar." Odysseus
stores the memory of this bitter meeting in his
heart.]

Are not the same; your very flesh
Is altered. Surely you are one
Of the immortal gods that have
Wide heaven for home. Show, now,
Compassion on us!"

            Then replied   860
Noble, long-tried Odysseus:

                  "Nay,
I am no god! Why liken me
To those that die not? I am he
Whom you so long have wept." His
    son,
Who could not yet believe that this   865
Could be his father, answered him
And said:

         "No, you are not Odysseus;
My own dear father! Some strange god
Enchants my eyes, to make me weep
In greater grief hereafter. Never   870
Could any mortal man so change."
Then Odysseus answered and said:

             "Telemachus,
It is unworthy of you thus
To stare and marvel beyond measure

         And now at evening,   889
Back came the swineherd to Odysseus
And his brave son, and there they made
Their supper ready. But Athene
Had first drawn near and touched
    Odysseus
With her gold wand, and once again
She made him agèd to behold   895
And meanly clad, lest the good swine-
    herd
Should look upon his face and know
    him,
And go to wise Penelope
And tell his tidings.   899

Now when the earliest dawn appeared
Rose-fingered, then Telemachus,
Dear son of great Odysseus, bound
Upon his feet his sandals fair
And took his mighty spear that fitted
His hand so readily. And now,   905
Ere he set forth to town, thus said he
To the good swineherd:
                    "Now, old friend,
I go to town so that my mother
May see me, for she will not cease,
I know, her piteous tears and weeping
Till she herself has seen me. This   911
I leave for you to do, to guide
This stranger to the town, that there
The man may beg his bread. Who
    chooses
May give him then a crust to eat,   915
A drink too from his cup. I have not
A home for every guest; too many
The troubles that come pressing on me
To vex my heart. So, if this stranger
Should take this ill, the worse for him!
I love, myself, plain speaking."
                         Then   921
Thus answered wise Odysseus:
                              "Nay,
Good friend, I have no wish to stay
    here.
In town a beggar fares far better
Than on the farm, for there a man   925
Can beg him food, and whoso will
May give him freely. I am now
Too old to live here on a farm
And labor at each task my master
May lay upon me. Go your way,   930
And, as for me, this man shall guide me
As you have bidden, after I
Have warmed me well beside the fire
And the sun gains in strength, for poorly
I now am clad; the frosts of morning
Might do me hurt: the town, they tell
    me,   936
Lies far away."
              So spoke Odysseus,
And now Telemachus went forth
Across the farmland. Fast he walked

With hurrying feet, still planning evil
Against the wooers.
                    And at last   941
He reached the stately house and set
The spear he carried in its place
By a great pillar. Then he entered
O'er the stone threshold. First of all
To see him was old Eurycleia,°   946
His nurse, as she was spreading fleeces
Upon the carven chairs. And swiftly
She came with flowing tears to meet
    him;
And kissed him on the face and shoul-
    ders.   950
And now there came forth from her
    room
Penelope, like Artemis,°
Or golden Aphrodite.° Weeping,
She cast her arms about her son
And kissed his face and his fair eyes,
And said, in winged words:
                    "Now at last   956
You come, Telemachus, more welcome
Than the sun's light. I thought my eyes
Should never see you more, when you
Went off so secretly to Pylos   960
Aboard your ship, to seek for tidings
Of your dear father."

[In the meantime, guided by the swineherd,
Odysseus approaches his own home. His beg-
gar's clothing serves him as a good disguise.
The first to recognize him is old Argos.]

                    Now a dog
Lay near, and heard, and straightway
    lifted
His head and ears. For this was Argos,
Steadfast Odysseus' dog — a dog   965
He reared long since, but never used,
For ere he used him, he went thence
To sacred Ilium.° Young men,

946. **Eurycleia** (ū′rĭ·klē′yà). 952. **Artemis**
(är′tê·mĭs): goddess of the moon and hunting;
the Romans called her Diana. 953. **Aphrodite**
(ăf·rô·dī′tê): goddess of love and beauty; the
Romans called her Venus. 968. **Ilium** (ĭl′ĭ·ŭm):
Troy.

In days now gone, would take the dog
To chase wild goats and deer and hares,
But now, his master far away,   971
He lay despised upon the dung
Left by the cattle and the mules
Heaped high before the doors. There
Argos, this dog, now lay, all foul   975
With vermin. Yet when he beheld,
Weak though he was, Odysseus near
  him,
He wagged his tail and dropped both
  ears,
Though he had now no strength to
  move
Nearer his master.
                And Odysseus   980
Saw him, but drew not near.

[While the wasteful suitors fail to recognize
Odysseus, he bides his time, planning their
murder. Penelope is gracious to the "stranger"
who she thinks brings news about her long-
absent husband. She sends for him and says:]

                        "Alas,
O stranger, but now all wherein
I once excelled, in form or face,
The gods laid waste that day the Ar-
  gives
Embarked for Ilium; for with them   985
My husband went away, Odysseus!
Would he might come again to watch
Over my life here: better far
Would be my fame, and fairer. Now
I can but suffer. Such the evil   990
Some power from on high has sent
For my affliction. So I give
But little heed to wanderers
Or suppliants or heralds serving
The people's need, but ever long   995
After Odysseus, wasting ever
My heart away.
                These men would hasten
My marriage day, so I must spin
A skein° of trickery. And first

999. **skein** (skān): a quantity of yarn or
thread put up after it is taken from the reel,
usually in a loose knot.

Some power whispered to my heart
That I should build me in my hall   1001
A great loom, and should weave me
  here
A robe, a garment rich and wide.
So then I said to all:
                        'Young men   1004
Who come to woo me — this I pray you:
Though great Odysseus now lie dead,
Forbear to urge this marriage. Wait
But till this robe I weave is finished —
I would not have its threads all wasted!
This is a shroud° for lord Laërtes°
When the dread doom of death shall
  take him   1011
And leave long sorrow. I must do this
Lest some Achæan woman blame me
In my own land, if he should lie
Without a shroud, who once was lord
Of wealth so great.'
                        So then I spoke,   1016
And their proud hearts agreed. And
  so
Each day I wove at my great web,
But every night I bade them bring
Torches to light me, and unraveled
All I had wrought by day. And thus
Three years I did, unseen, and ever
Deceived the wooers. But at length,
When the fourth year came round, my
  maids,
Ungrateful, like base dogs, betrayed
  me.   1025
The wooers came and caught me.
  Harshly
They railed° against me. So, com-
  pelled,
And through no will of mine, I brought
That weaving to its end. And now
I can no longer put off marriage   1030
Or shape me a new plan."

1010. **shroud:** garment for a corpse; **lord
Laërtes:** Odysseus' father is now a very old
man. The word *lord* is used to indicate
respect for his former greatness. 1027. **railed:**
scolded.

Indeed
Odysseus' heart was filled with pity
At his wife's weeping.
                                    But now,
When she with many a tear had taken
Her fill of sorrow, once again   1035
She spoke and answered:
                                    "Now I mean
To try you, stranger. I would know
If you in truth received my husband
As guest in your own hall."
                                    Answered
The wise Odysseus:
                                    "Noble lady,   1040
This is a hard thing to tell rightly
After so long a time, for now
Full twenty years have gone their way
Since he set forth and left my land.
Yet I will tell you how my heart   1045
Still sees his picture. Great Odysseus
Then wore a cloak of purple wool
In double fold. Upon it shone
A brooch of gold: two clasps it had.
And thus its front was carved: a
      dog   1050
Held with its paws a dappled fawn
Struggling, and gripped it in its jaws;
And all who saw it marveled how,
Though wrought of lifeless gold, that
      dog
Held the fawn gripped, and strangled
      it,   1055
While, striving to escape, the fawn
Still struggled with its feet. I marked
His tunic, too, that shone as bright
Upon his body as the skin
That gleams upon a sun-dried onion,
So smooth it was, and shining like 1061
The sun itself. And many a woman
Gazed at him wondering. And this
I say besides; mark well: I know not
If he was wont to wear this clothing
At home, or if some comrade gave it
When he embarked in his swift ship,
Or if some host had given it him,
For he was loved by many, few
So loved as he. And I myself   1070

Gave him a sword of bronze, a cloak
With double fold, of fairest purple,
And a fringed tunic, and so sent him,
With love and honor, on his way
In his good ship."
                                    So he spoke,   1075
And once again he waked in her
The need of weeping, for she knew
So well each token that Odysseus
Told her so clearly. But at length
She answered:
                                    "From this moment, stranger, 1080
You who have been a sight for pity,
Shall be beloved and honored. I
It was, with my own hand, who gave
      him
Those garments you have told of. First
In my own room, I folded them   1085
And fixed upon them the bright brooch,
That precious jewel. Yet I never
Shall greet him now, returning hither
To his own land."
                                    And thus Odysseus
Answered her, saying:
                                    "Honored wife   1090
Of great Odysseus, mar no more
Your lovely flesh, nor waste away
Your heart with weeping for your hus-
      band.
And yet I blame you not. No woman
But weeps to lose her lord, the man
She loved, whose children she has
      borne —   1096
Aye, even though he were far other
Than was Odysseus who, men say,
Is like the gods. But cease your weep-
      ing
And heed my words, for I will speak
Truth only and will hold back naught
Of all I lately heard: Odysseus,   1102
They say, is near at hand and safe,
I say that he is safe. Already
He is at hand: no longer now   1105
Will he delay and linger far
From friends and native land. Nay,
      more,
I add my oath. Be witness, now,

Zeus, highest of the gods and best,
And let this hearth of good Odys-
seus,   1110
Where I now stand, be witness too
That now, this very year, Odysseus
Shall come here, aye, as this moon
passes
And the new moon begins."

THINKING IT OVER

1. Why is Telemachus not at home in Ithaca when his father arrives there? Where is he?

2. When he first sees Odysseus, why does Telemachus fail to recognize him? Who is Odysseus' most powerful helper at this moment? What part does the minor character Eumæus play in helping Odysseus regain control of his home and kingdom?

3. Explain what is meant by the "skein of trickery" referred to by Penelope in line 999. What does this incident reveal about her?

4. Why has Penelope become as mistrustful of her serving maids as of the wooers?

5. What aspects of Odysseus' personality are shown to us by his own description of himself to his wife — especially lines 1062–75? What hints have you that he may have been enjoying himself and perhaps relishing the humor of the situation at this point?

PENELOPE DISCOVERS

THE STRANGER'S SECRET

[With the help of Telemachus, Odysseus kills the suitors in a bloody and merciless fight. The old nurse, who has kept silent though she recognized Odysseus even before the battle, rushes to Penelope to tell her that the suitors are dead, slain by none other than mighty Odysseus, her husband. Penelope replies:]

        "Dear nurse,
The gods have made you mad; for they
Can turn to folly even him   1116
Who is the wisest, and can set
The fool upon the way to wisdom.
And they have turned your wits astray.
Your mind, till now, was ever steady.

Why do you mock me, now my spirit
Is heavy with its grief, to tell me   1122
Such tales as this, awaking me
From the sweet sleep that held me fast
And sealed my eyes?"

        Then replied   1125
Her dear nurse Eurycleia:
          "Nay,
Dear child, I do not mock you. Here
In very truth, Odysseus now
Is with us, he himself. For he
Was the poor stranger every man   1130
Insulted in the hall. Long since,
Telemachus knew well that he
Was here among us, but with foresight
He hid his knowledge, that his father
Might all the better take his vengeance
For all the cruel wrongs these men   1136
Have wrought in arrogance."

        So said she.
Gladly her mistress heard and sprang
Up from her bed and cast her arms
Round the old woman. In winged words
She said:
      "Now, prithee, tell me truly,
My own dear nurse. If he indeed   1142
Is come again, as you are saying,
To his own home, how could he then
So quickly lay his hands in vengeance
Upon the shameless wooers — he   1146
Being but one, while they are many,
Thronging the house!"

        And thus replied
Her dear nurse Eurycleia:
         "Nay,
I saw not, and I heard no tidings,   1150
Nay, not a sound, save for the groans
Of those he slew. For we in fear
Sat shrinking in the farthest corner
Of our own sheltered room, fast barring
Its close-set doors, until at last   1155
I heard your son Telemachus
Call from the hall, for so his father
Had bid him call. I found Odysseus
Amidst the bodies of the slain,
For all about him they were lying   1160
Upon the trodden floor, aye, many,

Each close upon the other. Glad
Your heart too would have been, had you
But seen him then! Now all the bodies
Are gathered in a heap together   1165
Hard by the courtyard gate, while kindling
A mighty fire, he now is cleansing
The noble hall with brimstone.° Hither
I come to call you, for he bade me.
Follow me now that you may both
Enjoy your happiness together   1171
With loving hearts, for you have both
Borne many a sorrow."
                                    Then replied
Prudent Penelope:
                            "Dear nurse,
Now be not over-quick to boast   1175
And laugh with joy. You know indeed
How welcome he would be to all
In his own house, and most to me
And to the son I bore him. Yet
This tale you tell cannot be true: 1180
Alas, it is some god came hither
And slew those haughty wooers, angered
At the rash insults of their pride
And all their evil deeds. They honored
No man upon the earth, no man   1185
Or good or evil who dared come
Among them here. So for their crimes
They met this end. But far away
Odysseus now has lost forever
All hope of his returning hither —   1190
Nay, he himself is lost!"
                                    Then answered
Her dear nurse Eurycleia:
                                    "Child,
What words are these that now have passed
The portal of your teeth! To say   1194
That your own husband, he who now
Stands here upon his hearth, will never
Come home again! Your heart is ever
Slow to believe. Yet I can tell you

1168. **brimstone:** sulfur, burned as a cleansing agent.

Another sign, a sign yet surer,
The scar of the deep wound the boar
Once gave with his bright tusk. I spied it   1201
That day I washed his feet, and longed
To tell you what I saw. But he
Laid hand upon my mouth and so
With his wise foresight, stopped my speech."   1205
Then wise Penelope replied:
"Dear nurse, wise as you are, 'tis hard
To guard against the secret purpose
Of the eternal gods. And yet
Let us go down and seek my son   1210
And see these wooers who lie slain
And him that slew them."
                                    So she spoke,
And down she passed then from her room,
And sorely was her heart divided   1214
Whether to stand far off and question
Her own dear lord or stand beside him
And kiss his face and clasp his hand.
But when she entered and passed over
The threshold of carved stone, she went
And sat her down, facing Odysseus,
In firelight, by the farther wall.   1221
And he still sat with downcast eyes
By the tall pillar and awaited
In wonder if his stately wife
Would speak to him when she should turn   1225
Her eyes and see him. A long time
She sat in silence, and amazement
Was in her heart; then for a time
She gazed upon him face to face,
And then again she knew him not,   1230
For he still wore upon his body
A beggar's raiment.
                                    And her son,
Telemachus, now spoke, and said,
Reproaching her:
                            "Mother of mine,
Unmotherly, why is your heart   1235
So hard? Why do you ever keep
Far from my father? Why not sit
Close by his side, and question him,

And ask him all his story? Nay,
There is no other woman living   1240
Would stand aside thus, hardening
A stubborn heart against her husband
Who after many a peril past,
Comes, in the twentieth year, once
   more   1244
To his own land. Your heart is ever
Harder than stone!"
              Then thus replied
Prudent Penelope:
             "My son,
My spirit is amazed within me.
I have no power to speak or question
Or look upon his face. And yet,   1250
If this can be Odysseus' self,
And he has now come home, we two
May know each other far more surely
Than any other may, for we
Have secret tokens known to us,   1255
Hidden from all besides."
             So said she,
And great Odysseus smiled and quickly
Thus to Telemachus he spoke
In winged words:
           "Go, Telemachus,
And leave your mother in the hall   1260
To test me. She shall learn ere long
More surely what I am. But now,
Because I am unclean to see,
And wear base garments on my body,
She holds me in dishonor, saying   1265
That I am not her lord."

PENELOPE TESTS ODYSSEUS

[Odysseus leaves for a short while, to bathe
and dress himself in kingly garments. Athene
herself restores his former handsome appear-
ance.]
             So he came
Forth from the bath, and seemed in
   presence
Like the immortal gods. And thus
He came once more back to the seat
Whence he had risen, and there sat
Facing his wife. He spoke to her   1271
And said:

"O most perplexing woman,
Surely the dwellers on Olympus
Have given you a harder heart
Than other tender women."
           Answered   1275
The wise Penelope:
           "O man
Perplexing to my soul — nay, I
Am not held off by pride, nor scorn you,
But I am lost in wonder. Well
I know what you were once when, sail-
   ing   1280
Away in your oared ship, you left
Your home in Ithaca. But come
Now, Eurycleia, and make ready
His firm-built bed. Make it outside
The room he built him himself. Aye,
   move   1285
His firm-built bedstead forth and strew
Upon it bedding — fleeces, covers,
And bright-hued rugs."
           All this she said
To try her husband. But Odysseus   1289
Was angered at her words, and thus
He spoke to his true wife:
           "What, woman!
What words are these you now have
   said
To pierce my heart! Who can have set
My bed in a new place? That task
Would be a hard one, aye, too hard
Even for the cleverest, unless   1296
A god should come and easily
Remove it at his will and set it
In a new place. No mortal man
Of living men, in his full strength,   1300
Could ever move it easily
Out of its present place. For in it,
Wrought in its very frame, is hidden
A secret token, and no other
Wrought this, but I alone.
           There grew   1305
Within our yard an olive tree,
Long-leaved and thriving, strong of
   growth,
Thick as a pillar. Round its trunk
I shaped my room and built it thus

Till all was finished, walling it   1310
With massive stone, and well I fash-
   ioned
The roof to cover it and hung
And fitted its joined doors. And then,
From that long-leaved tall olive tree
I cut the crown away and squared,
Using my ax, the stem remaining   1316
Above the roots; then with the adz
I smoothed it and made true the line,
And thus I made my bedpost. Next
I bored it all with a keen auger   1320
And, so beginning, ever worked
On to the end, and it stood finished.
I decked it all with gold and silver
And ivory, and across it stretched
Long strips of oxhide bright and red.
This is the token that I mean.   1326
Now, wife, I do not know if still
That bed is standing there, or whether
Someone has cut that olive stem
And moved it elsewhere."
                   So he spoke,   1330
And at his words her knees grew weak
And all her soul within, for well
She knew this token that Odysseus
Had told so plainly. And she wept,
And straight to him she ran, and cast
Her arms about her husband's neck
And kissed his face and said:
                    "Odysseus,
Pray be not angry with me. You
Have ever been, through every fortune,
Wisest of men. The gods have sent   1340
Sore grief upon us, for they grudged us
That we should side by side together
Share the delight of youth and cross
The threshold of old age. Yet be not,
I pray you, wroth° with me or blame
   me,   1345
Because I did not, when I saw you,
Run thus to greet you! For my heart
Within my breast was shuddering ever
Lest some strange man should come
   and cheat me   1349
With lying words. For many a man

1345. wroth (rŏth): angry.

Will plot base deeds for gain. Lo, now
You quite convince this heart of mine,
Stubborn what though it be!"
                   So spoke she,
And stronger still there came upon him
A yearning need of tears, and there,
Holding his wise and faithful wife,   1356
He wept with joy. And she beside him,
Like men that see the land with glad-
   ness —
Seamen whose sturdy ship Poseidon
Has smitten on the deep and shattered
With storm and mighty seas, and few
Are they who from the foaming wa-
   ters   1362
Escape to swim to shore: their skin
Is crusted with the brine, but happy
They step to land once more, delivered
Out of their danger — with such glad-
   ness   1366
She gazed upon her husband.

THINKING IT OVER

1. What was the secret of Odysseus'
bedroom? Why did the stranger's knowledge of it convince Penelope that Odysseus was her husband?

2. How is the story of Odysseus and
the Sirens similar to that of "The Lorelei,"
the poem on page 381?

3. What enabled the nurse, Eurycleia,
to positively identify Odysseus?

4. Explain what sort of future you visualize for Odysseus, Penelope, and Telemachus after the end of the poem.

5. With what other epic tales are you
familiar? Why does the poem "The Song
of Hiawatha" qualify to be described as an
epic?

6. Both the Greeks and the Romans
were accustomed to refer to their gods
with certain descriptive words or phrases.
For example, Zeus was "Olympian";
Athene was often described as "flashing-
eyed." Occasionally just the descriptive
word or phrase was used by itself, as when
Zeus was called simply "the Thunderer."
The *Odyssey* contains many such descriptive adjectives and phrases. They are called
epithets. One occurs in lines 232–33: "The

god/Who shakes the earth, Poseidon." What epithets are used to refer to the dawn and the sea? Look for other epithets which Homer uses, and observe how effective they are in making the poetry more rich and the scenes and people more vividly real.

RECOGNIZING CLUES TO CHARACTER

1. Which of his many adventures seems to you to show Odysseus at his best as a courageous and resourceful leader?

2. Was Odysseus being kind or cruel when he dragged his men away from the land of the Lotus-eaters? Why?

3. When Telemachus recognizes his long-missing father, he weeps for joy. So does Odysseus when he makes his identity known to Penelope. Explain why this is not weakness of character in either man, and support your answer with other incidents or lines from the poem.

4. Explain why Penelope is reluctant to accept Odysseus' identity.

5. Select several incidents in the poem which prove that Odysseus really deserved the descriptive adjectives *crafty* and *shrewd;* select others which show Penelope deserving of being called *prudent* and *wise.*

6. Describe Odysseus as a father from the point of view of Telemachus; as a husband, from Penelope's; and as a leader of men from the point of view of his shipmates.

PEN AND PAPER

Write a composition of no fewer than 200 words on one of the following topics suggested by the *Odyssey:*

A Character Study of a Courageous Man
Why Athene Protected Odysseus
Even His Dog Remembered
Telemachus: A Worthy Son
Like Father, Like Son
Why Penelope Is the Ideal Wife and
    Mother

The Odyssey *in Art*

Like many great literary works, the *Odyssey* belongs to all lands and all ages. An illustration of this is the influence which Homer's epic has had on the art of different countries. The paintings for this text of the *Odyssey* were done by Robert Shore, who has used bold colors and dynamic design to express in modern terms the power of Homer's ancient epic. Below is a fragment of a Roman manuscript of the third century A.D., depicting the Trojan War — the battle in which Odysseus took part before his long journey home. On the next page are other episodes from the *Odyssey* as interpreted in the art of other countries.

"Penelope," fifteenth-century woodcut.

ABOVE: *"Ulysses Deriding Polyphemus."*

LEFT: *Fifty-century* B.C. *Greek vase.*

The Odyssey in Art (Cont.)

The woodcut at top of page opposite is from a manuscript printed in Germany in 1473; depicted is Penelope at her loom, with Odysseus and Telemachus slaying her suitors. *Bottom left, opposite,* is a Greek vase, fifth century B.C., with a decoration showing Odysseus using the ram to escape from the Cyclops. The print, *bottom right,* is from a painting by the nineteenth-century English artist, J. M. W. Turner, which depicts Odysseus outside the Cyclops' cave.

To your right is a bust of the *Odyssey's* author as conceived by a Greek artist, probably first century B.C.

Homer.

The Epic Tale

SUGGESTIONS FOR FURTHER READING

Asimov, Isaac, *Words from the Myths* (Houghton Mifflin, 1960)
A good exploration of myths with emphasis on our many everyday words which stem from the Greek legends.

Bates, Herbert, *The Odyssey of Homer* (McGraw-Hill, 1929)
A verse translation prepared especially for the high school student.

Benson, Sally, *Stories of the Gods and Heroes* (Dial Press, 1940)
Delightfully told myths based on Bulfinch's *The Age of the Fable.*

Braymer, Marjorie, *The Walls of Windy Troy* (Harcourt, Brace & World, 1960)
A biography of Heinrich Schliemann, whose dream of discovering the ruins of ancient Troy came true.

Ceram, C. W., *Gods, Graves, and Scholars* (Knopf, 1951)
Fascinating details of ancient civilizations as revealed by archeologists who have excavated these ancient cities — Troy among them.

Church, Alfred J., *The Iliad of Homer* (retold) and *The Odyssey of Homer* (retold) (Macmillan, 1951)
Prose versions of the two great stories told simply and well.

Colum, Padraic, *The Adventures of Odysseus and the Tale of Troy* (Macmillan, 1918)
All the dramatic highlights are here.

Coolidge, Olivia E., *Greek Myths* (Houghton Mifflin, 1949)
The more familiar stories from mythology are arranged according to their subjects and types. *The Trojan War* (Houghton Mifflin, 1952) will interest those who want to be better acquainted with Odysseus' early adventures.

Hamilton, Edith, *Mythology* (Little, Brown, 1940)
All the important Greek myths and legends, including the story of Odysseus.

Lamb, Charles, *The Odyssey*
For many readers, their favorite English translation.

Mireaux, Emile, *Daily Life in the Time of Homer* (Macmillan, 1959)
A study based on the poems of Homer.

Picard, Barbara L., *The Odyssey of Homer* (Walck, 1952)
A retelling of Odysseus' adventures.

Selincourt, Aubrey de, *Odysseus, the Wanderer* (Criterion, 1956)
A good introduction to the two great Homeric classics.

Trease, Geoffrey, *Young Traveler in Greece* (Dutton, 1956)
A young girl spends six months in modern Greece and becomes acquainted with places of legendary interest.

FOR YOUR LISTENING

An episode from the *Odyssey* can be heard on longplay record *Many Voices* 9A.

The Novel

Great Expectations

"Keep still . . . or I'll cut your throat!"

These are the words growled to a frightened little boy named Pip by a mud-stained, fearful-looking man wearing convict's clothes, an iron manacle chained to his leg. The scene is a graveyard outside a small village in England well over a hundred years ago.

Beginning with this startling opening, you will follow the career of young Pip as he goes through dramatic changes of fortune in one of the best mystery novels ever written. Early in life Pip learns that he has "great expectations" — that is, a highly promising future; and with its unfolding come many adventures — some tragic, some comic. Even though the events of the book are most dramatic and unusual, you will find Pip facing many of the problems of growing up that young people face today. Just as everyone has friends who influence and help him, so has Pip. In Joe, Biddy, Estella, and Herbert Pocket you may recognize people you know.

These characters — as real today as when they were first put down on paper — were created by a master. Knowing a little about Charles Dickens will help you to find mirrored in *Great Expectations* many incidents from his life. With this in mind, you may want to reread "Charles Dickens: Boy of the London Streets," on page 209 of this anthology, which gives such a vivid picture of Dickens' early life.

Dickens the Man

Born in 1812, Charles Dickens was still a child when his father, John Dickens, was arrested and put in Marshalsea Prison for debt. The Eng-

---

◀ This ceramic medallion was made in England in 1872 in the studio of Josiah Wedgwood, whose name has become world-recognized for the china which bears his imprint. High craftsmanship is a British tradition, as are the great English novels that have enriched the world's literature.

A London prison: engraving by Gustave Doré.

lish of those days saw no particular injustice in this act, not wondering how a man jailed for owing money could get his affairs settled while behind bars. Here was only one of the injustices which grew out of British laws during the nineteenth century. The works of Charles Dickens show that he felt such conditions to be wrong and in need of correction.

From his mother young Charles had learned to read and write and translate a little Latin before starting school. But because of his father's imprisonment he had to leave school and find work to help support his family.

Thus he was not even in his teens when an uncle gave him a job in a shoe-blacking factory. The England of that time had no laws to protect its laboring children, many of whom worked from sunrise until night in mills and factories. The memories of what Charles experienced were stored away in his mind.

Eventually John Dickens was released from prison and Charles could return to school. He wrote plays and edited a student newspaper. At fifteen his formal schooling ended. For a year he worked as a clerk in a law firm. As always, he watched and listened to the people around him. The details of Mr. Jaggers' unusual business transactions in *Great Ex-*

pectations no doubt stem from Dickens' observations as a law clerk.

He became a court reporter and then a newspaper reporter. He spent hours reading in the British Museum library. He had gone through a lonely childhood; now he finally found a friend, a young man of his own age, with whom he traveled about London much as do Pip and Herbert Pocket, whom you are soon to meet. And he fell in love. The girl, it seems, was as heartless and as careless of a man's feelings as Estella of *Great Expectations.*

Success as a writer came to Charles Dickens after the publication of some original articles and stories which he had sent to a magazine. They were signed with the pen name of "Boz." At first he was not paid for his writing, but readers liked his stories and demanded more. There would come a time when people lined up eagerly before the doors of magazine publishers for the newest installments of his novels.

With *The Pickwick Papers* Dickens tasted success. *Oliver Twist, Barnaby Rudge,* and *Nicholas Nickleby* followed, to magnify his fame at home and abroad.

In 1842 he planned a trip to America. By this time he was married — though not to the girl who served as the model for Estella. His wife went with him to America. They crossed a stormy Atlantic in a small steamboat which finally ended up on a mudbank near Halifax.

America greeted Dickens the way a film star or popular singer is welcomed in our day. He loved the fun and excitement of it all, but he saw things in America that provoked stinging, unflattering comments from him. His books were selling widely, yet no international copyright laws protected authors, so that he had not been paid for the American editions of his books. He spoke clearly and uncompromisingly of the injustice of this. He criticized slavery — as one might imagine he would after his childhood experience in the shoe-blacking factory. But Americans drew the line when he also criticized their social manners. By the time he sailed for home, Dickens had wearied of the attention that at first had been so enjoyable, and his huge American public no longer delighted in him.

He won them back with *A Christmas Carol* and *Dombey and Son.* Americans forgot that he had poked fun at them in his book *Martin Chuzzlewit.* And with *David Copperfield, A Tale of Two Cities,* and *Great Expectations,* the man who had been a poor and troubled boy won the highest honors and praise.

Dickens the Writer

Why is Dickens loved? Why have his books become a great heritage? To begin a Dickens novel is to enter a world where the characters are as warm and real as close personal friends. In his books we find wonderful companions like Pip, Joe, and Biddy (all in *Great Expectations*); David Copperfield and Mr. Micawber; Oliver Twist; and Tiny Tim and Scrooge (in *A Christmas Carol*). These are unforgettable characters.

One reason for Dickens' universal popularity is that he had a playwright's sense of drama. His stories abound with suspense and surprises. His London alleys and misty country marshes have the color

Charles Dickens, age 47.

The Thames embankment, London: engraving by Gustave Doré.

and the sounds of reality because he drew them from life. The village where Pip grows up is in fact the little village of Cooling, near London.

His characters are interesting, because he was interested in people and understood them. Dickens wrote about convicts as one who had met convicts, just as he had known pickpockets, beggars, and murderers. He makes his characters as real for us as they were real to him.

Great Expectations will leave many strong impressions with you. Pip grows into manhood during a time and in a country quite different from our own of the twentieth century. It is for you to decide which of Pip's problems and which of the decisions he has to make are similar in some ways to those confronting young people today.

The novel is divided into three main sections, called "stages." To help you avoid confusion, the names of most of the book's many characters are given at the headings of the chapters in which they first appear.

"Oh! Don't cut my throat, sir," I pleaded in terror. "Pray don't do it, sir."

The "I" speaking is Philip Pirrip, nicknamed "Pip." He is the narrator of the story and seven years old when it begins. Remember that this is a mystery novel you are reading; many events are not explained when they occur. Dickens planned to keep you puzzled. As you read, try to match your wits with Pip's now and again to see whether you can guess the meaning of some of the strange happenings. But by all means, be true to the code of the mystery fan: guessing is fair. Looking ahead to see how it all ends is not!

Great Expectations

A Novel by

CHARLES DICKENS

CHAPTER 1

In this chapter we meet Pip, who meets a convict in a graveyard.

MY FATHER'S FAMILY name being Pirrip, and my Christian name Philip, my infant tongue could make of both names nothing more explicit than Pip. So I called myself Pip, and came to be called Pip.

I gave Pirrip as my father's family name, on the authority of his tombstone and my sister — Mrs. Joe Gargery, who married the blacksmith. I never saw my father or my mother, and never saw a picture of either of them.

We lived in the marsh country, down by the river, within twenty miles of the sea. My first vivid impression of things seems to me to have been gained on a memorable raw afternoon toward evening. At such a time I found out for certain that this bleak place was the churchyard; that Philip Pirrip, late of this parish, and Georgiana, his wife, were dead and buried here. I knew that the dark flat wilderness beyond was the marshes; that the low leaden line beyond them was the river; that the distant savage lair from which the wind was rushing was the sea; and that the small bundle of shivers growing afraid of it all and beginning to cry was Pip.

"Hold your noise!" cried a terrible voice, as a man started up from among the graves. "Keep still, you little devil, or I'll cut your throat!"

A fearful man, all in coarse gray, with a great iron on his leg. A man with no hat, and with broken shoes, and with an old rag tied round his head. A man who had been soaked in water, and smothered in mud, and lamed by stones, and cut by flints, and stung by nettles, and torn by briers; who limped, and shivered, and glared, and growled; and whose teeth chattered in his head as he seized me by the chin.

"Oh! Don't cut my throat, sir," I pleaded in terror. "Pray don't do it, sir."

"Tell us your name!" said the man. "Quick!"

"Pip, sir."

"Once more," said the man, staring at me. "Give it mouth!"

"Pip. Pip, sir."

"Show us where you live," said the man. "Point out the place!"

I pointed to where our village lay, a mile or more from the church.

The man, after looking at me for a moment, turned me upside down and emptied my pockets. There was nothing in them but a piece of bread. He ate the bread ravenously.

Great Expectations by Charles Dickens, as abridged by Blanche Jennings Thompson, copyright, 1950, by Harcourt, Brace & World, Inc.

"Tell us your name!" said the man. "Quick!"

"You young dog," said the man, licking his lips. "What fat cheeks you ha' got. Darn me if I couldn't eat 'em, and if I han't half a mind to't!"

I held tighter to the tombstone on which he had put me; partly, to keep myself upon it; partly, to keep myself from crying.

"Now lookee here!" said the man. "Where's your mother and father?"

"There, sir!" said I, pointing to the tombstones.

He started, made a short run, and stopped and looked over his shoulder.

"Ha!" he muttered. "Who d'ye live with — supposin' you're kindly let to live, which I han't made up my mind about?"

"My sister, sir — Mrs. Joe Gargery — wife of Joe Gargery, the blacksmith, sir."

"Blacksmith, eh?" said he. And looked down at his leg.

After darkly looking at his leg and at me several times, he came closer, took me by both arms, and tilted me back as far as he could hold me.

"Now lookee here," he said, "the question being whether you're to be let to live. You know what a file is?"

"Yes, sir."

"And you know what wittles [1] is?"

"Yes, sir."

After each question he tilted me over a little more, so as to give me a greater sense of helplessness and danger.

"You get me a file." He tilted me again. "And you get me wittles." He tilted me again. "You bring 'em both to me." He tilted me again. "Or I'll have your heart and liver out."

I was dreadfully frightened, and so giddy that I clung to him with both hands and said, "If you would kindly please to let me keep upright, sir, perhaps I shouldn't be sick, and perhaps I could attend more."

He gave me a most tremendous dip and roll. Then he held me by the arms in an upright position and went on in these fearful terms:

"You bring me, tomorrow morning early, that file and them wittles to that old Battery [2] over yonder. You do it, and you never dare to say a word or dare to make a sign concerning your having seen such a person as me, or any person sumever, and you shall be let to live. You fail, or you go from my words in any partickler, no matter how small it is, and your heart and your liver shall be tore out, roasted, and ate. Now, I ain't alone, as you may think I am. There's a young man hid with me. That young man hears the words I speak. That young man has a secret way of getting at a boy, and at his heart, and at his liver. It is in wain for a boy to attempt to hide himself from that young man. A boy may lock his door, may be warm in bed, may tuck himself up, may draw the clothes over his head, may think himself comfortable and safe, but that young man will creep his way to him and tear him open. I am a-keeping that young man from harming of you at the present moment, with great difficulty. I find it wery hard to hold that young man off of your inside. Now, what do you say?"

I said that I would get him the file, and I would get him what broken bits of food I could, and I would come to him at the Battery early in the morning.

"Say, Lord strike you dead if you don't!" said the man.

I said so, and he took me down.

---

[1] **wittles:** victuals, food. (There are a number of other words in this book in which "v" is pronounced like "w" — a common speech habit of certain characters in this novel.)

[2] **Battery** (băt'ĕr·ĭ): a bank of earth on which large guns are mounted.

"Now," he pursued, "you remember what you've undertook, and you remember that young man, and you get home."

He hugged his shuddering body in both his arms and limped toward the low church wall. He got over it, like a man whose legs were numbed and stiff, and then turned round to look for me. I looked all around for the horrible young man, and could see no signs of him. But now I was frightened again, and ran home without stopping.

CHAPTER 2

We now meet Mrs. Joe Gargery, Pip's sister, and Joe Gargery the blacksmith, his brother-in-law.

MY SISTER, Mrs. Joe Gargery, was more than twenty years older than I, and had established a great reputation with herself and the neighbors because she had brought me up "by hand." [1] Knowing her to have a hard and heavy hand, and to be much in the habit of laying it upon her husband as well as upon me, I supposed that Joe Gargery and I were both brought up by hand.

She was not a good-looking woman, my sister; and I had a general impression that she must have made Joe Gargery marry her by hand. Joe was a fair man, with curls of flaxen hair on each side of his smooth face, and with eyes of a very undecided blue. He was a mild, good-natured, sweet-tempered, easygoing, foolish, dear fellow — a sort of Hercules [2] in strength, and also in

weakness. My sister, Mrs. Joe, with black hair and eyes, was tall and bony, and always wore a coarse apron, fastened over her figure behind with two loops.

Joe's forge adjoined our house, which was a wooden house, as many of the dwellings in our country were. When I ran home from the churchyard, the forge was shut up, and Joe was sitting alone in the kitchen. Joe and I being fellow sufferers, he warned me the moment I raised the latch of the door and peeped in at him.

"Mrs. Joe has been out a dozen times looking for you, Pip."

"Has she?"

"Yes, Pip," said Joe, "and what's worse, she's got Tickler with her."

At this dismal news, I twisted the only button on my waistcoat round and round, and looked dejectedly at the fire. Tickler was a wax-ended piece of cane, worn smooth by collision with my frame.

"She sot down," said Joe, "and she got up, and she made a grab at Tickler, and she Ram-paged [3] out. That's what she did," said Joe, "she Ram-paged out, Pip."

"Has she been gone long, Joe?" I always treated him as a larger child, and as no more than my equal.

"Well," said Joe, "she's been on the Ram-page, this last spell, about five minutes, Pip. She's a-coming! Get behind the door, old chap."

I took the advice. My sister, Mrs. Joe, throwing the door wide open, and finding an obstruction behind it, immediately applied Tickler. She concluded by throwing me at Joe, who passed me next to the chimney and quietly fenced me up there with his great leg.

[1] **by hand:** by personal looking after and responsibility.
[2] **Hercules** (hûr'kū·lēz): a mythological hero noted for his strength.

[3] **Ram-paged:** Joe is giving added emphasis to the word *rampage,* which means to storm about wildly.

"Where have you been, you young monkey?" said Mrs. Joe, stamping her foot. "Tell me directly what you've been doing to wear me away with fret and fright and worry, or I'd have you out of that corner if you was fifty Pips, and he was five hundred Gargerys."

"I have only been to the churchyard," said I, from my stool, crying and rubbing myself.

"Churchyard!" repeated my sister. "If it warn't for me you'd have been to the churchyard long ago, and stayed there. Who brought you up by hand?"

"You did," said I.

"And why did I do it, I should like to know?" exclaimed my sister.

I whimpered, "I don't know."

"*I* don't!" said my sister. "I'd never do it again! I know that. It's bad enough to be a blacksmith's wife, and him a Gargery, without being your mother."

My thoughts strayed from the question as I looked disconsolately at the fire. I fancied I saw the fugitive out on the marshes with the ironed leg, the mysterious young man, the file, the food I was about to steal, rise before me in the avenging coals.

Our supper was soon ready and my sister, as was her custom, sawed a very thick round off the loaf and hewed it into two halves, of which Joe got one, and I the other. Though I was hungry, I dared not eat my slice. I felt that I must have something in reserve for my dreadful acquaintance and his ally, the still more dreadful young man. I resolved to put my hunk of bread-and-butter down the leg of my trousers.

Joe was about to take a bite when his eye fell on me, and he saw that my bread-and-butter was gone.

The wonder and consternation [1] with which Joe stopped and stared at me were too evident to escape my sister's observation.

"What's the matter now?" said she.

"I say, you know!" muttered Joe, shaking his head at me in a very serious remonstrance. "Pip, old chap! You'll do yourself a mischief. It'll stick somewhere. You can't have chawed it, Pip."

"What's the matter *now?*" repeated my sister, more sharply than before.

"If you can cough any trifle of it up, Pip, I'd recommend you to do it," said Joe, all aghast. "Manners is manners, but still your 'elth's your 'elth."

By this time, my sister was quite desperate, so she pounced on Joe, and taking him by the two whiskers, knocked his head for a little while against the wall behind him while I sat in the corner looking guiltily on.

"Now, perhaps you'll mention what's the matter," said my sister, out of breath, "you staring great stuck pig."

Joe looked at her in a helpless way; then took a helpless bite and looked at me again.

"Been bolting his food, has he?" cried my sister.

"You know, old chap," said Joe, "I bolted, myself, when I was your age, but I never see your bolting equal yet, Pip."

My sister made a dive at me, and fished me up by the hair, saying nothing more than the awful words, "You come along and be dosed."

Some medical beast had revived tar water [2] in those days as a fine medicine, and Mrs. Joe always kept a supply of it in the cupboard. The urgency of my case demanded a pint of this mixture, which was poured down my throat, while Mrs. Joe held my head under her arm.

[1] **consternation** (kŏn'stēr·nā'shŭn): amazement or horror; dismay.

[2] **tar water:** a solution of tar and water regarded as a cure-all and also used as a tonic.

Conscience is a dreadful thing. I suffered the guilty knowledge that I was going to rob Mrs. Joe — I never thought I was going to rob Joe, for I never thought of any of the housekeeping property as his. This and the necessity of always keeping one hand on my bread-and-butter as I sat, or when I was ordered about the kitchen on any small errand, almost drove me out of my mind.

It was Christmas Eve, and I had to stir the pudding for next day with a copper stick. I tried it with the load upon my leg (and that made me think afresh of the man with the load on *his* leg), and found it quite unmanageable, so I slipped away and deposited that part of my conscience in my garret bedroom.

"Hark!" said I, when I had done my stirring, and was taking a final warm in the chimney corner before being sent up to bed. "Was that great guns, Joe?"

"Ah!" said Joe. "There's another convict off."

"What does that mean, Joe?" said I.

"There was a conwict off last night," said Joe, "after sunset-gun. And they fired warning of him. And now it appears they're firing warning of another."

"*Who's* firing?" said I.

"Drat that boy," interposed my sister, frowning at me over her work; "what a questioner he is. Ask no questions, and you'll be told no lies."

"Mrs. Joe," said I, after a long silence, "I should like to know — if you wouldn't much mind — where the firing comes from?"

"Drat that boy!" exclaimed my sister again. "From the Hulks!"

"And please what's Hulks?" said I.

"That's the way with this boy!" exclaimed my sister, pointing me out with her needle and thread, and shaking her head at me. "Answer him one question, and he'll ask you a dozen directly. Hulks are prison ships, right 'cross the marshes."

"I wonder who's put into prison ships, and why they're put there?" said I, in a general way, and with quiet desperation.

It was too much for Mrs. Joe, who immediately rose. "I tell you what, young fellow," said she; "I didn't bring you up by hand to badger people's lives out. People are put in the Hulks because they murder, and because they rob, and forge, and do all sorts of bad; and they always begin by asking questions. Now, you get along to bed!"

I was never allowed a candle to light me to bed, and, as I went upstairs in the dark, I was in mortal terror of the young man who wanted my heart and liver; I was in mortal terror of the man with the iron leg; I was in mortal terror of myself, from whom an awful promise had been extracted.

As soon as it was dawn, I got up and went downstairs, every board upon the way, and every crack in every board, calling after me, "Stop thief!" and "Get up, Mrs. Joe!" I had no time to spare. I stole some bread, some rind of cheese, and about half a jar of mince-meat (which I tied up in my pocket handkerchief with my last night's slice). I took some brandy from a stone bottle, diluting the stone bottle from a jug in the kitchen cupboard. Lastly, I took a meat bone with very little on it, and a beautiful round compact pork pie.

There was a door in the kitchen leading to the forge; I unlocked and unbolted that door and got a file from among Joe's tools. Then I put the fastenings as I had found them, opened the door at which I had entered when I ran home last night, shut it, and ran for the misty marshes.

CHAPTER 3

A second convict appears.

It was a very damp morning. On every rail and gate, wet lay clammy, and the marsh mist was thick. However fast I went, I couldn't warm my feet, to which the damp cold seemed riveted as the iron was riveted to the leg of the man I was running to meet. I knew my way to the Battery, because I had been down there with Joe, who had told me that, when I was apprenticed to him, we would have such larks [1] there! I had just crossed a ditch which I knew to be very near the Battery, and had scrambled up the mound beyond, when I saw the man sitting before me. His back was toward me, and he had his arms folded and was nodding forward, heavy with sleep, so I went forward softly and touched him on the shoulder. He instantly jumped up, and it was not the same man, but another man!

And yet this man was dressed in coarse gray, too, and had a great iron on his leg, and was lame, and hoarse, and cold, and everything that the other man was except that he had not the same face, and had a flat, broad-brimmed, low-crowned felt hat on. He swore an oath at me and then he ran into the mist, stumbling twice as he went.

"It's the young man!" I thought, feeling my heart shoot as I identified him. I dare say I should have felt a pain in my liver, too, if I had known where it was.

I was soon at the Battery, and there was the right man — hugging himself and limping to and fro, as if he had never all night left off hugging and limping — waiting for me. He was aw-

[1] larks: fun, as "going on a lark."

fully cold, to be sure. His eyes looked awfully hungry, too. He did not turn me upside down this time, but left me right side upward while I opened the bundle and emptied my pockets.

"What's in the bottle, boy?" said he.

"Brandy," said I.

He was already handing mincemeat down his throat in a violent hurry, but he left off to take some of the liquor. He shivered all the while violently.

"I think you have got the ague," [2] said I.

"I'm much of your opinion, boy," said he.

"It's bad about here," I told him. "You've been lying out on the marshes."

"I'll eat my breakfast afore they're the death of me," said he. "I'd do that if I was going to be strung up to that there gallows over there, directly afterward. I'll beat the shivers so far, *I'll* bet you."

He was gobbling mincemeat, meat bone, bread, cheese, and pork pie, all at once; staring distrustfully while he did so at the mist all around us, and often stopping to listen. Some real or fancied sound, some clink upon the river or breathing of beast upon the marsh, now gave him a start, and he said, suddenly:

"You're not a deceiving imp? You brought no one with you?"

"No, sir! No!"

"Well," said he, "I believe you. You'd be but a fierce young hound indeed, if at your time of life you could help to hunt a wretched creature, hunted as near death as this poor wretched creature is!"

Something clicked in his throat as if he had works in him like a clock, and was going to strike. And he smeared his ragged rough sleeve over his eyes.

Pitying him, I made bold to say, "I

[2] ague (ā′gū): a fever and chills.

am glad you enjoy it."

"Thankee, my boy. I do."

"I am afraid you won't leave any of it for him," said I, timidly. "There's no more to be got where that came from."

"Leave any for him? Who's him?" said my friend, stopping in his crunching of piecrust.

"The young man. That you spoke of. That was hid with you."

"Oh, ah!" he returned, with something like a gruff laugh. "Him? Yes, yes! *He* don't want no wittles."

"I thought he looked as if he did," said I.

The man stopped eating and regarded me with the keenest scrutiny and the greatest surprise.

"Looked? When?"

"Just now."

"Where?"

"Yonder," said I, pointing; "over there, where I found him nodding asleep, and thought it was you."

He held me by the collar, and stared at me so that I began to think his first idea about cutting my throat had revived.

"Dressed like you, you know, only with a hat," I explained, trembling; "and — and — " I was very anxious to put this delicately — "and with — the same reason for wanting to borrow a file. Didn't you hear the cannon last night?"

"When a man's alone on these flats, with a light head and a light stomach, perishing of cold and want, he hears nothin' all night but guns firing and voices calling. But this man — did you notice anything about him?"

"He had a badly bruised face," said I.

"Not here?" exclaimed the man, striking his left cheek.

"Yes, there!"

"Where is he?" He crammed what little food was left into the breast of his gray jacket. "Show me the way he went. I'll pull him down, like a bloodhound. Curse this iron on my sore leg! Give us hold of the file, boy."

He was down on the rank wet grass, filing at his iron like a madman, and not minding me or minding his own leg, which had an old chafe upon it and was bloody, but which he handled as roughly as if it had no more feeling in it than the file.

I was very much afraid of him again, now that he had worked himself into this fierce hurry, and I was likewise very much afraid of keeping away from home any longer. I told him I must go, but he took no notice, so I thought the best thing I could do was to slip off. The last I saw of him, his head was bent over his knee and he was working hard at his fetter, muttering at it and at his leg. The last I heard of him, I stopped in the mist to listen, and the file was still going.

CHAPTER 4

We meet the Christmas dinner guests: Mr. Wopsle, the parish clerk; Mr. and Mrs. Hubble, a wheelwright and his wife; and Mr. Pumblechook, Joe's uncle, a grain merchant.

I FULLY expected to find a constable in the kitchen, waiting to take me up. But not only was there no constable there, but no discovery had yet been made of the robbery. Mrs. Joe was prodigiously [1] busy in getting the house ready for

---

[1] **prodigiously** (prŏ·dĭj′ŭs·lĭ): extremely.

the festivities of Christmas.

"And where the deuce ha' *you* been?" was Mrs. Joe's Christmas salutation.

I said I had been down to hear the carols. "Ah, well!" observed Mrs. Joe. "You might ha' done worse." Joe secretly crossed his two forefingers and exhibited them to me as our token that Mrs. Joe was in a cross temper.

We were to have a superb dinner, consisting of a leg of pickled pork and greens, and a pair of roast stuffed fowls. A handsome mince pie had been made yesterday morning (which accounted for the mincemeat not being missed), and the pudding was already on the boil. My sister, having so much to do, was not going to church, but Joe and I were going. In his working clothes, Joe was a well-knit, characteristic-looking blacksmith; in his holiday clothes, he was more like a scarecrow than anything else. Nothing that he wore then fitted him or seemed to belong to him. As for me, when I was taken to have a new suit of clothes, the tailor had orders to make them like a kind of reformatory, and on no account to let me have the free use of my limbs. Joe and I going to church, therefore, must have been a moving spectacle for compassionate [1] minds. Yet what I suffered outside was nothing to what I underwent within. I was filled with terrors whenever Mrs. Joe went near the pantry, and I was remorseful under the weight of my wicked secret.

Mr. Wopsle, the clerk [2] at church, was to dine with us; and Mr. Hubble, the wheelwright, and Mrs. Hubble; and

---

[1] **compassionate** (kŏm-păsh'ŭn-ĭt): having sympathy and pity for the misfortunes of others.

[2] **clerk** (klärk): a church official whose duties were to assist the minister at church services and to teach in the local school.

Uncle Pumblechook, who was a well-to-do grain merchant in the nearest town, and drove his own carriage. The dinner hour was half-past one. When Joe and I got home, we found the table laid, and Mrs. Joe dressed, and the dinner dressing, and the front door unlocked (it never was at any other time) for the company to enter by, and everything most splendid. And still, not a word of the robbery.

The time came, without bringing with it any relief to my feelings, and the company came. Mr. Wopsle, besides a Roman nose and a large, shining, bald forehead, had a deep voice which he was uncommonly proud of. In church his reading of the psalms was a performance of dramatic vigor, and he was moreover somewhat given to competition with the minister. He punished the *amens* tremendously; and when he started the psalm he always looked around the congregation first, as much as to say, "You have heard our friend overhead; oblige me with your opinion of this style!"

I opened the door to the company, first to Mr. Wopsle, next to Mr. and Mrs. Hubble, and last of all to Uncle Pumblechook. (*I* was not allowed to call him "uncle," under the severest penalties.)

"Mrs. Joe," said Uncle Pumblechook — a large, hard-breathing, middle-aged, slow man, with a mouth like a fish, dull staring eyes, and sandy hair standing upright on his head, so that he looked as if he had just been all but choked, and had that moment come to — "I have brought you as the compliments of the season — I have brought you, mum, a bottle of sherry wine — and I have brought you, mum, a bottle of port wine." Every Christmas Day he presented himself, as a profound novelty, with exactly the same words, and carrying the two bottles like dumbbells.

We dined on these occasions in the kitchen, and adjourned, for the nuts and oranges and apples, to the parlor. Among this good company I should have felt myself, even if I hadn't robbed the pantry, in a false position. I should not have minded that if they would only have left me alone. But they wouldn't leave me alone. They seemed to think the opportunity lost if they failed to point the conversation at me, every now and then, and stick the point into me.

It began the moment we sat down to dinner. Mr. Wopsle said grace with theatrical declamation [1] and ended with the proper hope that we might be truly grateful. Upon which my sister fixed me with her eye and said in a low reproachful tone, "Do you hear that? Be grateful."

"Especially," said Mr. Pumblechook, "be grateful, boy, to them which brought you up by hand."

Joe always aided and comforted me when he could, in some way of his own, and he always did so at dinnertime by giving me gravy, if there were any. There being plenty of gravy today, Joe spooned into my plate, at this point, about half a pint.

"He was a world of trouble to you, ma'am," said Mrs. Hubble, sympathizing with my sister.

"Trouble?" echoed my sister. "Trouble?" And then entered on a fearful catalogue of all the illnesses I had been guilty of, and all the acts of sleeplessness I had committed, and all the high places I had tumbled from, and all the low places I had tumbled into, and all the injuries I had done myself, and all the times she had wished me in my grave, and I had stubbornly refused to go there. Everybody looked at me with indignation and abhorrence.

"Have a little brandy, uncle," said my sister presently.

O Heavens, it had come at last! He would find it was weak, he would say it was weak, and I was lost! I held tight to the leg of the table with both hands and awaited my fate.

My sister went for the stone bottle, came back with the stone bottle, and poured his brandy out: no one else taking any. The wretched man trifled with his glass — took it up, looked at it through the light, put it down — prolonged my misery. All this time Mrs. Joe and Joe were briskly clearing the table for the pie and pudding.

I couldn't keep my eyes off him. I saw the miserable creature finger his glass playfully, take it up, smile, throw his head back, and drink the brandy off. Instantly, the company was seized with unspeakable consternation, owing to his springing to his feet, turning round several times in an appalling whooping-cough dance, and rushing out at the door; he then became visible through the window, making the most hideous faces and apparently out of his mind.

I held on tight, while Mrs. Joe and Joe ran to him. I didn't know how I had done it, but I had no doubt I had murdered him somehow. In my dreadful situation, it was a relief when he was brought back, and, surveying the company all round as if *they* had disagreed with him, sank down into his chair with the one significant gasp, "Tar!"

I had filled up the bottle from the tar-water jug!

"Tar!" said my sister, in amazement. "Why, how ever could tar come there?"

But Uncle Pumblechook, who had the complete run of our kitchen, wouldn't hear the word, wouldn't hear

---

[1] **declamation** (dĕk'lá·mā'shŭn): high-flown speech in the manner of an oration.

I still held on to the leg of the table. . . .

of the subject, imperiously waved it away with his hand, and asked for hot gin-and-water. My sister now had to employ herself actively in getting the gin, the hot water, the sugar, and the lemon peel, and mixing them. For the time at least, I was saved. I still held on to the leg of the table, but clutched it now with the fervor of gratitude.

By degrees, I became calm enough to release my grasp and partake of pudding. Mr. Pumblechook partook of pudding. All partook of pudding. I began to think I should get over the day, when my sister said to Joe, "Clean plates — cold."

I clutched the leg of the table again immediately. I foresaw what was coming, and I felt that this time I really was gone.

"You must taste," said my sister, addressing the guests with her best grace, "you must taste, to finish with, a pie; a savory pork pie."

My sister went out to get it. I heard her steps proceed to the pantry. I saw Mr. Pumblechook balance his knife. I heard Joe say, "You shall have some, Pip." I felt that I could bear no more, and that I must run away. I released

the leg of the table and ran for my life.

But I ran no farther than the house door, for there I ran head foremost into a party of soldiers with their muskets, one of whom held out a pair of handcuffs to me, saying: "Here you are, look sharp, come on!"

CHAPTER 5

The sergeant finds the two convicts.

THE STRANGE sight of a file of soldiers ringing down the butt ends of their loaded muskets on our doorstep caused the dinner party to rise from table in confusion, and caused Mrs. Joe, re-entering the kitchen empty-handed, to stop short and stare in her wondering lament of "Gracious goodness gracious me, what's gone — with the — pie!"

The sergeant and I were in the kitchen when Mrs. Joe stood staring. It was the sergeant who had spoken to me, and he was now looking round at the company, with his handcuffs in his right hand, and his left on my shoulder.

"Excuse me, ladies and gentlemen," said the sergeant, "but I want the blacksmith."

"You see, blacksmith," said the sergeant, who had by this time picked out Joe with his eye, "we have had an accident with these, and I find the lock of one of 'em goes wrong. As they are wanted for immediate service, will you throw your eye over them?"

Joe threw his eye over them and pronounced that the job would necessitate the lighting of his forge fire, and would take nearer two hours than one. "Will it? Then will you set about it at once, blacksmith?" said the offhand sergeant, "as it's on His Majesty's service." With that he called to his men, who came trooping into the kitchen one after another and piled their arms in a corner.

I was still in an agony of fear; but seeing that the handcuffs were not for me, and that the pie had been for the moment forgotten, I collected a little of my scattered wits.

"How far might you call yourselves from the marshes, hereabouts? Not above a mile, I reckon?"

"Just a mile," said Mrs. Joe.

"That'll do. We begin to close in upon 'em about dusk. That'll do."

"Convicts, sergeant?" asked Mr. Wopsle, in a matter-of-course way.

"Aye!" returned the sergeant. "Two. They're pretty well known to be out on the marshes still, and they won't try to get clear of 'em before dusk. Anybody here seen anything of any such game?"

Everybody, myself excepted, said no, with confidence. Nobody thought of me.

"Well," said the sergeant, "they'll find themselves trapped in a circle. Now, blacksmith! If you're ready, His Majesty the King is."

Joe had got his coat and waistcoat and cravat [1] off, and his leather apron on, and passed into the forge. One of the soldiers opened its wooden windows, another lighted the fire, another turned to at the bellows, the rest stood round the blaze, which was soon roaring. Then Joe began to hammer and clink, hammer and clink, and we all looked on.

At last Joe's job was done, and the ringing and roaring stopped. As Joe got on his coat, he mustered courage to propose that some of us should go down with the soldiers and see what came of the hunt. Mr. Wopsle said he would go, if Joe would. Joe said he was agreeable and would take me.

The sergeant took a polite leave of the ladies, and his men resumed their muskets and fell in. Mr. Wopsle, Joe, and I received strict charge to keep in the rear and to speak no word after we reached the marshes. When we were all out in the raw air and were steadily moving toward our business, I whispered to Joe, "I hope, Joe, we shan't find them." And Joe whispered to me, "I'd give a shilling if they had escaped, Pip."

We were joined by no stragglers from the village, for the weather was cold and threatening, the way dreary, the footing bad, darkness coming on, and the people had good fires indoors, and were keeping the day. We struck out on the open marshes, through the gate at the side of the churchyard. A bitter sleet came rattling against us here on the east wind, and Joe took me on his back.

Now that we were out upon the dismal wilderness where I had been only eight or nine hours before, and had seen both men hiding, I considered for the first time, with great dread, if we should come upon them, would my par-

[1] cravat (krȧ·văt'): a necktie.

ticular convict suppose that it was I who had brought the soldiers there? He had asked me if I was a deceiving imp, and he said I should be a fierce young hound if I joined the hunt against him. Would he believe that I was both imp and hound in treacherous earnest, and had betrayed him?

It was of no use asking myself this question now. There I was, on Joe's back, and there was Joe beneath me, charging at the ditches like a hunter. The soldiers were in front of us, extending into a pretty wide line with an interval between man and man.

With my heart thumping at Joe's broad shoulder, I looked all about for any sign of the convicts. I could see none, I could hear none. The soldiers were moving on in the direction of the old Battery, and we were moving on a little way behind them, when, all of a sudden, we all stopped. For there had reached us, on the wings of the wind and rain, a long shout. It was repeated. The sergeant, a decisive man, ordered that the sound should not be answered, but that the course should be changed, and that his men should make toward it "at the double."

It was a run indeed now. Down banks and up banks, and over gates, and splashing into dikes, and breaking among coarse rushes, no man cared where he went. As we came nearer to the shouting, it became more and more apparent that it was made by more than one voice. After a while, we could hear one voice calling "Murder!" and another voice, "Convicts! Runaways! Guard! This way for the runaway convicts!" Then both voices would seem to be stifled in a struggle, and then would break out again. And when it had come to this, the soldiers ran like deer, and Joe too.

The sergeant ran in first, and two of his men ran in close upon him. Their pieces were cocked and leveled when we all ran in.

"Here are both men!" panted the sergeant, struggling at the bottom of a ditch. "Surrender, you two! and confound you for two wild beasts! Come asunder!"

Water was splashing, and mud was flying, and oaths were being sworn, and blows were being struck, when some more men went down into the ditch to help the sergeant, and dragged out, separately, my convict and the other one. Both were bleeding and panting and swearing and struggling; but of course I knew them both immediately.

"Mind," said my convict, wiping blood from his face with his ragged sleeves, and shaking torn hair from his fingers, "I took him! I give him up to you! Mind that!"

"It's not much to be particular about," said the sergeant. "It'll do you small good, my man, being in the same plight yourself. Handcuffs there!"

"I don't expect it to do me any good. I don't want it to do me more good than it does now," said my convict, with a greedy laugh. "I took him. He knows it. That's enough for me."

The other convict, in addition to the old bruised left side of his face, seemed to be bruised and torn all over. He could not so much as get his breath to speak, until they were both separately handcuffed, but leaned upon a soldier to keep himself from falling.

"Take notice, guard — he tried to murder me," were his first words.

"Tried to murder him?" said my convict disdainfully. "Try, and not do it? I took him, and giv' him up; that's what I done. I not only prevented him getting off the marshes, but I dragged him here. He's a gentleman if you please, this villain. Now the Hulks has got its gentleman again, through me. Murder him? When I could do worse and drag him back?"

The other one still gasped, "He tried — he tried — to — murder me. Bear — bear witness."

"Lookee here!" said my convict to the sergeant. "Singlehanded I got clear of the prison ship; I made a dash and I done it. I could ha' got clear of these death-cold flats likewise — look at my leg; you won't find much iron on it — if I hadn't made discovery that *he* was here. Let *him* go free? Let *him* profit by means as I found out? Let *him* make a tool of me afresh and again? Once more? No, no, no. If I had died at the bottom there," and he made an emphatic swing at the ditch with his manacled [1] hands, "I'd have held to him with that grip, that you should have been safe to find him in my hold."

The other fugitive, who was evidently in extreme horror of his companion, repeated, "He tried to murder me. I should have been a dead man if you had not come up."

"He lies!" said my convict, with fierce energy. "He's a liar born, and he'll die a liar. Look at his face; ain't it written there? Let him turn those eyes of his on me. I defy him to do it."

The other looked at the soldiers, and looked about at the marshes and at the sky, but certainly did not look at the speaker.

"Do you see him?" pursued my convict. "Do you see what a villain he is? Do you see those groveling and wandering eyes? That's how he looked when we were tried together. He never looked at me."

The other, turning his eyes restlessly about him far and near, did at last turn them for a moment on the speaker, with

[1] **manacled** (măn′*à*·k'ld): chained; handcuffed.

the words, "You are not much to look at," and with a half-taunting glance at the bound hands. At that point, my convict became so frantic that he would have rushed upon him but for the interposition of the soldiers. "Didn't I tell you," said the other convict then, "that he would murder me, if he could?" And anyone could see that he shook with fear, and that there broke out upon his lips curious white flakes, like thin snow.

"Enough of this!" said the sergeant. "Light those torches."

As one of the soldiers, who carried a basket, went down on his knee to open it, my convict looked round him for the first time and saw me. I had alighted from Joe's back on the brink of the ditch when we came up, and had not moved since. I looked at him eagerly when he looked at me, and slightly moved my hands and shook my head. I had been waiting for him to see me, that I might try to assure him of my innocence. He gave me a look that I did not understand, and it all passed in a moment. But he looked at me closely, and I knew I could not fail to remember his face ever afterward.

The soldier with the basket soon lighted three or four torches. Before we departed from that spot, four soldiers, standing in a ring, fired twice into the air. Presently we saw other torches kindled at some distance behind us, and others on the marshes on the opposite bank of the river. "All right," said the sergeant. "March."

We had not gone far when three cannon were fired ahead of us with a sound that seemed to burst something inside my ear. "You are expected on board," said the sergeant to my convict. "They know you are coming. Don't struggle, my man. Close up here."

The two were kept apart, and each walked surrounded by a separate guard.

I had hold of Joe's hand now, and Joe carried one of the torches. Mr. Wopsle had been for going back, but Joe was resolved to see it out, so we went on with the party. The two prisoners limped along in the midst of the muskets. We could not go fast, because of their lameness; and they were so spent, that two or three times we had to halt while they rested.

After an hour or so, we came to a rough wooden hut and a landing place. Then we went into the hut, where there was a smell of tobacco and whitewash, and a bright fire, and a lamp.

My convict never looked at me, except that once. While we stood in the hut, he turned to the sergeant and remarked:

"I wish to say something respecting this escape. It may prevent some persons laying under suspicion because of me."

"You can say what you like," returned the sergeant, standing coolly looking at him with his arms folded, "but you have no call to say it here. You'll have opportunity enough to say about it, and hear about it, before it's done with, you know."

"I know, but this is another matter. A man can't starve; at least *I* can't. I took some wittles, up at the village over yonder — "

"You mean stole," said the sergeant.

"And I'll tell you where from. From the blacksmith's."

"Halloa!" said the sergeant, staring at Joe.

"Halloa, Pip!" said Joe, staring at me.

"It was some broken wittles — that's what it was — and a dram of liquor, and a pie."

"Have you happened to miss such an article as a pie, blacksmith?" asked the sergeant confidentially.

"My wife did, at the very moment when you came in. Don't you know, Pip?"

"So," said my convict, turning his eyes on Joe in a moody manner, and without the least glance at me; "so you're the blacksmith, are you? Then I'm sorry to say, I've eat your pie."

"God knows you're welcome to it — so far as it was ever mine," returned Joe, with a saving remembrance of Mrs. Joe. "We don't know what you have done, but we wouldn't have you starved to death for it, poor miserable fellow creature. Would us, Pip?"

The something that I had noticed before clicked in the man's throat again, and he turned his back. The boat had returned, and his guard were ready, so we followed him to the landing place, and saw him put into the boat, which was rowed by a crew of convicts like himself. No one seemed surprised to see him, or interested in seeing him, or glad to see him, or sorry to see him, or spoke a word except that somebody in the boat growled as if to dogs, "Give way, you!" which was the signal for the dip of the oars. By the light of the torches, we saw the black Hulk lying out a little way from the mud of the shore, like a wicked Noah's ark. Cribbed and barred and moored by massive rusty chains, the prison ship seemed in my young eyes to be ironed like the prisoners. We saw the boat go alongside, and we saw him taken up the side and disappear. Then, the ends of the torches were flung hissing into the water, and went out, as if it were all over with him.

And so far as I could know it was all over with him, for I never mentioned him, or my pilfering in his behalf, to a living soul. I loved Joe — perhaps for no better reason in those days than because the dear fellow let me love him — and it was much on my mind that I ought to tell Joe the whole truth. Yet I did not, for I feared he would think me worse than I was. The fear of losing Joe's confidence tied my tongue. In a word, I was too cowardly to do what I knew to be right, just as I had been too cowardly to avoid doing what I knew to be wrong.

CHAPTER 6

We meet Mr. Wopsle's great-aunt and Biddy, her granddaughter.

WHEN I was old enough, I was to be apprenticed to Joe, and until I could assume that dignity I was not to be what Mrs. Joe called "Pompeyed," or (as I render it) pampered. Therefore, I was not only odd boy about the forge, but if any neighbor happened to want an extra boy to frighten birds, or pick up stones, or do any such job, I was favored with the employment. A money box was kept on the kitchen mantel shelf, into which it was publicly made known that all my earnings were dropped, but I had no hope of any personal claim to the treasure.

Mr. Wopsle's great-aunt kept an evening school in the village. She was a ridiculous old woman who used to go to sleep from six to seven every evening, in the company of youth who paid twopence [1] per week each for the improving opportunity of seeing her do it. She rented a small cottage, and Mr. Wopsle had the room upstairs, where we students used to overhear him reading aloud in a most dignified and terrific manner, and occasionally bumping on the ceiling. There was a pretense that

Mr. Wopsle "examined" the scholars once a quarter. What he did on those occasions was to turn up his cuffs, stick up his hair, and give us Mark Antony's oration over the body of Caesar. [2]

Mr. Wopsle's great-aunt, besides keeping this educational institution, kept — in the same room — a little general shop. She had no idea what stock she had, or what the price of anything in it was; but there was a little greasy memorandum book kept in a drawer, which served as a catalogue of prices, and by this list Biddy arranged all the shop transactions. Biddy was Mr. Wopsle's great-aunt's granddaughter. She was an orphan like myself; like me, too, she had been brought up by hand. Her hair always wanted brushing, her hands always wanted washing, and her shoes always wanted mending and pulling up at heel.

More by the help of Biddy than of Mr. Wopsle's great-aunt, I struggled through the alphabet as if it had been a bramblebush, getting considerably worried and scratched by every letter. After that, I fell among those thieves, the nine figures, who seemed every evening to do something new to disguise themselves and baffle recognition. But at last I began, in a groping way, to read, write, and cipher, [3] on the very smallest scale.

One night, I was sitting in the chimney corner with my slate, expending great efforts on the writing of a letter to Joe. I think it must have been a full year after our hunt upon the marshes, for it was a long time after, and it was winter and a hard frost. With an alphabet on the hearth at my feet for reference, I contrived in an hour or two to print and smear this epistle:

[1] twopence (tŭp'ĕns): an amount equaling about four cents in American money.

[2] Mark Antony's oration is from Shakespeare's play, Julius Caesar.
[3] cipher (sī'fēr): do sums in arithmetic.

mI deEr JO i opE U r krWitE wELl
i opE i shAl soN B haBell 4 2 teeDge
U JO aN theN wE shOrl b sO glOdd
aN wEn i M preNgtD 2 u JO woT
larX an blEvE ME inF xn PiP.

There was no necessity for my writing Joe a letter, inasmuch as he sat beside me and we were alone. But I delivered this written communication (slate
and all) with my own hand, and Joe
received it as a miracle of learning.

"I say, Pip, old chap!" cried Joe,
opening his blue eyes wide. "What a
scholar you are! Ain't you?"

"I should like to be," said I, glancing
at the slate as he held it, with a misgiv-
ing that the writing was rather hilly.

"Why, here's a J," said Joe, "and a O
equal to anythink! Here's a J and a O,
Pip, and a J-O, Joe."

I had never heard Joe read aloud
to any greater extent than this single
word, and I had observed at church
last Sunday, when I accidentally held
our prayer book upside down, that it
seemed to suit his convenience quite as
well as if it had been all right. Wishing
to find out whether, in teaching Joe, I
should have to begin quite at the beginning, I said, "Ah! But read the rest,
Joe."

"The rest, eh, Pip?" said Joe, looking
at it with a slowly searching eye. "One,
two, three. Why, here's three J's, and
three O's, and three J-O, Joe's, in it,
Pip!"

I leaned over Joe, and, with the aid
of my forefinger, read him the whole
letter.

"Astonishing!" said Joe, when I had
finished. "You *are* a scholar."

"How do you spell Gargery, Joe?" I
asked.

"I don't spell it at all," said Joe.

"But supposing you did?"

"It *can't* be supposed," said Joe.

"Tho' I'm uncommon fond of reading,
too."

"Are you, Joe?"

"Uncommon. Give me," said Joe, "a
good book, or a good newspaper, and
sit me down afore a good fire, and I ask
no better. Lord!" he continued, after
rubbing his knees a little, "when you *do*
come to a J and a O, and says you,
'Here, at last, is a J-O, Joe,' how interesting reading is!"

I derived from this last, that Joe's education was yet in its infancy. Pursuing
the subject, I inquired:

"Didn't you ever go to school, Joe,
when you were as little as me?"

"No, Pip."

"Why didn't you ever go to school,
Joe, when you were as little as me?"

"Well, Pip," said Joe, taking up the
poker, and settling himself to his usual
occupation, when he was thoughtful, of
slowly raking the fire between the lower bars, "I'll tell you. My father, Pip, he
were given to drink, and when he were
overtook with drink, he hammered
away at my mother most unmerciful.
My mother and me we ran away from
my father several times; and then my
mother she'd go out to work, and she'd
say, 'Joe,' she'd say, 'now, please God,
you shall have some schooling, child,'
and she'd put me to school. But my father were that good in his heart that he
couldn't a-bear to be without us. So, he
took us home and hammered us. Which,
you see, Pip," said Joe, "were a drawback on my learning."

"Certainly, poor Joe!"

"Though mind you, Pip," said Joe,
"rendering unto all their due, and
maintaining equal justice betwixt man
and man, my father were that good in
his heart, don't you see?"

I didn't see; but I didn't say so.

"'Consequence, my father didn't
make objections to my going to work;

so I went to work at my present calling, and I worked tolerable hard, I assure you, Pip. In time I were able to keep him, and I kept him till he went off in a purple leptic fit.[1] My mother, she were in poor 'elth, and quite broke. She weren't long of following, poor soul, and her share of peace come round at last."

Joe's blue eyes turned a little watery. "It were but lonesome then," said Joe, "living here alone, and I got acquainted with your sister. Now, Pip," Joe looked firmly at me, as if he knew I was not going to agree with him, "your sister is a fine figure of a woman."

I could not help looking at the fire, in an obvious state of doubt.

"Whatever family opinions, or whatever the world's opinions, on that subject may be, Pip, your sister is," Joe tapped the top bar with the poker after every word following, "a — fine — figure — of — a — woman!"

I could think of nothing better to say than "I am glad you think so, Joe."

"So am I," returned Joe. "When I offered to your sister to keep company, and to be asked in church, at such times as she was willing and ready to come to the forge, I said to her, 'And bring the poor little child. God bless the poor little child,' I said to your sister, 'there's room for *him* at the forge!' "

I broke out crying and hugged Joe round the neck. Joe dropped the poker to hug me, and to say, "Ever the best of friends; ain't us, Pip? Don't cry, old chap!"

When this little interruption was over, Joe resumed:

"Well, you see, Pip, and here we are! Now, when you take me in hand in my learning, Pip (and I tell you before-

[1] **purple leptic fit:** Joe probably means to say "apoplectic (ăp'ō·plĕk'tĭk)." Apoplexy is a sudden paralysis or loss of consciousness, sometimes called a "stroke."

hand I am awful dull, most awful dull), Mrs. Joe mustn't see too much of what we're up to. It must be done, as I may say, on the sly. I'll tell you why, Pip.

"Your sister ain't overpartial to having scholars on the premises," Joe continued, "and in partickler would not be overpartial to my being a scholar, for fear as I might rise. Like a sort of rebel, don't you see?"

Young as I was, I believe that I dated a new admiration of Joe from that night. We were equals afterward, as we had been before; but afterward, at quiet times when I sat looking at Joe and thinking about him, I had a new sensation of feeling conscious that I was looking up to Joe in my heart.

"However," said Joe, rising to feed the fire, "here's the Dutch clock a-working himself up to being equal to strike eight of them, and she's not home yet!"

Mrs. Joe made occasional trips with Uncle Pumblechook on market days to assist him in buying such household stuffs and goods as required a woman's judgment, Uncle Pumblechook being a bachelor. This was market day, and Mrs. Joe was out on one of these expeditions.

Joe made the fire and swept the hearth, and then we went to the door to listen for the carriage. It was a dry, cold night.

"Here comes the mare," said Joe, "ringing like a peal of bells!"

Mrs. Joe was soon landed, and Uncle Pumblechook was soon down too, and we were soon all in the kitchen, carrying so much cold air with us that it seemed to drive all the heat out of the fire.

"Now," said Mrs. Joe, unwrapping herself with haste and excitement, and throwing her bonnet back on her shoulders, where it hung by the strings, "if

"I say, Pip, old chap!" cried Joe. . . . "What a scholar you are! Ain't you?"

this boy ain't grateful this night, he never will be!"

I looked as grateful as any boy possibly could who was wholly uninformed why he ought to be grateful.

"It's only to be hoped," said my sister, "that he won't be Pompeyed. But I have my fears."

"She ain't like that, mum," said Mr. Pumblechook. "She knows better."

She? I looked at Joe, making the motion with my lips and eyebrows. "She?" Joe looked at me, making the motion with *his* lips and eyebrows. "She?" My sister catching him in the act, he drew the back of his hand across his nose with his usual air on such occasions, and looked at her.

"Well?" said my sister, in her snappish way. "What are you staring at? Is the house afire?"

"Some indiwidual," Joe politely hinted, "mentioned she."

"And she is a she, I suppose?" said my sister. "Unless you call Miss Havisham a he. And I doubt if even you'll go so far as that."

"Miss Havisham uptown?" said Joe.

"Is there any Miss Havisham downtown?" returned my sister. "She wants this boy to go and play there. And of course he's going. And he had better play there," said my sister, shaking her head at me as an encouragement to be extremely light and sportive, "or I'll work him."

I had heard of Miss Havisham uptown — everybody for miles round had heard of Miss Havisham uptown — as an immensely rich and grim lady who lived in a large and dismal house barricaded against robbers, and who led a life of seclusion.

"Well, to be sure!" said Joe, astounded. "I wonder how she comes to know Pip!"

"Noodle!" cried my sister. "Who said she knew him?"

"Some indiwidual," Joe again politely hinted, "mentioned that she wanted him to go and play there."

"And couldn't she ask Uncle Pumblechook if he knew of a boy to go and play there? Isn't it just barely possible that Uncle Pumblechook may be a tenant of hers, and that he may sometimes go there to pay his rent? And couldn't she then ask Uncle Pumblechook if he knew of a boy to go and play there? And couldn't Uncle Pumblechook — being always considerate and thoughtful for us, though you may not think so, Joseph — then mention this boy that I have forever been a willing slave to?" My sister spoke in a tone of deepest reproach as if Joe were the most callous of nephews.

"Good again!" cried Uncle Pumblechook. "Well put! Good indeed! Now, Joseph, you know the case."

"No, Joseph," said my sister, in a reproachful manner, "you do not yet — though you may not think it — know the case. Uncle Pumblechook, being sensible that this boy's fortune may be made by his going to Miss Havisham's, has offered to take him into town tonight in his own carriage, and to keep him tonight and to take him with his own hands to Miss Havisham's tomorrow morning. And Lor-a-mussy me!" cried my sister, casting off her bonnet in sudden desperation, "here I stand talking, with Uncle Pumblechook waiting, and the mare catching cold at the door, and the boy grimed with crock and dirt from the hair of his head to the sole of his foot!"

With that she pounced on me, like an eagle on a lamb, and my face was squeezed into wooden bowls in sinks, and my head was put under taps of water butts, and I was soaped, and kneaded, and toweled, and thumped, and harrowed, and rasped, until I really was quite beside myself.

When my washing was completed, I was put into clean linen of the stiffest character, and was trussed up in my tightest and fearfulest suit. I was then delivered over to Mr. Pumblechook, who formally received me as if he were the sheriff, and who let off upon me the

speech that I knew he had been dying to make all along: "Boy, be forever grateful to all friends, but especially unto them which brought you up by hand!"

"Good-by, Joe!"

"God bless you, Pip, old chap!"

I had never parted from him before, and what with my feelings and what with soapsuds, I could at first see no stars from the carriage. But they twinkled out one by one, without throwing any light on the question why on earth I was going to play at Miss Havisham's, and what on earth I was expected to play at.

CHAPTER 7

We are introduced to Miss Havisham and her ward Estella.

UPON REACHING Mr. Pumblechook's grain and seed shop on the High Street of the market town, I was sent straight to bed in an attic with a sloping roof, which was so low in the corner where the bedstead was that I calculated the tiles as being within a foot of my eyebrows.

Mr. Pumblechook and I breakfasted at eight o'clock in the parlor behind the shop while his shopman took his mug of tea and hunk of bread-and-butter on a sack of peas in the front premises. I considered Mr. Pumblechook wretched company. Besides giving me as much crumb as possible in combination with as little butter, and putting a great quantity of warm water in my milk, his conversation consisted of nothing but arithmetic. On my politely bidding him good morning, he said pompously, "Seven times nine, boy?" And how should *I* be able to answer, dodged in that way, in a strange place, on an empty stomach! I was hungry, but before I had swallowed a morsel, he began a running sum that lasted all through the breakfast. "Seven?" "And four?" "And eight?" "And six?" "And two?" "And ten?" And so on.

I was very glad when ten o'clock came and we started for Miss Havisham's. Within a quarter of an hour we came to Miss Havisham's house, which was of old brick, and dismal, and had a great many iron bars to it. Some of the windows had been walled up; of those that remained, all the lower were rustily barred. There was a courtyard in front, and that was barred; so we had to wait, after ringing the bell, until someone should come to open it. While we waited at the gate, I saw that at the side of the house there was a large brewery. No brewing was going on in it, and none seemed to have gone on for a long time.

A window was raised, and a clear voice demanded, "What name?" To which my conductor replied, "Pumblechook." The voice returned, "Quite right," and the window was shut again, and a young lady came across the courtyard, with keys in her hand.

"This," said Mr. Pumblechook, "is Pip."

"This is Pip, is it?" returned the young lady, who was very pretty, and seemed very proud. "Come in, Pip."

Mr. Pumblechook was coming in also, when she stopped him with the gate.

"Oh!" she said. "Did you wish to see Miss Havisham?"

"If Miss Havisham wished to see me," returned Mr. Pumblechook, somewhat confused.

"Ah!" said the girl. "But you see she doesn't."

She said it so finally, that Mr. Pumblechook could not protest. But he eyed me severely — as if *I* had done anything to him! — and departed with the words reproachfully delivered: "Boy! Let your behavior here be a credit unto them which brought you up by hand!"

My young conductress locked the gate, and we went across the courtyard. It was paved and clean, but grass was growing in every crevice. The brewery beyond stood open, and all was empty and disused. The cold wind seemed to blow colder there than outside the gate; and it made a shrill noise in howling in and out at the open sides of the brewery, like the noise of wind in the rigging of a ship at sea.

"What is the name of this house, miss?"

"Its name was Satis; which is Greek, or Latin, or Hebrew, or all three — or all one to me — for enough."

"Enough House!" said I. "That's a curious name, miss."

"Yes," she replied, "but it means more than it says. It meant, when it was given, that whoever had this house, could want nothing else. They must have been easily satisfied in those days, I should think. But don't loiter, boy."

Though she called me "boy" so often, and with a carelessness that was far from complimentary, she was of about my own age. She seemed much older than I, of course, being a girl, and beautiful and self-possessed; and she was as scornful of me as if she had been one-and-twenty, and a queen.

We went into the house by a side door — the great front entrance had two chains across it outside — and the first thing I noticed was that the passages were all dark, and that she had left a candle burning there. She took it up, and we went through more passages and up a staircase, and still it was all dark, and only the candle lighted us.

At last we came to the door of a

room, and she said, "Go in."

I answered, more in shyness than politeness, "After you, miss."

To this she returned, "Don't be ridiculous, boy; I am not going in." And scornfully walked away, and — what was worse — took the candle with her.

This was very uncomfortable, and I was half afraid. However, the only thing to be done being to knock at the door, I knocked, and was told from within to enter. I entered, therefore, and found myself in a pretty large room, well lighted with wax candles. No glimpse of daylight was to be seen in it. It was a dressing room, as I supposed from the furniture. But prominent in it was a draped table with a gilded looking glass, and that I made out at first sight to be a fine lady's dressing table.

In an armchair, with an elbow resting on the table and her head leaning on that hand, sat the strangest lady I have ever seen, or shall ever see.

She was dressed in rich materials — satins, and lace, and silks — all of white. Her shoes were white. She had a long white veil hanging from her hair, and she had bridal flowers in her hair, but her hair was white. Some bright jewels sparkled on her neck and on her hands, and some other jewels lay sparkling on the table. Dresses and half-packed trunks were scattered about. She had not quite finished dressing, for she had but one shoe on — the other was on the table near her hand — her veil was but half arranged, her watch and chain were not put on, and her handkerchief and gloves, some flowers, and a prayer book lay all confusedly heaped about the looking glass.

But I saw that everything within my view which ought to be white had lost its luster, and was faded and yellow. I saw that the bride within the bridal dress had withered like the dress, and like the flowers, and had no brightness left but the brightness of her sunken eyes. I saw that the dress had been put upon the rounded figure of a young woman, and that the figure upon which it now hung loose had shrunk to skin and bone.

"Who is it?" said the lady at the table.

"Pip, ma'am."

"Pip?"

"Mr. Pumblechook's boy, ma'am. Come — to play."

"Come nearer; let me look at you. Come closer."

It was when I stood before her, avoiding her eyes, that I took note of the surrounding objects in detail, and saw that her watch had stopped at twenty minutes to nine, and that a clock in the room had stopped at twenty minutes to nine.

"Look at me," said Miss Havisham. "You are not afraid of a woman who has never seen the sun since you were born?"

I regret to state that I was not afraid of telling an enormous lie in the answer, "No."

"Do you know what I touch here?" she said, laying her hands, one upon the other, on her left side.

"Yes, ma'am."

"What do I touch?"

"Your heart."

"Broken!"

She uttered the word with an eager look, and with strong emphasis, and with a weird smile that had a kind of boast in it.

"I am tired," said Miss Havisham. "I sometimes have sick fancies, and I have a sick fancy that I want to see some play. There, there!" with an impatient movement of the fingers of her right hand, "play, play, play!"

I stood looking at Miss Havisham in what I suppose she took for a stubborn manner, inasmuch as she said, when we had taken a good look at each other:

"Are you sullen and obstinate?"

"No, ma'am, I am very sorry for you, and very sorry I can't play just now. If you complain of me, I shall get into trouble with my sister, so I would do it if I could; but it's so new here, and so strange, and so fine — and sad — " I stopped, fearing I might say too much, or had already said it, and we took another look at each other.

Before she spoke again, she turned her eyes from me, and looked at the dress she wore, and at the dressing table, and finally at herself in the looking glass.

"So new to him," she muttered, "so old to me; so strange to him, so familiar to me; so sad to both of us! Call Estella."

As she was still looking at the reflection of herself, I thought she was still talking to herself, and kept quiet.

"Call Estella," she repeated, flashing a look at me. "You can do that. Call Estella. At the door."

I called, and the scornful young lady answered at last, and her light came along the dark passage like a star.

Miss Havisham beckoned her to come close, and took up a jewel from the table, and tried its effect against her pretty brown hair. "Your own, one day, my dear, and you will use it well. Let me see you play cards with this boy."

"With this boy! Why, he is a common laboring boy!"

I thought I overheard Miss Havisham answer — only it seemed so unlikely — "Well? You can break his heart."

"What do you play, boy?" asked Estella of me, with the greatest disdain.

"Nothing but beggar my neighbor, miss."

"Beggar him," said Miss Havisham to Estella. So we sat down to cards.

It was then I began to understand that everything in the room had stopped, like the watch and the clock, a long time ago. I noticed that Miss Havisham put down the jewel exactly on the spot from which she had taken it up. As Estella dealt the cards, I glanced at the dressing table again, and saw that the shoe upon it, once white, now yellow, had never been worn. I glanced down at the foot from which the shoe was absent, and saw that the silk stocking on it, once white, now yellow, had been trodden ragged.

Miss Havisham sat, corpselike, as we played at cards.

"He calls the knaves jacks, this boy!" said Estella with disdain, before our first game was out. "And what coarse hands he has! And what thick boots!"

I had never thought of being ashamed of my hands before; but her contempt for me was so strong that it became infectious, and I caught it.

She won the game, and I dealt. I misdealt, as was only natural when I knew she was lying in wait for me to do wrong; and she denounced me for a stupid, clumsy, laboring boy.

"You say nothing of her," remarked Miss Havisham to me, as she looked on. "She says many hard things of you, yet you say nothing of her. What do you think of her?"

"I don't like to say," I stammered.

"Tell me in my ear," said Miss Havisham, bending down.

"I think she is very proud," I replied, in a whisper.

"Anything else?"

"I think she is very pretty."

"Anything else?"

"I think she is very insulting." (She

She was dressed in rich materials — satins, and lace, and silks — all of white.

was looking at me then with a look of supreme distaste.)

"Anything else?"

"I think I should like to go home."

"And never see her again, though she is so pretty?"

"I am not sure that I shouldn't like to see her again, but I should like to go home now."

"You shall go soon," said Miss Havisham aloud. "Play the game out."

I played the game to an end with Estella, and she won of me. She threw the cards down on the table when she had won them all, as if she despised them for having been won of me.

"When shall I have you here again?" said Miss Havisham. "Let me think. Come again after six days. You hear?"

"Yes, ma'am."

"Estella, take him down. Let him have something to eat, and let him roam and look about him while he eats. Go, Pip."

I followed the candle down, as I had followed the candle up, and she stood it in the place where we had found it.

"You are to wait here, you boy," said Estella. She disappeared and closed the door.

I took the opportunity of being alone to look at my coarse hands and my common boots. They had never troubled me before, but they troubled me now. I determined to ask Joe why he had ever taught me to call those picture cards jacks, which ought to be called knaves. I wished Joe had been better brought up, and then I should have been so too.

She came back, with some bread and meat and a little mug of beer. She put the mug down on the stones of the yard, and gave me the bread and meat without looking at me, as insolently as if I were a dog in disgrace. I was so humiliated, hurt, spurned, offended, angry,

sorry, that tears started to my eyes. The moment they sprang there, the girl looked at me with a quick delight in having been the cause of them. This gave me power to keep them back and to look at her; so she gave a contemptuous toss — but with a sense, I thought, of having made too sure that I was so wounded — and left me.

But, when she was gone, I got behind one of the gates in the brewery lane, and leaned my sleeve against the wall there, and leaned my forehead on it, and cried. As I cried, I kicked the wall, and took a hard twist at my hair, so bitter were my feelings.

I got rid of my injured feelings for the time, by kicking them into the brewery wall, and twisting them out of my hair, and then I smoothed my face with my sleeve, and came from behind the gate. The bread and meat were acceptable, and the beer was warming and tingling.

Soon I saw Estella approaching with the keys to let me out. She gave me a triumphant glance in passing me, as if she rejoiced that my hands were so coarse and my boots were so thick, and she opened the gate and stood holding it. I was passing out without looking at her, when she touched me with a taunting hand.

"Why don't you cry?"

"Because I don't want to."

"You do," said she. "You have been crying till you are half blind, and you are near crying again now."

She laughed, pushed me out, and locked the gate upon me. I went straight to Mr. Pumblechook's, and was immensely relieved to find him not at home. So, leaving word with the shopman on what day I was wanted at Miss Havisham's again, I set off on the four-mile walk to our forge. As I went along, I thought on all I had seen, and that I was a common laboring boy; that my hands were coarse; that my boots were thick; that I was much more ignorant than I had considered myself last night; and generally that I was in a bad way.

CHAPTER 8

Pip tells some tall tales.

WHEN I reached home, my sister was very curious to know all about Miss Havisham's, and asked a number of questions. And I soon found myself getting heavily bumped from behind in the nape of the neck and the small of the back, and having my face shoved against the kitchen wall, because I did not answer those questions at sufficient length.

I felt convinced that if I described Miss Havisham's as my eyes had seen it, I should not be understood. Not only that, but I felt convinced that Miss Havisham too would not be understood. I felt that there would be something coarse and treacherous in my dragging her as she really was (to say nothing of Miss Estella) before the attention of Mrs. Joe. Consequently, I said as little as I could, and had my face shoved against the kitchen wall.

The worst of it was that bullying old Pumblechook, who had a devouring curiosity to be informed of all I had seen and heard. He came gaping over in his carriage at teatime, to have the details related to him.

"Well, boy," Uncle Pumblechook began, as soon as he was seated in the chair of honor by the fire. "How did you get on uptown?"

I answered, "Pretty well, sir," and my sister shook her fist at me.

"Pretty well?" Mr. Pumblechook repeated. "Pretty well is no answer. Tell us what you mean by pretty well, boy!"

My sister with an exclamation of impatience was going to fly at me — I had no shadow of defense, for Joe was busy in the forge — when Mr. Pumblechook interposed with "No! Don't lose your temper. Leave this lad to me, ma'am; leave this lad to me." Mr. Pumblechook then turned me toward him, as if he were going to cut my hair, and said:

"Boy! What is Miss Havisham like?" Mr. Pumblechook began again, folding his arms tight on his chest.

"Very tall and dark," I told him.

"Is she, uncle?" asked my sister.

Mr. Pumblechook winked assent, from which I at once gathered that he had never seen Miss Havisham, for she was nothing of the kind.

"Good!" said Mr. Pumblechook, conceitedly. "This is the way to have him! We are beginning to hold our own, I think, mum?"

"I am sure, uncle," returned Mrs. Joe; "I wish you had him always; you know so well how to deal with him."

"Now, boy! What was she a-doing of, when you went in today?" asked Mr. Pumblechook.

"She was sitting," I answered, "in a black velvet coach."

Mr. Pumblechook and Mrs. Joe stared at one another — as they well might — and both repeated, "In a black velvet coach?"

"Yes," said I. "And Miss Estella — that's her niece, I think — handed her in cake and wine at the coach window, on a gold plate. And we all had cake and wine on gold plates. And I got up behind the coach to eat mine, because she told me to."

Mr. Pumblechook and Mrs. Joe

stared at one another again, in utter amazement. I was perfectly frantic — a reckless witness under the torture — and would have told them anything.

"Did you ever see her in it, uncle?" asked Mrs. Joe.

"How could I," he returned, forced to tell the truth, "when I never see her in my life? Never clapped eyes upon her!"

"Goodness, uncle! And yet you have spoken to her?"

"Why, don't you know," said Mr. Pumblechook testily, "that when I have been there, I have been took up to the outside of her door, and the door has stood ajar, and she spoken to me that way. What did you play at, boy?"

"We played with flags," I said. (I beg to observe that I think of myself with amazement, when I recall the lies I told on this occasion.)

"Flags!" echoed my sister.

"Yes," said I. "Estella waved a blue flag, and I waved a red one, and Miss Havisham waved one sprinkled all over with little gold stars, out at the coach window. And then we all waved our swords and hurrahed."

If they had asked me any more questions, I should undoubtedly have betrayed myself, but Joe came in then to have a cup of tea, and my sister began to tell him of my pretended experiences.

Now, when I saw Joe open his blue eyes and roll them all round the kitchen in helpless amazement, I was overtaken by repentance. Toward Joe, and Joe only, I considered myself a young monster, while they sat debating what results would come to me from Miss Havisham's acquaintance and favor. They had no doubt that Miss Havisham would "do something" for me. My sister thought it would be "property." Mr. Pumblechook was in favor of a hand-

some premium [1] for binding me apprentice to some trade.

After Mr. Pumblechook had driven off, and when my sister was washing up, I stole into the forge to Joe, and remained by him until he had done for the night. Then I said, "Before the fire goes out, Joe, I should like to tell you something."

"Should you, Pip?" said Joe, drawing his shoeing stool near the forge. "Then tell us. What is it, Pip?"

"Joe," said I, taking hold of his rolled-up shirt sleeve, and twisting it between my finger and thumb, "you remember all about that Miss Havisham's?"

"Remember?" said Joe. "I believe you! Wonderful!"

"It's a terrible thing, Joe; it ain't true."

"What are you telling of, Pip?" cried Joe, falling back in the greatest amazement. "You don't mean to say it's — "

"Yes, I do; it's lies, Joe."

As I fixed my eyes hopelessly on Joe, he looked at me in dismay. "Pip, old chap! This won't do, old fellow! I say! Where do you expect to go to?"

"It's terrible, Joe; ain't it?"

"Terrible?" cried Joe. "Awful! What possessed you?"

"I don't know what possessed me, Joe," I replied, letting his shirt sleeve go, and sitting down in the ashes at his feet, hanging my head; "but I wish you hadn't taught me to call knaves at cards jacks, and I wish my boots weren't so thick nor my hands so coarse."

And then I told Joe that I felt very

[1] premium (prē′mĭ·ŭm): an initial fee paid to a master workman by a prospective apprentice. In former times, apprenticeship was the most common way to learn a trade. A boy (with his parents or guardian) signed a contract, called "indentures," by which he was bound to serve a master workman without pay for five to seven years. In return for this service, he was taught the workman's trade.

miserable, and that I hadn't been able to explain myself to Mrs. Joe and Pumblechook, who were so rude to me, and that there had been a beautiful young lady at Miss Havisham's who was dreadfully proud, and that she had said I was common, and that I knew I was common, and that I wished I was not common, and that the lies had come of it somehow, though I didn't know how.

"There's one thing you may be sure of, Pip," said Joe, "namely, that lies is lies. However they come, they didn't ought to come, and they come from the father of lies, and work round to the same. Don't you tell me no more of 'em, Pip. *That* ain't the way to get out of being common, old chap. And as to being common, I don't make it out at all clear. You are uncommon in some things. You're uncommon small. Likewise you're a uncommon scholar."

"No, I am ignorant and backward, Joe."

"Why, see what a letter you wrote last night! Wrote in print even! I've seen letters — ah! and from gentlefolks! — that I'll swear weren't wrote in print," said Joe.

"I have learned next to nothing, Joe. You think much of me. It's only that."

"Well, Pip," said Joe, "you must be a common scholar afore you can be a uncommon one, I should hope!"

"You are not angry with me, Joe?"

"No, old chap. That's all, old chap, and don't never do it no more."

When I got up to my little room and said my prayers, my young mind was in a disturbed and unthankful state. I thought long how common Estella would consider Joe, a mere blacksmith, how thick his boots, and how coarse his hands. I thought how Joe and my sister were then sitting in the kitchen, and how I had come up to bed from the kitchen, and how Miss Havisham and Estella never sat in a kitchen, but were far above the level of such common doings. I fell asleep recalling what I "used to do" when I was at Miss Havisham's; as though I had been there weeks or months, instead of hours.

That was a memorable day to me, for it made great changes in me. But it is the same with any life. Imagine one selected day struck out of it, and think how different its course would have been. Pause, you who read this, and think for a moment of the long chain of iron or gold, of thorns or flowers, that would never have bound you, but for the formation of the first link on one memorable day.

CHAPTER 9

A mysterious stranger appears with a surprise for Pip.

THE IDEA occurred to me a morning or two later when I woke, that the best step I could take toward making myself uncommon was to get out of Biddy everything she knew. I mentioned to Biddy when I went to Mr. Wopsle's great-aunt's at night, that I had a particular reason for wishing to get on in life, and that I should feel very much obliged to her if she would impart all her learning to me. Biddy, who was the most obliging of girls, immediately said she would, and indeed began to carry out her promise within five minutes.

The educational scheme or course established by Mr. Wopsle's great-aunt may be summarized briefly. The pupils ate apples and put straws down one another's backs until Mr. Wopsle's great-aunt collected her energies and tottered at us with a birch rod. After receiving

Biddy and Pip.

the charge with every mark of derision,[1] the pupils formed a line and buzzingly passed a ragged book from hand to hand. The book had an alphabet in it, some figures and tables, and a little spelling. Biddy gave out the number of the page, and then we all read aloud in a frightful chorus. Biddy led with a high shrill voice, and none of us had the least notion of, or respect for, what we were reading.

It appeared to me that it would take time to become uncommon under these circumstances; nevertheless, I resolved to try it, and that very evening Biddy entered on our special agreement by lending me, to copy at home, a large Old English *D* which she had imitated from the heading of some newspaper, and which I supposed, until she told me what it was, to be a design for a buckle.

Of course there was a public house in the village, and of course Joe liked sometimes to smoke his pipe there. I had received strict orders from my sister to call for him at the Three Jolly

[1] **derision** (dė·rĭzh'ŭn): ridicule; scorn.

Bargemen that evening, on my way from school, and bring him home at my peril. To the Three Jolly Bargemen, therefore, I directed my steps.

I found Joe there, smoking his pipe in company with Mr. Wopsle and a stranger. Joe greeted me as usual with "Halloa, Pip, old chap!" and the moment he said that, the stranger turned his head and looked at me.

He was a secret-looking man whom I had never seen before. His head was all on one side, and one of his eyes was half shut up, as if he were taking aim at something with an invisible gun. He had a pipe in his mouth, and he took it out, and, after slowly blowing all his smoke away and looking hard at me all the time, nodded. So I nodded, and then he nodded again, and made room on the settle beside him that I might sit down there.

But, as I was used to sit beside Joe whenever I entered that place of resort, I said, "No, thank you, sir," and fell into the space Joe made for me on the opposite settle. The strange man, after glancing at Joe, and seeing that his attention was otherwise engaged, nodded to me again when I had taken my seat, and then rubbed his leg — in a very odd way, it struck me.

"You were saying," said the strange man, turning to Joe, "that you was a blacksmith. What'll you drink, Mr. Gargery? At my expense? To top up with?"

"Well," said Joe, "to tell you the truth, I ain't much in the habit of drinking at anybody's expense but my own."

"Habit? No," returned the stranger, "but once and away, and on a Saturday night, too. Come! Put a name to it, Mr. Gargery."

"I wouldn't wish to be stiff company," said Joe. "Rum."

"Rum," repeated the stranger. "And the other gentleman?"

"Rum," said Mr. Wopsle.

"Three rums!" cried the stranger, calling to the landlord. "Glasses round!"

The stranger put his legs up on the settle that he had to himself. He wore a flapping broad-brimmed traveler's hat and under it a handkerchief tied over his head in the manner of a cap, so that he showed no hair.

"I am not acquainted with this country, gentlemen, but it seems a solitary country toward the river."

"Most marshes is solitary," said Joe.

"No doubt, no doubt. Do you find any gypsies, now, or tramps, or vagrants of any sort, out there?"

"No," said Joe; "none but a runaway convict now and then. And we don't find *them* easy."

"Seems you have been out after such?" asked the stranger.

"Once," returned Joe. "Not that we wanted to take them, you understand; we went out as lookers-on, me and Mr. Wopsle and Pip. Didn't us, Pip?"

"Yes, Joe."

The stranger looked at me again and said, "He's a likely young parcel of bones, that. What is it you call him?"

"Pip," said Joe.

"Christened Pip?"

"No, not christened Pip."

"Surname Pip?"

"No," said Joe; "it's a kind of a family name what he gave himself when a infant, and is called by."

"Son of yours?"

"Well —" said Joe slowly, "well — no. No, he ain't."

"Nevvy?" [1] said the strange man.

"Well," said Joe, "he is not — no, not to deceive you, he is *not* — my nevvy."

"What the blue blazes is he?" asked the stranger.

Mr. Wopsle then explained the ties

[1] **Nevvy:** nephew.

between Joe and me, and all the while the strange man looked at nobody but me. He said nothing until the glasses were brought. Then he stirred his rum-and-water pointedly at me. And he stirred it not with a spoon that was brought to him, but *with a file.*

He did this so that nobody but me saw the file; and when he had done it, he wiped the file and put it in a breast pocket. I knew it to be Joe's file, and I knew that he knew my convict, the moment I saw the file. I sat gazing at him, spellbound. Joe got up to go, and took me by the hand.

"Stop half a moment, Mr. Gargery," said the strange man. "I think I've got a bright new shilling somewhere in my pocket, and if I have, the boy shall have it."

He looked it out from a handful of small change, folded it in some crumpled paper, and gave it to me. "Yours!" said he. "Mind! Your own."

I thanked him, staring at him far beyond the bounds of good manners, and holding tight to Joe. On the way home I could think of nothing else but this strange meeting.

My sister was not in a very bad temper when we presented ourselves in the kitchen, and Joe was encouraged by that unusual circumstance to tell her about the bright shilling. "A bad un, I'll be bound," said Mrs. Joe triumphantly, "or he wouldn't have given it to the boy. Let's look at it."

I took it out of the paper, and it proved to be a good one. "But what's this?" said Mrs. Joe, throwing down the shilling and catching up the paper. "Two one-pound notes?" [2]

Joe caught up his hat again, and ran

[2] **Two one-pound notes:** forty shillings, or almost ten dollars in American money in Dickens' time. It should be remembered that ten dollars was a considerable sum of money at that time.

with them to the Jolly Bargemen to re-store them to their owner. While he was gone I sat down on my usual stool and looked vacantly at my sister, feeling pretty sure that the man would not be there.

Presently Joe came back, saying that the man was gone, but that he, Joe, had left word at the Three Jolly Bargemen concerning the notes. Then my sister sealed them up in a piece of paper, and put them under some dried rose leaves in an ornamental teapot on the top of a press in the parlor. There they remained a nightmare to me many and many a night and day.

I had sadly broken sleep when I got to bed, through thinking of the strange man and of the guiltily coarse and common thing it was to be on secret terms of conspiracy with convicts — a feature in my low career that I had previously forgotten. I was haunted by the file too. A dread possessed me that when I least expected it, the file would reappear. I coaxed myself to sleep by thinking of Miss Havisham's next Wednesday; and in my sleep I saw the file coming at me out of a door, without seeing who held it, and I screamed myself awake.

CHAPTER 10

We meet Camilla and her husband, Miss Sarah Pocket, Georgiana, and a pale young gentleman.

At the appointed time I returned to Miss Havisham's, and my hesitating ring at the gate brought out Estella. She took me to a small paved courtyard, the opposite side of which was formed by a detached dwelling house. There was a clock in the outer wall of this house. Like the clock in Miss Havisham's room, and like Miss Havisham's watch, it had stopped at twenty minutes to nine.

We went in at the door, which stood open, and into a gloomy room with a low ceiling, on the ground floor at the back. There was some company in the room, and Estella said, "You are to go and stand there, boy, till you are wanted." "There" being the window, I crossed to it and stood "there," in a very uncomfortable state of mind, looking out.

The other occupants of the room had stopped conversation and were looking at me closely. There were three ladies in the room and one gentleman. Before I had been standing at the window five minutes, they somehow conveyed to me that they were all toadies and humbugs.

One lady, whose name was Camilla, was speaking of Miss Havisham, whom she called a "poor, dear soul" without much sympathy, I thought. Having nothing else to do but stand, nervously, I listened and discovered, from the conversation, that the gentleman in the room was this lady's husband. The two other ladies were Sarah Pocket and someone, who hardly spoke at all, named Georgiana. I discovered, also, that while they addressed each other as "Cousin," none seemed to approve of the others — and together they obviously disapproved of a gentleman named Cousin Matthew, who was not present.

The ringing of a distant bell, combined with the echoing of some cry or call along the passage by which I had come, interrupted the conversation and caused Estella to say to me, "Now, boy!" On my turning round, they all looked at me with the utmost contempt, and as I went out, I heard Sarah Pocket say, "Well, I am sure! What next!" and

Camilla added, with indignation, "Was there ever such a fancy! The i-de-a!"

As we were going with our candle along the dark passage, Estella stopped all of a sudden and, facing round, said in her taunting manner, with her face quite close to mine:

"Well?"

"Well, miss," I answered, almost falling over her and checking myself.

She stood looking at me, and of course I stood looking at her.

"Am I pretty?"

"Yes; I think you are very pretty."

"Am I insulting?"

"Not so much so as you were last time," said I.

"Not so much so?"

"No."

She slapped my face with such force as she had.

"Now?" said she. "You little coarse monster, what do you think of me now?"

"I shall not tell you."

"Because you are going to tell upstairs. Is that it?"

"No," said I, "that's not it."

"Why don't you cry again, you little wretch?"

"Because I'll never cry for you again," said I. Which was, I suppose, as false a declaration as ever was made; for I was inwardly crying for her then, and I know what I know of the pain she cost me afterward.

We went on our way upstairs after this episode; and, as we were going up, we met a gentleman groping his way down.

"Whom have we here?" asked the gentleman, stopping and looking at me.

"A boy," said Estella.

He was a burly man of an exceedingly dark complexion, with an exceedingly large head. He took my chin in his large hand and turned up my face to have a look at me by the light of the candle. He was bald on the top of his head, and had bushy black eyebrows that wouldn't lie down, but stood up bristling. His eyes were set very deep in his head, and were disagreeably sharp and suspicious. He had a large watch chain, and strong black dots where his beard and whiskers would have been if he had let them grow. He was nothing to me, and I could have had no foresight then that he ever would be anything to me, but it happened that I had this opportunity of observing him well.

"Boy of the neighborhood? Hey?" said he.

"Yes, sir," said I.

"How do *you* come here?"

"Miss Havisham sent for me, sir," I explained.

"Well! Behave yourself. I have a pretty large experience of boys, and you're a bad set of fellows. Now mind!" said he, biting the side of his great forefinger, as he frowned at me, "you behave yourself!"

With these words he released me — which I was glad of, for his hand smelt of scented soap — and went his way downstairs. We were soon in Miss Havisham's room. Estella left me standing near the door, and I stood there until Miss Havisham cast her eyes upon me from the dressing table.

"So!" she said. "The days have worn away, have they?"

"Yes, ma'am. Today is — "

"There, there, there!" with the impatient movement of her fingers. "I don't want to know. Are you ready to play?"

I was obliged to answer in some confusion, "I don't think I am, ma'am."

"Not at cards again?" she demanded with a searching look.

"Yes, ma'am; I could do that, if I was wanted."

"Since this house strikes you old and grave, boy," said Miss Havisham impatiently, "and you are unwilling to play, are you willing to work?"

I could answer this inquiry with a better heart than I had been able to find for the other question, and I said I was quite willing.

"Then go into that opposite room," said she, pointing at the door behind me with her withered hand, "and wait there till I come."

I crossed the staircase landing and entered the room she indicated. From that room, too, the daylight was completely excluded, and it had an airless smell that was oppressive. Everything in it was covered with dust and mold, and dropping to pieces. The most prominent object was a long table with a tablecloth spread on it, as if a feast had been in preparation when the house and the clocks all stopped together. A centerpiece of some kind was in the middle of this cloth; at one time it must have been a wedding cake, but now it was so heavily overhung with cobwebs that its form was quite undistinguishable. I saw speckled-legged spiders with blotchy bodies running home to it, and running out from it.

I heard the mice, too, rattling behind the panels.

These crawling things had fascinated my attention, and I was watching them from a distance when Miss Havisham laid a hand upon my shoulder. In her other hand she had a crutch-headed stick on which she leaned, and she looked like a witch.

"This," said she, pointing to the long table with her stick, "is where I will be laid when I am dead. They shall come and look at me here."

"What do you think that is," she asked me, again pointing with her stick; "that, where those cobwebs are?"

"I can't guess, ma'am."

"It's a great cake. A bride cake. Mine!"

She looked all round the room in a glaring manner, and then said, leaning on me while her hand twitched my shoulder, "Come, come, come! Walk me, walk me!"

I made out from this that the work I had to do was to walk Miss Havisham round and round the room. Accordingly, she leaned on my shoulder and we started away round and round the room.

Estella entered and became a spectator of our proceedings. With her she had brought the three ladies and the gentleman whom I had seen below.

"Dear Miss Havisham," said Miss Sarah Pocket. "How well you look!"

"I do not," returned Miss Havisham. "I am yellow skin and bone."

Camilla brightened when Miss Pocket met with this rebuff; and she murmured, as she plaintively contemplated [1] Miss Havisham, "Poor dear soul! Certainly not to be expected to look well, poor thing. The idea!"

"And how are *you?*" said Miss Havisham to Camilla. As we were close to Camilla then, I would have stopped as a matter of course, only Miss Havisham wouldn't stop. We swept on, and I felt that I was highly obnoxious to Camilla.

"Thank you, Miss Havisham," she returned. "I am as well as can be expected."

"Why, what's the matter with you?" asked Miss Havisham, with exceeding sharpness.

"Nothing worth mentioning," replied Camilla. "I don't wish to make a display of my feelings, but I have habitually thought of you more in the night than I am quite equal to."

[1] **plaintively contemplated** (plān′tĭv·lĭ kŏn′-tĕm·plāt·ĕd): sorrowfully gazed at.

"Then don't think of me," retorted Miss Havisham.

"Oh!" cried Camilla. "It's a weakness to be so affectionate, but I can't help it."

Miss Havisham and I kept going round and round the room; now brushing against the skirts of the visitors; now giving them the whole length of the dismal chamber.

"There's Matthew!" said Camilla. "Never mixing with any natural ties, never coming here to see how Miss Havisham is!"

When this same Matthew was mentioned, Miss Havisham stopped me and herself, and stood looking at the speaker. This change had a great influence in bringing Camilla's weeping manner to a sudden end.

"Matthew will come and see me at last," said Miss Havisham sternly, "when I am laid on that table. That will be his place — there," striking the table with the stick, "at my head! And yours will be there! And your husband's there! And Sarah Pocket's there! And Georgiana's there! Now you all know where to take your stations when you come to feast upon me.[1] And now go!"

At the mention of each name, she had struck the table with her stick in a new place. She now said, "Walk me, walk me!" and we went on again.

While Estella was away lighting them down, Miss Havisham still walked with her hand on my shoulder, but more and more slowly. At last she stopped before the fire and said, after muttering and looking at it some seconds:

"This is my birthday, Pip."

I was going to wish her many happy returns, when she lifted her stick.

"I don't permit it to be spoken of. I don't permit those who were here just now, or anyone, to speak of it. They come here on the day, but they dare not refer to it."

Of course I made no further effort to refer to it.

"On this day of the year, long before you were born, this heap of decay," stabbing with her crutched stick at the pile of cobwebs on the table, but not touching it, "was brought here. It and I have worn away together. The mice have gnawed at it, and sharper teeth than teeth of mice have gnawed at me."

She held the head of her stick against her heart as she stood looking at the table; she in her once white dress, all yellow and withered; the once white cloth all yellow and withered; everything around in a state to crumble under a touch.

"When the ruin is complete," said she, with a ghastly look, "and when they lay me dead, in my bride's dress on the bride's table — which shall be done, and which will be the finished curse upon him — so much the better if it is done on this day!"

I remained quiet. Estella returned, and she too remained quiet. At length, Miss Havisham said, "Let me see you two play at cards; why have you not begun?" With that, we returned to her room, and sat down as before; I was beaten as before, and again, as before, Miss Havisham watched us all the time, directed my attention to Estella's beauty, and made me notice it the more by trying her jewels on Estella's breast and hair.

Estella, for her part, treated me as before, except that she did not condescend to speak. When we had played some half dozen games, a day was appointed for my return, and I was taken down into the yard to be fed in the former doglike manner. There, too, I

[1] **Now . . . me:** That is, to collect their shares of her will after her death.

was again left to wander about as I liked.

I strolled into the garden and found myself in the dismal corner which I had seen out of a window. Never questioning for a moment that the house was now empty, I looked in a window, and found myself, to my great surprise, exchanging a broad stare with a pale young gentleman with red eyelids and light hair.

This pale young gentleman quickly appeared beside me. He had been at his books when I had found myself staring at him, and I now saw that he was inky.

"Who let *you* in?" said he.

"Miss Estella."

"Who gave you leave to prowl about?"

"Miss Estella."

"Come and fight," said the pale young gentleman.

What could I do but follow him? I have often asked myself the question since; but, what else could I do? His manner was so final and I was so astonished that I followed where he led, as if I had been under a spell.

"Stop a minute, though," he said, wheeling round before we had gone many paces. "I ought to give you a reason for fighting, too. There it is!" In a most irritating manner he instantly slapped his hands against one another, daintily flung one of his legs up behind him, pulled my hair, slapped his hands again, dipped his head, and butted it into my stomach.

I hit out at him, and was going to hit out again, when he said, "Aha! Would you?" and began dancing backward and forward in a manner quite unparalleled [1] within my limited experience.

"Laws of the game!" said he. Here, he skipped from his left leg on to his right. "Regular rules!" Here, he skipped

[1] **unparalleled** (ŭn·păr′ȧ·lĕld): unequaled.

from his right leg on to his left. "Come to the ground, and go through the preliminaries!" Here, he dodged backward and forward, and did all sorts of things while I looked helplessly at him.

I was secretly afraid of him when I saw him so skillful; but I followed him without a word to a retired nook of the garden. On his asking me if I was satisfied with the ground, and on my replying "Yes," he obtained from the house a bottle of water and a sponge dipped in vinegar. "Available for both," he said, and fell to pulling off, not only his jacket and waistcoat, but his shirt, too, in a manner at once lighthearted, businesslike, and bloodthirsty. Although he did not look very healthy, these dreadful preparations quite appalled me. I judged him to be about my own age, but he was much taller.

My heart failed me when I saw him squaring at me with every demonstration of mechanical skill. I never have been so surprised in my life as I was when I let out the first blow and saw him lying on his back, looking up at me with a bloody nose.

But he was on his feet directly, and after sponging himself began squaring again. The second greatest surprise I have ever had in my life was seeing him on his back again, looking up at me out of a black eye.

His spirit inspired me with great respect. He seemed to have no strength, and he never once hit me hard, and he was always knocked down. He got heavily bruised, but he came again and again until at last he got a bad fall with the back of his head against the wall. Even after that, he got up and turned round confusedly a few times; but finally went on his knees to his sponge and threw it up, panting out, "That means you have won."

He seemed so brave and innocent

I found Estella waiting with the keys. . . .

that although I had not proposed the contest, I felt but a gloomy satisfaction in my victory. However, I got dressed and said, "Can I help you?" and he said, "No, thankee," and I said, "Good afternoon," and *he* said, "Same to you."

When I got into the courtyard, I found Estella waiting with the keys. But she neither asked me where I had been, nor why I had kept her waiting; and there was a bright flush upon her face, as though something had happened to delight her. Instead of going straight to the gate, too, she stepped back into the passage and beckoned me.

"Come here! You may kiss me if you like."

I kissed her cheek as she turned it to me. I think I would have gone through a great deal to kiss her cheek. But I felt that the kiss was given to the coarse common boy as a piece of money might have been, and that it was worth nothing.

What with the birthday visitors, and what with the cards, and what with the fight, my stay had lasted so long that when I neared home, the light off the point on the marshes was gleaming against a black night sky, and Joe's furnace was flinging a path of fire across the road.

CHAPTER 11

Pip becomes Joe's apprentice.

MY MIND grew very uneasy on the subject of the pale young gentleman. The more I thought of the fight, and recalled the pale young gentleman on his back, the more certain it appeared that something would be done to me. When the day came round for my return to the scene of the deed of violence, my terrors reached their height. However, go to Miss Havisham's I must, and go I did. And behold; nothing came of the late struggle. It was not mentioned in any way, and no pale young gentleman was to be seen anywhere.

On the broad landing between Miss Havisham's own room and that other room in which the long table was laid out, I saw a light chair on wheels. I entered, beginning with that day, on a regular occupation of pushing Miss Havisham in this chair (when she was tired of walking with her hand upon my shoulder) round her own room, and across the landing, and round the other room. Over and over and over again, we would make these journeys, and sometimes they would last as long as three hours at a stretch.

As we began to be more used to one another over a period of some eight or ten months, Miss Havisham talked more to me, and asked me such questions as what had I learned and what was I going to be? I told her I was going to be apprenticed to Joe, I believed; and I enlarged upon my knowing nothing and wanting to know everything, in the hope that she might offer some help toward that desirable end. But she did not; on the contrary, she seemed to prefer my being ignorant. Neither did she ever give me any money or anything but my daily dinner — nor even suggest that I should be paid for my services.

Estella was always about, and always let me in and out, but never told me I might kiss her again. Sometimes, she would be quite familiar with me; sometimes, she would tell me energetically that she hated me. Miss Havisham would often ask me in a whisper, or when we were alone, "Does she grow prettier and prettier, Pip?" And when I said "Yes" (for indeed she did), would seem to enjoy it greedily. Also, when we played at cards Miss Havisham would look on, relishing Estella's moods, whatever they were. Sometimes, when her moods were so many and so contradictory that I was puzzled what to say or do, Miss Havisham would embrace her with lavish fondness, murmuring something in her ear that sounded like "Break their hearts, my pride and hope, break their hearts and have no mercy!"

Perhaps I might have told Joe of my adventures, had I not previously been betrayed into those enormous lies to which I had confessed. As it was, I reposed complete confidence in no one but Biddy; but I told poor Biddy everything. Why it came natural for me to do so, and why Biddy had a deep concern in everything I told her, I did not know then, though I think I know now.

Meanwhile, councils went on in the kitchen at home. That fool Pumblechook and my sister would pair off in nonsensical speculations about Miss Havisham, and about what she would do with me and for me. In these discussions, Joe bore no part. But he was often talked at, while they were in progress, by reason of Mrs. Joe's perceiving that he was not favorable to my being taken from the forge.

We went on in this way for a long time, when, one day, Miss Havisham stopped short as she and I were walking and said with some displeasure:

"You are growing tall, Pip!"

She said no more at the time, but she presently stopped and looked at me again; and after that looked frowning and moody. The next day she stayed me with a movement of her impatient fingers:

"Tell me the name again of that blacksmith of yours."

"Joe Gargery, ma'am."

"Meaning the master you were to be apprenticed to?"

"Yes, Miss Havisham."

"You had better be apprenticed at once. Would Gargery come here with you, and bring your indentures,[1] do you think?"

[1] indentures (ĭn·dĕn′tŭrz): a contract binding an apprentice to a master.

"At any particular time, Miss Havisham?"

"There, there! I know nothing about times. Let him come soon, and come along with you."

When I delivered this message at home, my sister "went on the Rampage," threw a candlestick at Joe, got out the dustpan — always a very bad sign — and fairly cleaned us out of house and home. It was ten o'clock at night before we ventured to creep in again — and all because Miss Havisham had asked for Joe and had not included my sister.

It was a trial to my feelings, on the next day but one, to see Joe arraying himself in his Sunday clothes to accompany me to Miss Havisham's. At breakfast time, my sister declared her intention of going to town with us, and being left at Uncle Pumblechook's and called for "when we had done with our fine ladies."

The forge was shut up for the day, and Joe inscribed in chalk upon the door (as it was his custom to do on the very rare occasions when he was not at work) the monosyllable HOUT,[1] accompanied by a sketch of an arrow supposed to be flying in the direction he had taken. When we came to Pumblechook's, my sister bounced in and left us. As it was almost noon, Joe and I held straight on to Miss Havisham's house. Estella opened the gate as usual, and led us the way that I knew so well.

Estella told me we were both to go in, so I took Joe by the coat cuff and conducted him into Miss Havisham's presence. She was seated at her dressing table, and looked round at us immediately.

"Oh!" said she to Joe. "You are the husband of the sister of this boy?"

[1] **hout**: out.

I could hardly have imagined dear old Joe looking so unlike himself or so like some extraordinary bird, standing, as he did, speechless, with his tuft of feathers ruffled, and his mouth open as if he wanted a worm.

"You are the husband," repeated Miss Havisham, "of the sister of this boy?"

It was very aggravating; but, throughout the interview, Joe persisted in addressing me instead of Miss Havisham. It was quite impossible for me to make him understand that he ought to speak to Miss Havisham. The more I made faces and gestures to him to do it, the more confidential, argumentative, and polite he persisted in being to me.

"Have you brought his indentures with you?" asked Miss Havisham.

"Well, Pip, you know," replied Joe, as if that were a little unreasonable, "you yourself see me put 'em in my 'at, and therefore you know as they are here." With which he took them out, and gave them, not to Miss Havisham, but to me. I am afraid I was ashamed of the dear good fellow — I *know* I was ashamed of him — when I saw that Estella laughed mischievously. I took the indentures out of his hand and gave them to Miss Havisham.

"You expected," said Miss Havisham, as she looked them over, "no premium with the boy?"

"Joe!" I remonstrated; for he made no reply at all. "Why don't you answer — "

"Pip," returned Joe, cutting me short as if he were hurt, "which I meantersay that were not a question requiring a answer betwixt yourself and me, and which you know the answer to be full well 'No.' You know it to be 'No,' Pip, and wherefore should I say it?"

Miss Havisham glanced at him as if she understood what he really was, better than I had thought possible. She took up a little bag from the table beside her.

"Pip has earned a premium here," she said, "and here it is. There are five-and-twenty guineas [1] in this bag. Give it to your master, Pip."

Joe, even at this pass, persisted in addressing me. "This is very liberal on your part, Pip," said Joe, "and it is as such received and grateful welcome, though never looked for. And now, old chap," said Joe, "may you and me do our duty, one to another!"

"Good-by, Pip!" said Miss Havisham. "Let them out, Estella."

"Am I to come again, Miss Havisham?" I asked.

"No. Gargery is your master now. Gargery! One word!"

Thus calling him back as I went out of the door, I heard her say to Joe, in a distinct emphatic voice, "The boy has been a good boy here, and that is his reward. Of course, as an honest man, you will expect no other and no more."

In another minute we were outside the gate, and it was locked, and Estella was gone. When we stood in the daylight alone again, Joe backed up against a wall and said to me, "Astonishing!" And there he remained so long, saying "Astonishing" at intervals so often that I began to think his senses were never coming back. At length he said, "Pip, I do assure *you* this is as-TON-ishing!" and so, by degrees, became conversational and able to walk away.

"Well!" cried my sister, addressing us both at once, when we arrived at Pumblechook's. "I wonder you condescend to come back to such poor society as this, I am sure I do! Well, what did she give this boy here?"

"To be partick'ler," said Joe, handing the bag to my sister, "it's five-and-twenty pound."

"It's five-and-twenty pound, mum," echoed that basest of swindlers, Pumblechook, rising to shake hands with her; "and it's no more than your merits (as I said when my opinion was asked), and I wish you joy of the money!"

"Goodness knows, Uncle Pumblechook," said my sister (grasping the money), "we're deeply beholden to you."

"Never mind me, mum," returned that diabolical [2] grain merchant. "A pleasure's a pleasure all the world over. But this boy, you know; we must have him bound. I said I'd see to it — to tell you the truth."

The justices were sitting in the town hall near at hand, and we at once went over to have me bound apprentice to Joe. I say, we went over, but I was pushed over by Pumblechook, exactly as if I had that moment picked a pocket or set a house afire. Indeed, it was the general impression in court that I had been taken red-handed; for, as Pumblechook shoved me before him through the crowd, I heard some people say, "What's he done?" and others, "He's a young 'un, too, but looks bad, don't he?" One person of pious appearance even gave me a pamphlet entitled, TO BE READ IN MY CELL.

When we had come out again, we went back to Pumblechook's. And there my sister became so excited by the twenty-five guineas that nothing would serve her but we must have a dinner at the Blue Boar, and that Mr. Pumblechook must go over in his cart and bring the Hubbles and Mr. Wopsle.

My only remembrances of the great

---

[1] **guinea** (gĭn'ĭ): a gold coin worth twenty-one shillings, a little over $5 in American money then.

[2] **diabolical** (dī'*à*·bŏl'ĭ·k*ă*l): literally, devilish; in this context, "scheming" is perhaps closer to Dickens' meaning.

festival are that they wouldn't let me go to sleep, but whenever they saw me dropping off, woke me up and told me to enjoy myself and that when I got into my little bedroom, I was truly wretched, and had a strong conviction on me that I should never like Joe's trade. I had liked it once, but once was not now.

It is a most miserable thing to feel ashamed of home. Home had never been a very pleasant place to me, because of my sister's temper. But Joe had blessed it, and I believed in it. Within a single year all this was changed. Now, it was all coarse and common, and I would not have had Miss Havisham and Estella see it on any account.

How much of my ungracious condition of mind may have been my own fault, how much Miss Havisham's, how much my sister's, is now of no importance. The change was made in me; the thing was done. Well or ill done, it was done.

Once it had seemed to me that when I should at last roll up my shirt sleeves and go into the forge, Joe's 'prentice, I should be distinguished and happy. Now I only felt that I was dusty with the dust of the small coal, and that I had a weight upon my daily remembrance to which the anvil was a feather. There have been occasions in my later life when I have felt for a time as if a thick curtain had fallen on all its interest and romance, to shut me out from anything save dull endurance any more. Never has that curtain dropped so heavy and blank, as when my way in life lay stretched out straight before me through the newly entered road of apprenticeship to Joe.

But I am glad to know that I never breathed a murmur to Joe while my indentures lasted. It is about the only thing I *am* glad to know of myself in that connection. It was not because I was faithful, but because Joe was faithful, that I never ran away and became a soldier or a sailor. It was not because I had a strong sense of the virtue of industry, but because Joe did, that I worked with tolerable zeal against the grain. It is not possible to know how far the influence of any amiable, honesthearted, duty-doing man flies out into the world, but I know right well that any good that intermixed itself with my apprenticeship came of plain, contented Joe, and not of restless, aspiring, discontented me.

What I dreaded most was that in some unlucky hour I, being at my grimiest and commonest, should lift up my eyes and see Estella looking in at one of the wooden windows of the forge. I was haunted by the fear that she would, sooner or later, find me out, with a black face and hands, doing the coarsest part of my work, and would exult over me and despise me. Often after dark, when I was pulling the bellows for Joe, I would fancy that I saw her just drawing her face away, and would believe that she had come at last.

After that, when we went in to supper, the place would have a more homely look than ever, and I would feel more ashamed of home than ever, in my own ungracious breast.

CHAPTER 12

Introducing Orlick.

As I was getting too big for Mr. Wopsle's great-aunt's room, my education under that ridiculous female ended; not, however, until Biddy had imparted to me everything she knew, from the little catalogue of prices to a comic song she had once bought for a half-penny. Although the only coherent part of the latter piece of literature was the opening lines,

When I went to Lunnon town, sirs,
      Too rul loo rul!
      Too rul loo rul!
Wasn't I done very brown, sirs?
      Too rul loo rul!
      Too rul loo rul!

— still, in my desire to be wiser, I got this composition by heart with the utmost care. Moreover, in my hunger for information, I made proposals to Mr. Wopsle to bestow some intellectual crumbs upon me; with which he kindly complied. As it turned out, however, he wanted me only as a dramatic assistant for his reading of Shakespeare, to be contradicted and embraced and wept over and bullied and clutched and stabbed and knocked about in a variety of ways. I soon declined that course of instruction, though not until Mr. Wopsle in his poetic fury had severely mauled me.

Whatever I acquired, I tried to impart to Joe. This statement sounds so well that I cannot in my conscience let it pass unexplained. I wanted to make Joe less ignorant and common, that he might be worthier of my society and less open to Estella's reproach.

The old Battery out on the marshes was our place of study, and a broken slate and a short piece of slate pencil were our educational implements, to which Joe always added a pipe of tobacco. I never knew Joe to remember anything from one Sunday to another, or to acquire, under my tuition, any piece of information whatever. Yet he would smoke his pipe at the Battery with a far wiser air than anywhere else — even with a learned air — as if he considered himself to be advancing immensely. Dear fellow, I hope he did.

It was pleasant and quiet, out there with the sails on the river. Whenever I watched the vessels standing out to sea with their white sails spread, I somehow thought of Miss Havisham and Estella and the strange house and the strange life that was so picturesque. One Sunday I resolved to mention a thought concerning them that had been much in my head.

"Joe," said I, "don't you think I ought to pay Miss Havisham a visit?"

"Well, Pip," returned Joe, slowly considering. "What for?"

"What for, Joe? What is any visit made for?"

"There is some wisits p'r'aps," said Joe, "as forever remains open to the question, Pip. But in regard of wisiting Miss Havisham. She might think you wanted something — expected something of her."

I had thought of that too, and it was very far from comforting to me to find that he had thought of it; for it seemed to render it more probable.

"But, Joe."

"Yes, old chap."

"Here am I, getting on in the first year of my time, and since the day of my being bound I have never thanked Miss Havisham, or asked after her, or shown that I remember her."

"Well," said Joe, "if I was yourself, Pip, I wouldn't. No, I would *not*."

"But, Joe; what I wanted to say was, that as we are rather slack just now, if you would give me a half holiday tomorrow, I think I would go uptown and make a call on Miss Est— Havisham."

"Her name," said Joe gravely, "ain't Estavisham, Pip, unless she has been rechristened."

"I know, Joe. It was a slip. What do you think of it, Joe?"

Joe decided that if I thought well of

it, he thought well of it. But he insisted that if I were not received with cordiality, or if I were not encouraged to repeat my visit, then this experimental trip should have no successor. By these conditions I promised to abide.

Now, Joe kept a journeyman[1] at weekly wages whose name was Orlick. He was a broad-shouldered, loose-limbed, swarthy fellow of great strength, never in a hurry, and always slouching. He never even seemed to come to his work on purpose, but would slouch in as if by mere accident. He lodged at a sluice keeper's[2] out on the marshes, and on working days would come slouching in with his hands in his pockets and his dinner loosely tied in a bundle round his neck and dangling on his back.

This sullen journeyman had no liking for me. When I was very small and timid, he gave me to understand that the Devil lived in a black corner of the forge, and that he knew the fiend very well; also that it was necessary to make up the fire, once in seven years, with a live boy, and that I might consider myself fuel. When I became Joe's 'prentice, Orlick was perhaps confirmed in some suspicion that I should displace him and he liked me still less.

Orlick was at work and present, next day, when I reminded Joe of my half holiday. He said nothing at the moment, for he and Joe had just got a piece of hot iron between them, and I was at the bellows; but by and by he said, leaning on his hammer:

"Now, master! Sure you're not a-going to favor only one of us. If

---

[1] **journeyman** (jûr′nĭ·măn): one who has learned a craft and is no longer an apprentice, but who still works for a master craftsman.

[2] **sluice** (sloōs) **keeper**: the person in charge of a gate which regulates the flow of water in a sluice, a man-made stream used for drainage or irrigation purposes.

Young Pip has a half holiday, do as much for Old Orlick." I suppose he was about five-and-twenty, but he usually spoke of himself as an ancient person.

"Why, what'll you do with a half holiday if you get it?" said Joe.

"What'll *I* do with it? What'll *he* do with it? I'll do as much with it as *him*," said Orlick.

"As to Pip, he's going uptown," said Joe.

"Well then, as to Old Orlick, *he's* a-going uptown," retorted that worthy. "Two can go uptown. 'Tain't only one wot can go uptown."

"Don't lose your temper," said Joe.

"Shall if I like," growled Orlick. "Now, master! Come. No favoring in this shop. Be a man!"

"Then, as in general you stick to your work as well as most men," said Joe, "let it be a half holiday for all."

My sister had been standing silent in the yard, within hearing — she was a most unashamed spy and listener — and she instantly looked in at one of the windows.

"Like you, you fool!" said she to Joe, "giving holidays to great idle hulkers like that. You are a rich man, upon my life, to waste wages in that way. I wish *I* was his master!"

"You'd be everybody's master if you durst," retorted Orlick, with an ill-favored grin.

"Let her alone," said Joe.

"I'd be a match for all noodles and all rogues," returned my sister, beginning to work herself into a mighty rage. "And I couldn't be a match for the noodles without being a match for your master, who's the dunderheaded king of the noodles. And I couldn't be a match for the rogues without being a match for you, who are the blackest-looking and the worst rogue between this and France. Now!"

They went at one another like two giants.

"You're a foul shrew,[1] Mother Gargery," growled the journeyman. "If that makes a judge of rogues, you ought to be a good 'un."

"Let her alone, will you?" said Joe.

"What did you say?" cried my sister, beginning to scream. "What did you say? What did that fellow Orlick say to me, Pip? What did he call me, with my husband standing by? Oh! Oh! Oh!" Each of these exclamations was a shriek. "Oh! Hold me! Oh!"

"Ah-h-h!" growled the journeyman, between his teeth. "I'd hold you, if you was my wife. I'd hold you under the pump and choke it out of you."

"I tell you, let her alone," said Joe.

"Oh! To hear him!" cried my sister, with a clap of her hands and a scream together. "To hear the names he's giving me! That Orlick! In my own house! Me, a married woman! With my husband standing by! Oh! Oh!"

What could the wretched Joe do now but stand up to his journeyman? They went at one another like two giants. But if any man in that neighborhood could stand up long against Joe, I never saw the man. Orlick was very soon

[1] **shrew:** noisy, scolding woman.

among the coal dust, and in no hurry to come out of it. Then Joe picked up my sister, who had fainted at the window, and carried her into the house. Afterward came that calm and silence which succeed all uproars — and I went upstairs to dress.

When I came down again, I found Joe and Orlick sweeping up, without any other traces of the fight than a slit in one of Orlick's nostrils. A pot of beer had appeared from the Jolly Bargemen, and they were sharing it by turns in a peaceable manner. Joe followed me out into the road to say, as an observation that might do me good, "On the Rampage, Pip, and off the Ram-page, Pip — such is life!"

When I found myself again going to Miss Havisham's, I passed and repassed the gate many times before I could make up my mind to ring.

Miss Sarah Pocket came to the gate. No Estella.

"How, then? You here again?" said Miss Pocket. "What do you want?"

When I said that I only came to see how Miss Havisham was, Sarah let me in, and presently brought the sharp message that I was to "come up."

Everything was unchanged, and Miss Havisham was alone. "Well!" said she, fixing her eyes upon me. "I hope you want nothing? You'll get nothing."

"No indeed, Miss Havisham. I only wanted you to know that I am doing very well in my apprenticeship, and am always much obliged to you."

"There, there!" with the old restless fingers. "Come now and then; come on your birthday. — Aye!" she cried suddenly, turning herself and her chair toward me. "You are looking round for Estella? Hey?"

I had been looking round — in fact, for Estella — and I stammered that I hoped she was well.

"Abroad," said Miss Havisham; "educating for a lady; far out of reach; prettier than ever; admired by all who see her. Do you feel that you have lost her?"

There was such a wicked enjoyment in her utterance of the last words, and she broke into such a disagreeable laugh, that I was at a loss what to say. She spared me the trouble of considering, by dismissing me. When the gate was closed upon me, I felt more than ever dissatisfied with my home and with my trade and with everything.

As I was loitering along the High Street, looking at the shop windows and thinking what I would buy if I were a gentleman, who should come out of the bookshop but Mr. Wopsle. He was on his way to drink tea at the Pumblechookian parlor and insisted on my accompanying him. I made no great resistance; consequently, we turned into Pumblechook's just as the street and shops were lighting up.

It was a very dark night with a heavy mist when I set out with Mr. Wopsle on the walk home, and the turnpike lamp was a blur. Suddenly we came upon a man, slouching under the lee of the turnpike house.

"Halloa!" we said, stopping. "Orlick there?"

"Ah!" he answered, slouching out. "I was standing by a minute on the chance of company."

"You are late," I remarked.

Orlick not unnaturally answered, "Well? And *you're* late."

"We have been," said Mr. Wopsle, "indulging, Mr. Orlick, in an intellectual evening."

Old Orlick growled, as if he had nothing to say about that, and we all went on together. I asked him presently whether he had been spending his half holiday up and down town?

"Yes," said he, "all of it. I come in behind yourself. I didn't see you, but I must have been pretty close behind you. By the bye, the guns is going again."

"At the Hulks?" said I.

"Aye! There's some of the birds flown from the cages. The guns have been going since dark, about. You'll hear one presently."

We had not walked many yards farther when the well-remembered boom came toward us, deadened by the mist.

"A good night for cutting off in," said Orlick. "We'd be puzzled how to bring down a jailbird on the wing tonight." Orlick, with his hands in his pockets, slouched heavily at my side. I thought he had been drinking, but he was not drunk.

Thus we came to the village. We approached the Three Jolly Bargemen, which we were surprised to find — it being eleven o'clock — in a state of commotion, with the door wide open, and lights scattered about. Mr. Wopsle dropped in to ask what was the matter (thinking that a convict had been taken), but came running out in a great hurry.

"There's something wrong," said he, without stopping, "up at your place, Pip. Run all!"

"What is it?" I asked, keeping up with him. So did Orlick, at my side.

"I can't quite understand. The house seems to have been violently entered when Joe Gargery was out. Supposed by convicts. Somebody has been attacked and hurt."

We were running too fast to admit of more being said, and we made no stop until we got into our kitchen. It was full of people; the whole village was there or in the yard, and there was a surgeon, and there was Joe, and there was a group of women, all on the floor in the midst of the kitchen. The bystanders drew back when they saw me, and so I became aware of my sister — lying without sense or movement on the bare boards where she had been knocked down by a tremendous blow on the back of the head, dealt by some unknown hand when her face was turned toward the fire — destined never to be on the Ram-page again, while she was the wife of Joe.

Joe had been at the Three Jolly Bargemen, smoking his pipe, from a quarter after eight o'clock to a quarter before ten. While he was there, my sister had been seen standing at the kitchen door and had exchanged good night with a farm laborer going home. When Joe went home at five minutes before ten, he found her struck down on the floor, and promptly called in assistance.

Nothing had been taken away from any part of the house. But there was one remarkable piece of evidence on the spot. She had been struck with something blunt and heavy, on the head and spine; after the blows were dealt, something heavy had been thrown down at her with considerable violence, as she lay on her face. And on the ground beside her, when Joe picked her up, was a convict's leg iron which had been filed asunder.

Now, Joe, examining this iron with a smith's eye, declared it to have been filed asunder some time ago. Officials from the Hulks testified that this leg iron had not been worn by either of two convicts who had escaped last night. Further, one of those two was already retaken, and had not freed himself of his iron.

Knowing what I knew, I believed the iron to be my convict's iron — the iron I had seen and heard him filing at, on the marshes — but my mind did not accuse him of having put it to its latest use. For I believed one of two other persons to have become possessed of it, and to have turned it to this cruel account. Either Orlick, or the strange man who had shown me the file.

Now, as to Orlick; he had gone to town exactly as he told us when we picked him up at the turnpike, he had been seen about town all the evening, he had been in several public houses, and he had come back with myself and Mr. Wopsle. There was nothing against him, save the quarrel; and my sister had quarreled with him, and with everybody else about her, ten thousand times. As to the strange man: if he had come back for his two bank notes, there could have been no dispute about them, because my sister was fully prepared to restore them. Besides, there had been no argument; the assailant had come in so silently and suddenly that she had been felled before she could look round.

The constables were about the house for a week or two, searching for evidence by which to take the culprit. But they found nothing, and neither did they find the culprit. For a long time my sister lay ill in bed. Her sight was disturbed, so that she saw objects multiplied; her hearing was greatly impaired; her memory also; and her speech was unintelligible. It was necessary to keep my slate always by her, that she might indicate in writing what she could not indicate in speech.

However, her temper was greatly improved, and she was patient. We were at a loss to find a suitable attendant for her, until a circumstance happened conveniently to relieve us. Mr. Wopsle's great-aunt died, and Biddy became part of our establishment. Biddy came to us with a small speckled box containing the whole of her worldly effects and became a blessing to the household. Above all she was a blessing to Joe, for the dear old fellow was sadly cut up by the constant sight of the wreck of his wife. Biddy instantly taking the cleverest charge of her, Joe became able in some sort to appreciate the greater quiet of his life, and to get down to the Jolly Bargemen now and then for a change that did him good.

Biddy's first triumph in her new office was to solve a difficulty that had completely puzzled me. Again and again and again, my sister had traced upon the slate a character that looked like a curious *T*, and then with the utmost eagerness had called our attention to it as something she particularly wanted. I had in vain tried everything that began with a *T*, from tar to toast and tub. At length it had come into my head that the sign looked like a hammer, and on my lustily shouting that word in my sister's ear, she had begun to hammer on the table and had confirmed my guess. Thereupon, I had brought in all our hammers, one after another, but without avail.

When my sister found that Biddy was very quick to understand her, this mysterious sign reappeared on the slate. Biddy looked thoughtfully at it, heard my explanation, looked thoughtfully at my sister, looked thoughtfully at Joe, and ran into the forge, followed by Joe and me.

"Why, of course!" cried Biddy with an exultant face. "Don't you see? It's *him!*"

Orlick, without a doubt! She had lost his name, and could only signify him by his hammer. We told him why we wanted him to come into the kitchen, and he slowly laid down his hammer, wiped his brow with his arm, took another wipe at it with his apron, and came slouching out.

I confess that I expected to see my sister denounce him, and that I was disappointed by the different result. She showed the greatest anxiety to be on good terms with him, was evidently much pleased by his being at length produced, and motioned that she would have him given something to drink. She watched his face as if she particularly hoped that he took kindly to his reception. After that, a day rarely passed without her drawing the hammer on her slate, and without Orlick's slouching in and standing doggedly before her, as if he knew no more than I did what to make of it.

CHAPTER 13

Pip opens his heart to Biddy.

I NOW fell into a regular routine of apprenticeship life, which was varied, beyond the limits of the village and the marshes, by no more remarkable circumstance than the arrival of my birthday and my paying another visit to

Miss Havisham. The interview lasted but a few minutes, and she gave me a guinea when I was going, and told me to come again on my next birthday. I may mention at once that this became an annual custom. I tried to decline taking the guinea on the first occasion, causing her to ask me angrily if I expected more. After that, I took it. So unchanging was the dull old house, it bewildered me, and under its influence I continued at heart to hate my trade and to be ashamed of home.

Slowly I became conscious of a change in Biddy, however. Her shoes came up at the heel, her hair grew bright and neat, her hands were always clean. She was not beautiful — she was common, and could not be like Estella — but she was pleasant and wholesome and sweet-tempered. I observed to myself one evening that she had curiously thoughtful and attentive eyes; eyes that were very pretty and very good. I laid down my pen, and Biddy stopped in her needlework without laying it down.

"Biddy," said I, "how do you manage it? Either I am very stupid, or you are very clever."

"What is it that I manage? I don't know," returned Biddy, smiling.

She managed our whole domestic life, and wonderfully too; but I did not mean that, though that made what I did mean more surprising.

"How do you manage, Biddy," said I, "to learn everything that I learn, and always to keep up with me?" I was beginning to be rather vain of my knowledge, for I spent my birthday guineas on it and the greater part of my pocket money.

"I suppose I must catch it — like a cough," said Biddy quietly, and went on with her sewing.

I looked at Biddy and began to think

her rather an extraordinary girl.

"You are one of those, Biddy," said I, "who make the most of every chance. You never had a chance before you came here, and see how improved you are!"

Biddy looked at me for an instant and went on with her sewing. "I was your first teacher, though, wasn't I?" said she, as she sewed.

"Yes, Biddy," I observed, "you were my first teacher, and that at a time when we little thought of ever being together like this in this kitchen. I must consult you a little more, as I used to do. Let us have a quiet walk on the marshes next Sunday, Biddy, and a long chat."

My sister was never left alone now; but Joe undertook the care of her on that Sunday afternoon, and Biddy and I went out together. It was summertime and lovely weather. When we came to the riverside and sat down on the bank, I resolved that it was a good time and place for the admission of Biddy into my inner confidence.

"Biddy," said I, after binding her to secrecy, "I want to be a gentleman."

"Oh, I wouldn't, if I was you!" she returned. "I don't think it would be right."

"Biddy," said I, with some severity, "I have particular reasons for wanting to be a gentleman."

"You know best, Pip; but don't you think you are happier as you are?"

"Biddy," I exclaimed impatiently, "I am not at all happy as I am. I am disgusted with my calling and with my life. Don't be absurd."

"Was I absurd?" said Biddy, quietly raising her eyebrows. "I am sorry for that; I didn't mean to be. I only want you to do well and be comfortable."

"Well, then, understand once for all that I never shall or can be comfortable

— or anything but miserable — there, Biddy! — unless I can lead a very different sort of life from the life I lead now."

"That's a pity!" said Biddy, shaking her head with a sorrowful air.

"If I could have settled down," I said to Biddy, "I know it would have been much better for me. Joe and I would perhaps have gone partners, and I might have grown up to keep company with you. Instead of that, see how I am going on. Dissatisfied and uncomfortable, and — what would it signify to me, being coarse and common, if nobody had told me so!"

Biddy turned her face suddenly toward mine and looked attentively at me.

"It was neither a very true nor a very polite thing to say," she remarked. "Who said it?"

"The beautiful young lady at Miss Havisham's, and she's more beautiful than anybody ever was, and I admire her dreadfully, and I want to be a gentleman on her account."

"Do you want to be a gentleman to spite her or to gain her over?" Biddy quietly asked me, after a pause.

"I don't know," I moodily answered.

"Because, if it is to spite her," Biddy pursued, "I should think — but you know best — that might be better and more independently done by caring nothing for words. And if it is to gain her over, I should think — but you know best — she was not worth gaining over."

"It may be all quite true," said I to Biddy, "but I admire her dreadfully."

I turned over on my face when I came to that, and got a good grasp on the hair on each side of my head, and wrenched it well. Biddy was the wisest of girls, and she tried to reason no more

with me. She put her hand, which was a comfortable hand though roughened by work, on my shoulder in a soothing way, while with my face upon my sleeve I cried a little — exactly as I had done in the brewery yard long ago — and felt vaguely convinced that I was very much ill-used by somebody, or by everybody; I can't say which.

"I am glad of one thing," said Biddy, "and that is, that you have felt you could give me your confidence, Pip." So, with a quiet sigh for me, Biddy rose from the bank and said, with a fresh and pleasant change of voice, "Shall we walk a little farther or go home?"

"Biddy," I cried, getting up, putting my arm around her neck, and giving her a kiss, "I shall always tell you everything."

"Till you're a gentleman," said Biddy.

"You know I never shall be, so that's always. Not that I have any occasion to tell you anything, for you know everything I know — as I told you at home the other night."

"Ah!" said Biddy, quite in a whisper, and then repeated, with her former pleasant change, "shall we walk a little farther or go home?"

We talked a good deal as we walked, and all that Biddy said seemed right. Biddy was never insulting, or changeable, or Biddy today and somebody else tomorrow; she would have derived only pain, and no pleasure, from giving me pain. I began to consider whether I was not happier in these circumstances, after all, than being despised by Estella. How could it be, then, that I did not like her much the better of the two?

"Biddy," said I, when we were walking homeward, "I wish you could put me right."

"I wish I could!" said Biddy.

"If I could only get myself to fall in

love with you — you don't mind my speaking so openly to such an old acquaintance?"

"Oh, dear, not at all!" said Biddy. "Don't mind me."

"If I could only get myself to do it, *that* would be the thing for me."

"But you never will, you see," said Biddy.

When we came near the churchyard, we had to cross an embankment and there started up, from the rushes, Old Orlick.

"Halloa!" he growled. "Where are you two going?"

"Where should we be going, but home?"

"Well, then," said he, "I'm jiggered if I don't see you home!"

Biddy said to me in a whisper, "Don't let him come; I don't like him." As I did not like him either, I took the liberty of saying that we thanked him, but we didn't want seeing home. He dropped back, but came slouching after us at a little distance.

Curious to know whether Biddy suspected him of having had a hand in that murderous attack of which my sister had never been able to give any account, I asked her why she did not like him.

"Oh," she replied, glancing over her shoulder as he slouched after us, "because I — I am afraid he likes me!"

"Did he ever tell you he liked you?" I asked indignantly.

"No," said Biddy, glancing over her shoulder again, "he never told me so; but he looks at me strangely whenever he can catch my eye."

I kept an eye on Orlick after that night. He had struck root in Joe's establishment, by reason of my sister's sudden fancy for him, or I should have tried to get him dismissed. He quite understood my distaste for him and re-

turned it in good measure, as I had reason to know thereafter.

And now my mind was confused. At times, I would decide that my drawing away from dear old Joe and the forge was ended, and that I was growing up in a fair way to be partners with Joe and to keep company with Biddy — when all in a moment some remembrance of the Havisham days would fall upon me and scatter my wits again. Scattered wits take a long time picking up; and often they would be dispersed in all directions by one stray thought, that perhaps after all Miss Havisham was going to make my fortune when my time was out.

If my time had run out, it would have left me still at the height of my perplexities, I dare say. It never did run out, however, but was brought to an early end, as I proceed to relate.

CHAPTER 14

Mr. Jaggers, a lawyer, brings astonishing news.

It was in the fourth year of my apprenticeship to Joe, and it was a Saturday night. There was a group assembled round the fire at the Three Jolly Bargemen, attentive to Mr. Wopsle as he read the newspaper aloud. Of that group I was one.

I became aware of a strange gentleman leaning over the back of the settle opposite me, looking on. There was an expression of contempt on his face, and he bit the side of a great forefinger as he watched the group of faces.

"Well!" said the stranger to Mr. Wopsle, when the reading was done. "You have settled it all to your own satisfaction, I have no doubt?"

The strange gentleman had an air of authority not to be disputed, and a manner expressive of knowing something secret about every one of us.

"From information I have received," said he, looking round at us as we all quailed before him, "I have reason to believe there is a blacksmith among you, by name Joseph — or Joe — Gargery. Which is the man?"

"Here is the man," said Joe.

The strange gentleman beckoned him out of his place, and Joe went.

"You have an apprentice," pursued the stranger, "commonly known as Pip? Is he here?"

"I am here!" I cried.

The stranger did not recognize me, but I recognized him as the gentleman I had met on the stairs on the occasion of my second visit to Miss Havisham. I had known him the moment I saw him looking over the settle. I checked off again in detail his large head, his dark complexion, his deep-set eyes, his bushy black eyebrows, his large watch chain, his strong black dots of beard and whisker, and even the smell of scented soap on his great hand.

"I wish to have a private conference with you two," said he, when he had surveyed me at his leisure. "It will take a little time. Perhaps we had better go to your place of residence."

Amidst a wondering silence, we three walked out of the Jolly Bargemen and in a wondering silence walked home. Joe went on ahead to open the front door. Our conference was held in the parlor, which was feebly lighted by one candle.

It began with the strange gentleman's sitting down at the table, drawing the candle to him, and looking over some entries in his pocketbook.

"My name," he said, "is Jaggers, and I am a lawyer in London. I am pretty well known. I have unusual business to transact with you, and I commence by explaining that it is not of my originating. If my advice had been asked, I should not have been here. It was not asked, and you see me here. What I have to do as the confidential agent of another, I do. No less, no more.

"Now, Joseph Gargery, I am the bearer of an offer to relieve you of this young fellow, your apprentice. You would not object to cancel his indentures at his request and for his good? You would want nothing for so doing?"

"Lord forbid that I should want anything for not standing in Pip's way," said Joe, staring.

"Lord forbidding is pious, but not to the purpose," returned Mr. Jaggers. "The question is, would you want anything? Do you want anything?"

"The answer is," returned Joe sternly, "no."

I thought Mr. Jaggers glanced at Joe, as if he considered him a fool for his unselfishness. But I was too much bewildered between breathless curiosity and surprise to be sure of it.

"Very well," said Mr. Jaggers. "Now, I return to this young fellow. And the communication I have got to make is that he has Great Expectations."

Joe and I gasped and looked at one another.

"I am instructed to communicate to him," said Mr. Jaggers, throwing his finger at me sideways, "that he will come into a handsome property. Further, that it is the desire of the present possessor of that property that he be immediately removed from his present sphere of life and from this place and be brought up as a gentleman — in a word, as a young fellow of great expectations."

My dream was out; my wild fancy

was surpassed by sober reality; Miss Havisham was going to make my fortune on a grand scale.

"Now, Mr. Pip," pursued the lawyer, "I address the rest of what I have to say to you. You are to understand, first, that it is the request of the person from whom I take my instructions that you always bear the name of Pip. You will have no objection, I dare say, but if you have any objection, this is the time to mention it."

My heart was beating so fast, and there was such a singing in my ears, that I could scarcely stammer I had no objection.

"I should think not! Now you are to understand, secondly, Mr. Pip, that the name of the person who is your liberal benefactor remains a profound secret until the person chooses to reveal it at first hand by word of mouth to yourself. When or where that intention may be carried out, no one can say. It may be years hence. It is not important what the reasons of this prohibition are; they may be the strongest and gravest reasons, or they may be a mere whim. This is not for you to inquire into. The condition is laid down. Your acceptance of it, and your observance of it as binding, is the only remaining condition that I am charged with by the person from whom I take my instructions. That person is the person from whom you derive your expectations, and the secret is solely held by that person and by me. If you have any objection to it, this is the time to mention it. Speak out."

Once more, I stammered that I had no objection.

"I should think not! Now, Mr. Pip, I have done with stipulations.[1] We come

---

[1] **stipulations** (stĭp′ū·lā′shŭns): conditions of agreement.

next to mere details of arrangement. You must know that although I have used the term 'expectations' more than once, you are not endowed with expectations only. There is already lodged in my hands a sum of money amply sufficient for your suitable education and maintenance. You will please consider me your guardian.

"Oh!" he said, just as I was going to thank him. "I tell you at once, I am paid for my services, or I shouldn't render them. It is considered that you must be better-educated, in accordance with your altered position."

I said I had always longed for it.

"Never mind what you have always longed for, Mr. Pip," he retorted. "Keep to the record. If you long for it now, that's enough. Am I answered that you are ready to be placed at once under some proper tutor? Is that it?"

I stammered yes, that was it.

"There is a certain tutor who I think might suit the purpose," said Mr. Jaggers. "The gentleman I speak of is one Mr. Matthew Pocket."

Ah! I caught at the name directly. Miss Havisham's relation. The Matthew whom Mr. and Mrs. Camilla had spoken of. The Matthew whose place was to be at Miss Havisham's head when she lay dead in her bride's dress on the bride's table.

"You know the name?" said Mr. Jaggers, looking shrewdly at me. "What do you say of it?"

I said that I was much obliged to him for his mention of Mr. Matthew Pocket, and that I would gladly try that gentleman.

"Good. You had better try him in his own house. The way shall be prepared for you, and you can see his son first, who is in London. When will you come to London?"

I said (glancing at Joe, who stood

"And the communication I have got to make is that he has Great Expectations."

looking on, motionless) that I supposed I could come directly.

"First," said Mr. Jaggers, "you should have some new clothes to come in, and they should not be working clothes. Say this day week.[1] You'll want some money. Shall I leave you twenty guineas?"

He produced a long purse, with the greatest coolness, and counted them out on the table and pushed them over to me, and sat swinging his purse and eyeing Joe.

"Well, Joseph Gargery? You look dumfoundered?"

"I *am!*" said Joe, in a very decided manner.

"It was understood that you wanted nothing for yourself, remember?"

"It were understood," said Joe. "And it are understood. And it ever will be the same."

"But what," said Mr. Jaggers, swinging his purse, "what if it was in my instructions to make you a present, as compensation?"

"As compensation what for?" Joe demanded.

"For the loss of his services."

Joe laid his hand upon my shoulder with the touch of a woman. "Pip is that hearty welcome," said Joe, "to go free with his services, to honor and fortun', as no words can tell him. But if you think as money can make compensation to me for the loss of the little child — what come to the forge — and ever the best of friends! — "

Oh, dear good Joe, whom I was so ready to leave and so unthankful to, I see you again, with your muscular blacksmith's arm before your eyes, and your broad chest heaving, and your voice dying away.

But I encouraged Joe at the time. I

---

[1] **this day week:** a week from today.

begged Joe to be comforted, for (as he said) we had ever been the best of friends, and (as I said) we ever would be so. Joe scooped his eyes with his wrist, but said not another word.

Mr. Jaggers, looking on at this, said, "Now, Joseph Gargery, I warn you this is your last chance. If you mean to take a present that I have in charge to make you, speak out, and you shall have it. If on the contrary you mean to say — " Here, to his great amazement, he was stopped by Joe's suddenly assuming a fighting air.

"Which I meantersay," cried Joe, "that if you come into my place bull-baiting and badgering me, come out! Which I meantersay as sech if you're a man, come on!"

I drew Joe away, and he immediately became peaceful. Mr. Jaggers backed near the door and there delivered his last remarks:

"Well, Mr. Pip, I think the sooner you leave here, the better. Let it stand for this day week, and you shall receive my printed address in the meantime. You can take a coach at the stagecoach office in London, and come straight to me."

Something came into my head which induced me to run after him.

"I beg your pardon, Mr. Jaggers."

"Halloa!" said he. "What's the matter?"

"I wish to be quite right, Mr. Jaggers. Would there be any objection to my taking leave of anyone I know about here, before I go away?"

"No," said he, looking as if he hardly understood me.

"I don't mean in the village only, but uptown?"

"No," said he. "No objection."

I thanked him and ran home again, and there I found Joe seated by the kitchen fire with a hand on each knee, gazing intently at the burning coals. I too sat down before the fire and gazed at the coals, and nothing was said for a long time.

My sister was in her cushioned chair in her corner, and Biddy sat at her needlework before the fire, and Joe sat next Biddy.

At length I got out, "Joe, have you told Biddy?"

"No, Pip," returned Joe, "I left it to yourself, Pip."

"I would rather you told, Joe."

"Pip's a gentleman of fortun', then," said Joe, "and God bless him in it!"

Biddy dropped her work and looked at me. Joe held his knees and looked at me. I looked at both of them. After a pause they both heartily congratulated me; but there was a certain touch of sadness in their congratulations that I rather resented.

I took it upon myself to impress Biddy (and through Biddy, Joe) with the grave obligation I considered my friends under, to know nothing and say nothing about the maker of my fortune. They said they would be very particular and then they congratulated me again, and went on to express so much wonder at the notion of my being a gentleman that I didn't half like it.

"Saturday night," said I, when we sat at our supper of bread-and-cheese and beer. "Five more days, and then the day before *the* day! They'll soon go."

"Yes, Pip," observed Joe, whose voice sounded hollow in his beer mug. "They'll soon go."

"I have been thinking, Joe, that when I go downtown on Monday and order my new clothes, I shall tell the tailor that I'll come and put them on there, or that I'll have them sent to Mr. Pumblechook's. It would be very disagreeable to be stared at by all the people here."

"Mr. and Mrs. Hubble might like to see you in your new genteel figure, too, Pip," said Joe. "So might Wopsle. And the Jolly Bargemen might take it as a compliment."

"That's just what I don't want, Joe. They would make such a business of it — such a coarse and common business — that I couldn't bear myself."

Biddy asked me here, "Have you thought about when you'll show yourself to Mr. Gargery, and your sister, and me? You will show yourself to us, won't you?"

"Biddy," I returned with some resentment, "you are so exceedingly quick that it's difficult to keep up with you. I shall bring my clothes here in a bundle one evening — most likely on the evening before I go away."

Biddy said no more. Handsomely forgiving her, I soon exchanged an affectionate good night with her and Joe, and went up to bed. When I got into my little room, I sat down and took a long look at it, as a mean little room that I should soon be parted from and raised above forever.

As I put the window open and stood looking out, I saw Joe come slowly forth at the dark door below and take a turn or two in the air; and then I saw Biddy come and bring him a pipe and light it for him. He never smoked so late, and it seemed to hint to me that he wanted comforting, for some reason or other. I drew away from the window and sat down in my one chair by the bedside, feeling it very sorrowful and strange that this first night of my bright fortunes should be the loneliest I had ever known.

I put my light out and crept into bed; and it was an uneasy bed now, and I never slept the old sound sleep in it any more.

CHAPTER 15

*Pip visits Trabb, the tailor,
and has a brief encounter
with Trabb's boy.*

MORNING made a considerable difference in my general prospect of life. After breakfast, Joe brought out my indentures from the press in the best parlor, and we put them in the fire, and I felt that I was free.

After our early dinner, I strolled out alone. As I passed the church, I thought — with something akin to shame — of my companionship with the fugitive whom I had once seen limping among those graves. My comfort was that it happened a long time ago, and that he had doubtless been transported a long way off, and that he was dead to me, and might be dead into the bargain. I made my way to the old Battery, and, lying down there to consider the question whether Miss Havisham intended me for Estella, fell asleep.

When I awoke, I was much surprised to find Joe sitting beside me, smoking his pipe. He greeted me with a cheerful smile on my opening my eyes, and said:

"As being the last time, Pip, I thought I'd foller."

"And, Joe, I am very glad you did so."

"Thankee, Pip."

"You may be sure, dear Joe," I went on, after we had shaken hands, "that I shall never forget you."

"No, no, Pip!" said Joe, in a comfortable tone. "I'm sure of that. Aye, aye, old chap!"

I told Joe of my former thoughts in this very place, that I had long wanted to be a gentleman. "It's a pity now,

Joe," said I, "that you did not get on a little more when we had our lessons here, isn't it?"

"Well, I don't know," returned Joe. "I'm so awful dull, I'm only master of my own trade. It were always a pity as I was so awful dull; but it's no more of a pity now than it was — this day twelvemonth [1] — don't you see!"

What I had meant was that when I came into my property and was able to do something for Joe, it would have been much more agreeable if he had been better qualified for a rise in station. He was so perfectly unaware of my meaning, however, that I thought I would mention it to Biddy in preference.

So, when we had walked home and had had tea, I took Biddy into our little garden and said I had a favor to ask of her.

"And it is, Biddy," said I, "that you will not omit any opportunity of helping Joe on a little."

"How helping him on?" asked Biddy, with a steady sort of glance.

"Well! Joe is a dear good fellow — in fact, I think he is the dearest fellow that ever lived — but he is rather backward in some things. For instance, Biddy, in his learning and his manners."

"Oh, his manners! Won't his manners do, then?" asked Biddy, plucking a black-currant leaf.

"My dear Biddy, they do very well here — "

"Oh! they *do* very well here?" interrupted Biddy, looking closely at the leaf in her hand.

"Hear me out — but if I were to remove Joe into a higher sphere, as I shall hope to remove him when I fully come into my property, they would hardly do him justice."

---

[1] this day twelvemonth: a year ago today.

"And don't you think he knows that?" asked Biddy.

It was such a provoking question (for it had never in the most distant manner occurred to me) that I said, snappishly, "Biddy, what do you mean?"

"Have you never considered that he may be proud?"

"Proud?" I repeated, with disdainful emphasis.

"Oh! there are many kinds of pride," said Biddy, looking full at me and shaking her head; "pride is not all of one kind — "

"Well? What are you stopping for?" said I.

"Not all of one kind," resumed Biddy. "He may be too proud to let anyone take him out of a place that he is competent to fill, and fills well and with respect."

"Now, Biddy," said I, "I am very sorry to see this in you. You are envious, Biddy, and grudging. You are dissatisfied on account of my rise in fortune, and you can't help showing it."

"If you have the heart to think so," returned Biddy, "say so. Say so over and over again, if you have the heart to think so."

"If you have the heart to be so, you mean, Biddy," said I, in a virtuous and superior tone. "Don't put it off upon me. I am extremely sorry to see this in you, Biddy. It's a — it's a bad side of human nature."

I walked away from Biddy, and Biddy went into the house, and I went out at the garden gate and took a dejected stroll until suppertime, again feeling it very sorrowful and strange that this, the second night of my bright fortunes, should be as lonely and unsatisfactory as the first.

But morning once more brightened my view. I went into town as early as I could hope to find the shops open, and presented myself before Mr. Trabb, the tailor, who was having his breakfast in the parlor behind his shop, and who did not think it worth his while to come out to me, but called me in to him.

"Well!" said Mr. Trabb, in a hail-fellow-well-met kind of way. "How are you, and what can I do for you?"

"Mr. Trabb," said I, "it's an unpleasant thing to have to mention, because it looks like boasting, but I have come into a handsome property."

A change passed over Mr. Trabb. He got up from the bedside and wiped his fingers on the tablecloth, exclaiming, "Lord bless my soul!"

"I am going up to my guardian in London," said I, casually drawing some guineas out of my pocket and looking at them, "and I want a fashionable suit of clothes to go in. I wish to pay for them," I added, "with ready money."

"My dear sir," said Mr. Trabb, "may I venture to congratulate you? Would you do me the favor of stepping into the shop?"

Mr. Trabb's boy was the boldest boy in all that countryside. When I had first entered, he was sweeping the shop, and he sweetened his labors by sweeping over me. He was still sweeping when I came out into the shop with Mr. Trabb, and he knocked the broom against all possible corners and obstacles, to express equality with any blacksmith, alive or dead.

"Hold that noise," said Mr. Trabb with the greatest sternness, "or I'll knock your head off! Do me the favor to be seated, sir. Now, sir," said Mr. Trabb, taking down a roll of cloth.

I selected the materials for a suit, and re-entered the parlor to be measured. When he had at last done and had arranged to send the articles to Mr. Pumblechook's, he said, "I know, sir, that

London gentlemen cannot be expected to patronize local work, as a rule; but if you would give me a turn now and then, I should greatly esteem it. Good morning, sir, much obliged. — Door!"

The last word was flung at the boy, who had not the least notion what it meant. But I saw him collapse as his master rubbed me out with his hands, and my first decided experience of the stupendous power of money was that it had morally laid upon his back Trabb's boy.

After this memorable event I went to the hatter's, and the bootmaker's, and the hosier's, and felt rather like Mother Hubbard's dog whose outfit required the services of so many trades. I also went to the coach office and took my place for seven o'clock on Saturday morning. When I had ordered everything I wanted, I directed my steps toward Pumblechook's, and, as I approached that gentleman's place of business, I saw him standing at his door.

He was waiting for me with great impatience. He had been out early with the carriage, and had called at the forge and heard the news. He had prepared a luncheon for me in the parlor, and he too ordered his shopman to "come out of the gangway" as my sacred person passed.

"To think," said Mr. Pumblechook, after snorting admiration at me for some moments, "that I should have been the humble instrument of leading up to this, is a proud reward."

I begged Mr. Pumblechook to remember that nothing was to be ever said or hinted on that point. I mentioned that I wished to have my new clothes sent to his house, and he was delighted on my so distinguishing him. I mentioned my reason for wishing to avoid observation in the village, and he lauded it to the skies.

There followed many glasses of wine, the drinking of which was constantly interrupted by Mr. Pumblechook's rising from his chair, extending a fervent hand, and clasping my own, with the request that he might shake it.

There was nobody but himself, he intimated, worthy of my confidence. Then he asked me tenderly if I remembered our boyish games at sums, and how we had gone together to have me bound apprentice, and, in effect, how he had ever been my favorite fancy and my chosen friend. If I had taken ten times as many glasses of wine, I should have known that he never stood in that relation to me, and should in my heart of hearts have repudiated the idea.

Tuesday, Wednesday, and Thursday passed, and on Friday morning I went to Mr. Pumblechook's to put on my new clothes and pay my visit to Miss Havisham. My clothes were rather a disappointment, of course. Probably every new and eagerly expected garment ever put on fell a trifle short of the wearer's expectation. But after I had had my new suit on some half an hour, it seemed to fit me better.

I went to Miss Havisham's by all the back ways, and rang at the bell. Sarah Pocket came to the gate and positively reeled back when she saw me so changed.

"You?" said she. "You? Good gracious! What do you want?"

"I am going to London, Miss Pocket," said I, "and want to say good-by to Miss Havisham."

I was not expected, for she left me locked in the yard while she went to ask if I were to be admitted. After a very short delay, she returned and took me up, staring at me all the way.

Miss Havisham was taking exercise

in the room with the long table, leaning on her crutch stick. The room was lighted as usual, and at the sound of her entrance, she stopped and turned. She was then just abreast of the rotted bride cake.

"Don't go, Sarah," she said. "Well, Pip?"

"I start for London, Miss Havisham, tomorrow." I was exceedingly careful what I said. "And I thought you would kindly not mind my taking leave of you."

"This is a gay figure, Pip," said she, making her crutch stick play round me, as if she, the fairy godmother who had changed me, were bestowing the finishing gift.

"I have come into such good fortune since I saw you last, Miss Havisham," I murmured. "And I am so grateful for it, Miss Havisham!"

"Aye, aye!" said she, looking at the envious Sarah with delight. "I have seen Mr. Jaggers. I have heard about it, Pip. So you go tomorrow?"

"Yes, Miss Havisham."

"And you are adopted by a rich person?"

"Yes, Miss Havisham."

"Not named?"

"No, Miss Havisham."

"And Mr. Jaggers is made your guardian?"

"Yes, Miss Havisham."

She quite gloated on these questions and answers, so keen was her enjoyment of Sarah Pocket's jealous dismay. "Well!" she went on. "You have a promising career before you. Be good — deserve it — and abide by Mr. Jaggers' instructions." She looked at me, and looked at Sarah, and Sarah's face wrung out of her watchful face a cruel smile. "Good-by, Pip! — you will always keep the name of Pip, you know."

"Yes, Miss Havisham."

"Good-by, Pip!"

She stretched out her hand, and I went down on my knee and put it to my lips. I had not considered how I should take leave of her; it came naturally to me at the moment to do this. She looked at Sarah Pocket with triumph in her weird eyes, and so I left my fairy godmother, with both her hands on her crutch stick, standing in the midst of the dimly lighted room beside the rotten bride cake that was hidden in cobwebs.

And now, those six days which were to have run out so slowly had run out fast and were gone, and tomorrow looked me in the face more steadily than I could look at it. As the six evenings had dwindled away, I had become more and more appreciative of the society of Joe and Biddy. On this last evening, I dressed myself out in my new clothes for their delight and sat in my splendor until bedtime. We had a hot supper on the occasion, graced by the inevitable roast fowl. We were all very low, and none the higher for pretending to be in spirits.

I was to leave our village at five in the morning, and I had told Joe that I wished to walk away all alone. I am afraid that this purpose originated in my sense of the contrast there would be between me and Joe if we went to the coach together. I had pretended with myself that there was nothing of this taint in the arrangement; but when I went up to my little room on this last night, I felt compelled to admit that it was so, and had an impulse to go down again and entreat Joe to walk with me in the morning. I did not.

It was a hurried breakfast with no taste in it. I got up from the meal, saying with a sort of briskness, as if it had only just occurred to me, "Well! I suppose I must be off!" and then I kissed my sister, who was nodding and shaking in her usual chair, and kissed Biddy, and threw my arms around Joe's neck. The last I saw of them was when dear old Joe waved his strong right arm above his head, crying huskily, "Hooroar!" and Biddy put her apron to her face.

I walked away at a good pace, thinking it was easier to go than I had supposed it would be. The village was very peaceful and quiet, and all beyond was so unknown and great that in a moment with a strong heave and sob I broke into tears. I was better after I had cried than before — more sorry, more aware of my own ingratitude, more gentle. If I had cried before, I should have had Joe with me then.

When I was on the coach, and it was clear of the town, I deliberated with an aching heart whether I would not get down when we changed horses and walk back, and have another evening at home, and a better parting.

We changed horses after a while and it was now too late and too far to go back, and I went on. And the mists had all solemnly risen now, and the world lay spread before me.

This Is the End of the First Stage of Pip's Expectations.

THE THREADS OF THE PLOT

At this point in the novel you will see that Dickens, like a master weaver at his loom, is working with many "threads" of story at once. We are not yet able, even if we wished, to see what the whole great "tapestry" is going to be. But it is important to trace some of the story "threads" that compose this first section. Thoughtful answers to these questions will help you review the events covered in the First Stage.

1. How much do we know about the two convicts on the marsh? Explain why Pip calls one of them "his" convict. Why was this man startled when Pip told him that he had seen a second convict?

2. How is Estella related to Miss Havisham?

3. How much of Miss Havisham's story do we know up to now? Why did she send for Pip? Explain what she may have meant by the words he thought she said (page 596), "Break their hearts, my pride and hope, break their hearts and have no mercy!"

4. What possible connection does the attack on Mrs. Joe have with the convicts? With what weapon was she struck? Why did she fail to see who struck her?

5. What is Mr. Jaggers' relation to Miss Havisham? to Pip? What conclusion does Pip draw about Miss Havisham, Mr. Jaggers, and himself?

6. Who first uses the words "great expectations"? What is specifically meant by the phrase?

GETTING TO KNOW THE CHARACTERS

As we review the various interwoven story threads running through the First Stage of *Great Expectations*, we must not lose sight of the fact that the main characters have been developing and changing just as real people do when various events influence their lives. These questions will help you decide how well you have followed the development of the characters.

7. Pip is a small boy in the very first scene; he is just beginning to understand what it can mean to be an orphan, especially in terms of the future. Compare the child he is in Chapter 1 with the Pip who leaves for London. Explain the different ways in which he has changed.

8. We know that Pip's convict is a dangerous criminal, yet we like him, just as Pip does. What makes us feel sorry for him? When his actions earn Pip's gratitude, what does this show about him?

9. Miss Havisham treats Pip cruelly, but there is something about her which also wins our sympathy. Explain what you think is the reason for her cruelty — and what she does that is kindhearted.

10. Describe Estella's treatment of Pip. Does it seem reasonable that a boy should love a girl who behaves in this way? Defend your answer; you will find some members of your class disagreeing with you! Does Estella's attitude change toward Pip? If you think it does, explain why.

11. What makes Pip's sister, Mrs. Joe, seem harsh? Point out an example of her strict honesty — and try to offer reasons for the severity of her speech and actions. How does she change after the attack made on her?

12. What traits of character make Joe such a warm and lovable human being? Why is Biddy so appealing?

13. What traits of character make Orlick so unlikable? Mr. Pumblechook? Miss Havisham's relatives?

IDEAS TO TALK OVER

14. That money has power to change people's attitudes toward one another was a favorite subject of Charles Dickens. The curious behavior of Miss Havisham's relatives on her birthday is directly connected with this subject. Can you explain why?

15. Pip is quick to notice that some people treat him differently the minute they learn he has come into money. Mr. Pumblechook, Trabb, the tailor, and Trabb's foolish boy — who seems to be the village clown — are among the first to alter their manner toward Pip. Explain what each does and what those actions reveal about the person. How does Miss Havisham act when Pip gives her the news? What effect has his good fortune on Sarah Pocket?

LOOKING AHEAD

16. We shall now accompany Pip to London. He has said good-by to the only home and family he has known. He admits to himself that he has been ungrateful. By now he is a young man, and he has been assured of a bright future. But like all young people, when he departs for London, he cannot leave behind him, like so much unwanted luggage, the problems that go with growing up. His love for Estella is an unsolved problem. Another is the unpleasant feeling that he has not been sufficiently grateful to Joe and Mrs. Joe. Is it likely, do you think, that the tremendous change in his life and fortunes will automatically solve these problems for Pip? Is it possible that his personality will fail to be affected by the upheaval in his life or by the continuing presence of those unsolved problems? Give your reasons for thinking as you do.

17. Perhaps, as you begin the Second Stage of *Great Expectations*, you might like to try to predict what lies ahead for Pip. What is your guess? Take warning, however. Your predictions might be accurate, your understanding of Pip's character good, but Dickens has many a surprise ahead — for you as well as for the ambitious young Pip!

FOR YOUR VOCABULARY: WORD HISTORIES

As a blacksmith, Joe has two helpers, Pip and Orlick. They are his *apprentice* and his *journeyman*, respectively, and Joe is their *master*. The apprenticeship system is very old, going back as far as ancient Babylonia and Egypt. Today's trade unions make use of these same terms; many high schools offer *pre-apprentice* shop courses.

In the England of Pip's day, a boy's apprenticeship had to be paid for; that is, a legal contract called his "indentures" provided that his master be paid a certain sum, in return for which the boy received his board, room, and training in the master's craft or trade.

Then as now, a journeyman was a workman who had completed his apprenticeship and was qualified to earn wages in his trade.

Our language draws on these old terms and titles. The *master* plumber is the man you call to fix a leaky sink; by the same token, you would prefer not to have an *apprentice* carpenter build your new garage. We also use such expressions as "He is a journeyman playwright" and "George is a master architect." What do these expressions mean? What other examples can you mention in which old terms are used in the language of today?

The Second Stage of Pip's Expectations

CHAPTER 16

Pip meets Wemmick, Mr. Jaggers' clerk, and Herbert Pocket.

THE JOURNEY from our town to London was one of about five hours. It was a little past midday when the four-horse stagecoach in which I was passenger got into the ravel of traffic in London. If we Britons had not at one time decided that it was treasonable to doubt our having and our being the best of everything, I would have been scared by the immensity of London, and I think I might have had some faint doubts whether it was not rather ugly, crooked, narrow, and dirty.

Mr. Jaggers had sent me his address: it was in a section called Little Britain. I was soon taken there by hackney coach and deposited at certain offices with an open door, whereon was painted MR. JAGGERS.

I went into the front office and asked, was Mr. Jaggers at home?

"He is not," returned the clerk. "He is in court at present. Am I addressing Mr. Pip?"

I signified that he was addressing Mr. Pip.

"Mr. Jaggers left word would you wait in his room. He couldn't say how long he might be, having a case on. But it stands to reason, his time being valuable, that he won't be longer than he can help."

With those words, the clerk opened a door and ushered me into an inner chamber at the back. Mr. Jaggers' room was lighted by a skylight only, and was a most dismal place. I sat wondering and waiting in Mr. Jaggers' close room, until I really could not bear the dust and grit that lay thick on everything, and got up and went out.

I told the clerk that I would take a turn in the air while I waited, and went out into the streets, where I saw the great black dome of Saint Paul's bulging at me from behind a grim stone building which a bystander said was Newgate Prison. Following the wall of the jail, I found a number of people standing about, smelling strongly of beer. I learned that the trials were on.

I dropped into the office to ask if Mr. Jaggers had come in yet, and I found he had not, and I strolled out again. I became aware that other people were waiting about for Mr. Jaggers, as well as I. There were two men of secret appearance lounging nearby, one of whom said to the other when they first passed me that "Jaggers would do it if it was to be done." There were two women standing at a corner, and one of the women was crying on her dirty shawl, and the other comforted her by saying as she pulled her own shawl over her shoulders, "Jaggers is for him, 'Melia, and what more *could* you have?" These testimonies to the popularity of my guardian made a deep impression on me, and I admired and wondered more than ever.

At length I saw Mr. Jaggers coming across the road toward me. All the others who were waiting saw him at the same time, and there was quite a rush at him. Mr. Jaggers addressed himself to his followers.

First, he took the two secret men.

"Now, I have nothing to say to *you*," said Mr. Jaggers. "I told you from the first it was a tossup. Have you paid Wemmick?"

"Yes, sir," said both the men together.

"Very well; then you may go. If you say a word to me, I'll throw up the case."

"We thought, Mr. Jaggers — " one of the men began, pulling off his hat.

"That's what I told you not to do," said Mr. Jaggers. "*You* thought! I think for you; that's enough for you."

"And now *you!*" said Mr. Jaggers, suddenly stopping and turning on the two women with the shawls. "Once for all; if you come here, bothering about your Bill, I'll make an example of both your Bill and you, and let him slip through my fingers. Have you paid Wemmick?"

"Oh, yes, sir! Every farthing."

"Very well. Say another word — one single word — and Wemmick shall give you your money back." This terrible threat caused the two women to fall off immediately.

Without further interruption we reached the front door. My guardian then took me into his own room, and while he lunched, he informed me what arrangements he had made for me. I was to go to Barnard's Inn, to young Mr. Pocket's rooms, where a bed had been sent in for my accommodation; I was to remain with young Mr. Pocket until Monday; on Monday I was to go with him to his father's house on a visit. Also, I was told what my allowance was

Pip's London.

to be — it was a very liberal one — and had handed to me the cards of certain tradesmen with whom I was to deal for all kinds of clothes and such other things as I should want. "You will find your credit good, Mr. Pip," said my guardian, "but I shall by this means be able to check your bills, and to pull you up if I find you spending too much. Of course you'll go wrong somehow, but that's no fault of mine."

After I had pondered a little over this encouraging sentiment, I asked Mr. Jaggers if I could send for a coach. He said it was not worth while, I was so near my destination; Wemmick should walk round with me, if I pleased.

I then found that Wemmick was the clerk in the next room. I accompanied him into the street, after shaking hands with my guardian. We found a new set of people lingering outside, but Wemmick made a way among them by saying coolly yet decisively, "I tell you it's no use; he won't have a word to say to one of you"; and we soon got clear of them and went on side by side.

Casting my eyes on Mr. Wemmick as we went along, to see what he was like in the light of day, I found him to be a dry man, rather short in stature, with a square wooden face. He wore his hat on the back of his head, and looked straight before him, walking in a self-contained way as if there were nothing in the streets to claim his attention.

"Do you know where Mr. Matthew Pocket lives?" I asked Mr. Wemmick.

"Yes," said he, nodding in the direction. "At Hammersmith, west of London."

"Is that far?"

"Well! Say five miles."

"Do you know him?"

"Why, you are a regular cross-examiner!" said Mr. Wemmick, looking at me with an approving air. "Yes, I know him. *I* know him!"

Soon he said here we were at Barnard's Inn. It was the dingiest collection of shabby buildings ever squeezed together in a rank corner as a club for tomcats. We entered a melancholy little square that looked to me like a flat burying ground. I thought it had the most dismal trees in it, and the most dismal sparrows, and the most dismal cats, and the most dismal houses that I had ever seen. The windows of the houses were in every stage of dilapidated [1] blind and curtain, crippled flowerpot, cracked glass, dusty decay, and miserable makeshift.

So imperfect was this realization of the first of my great expectations that I looked in dismay at Mr. Wemmick. He led me up a flight of stairs, which appeared to be slowly collapsing into sawdust, to a set of chambers on the top floor. Mr. Pocket, Jun., was painted on the door, and there was a label on the letter box, "Return shortly."

"He hardly thought you'd come so soon," Mr. Wemmick explained. "You don't want me any more?"

"No, thank you," said I.

"As I keep the cash," Mr. Wemmick observed, "we shall most likely meet pretty often. Good day."

When he was gone, I opened the staircase window and nearly beheaded myself, for the ropes had rotted away, and it came down like the guillotine. [2] After this escape, I was content to stand dolefully looking out, saying to myself that London was decidedly overrated.

Mr. Pocket, Junior's, idea of "shortly" was not mine, for I had nearly maddened myself with looking out for half an hour, and had written my name with

[1] **dilapidated** (dĭ·lăp′ĭ·dāt′ĕd): falling apart.
[2] **guillotine** (gĭl′ô·tēn): a machine for beheading a person by means of a heavy blade.

my finger several times in the dirt of every pane in the window, before I heard footsteps on the stairs. Gradually there arose before me the hat, head, waistcoat, trousers, boots, of a member of society of about my own standing. He had a paper bag under each arm and a basket of strawberries in one hand, and was out of breath.

"Mr. Pip?" said he.

"Mr. Pocket?" said I.

"Dear me!" he exclaimed, "I am extremely sorry; but I knew there was a coach from your part of the country at midday, and I thought you would come by that one. The fact is, I have been out on your account — not that that is any excuse — for I thought, coming from the country, you might like a little fruit after dinner, and I went to Covent Garden Market to get it."

For a certain reason, I felt as if my eyes would start out of my head. I began to think this was a dream.

"Pray come in," said Mr. Pocket, Junior. "Allow me to lead the way. I am rather bare here, but I hope you'll be able to make out tolerably well till Monday. My father thought you might like to take a walk about London with me. I am sure I shall be very happy to show London to you. Our food will be supplied from our coffeehouse here, and (it is only right I should add) at your expense, such being Mr. Jaggers' directions. As to our lodging, it's not by any means splendid, because I have my own bread to earn, and my father hasn't anything to give me, and I shouldn't be willing to take it if he had. This is our sitting room — just such chairs and tables and carpet and so forth, you see, as they could spare from home. This is my little bedroom; rather musty, but Barnard's *is* musty. This is your bedroom; the furniture's hired for the occasion, but I trust it will answer the purpose; if you should want anything, I'll go and fetch it. The chambers are retired,[1] and we shall be alone together, but we shan't fight, I dare say."

As I stood opposite to Mr. Pocket, Junior, I saw the sudden recognition come into his own eyes that I knew to be in mine, and he said, falling back:

"Lord bless me, you're the prowling boy!"

"And you," said I, "are the pale young gentleman!"

CHAPTER 17

Pip gets a new name.

THE PALE young gentleman and I stood contemplating one another in Barnard's Inn, until we both burst out laughing.

"The idea of its being you!" said he. "The idea of its being *you!*" said I. And then we stared at one another afresh, and laughed again. "Well!" said the pale young gentleman, reaching out his hand good-humoredly, "it's all over now, I hope, and it will be good of you if you'll forgive me for having knocked you about so."

I derived from this speech that Mr. Herbert Pocket (for Herbert was the pale young gentleman's name) still rather confused his intentions with his actions. But I made a modest reply, and we shook hands warmly.

"You hadn't come into your good fortune at that time?" said Herbert Pocket.

"No," said I.

"No," he agreed, "I heard it had happened very lately. *I* was rather on the lookout for good fortune then."

"Indeed?"

"Yes. Miss Havisham had sent for me,

[1] **retired:** secluded; having few neighbors.

to see if she could take a fancy to me. But she couldn't — at all events, she didn't."

I thought it polite to remark that I was surprised to hear that.

"Bad taste," said Herbert, laughing, "but a fact. Yes, she had sent for me on a trial visit, and if I had come out of it successfully, I suppose I should have been provided for; perhaps I should have been what-you-may-called-it to Estella."

"What's that?" I asked, with sudden anxiety.

He was arranging his fruit in plates while we talked, which divided his attention, and was the cause of his having made this lapse of a word. "Engaged," he explained, still busy with the fruit. "Betrothed."

"How did you bear your disappointment?" I asked.

"Pooh!" said he. "I didn't care much for it. *She's* a Tartar." [1]

"Miss Havisham?"

"I don't say no to that, but I meant Estella. That girl's hard and haughty and unreasonable to the last degree, and has been brought up by Miss Havisham to wreak vengeance on all the male sex."

"What relation is she to Miss Havisham?"

"None," said he. "Only adopted."

"Why should she wreak revenge on all the male sex? What revenge?"

"Lord, Mr. Pip!" said he. "Don't you know?"

"No," said I.

"Dear me! It's quite a story, and shall be saved till dinnertime. Mr. Jaggers is your guardian, I understand?" he went on.

"Yes."

"You know he is Miss Havisham's man of business and solicitor,[2] and has her confidence when nobody else has?"

This was bringing me (I felt) toward dangerous ground. I answered cautiously that I had seen Mr. Jaggers in Miss Havisham's house on the very day of our combat, but never at any other time, and that I believed he had no recollection of having ever seen me there.

"He was so obliging as to suggest my father for your tutor, and he called on my father to propose it. Of course he knew about my father from his connection with Miss Havisham. My father is Miss Havisham's cousin; not that that implies friendly intercourse between them, for he makes no effort to court her favor."

Herbert Pocket had a frank and easy way with him that was very taking. I have never seen anyone who had a greater natural inability to do anything secret and mean. There was something wonderfully hopeful about his general air, and something that at the same time whispered to me he would never be very successful or rich. He was still a pale young gentleman, without much strength. He had not a handsome face, but it was better than handsome, being extremely amiable and cheerful.

As he was so outspoken himself, I told him my small story, and laid stress on my being forbidden to inquire who my benefactor was. I further mentioned that as I had been brought up a blacksmith in a country place, and knew very little of the ways of politeness, I would take it as a great kindness in him if he would give me a hint whenever he saw me at a loss or going wrong.

"With pleasure," said he, "though I venture to prophesy that you'll want very few hints. Will you begin at once

[1] **Tartar:** a person of cruel and unrelenting nature, impossible to deal with.

[2] **solicitor** (sȯ·lĭs′ĭ·tẽr): in England, a lawyer who handles his clients' legal affairs, as distinguished from a barrister (băr′ĭs·tẽr), who pleads cases in court.

to call me by my Christian name, Herbert?"

I thanked him and said I would. I informed him in exchange that my Christian name was Philip.

"I don't take to Philip," said he, smiling, "for it sounds like one of those dull boys out of the spelling book. Would you mind Handel for a familiar name? There's a charming piece of music by Handel, called the Harmonious Blacksmith."

"I should like it very much."

"Then, my dear Handel," said he, turning round as the door opened, "here is the dinner."

We had made some progress in the dinner, when I reminded Herbert of his promise to tell me about Miss Havisham.

"True," he replied. "Let me introduce the topic, Handel, by mentioning that in London it is not the custom to put the knife in the mouth — for fear of accidents — and that while the fork is reserved for that use, it is not put farther in than necessary. It is scarcely worth mentioning, only it's as well to do as other people do. Also, the spoon is not generally used overhand, but under. This has the advantage that you get at your mouth better (which after all is the object)."

He offered these friendly suggestions in such a lively way that we both laughed.

"Now," he pursued, "Miss Havisham was a spoiled child. Her mother died when she was a baby, and her father denied her nothing. He was very rich and very proud. So was his daughter."

"Miss Havisham was an only child?" I asked.

"Stop a moment, I am coming to that. No, she was not an only child; she had a half brother. Her father privately married again — his cook, I rather think."

"I thought he was proud," said I.

"My good Handel, so he was. He married his second wife privately, because he *was* proud, and in the course of time she died also. When his second wife died, Havisham told his daughter what he had done, and then the son became a part of the family, residing in the house you are acquainted with. As the son became a young man, he turned out riotous, extravagant, undutiful — altogether bad. At last his father disinherited him; but he softened when he was dying and left him well off, though not nearly so well off as Miss Havisham.

"Miss Havisham was now an heiress, and was looked after as a great match. Her half brother had ample means again, but wasted them most fearfully. There were strong differences between him and her, and it is suspected that he cherished a deep and mortal grudge against her. Now, I come to the cruel part of the story.

"There appeared upon the scene a certain man, who made love to Miss Havisham. I have heard my father mention that he was a showy man, and the kind of man for the purpose. But he was not to be mistaken for a gentleman. Well! This man pursued Miss Havisham and professed to be devoted to her. There is no doubt that she perfectly idolized him. He got great sums of money from her, and he induced her to buy her brother out of a share in the family property at an immense price, on the plea that when he was her husband he must hold and manage it all.

"Now, your guardian was not at that time in Miss Havisham's councils, and she was too haughty and too much in love to be advised by anyone. Her relations were poor and scheming, with the exception of my father; he was poor enough, but not slavish or jealous. The only independent one among them, he warned her that she was doing too much for this man, and was placing herself in his power. She angrily ordered my father out of the house, in his presence, and my father has never seen her since."

I now recalled having heard Miss Havisham say, "Matthew will come and see me at last when I am laid dead upon that table."

"To return to the man and make an end of him. The marriage day was fixed, the wedding dresses were bought, the wedding guests were invited. The day came, but not the bridegroom. He wrote a letter — "

"Which she received," I struck in, "when she was dressing for her marriage? At twenty minutes to nine?"

"At the hour and minute," said Herbert, nodding, "at which she afterward stopped all the clocks. What was in it, further than that it most heartlessly broke the marriage off, I can't tell you, because I don't know. When she recovered from a bad illness, she laid the whole place waste, as you have seen it, and she has never since looked upon the light of day."

"Is that all the story?" I asked, after considering it.

"All I know of it. Oh, I have forgotten one thing. It has been supposed that the man to whom she gave her misplaced confidence acted in concert with her half brother; that it was a conspiracy between them; and that they shared the profits."

"What became of the two men? Are they alive now?"

"I don't know."

"You said just now that Estella was not related to Miss Havisham, but adopted. When adopted?"

Herbert shrugged his shoulders. "There has always been an Estella,

since I have heard of a Miss Havisham. I know no more."

"And all I know," I replied, "you know."

"I fully believe it. And as to the condition of your expected fortune — namely, that you are not to inquire or discuss to whom you owe it — you may be very sure that it will never be even approached by me."

He said this with so much delicacy that I felt he as perfectly understood Miss Havisham to be my benefactress as I understood the fact myself.

We were very gay and sociable, and I asked him in the course of conversation what he was. He replied, "An insurer of ships."

I had grand ideas of the wealth and importance of insurers of ships, and was further impressed when he continued, "I shall not rest satisfied with merely insuring ships. I think I shall trade," said he, leaning back in his chair, "to the East Indies for shawls, spices, dyes, drugs, and precious woods. It's an interesting trade."

Quite overpowered by the magnificence of these dealings, I asked him where the ships he insured mostly traded to at present.

"I haven't begun insuring yet," he replied. "I am looking about me."

Somehow, that pursuit seemed more in keeping with Barnard's Inn. I said (in a tone of conviction), "Ah-h!"

"Yes. I am in a countinghouse,[1] and looking about me."

"Is a countinghouse profitable?" I asked.

"Why, n-no; not to me. Not directly profitable. That is, it doesn't pay me anything, and I have to — keep myself. But the thing is, that you look about

---

[1] **countinghouse:** an office or building where business is transacted.

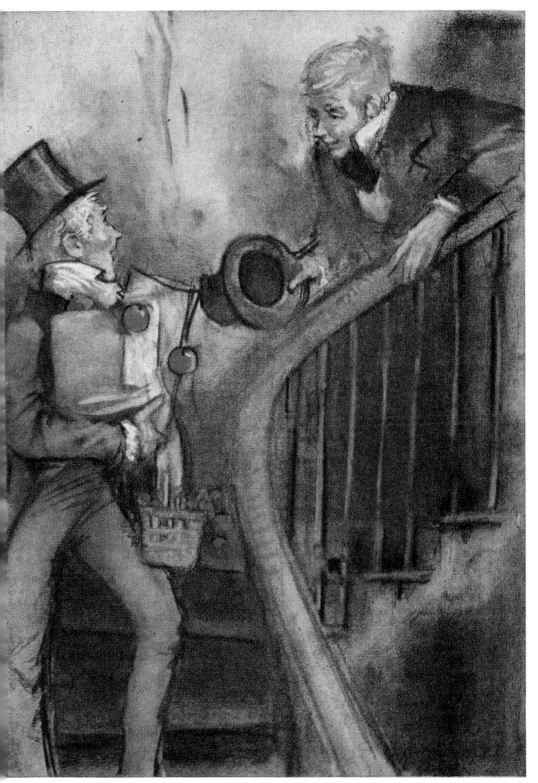

"Mr. Pip?" said he. "Mr. Pocket?" said I.

you. *That's* the grand thing. You are in a countinghouse, you know, and you look about you."

This was very like his way of conducting that encounter in the garden; very like. His manner of bearing his poverty, too, exactly corresponded to his manner of bearing that defeat. It seemed to me that he took all blows and buffets now, with just the same air as he had taken mine then. It was evident that he owned nothing but the simplest necessaries and that everything else turned out to have been sent in on my account from the coffeehouse or somewhere else, yet his imaginary good fortune made him cheerful. I liked him and we got on famously together.

CHAPTER 18

Pip's friendships increase.

ON MONDAY MORNING at a quarter of nine, Herbert went to the countinghouse — to look around him, I suppose — and I bore him company. He was to come out in an hour or two and accompany me to Hammersmith, where I was to stay under the roof and under the instruction of Mr. Matthew Pocket. When Herbert came, we went and had lunch and then took a coach for his family's home, where we arrived at two or three o'clock in the afternoon. Lifting the latch of a gate, we passed into a garden overlooking the river, where Mr. Pocket's children were playing about.

Mr. Pocket came out to make my acquaintance. He was a gentleman with a rather perplexed expression of face, with very gray hair disordered on his head, as if he didn't quite see how to put anything straight. Mr. Pocket said

he was glad to see me, and he hoped I was not sorry to see him. "For I am really not," he added, with his son's smile, "an alarming person." He was a young-looking man, despite his perplexities and his gray hair, and his manner seemed quite natural. Later and by degrees I learned, chiefly from Herbert, that Mr. Pocket had educated himself at Harrow and Cambridge,[1] where he had distinguished himself. He had come to London and here, after failing in loftier hopes, he turned to the meager rewards to be had from tutoring backward young men and from routine literary tasks.

Mr. Pocket took me into the house and showed me my room, which was a pleasant one. He then knocked at the doors of two other similar rooms, and introduced me to their occupants, by name Drummle and Startop. Drummle, an old-looking young man of a heavy order of physique, was whistling. Startop, younger in years and appearance, was reading and holding his head, as if he thought himself in danger of exploding it with too strong a charge of knowledge.

In the evening there was rowing on the river. As Drummle and Startop had each a boat, I resolved to set up mine, and to best them both. I was pretty good at most exercises in which country boys are skillful, but I was conscious of wanting elegance of style for the Thames.[2] Therefore I at once engaged an expert boatman nearby, to whom I was introduced by my new friends.

After two or three days, when I had established myself in my room and had gone backward and forward to London

[1] **Harrow and Cambridge:** Harrow is a famous preparatory school, and Cambridge a famous university in England.
[2] **Thames** (tĕmz): a river passing through London near Mr. Pocket's house.

several times, Mr. Pocket and I had a long talk together. I learned that he had been told by Mr. Jaggers that I was not designed for any profession, and that I should be well enough educated for my destiny if I could "hold my own" with the average of young men in prosperous circumstances.

When I had begun to work in earnest, it occurred to me that if I could retain my bedroom in Barnard's Inn, my life would be agreeably varied, while my manners would be none the worse for Herbert's society; so I went off to impart my wish to Mr. Jaggers.

"If I could buy the furniture now hired for me," said I, "and one or two other little things, I should be quite at home there."

"Go it!" said Mr. Jaggers, with a short laugh. "I told you you'd get on. Well! How much do you want?"

I said I didn't know how much.

"Come!" retorted Mr. Jaggers. "How much? Fifty pounds?"

"Oh, not nearly so much."

"Five pounds?" said Mr. Jaggers.

This was such a great fall, that I said in disappointment, "Oh! more than that."

"More than that, eh!" retorted Mr. Jaggers. "How much more?"

"It is so difficult to fix a sum," said I, hesitating.

"Wemmick!" said Mr. Jaggers, opening his office door. "Take Mr. Pip's written order, and pay him twenty pounds."

This strongly marked way of doing business made a strongly marked impression on me, and that not of an agreeable kind. As he happened to go out now, and as Wemmick was brisk and talkative, I said to Wemmick that I hardly knew what to make of Mr. Jaggers' manner.

"Tell him that, and he'll take it as a compliment," answered Wemmick. "He don't mean that you *should* know what to make of it. — Oh!" for I looked surprised, "it's not personal; it's professional, only professional."

He went on to say in a friendly manner:

"If at any odd time when you have nothing better to do, you wouldn't mind coming over to see me at Walworth, I could offer you a bed, and I should consider it an honor. I have not much to show you but such two or three curiosities as I have and a bit of garden and a summerhouse."

I said I should be delighted to accept his hospitality.

"Thankee," said he. "Then we'll consider that it's to come off, when convenient to you. Have you dined with Mr. Jaggers yet?"

"Not yet."

"Well," said Wemmick, "he'll give you wine, and good wine. I'll give you punch, and not bad punch. And now I'll tell you something. When you go to dine with Mr. Jaggers, look at his housekeeper."

"Shall I see something very uncommon?"

"Well," said Wemmick, "you'll see a wild beast tamed. It won't lower your opinion of Mr. Jaggers' powers. Keep your eye on it."

I told him I would do so, but it was to be some time before my interest and curiosity were satisfied.

As the weeks passed at Mr. Pocket's home, I came to know better the nature of my fellow students. Bentley Drummle, who was so sulky a fellow that he even took up a book as if its writer had done him an injury, did not take up with new acquaintances in a more agreeable spirit. Heavy in figure, movement, and comprehension, he was idle, proud, niggardly, reserved, and suspicious. He came of a rich family who had nursed this combination of qualities until they made the discovery that it was just of age and a blockhead. Thus, Bentley Drummle had come to Mr. Pocket when he was a head taller than that gentleman, and half a dozen heads thicker than most gentlemen.

Startop had been spoiled by a weak mother and kept at home when he ought to have been at school, but he was devotedly attached to her and admired her beyond measure. He had a woman's delicacy of feature. It was but natural that I should take to him much more kindly than to Drummle. Even in the earliest evenings of our boating, he and I would pull homeward abreast of one another, conversing from boat to boat, while Bentley Drummle came up in our wake alone.

Herbert was my intimate companion and friend. I presented him with a half share in my boat, which was the occasion of his often coming down to Hammersmith; and my possession of a half share in his chambers often took me up to London. We used to walk between the two places at all hours.

These were the surroundings among which I settled down and applied myself to my education. I soon contracted expensive habits and began to spend an amount of money that a few short months before I should have thought almost impossible. But through good and evil I stuck to my books. Between Mr. Pocket and Herbert I got on fast.

I had not seen Mr. Wemmick for some weeks when I thought I would write him a note and propose to go home with him on a certain evening. He replied that it would give him much pleasure, and that he would expect me at the office at six o'clock. Thither I went, and there I found him, putting the key of his safe down his back as the clock struck.

"Did you think of walking down to Walworth?" said he.

"Certainly," said I, "if you approve."

"Very much," was Wemmick's reply, "for I have had my legs under the desk all day, and shall be glad to stretch them. Now I'll tell you what I've got for supper — a cold roast fowl. You don't object to an aged [1] parent, I hope?"

I really thought he was still speaking of the fowl, until he added, "Because I have got an aged parent at my place." I then said what politeness required.

"So you haven't dined with Mr. Jaggers yet?" he pursued, as we walked along.

"Not yet."

"He told me so this afternoon. I expect you'll have an invitation tomorrow. He's going to ask your pals, too. Three of 'em, ain't there? Well, he's going to ask the whole gang."

Mr. Wemmick and I beguiled [2] the time talking, until he gave me to understand that we had arrived in the district of Walworth. It appeared to be a rather dull collection of back lanes, ditches, and little gardens. Wemmick's house was a little wooden cottage in the midst of plots of garden, looking like a miniature castle, with the top of it cut out and painted like a battery mounted with guns.

"My own doing," said Wemmick. "Looks pretty, don't it?"

I highly commended it. I think it was the smallest house I ever saw.

"That's a real flagstaff, you see," said Wemmick, "and on Sundays I run up a real flag. Then look here. After I have crossed this bridge, I hoist it up — so — and cut off the communication."

[1] **aged** (ā'jĕd).
[2] **beguiled** (bē·gīld'): whiled away.

The bridge was a plank, and it crossed a chasm about four feet wide and two deep. But it was very pleasant to see the pride with which he hoisted it up and made it fast, smiling as he did so, with a relish and not merely mechanically.

"At nine o'clock every night, Greenwich time,"[1] said Wemmick, "the gun fires. There he is, you see! And when you hear him go, I think you'll say he's a Stinger."

The miniature cannon referred to was mounted in a separate fortress, constructed of latticework. It was protected from the weather by an ingenious little tarpaulin umbrella.

"Then, at the back," said Wemmick, "there's a pig, and there are fowls and rabbits; and I grow cucumbers. So, sir," said Wemmick, smiling again, but seriously, too, as he shook his head, "if you can suppose the little place besieged, it would hold out a devil of a time with so many provisions."

Then he conducted me to a bower about a dozen yards off, and in this retreat our glasses were already set forth.

"I am my own engineer, and my own carpenter, and my own plumber, and my own gardener, and my own Jack-of-all-trades," said Wemmick, in acknowledging my compliments. "Well, it's a good thing, you know. It brushes the Newgate[2] cobwebs away, and pleases the Aged. You wouldn't mind being at once introduced to the Aged, would you? It wouldn't put you out?"

I expressed readiness and we went into the castle. There we found, sitting by a fire, a very old man in a flannel coat; clean, cheerful, comfortable, and well cared for, but intensely deaf.

"Well, Aged Parent," said Wemmick, shaking hands with him in a cordial way, "how am you?"

"All right, John; all right!" replied the old man.

"Here's Mr. Pip, Aged Parent," said Wemmick, "and I wish you could hear his name. Nod away at him, Mr. Pip; that's what he likes. Nod away at him, if you please."

"This is a fine place of my son's, sir," cried the old man, while I nodded as hard as I possibly could.

"You're as proud of it as Punch; ain't you, Aged?" said Wemmick, contemplating the old man, with his hard face really softened; "there's a nod for you," giving him a tremendous one; "there's another for you," giving him a still more tremendous one; "you like that, don't you? If you're not tired, Mr. Pip — though I know it's tiring to strangers — will you nod him one more? You can't think how it pleases him."

I nodded him several more, and he was in great spirits. There was a neat serving girl in attendance, who looked after the Aged during the day. She set about laying the supper cloth while Wemmick and I engaged in conversation. He told me, as he smoked a pipe, that it had taken him a good many years to bring the property up to its present pitch of perfection.

"I hope Mr. Jaggers admires it," I said.

"Never seen it," said Wemmick. "Never heard of it. Never seen the Aged. Never heard of him. No; the office is one thing, and private life is another. When I go into the office, I leave the Castle behind me, and when I come into the Castle, I leave the office behind me. If it's not in any way disagreeable to you, you'll oblige me by doing the

---

[1] **Greenwich** (grĕn'ĭch) **time:** the official basis of standard time throughout the world.

[2] **Newgate:** Newgate Prison. Mr. Wemmick's dealings as Mr. Jaggers' clerk were largely with persons who sought either to get out or keep out of Newgate.

same. I don't wish it professionally spoken about."

Of course I felt my good faith involved in the observance of his request. The punch being very nice, we sat there drinking it and talking until it was almost nine o'clock. "Getting near gunfire," said Wemmick then, as he laid down his pipe. "It's the Aged's treat."

The Aged heated the poker, with expectant eyes, as a preliminary to the performance of this great nightly ceremony. Wemmick stood with his watch in his hand until the moment was come for him to take the red-hot poker from the Aged, and repair [1] to the battery. He took it, and went out, and presently the Stinger went off with a bang that shook the crazy little box of a cottage as if it must fall to pieces, and made every glass and teacup in it ring. Upon this the Aged — who I believe would have been blown out of his armchair but for holding on by the elbows — cried out exultingly, "He's fired! I heared him!" and I nodded at the old gentleman until I absolutely could not see him.

The supper, which was served shortly, was excellent. I was heartily pleased with my whole entertainment. Nor was there any drawback to my little turret bedroom.

Our breakfast was as good as the supper, and at half-past eight we started for Little Britain. By degrees, Wemmick seemed to get drier and harder as we went along. At last when we got to his place of business and he pulled out his key, he looked as unconscious of his Walworth property as if the Castle and the drawbridge and the arbor and the Aged had all been blown into space together by the last discharge of the Stinger.

[1] repair: go.

CHAPTER 19

Pip has dinner at Mr. Jaggers' and observes his housekeeper.

IT HAPPENED, as Wemmick had told me it would, that my guardian gave me the invitation for myself and friends. "No ceremony," Mr. Jaggers said, "and no dinner dress, and say tomorrow."

At six o'clock the next day Mr. Jaggers conducted my friends and me to Gerrard Street, Soho, to a rather stately house, but dolefully in want of painting, and with dirty windows. We went up a dark brown staircase into a series of three dark brown rooms on the first floor.

Dinner was laid in the best of these rooms. The table was comfortably laid and at Mr. Jaggers' side was a dumbwaiter, with a variety of bottles and decanters on it and four dishes of fruit for dessert. I noticed throughout that he kept everything under his own hand, and distributed everything himself.

As he had scarcely seen my three companions until now — for he and I had walked together — he stood on the hearthrug, after ringing the bell, and took a searching look at them. To my surprise, he seemed at once to be principally, if not solely, interested in Drummle.

"Pip," said he, putting his large hand on my shoulder and moving me to the window, "I don't know one from the other. Who's the Spider?"

"The Spider?" said I.

"The blotchy, sprawly, sulky fellow."

"That's Bentley Drummle," I replied. "The one with the delicate face is Startop."

Not taking the least account of Startop, he returned, "Bentley Drummle is his name, is it? I like the look of that fellow."

He immediately began to talk to Drummle. I was looking at the two when there came between me and them the housekeeper, with the first dish for the table.

She was a woman of about forty, tall, of a lithe, nimble figure, extremely pale, with large faded eyes and a quantity of streaming hair. She set the dish on, touched my guardian quietly on the arm with a finger to notify that dinner was ready, and vanished. No other attendant appeared.

Induced to take particular notice of the housekeeper, both by her own striking appearance and by Wemmick's preparation, I observed that whenever she was in the room, she kept her eyes attentively on my guardian. I fancied that I could detect in his manner a purpose of always holding her in suspense.

Dinner went off gaily, and although my guardian seemed to follow rather than suggest subjects, I knew that he wrenched the weakest part of our dispositions out of us. I found that I was expressing my tendency to spend extravagantly, and to patronize [1] Herbert, and to boast of my great prospects. It was so with all of us, but with no one more than Drummle. He informed our host that he much preferred our room to our company, and that as to skill he was more than our master, and that as to strength he could scatter us like chaff. He began baring and flexing his arm to show how muscular it was, and we all began to bare and flex our arms in a ridiculous manner.

Now the housekeeper was at that time clearing the table, my guardian taking no heed of her. Suddenly, he

[1] **patronize** (pā′trŭn-īz): act in a superior manner toward someone.

clapped his large hand on the housekeeper's like a trap, as she stretched it across the table.

"If you talk of strength," said Mr. Jaggers, "I'll show you a wrist. Molly, let me see your wrist."

Her entrapped hand was on the table, but she had already put her other hand behind her waist. "Master," she said, in a low voice, with her eyes attentively and entreatingly fixed upon him. "Don't."

"I'll show you a wrist," repeated Mr. Jaggers, with an immovable determination to show it. "Molly, let them see your wrist."

"Master," she again murmured. "Please!"

"Molly," said Mr. Jaggers, not looking at her, "let them see *both* your wrists. Show them. Come!"

He took his hand from hers, and turned that wrist up on the table. She brought her other hand from behind her, and held the two out side by side. The last wrist was much disfigured — deeply scarred and scarred across and across. When she held her hands out, she took her eyes from Mr. Jaggers, and turned them watchfully on every one of the rest of us in succession.

"There's power here," said Mr. Jaggers, coolly tracing out the sinews with his forefinger. "Very few men have the power of wrist that this woman has. It's remarkable what mere force of grip there is in these hands. I have had occasion to notice many hands; but I never saw stronger in that respect, man's or woman's, than these. That'll do, Molly. You can go." She withdrew her hands and went out of the room, and Mr. Jaggers filled his glass and passed round the wine.

"At half-past nine, gentlemen," said he, "we must break up. Pray make the best use of your time. I am glad to see you all. Mr. Drummle, I drink to you."

If his object in singling out Drummle were to bring him out still more, it perfectly succeeded. In a sulky triumph Drummle showed his poor opinion of the rest of us in a more and more offensive degree, until he became downright intolerable. Through all his stages, Mr. Jaggers followed him with the same strange interest.

In our boyish want of discretion I dare say we took too much to drink, and I know we talked too much. We became particularly hot upon some sneer of Drummle's, to the effect that we were too free with our money. Startop tried to turn the discussion aside with some small pleasantry that made us all laugh. Resenting this little success more than anything, Drummle, without any threat or warning, pulled his hands out of his pockets, dropped his round shoulders, swore, took up a large glass, and would have flung it at Startop's head, but for our entertainer's dexterously [1] seizing it at the instant it was raised.

"Gentlemen," said Mr. Jaggers, deliberately putting down the glass, "I am exceedingly sorry to announce that it's half-past nine."

On this hint we all rose to depart. Before we got to the street door, Startop was cheerily calling Drummle "old boy," as if nothing had happened. But the old boy would not even walk to Hammersmith on the same side of the way. Herbert and I, who remained in town, saw them going down the street on opposite sides, Startop leading, and Drummle lagging behind in the shadow of the houses.

In about a month after that, the Spider's time with Mr. Pocket was up for good, and, to the great relief of all the house, he went home to his family.

[1] **dexterously** (dĕk′stĕr·ŭs·lĭ): skillfully.

CHAPTER 20

Pip has a visitor.

MY DEAR MR. PIP:

I write this by request of Mr. Gargery, for to let you know that he is going to London in company with Mr. Wopsle and would be glad if agreeable to be allowed to see you. He would call at Barnard's Hotel Tuesday morning at nine o'clock, when if not agreeable please leave word. Your poor sister is much the same as when you left. We talk of you in the kitchen every night, and wonder what you are saying and doing. If now considered in the light of a liberty, excuse it for the love of poor old days. No more, dear Mr. Pip, from

Your ever obliged,
and affectionate servant,
Biddy.

P.S. He wishes me most particular to write *what larks.* He says you will understand. I hope and do not doubt it will be agreeable to see him even though a gentleman, for you had ever a good heart, and he is a worthy worthy man. I have read him all excepting only the last little sentence, and he wishes me most particular to write again *what larks.*

I received this letter by post on Monday morning, and therefore its appointment was for next day. Let me confess exactly with what feelings I looked forward to Joe's coming.

Not with pleasure, though I was bound to him by so many ties; no, with considerable disturbance and some mortification.[2] If I could have kept him away by paying money, I certainly would have paid money. My greatest reassurance was that he was coming to Barnard's Inn, not to Hammersmith. I had little objection to his being seen

[2] **mortification** (môr′tĭ·fĭ·kā′shŭn): shame and hurt pride.

by Herbert or his father, for both of whom I had respect; but I had the sharpest sensitiveness as to his being seen by Drummle, whom I held in contempt. So throughout life, our worst weaknesses and meannesses are usually committed for the sake of the people whom we most despise.

I had got on so expensively of late that I had even hired a serving boy and had clothed him with a blue coat, canary waistcoat, white tie, creamy breeches, and top boots. I had to find him a little to do and a great deal to eat; and with both of these requirements he haunted my existence.

I came into town on Monday night to be ready for Joe, and I got up early in the morning, and caused the sitting room and breakfast table to assume their most splendid appearance.

Presently I heard Joe on the staircase. I knew it was Joe by his clumsy manner of coming upstairs. When at last he stopped outside our door, I could hear his finger tracing over the painted letters of my name. Finally he gave a faint single rap, and my serving boy announced, "Mr. Gargery!" and he came in.

"Joe, how are you, Joe?"

"Pip, how AIR you, Pip?"

With his good honest face all glowing and shining, and his hat put down on the floor between us, he caught both my hands and worked them straight up and down.

"I am glad to see you, Joe. Give me your hat."

But Joe, taking it up carefully with both hands, like a bird's nest with eggs in it, wouldn't hear of parting with that piece of property.

"You have that growed," said Joe, "and that gentlefolked," Joe considered a little before he discovered this word; "as to be a honor to your king and country."

"And you, Joe, look wonderfully well."

"Thank God," said Joe, "I'm equal to most. And your sister, she's no worse than she were. And Biddy, she's ever right and ready."

Herbert had entered the room, so I presented Joe to Herbert. Joe, being invited to sit down to table, looked all round the room for a suitable spot on which to deposit his hat and ultimately stood it on an extreme corner of the chimney piece, from which it ever afterward fell off at intervals.

"Do you take tea or coffee, Mr. Gargery?" asked Herbert, who always presided of a morning.

"Thankee, sir," said Joe, stiff from head to foot, "I'll take whichever is most agreeable to yourself."

"Say tea, then," said Herbert, pouring it out.

Here Joe's hat tumbled off the mantelpiece, and he started out of his chair and picked it up, and fitted it to the same exact spot.

"When did you come to town, Mr. Gargery?"

"Were it yesterday afternoon?" said Joe, after coughing behind his hand. "No it were not. Yes it were. Yes. It were yesterday afternoon" (with an appearance of mingled wisdom, relief, and strict impartiality).

"Have you seen anything of London, yet?"

"Why, yes, sir," began Joe, but his attention was attracted by his hat, which was toppling. Indeed, it demanded from him a constant attention. He made extraordinary play with it, and showed the greatest skill, now rushing at it and catching it neatly as it dropped, now merely stopping it midway, beating it up, finally splashing it into the slop basin, where

Joe visits Pip.

I took the liberty of laying hands upon it.

Then he fell into such unaccountable fits of meditation, with his fork midway between his plate and his mouth; had his eyes attracted in such strange directions; was afflicted with such remarkable coughs; sat so far from the table; and dropped so much more than he ate, and pretended that he hadn't dropped it; that I was heartily glad when Herbert left us for the city.

I had neither the good sense nor the good feeling to know that this was all my fault, and that if I had been easier with Joe, Joe would have been easier with me. I felt impatient of him and out of temper with him.

"Us two being now alone, sir — " began Joe.

"Joe," I interrupted pettishly, "how can you call me sir?"

Joe looked at me for a single instant with something like reproach. I was conscious of a sort of dignity in the look.

"Us two being now alone," resumed Joe, "and me having the intentions and abilities to stay not many minutes more, I will now conclude — leastways begin — to mention what have led to my having had the present honor.

"Well, sir, this is how it were. I were at the Bargemen t'other night, Pip" (whenever he subsided into affection, he called me Pip, and whenever he relapsed into politeness he called me sir), "when there come in Pumblechook. Well, Pip; this same identical come to me at the Bargemen and his word were, 'Joseph, Miss Havisham she wished to speak to you.'"

"Miss Havisham, Joe?"

"'She wished,' were Pumblechook's word, 'to speak to you.'" Joe sat and rolled his eyes at the ceiling.

"Yes, Joe? Go on, please."

"Next day, sir," said Joe, looking at me as if I were a long way off, "having cleaned myself, I go and I see Miss A."

"Miss A., Joe? Miss Havisham?"

"Which I say, sir," replied Joe, with an air of legal formality, as if he were making his will, "Miss A., or otherways Havisham.[1] Her expression air then as follering: 'Mr. Gargery. You air in correspondence with Mr. Pip?' Having had a letter from you, I were able to say 'I am.' 'Would you tell him, then,' said she, 'that Estella has come home, and would be glad to see him.'"

I felt my face fire up as I looked at Joe.

"Biddy," pursued Joe, "when I got home and asked her fur to write the message to you, a little hung back. Biddy says, 'I know he will be very glad to have it by word of mouth; it is holiday time, you want to see him, go!' I

[1] Joe pronounced Havisham "'avisham."

have now concluded, sir," said Joe, rising from his chair, "and, Pip, I wish you ever well and ever prospering to a greater and greater height."

"But you are not going now, Joe?"

"Yes I am," said Joe.

"But you are coming back to dinner, Joe?"

"No I am not," said Joe.

Our eyes met, and all the "sir" melted out of that manly heart as he gave me his hand.

"Pip, dear old chap, life is made of ever so many partings welded together, as I may say, and one man's a blacksmith, and one's a whitesmith,[1] and one's a goldsmith, and one's a coppersmith. Diwisions among such must come, and must be met as they come. If there's been any fault at all today, it's mine. You and me is not two figures to be together in London; nor yet anywheres else but what is private, and beknown, and understood among friends. It ain't that I am proud, but that I want to be right, as you shall never see me no more in these clothes. I'm wrong in these clothes. I'm wrong out of the forge, the kitchen, or off th' marshes. You won't find half so much fault in me if you think of me in my forge dress, with my hammer in my hand, or even my pipe. You won't find half so much fault in me if, supposing as you should ever wish to see me, you come and put your head in at the forge window and see Joe the blacksmith, there at the old anvil, in the old burned apron, sticking to the old work. I'm awful dull, but I hope I've beat out something nigh the rights of this at last. And so God bless you, dear old Pip, old chap, God bless you!"

I had not been mistaken in my fancy that there was a simple dignity in him.

[1] **whitesmith:** a tinsmith.

The fashion of his dress could no more come in its way when he spoke these words than it could come in its way in Heaven. He touched me gently on the forehead, and went out. As soon as I could recover myself sufficiently, I hurried out after him and looked for him in the neighboring streets; but he was gone.

CHAPTER 21

The mysterious stranger returns, and so does Orlick.

IT WAS clear that I must go to our town next day, and in the first flow of my repentance it was equally clear that I must stay at Joe's. But when I secured my place on the coach, I began to invent reasons for putting up at the Blue Boar. All other swindlers upon earth are nothing to the self-swindlers, and with such pretenses did I cheat myself. I settled that I must go to the Blue Boar.

At that time it was customary to carry convicts down to the dockyards by stagecoach. As I had often seen them on the highroad dangling their ironed legs over the coach roof, I had no cause to be surprised when Herbert came up and told me there were two convicts going down with me. But I had a reason that was an old reason now for faltering whenever I heard the word convict.

"You don't mind them, Handel?" said Herbert.

"Oh, no!"

"You just now looked as if you didn't like them?"

"I can't pretend that I do like them, and I suppose you don't particularly. But I don't mind them."

"See! There they are," said Herbert, "and what a degraded and vile sight it is!"

The two convicts were handcuffed together, and had irons on their legs — irons of a pattern that I knew well. They wore the dress that I likewise knew well. One was a taller and stouter man than the other, and his attire disguised him, but I knew his half-closed eye at one glance. There stood the man whom I had seen on the settle at the Three Jolly Bargemen on a Saturday night!

But this was not the worst of it. It turned out that the whole of the back of the coach had been taken by a family, and that there were no places for the two prisoners but on the seat in front, behind the coachman. I sat with the coachman, and the convict I had recognized sat behind me with his breath on the hair of my head!

"Good-by, Handel!" Herbert called out as we started. I thought what a blessed fortune it was that he had found another name for me than Pip.

The weather was miserably raw. Cowering forward for warmth and to make me a screen against the wind, the convicts moved closer to me than before. The very first words I heard them interchange were the words of my own thought, "Two one-pound notes."

"How did he get 'em?" said the convict I had never seen.

"How should I know?" returned the other. "He had 'em stowed away somehows. Give him by friends, I expect."

"I wish," said the other, with a bitter curse upon the cold, "that I had 'em here."

"Two one-pound notes, or friends?"

"Two one-pound notes. I'd sell all the friends I ever had, for one, and think it a blessed good bargain. Well? So he says — ?"

"So he says," resumed the convict I had recognized " — it was all said and done in half a minute, behind a pile of timber in the dockyards — 'You're a-going to be discharged!' Yes, I was. Would I find out that boy that had fed him and kep' his secret, and give him them two one-pound notes? Yes, I would. And I did."

"More fool you," growled the other. "I'd have spent 'em on wittles and drink. He must have been a green one. Mean to say he knowed nothing of you?"

"Not a thing. Different gangs and different ships. He was tried again for prison breaking, and got made a lifer."

"And was that the only time you worked out, in this part of the country?"

"The only time."

"What might have been your opinion of the place?"

"A most beastly place. Mudbank, mist, swamp, and work; work, swamp, mist, and mudbank."

They both cursed the place in very strong language, and gradually growled themselves out, and had nothing left to say.

After overhearing this dialogue, I resolved to alight as soon as we touched the town and put myself out of his reach. This device I executed successfully. As to the convicts, they went their way with the coach, and I knew at what point they would be spirited off to the river. In my fancy, I saw the boat with its convict crew waiting for them at the slime-washed stairs — again heard the gruff "Give way, you!" like an order to dogs — again saw the wicked Hulks lying out on the black water. I could not have said what I was afraid of, but there was great fear upon me.

In the morning I was up and out of

the Blue Boar too early, so I loitered into the country on Miss Havisham's side of town, thinking about my patroness, and painting brilliant pictures of her plans for me.

She had adopted Estella, she had as good as adopted me, and it could not fail to be her intention to bring us together. Estella had taken strong possession of me. I loved Estella with the love of a man; I loved her simply because I found her, in my memory, irresistible. I knew to my sorrow, often and often, if not always, that I loved her against reason, against promise, against peace, against hope, against happiness, against all discouragement that could be. I loved her none the less because I knew it, and it had no more influence in restraining me than if I had devoutly believed her to be human perfection.

I so shaped out my walk as to arrive at the gate at my old time. I heard the side door open, and steps come across the courtyard, and started to see myself confronted by a man in a sober gray dress — the last man I should have expected to see in that place of porter at Miss Havisham's door.

"Orlick!"

"Ah, young master, there's more changes than yours. But come in, come in. It's opposed to my orders to hold the gate open."

I entered and he swung it, and locked it, and took the key out. "Yes!" said he, facing round. "Here I am!"

"How did you come here?"

"I come here," he retorted, "on my legs."

"Are you here for good?"

"I ain't here for harm, young master, I suppose."

I was not so sure of that. "Then you have left the forge?" I said.

"Do this look like a forge?" replied

Orlick, leading me to the house.

Recalling how I had gone up the staircase in the dark, many a time, I ascended it now and tapped in my old way at the door of Miss Havisham's room. "Pip's rap," I heard her say, immediately; "come in, Pip."

She was in her chair near the old table, in the old dress, with her two hands crossed on her stick, her chin resting on them. Sitting near her was an elegant lady whom I had never seen.

"Come in, Pip," Miss Havisham continued. "Come in, Pip. How do you do, Pip? So you kiss my hand as if I were a queen, eh? — Well?"

"I heard, Miss Havisham," said I, rather at a loss, "that you were so kind as to wish me to come and see you, and I came directly."

"Well?"

The lady whom I had never seen before lifted up her eyes and looked archly at me, and then I saw that the eyes were Estella's eyes. But she was so much changed, was so much more beautiful, so much more womanly, that I slipped hopelessly back into the coarse and common boy again. Oh, the sense of distance and difference that came upon me, and the inaccessibility that came about her!

"Do you find her much changed, Pip?" asked Miss Havisham, with her greedy look, and striking her stick upon a chair that stood between them as a sign for me to sit down there.

"When I came in, Miss Havisham, I thought there was nothing of Estella in the face or figure; but now it all settles down so curiously into the old — "

"What? You are not going to say into the old Estella?" Miss Havisham interrupted. "She was proud and insulting, and you wanted to go away from her. Don't you remember?"

I said confusedly that that was long ago, and that I knew no better then. Estella smiled with perfect composure and said she had no doubt of my having been quite right, and of her having been very disagreeable.

"Is *he* changed?" Miss Havisham asked her.

"Very much," said Estella, looking at me.

"Less coarse and common?" said Miss Havisham, playing with Estella's hair.

Estella laughed. She treated me as a boy still, but she lured me on.

It was settled that I should stay there all the rest of the day, and return to the hotel at night, and to London tomorrow. When we had conversed for a while, Miss Havisham sent us two out to walk. Estella and I went into the garden, I trembling in spirit and worshiping the very hem of her dress; she, quite composed and decidedly not worshiping anything in me.

As the garden was too overgrown and rank for walking, we came out again into the brewery yard. I showed her where I had seen her walking that first old day, and she said with a cold and careless look in that direction, "Did I?" I reminded her where she had come out of the house and given me my meat and drink, and she said, "I don't remember." "Not remember that you made me cry?" said I. "No," said she, and shook her head and looked about her. I verily believe that her not remembering and not minding in the least made me cry again, inwardly — and that is the sharpest crying of all.

"You must know," said Estella, condescending to me as a brilliant and beautiful woman might, "that I have no heart — if that has anything to do with my memory. I have no softness there, no — sympathy — sentiment — nonsense. If we are to be thrown much together, you had better believe it at once."

Her handsome dress had trailed upon the ground. She held it in one hand now, and with the other lightly touched my shoulder as we walked. We walked round the ruined garden twice or thrice more. At last we went back into the house, and there I heard with surprise that my guardian had come down to see Miss Havisham on business, and would come back to dinner. Estella left us to prepare herself, and Miss Havisham turned to me and said in a whisper:

"Is she beautiful, graceful, well grown? Do you admire her?"

"Everybody must who sees her, Miss Havisham."

She put an arm around my neck and drew my head close down to hers as she sat in the chair. "Love her, love her, love her! How does she treat you?"

Before I could answer (if I could have answered so difficult a question at all), she repeated, "Love her, love her, love her! If she favors you, love her. If she wounds you, love her. If she tears your heart to pieces — and as it gets older and stronger it will tear deeper — love her, love her, love her! Hear me, Pip! I adopted her to be loved. I bred her and educated her to be loved. I developed her into what she is, that she might be loved. Love her!"

"I'll tell you," she went on in the same hurried passionate whisper, "what real love is. It is blind devotion, unquestioning self-humiliation, utter submission, trust and belief against yourself and against the whole world, giving up your whole heart and soul to someone who smites it — as I did!"

She rose up in the chair, in her shroud of a dress, and struck at the air as if she would as soon have struck herself against the wall and fallen dead. All this passed in a few seconds. As I drew her down into her chair, I turned and saw my guardian in the room.

Miss Havisham had seen him as soon as I, and was (like everybody else) afraid of him. She made a strong attempt to compose herself, and stammered that he was as punctual as ever.

"As punctual as ever," he repeated. "And so you are here, Pip?"

I told him when I had arrived, and how Miss Havisham wished me to come and see Estella.

"Well, Pip! How often have you seen Miss Estella before?" said he.

"How often?"

"Jaggers," interposed Miss Havisham, much to my relief; "leave my Pip alone, and go with him to your dinner."

He complied, and we groped our way down the dark stairs together. "Pray, sir," said I, "may I ask you a question?"

"You may," said he, "and I may decline to answer it. Put your question."

"Estella's name, is it Havisham or — ?" I had nothing to add.

"Or what?" said he.

"Is it Havisham?"

"It is Havisham."

This brought us to the dinner table, where Estella awaited us. Mr. Jaggers scarcely directed his eyes to Estella's face once during dinner. When she spoke to him, he listened, and in due course answered, but never looked at her that I could see. On the other hand, she often looked at him, with interest and curiosity, if not distrust, but his face never showed the least consciousness.

Afterward we went up to Miss Havisham's room, and we four played at whist.[1] We played until nine o'clock,

<hr>

[1] whist: a card game, the forerunner of modern contract bridge.

and then, before our leaving, it was arranged that when Estella came to London I should be forewarned of her coming and should meet her at the coach; and then I took leave of her, and touched her and left her.

My guardian slept at the Boar in the next room to mine. Far into the night, Miss Havisham's words, "Love her, love her, love her!" sounded in my ears. I said to my pillow, "I love her, I love her, I love her!" hundreds of times.

Ah me! I thought those were high and great emotions. But I never thought there was anything low and small in my keeping away from Joe, because I knew she would be scornful of him. It was but a day gone, and Joe had brought the tears into my eyes; they had soon dried, God forgive me! soon dried.

CHAPTER 22

Trabb's boy has some fun with Pip.

AFTER well considering the matter while I was dressing at the Blue Boar in the morning, I resolved to tell my guardian that I doubted Orlick's being the right sort of man to fill a post of trust at Miss Havisham's. He listened in a satisfied manner while I told him what knowledge I had of Orlick. "Very good, Pip," he observed, when I had concluded. "I'll go round presently and pay our friend off." Rather alarmed by this hasty action, I was for a little delay, and even hinted that our friend might be difficult to deal with. "Oh, no, he won't," said my guardian. "I should like to see him argue the question with *me*."

As we were going back together to London by the midday coach, and as I breakfasted under such terrors of seeing the hypocritical Pumblechook that I could scarcely hold my cup, I left the Blue Boar immediately after breakfast, making a loop of a couple of miles into the open country at the back of Pumblechook's premises to get round into the High Street again. Then I felt myself in comparative security.

It was interesting to be in the quiet old town once more, and it was not disagreeable to be here and there suddenly recognized and stared after. My position was a distinguished one, and I was not at all dissatisfied with it, until Fate threw me in the way of that unlimited miscreant,[1] Trabb's boy.

Casting my eyes along the street at a certain point of my progress, I beheld Trabb's boy approaching. Suddenly the knees of Trabb's boy knocked together, his hair uprose, his cap fell off, he staggered out into the road, and crying to the populace, "Hold me! I'm so frightened!" pretended to be in a fit of terror occasioned by the dignity of my appearance. As I passed him, his teeth loudly chattered in his head, and with every mark of extreme humiliation, he prostrated himself in the dust.

This was a hard thing to bear, but this was nothing. I had not advanced another two hundred yards, when, to my inexpressible amazement and indignation, I again beheld Trabb's boy approaching. He was coming round a narrow corner. He staggered round and round me with knees more afflicted, and with uplifted hands as if beseeching for mercy. His sufferings were hailed with the greatest joy by a knot of spectators, and I felt utterly confounded.

[1] miscreant (mĭs′krė-ánt): villain, wrongdoer.

I had not got as much farther down the street as the post office when I again beheld Trabb's boy shooting round by a back way attended by a company of delighted young friends to whom he exclaimed, with a wave of his hand, "Don't know yah!" Afterward he took to crowing at me, pursuing me across the bridge, and completing the disgrace with which I left town.

The coach, with Mr. Jaggers inside, came up in due time, and I took my box seat again, and arrived in London safe — but not sound, for my heart was gone. As soon as I arrived, I sent a codfish and a barrel of oysters to Joe (as reparation for not having gone myself), and then went on to Barnard's Inn.

I found Herbert dining on cold meat, and delighted to welcome me back, and I felt that I must open my heart that very evening to my friend and chum. Dinner done and we sitting with our feet upon the fender, I said to Herbert, "My dear Herbert, I have something very particular to tell you."

"My dear Handel," he returned, "I shall respect your confidence."

"It concerns myself, Herbert," said I, "and one other person."

Herbert looked at the fire with his head on one side, and looked at me because I didn't go on.

"Herbert," said I, laying my hand upon his knee, "I love — I adore — Estella. I have never left off adoring her. And she has come back, a most beautiful and most elegant creature. And I saw her yesterday. And if I adored her before, I now doubly adore her."

"Lucky for you then, Handel," said Herbert, "that you are picked out for her and allotted to her. Have you any idea yet of Estella's views on the adoration question?"

I shook my head gloomily. "Oh! She

is thousands of miles away from me," said I.

"Patience, my dear Handel; time enough, time enough. But you have something more to say?"

"I am ashamed to say it," I returned, "and yet it's no worse to say it than to think it. You call me a lucky fellow. Of course, I am. I was a blacksmith's boy but yesterday; I am — what shall I say I am — today?"

"Say a good fellow, if you want a phrase," returned Herbert, smiling, "a good fellow, with boldness and hesitation, action and dreaming, curiously mixed in him."

"Herbert," I went on, "you say I am lucky, and yet, when I think of Estella, I cannot tell you how dependent and uncertain I feel. I may say that on the constancy of one person (naming no person) all my expectations depend. And at the best, how indefinite and unsatisfactory, only to know so vaguely what they are!"

"Now, Handel," Herbert replied, in his gay, hopeful way, "it seems to me that we are looking into our gift horse's mouth with a magnifying glass. Didn't you tell me that your guardian, Mr. Jaggers, told you in the beginning that you were not endowed with expectations only? And even if he had not told you so, could you believe that of all men in London, Mr. Jaggers is the man to hold his present relations toward you unless he was sure of his ground?"

"What a hopeful disposition you have!" said I, gratefully admiring his cheery ways.

"I ought to have," said Herbert, "for I have not much else. And now, I want to make myself seriously disagreeable to you for a moment — positively repulsive."

"You won't succeed," said I.

"Oh, yes, I shall!" said he. "I have been thinking that Estella cannot surely be a condition of your inheritance, if she was never referred to by your guardian. Am I right in so understanding what you have told me, as that he never referred to her, directly or indirectly, in any way? Never even hinted, for instance, that your patron might have views as to your marriage ultimately?"

"Never."

"Now, Handel, I am quite free from the flavor of sour grapes, upon my soul and honor! Not being bound to her, can you not detach yourself from her? — I told you I should be disagreeable."

I turned my head aside, for, with a rush and a sweep, a feeling like that which subdued me on the morning when I left the forge, smote upon my heart again. There was silence between us for a little while.

"My dear Handel," Herbert went on, "think of her bringing-up, and think of Miss Havisham. Think of what she is herself. This may lead to miserable things."

"I know it, Herbert," said I, with my head still turned away, "but I can't help it."

"Well!" said Herbert, getting up with a lively shake as if he had been asleep, and stirring the fire. "Now I'll endeavor to make myself agreeable again! I was going to say a word or two, Handel, concerning my father's son. I am afraid it is scarcely necessary to go round the point. I am myself committed to another."

"You mean you are engaged?" I asked.

"I am," said Herbert; "but it's a secret."

"May I ask the name?" I said.

"Name of Clara," said Herbert.

"Live in London?"

"Yes. Her father had to do with the supplying of passenger ships. I think he was a kind of purser."

"What is he now?" said I.

"He's an invalid now," replied Herbert. "I have never seen him, for he has always kept his room overhead since I have known Clara. But I have heard him constantly. He makes tremendous rows — roars, and pegs at the floor with some frightful instrument." Herbert looked at me and laughed heartily.

"Don't you expect to see him?" said I.

"Oh, yes, I constantly expect to see him," returned Herbert, "because I never hear him, without expecting him to come tumbling through the ceiling. But I don't know how long the rafters may hold."

When he had once more laughed heartily, he became meek and told me that the moment he began to make money, it was his intention to marry this young lady. He added, sadly, "But you *can't* marry, you know, while you're looking about you."

CHAPTER 23

Estella arrives in London.

ONE DAY when I was busy with my books, I received a note by the post. It had no set beginning, as Dear Mr. Pip, or Dear Pip, or Dear Sir, or Dear Anything, but ran thus:

I am to come to London the day after tomorrow by the midday coach. I believe it was settled you should meet me? At all events Miss Havisham has that impression, and I write in obedience to it. She sends you her regard. — Yours, ESTELLA.

My appetite vanished instantly, and I knew no peace or rest until the day arrived. Then I was worse than ever, and began haunting the coach office in Wood Street even before the coach had left the Blue Boar in our town. I felt I could not let the coach office be out of my sight longer than five minutes at a time, and so I underwent a watch of four or five hours. Finally I saw her face at the coach window and her hand waving to me.

In her furred traveling dress, Estella seemed more delicately beautiful than ever. Her manner was more winning than before, and I thought I saw Miss Havisham's influence in the change.

"I am going to Richmond," she told me. "The distance is ten miles. I am to have a carriage, and you are to take me. This is my purse, and you are to pay my charges out of it. Oh, you must take the purse! We have no choice, you and I, but to obey our instructions. We are not free to follow our own devices, you and I."

As she looked at me in giving me the purse, I hoped there was an inner meaning in her words. She said them slightingly, but not with displeasure.

"A carriage will have to be sent for, Estella. Will you rest here a little?"

"Yes, I am to rest here a little, and I am to drink some tea, and you are to take care of me the while."

She drew her arm through mine, as if it must be done, and I requested a waiter to show us a private sitting room. On my objecting to a first room he showed us, which was a black hole of a place, he took us into another room with a dinner table for thirty. I was aware that the air of this chamber, in its strong combination of stable with soup stock, might have led one to infer that the coaching department was not doing well, and that the enterprising proprietor was boiling down the horses for the refreshment department. Yet the room was all in all to me, Estella being in it. I thought that with her I could have been happy there for life. (I was not at all happy there at the time, observe, and I knew it well.)

"Where are you going to, at Richmond?" I asked Estella.

"I am going to live," said she, "at a great expense, with a lady there, who has the power— or says she has — of taking me about and introducing me and showing people to me and showing me to people. How do you thrive with Mr. Pocket?"

"I live quite pleasantly there; at least —" It appeared to me that I was losing a chance.

"At least?" repeated Estella.

"As pleasantly as I could anywhere, away from you."

"You silly boy," said Estella, quite composedly, "how can you talk such nonsense? Your friend Mr. Matthew, I believe, is superior to the rest of his family?"

"Very superior indeed."

"He really is disinterested, and above small jealousy and spite?" Estella asked.

"I am sure I have every reason to say so."

"You have not every reason to say so of the rest of the family, of Sarah Pocket, Camilla, and the others," said she, "for they beset Miss Havisham with reports to your disadvantage. They watch you, misrepresent you, write letters about you (anonymous sometimes), and you are the torment and occupation of their lives. You can scarcely realize the hatred those people feel for you."

"They do me no harm, I hope?"

"No, no, you may be sure of that," said Estella. "Oh, what satisfaction it gives me to see those people thwarted! Two things I can tell you. First, these people will never impair your ground with Miss Havisham, in any particular, great or small. Second, I am indebted to you as the cause of their being so busy and so mean in vain, and there is my hand upon it."

As she gave it to me playfully, I held it and put it to my lips. "You ridiculous boy," said Estella, "will you never take warning? Or do you kiss my hand in the same spirit in which I once let you kiss my cheek?"

"If I say yes, may I kiss the cheek again?"

"You should have asked before you touched the hand. But, yes, if you like."

I leaned down, and her calm face was like a statue's. "Now," said Estella, gliding away the instant I touched her cheek, "you are to take care that I have some tea, and you are to take me to Richmond."

Her reverting to this tone as if our association were forced upon us and we were mere puppets, gave me pain; but everything in our intercourse did give me pain. Whatever her tone with me happened to be, I could put no trust in it, and build no hope on it; and yet I went on against trust and against hope. Why repeat it a thousand times? So it always was.

I rang for the tea, and the waiter brought in by degrees some fifty articles associated with that refreshment, but of tea not a glimpse. A teaboard, cups and saucers, plates, knives and forks, spoons, saltcellars, a meek little muffin confined with the utmost precaution under a strong iron cover, a fat family teapot. After a long absence he came in with a box of precious appearance containing the tea twigs. These I steeped in hot water and extracted one

"You silly boy," said Estella, quite composedly.

cup of I don't know what, for Estella.

The bill paid, and the waiter remembered, and the chambermaid taken into consideration — in a word, the whole house bribed into a state of contempt and animosity,[1] and Estella's purse much lightened — we got into our post coach and drove away. Turning into Cheapside and rattling up Newgate Street, we were soon under the walls of the prison.

"Mr. Jaggers," said I, reminded of my guardian by the passing sight, "has the reputation of being more in the secrets of that dismal place than any man in London."

"He is more in the secrets of every place, I think," said Estella, in a low voice.

"You have been accustomed to see him often, I suppose?"

"I have been accustomed to see him at uncertain intervals ever since I can remember. But I know him no better now than I did before I could speak plainly. What is your own experience of him?"

"Once used to his distrustful manner," said I, "I have done very well."

"Are you intimate?"

"I have dined with him at his private house."

"I fancy," said Estella, shrinking, "that must be a curious place."

"It is a curious place."

I should have been cautious about discussing my guardian too freely even with her; but I should have gone on with the subject so far as to describe the dinner in Gerrard Street, if we had not then come into a sudden glare of gaslight. When we were out of it, we fell into other talk, principally about the way by which we were traveling and about London.

[1] **animosity** (ăn´ĭ·mŏs´ĭ·tĭ): ill will; resentment.

It was impossible for me to avoid seeing that she cared to attract me; that she made herself winning; and would have won me even if the task had needed pains. Yet this made me none the happier, for I felt that she held my heart in her hand because she willfully chose to do it.

When we passed through Hammersmith, I showed her where Mr. Matthew Pocket lived, and said it was no great way from Richmond, and that I hoped I should see her sometimes.

"Oh, yes, you are to see me; you are to come when you think proper; you are to be mentioned to the family; indeed you are already mentioned."

I inquired was it a large household she was going to be a member of?

"No, there are only two, mother and daughter. The mother is a lady of some social station, I believe, though not averse to increasing her income."

"I wonder Miss Havisham could part with you again so soon."

"It is a part of Miss Havisham's plans for me, Pip," said Estella, with a sigh, as if she were tired. "I am to write to her constantly and see her regularly, and report how I go on — I and the jewels — for they are nearly all mine now."

It was the first time she had ever called me by name. Of course she did so purposely, and knew that I should treasure it up.

We came to Richmond all too soon, and at our destination two cherry-colored maids came fluttering out to receive Estella. The doorway soon absorbed her boxes, and she gave me her hand and a smile, and said good night, and was absorbed likewise. And still I stood looking at the house, thinking how happy I should be if I lived there with her, and knowing that I never was happy with her, but always miserable.

CHAPTER 24

Pip and Herbert examine their affairs.

As I HAD grown accustomed to my expectations, I had insensibly begun to notice their effect upon myself and those around me. Their influence on my own character I disguised from my recognition as much as possible, but I knew very well that it was not all good. I lived in a state of chronic uneasiness respecting my behavior to Joe. My conscience was not by any means comfortable about Biddy. When I woke up in the night I used to think, with a weariness on my spirits, that I should have been happier and better if I had never seen Miss Havisham's face, and had risen to manhood content to be partners with Joe in the honest old forge. Many a time of an evening, when I sat alone looking at the fire, I thought, after all, there was no fire like the forge fire and the kitchen fire at home.

Now, concerning the influence of my position on others, I perceived it was not beneficial to anybody, and above all, that it was not beneficial to Herbert. My lavish habits led his easy nature into expenses he could not afford, corrupted the simplicity of his life, and disturbed his peace with anxieties and regrets. I began to contract a quantity of debt. I could hardly begin but Herbert must begin too, so he soon followed.

In my confidence in my own resources, I would willingly have taken Herbert's expenses on myself; but Herbert was proud, and I could make no such proposal to him. So he got into difficulties in every direction, and continued to look about him. When we gradually fell into keeping late hours and late company, I noticed that he looked about him with a desponding eye at breakfast time; that he began to look about him more hopefully about midday; that he drooped when he came in to dinner; and that about two o'clock in the morning he became so deeply despondent again as to talk of buying a rifle and going to America, with a general purpose of compelling buffaloes to make his fortune.

We spent as much money as we could, and got as little for it as people could make up their minds to give us. We were always more or less miserable, and most of our acquaintance were in the same condition. There was a gay fiction among us that we were constantly enjoying ourselves, and a skeleton truth that we never did. To the best of my belief, our case was in the last respect a rather common one.

At certain times I would say to Herbert, as if it were a remarkable discovery:

"My dear Herbert, we are getting on badly."

"My dear Handel," Herbert would say to me, in all sincerity, "if you will believe me, those very words were on my lips, by a strange coincidence."

"Then, Herbert," I would respond, "let us look into our affairs."

We always derived profound satisfaction from making an appointment for this purpose. Dinner over, we produced a bundle of pens, a copious supply of ink, and a goodly show of writing and blotting paper. There was something very comfortable in having plenty of stationery.

I would then take a sheet of paper, and write across the top of it, in a neat hand, the heading, "Memorandum of Pip's debts." Herbert would also take a sheet of paper, and write across it, "Memorandum of Herbert's debts."

Each of us would then refer to a confused heap of bills at his side. The sound of our pens going refreshed us exceedingly, insomuch that I sometimes found it difficult to distinguish between this business proceeding and actually paying the money.

When we had written a little while, I would ask Herbert how he got on.

"They are mounting up, Handel," Herbert would say; "upon my life they are mounting up."

"Be firm, Herbert," I would retort. "Look the thing in the face. Look into your affairs. Stare them out of countenance."

"So I would, Handel, only they are staring *me* out of countenance."

However, my determined manner would have its effect, and Herbert would fall to work again. After a time he would give up once more, on the plea that he had not got Cobbs's bill, or Lobbs's, or Nobbs's, as the case might be.

"Then, Herbert, estimate; estimate it in round numbers, and put it down."

"What a fellow of resource you are!" my friend would reply, with admiration. "Really, your business powers are very remarkable."

I thought so too. I established with myself, on these occasions, the reputation of a first-rate man of business — prompt, decisive, energetic, clear, coolheaded. When I had got all my responsibilities down upon my list, I compared each with the bill, and ticked it off. My self-approval when I ticked an entry was quite a luxurious sensation. When I had no more ticks to make, I folded all my bills up uniformly, docketed each on the back, and tied the whole into a symmetrical bundle. Then I did the same for Herbert (who modestly said he had not my administrative genius), and felt that I had brought his affairs into focus for him.

But there was a calm, a rest, a virtuous hush, consequent on these examinations of our affairs, that gave me, for the time, an admirable opinion of myself. Soothed by my exertions, my method, and Herbert's compliments, I would sit with his symmetrical bundle and my own on the table before me among the stationery, and feel like a bank of some sort, rather than a private individual.

We shut our outer door on these solemn occasions in order that we might not be interrupted. I had fallen into my serene state one evening, when we heard a letter drop through the slit in the said door and fall on the ground. "It's for you, Handel," said Herbert, going out and coming back with it, "and I hope there is nothing the matter." This was in allusion [1] to its heavy black seal and border.

The letter was signed TRABB & CO., and its contents were to inform me that Mrs. J. Gargery had departed this life on Monday last at twenty minutes past six in the evening, and that my attendance was requested at the funeral on Monday next at three o'clock in the afternoon.

CHAPTER 25

Pip returns to the forge.

IT WAS the first time that a grave had opened in my road of life, and the figure of my sister in her chair by the kitchen fire haunted me night and day.

[1] **allusion** (ă·lū′zhŭn): a hinted or indirect reference.

Whatever my fortunes might have been, I could scarcely have recalled my sister with much tenderness. But I suppose there is a shock of regret which may exist without much tenderness.

I went down early in the morning and alighted at the Blue Boar, in good time to walk over to the forge. At last I came within sight of the house, and saw that Trabb and Co. had taken possession. Poor dear Joe, entangled in a little black cloak tied in a large bow under his chin, was seated apart at the upper end of the room, where, as chief mourner, he had evidently been stationed by Trabb. When I bent down and said to him, "Dear Joe, how are you?" he said, "Pip, old chap, you know'd her when she were a fine figure of a woman —" and clasped my hand and said no more.

Biddy, looking very neat and modest in her black dress, went quietly here and there, and was very helpful. When I had spoken to Biddy, as I thought it not a time for talking, I went and sat down near Joe.

"Pocket handkerchiefs out, all!" cried Mr. Trabb at this point, in a depressed businesslike voice — "Pocket handkerchiefs out! We are ready!"

So, we all put our pocket handkerchiefs to our faces and filed out two and two: Joe and I, Biddy and Pumblechook, Mr. and Mrs. Hubble, the remains of my poor sister being carried by six bearers.

We walked the length of the village, and now the range of marshes lay clear before us, and we went into the churchyard, close to the graves of my unknown parents, Philip Pirrip, late of this parish, and Georgiana, his wife. And there my sister was laid quietly in the earth while the larks sang high above it, and the light wind strewed it with beautiful shadows of clouds and trees.

When we got back and when they were all gone, Biddy, Joe, and I had a cold dinner together; but we dined in the best parlor, not in the old kitchen, and Joe was so exceedingly particular what he did with his knife and fork and the saltcellar and what not, that there was great restraint upon us. But after dinner, when I made him take his pipe, and when I loitered with him about the forge, and when we sat down together on the great block of stone outside it, we got on better.

He was very much pleased by my asking if I might sleep in my own little room, and I was pleased too; for I felt that I had done rather a great thing in making the request.

When the shadows of evening were closing in, I took an opportunity of getting into the garden with Biddy for a little talk.

"Biddy," said I, "I think you might have written to me about these sad matters."

"Do you, Mr. Pip?" said Biddy. "I should have written if I had thought that."

She was so quiet, and had such an orderly, good, and pretty way with her that I did not like the thought of making her cry again. After looking a little at her downcast eyes as she walked beside me, I gave up that point.

"I suppose it will be difficult for you to remain here now, Biddy, dear?"

"Oh! I can't do so, Mr. Pip," said Biddy, in a tone of regret, but still of quiet conviction. "I have been speaking to Mrs. Hubble, and I am going to her tomorrow. I hope we shall be able to take some care of Mr. Gargery together until he settles down."

"How are you going to live, Biddy? If you want any mo—"

"How am I going to live?" repeated Biddy, striking in, with a momentary flush upon her face. "I'll tell you, Mr. Pip. I am going to try to get the place of mistress in the new school nearly finished here. I can be well recommended by all the neighbors, and I hope I can be industrious and patient, and teach myself while I teach others. The new schools are not like the old, but have had time since then to improve."

"I think you would always improve, Biddy, under any circumstances." As we walked on, I said, "I have not heard the particulars of my sister's death, Biddy."

"They are very slight, poor thing. She had been in one of her bad states for four days, when she came out of it in the evening, just at teatime, and said quite plainly, 'Joe.' As she had never said any word for a long while, I ran and fetched in Mr. Gargery from the forge. She made signs to me that she wanted him to sit down close to her, and wanted me to put her arms round his neck. So I put them round his neck, and she laid her head down on his shoulder quite content and satisfied. And so she presently said 'Joe' again, and once 'Pardon,' and once 'Pip.' And so she never lifted her head up any more, and it was just an hour later when we laid it down on her own bed, because we found she was gone."

Biddy cried; the darkening garden, and the lane, and the stars that were coming out, were blurred in my own sight.

"Nothing was ever discovered, Biddy?"

"Nothing."

"Do you know what is become of Orlick?"

"I should think from the color of his clothes that he is working in the quarries."

"Of course you have seen him then?

Why are you looking at that dark tree in the lane?"

"I saw him there on the night she died."

"That was not the last time either, Biddy?"

"No; I have seen him there since we have been walking here. It is of no use," said Biddy, laying her hand upon my arm, as I was for running out. "You know I would not deceive you; he was not there a minute, and he is gone."

It revived my utmost indignation to find that she was still pursued by this fellow, and I told her that I would spend any money or take any pains to drive him out of that country. By degrees she led me into more temperate talk, and she told me how Joe loved me, and how Joe never complained of anything — she didn't say, of me; she had no need; I knew what she meant — but ever did his duty in his way of life, and with a strong hand, a quiet tongue, and a gentle heart.

"Indeed, it would be hard to say too much for him," said I, "and of course I shall be often down here now. I am not going to leave poor Joe alone."

"Are you quite sure, then, that you *will* come to see him often?" asked Biddy, stopping in the narrow garden walk, and looking at me with a clear and honest eye.

"Oh, dear me!" said I angrily. "This really is a very bad side of human nature! Don't say any more, if you please, Biddy. This shocks me very much."

For which reason I kept Biddy at a distance during supper, and when I went up to my own little room, took as stately a leave of her as I could. As often as I was restless in the night, and that was every quarter of an hour, I reflected what an unkindness, what an in-

jury, what an injustice, Biddy had done me.

Early in the morning I was to go. Early in the morning I was out, and looking in, unseen, at one of the wooden windows of the forge. There I stood, for minutes, looking at Joe, already at work with a glow of health and strength upon his face that made it show as if the bright sun of the life in store for him were shining on it.

"Good-by, dear Joe! No, don't wipe it off — give me your blackened hand! I shall be down soon and often."

"Never too soon, sir," said Joe, "and never too often, Pip!"

Biddy was waiting for me at the kitchen door, with a mug of new milk and a crust of bread. "Biddy," said I, when I gave her my hand at parting, "I am not angry, but I am hurt."

"No, don't be hurt," she pleaded quite pathetically, "let only me be hurt, if I have been ungenerous."

Once more, the mists were rising as I walked away. If they disclosed to me, as I suspect they did, that I should *not* come back, and that Biddy was quite right, all I can say is — they were quite right too.

CHAPTER 26

Miss Skiffins helps serve tea.

HERBERT and I went on from bad to worse, in the way of increasing our debts; and time went on; and I came of age. Herbert himself had come of age, eight months before me. As he had no property to come into, the event did not make a profound sensation in Barnard's Inn. But we had looked forward to my one-and-twentieth birthday with a crowd of speculations and anticipations, for we had both considered that my guardian could hardly help saying something definite on that occasion.

I had taken care to have it well understood in Little Britain when my birthday was. On the day before it, I received an official note from Wemmick, informing me that Mr. Jaggers would be glad if I would call upon him at five in the afternoon of the next day. This convinced us that something great was to happen, and threw me into an unusual flutter when I hurried to my guardian's office, a model of punctuality.

Wemmick offered me his congratulations, and incidentally rubbed the side of his nose with a folded piece of tissue paper that I liked the look of. It was November, and my guardian was standing before his fire with his hands under his coattails.

"Well, Pip," said he, "I must call you Mr. Pip today. Congratulations, Mr. Pip."

We shook hands and I thanked him.

"Take a chair, Mr. Pip," said my guardian.

As I sat down, I felt at a disadvantage which reminded me of that old time when I had been put upon a tombstone.

"Now, my young friend," my guardian began, as if I were a witness in the box, "I am going to have a word or two with you."

"If you please, sir."

"What do you suppose," said Mr. Jaggers, "you are living at the rate of?"

"At the rate of, sir?"

"At," repeated Mr. Jaggers, "the — rate — of?"

Reluctantly, I confessed myself quite unable to answer the question. This reply seemed agreeable to Mr. Jaggers, who said, "I thought so! Now, I have asked *you* a question, my friend. Have you anything to ask *me?*"

"Of course it would be a great relief to me to ask you several questions, sir."

"Ask one," said Mr. Jaggers.

"Is my benefactor to be made known to me today?"

"No. Ask another."

"Is that confidence to be imparted to me soon?"

"Waive [1] that a moment," said Mr. Jaggers, "and ask another."

"Have — I — anything to receive, sir?" On that, Mr. Jaggers said, triumphantly, "I thought we should come to it!" and called to Wemmick to give him that piece of paper. Wemmick appeared, handed it in, and disappeared.

"Now, Mr. Pip," said Mr. Jaggers, "attend if you please. You have been drawing pretty freely here; your name occurs pretty often in Wemmick's cashbook; but you are in debt, of course?"

"I am afraid I must say yes, sir."

"You know you must say yes, don't you?" said Mr. Jaggers.

"Yes, sir."

"I don't ask you what you owe, because you don't know; and if you did know, you wouldn't tell me; you would say less. Yes, yes, my friend," cried Mr. Jaggers, waving his forefinger to stop me, as I made a show of protesting; "it's likely enough that you think you wouldn't, but you would. Now, take this piece of paper in your hand. Now, unfold it and tell me what it is."

"This is a bank note," said I, "for five hundred pounds."

"You consider it, undoubtedly, a handsome sum of money. Now, that handsome sum of money, Pip, is your own. It is a present to you on this day, as part of your expectations. And at the rate of that handsome sum of money annually, and at no higher rate, you are to live until your donor appears. That

---

[1] **waive** (wāv): put aside; disregard.

is to say, you will now take your money affairs entirely into your own hands, and you will draw from Wemmick one hundred and twenty-five pounds quarterly,[1] until you know your benefactor. As I have told you before, I am the mere agent. I execute my instructions, and I am paid for doing so. I think them unwise, but I am not paid for giving any opinion on their merits."

After a pause, I hinted:

"There was a question just now, Mr. Jaggers, which you desired me to waive for a moment. I hope I am doing nothing wrong in asking it again?"

"What is it?" said he.

"Is it likely," I said, after hesitating, "that my patron, Mr. Jaggers, will soon come to London," said I, "or summon me anywhere else?"

"Now here," replied Mr. Jaggers, fixing me for the first time with his dark deep-set eyes, "we must go back to the evening when we first encountered one another in your village. What did I tell you then, Pip?"

"You told me, Mr. Jaggers, that it might be years hence when that person appeared."

"Just so," said Mr. Jaggers. "That's my answer."

"Do you suppose it will still be some years hence, Mr. Jaggers?"

"Come!" said Mr. Jaggers. "I'll be plain with you, my friend Pip. That's a question I must not be asked. When that person discloses, you and that person will settle your own affairs. My part in this business will cease. And that's all I have got to say."

"If that is all you have to say, sir," I remarked, "there can be nothing left for me to say."

He nodded assent and asked me where I was going to dine. I replied at

my own chambers, with Herbert. As a necessary sequence, I asked him if he would favor us with his company, and he promptly accepted the invitation. But first he had a letter or two to write, and I said I would go into the outer office and talk to Wemmick.

The fact was that when the five hundred pounds had come into my pocket, a thought had come into my head; and it appeared to me that Wemmick was a good person to advise with.

"Mr. Wemmick," said I, "I want to ask your opinion. I am very desirous to serve a friend. This friend is trying to get on in commercial life, but has no money and finds it difficult and disheartening to make a beginning. Now, I want somehow to help him to a beginning."

"With money down?" said Wemmick, in a tone drier than any sawdust.

"With *some* money down," I replied, for an uneasy remembrance shot across me of that symmetrical bundle of papers at home; "with *some* money down, and perhaps some anticipation of my expectations."

"Mr. Pip," said Wemmick, "pitch your money into the Thames and you know the end of it. Serve a friend with it, and you may know the end of it too — but it's a less pleasant and profitable end."

"And that," said I, "is your deliberate opinion, Mr. Wemmick?"

"That," he returned, "is my deliberate opinion in this office."

"Ah!" said I, pressing him, for I thought I saw a loophole here; "but would that be your opinion at Walworth?"

"Mr. Pip," he replied, "Walworth is one place, and this office is another. Much as the Aged is one person, and Mr. Jaggers is another. They must not be confounded together. My Walworth

[1] **quarterly:** four times a year.

sentiments must be taken at Walworth; none but my official sentiments can be taken in this office."

"Very well," said I, much relieved, "then I shall look you up at Walworth, you may depend upon it."

"Mr. Pip," he returned, "you will be welcome there, in a private and personal capacity."

We had held this conversation in a low voice, well knowing my guardian's ears to be the sharpest of the sharp. As he now appeared in his doorway, we all three went into the street together, and from the doorstep Wemmick turned his way, and Mr. Jaggers and I turned ours.

I devoted the next Sunday afternoon to a pilgrimage to the Castle. On arriving before the battlements, I found the Union Jack flying and the drawbridge up, but undeterred [1] by this show of defiance and resistance, I rang at the gate, and was admitted by the Aged.

"My son, sir," said the old man, after securing the drawbridge, "left word that he would soon be home from his afternoon's walk. He is very regular in his walks, is my son. Very regular in everything, is my son."

I nodded at the old gentleman, and we went in and sat down by the fireside.

"You made acquaintance with my son, sir," said the old man, in his chirping way, while he warmed his hands at the blaze, "at his office, I expect?" I nodded. "Hah! I have heared that my son is a wonderful hand at his business."

I was startled just then by a sudden click in the wall on one side of the chimney, and the ghostly tumbling open of a little wooden flap with "John" upon it. The old man, following my eyes, cried with great triumph, "My

[1] **undeterred** (ŭn′dê·tûrd′): not frightened or turned aside.

son's come home!" and we both went out to the drawbridge. The Aged was so delighted to work the drawbridge that I made no offer to assist him, but stood quiet until Wemmick had come across, and had presented me to Miss Skiffins, a lady by whom he was accompanied.

Miss Skiffins was of a wooden appearance, like her escort. The cut of her dress from the waist upward, both before and behind, made her figure very like a boy's kite, and I might have pronounced her gown a little too decidedly orange and her gloves a little too intensely green; but she seemed to be a good sort of person, and showed a high regard for the Aged. I was not long in discovering that she was a frequent visitor at the Castle.

While Miss Skiffins was taking off her bonnet (she retained her green gloves during the evening as an outward and visible sign that there was company), Wemmick invited me to take a walk with him round the property and see how the island looked in wintertime. Thinking that he did this to give me an opportunity of taking his Walworth sentiments, I seized the opportunity as soon as we were out of the Castle.

I informed Wemmick that I was anxious in behalf of Herbert Pocket, and I told him how we had first met, and how we had fought. I alluded to the advantages I had derived in my first ignorance from his society, and I confessed that I feared I had but ill repaid them. He might have done better without me and my expectations. For these reasons (I told Wemmick), and because he was my young companion and friend, I sought advice on how I could best help Herbert to some present income — say of a hundred a year, to keep him in good hope and heart — and gradually to buy him into some small part-

Wemmick, Miss Skiffins, and Aged Parent.

nership. I begged Wemmick to understand that my help must always be rendered without Herbert's knowledge or suspicion, and that there was no one else in the world with whom I could advise. I wound up by laying my hand upon his shoulder and saying, "I can't help confiding in you, though I know it must be bothersome to you; but that is your fault in having ever brought me here."

Wemmick was silent for a little while, and then said, "Mr. Pip, I'll put on my considering cap, and I think all you want to do may be done by degrees. Skiffins (that's her brother) is an accountant and agent. I'll look him up and go to work for you."

After a little further conversation to the same effect, we returned into the Castle, where we found Miss Skiffins preparing tea. The responsible duty of making the toast was delegated to the Aged, and that excellent old gentleman prepared such a haystack of buttered toast that I could scarcely see him over it. We ate the whole of the toast and drank tea in proportion, and it was delightful to see how warm and greasy we all got after it. The Aged especially might have passed for some clean old chief of a savage tribe, just oiled. Then we drew round the fire, and Wemmick said, "Now, Aged Parent, read us the paper."

Wemmick explained to me while the Aged got his spectacles out that this was according to custom, and that it gave the old gentleman infinite satisfaction to read the news aloud. "I won't offer an apology," said Wemmick, "for he isn't capable of many pleasures — are you, Aged P.?"

"All right, John, all right," returned the old man, seeing himself spoken to.

"Only tip him a nod every now and then when he looks off his paper," said Wemmick, "and he'll be as happy as a king. We are all attention, Aged One."

As Wemmick and Miss Skiffins sat side by side, I observed him slowly and gradually stealing his arm round Miss Skiffins' waist. In course of time I saw his hand appear on the other side of Miss Skiffins; but at that moment Miss Skiffins neatly stopped him with the green glove, unwound his arm again as if it were an article of dress, and with the greatest deliberation laid it on the table before her. Miss Skiffins' composure while she did this was one of the most remarkable sights I have ever seen.

At last the Aged read himself into a light slumber. Of course I knew better than to offer to see Miss Skiffins home, and under the circumstances I thought I had best go first; which I did, taking a cordial leave of the Aged, and having passed a pleasant evening.

Before a week was out, I received a note from Wemmick stating that he had made some advance in that matter pertaining to our private and personal relations. The upshot was that we found a worthy young merchant, not long established in business, who wanted intelligent help, and who wanted capital, and who in due course of time would want a partner. Between him and me secret articles were signed of which Herbert was the subject, and I paid him half of my five hundred pounds down, and engaged for other payments; some to fall due at certain dates out of my income; some on my coming into my property. Miss Skiffins' brother conducted the negotiation.

The whole business was so cleverly managed that Herbert had not the least suspicion of my hand being in it. I never shall forget the radiant face with which he came home one afternoon, and told me, as a mighty piece of news, of his having fallen in with one Clarriker (the young merchant's name), and of his belief that the opening had come at last. Day by day as his hopes grew stronger and his face brighter, he must have thought me a more and more affectionate friend, for I had the greatest difficulty in restraining my tears of triumph when I saw him so happy. At length, the thing being done, and he having that day entered Clarriker's House, and he having talked to me for a whole evening in a flush of pleasure and success, I did really cry in good earnest when I went to bed, to think that my expectations had done some good to somebody.

A great event in my life, the turning point of my life, now opens on my view. But, before I proceed to narrate it, and before I pass on to all the changes it involved, I must give one chapter to Estella. It is not much to give to the theme that so long filled my heart.

CHAPTER 27

Estella warns Pip.

THE LADY with whom Estella was placed, Mrs. Brandley by name, was a widow, with one daughter several years older than Estella. They were in what is called a good position, and they visited, and were visited by, numbers of people.

In Mrs. Brandley's house and out of Mrs. Brandley's house, I suffered every kind and degree of torture that Estella could cause me. She made use of me to tease other admirers; she turned the very familiarity between herself and me to this account, and while I think it likely that it almost maddened her other lovers, I knew too certainly that it almost maddened me. She had admirers without end. No doubt my jealousy made an admirer of everyone who went near her; but there were more than enough of them without that.

I saw her often at Richmond, I heard of her often in town, and I used often to take her and the Brandleys on all sorts of pleasures — and they were all miseries to me. I never had one hour's happiness in her society, and yet my mind all round the four-and-twenty

hours was harping on the happiness of having her with me unto death. There were times, however, when she would come to a sudden check and would seem to pity me.

"Pip, Pip," she said one evening, when we sat apart at a darkening window of the house in Richmond; "will you never take warning?"

"Of what?"

"Of me."

"Warning not to be attracted by you, do you mean, Estella?"

"Do I mean! If you don't know what I mean, you are blind."

"At any rate," said I, "I have no warning given me just now, for you wrote to me to come to you this time."

"That's true," said Estella, with a cold careless smile that always chilled me. "The time has come round when Miss Havisham wishes to have me for a day at Satis House. You are to take me there, and bring me back, if you will. She would rather I did not travel alone, and objects to receiving my maid, for she has a sensitive horror of being talked of by such people. Can you take me?"

"Can I take you, Estella!"

"You can then? The day after tomorrow, if you please. You are to pay all charges out of my purse. You hear the condition of your going?"

"And must obey," said I.

We went down on the next day but one, and we found Miss Havisham in the room where I had first beheld her. She hung upon Estella's beauty, hung upon her words, hung upon her gestures, and looked at her, as though she were devouring the beautiful creature she had reared.

From Estella she looked at me, with a searching glance that seemed to pry into my heart and probe its wounds. "How does she use you, Pip, how does she use you?" she asked me again, with her witchlike eagerness, even in Estella's hearing. When we sat by the flickering fire at night, she was most weird, exhorting Estella to tell her the names and feelings of men she had fascinated. But I saw in this that Estella was set to wreak Miss Havisham's revenge on men. I, too, was tormented even while the prize was reserved for me. I saw in this the reason for my being staved off so long, and the reason for my late guardian's declining to commit himself to the formal knowledge of such a scheme.

As I looked about the room, at the pale gloom of the candlelight, and at the stopped clock, and at the withered articles of bridal dress upon the table and the ground, and at her own awful figure with its ghostly reflection thrown large by the fire upon the ceiling and the wall, I saw in everything the intensity of Miss Havisham's mortally hurt and diseased mind.

It happened on the occasion of this visit that some sharp words arose between Estella and Miss Havisham. It was the first time I had ever seen them opposed.

Miss Havisham still clutched Estella's hand in hers, when Estella gradually began to detach herself. She had shown a proud impatience more than once before, and had rather endured that fierce affection than accepted or returned it.

"What!" said Miss Havisham, flashing her eyes upon it. "Are you tired of me?"

"Only a little tired of myself," replied Estella, removing her arm.

"Speak the truth, you ingrate!" cried Miss Havisham, passionately striking her stick upon the floor. "You are tired of me."

Estella looked at her with perfect composure, and again looked down at the fire. Her graceful figure and her beautiful face expressed a self-possessed indifference to the wild heat of the other that was almost cruel.

"You stock and stone!" exclaimed Miss Havisham. "You cold, cold heart!"

"What!" said Estella. "Do you reproach me for being cold? You?"

"Are you not?" was the fierce retort.

"You should know," said Estella. "I am what you have made me."

"So proud, so proud!" moaned Miss Havisham, pushing away her gray hair with both her hands.

"Who taught me to be proud?" returned Estella. "Who praised me when I learned my lesson?"

"So hard, so hard!" moaned Miss Havisham, with her former action.

"Who taught me to be hard?" returned Estella. "Who praised me when I learned my lesson?"

"But to be proud and hard to *me!*" Miss Havisham quite shrieked, as she stretched out her arms. "Estella, Estella, Estella, to be proud and hard to *me!*"

"So," said Estella, "I must be taken as I have been made. The success is not mine, the failure is not mine, but the two together make me."

Miss Havisham had settled down, upon the floor, among the faded bridal relics with which it was strewn. I took advantage of the moment — I had sought one from the first — to leave the room, after beseeching Estella's attention to her with a movement of my hand. When I left, Estella was yet standing by the great chimney piece, just as she had stood throughout. Miss Havisham's gray hair was all adrift upon the ground, among the other bridal wrecks, and was a miserable sight to see.

It was with a depressed heart that I walked in the starlight for an hour and more, about the courtyard, and about the brewery, and about the ruined garden. When I at last took courage to return to the room, I found Estella sitting at Miss Havisham's knee. Afterward Estella and I played cards, as of yore — only we were skillful now, and played French games — and so the evening wore away, and I went to bed.

I lay in that separate building across the courtyard. It was the first time I had ever lain down to rest in Satis House, and sleep refused to come near me. At last I felt that I absolutely must get up. I put on my clothes and went out across the yard into the long stone passage. But I was no sooner in the passage than I extinguished my candle, for I saw Miss Havisham moving along the corridor in a ghostly manner, making a low cry. I followed her at a distance and saw her go up the staircase. She carried a bare candle in her hand and was a most unearthly object by its light. Standing at the bottom of the staircase, I heard her walking across into her own room, never ceasing the low cry. Again and again I heard her footstep, saw her candle pass above, and heard her ceaseless low cry.

Before we left next day, there was no revival of the difference between her and Estella, nor was it ever revived on any similar occasions; and there were four similar occasions, to the best of my remembrance.

It is impossible to turn this leaf of my life without putting Bentley Drummle's name upon it, or I would, very gladly.

It became known to me, through a London club of which we were both members, that Drummle was acquainted with Estella and had called on her at Richmond. I tell this lightly, but it was no light thing to me. For I cannot express what pain it gave me to think that Estella should show any favor to a contemptible, clumsy, sulky booby, so very far below the average.

It was easy for me to find out, and I did soon find out, that Drummle had begun to follow her closely, and that she allowed him to do it. A little while, and he was always in pursuit of her, and Estella held him on; now with encouragement, now with discouragement, now almost flattering him, now openly despising him. The Spider, as Mr. Jaggers had called him, was used to lying in wait, however, and had the patience of his tribe.

At a certain Assembly Ball at Richmond, I resolved to speak to her concerning him. I took the opportunity when she was waiting for Mrs. Brandley to take her home.

"Are you tired, Estella?"

"Rather, Pip."

"You should be."

"Say, rather, I should not be; for I have my letter to Satis House to write before I go to sleep."

"Recounting tonight's triumph?" said I. "Surely a very poor one, Estella."

"What do you mean?"

"Estella," said I, "look at that fellow in the corner who is looking over here at us."

"Why should I look at him?" returned Estella. "What is there in that fellow in the corner that I need look at?"

"Indeed, that is the very question I want to ask you," said I. "He has been hovering about you all night."

"Moths and all sorts of ugly creatures," replied Estella, with a glance toward him, "hover about a lighted candle. Can the candle help it?"

"But, Estella, do hear me speak. It makes me wretched that you should encourage a man so generally despised as Drummle. You know he is despised."

"Well?" said she.

"You know he is an ill-tempered, lowering, stupid fellow."

"Well?" said she.

"You know he has nothing to recommend him but money, don't you?"

"Pip," said Estella, casting her glance over the room, "don't be foolish about its effect on you. It may have its effect on others, and may be meant to have. It's not worth discussing."

"Yes, it is," said I, "because I cannot bear that people should say, 'she throws away her graces and attractions on a mere boor, the lowest in the crowd.'"

"I can bear it," said Estella.

"Oh! don't be so proud, Estella, and so inflexible."

"Calls me proud and inflexible in this breath!" said Estella, opening her hands. "And in his last breath reproached me for stooping to a boor!"

"There is no doubt you do," said I, "for I have seen you give him looks and smiles this very night, such as you never give to — me."

"Do you want me then," said Estella, turning suddenly with a fixed and serious look, "to deceive and entrap you?"

"Do you deceive and entrap him, Estella?"

"Yes, and many others — all of them but you. Here is Mrs. Brandley. I'll say no more."

And now that I have given the one chapter to the theme that so filled my heart, and so often made it ache and ache again, I pass on to the event that had impended over me longer yet; the event that had begun to be prepared for before I knew that the world held Estella.

All the work, near and afar, that tended to the end, had been accomplished; and in an instant the blow was struck, and the roof of my present life dropped upon me.

CHAPTER 28

Pip has a midnight caller.

I was three-and-twenty years of age. Not another word had I heard to enlighten me on the subject of my expectations. We had left Barnard's Inn a year before, and lived in the Temple.[1] Our chambers were in Garden Court, down by the river. Mr. Pocket and I had for some time parted company as to our original relations, though we continued on the best terms.

Business had taken Herbert on a journey to Marseilles.[2] I was alone, and had a dull sense of being alone. I sadly missed the cheerful face and ready response of my friend. It was wretched weather; stormy and wet, stormy and wet; mud, mud, mud, deep in all the streets. We lived at the top of the last house, and the wind rushing up the river shook the house that night, like discharges of cannon or breakings of a sea. I saw that the lamps in the court were blown out, and that the lamps on the bridges and the shore were shuddering, and that the coal fires in barges on the river were being carried away before the wind like red-hot splashes in the rain.

I read with my watch upon the table, purposing to close my book at eleven o'clock. As I shut it, all the church clocks in the city struck that hour. The sound was curiously flawed by the wind; and I was listening, when I heard a footstep on the stair.

What nervous folly made me start, and awfully connect it with the footstep

[1] **Temple:** several groups of famous buildings, built on courtyards near the Thames River, which were occupied by lawyers and court officials and clerks.
[2] **Marseilles** (mär·sālz′): a seaport in France.

of my dead sister, matters not. It was past in a moment, and I listened again, and heard the footstep coming on. Remembering then that the staircase lights were blown out, I took up my reading lamp and went out to the stairhead. Whoever was below had stopped on seeing my lamp, for all was quiet.

"There is someone down there, is there not?" I called out, looking down.

"Yes," said a voice from the darkness beneath.

"What floor do you want?"

"The top — Mr. Pip."

"That is my name. There is nothing the matter?"

"Nothing the matter," returned the voice. And the man came on.

I stood with my lamp held out over the stair rail, and as he came slowly within its light, I saw a face that was strange to me, looking up with a strange air of being touched and pleased by the sight of me.

Moving the lamp as the man moved, I made out that he was substantially dressed, but roughly, like a voyager by sea. That he had long iron-gray hair. That his age was about sixty. That he was a muscular man, strong on his legs, and that he was browned and hardened by exposure to weather. As he ascended the last stair or two, I saw, with a stupid kind of amazement, that he was holding out both his hands to me.

"Pray what is your business?" I asked him.

"My business?" he repeated, pausing. "Ah! Yes. I will explain my business, by your leave."

"Do you wish to come in?"

"Yes," he replied. "I wish to come in, master."

I took him into the room I had just left and, having set the lamp on the table, asked him as civilly as I could to explain himself.

He looked about him with the strangest air — an air of wondering pleasure, as if he had some part in the things he admired — and he pulled off a rough outer coat, and his hat. Then I saw that his head was furrowed and bald, and that the long iron-gray hair grew only on its sides. But I saw nothing that in the least explained him. On the contrary, I saw him next moment once more holding out both his hands to me.

"What do you mean?" said I, half suspecting him to be mad.

He stopped in his looking at me and slowly rubbed his right hand over his head. "It's disappointing to a man," he said, in a coarse broken voice, "arter having looked for'ard so distant, and come so fur; but you're not to blame for that — neither on us is to blame for that. I'll speak in half a minute. Give me half a minute, please."

He sat down on a chair that stood before the fire, and covered his forehead with his large brown hands. I looked at him attentively then, and recoiled a little from him; but I did not know him.

"There's no one nigh," said he, looking over his shoulder, "is there?"

"Why do you, a stranger coming into my rooms at this time of the night, ask that question?" said I.

"You're a game one," he returned. "I'm glad you've grow'd up a game one! But don't catch hold of me. You'd be sorry arterwards to have done it."

I relinquished the intention he had detected, for I knew him! Even yet I could not recall a single feature, but I knew him! If the wind and the rain had swept up to the churchyard where we first stood face to face I could not have known my convict more distinctly than I knew him now, as he sat in the chair before the fire. No need to take a file from his pocket and show it to me; no need to take the handkerchief from his neck and twist it round his head; no need to hug himself with both his arms, and take a shivering turn across the room, looking back at me for recognition. I knew him before he gave me one of those aids, though a moment before I had not been conscious of remotely suspecting his identity.

He came back to where I stood and again held out both his hands. Not knowing what to do — for in my astonishment I had lost my self-possession — I reluctantly gave him my hands. He grasped them heartily, raised them to his lips, kissed them, and still held them.

"You acted nobly, my boy," said he. "Noble Pip! And I have never forgot it!"

At a change in his manner as if he were even going to embrace me, I laid a hand upon his breast and put him away.

"Stay!" said I. "Keep off! If you are grateful to me for what I did when I was a little child, I hope you have shown your gratitude by mending your way of life. If you have come here to thank me, it was not necessary. There must be something good in the feeling that has brought you here, and I will not repulse you; but surely you must understand — I — "

My attention was so attracted by the strangeness of his fixed look at me that the words died away on my tongue.

"You was a-saying," he observed, when we had confronted one another in silence, "that surely I must understand. What surely must I understand?"

"That I cannot wish to renew that chance intercourse with you of long ago, under these different circumstances. I am glad to believe you have repented and recovered yourself. I am glad to tell you so. I am glad that, thinking I deserved to be thanked, you have come to thank me. But our ways are different ways, none the less. You are wet, and you look weary. Will you drink something before you go?"

He had replaced his neckerchief loosely, and had stood, keenly observant of me, biting a long end of it. "I think," he answered, still observant of me, "that I *will* drink (I thank you) afore I go."

I made him some hot rum-and-water. I tried to keep my hand steady while I did so. When at last I put the glass to him, I saw with amazement that his eyes were full of tears. I was softened by the softened aspect of the man, and felt a touch of reproach. "I hope," said I, "that you will not think I spoke harshly to you just now. I had no intention of doing it, and I am sorry for it if I did. I wish you well and happy!"

As I put my glass to my lips, he stretched out his hand. I gave him mine, and then he drank, and drew his sleeve across his eyes and forehead.

"How are you living?" I asked him.

"I've been a sheep farmer, stockbreeder, other trades besides, away in the new world," said he; "many a thousand mile of stormy water off from this."

"I hope you have done well?"

"I've done wonderful well. No man has done nigh as well as me. I'm famous for it."

"I'm glad to hear it."

"I hope to hear you say so, my dear boy."

Without stopping to try to understand those words or the tone in which they were spoken, I turned off to a point that had just come into my mind.

"Have you ever seen a messenger you once sent to me," I inquired, "since he undertook that trust?"

"Never set eyes upon him. I warn't likely to."

"He came faithfully, and he brought me the two one-pound notes. I was a poor boy then, as you know, and to a poor boy they were a little fortune. But, like you, I have done well since, and you must let me pay them back. You can put them to some other poor boy's use." I took out my purse.

He watched me as I laid my purse upon the table and opened it, and he watched me as I separated two one-pound notes from its contents. They were clean and new, and I spread them out and handed them over to him. Still watching me, he laid them one upon the other, folded them longwise, gave them a twist, set fire to them at the lamp, and dropped the ashes into the tray.

"May I make so bold," he said then, with a smile that was like a frown, and with a frown that was like a smile, "as to ask you *how* you have done well, since you and me was out on them lone shivering marshes?"

He emptied his glass, got up, and stood at the side of the fire, with his heavy brown hand on the mantelshelf. He put a foot up to the bars to dry and warm it, and the wet boot began to steam; but he neither looked at it nor at the fire, but steadily looked at me. It was only now that I began to tremble.

When my lips had parted, I forced myself to tell him that I had been chosen to succeed to some property.

"Might a mere warmint [1] ask what property?" said he.

I faltered, "I don't know."

"Might a mere warmint ask whose property?" said he.

I faltered again, "I don't know."

[1] **warmint** (wär′mĭnt): a mispronunciation of the word *varment,* or *vermin,* meaning lowly creature.

"Pray what is your business?" I asked him.

"Could I make a guess, I wonder," said the convict, "at your income since you come of age? As to the first figure, now. Five?"

With my heart beating like a heavy hammer of disordered action, I rose out of my chair, and stood with my hand upon the back of it, looking wildly at him.

"Concerning a guardian," he went on. "There ought to have been some guardian, while you was a minor. Some lawyer, maybe. As to the first letter of that lawyer's name, now. Would it be J?"

All the truth of my position came flashing on me; and its disappointments, dangers, disgraces, consequences of all kinds, rushed in in such a multitude that I was borne down by them and had to struggle for every breath I drew. "Put it," he resumed, "as the employer of that lawyer whose name begun with a J, and might be Jaggers — put it as he had come over sea to Portsmouth, and had landed there, and had wanted to come on to you. Well! however did I find you out? Why, I wrote from Portsmouth to a person in London for particulars of your address. That person's name? Why, Wemmick."

I could not have spoken one word, though it had been to save my life. I stood, with a hand on the chair back and a hand on my breast, where I seemed to be suffocating — I stood so, looking wildly at him, until I grasped at the chair, when the room began to surge and turn. He caught me, drew me to the sofa, put me up against the cushions, and bent on one knee before me: bringing the face that I now well remembered, and that I shuddered at, very near to mine.

"Yes, Pip, dear boy, I've made a gentleman on you! It's me wot has done it! I swore that time, sure as ever I earned a guinea, that guinea should go to you. I swore arterwards, sure as ever I spec'-lated and got rich, you should get rich. I lived rough, that you should live smooth; I worked hard that you should be above work. What odds, dear boy? Do I tell it fur you to feel a obligation? Not a bit. I tell it fur you to know as that there hunted dog wot you kept life in got his head so high that he could make a gentleman — and, Pip, you're him!"

The abhorrence in which I held the man, the dread I had of him, the repugnance with which I shrank from him, could not have been exceeded if he had been some terrible beast.

"Look'ee here, Pip. I'm your second father. You're my son — more to me nor any son. I've put away money, only for you to spend. When I was a hired-out shepherd in a solitary hut, not seeing no faces but faces of sheep till I half forgot wot men's and women's faces was like, I see yours. I drops my knife many a time in that hut when I was a-eating my dinner or my supper, and I says, 'Here's the boy again, a-looking at me whiles I eats and drinks!' I see you there a many times as plain as ever I see you on them misty marshes. I says each time, 'If I gets liberty and money, I'll make that boy a gentleman!' And I done it. Why, look at you, dear boy! Look at these here lodgings of yours, fit for a lord! A lord? Ah! You shall show money with lords for wagers, and beat 'em!"

In his heat and triumph, and in his knowledge that I had been nearly fainting, he did not notice my horror-stricken reception of all this. It was the one grain of relief I had. Again he took both my hands and put them to his lips, while my blood ran cold within me.

"Don't you mind talking, Pip," said he. "You ain't looked slowly forward to this as I have; you wasn't prepared for this, as I was. But didn't you never think it might be me?"

"Oh no, no, no," I returned. "Never, never!"

"Well, you see it *was* me, and single-handed. Never a soul in it but my own self and Mr. Jaggers."

"Was there no one else?" I asked.

"No," said he, with a glance of surprise. "Who else should there be? And, dear boy, how good-looking you have growed! There's bright eyes some-wheres — eh? Isn't there bright eyes somewheres, wot you love the thoughts on?"

O Estella, Estella!

"They shall be yours, dear boy, if money can buy 'em. Let me finish wot I was a-telling you, dear boy. From that there hut and that there hiring-out, I got money and got my liberty and went for myself. It all prospered wonderful. As I giv' you to understand just now, I'm famous for it. It was the gains of the first few year wot I sent home to Mr. Jaggers — all for you — when he first come after you, following my letter."

Oh, that he had never come! That he had left me at the forge — far from con-tented, yet, by comparison, happy!

"And, dear boy, I held steady afore my mind that I would for certain come one day and see my boy, and make my-self known to him, on his own ground."

He laid his hand on my shoulder. I shuddered at the thought that for any-thing I knew his hand might be stained with blood.

"Where will you put me?" he asked presently. "I must be put somewheres, dear boy."

"To sleep?" said I.

"Yes. And to sleep long and sound," he answered, "for I've been sea-tossed and sea-washed, months and months."

"My friend and companion," said I,

rising from the sofa, "is absent; you must have his room."

"He won't come back tomorrow, will he?"

"No," said I, answering almost me-chanically, "not tomorrow."

"Because, look'ee here, dear boy," he said, dropping his voice, and laying a long finger on my breast in an impres-sive manner, "caution is necessary."

"How do you mean? Caution?"

"It's death!"

"What's death?"

"I was sent for life. It's death to come back. There's been overmuch coming back of late years, and I should of a certainty be hanged if took."

Nothing was needed but this; the wretched man, after loading me with his wretched gold and silver chains for years, had risked his life to come to me, and I held it there in my keeping!

My first care was to close the shutters so that no light might be seen from without, and then to close and make fast the doors. He asked me for some of my "gentleman's linen" to put on in the morning. I brought it out, and laid it ready for him, and my blood again ran cold when he took me by both hands to give me good night.

I got away from him, without know-ing how I did it, and for an hour or more I remained too stunned to think. It was not until I began to think that I began fully to know how wrecked I was, and how the ship in which I had sailed was gone to pieces.

Miss Havisham's intentions toward me, all a mere dream; Estella not de-signed for me; I was only allowed in Satis House as a convenience, a sting for the greedy relations, a model with a mechanical heart to practice on when no other practice was at hand. But sharpest and deepest pain of all — it was for the convict, guilty of I knew not what crimes — that I had deserted Joe.

In every rage of wind and rush of rain, I heard pursuers. Twice I could have sworn there was a knocking and whispering at the outer door. With these fears upon me, a half-formed terror filled the room and impelled me to go in and look at my dreadful burden.

He had rolled a handkerchief round his head, his face was set and lowering in his sleep, and he had a pistol lying on the pillow. I softly removed the key to the outside of his door, and turned it on him before I again sat down by the fire. Gradually I slipped from the chair and lay on the floor. When I awoke, the clocks were striking five, the candles were wasted out, the fire was dead, and the wind and rain intensified the thick black darkness.

This Is the End of the Second Stage of Pip's Expectations.

DISCUSSING THE MAIN CHARACTER: PIP

1. At the conclusion of the First Stage you were invited to guess what might be ahead for Pip. How accurate was your guess? Did you foresee that his new way of life would not solve his problems, but turn him into a snob instead?

2. Pip has changed. In the First Stage you were asked to describe him as he was at the beginning of the story, compared with the Pip who left for London. We become uncomfortably aware of what a snob he is when Joe visits him in London. How little Pip does to put poor awkward Joe at his ease! Do you think that he *meant* to fail his kind friend so badly? If you were disappointed in Pip, in all fairness to him recall what he does after Joe leaves, at the end of Chapter 20. How does this clue suggest the possibility that, after all, Pip is a better person than his snobbishness might indicate? Can you show any other indications of this?

3. The change in Pip demonstrates for you an important difference between the novel and the short story. The characters in a novel are many-sided; they go through a variety of changes, over a longer range of time. Many people and many influences have been wrenching Pip away from the simple, trusting affection and loyalty held out to him as an example by Joe. Exactly in what way has he been influenced?

4. To gain deeper understanding of Pip, it is well to take a good long look at the people and events that have changed him. You can chart the changes in Pip in a most dramatic way by drawing up a two-column list. Jot down in one column the names of the people and the events that have influenced Pip to become a snob. In the other column, list the people and events that may have the power to save him from remaining selfish and snobbish. To simplify matters, head your columns "Good Influences" and "Bad Influences." You may find yourself unable to decide about some of the people and events. Make choices — and see whether the developments in the Third Stage lead you to change your mind. By all means, save the list in your notebook; you will want to refer to it several times before you have finished the novel. Preparing such a list will also help you to keep track of the story threads; it is a good way to prove to yourself that you are reading with insight and understanding. You may wish to add others, but your list should certainly include the following people:

> Joe
> Estella
> Biddy
> Pip's Convict
> Miss Havisham
> Mr. Jaggers
> Mr. Wemmick
> Herbert Pocket
> Drummle

5. Under which heading would you list these characters? The choice is not always easy. Is Herbert Pocket basically a snob, for instance? Miss Havisham has under-

gone a change since the First Stage — is she now a good or bad influence?

6. In listing the events and situations which have influenced Pip to behave like a snob, or a good, loyal friend, be sure to include:

Pip's first visit home
Pip's hiring a servant
The death of Mrs. Joe
Pip's London meeting with Estella
The arrival of Pip's convict

7. Look over your list and try to decide in every case what the effect is of each person and event on Pip. Compare your notes and opinions with those of your classmates. By discussing him, you will come to know him thoroughly — a fully drawn main character, such as novels offer.

FOLLOWING THE THREADS OF THE PLOT

8. By the end of the First Stage, most of the plot threads of the story had been revealed. In the Second Stage, each of these threads was expanded — Pip and the convict, the injury to Mrs. Joe, the question of Pip's benefactor. Can you name the other major threads of the plot? How were these brought farther along in the Second Stage? What new threads were introduced?

IDEAS TO TALK OVER

9. How does it happen that the possession of money can cause some people to become snobs? Have you observed examples of snobbishness in young people? Are teen-agers more prone than adults to act snobbishly? In cases you know, would you blame a tendency to "follow the crowd" or an attempt to be "different"?

10. Another point to think about and discuss is the question of values. How confused Pip has become! Take a look at your notebook list. In just a few words, add under each character's name what you think are the values he holds most dear. In some instances it will be loyalty or friendship; in others, money or power. Is it any wonder that Pip is torn this way and that in his search for happiness, when so many of his associates have conflicting values?

11. Pip is now twenty-three and a "gentleman." How would you rate his actions according to *your* definition of a true gentleman?

12. How would you interpret Mrs. Joe's dying words (page 650) "Joe . . . Pardon . . . Pip"? There are two possible interpretations.

13. Estella has not lost her ability to make Pip feel "a coarse and common boy." Even the silly clowning of Trabb's boy bothers him, though one would suppose that a sophisticated young man of London would laugh at it. In short, Pip is as insecure and unhappy as he was the day he left the forge. And with the return of the convict Pip is overcome by two shocking realizations: his dreams about the future are shattered, and he has deserted Joe. What has made him realize these two truths about himself?

14. Consider, now, what new decision confronts Pip: Shall he refuse shelter to the convict, and thus betray the man's trust, or shall he hide him and run the risk of harboring a wanted criminal? Will he continue to make the wrong choices?

FOR YOUR VOCABULARY: SHADES OF MEANINGS

In Chapter 22 Pip speaks of "the *hypocritical* Pumblechook." Earlier in the story he refers to Miss Havisham's greedy relatives as "toadies and humbugs." The word *hypocritical* is from the Greek word *hypo-kritēs*, one who tries to give the impression that he is better or kinder (or perhaps more honest) than he is.

A *toady* plays up to people because they are influential or rich. Some dictionaries define a toady as a "toadeater" — a vivid, if unpleasant, description! A *humbug* is someone whose actions are deliberately misleading.

Today we should be more apt to use the word *snob* than either *toady* or *humbug* in discussing the Havisham relatives. According to the dictionary, a *snob* seeks to associate with those whom he regards as his superiors; he is quite cool toward people who in his opinion are his own inferiors.

Why is *hypocritical* a better word to use for Mr. Pumblechook than *humbug*, *toady*, or *snob*?

The Third Stage of Pip's Expectations

CHAPTER 29

Pip confronts Jaggers.

IT WAS fortunate that I had to take precautions to insure (so far as I could) the safety of my dreaded visitor. The impossibility of keeping him concealed in the chambers was self-evident. Having some time previously rid myself of my expensive serving boy, I was looked after by an old female, assisted by her niece; and to keep a room secret from them would be to invite curiosity. I resolved to announce in the morning that my uncle had unexpectedly come from the country.

This course I decided on while I was yet groping about in the darkness for the means of getting a light. I went out to get the watchman to come with his lantern. Now, in groping my way down the black staircase, I fell over something, and that something was a man crouching in a corner. As the man made no answer when I asked him what he did there, I ran to the court and urged the watchman to come quickly. We examined the staircase from the bottom to the top and found no one there.

It troubled me that there should have been a lurker on the stairs on that night of all nights in the year, and I asked the watchman whether he had admitted at his gate any gentleman who had been dining out.

"The night being so bad, sir," said the watchman, "uncommon few have come in at my gate. Besides them three gentlemen that I know, I don't call to mind another since about eleven o'clock, when a stranger asked for you."

"My uncle," I muttered. "Yes."

"You saw him, sir?"

"Yes. Oh, yes."

"Likewise the person with him?"

"Person with him!" I repeated. "What sort of person?"

The watchman had not particularly noticed; he should say a working person; to the best of his belief, he had a dust-colored kind of clothes on, under a dark coat.

My mind was much troubled by these two circumstances taken together. As the night passed, I was not able to consider my own situation, nor could I do so yet. At last the old woman and the niece came in. I imparted how my uncle had come in the night and was then asleep, and how the breakfast preparations were to be modified accordingly.

By-and-by, his door opened and he came out. I could not bring myself to bear the sight of him, and I thought he had a worse look by daylight.

"I do not even know," said I, speaking low as he took his seat at the table, "by what name to call you. I have given out that you are my uncle."

"That's it, dear boy! Call me uncle."

"You assumed some name, I suppose, on board ship?"

"Yes, dear boy. I took the name of Provis."

"Do you mean to keep that name?"

"Why, yes, dear boy, it's as good as another — unless you'd like another."

"What is your real name?" I asked him in a whisper.

"Magwitch," he answered in the same tone; "christened Abel."

"When you came into the Temple last night," said I, "and asked the watchman the way here, had you anyone with you?"

"With me? No, dear boy."

"But there was someone there?"

"I didn't take particular notice," he said dubiously, "not knowing the ways of the place."

"Are you known in London?"

"I hope not," said he, giving his neck a jerk with his forefinger that made me turn hot and sick.

"Were you known in London once?"

"Not over and above, dear boy. I was in the provinces mostly."

"Were you — tried — in London?"

"Which time?" said he, with a sharp look.

"The last time."

He nodded. "First knowed Mr. Jaggers that way. Jaggers was for me. And what I done is worked out and paid for!"

He ate in a ravenous way that was very disagreeable, and all his actions were uncouth, noisy, and greedy. Some of his teeth had failed him since I saw him eat on the marshes, and as he turned his food in his mouth, and turned his head sideways to bring his strongest fangs to bear upon it, he looked terribly like a hungry old dog.

"I'm a heavy grubber, dear boy," he said, as a polite kind of apology when he had made an end of his meal. "Similarly, I must have my smoke." He got up and brought out a short black pipe and a handful of loose tobacco. Having filled his pipe, he took a live coal from the fire with the tongs and lighted his pipe at it, and turned round on the hearthrug with his back to the fire. He took out of his pocket a great thick pocketbook, bursting with papers, and tossed it on the table.

"There's something worth spending in that there book, dear boy. It's yours. All I've got ain't mine; it's yours. Don't you be afeerd on it. There's more where that come from. I've come to the old country fur to see my gentleman spend his money *like* a gentleman. That'll be *my* pleasure. *My* pleasure 'ull be fur to see him do it. And blast you all!" he wound up. "Blast you every one, from the judge in his wig to the colonist a-stirring up the dust, I'll show a better gentleman than the whole kit on you put together!"

"Stop!" said I, almost in a frenzy of fear and dislike. "I want to speak to you. I want to know what is to be done. I want to know how you are to be kept out of danger, how long you are going to stay, what projects you have."

"Look'ee here, Pip," said he, laying his hand on my arm in a suddenly altered and subdued manner. "I forgot myself half a minute ago. What I said was low; that's what it was; low. Look-'ee here, Pip. Overlook it. I ain't a-going to be low."

"First," I resumed, half groaning, "what precautions can be taken against your being recognized and seized?"

"Well, dear boy, the danger ain't so great. Unless I was informed agen, the danger ain't so much. There's Jaggers, and there's Wemmick, and there's you. Who else is there to inform?"

"Is there no chance person who might identify you in the street?" said I.

"Well," he returned, "there ain't

Pip and Magwitch.

It appeared to me that I could do no better than secure him some quiet lodging nearby. That the secret must be confided to Herbert was plain to me. But it was by no means so plain to Mr. Provis (I resolved to call him by that name), who reserved his consent to Herbert's participation until he should have seen him. "And even then, dear boy," said he, pulling a greasy little clasped black Testament out of his pocket, "we'll have him on his oath." The book had the appearance of having been stolen from some court of justice.

There being a respectable lodging-house in Essex Street, almost within hail of my windows, I went there and was so fortunate as to secure the second floor for my uncle, Mr. Provis. I then went from shop to shop, making such purchases as were necessary to change his appearance. This business transacted, I turned my face, on my own account, to Little Britain. Mr. Jaggers was at his desk, but seeing me enter, got up immediately and stood before his fire.

"Now, Pip," said he, "be careful."

"I will, sir," I returned.

"Don't commit yourself," said Mr. Jaggers, "and don't commit anyone. You understand — anyone."

Of course I saw that he knew the man had come.

"I merely want, Mr. Jaggers," said I, "to assure myself what I have been told is true. I have been informed by a person named Abel Magwitch that he is the benefactor so long unknown to me."

"That is the man," said Mr. Jaggers, " — in New South Wales." [1]

[1] **New South Wales:** now a state in Australia; formerly a territory to which many convicts were transported, or exiled. Magwitch, as a desperate criminal, had been sentenced to transportation for life.

many. Still, look'ee here, Pip. If the danger had been fifty times as great, I should ha' come to see you, mind you, just the same."

"And how long do you remain?"

"How long?" said he, taking his black pipe from his mouth and dropping his jaw as he stared at me. "I'm not a-going back. I've come for good."

"Where are you to live?" said I. "What is to be done with you? Where will you be safe?"

"Dear boy," he returned, "there's disguising wigs can be bought for money, and there's hair powder, and spectacles, and black clothes — and what not. As to the where and how of living, dear boy, give me your own opinions on it."

"And only he?" said I.

"And only he," said Mr. Jaggers.

"I am not so unreasonable, sir, as to think you at all responsible for my wrong conclusions; but I always supposed it was Miss Havisham."

"As you say, Pip," returned Mr. Jaggers, "I am not at all responsible for that."

"And yet it looked so like it, sir," I pleaded with a downcast heart.

"Not a particle of evidence, Pip," said Mr. Jaggers. "Take nothing on its looks; take everything on evidence. There's no better rule."

"I have no more to say," said I, with a sigh, after standing silent for a little while. "I have verified my information, and there's an end."

"Quite," said Mr. Jaggers. "I communicated to Magwitch — in New South Wales — when he first wrote to me — from New South Wales — the caution that he was not at all likely to obtain a pardon and that his presenting himself in this country would be an act of felony, rendering him liable to the extreme penalty of the law. I gave Magwitch that caution," said Mr. Jaggers, looking hard at me. "I wrote it to New South Wales. He guided himself by it, no doubt."

"No doubt," said I.

"I have been informed by Wemmick," pursued Mr. Jaggers, still looking hard at me, "that he has received a letter, from a colonist of the name of Purvis, or — "

"Or Provis," I suggested.

"Or Provis — thank you, Pip. Perhaps it *is* Provis? Perhaps you know it's Provis?"

"Yes," said I.

"You know it's Provis. A letter from a colonist of the name of Provis, asking for the particulars of your address, on behalf of Magwitch. Wemmick sent him the particulars, I understand, by return post. Probably it is through Provis that you have received the explanation of Magwitch — in New South Wales?"

"It came through Provis," I replied.

"Good day, Pip," said Mr. Jaggers, offering his hand. "Glad to have seen you. In writing by post to Magwitch — in New South Wales — or in communicating with him through Provis, have the goodness to mention that the particulars and vouchers [1] of our long account shall be sent to you, together with the balance; for there is still a balance remaining. Good day, Pip!"

Next day the clothes I had ordered came, and Provis put them on, but there was something in him that made it hopeless to attempt to disguise him. The more I dressed him, and the better I dressed him, the more he looked like the slouching fugitive on the marshes. He dragged one of his legs as if there were still a weight of iron on it, and from head to foot there was convict in the very grain of the man.

For five days, expecting Herbert all the time, I dared not go out except when I took Provis for an airing after dark. At length, one evening when dinner was over I was roused by the welcome footstep on the staircase. Provis, who had been asleep too, staggered up at the noise I made, and in an instant I saw his jackknife shining in his hand.

"Quiet! It's Herbert!" I said.

"Handel, my dear fellow, how are you, and again how are you, and again how are you? I seem to have been gone a twelvemonth! Why, so I must have been, for you have grown quite thin and pale! Handel, my — Halloa! I beg your pardon."

He was stopped in his running on

[1] **vouchers:** receipts for payment of debt.

and in his shaking hands with me, by seeing Provis. Provis, regarding him with a fixed attention, was slowly putting up his jackknife and groping in another pocket for something else.

"Herbert, my dear friend," said I, shutting the double doors, while Herbert stood staring and wondering, "something very strange has happened. This is — a visitor of mine."

"It's all right, dear boy!" said Provis, coming forward, with his little clasped black book, and then addressing himself to Herbert. "Take it in your right hand. Lord strike you dead on the spot if ever you split in any way sumever. Kiss it!"

"Do so, as he wishes it," I said to Herbert. So Herbert, looking at me with a friendly uneasiness and amazement, complied, and Provis immediately shaking hands with him, said, "Now, you're on your oath, you know. And never believe me on mine, if Pip shan't make a gentleman on you!"

CHAPTER 30

Two men, named Compeyson and Arthur, step out of the past.

In vain should I attempt to describe the astonishment and disquiet of Herbert, when he and I and Provis sat down before the fire, and I recounted the whole of the secret. Enough that I saw my own feelings reflected in Herbert's face, and, not least among them, my repugnance toward the man who had done so much for me.

"Look'ee here, Pip's comrade," he said to Herbert, after having discoursed for some time, "I know very well that once since I come back I've been low. But don't you fret yourself on that score. I ain't made Pip a gentleman, and Pip ain't a-goin' to make you a gentleman, not fur me not to know what's due to ye both."

Herbert said, "Certainly," but remained perplexed and dismayed. We were anxious for the time when he would go to his lodging and leave us together, but it was midnight before I saw him safely in at his own dark door. When it closed upon him, I experienced the first moment of relief I had known since the night of his arrival.

Herbert received me with open arms, and I had never felt before so blessedly what it is to have a friend. When he had spoken some sound words of sympathy and encouragement, we tried to consider the question of what was to be done.

"What," said I to Herbert, "what is to be done? He is intent upon various new expenses — horses, and carriages, and lavish appearances of all kinds. He must be stopped somehow."

"You mean that you can't accept — "

"How can I?" I interposed, as Herbert paused. "Think of him! Look at him!"

An involuntary shudder passed over both of us.

"Then," said I, "after all, stopping short here, never taking another penny from him, think what I owe him already! Then again, I am heavily in debt — very heavily for me, who have now no expectations — and I have been bred to no calling, and I am fit for nothing."

"Well, well, well!" Herbert remonstrated. "Don't say fit for nothing. You might go into Clarriker's house, small as it is. I am working up toward a partnership, you know."

Poor fellow! He little suspected with whose money.

"But there is another question," said Herbert. "This is an ignorant determined man, who has long had one fixed idea. More than that, he seems to me (I may misjudge him) to be a man of a desperate and fierce character. Think of this! He comes here at the peril of his life, for the realization of his fixed idea. After all his toil and waiting, you destroy his idea, and make his gains worthless to him. Do you see nothing that he might do under the disappointment?"

"I have seen it, Herbert. Nothing has been in my thoughts so distinctly as his putting himself in the way of being taken."

"Then you may rely upon it," said Herbert. "That would be his reckless course if you forsook him. The first and the main thing to be done is to get him out of England. You will have to go with him, and then he may be induced to go. That done, extricate yourself, in Heaven's name, and we'll see it out together, dear old boy."

Provis came round at breakfast time, took out his jackknife, and sat down to his meal. He was full of lavish plans for my future and urged me to begin speedily upon the pocketbook, which he had left in my possession. When he had made an end of his breakfast, and was wiping his knife on his leg, I said to him, without a word of preface:

"After you were gone last night, I told my friend of the struggle that the soldiers found you engaged in on the marshes. You remember?"

"Remember!" said he. "I think so!"

"We want to know something about that man — and about you. It is strange to know no more about either, and particularly you, than I was able to tell last night. Is not this as good a time as an-other for our knowing more?"

"Well," he said, after consideration. "You're on your oath, you know, Pip's comrade?"

"Assuredly," replied Herbert.

"And look'ee here! Wotever I done, is worked out and paid for," he insisted again.

He stuck his pipe in a buttonhole of his coat, spread a hand on each knee, and, after turning an angry eye on the fire for a few silent moments, looked around at us and said what follows:

"Dear boy and Pip's comrade, I am not a-going fur to tell you my life, like a song or a storybook. But to give it you short and handy, I'll put it at once into a mouthful of English. In jail and out of jail, in jail and out of jail, in jail and out of jail. There, you've got it. That's *my* life pretty much, down to such times as I got shipped off, arter Pip stood my friend.

"I've been done everything to, pretty well — except hanged. I've been locked up, and stuck in the stocks, and whipped and worried and drove. I've no notion where I was born. I knowed my name to be Magwitch, christened Abel, that's all I knowed. So fur as I could find, there warn't a soul that see young Abel Magwitch, with as little in him as on him, but wot caught fright at him, and either drove him off or put him under arrest. When I was a ragged little creetur as much to be pitied as ever I see, I got the name of being hardened. 'This is a terrible hardened one,' they says to prison wisitors, picking out me. 'May be said to live in jails, this boy.' They always went on agen me about the Devil. But what the devil was I to do? I must put something into my stomach, mustn't I?

"Tramping, begging, thieving, working sometimes when I could — though that warn't as often as you may think, till you put the question whether you would ha' been overready to give me work yourselves — a bit of a poacher, a bit of a laborer, a bit of a wagoner, a bit of a haymaker, a bit of a hawker,[1] a bit of most things that don't pay and lead to trouble, I got to be a man.

"At Epsom races, a matter of over twenty year ago, I got acquainted wi' a man whose skull I'd crack wi' this poker, like the claw of a lobster, if I'd got it on this hob. His right name was Compeyson; and that's the man, dear boy, what you see me a-pounding in the ditch. He set up fur a gentleman, this Compeyson, and had learning. He was a smooth one to talk and imitated the ways of gentlefolk. He was good-looking too.

"Compeyson took me on to be his man and pardner. And what was Compeyson's business in which we was to go pardners? Compeyson's business was the swindling, handwriting forging, stolen bank-note passing, and suchlike. All sorts of traps as Compeyson could set with his head, and let another man in for, was Compeyson's business. He'd no more heart than a iron file, he was as cold as death, and he had the head of the Devil.

"There was another man in with Compeyson, as was called Arthur. Him and Compeyson had been in a bad thing with a rich lady some years afore, and they made a pot of money by it; but Compeyson betted and gamed it all away. So, Arthur was a-dying and a-dying poor and with the horrors on him, and Compeyson's wife was having pity on him when she could and Compeyson was a-having pity on nothing and nobody.

"I might a-took warning by Arthur, but I didn't. I begun wi' Compeyson,

[1] hawker: a peddler.

and a poor tool I was in his hands. Arthur lived at the top of Compeyson's house. The second or third time as ever I see him, he came a-tearing down into Compeyson's parlor late at night, in only a flannel gown, with his hair all in a sweat, and he says to Compeyson's wife, 'Sally, she really is upstairs along-er me, now, and I can't get rid of her. She's all in white,' he says, 'wi' white flowers in her hair, and she's got a shroud hanging over her arm, and she says she'll put it on me at five in the morning.'

"Says Compeyson: 'Why, you fool, she's alive! How should she be up there, without coming through the door, or in at the window, and up the stairs?'

"'I don't know how she's there,' says Arthur, shivering dreadful with the horrors, 'but she's standing in the corner at the foot of the bed. And over where her heart's broke — you broke it! — there's drops of blood.'

"Compeyson's wife and me took him up to bed agen, and he raved most dreadful. 'Why, look at her!' he cries out. 'She's a-shaking the shroud at me! She'll put it on me, and then I'm done for! Take it away from her, take it away!' And then he kept on talking to her, and answering of her, till I half believed I see her myself.

"He rested pretty quiet a few minutes and then he screams out, 'Here she is! She's got the shroud again. She's unfolding it. She's coming out of the corner. She's coming to the bed. Hold me, both of you — one on each side — don't let her touch me with it.' Then he lifted himself up hard, and was dead.

"Compeyson took it easy as a good riddance for both sides. Him and me was soon busy, and I'll simply say to you, dear boy, and Pip's comrade, that that man got me into such nets as made me his slave. I was always in debt to him, always under his thumb, always a-working, always a-getting into danger. My missis as I had the hard time wi' — Stop though! I ain't brought *her* in —"

He looked about him in a confused way, turned his face to the fire, and spread his hands broader on his knees. "There ain't no need to go into it," he said, looking round once more. "At last, me and Compeyson was both committed for felony — on a charge of putting stolen notes in circulation. Compeyson says to me, 'Separate defenses, no communication,'[1] and that was all. And I was so miserable poor that I sold all the clothes I had, except what hung on my back, afore I could get Jaggers.

"When he was put in the dock,[2] I noticed first of all what a gentleman Compeyson looked, wi' his curly hair and his black clothes and his white pocket handkercher, and what a common sort of a wretch I looked. When the prosecution opened, I noticed how heavy it all bore on me, and how light on him. When the evidence was give in the box,[3] I noticed how it was always me that had come for'ard, and could be swore to, how it was always me that the money had been paid to, how it was always me that had seemed to work the thing and get the profit. But when the defense come on, then I see the plan plainer; for, says the counselor for Compeyson, 'My lord and gentlemen, here you have afore you, side by side, two persons as your eyes can separate wide; one well brought up, one ill brought up.'

"And when the verdict come, warn't it Compeyson as was recommended to mercy on account of good character and bad company, and giving up all the information he could agen me, and warn't it me as got never a word but guilty? And when I says to Compeyson, 'Once out of this court, I'll smash that face of yours!' ain't it Compeyson as prays the judge to be protected, and gets two turnkeys stood betwixt us? And when we're sentenced, ain't it him as gets seven year, and me fourteen, and ain't it him as the judge is sorry for, because he might a-done so well, and ain't it me as the judge perceives to be a old offender of wiolent passion, likely to come to worse?"

He had worked himself into a state of great excitement, but he checked it, and stretching out his hand toward me, said, "I ain't a-going to be low, dear boy!

"We was in the same prison ship, but I couldn't get at him for long, though I tried. At last I come behind him and hit him on the cheek to turn him round and get a smashing one at him, when I was seen and seized. The black hole[4] of that ship warn't a strong one. I escaped to the shore, and I was a-hiding among the graves there, envying them as was in 'em and all over, when I first see my boy!"

He regarded me with a look of affection that made him almost abhorrent to me again, though I had felt great pity for him.

"By my boy, I was give to understand as Compeyson was out on them marshes too. Upon my soul, I half believe he escaped in his terror to get quit of me, not knowing it was me as had got ashore. I hunted him down. I smashed his face. 'And now,' says I, 'as

[1] **Separate . . . communication:** each man would handle his own case and there would be no communication between them while defending themselves.
[2] **dock:** the place where prisoners stand before the court.
[3] **box:** the witness chair, as it would be called in American courts.

[4] **black hole:** a lockup room or cell.

the worst thing I can do, caring nothing for myself, I'll drag you back.' And I'd have swum off, towing him by the hair, if it had come to that, and I'd a got him aboard without the soldiers.

"Of course he'd much the best of it to the last and his punishment was light. I was put in irons, brought to trial again, and sent for life. I didn't stop for life, dear boy and Pip's comrade, being here."

He slowly took his tangle of tobacco from his pocket, plucked his pipe from his buttonhole, slowly filled it, and began to smoke.

"Is he dead?" I asked after a silence.

"Is who dead, dear boy?"

"Compeyson."

"He hopes *I* am, if he's alive, you may be sure," with a fierce look. "I never heard no more of him."

Herbert had been writing with his pencil in the cover of a book. He softly pushed the book over to me, as Provis stood smoking with his eyes on the fire, and I read in it:

"Young Havisham's name was Arthur. Compeyson is the man who professed to be Miss Havisham's lover."

I shut the book and nodded slightly to Herbert, and put the book by; but we neither of us said anything, and both looked at Provis as he stood smoking by the fire.

CHAPTER 31

Pip and Drummle exchange
sharp words.

A NEW fear had entered in my mind at Provis' narrative. If Compeyson were alive and should discover his return, I could hardly doubt the consequence.

That Compeyson would hesitate to release himself for good from a dreaded enemy by the safe means of becoming an informer, was scarcely to be imagined.

Never had I breathed, and never would I breathe — or so I resolved — a word of Estella to Provis. But I said to Herbert that before I could go abroad, I must see both Estella and Miss Havisham. On my presenting myself at Mrs. Brandley's, Estella's maid was called to tell me that Estella had gone into the country. Where? To Satis House. She had never gone there before without me, and I went home again in complete discouragement.

Next day, I had the meanness to pretend that I was under a binding promise to go down to Joe. Provis was to be strictly careful while I was gone, and Herbert was to take the charge of him that I had taken.

Having thus cleared the way for my expedition to Miss Havisham's, I set off by the early morning coach, and when we drove up to the Blue Boar, whom should I see come out under the gateway, toothpick in hand, to look at the coach, but Bentley Drummle!

As he pretended not to see me, I pretended not to see him. It was a very lame pretense on both sides; the lamer because we both went into the coffee-room. I sat at my table while he stood before the fire. By degrees it became an enormous injury to me that he stood there enjoying the fire, and I got up, determined to have my share of it. I had to put my hands behind his legs for the poker when I went up to the fireplace to stir the fire, but still pretended not to know him.

"Is this a cut?" [1] said Mr. Drummle.

"Oh?" said I, poker in hand. "It's you, is it? How do you do? I was wondering

[1] a cut: a refusal to recognize a person.

who it was who kept the fire off."

With that I poked tremendously, and having done so, planted myself side by side with Mr. Drummle, my shoulders squared, and my back to the fire.

"Large tract of marshes about here, I believe?" said Drummle.

"Yes. What of that?" said I.

Mr. Drummle looked at me and laughed.

"Are you amused, Mr. Drummle?"

"No," said he, "not particularly. I am going out for a ride in the saddle. I mean to explore those marshes for amusement. Out-of-the-way villages there, they tell me. Curious little public houses — and smithies [1] — and that. Waiter!"

"Yes, sir."

"Is that horse of mine ready?"

"Brought round to the door, sir."

"I say. Look here. The lady won't ride today; the weather won't do."

"Very good, sir."

"And I don't dine, because I am going to dine at the lady's."

"Very good, sir."

Then Drummle glanced at me with an insolent triumph. One thing was manifest to both of us, and that was that until relief came, neither of us could relinquish the fire. There we stood, well squared up before it, shoulder to shoulder and foot to foot, with our hands behind us, not budging an inch.

After glancing at him once or twice, in an increased state of smoldering anger, I said:

"Mr. Drummle, I did not seek this conversation, and I don't think it's an agreeable one."

"I am sure it's not," said he over his shoulder.

"And therefore," I went on, "with your leave, I will suggest that we hold

[1] smithies: blacksmith shops.

Pip and Drummle.

no kind of communication in future."

"Quite my opinion," said Drummle. "But don't lose your temper. Haven't you lost enough without that?"

"What do you mean, sir?"

"Waiter," said Drummle, by way of answering me.

The waiter reappeared.

"Look here, you sir. You quite understand that the young lady don't ride today, and that I dine at the young lady's?"

"Quite so, sir!"

He left abruptly, and I saw him through the window, seizing his horse's mane, mounting in his blundering brutal manner, and calling for a light for the cigar in his mouth. A man in a dust-colored dress appeared, and as Drummle leaned down from the saddle and lighted his cigar and laughed, with a jerk of his head toward the coffeeroom windows, the slouching shoulders and ragged hair of this man, whose back was toward me, reminded me of Orlick.

Too heavily out of sorts to care, I washed the weather and the journey from my face and hands and went out to the memorable old house that it would have been so much the better for me never to have entered, never to have seen.

In the room where the dressing table stood, and where the wax candles burned on the wall, I found Miss Havisham and Estella; Miss Havisham seated on a settee near the fire, and Estella on a cushion at her feet. Estella was knitting and Miss Havisham was looking on. They both raised their eyes as I went in, and both saw an alteration in me. I derived that from the look they interchanged.

"And what wind," said Miss Havisham, "blows you here, Pip?"

Though she looked steadily at me, I saw that she was rather confused. Estella paused a moment in her knitting with her eyes upon me.

"Miss Havisham," said I, "I went to Richmond yesterday to speak to Estella; and finding that some wind had blown *her* here, I followed. What I had to say to Estella, Miss Havisham, I will say before you presently — in a few moments. It will not surprise you; it will not displease you. I am as unhappy as you can ever have meant me to be."

Miss Havisham continued to look steadily at me. I could see in the action of Estella's fingers as they worked that she attended to what I said, but she did not look up.

"I have found out who my patron is. It is not a fortunate discovery, and is not likely ever to enrich me in reputation, station, fortune, anything. There are reasons why I must say no more of that. It is not my secret, but another's. When you first caused me to be brought here, Miss Havisham; when I belonged to the village over yonder, that I wish I had never left; I suppose I did really come here, as any other chance boy might have come — as a kind of servant, to gratify a want or a whim, and to be paid for it?"

"Aye, Pip," replied Miss Havisham, steadily nodding her head, "you did."

"And that Mr. Jaggers —"

"Mr. Jaggers," said Miss Havisham, taking me up in a firm tone, "had nothing to do with it, and knew nothing of it. His being my lawyer, and his being the lawyer of your patron is a coincidence."

"But when I fell into the mistake I have so long remained in, at least you led me on?" said I.

"Yes," she returned, again nodding steadily, "I let you go on."

"Was that kind?"

"Who am I," cried Miss Havisham, striking her stick upon the floor and flashing into wrath so suddenly that Estella glanced up at her in surprise, "who am I that I should be kind?"

"I was liberally paid for my old attendance here," I said, to soothe her, "in being apprenticed, and I have asked these questions only for my own information. What follows has another purpose. In humoring my mistake, Miss Havisham, you punished your self-seeking relations?"

"I did. Why, they would have it so! So would you. You made your own snares. *I* never made them."

Waiting until she was quiet again — for this, too, flashed out of her in a wild and sudden way — I went on.

"I have been thrown among one family of your relations, Miss Havisham, since I went to London. And I should be false and base if I did not tell you that you deeply wrong both Mr. Matthew Pocket and his son Herbert, if you suppose them to be otherwise than generous, upright, open, and incapable of anything designing or mean."

"They are your friends," said Miss Havisham.

"They made themselves my friends," said I, "when Sarah Pocket, Miss Georgiana, and Mistress Camilla were not my friends, I think."

This contrasting of them with the rest seemed, I was glad to see, to do them good with her. She looked at me keenly for a little while, and then said quietly:

"What do you want for them?"

"I do want something, Miss Havisham. If you could spare the money to do my friend Herbert a lasting service in life, but which from the nature of the case must be done without his knowledge, I could show you how."

"Why must it be done without his knowledge?" she asked, settling her hands upon her stick that she might regard me the more attentively.

"Because," said I, "I began the service myself, more than two years ago, without his knowledge, and I don't want to be betrayed. Why I fail in my ability to finish it, I cannot explain. It is a part of the secret which is another person's and not mine."

"What else?"

"Estella," said I, turning to her now, and trying to command my trembling voice, "you know I love you. You know that I have loved you long and dearly."

She raised her eyes to my face on being thus addressed, and her fingers plied their work, and she looked at me with an unmoved countenance. I saw that Miss Havisham glanced from me to her, and from her to me.

"I should have said this sooner, but for my long mistake. It induced me to hope that Miss Havisham meant us for one another. But I must say it now."

Preserving her unmoved countenance, and with her fingers still going, Estella shook her head.

"I know," said I, in answer to that action; "I know. I have no hope that I shall ever call you mine, Estella. I am ignorant what may become of me very soon, how poor I may be, or where I may go. Still, I love you. I have loved you ever since I first saw you in this house."

Looking at me perfectly unmoved and with her fingers busy, she shook her head again.

"It would have been cruel in Miss Havisham to torture me through all these years with a vain hope and an idle pursuit, if she had reflected on the gravity of what she did. But I think she did not. I think that in the endurance of her own trial, she forgot mine, Estella."

I saw Miss Havisham put her hand to her heart and hold it there, as she sat looking by turns at Estella and at me.

"It seems," said Estella very calmly, "that there are sentiments, fancies — I don't know how to call them — which I am not able to comprehend. When you say you love me, I know what you mean, as a form of words, but nothing more. You address nothing in my breast, you touch nothing there."

"Is it not true," said I, "that Bentley Drummle is in town here, and pursuing you?"

"It is quite true," she replied, referring to him with the indifference of utter contempt.

"That you encourage him, and ride out with him, and that he dines with you this very day?"

She seemed a little surprised that I should know it, but again replied, "Quite true."

"You cannot love him, Estella?"

Her fingers stopped for the first time, as she retorted rather angrily, "What have I told you? Do you still think, in spite of it, that I do not mean what I say?"

"You would never marry him, Estella?"

She looked toward Miss Havisham. Then she said, "Why not tell you the truth? I am going to be married to him."

I dropped my face into my hands, but was able to control myself better than I could have expected, considering what agony it gave me to hear her say those words.

"Estella, dearest, dearest Estella, do not let Miss Havisham lead you into this fatal step. Put me aside forever — you have done so, I well know — but bestow yourself on some worthier person than Drummle. Miss Havisham gives you to him, as the greatest slight and injury that could be done to the many far better men who admire you, and to the few who truly love you. Among those few, there may be one who loves you even as dearly, though he has not loved you as long, as I. Take him, and I can bear it better for your sake!"

My earnestness awoke a wonder in her.

"I am going," she said again, in a gentler voice, "to be married to him. The preparations for my marriage are making, and I shall be married soon. I shall do well enough, and so will my husband. As to leading me into what you call this fatal step, Miss Havisham would have had me wait, and not marry yet; but I am tired of the life I have led, which has very few charms for me, and I am willing enough to change it. Say no more. We shall never understand each other."

"Such a mean brute, such a stupid brute!" I urged in despair.

"Don't be afraid of my being a blessing to him," said Estella. "I shall not be that. Come! Here is my hand."

"Oh, Estella!" I answered, as my bitter tears fell fast on her hand, do what I would to restrain them. "Even if I remained in England and could hold my head up with the rest, how could I see you Drummle's wife?"

"Nonsense," she returned, "nonsense. This will pass in no time."

"Never, Estella!"

"You will get me out of your thoughts in a week."

"Out of my thoughts! You are part of my existence, part of myself. You have been in every line I have ever read, since I first came here, the rough common boy whose poor heart you wounded even then. Estella, to the last hour of my life, you cannot choose but remain part of my character, part of the little good in me, part of the evil. But I associate you only with the good, for you must have done me far more good than harm. Oh, God bless you, God forgive you!"

I held her hand to my lips some lingering moments, and so I left her. But afterward, I remembered that the spectral figure of Miss Havisham, her hand still covering her heart, seemed all resolved into a ghastly stare of pity and remorse.

It was past midnight when I crossed London Bridge. I was not expected till tomorrow, but I had my keys, and, if Herbert were gone to bed, could get to bed myself without disturbing him.

The night porter examined me with much attention as he held the gate a little way open for me to pass in. To help his memory I mentioned my name.

"I was not quite sure, sir, but I thought so. Here's a note, sir. The messenger that brought it said would you be so good as to read it by my lantern?"

Much surprised by the request, I took the note. It was directed to Philip Pip, Esquire, and on the top of the superscription were the words, "PLEASE READ THIS HERE." I opened it, the watchman holding up his light, and read inside, in Wemmick's writing:

"DON'T GO HOME."

CHAPTER 32

Pip meets Clara, Herbert's fiancée.

TURNING from the Temple gate as soon as I had read the warning, I made the best of the way to Fleet Street, and there got a late hackney [1] and drove to Covent Garden, where I secured a room for the night. The porter lighted the candle next in order on his shelf, and showed me straight into the bedroom next on his list.

What a doleful night! How anxious, how dismal, how long! The closet whispered, the fireplace sighed, the little washstand ticked, and one guitar string played occasionally in the chest of drawers. Why I was not to go home, and what had happened at home, and when I should go home, and whether Provis was safe at home, were questions occupying my mind so busily that one might have supposed there could be no more room in it for any other

[1] **hackney:** a horse-drawn cab.

theme. Even when I thought of Estella, and how we had parted that day forever, I was pursuing here and there and everywhere the caution DON'T GO HOME. At last I dozed, in sheer exhaustion of mind and body.

I had left directions that I was to be called at seven; for it was plain that I must see Wemmick before seeing anyone else, and equally plain that this was a case in which his Walworth sentiments only could be taken.

The Castle battlements arose upon my view at eight o'clock. The little servant happening to be entering the fortress with two hot rolls, I crossed the drawbridge in her company and so came without announcement into the presence of Wemmick as he was making tea for himself and the Aged.

"Halloa, Mr. Pip!" said Wemmick. "You did come home, then?"

"Yes," I returned, "but I didn't go home."

"That's all right," said he, rubbing his hands. "I left a note for you at each of the Temple gates, on the chance. Which gate did you come to?"

I told him.

"I'll go round to the others in the course of the day and destroy the notes," said Wemmick. "It's a good rule never to leave documentary evidence [2] if you can help it. Now, Mr. Pip, you and I understand one another. I accidentally heard, yesterday morning, that a certain person not altogether of uncolonial pursuits, and not unpossessed of portable property — we won't name this person — "

"Not necessary," said I.

" — this person had made some little stir by disappearing from a certain part of the world and being no more heard of thereabouts. I also have heard that

[2] **documentary evidence:** written or printed evidence.

you at your chambers in Garden Court, Temple, had been watched, and might be watched again."

"By whom?" said I.

"I wouldn't go into that," said Wemmick evasively. "It might clash with official responsibilities. I heard it."

I saw that he was restrained by loyalty to Little Britain from saying as much as he could. But I told him, after a little meditation over the fire, that I would like to ask him a question, subject to his answering or not answering, as he deemed right.

"You have heard of a man of bad character, whose true name is Compeyson?"

He answered with one nod.

"Is he living?"

One other nod.

"Is he in London?"

He gave me one last nod and went on with his breakfast.

"Now," said Wemmick, "questioning being over," which he emphasized and repeated for my guidance; "I come to what I did, after hearing what I heard. I went to Garden Court to find you; not finding you, I went to Clarriker's to find Mr. Herbert."

"And you found him?" said I, with great anxiety.

"And I found him. Without mentioning any names or going into any details, I gave him to understand that if he was aware of anybody — Tom, Jack, or Richard — being about the chambers, or about the immediate neighborhood, he had better get Tom, Jack, or Richard out of the way while you were out of the way."

"He would be greatly puzzled what to do?"

"He *was* puzzled what to do; not the less because I gave him my opinion that it was not safe to try to get Tom, Jack, or Richard too far out of the way at present. Mr. Pip, I'll tell you something. Under existing circumstances there is no place like a great city when you are once in it. Don't break cover too soon. Lie close. Wait till things slacken before you try the open, even for foreign air."

I thanked him for his valuable advice, and asked him what Herbert had done.

"Mr. Herbert," said Wemmick, "after being all of a heap for half an hour, struck out a plan. He mentioned to me as a secret that he is courting a young lady who has, as no doubt you are aware, a bedridden pa. Which pa, having been in the shipping line of life, lies a-bed in a bow window where he can see the ships sail up and down the river. You are acquainted with the young lady, most probably?"

"Not personally," said I.

"The house with the bow window," said Wemmick, "being kept, it seems, by a very respectable widow, who has a furnished upper floor to let, Mr. Herbert put it to me, what did I think of that as a temporary tenement for Tom, Jack, or Richard? Now, I thought very well of it, for three reasons. Firstly. It is well out of the way. Secondly. Without going near it yourself, you could always hear of the safety of Tom, Jack, or Richard. Thirdly. After a while, and when it might be prudent, if you should want to slip Tom, Jack, or Richard on board a packet boat,[1] there he is — ready."

Much comforted by these considerations, I thanked Wemmick again and again, and begged him to proceed.

"Well, sir! Mr. Herbert threw himself into the business with a will, and by nine o'clock last night he housed Tom, Jack, or Richard — whichever it may

---

[1] **packet boat:** a boat, in this instance a steam-driven, paddle-wheeled boat which carried mail and passengers from England to the Continent.

be — you and I don't want to know — quite successfully. At the old lodgings it was understood that he was summoned to Dover. Now, another advantage of all this is that it was done without you. This diverts suspicion and brings confusion, and you want confusion."

Wemmick, having finished his breakfast, here looked at his watch, and began to get his coat on.

"And now, Mr. Pip," said he, with his hands still in the sleeves, "I have probably done the most I can do. Here's the address. There can be no harm in your going here tonight and seeing for yourself that all is well with Tom, Jack, or Richard, before you go home."

Eight o'clock had struck before I got into the air that was scented, not disagreeably, by the chips and shavings of the longshore boatbuilders, and mast, oar, and blockmakers. All that waterside region of the upper and lower Pool below London Bridge was unknown ground to me, and when I struck down by the river, I found that the spot I wanted was anything but easy to find. It was called Mill Pond Bank, Chinks's Basin; and I had no other guide to Chinks's Basin than the Old Green Copper Rope-Walk.

Selecting from the few queer houses upon Mill Pond Bank a house with a wooden front and three stories of bow window, I looked at the plate upon the door, and read there Mrs. Whimple. That being the name I wanted, I knocked, and an elderly woman of a pleasant and thriving appearance responded. She was immediately deposed, however, by Herbert, who silently led me into the parlor and shut the door.

"All is well, Handel," said Herbert, "and he is quite satisfied, though eager to see you. My dear girl is with her father, and if you'll wait till she comes down, I'll make you known to her, and then we'll go upstairs. — *That's* her father."

I had become aware of an alarming growling overhead, and had probably expressed the fact in my countenance.

"I am afraid he is a sad old rascal," said Herbert, smiling, "but I have never seen him. Don't you smell rum? He is always at it." While he spoke, the growling noise became a prolonged roar, and died away.

"To have Provis for an upper lodger is quite a godsend to Mrs. Whimple," said Herbert, "for of course people in general won't stand that noise."

As we were thus conversing, a very pretty, slight, dark-eyed girl of twenty or so came in, and Herbert presented her proudly, as "Clara." There was something confiding, loving, and innocent in her modest manner of yielding herself to Herbert's embracing arm. I was looking at her with pleasure and admiration when suddenly the growl swelled into a roar again, and a frightful bumping noise was made on the ceiling. Upon this, Clara said to Herbert, "Papa wants me, darling!" and ran away.

Clara returned soon afterward, and Herbert accompanied me upstairs to see our charge. I found Provis comfortably settled. He expressed no alarm, and seemed to feel none that was worth mentioning; but it struck me that he was softened in some indefinable way. I was fully determined to say nothing to him respecting Compeyson. For anything I knew, his hatred of the man might otherwise lead to his seeking him out and rushing on his own destruction. Therefore, when Herbert and I sat down with him by his fire, I asked him first of all whether he relied on Wemmick's judgment and sources of information.

"Aye, aye, dear boy!" he answered with a grave nod. "Jaggers knows."

"Then I have talked with Wemmick," said I, "and have come to tell you what caution he gave me and what advice."

I told him how Wemmick had heard in Newgate Prison that he was under suspicion, and that my chambers had been watched; how Wemmick had recommended his keeping close for a time, and my keeping away from him; and what Wemmick had said about getting him abroad. I added that of course I should go with him. What was to follow that, I did not touch upon; neither indeed was I at all clear or comfortable about it in my own mind, now that I saw him in that softer condition, and in great peril for my sake.

He was very reasonable throughout. His coming to England was a venture, he said, and he had always known it to be a venture, and he had very little fear of his safety with such good help.

Herbert, who had been looking at the fire and pondering, here said, "We are both good watermen, Handel, and could take him down the river ourselves when the right time comes. No boat would then be hired for the purpose, and no boatmen; that would save at least a chance of suspicion, and any chance is worth saving. Don't you think it might be a good thing if you began at once to keep a boat at the Temple stairs, and were in the habit of rowing up and down the river? You fall into that habit, and then who notices or minds? Do it twenty or fifty times, and there is nothing special in your doing it the twenty-first or fifty-first."

I liked this scheme, and Provis was quite elated by it. We agreed that it should be carried into execution, and that Provis should never recognize us if we came below London Bridge and rowed past Mill Pond Bank. But we further agreed that he should pull down the blind in that part of his window which faced upon the east whenever he saw us and all was right.

Our conference being now ended, and everything arranged, I rose to go, remarking to Herbert that he and I had better not go home together, and that I would take half an hour's start of him. "I don't like to leave you here," I said to Provis, "though I cannot doubt your being safer here than near me. Good-by!"

"Dear boy," he answered, clasping my hands, "I don't know when we may meet again, and I don't like good-by. Say good night!"

"Good night! Herbert will go regularly between us, and when the time comes, you may be certain I shall be ready. Good night, good night!" Looking back at him, I thought of the first night of his return, when our positions were reversed, and when I little supposed my heart could ever be as heavy and anxious at parting from him as it was now.

Next day, I set myself to get the boat. It was soon done, and the boat was brought round to the Temple stairs, and lay where I could reach her within a minute or two. Then I began to go out as for training and practice, sometimes alone, sometimes with Herbert. I was often out in cold, rain, and sleet, but nobody took much note of me after I had been out a few times. At first, I kept above Blackfriars Bridge; but as the hours of the tide changed, I took toward London Bridge. The first time I passed Mill Pond Bank, Herbert and I were pulling a pair of oars; and, both in going and returning, we saw the blind toward the east come down. Herbert was rarely there less frequently than three times in a week, and he never brought me a single word of news that was at all alarming.

Still, I was always full of fears for the rash man who was in hiding. Herbert had sometimes said to me that he found it pleasant to stand at one of our windows after dark, when the tide was running down, and to think that it was flowing, with everything it bore, toward Clara. But I thought with dread that it was flowing toward Magwitch, and that any black mark on its surface might be his pursuers, going swiftly, silently, and surely to take him.

CHAPTER 33

Wemmick tells Pip the story of Molly.

SOME weeks passed without bringing any change. We waited for Wemmick, and he made no sign. My worldly affairs began to wear a gloomy appearance, and I was pressed for money by more than one creditor. Even I myself began to know the want of ready money in my own pocket, and to relieve it by converting some easily spared articles of jewelry into cash. But I had quite determined that it would be a heartless fraud to take more money from my patron in the existing state of my uncertain thoughts and plans. Therefore, I had sent him the unopened pocketbook by Herbert, to hold in his own keeping, and I felt a kind of satisfaction in not having profited by his generosity since his revelation of himself.

It was an unhappy life that I lived. Condemned to inaction and a state of constant restlessness and suspense, I rowed about in my boat, and waited, waited, waited, as I best could.

One afternoon, late in February, I came ashore at the wharf at dusk. I had pulled down as far as Greenwich with the ebb tide and had turned with the tide. It had been a fine bright day, but had become foggy as the sun dropped, and I had had to feel my way back among the shipping pretty carefully. Both in going and returning, I had seen the signal in his window, all well.

I had strolled up into Cheapside when a large hand was laid upon my shoulder, by someone overtaking me. It was Mr. Jaggers' hand, and he passed it through my arm.

"As we are going in the same direction, Pip, we may walk together. Come and dine with me."

I was going to excuse myself, when he added, "Wemmick's coming." So I changed my excuse into an acceptance.

"Did you send that note of Miss Havisham's to Mr. Pip, Wemmick?" Mr. Jaggers asked, soon after we began dinner in his house, once again in the dark brown room on the first floor.

"No, sir," returned Wemmick; "it was going by post, when you brought Mr. Pip into the office. Here it is." He handed it to his principal, instead of to me.

"It's a note of two lines, Pip," said Mr. Jaggers, handing it on, "sent up to me by Miss Havisham, on account of her not being sure of your address. She tells me that she wants to see you on a little matter of business you mentioned to her. You'll go down?"

"Yes," said I, casting my eyes over the note, which was exactly in those terms.

"When do you think of going down?"

"I have an impending engagement," said I, glancing at Wemmick, "that renders me rather uncertain of my time. At once, I think."

"If Mr. Pip has the intention of going

Molly.

"So, here's to Mrs. Bentley Drummle," said Mr. Jaggers, taking a decanter of choicer wine from his dumbwaiter, and filling for each of us and for himself. "Now, Molly, Molly, Molly, Molly, how slow you are today!"

She was at his elbow when he addressed her, putting a dish upon the table. As she withdrew her hands from it, she fell back a step or two, nervously muttering some excuse. And a certain action of her fingers as she spoke arrested my attention.

"What's the matter?" said Mr. Jaggers.

"Nothing. Only the subject we were speaking of," said I, "was rather painful to me."

The action of her fingers was like the action of knitting. She stood looking at her master, not understanding whether she was free to go, or whether he had more to say to her and would call her back if she did go. Her look was very intent. Surely, I had seen exactly such eyes and such hands on a memorable occasion very lately!

He dismissed her, and she glided out of the room. But she remained before me, as plainly as if she were still there. I looked at those hands, I looked at those eyes, I looked at that flowing hair; and I compared them with other hands, other eyes, other hair, that I knew of, and with what those might be after twenty years of a brutal husband and a stormy life. I looked again at those hands and eyes of the housekeeper. And I felt absolutely certain that this woman was Estella's mother. Only twice more did the housekeeper reappear, and then her stay in the room was very short, and Mr. Jaggers was sharp with her. But her hands were Estella's hands, and her eyes were Estella's eyes, and if she had reappeared a hundred times I could have been nei-

at once," said Wemmick to Mr. Jaggers, "he needn't write an answer, you know."

Receiving this as a warning that it was best not to delay, I settled that I would go tomorrow, and said so. Wemmick drank a glass of wine and looked with a grimly satisfied air at Mr. Jaggers, but not at me.

"So, Pip! Our friend the Spider," said Mr. Jaggers, "has played his cards. He has won the pool."

It was as much as I could do to assent.

ther more sure nor less sure that my conviction was the truth.

Wemmick and I took our leave early, and left together. I asked him if he had ever seen Miss Havisham's adopted daughter, Mrs. Bentley Drummle? He said no. To avoid being too abrupt, I then spoke of the Aged, and of Miss Skiffins. He looked rather sly when I mentioned Miss Skiffins.

"Wemmick," said I, "do you remember telling me, before I first went to Mr. Jaggers' private house, to notice that housekeeper?"

"Did I?" he replied. "Ah, I dare say I did."

"I wish you would tell me her story. I feel a particular interest in being acquainted with it. You know that what is said between you and me goes no further."

"Well!" Wemmick replied. "I don't know her story—that is, I don't know all of it. But what I do know, I'll tell you. We are in our private and personal capacities, of course."

"Of course."

"A score or so of years ago that woman, known to you as Molly, was tried at the Old Bailey for murder and was acquitted. She was a very handsome young woman, and I believe had some gypsy blood in her. Anyhow, it was hot enough when it was up, as you may suppose."

"But she was acquitted."

"Mr. Jaggers was for her," pursued Wemmick, with a look full of meaning, "and worked the case in a way quite astonishing. It was a desperate case. The murdered person was a woman, a good ten years older, very much larger, and very much stronger. It was a case of jealousy. They both led tramping lives, and Molly had been married very young to a tramping man, and was a perfect fury in point of jealousy. The murdered woman—more a match for the man, certainly, in point of years—was found dead in a barn. There had been a violent struggle, perhaps a fight. She was bruised and scratched and torn, and had been held by the throat at last and choked. Now, there was reasonable evidence to implicate Molly, but it was on the physical improbability of her having been able to do it that Mr. Jaggers principally rested his case. You may be sure," said Wemmick, touching me on the sleeve, "that he never dwelt upon the strength of her hands then, though he sometimes does now."

I had told Wemmick of his showing us her wrists that day of the dinner party.

"Well, sir!" Wemmick went on. "This woman was so artfully dressed that she looked much slighter than she really was; her sleeves were so skillfully contrived that her arms had a delicate look. Yet the backs of her hands were scarred, and the question was, was it with fingernails? Now, Mr. Jaggers showed that she had struggled through a great lot of brambles and so cut her hands; and bits of those brambles were actually found in her skin and put in evidence. But the boldest point he made was this. It was attempted to be set up in proof of her jealousy that she was under strong suspicion of having, at about the time of the murder, frantically destroyed her child by this man—a child some three years old—to revenge herself upon him. Mr. Jaggers worked that charge against her in this way. 'You say that the scratches are the marks of fingernails, and we show you the brambles. Now you say that she may have destroyed her child. What then? You are not trying her for the murder of her child; why don't you? As to *this* case, the matter is irrelevant.'

"To sum up, sir," added Wemmick, "Mr. Jaggers was altogether too many for the jury, and they gave in."

"Has she been in his service ever since?"

"Yes," said Wemmick, "she went into his service immediately after her acquittal, tamed as she is now."

"Do you remember the sex of the child?"

"Said to have been a girl."

"You have nothing more to say to me tonight?"

"Nothing. I got your letter and destroyed it. Nothing."

We exchanged a cordial good night, and I went home, with new matter for my thoughts, though with no relief from the old.

CHAPTER 34

Pip visits Miss Havisham
for the last time.

PUTTING Miss Havisham's note in my pocket, I went down by coach next day. The best light of the day had gone when I passed the High Street. The cathedral chimes had at once a sadder and more remote sound to me; they seemed to call to me that the place was changed, and that Estella was gone out of it forever.

Miss Havisham was not in her own room, but was in the larger room across the landing. Looking in at the door, after knocking in vain, I saw her sitting on the hearth in a ragged chair, close before the ashy fire. I went in and stood where she could see me when she raised her eyes. There was an air of utter loneliness upon her. As I stood pitying her,

and thinking how in the progress of time I too had come to be a part of the wrecked fortunes of that house, her eyes rested on me. She stared and said in a low voice, "Is it real?"

"It is I, Pip. Mr. Jaggers gave me your note yesterday, and I have lost no time."

"Thank you. Thank you."

"I want," she said, "to pursue that subject you mentioned to me when you were last here, and to show you that I am not all stone. You said, speaking for your friend, that you could tell me how to do something useful and good. Something that you would like done, is it not?"

"Something that I would like done very, very much."

"What is it?"

I explained to her the secret history of the partnership I had set up for Herbert, and my present fear of failing him.

"So!" said she, assenting with her head, but not looking at me. "And how much money is wanting to complete the purchase?"

I was rather afraid of stating it, for it sounded a large sum. "Nine hundred pounds."

"If I give you the money for this purpose, will you keep my secret as you have kept your own?"

"Quite as faithfully."

"And your mind will be more at rest?"

"Much more at rest."

"Are you very unhappy now?"

"I am far from happy, Miss Havisham; but I have other causes of disquiet than any you know of. They are the secrets I have mentioned."

After a little while, she raised her head and looked at the fire again.

"Can I only serve you, Pip, by serving your friend? Regarding that as done, is there nothing I can do for you yourself?"

"Nothing. I thank you for the question. I thank you even more for the tone of the question. But, there is nothing."

She presently rose from her seat and looked about for the means of writing. There were none there, and she took from her pocket a yellow set of ivory tablets, mounted in tarnished gold, and wrote upon them with a pencil in a case of tarnished gold that hung from her neck.

"You are still on friendly terms with Mr. Jaggers?"

"Quite. I dined with him yesterday."

"This is an authority to him to pay you that money, to lay out at your discretion for your friend. I keep no money here; but if you would rather Mr. Jaggers knew nothing of the matter, I will send it to you."

"Thank you, Miss Havisham; I have not the least objection to receiving it from him."

She read me what she had written, and it was direct and clear, and evidently intended to absolve me from any suspicion of profiting by the receipt of the money. I took the tablets from her hand and it trembled as she took off the chain to which the pencil was attached, and put it in mine.

"My name is on the first leaf. If you can ever write under my name, 'I forgive her,' though ever so long after my broken heart is dust — pray do it!"

"Oh, Miss Havisham," said I, "I can do it now. I want forgiveness and direction far too much to be bitter with you."

She turned her face to me for the first time since she averted it, and to my amazement she dropped on her knees at my feet with her folded hands raised. To see her with her white hair and her worn face, kneeling at my feet, gave me a shock through all my frame.

"Oh!" she cried despairingly. "What have I done! What have I done!"

"If you mean, Miss Havisham, what have you done to injure me, let me answer. Very little. I should have loved her under any circumstances. Is she married?"

"Yes!"

It was a needless question, for a new desolation in the desolate house had told me so.

"What have I done! What have I done!" She wrung her hands, and crushed her white hair, and returned to this cry over and over again. "What have I done! Until you spoke to her the other day, and until I saw in you a looking glass that showed me what I once felt myself, I did not know what I had done. What have I done! What have I done!"

"Miss Havisham," I said, when her cry had died away, "you may dismiss me from your mind and conscience. But Estella is a different case."

"Yes, yes, I know it. But, Pip — my dear!" There was an earnest womanly compassion for me in her new affection. "My dear! Believe this: when she first came to me, I meant to save her from misery like my own. At first I meant no more. But as she grew, and promised to be very beautiful, I gradually did worse, and with my praises, and with my jewels, and with my teachings, I stole her heart away and put ice in its place."

"Better," I could not help saying, "to have left her a natural heart, even to be bruised or broken."

"If you knew all my story," she pleaded, "you would have some compassion for me and a better understanding of me."

"Miss Havisham," I answered, as delicately as I could, "I believe I may say that I do know your story, and have known it ever since I first left this neighborhood. Does what has passed

I saw her running at me, shrieking, with a whirl of fire blazing all about her. . . .

between us give me any excuse for asking you a question relative to Estella?"

She was seated on the ground, with her arms on the ragged chair, and her head leaning on them. She looked full at me and replied, "Go on."

"Whose child was Estella?"

She shook her head.

"You don't know?"

She shook her head again.

"But Mr. Jaggers brought her here, or sent her here?"

"Brought her here."

"Will you tell me how that came about?"

She answered in a low whisper and with caution, "I had been shut up in these rooms a long time when I told him that I wanted a little girl to rear and love, and save from my fate. He told me that he would look about him for such an orphan child. One night he brought her here asleep, and I called her Estella."

"Might I ask her age then?"

"Two or three. She herself knows nothing, but that she was left an orphan and I adopted her."

So convinced I was of that woman's being her mother that I wanted no evidence to establish the fact in my mind. But, to any mind, the connection here was clear and straight.

What more could I hope to do by prolonging the interview? I had succeeded on behalf of Herbert, Miss Havisham had told me all she knew of Estella, I had said and done what I could to ease her mind.

Twilight was closing in when I went downstairs into the natural air. I called to the woman who had opened the gate when I entered that I would not trouble her just yet, but would walk round the place before leaving. For I had a feeling that I should never be there again, and I felt that the dying light was suited to

my last view of it.

I made my way to the ruined garden. I went all round it; round by the corner where Herbert and I had fought our battle; round by the paths where Estella and I had walked. So cold, so lonely, so dreary all!

Suddenly I had a strange premonition [1] of disaster to Miss Havisham. Passing on into the front courtyard, I hesitated whether to call the woman to let me out at the locked gate, of which she had the key, or first to go upstairs and assure myself that Miss Havisham was as safe and well as I had left her. I took the latter course and went up.

I looked into the room where I had left her, and I saw her seated in the ragged chair upon the hearth close to the fire, with her back toward me. In the moment when I was withdrawing my head to go quietly away, I saw a great flaming light spring up. In the same moment I saw her running at me, shrieking, with a whirl of fire blazing all about her, and soaring at least as many feet above her head as she was high.

I had a double-caped greatcoat on, and over my arm another thick coat. I got them off, closed with her, threw her down, and got them over her; I dragged the great cloth from the table for the same purpose, and with it dragged down the heap of rottenness in the midst and all the ugly things that sheltered there. The closer I covered her, the more wildly she shrieked and tried to free herself. I knew that we were on the floor by the great table, and that patches of tinder yet alight were floating in the smoky air, which a moment ago had been her faded bridal dress.

Then I looked round and saw the disturbed beetles and spiders running away over the floor, and the servants

---

[1] **premonition** (prē'mō·nĭsh'ŭn): forewarning.

coming in with breathless cries at the door. She was insensible, and I was afraid to have her moved, or even touched. Assistance was sent for, and when the surgeon came, I was astonished to see that my hands were burned.

On examination it was pronounced that she had received serious hurts, but that the danger lay mainly in the nervous shock. By the surgeon's directions, her bed was carried into that room and laid upon the great table. When I saw her again, an hour afterward, she lay indeed where I had seen her strike her stick, and had heard her say she would lie one day.

Toward midnight she began to wander in her speech and said innumerable times, in a low solemn voice, "What have I done!" And then, "When she first came, I meant to save her from misery like mine." And then, "Take the pencil and write under my name, 'I forgive her'!" She never changed the order of these three sentences.

As I could do no service there, and as I had, nearer home, a pressing reason for anxiety and fear, I decided that I would return by the early morning coach. At about six o'clock in the morning, therefore, I leaned over her and touched her lips with mine, just as they said, "Take the pencil and write under my name, 'I forgive her.'"

CHAPTER 35

Pip hears more about Provis.

MY HANDS had been dressed twice or thrice in the night, and again in the morning. My left arm was a good deal burned to the elbow, and less severely as high as the shoulder; it was very painful, but I felt thankful it was no worse. My right hand was not so badly burned but that I could move the fingers. My left hand and arm I carried in a sling; and I could only wear my coat like a cloak, loose over my shoulders and fastened at the neck.

Herbert devoted the day to attending on me. He was the kindest of nurses, and at stated times took off the bandages and steeped them in the cooling liquid that was kept ready, and put them on again, with a patient tenderness that I was deeply grateful for.

Neither of us spoke of the boat, but we both thought of it. That was made apparent by our avoidance of the subject and by our agreeing to make my recovery of the use of my hands a question of so many hours, not of so many weeks.

My first question when I saw Herbert had been, of course, whether all was well down the river.

"I sat with Provis two hours, Handel, two good hours. He was very communicative last night, and told me more of his life. You remember his breaking off here about some woman that he had had great trouble with? He went into that part of his life, and a dark wild part it is. Shall I tell you?"

"Tell me by all means!"

"Rest easy, my dear Handel," Herbert said. "It seems," he went on, "that the woman was young, jealous, and revengeful to the last degree."

"To what last degree?"

"Murder! She was tried for it, and Mr. Jaggers defended her, and the reputation of that defense first made his name known to Provis. It was another and a stronger woman who was the victim, and there had been a struggle — in a barn."

"Was the woman brought in guilty?"

"No; she was acquitted. This acquitted young woman and Provis had a little child, a little child of whom Provis was exceedingly fond. On the evening of the very night when the object of her jealousy was strangled, the young woman presented herself before Provis for one moment, and swore that she would destroy the child (which was in her possession), and he should never see it again; then she vanished. You don't think your breathing is affected by the burns, my dear boy? You seem to breathe quickly."

"Perhaps I do, Herbert. Did the woman keep her oath?"

"There comes the darkest part of Provis's life. She did."

"That is, he says she did."

"Why, of course, my dear boy," returned Herbert, in a tone of surprise, and again bending forward to get a nearer look at me. "He says it all. I have no other information."

"No, to be sure."

"Now, whether," pursued Herbert, "he had used the child's mother ill, Provis doesn't say; but she had shared some four or five years of the wretched life he described to us at his fireside, and he seems to have felt pity for her. Therefore, fearing he should be called upon to testify about this destroyed child, and so be the cause of her death, he hid himself (much as he grieved for the child), kept himself dark, as he says, out of the way and out of the trial, and was only vaguely talked of as a certain man called Abel, out of whom the jealousy arose. After the acquittal she disappeared, and thus he lost the child and the child's mother."

"I want to ask — "

"A moment, my dear boy, and I have done. That evil genius, Compeyson, the worst of scoundrels, knowing of his keeping out of the way at that time, of course afterward held the knowledge over his head as a means of keeping him poorer and working him harder."

"I want to know," said I, "and particularly, Herbert, whether he told you when this happened?"

"Particularly? Let me remember, then, what he said as to that. His expression was, 'a round score o' year ago, and a'most directly after I took up wi' Compeyson.' How old were you when you came upon him in the little churchyard?"

"I think in my seventh year."

"Aye. It had happened some three or four years then, he said, and you brought into his mind the little girl so tragically lost, who would have been about your age."

"Herbert," said I, after a short silence, "the man we have hiding down the river is Estella's father."

CHAPTER 36

Pip receives a mysterious letter.

EARLY the next morning I went to Little Britain and there obtained from Mr. Jaggers — after a long account of the disaster at Satis House — a check for the money Miss Havisham was assigning to Herbert's credit. From Little Britain I went, with my check in my pocket, to Miss Skiffins' brother, the accountant; and he going straight to Clarriker's and bringing Clarriker to me, I had the great satisfaction of concluding that arrangement. It was the only good thing I had done, and the only completed thing I had done, since I was first told of my great expectations.

Clarriker informed me that he would now be able to establish a small branch house in the East and that Herbert in his new partnership capacity would go out and take charge of it. And now indeed I felt as if my last anchor were loosening its hold, and I should soon be driving with the winds and waves.

We had now got into the month of March. My left arm took in the natural course so long to heal that I was still unable to get a coat on. My right arm was tolerably restored — disfigured, but fairly serviceable.

On a Monday morning, when Herbert and I were at breakfast, I received the following letter from Wemmick by the post.

Walworth. Burn this as soon as read. Early in the week, or say Wednesday, you might do what you know of, if you felt disposed to try it. Now burn.

When I had shown this to Herbert and had put it in the fire — but not before we had both got it by heart — we considered what to do. For, of course, my being disabled could now be no longer kept out of view.

"I have thought it over again and again," said Herbert, "and I think I know a better course than taking a Thames waterman. Take Startop. A good fellow, a skilled hand, fond of us, and enthusiastic and honorable."

I had thought of him more than once.

"But how much would you tell him, Herbert?"

"It is necessary to tell him very little. Let him suppose it a mere freak, but a secret one, until the morning comes; then let him know that there is urgent reason for your getting Provis aboard and away. You go with him?"

"No doubt."

"Where?"

It seemed to me almost indifferent what port we made for — Hamburg, Rotterdam, Antwerp — the place signified little, so that he was out of England. Any foreign steamer that fell in our way and would take us up would do. As foreign steamers would leave London at about the time of high water, our plan would be to get down the river by a previous ebb tide, and lie by in some quiet spot until we could pull off to one. The time when one would be due where we lay, wherever that might be, could be calculated pretty nearly, if we made inquiries beforehand.

Herbert assented to all this, and we went out immediately after breakfast to pursue our investigations. We found that a steamer for Hamburg was likely to suit our purpose best, and we directed our thoughts chiefly to that vessel. But we noted down what other foreign steamers would leave London with the same tide, and we satisfied ourselves that we knew the build and color of each. We then separated for a few hours; I to get at once such passports as were necessary; Herbert, to see Startop at his lodgings. When we met again at one o'clock I, for my part, was prepared with passports; Herbert had seen Startop, and he was more than ready to join.

Those two would pull a pair of oars, we settled, and I would steer; our charge would be sitter, and keep quiet. We arranged that Herbert should prepare Provis to come down some stairs nearby the house, on Wednesday, when he saw us approach, and not sooner. All arrangements with him should be concluded that Monday night. These precautions well understood by both of us, I went home.

On opening the outer door of our chambers with my key, I found a letter in the box, directed to me — a very dirty letter, though not ill written. It had been delivered by hand and its contents were these:

If you are not afraid to come to the old marshes tonight or tomorrow night at nine, and to come to the little sluice house by the limekiln,[1] you had better come. If you want information regarding *your uncle Provis,* you had much better come and tell no one and lose no time. *You must come alone.* Bring this with you.

What to do now, I could not tell. And the worst was that I must decide quickly, or I should miss the afternoon coach, which would take me down in time for tonight. Tomorrow night I could not think of going, for it would be too close upon the time of the flight. For anything I knew, the information might have some important bearing on the flight itself. I resolved to go.

I had to read this mysterious letter again, twice, before its injunction to me to be secret got into my mind. Yielding to it, I left a note in pencil to Herbert, telling him that I had decided to go down to see how Miss Havisham was faring. I hurried out and caught the coach just as it came out of the yard. I was the only inside passenger, jolting away knee-deep in straw. And now I began to wonder at myself for being in the coach, and to doubt whether I had sufficient reason for being there, and to consider whether I should get out presently and go back, and to argue against ever heeding an anonymous communication, and, in short, to pass through all phases of contradiction and indecision. Still, the reference to Provis by name mastered everything. I feared that in case any harm should befall him through my not going, I could never forgive myself.

[1] **limekiln** (līm′kĭl′; -kīln′): a furnace in which limestone or shells are burned to produce lime.

It was dark before we got down. Avoiding the Blue Boar, I put up at an inn downtown and ordered some dinner. While it was preparing, I went to Satis House and inquired for Miss Havisham; she was still very ill, though considered somewhat better.

As I was not able to cut my dinner, the old landlord with a shining bald head did it for me. This bringing us into conversation, he was so good as to entertain me with my own story — of course with the popular feature that Pumblechook was my earliest benefactor and the founder of my fortunes.

"Do you know the young man?" said I.

"Know him?" repeated the landlord. "Ever since he was — no height at all."

"Does he ever come back to this neighborhood?"

"Aye, he comes back," said the landlord, "to his great friends, now and again, and gives the cold shoulder to the man that made him."

"What man is that?"

"Him that I speak of," said the landlord. "Mr. Pumblechook."

"Is he ungrateful to no one else?"

"No doubt he would be, if he could," returned the landlord, "but he can't. And why? Because Pumblechook done everything for him."

"Does Pumblechook say so?"

"Say so!" replied the landlord. "He han't no call to say so."

"But does he say so?"

"It would turn a man's blood to white wine winegar to hear him tell of it, sir," said the landlord.

I thought, "Yet Joe, dear Joe, *you* never tell of it. Long-suffering and loving Joe, *you* never complain. Nor you, sweet-tempered Biddy!"

I had never been struck at so keenly for my thanklessness to Joe, as through the brazen impostor Pumblechook. The falser he, the truer Joe; the meaner he, the nobler Joe.

My heart was deeply and most deservedly humbled as I mused over the fire for an hour or more. The striking of the clock aroused me, and I got up and had my coat fastened round my neck, and went out. I had previously sought in my pockets for the letter, that I might refer to it again, but I could not find it, and was uneasy to think that it must have been dropped in the straw of the coach. I knew very well, however, that the appointed place was the little sluice house by the limekiln on the marshes, and the hour nine. Toward the marshes I now went straight, having no time to spare.

CHAPTER 37

Trabb's boy leads a rescue party.

IT WAS a dark night, there was a melancholy wind, and the marshes were very dismal. A stranger would have found them unbearable, and even to me they were so oppressive that I hesitated, half inclined to go back. It was a half hour before I drew near to the kiln. The lime was burning with a sluggish, stifling smell, but the fires were made up and left, and no workmen were visible. Nearby was a small stone quarry.

Coming up to the marsh level out of this quarry, I saw a light in the old sluice house. I quickened my pace and knocked at the door. There was no answer, and I knocked again. No answer still, and I tried the latch.

The door yielded. Looking in, I saw a lighted candle on a table, a bench, and a mattress on a low bedstead. As there was a loft above, I called, "Is there anyone here?" but no voice answered.

Then I looked at my watch, and finding that it was past nine, called again, "Is there anyone here?" There being still no answer, I went out at the door, uncertain what to do.

It was beginning to rain fast. Seeing nothing, I turned back into the house. Considering that someone must have been there lately and must soon be coming back, or the candle would not be burning, it came into my head to look if the wick were long. I had taken up the candle in my hand, when it was extinguished by some violent shock, and the next thing I knew was that I had been caught in a strong running noose, thrown over my head from behind.

"Now," said a suppressed voice with an oath, "I've got you!"

"What is this?" I cried, struggling. "Who is it? Help, help, help!"

Not only were my arms pulled close to my side, but the pressure on my bad arm caused me extreme pain. A strong man's hand was set against my mouth to deaden my cries, and with a hot breath always close to me, I struggled in the dark until I was fastened tight to the wall. "And now," said the suppressed voice with another oath, "call out again, and I'll make short work of you!"

Faint and sick with pain, I tried to ease my arm, but I was bound too tight. After groping about for a little, my attacker began to strike a light. Presently I saw the man's lips breathing on the tinder, and then a flare of light flashed up and showed me Orlick.

Whom I had looked for, I don't know. I had not looked for him. Seeing him, I felt that I was in great danger indeed, and I kept my eyes upon him.

He lighted the candle from the flaring match with great deliberation, and dropped the match, and trod it out. Then he put the candle away from him on the table, so that he could see me, and sat with his arms folded on the table, and looked at me. I made out that I was fastened to a stout perpendicular ladder a few inches from the wall — a fixture there — the means of ascent to the loft above.

"Now," said he, when we had surveyed one another for some time, "I've got you."

"Why have you lured me here?"

"Don't you know?" said he, with a deadly look.

"Why have you set upon me in the dark?"

"Because I mean to do it all myself. One keeps a secret better than two. Oh, you enemy, you enemy!"

His enjoyment of the spectacle I furnished, as he sat with his arms folded on the table, shaking his head at me, made me tremble. As I watched him in silence, he put his hand into the corner at his side, and took up a gun with a brass-bound stock that I had seen beside him at Satis House during our brief encounter there.

"Do you know this?" said he, making as if he would take aim at me. "Do you know where you saw it afore? Speak, wolf!"

"Yes," I answered.

"You cost me that place. You did. Speak!"

"What else could I do?"

"You did that, and that would be enough, without more. How dared you come betwixt me and a young woman I liked?"

"When did I?"

"When didn't you? It was you as always give Old Orlick a bad name to her."

"You gave it to yourself; you gained it for yourself. I could have done you no harm, if you had done yourself none."

"You're a liar. And you'll take any pains, and spend any money, to drive me out of this country, will you?" said he, repeating my words to Biddy in the last interview I had with her. "Now, I'll tell you a piece of information. It was never so worth your while to get me out of this country as it is tonight." As he shook his heavy hand at me, with his mouth snarling like a tiger's, I felt that it was true.

"What are you going to do to me?"

"I'm a-going," said he, bringing his fist down upon the table with a heavy blow, and rising as the blow fell, to give it greater force, "I'm a-going to have your life!"

He leaned forward staring at me, slowly unclenched his hand and drew it across his mouth as if his mouth watered for me, and sat down again.

"You was always in Old Orlick's way since ever you was a child. You goes out of his way this present night. He'll have no more on you. You're dead."

I felt that I had come to the brink of my grave. For a moment I looked wildly round my trap for any chance of escape; but there was none.

"More than that," said he, "I won't have a rag of you, I won't have a bone of you, left on earth. I'll put your body in the kiln — I'd carry two such to it, on my shoulders — and, let people suppose what they may of you, they shall never know nothing."

My mind rapidly considered all the consequences of such a death. Estella's father would believe I had deserted him, would be taken, would die accusing me; even Herbert would doubt me when he compared the letter I had left for him with the fact that I had called at Miss Havisham's gate for only a moment; Joe and Biddy would never know how sorry I had been that night.

Orlick had been drinking, and his eyes were red and bloodshot. Around his neck was slung a tin bottle, and he took a fiery drink from it.

"Wolf!" said he, folding his arms again. "Old Orlick's a-going to tell you something. It was you as did for your shrew sister."

"It was you, villain," said I.

"I tell you it was your doing — I tell you it was done through you," he retorted, catching up the gun, and making a blow with the stock at the vacant air between us. "I come upon her from behind, as I come upon you tonight. I give it to her! I left her for dead, and if there had been a limekiln as nigh her as there is now nigh you, she shouldn't have come to life again. But it warn't Old Orlick as did it; it was you. You was favored, and he was bullied and beat. Old Orlick bullied and beat, eh? Now you pays for it. You done it; now you pays for it."

He drank again, and became more ferocious. He took up the candle, and shading it with his murderous hand so as to throw its light on me, stood before me, looking at me and enjoying the sight.

"Wolf, I'll tell you something more. It was Old Orlick as you tumbled over on your stairs that night. And why was Orlick there? I'll tell you something more. I've had a firm mind and a firm will to have your life, since you was down here at your sister's burying. I hadn't seen a way to get you safe, and I've looked after you to know your ins and outs. For, says Old Orlick to himself, 'Somehow or another I'll have him!' What! When I looks for you, I finds your Uncle Provis, eh?

"*You* with a uncle, too! But when Old Orlick come for to hear that your Uncle Provis had mostlike wore the leg iron wot Old Orlick had picked up on these marshes long ago, and wot he kept by him till he dropped your sister with it — when he come to hear that — hey? — "

In his savage taunting, he flared the candle so close to me that I turned my face aside to save it from the flame.

"Ah!" he cried, laughing, after doing it again. "The burned child dreads the fire! Old Orlick knowed you was burned, Old Orlick knowed you was a-smuggling your Uncle Provis away, Old Orlick's a match for you and knowed you'd come tonight! Now I'll tell you something more, wolf, and this ends it. There's them that's as good a match for your Uncle Provis as Old Orlick has been for you. There's them that can't and that won't have Magwitch — yes, *I* know the name! — alive in the same land with them, and that's had sure information of him when he was alive in another land, as that he shouldn't leave it and put them in danger. Beware of Compeyson, Magwitch, and the gallows!"

There was a clear space of a few feet between the table and the opposite wall. Within this space he now slouched backward and forward with his hands hanging loose and heavy at his sides, and with his eyes scowling at me. I had no grain of hope left.

Of a sudden he stopped, took the cork out of his bottle, and tossed it away. Light as it was, I heard it fall like a plummet.[1] He swallowed slowly, tilting up the bottle by little and little, and now he looked at me no more. The last few drops of liquor he poured into the palm of his hand and licked up. Then with a sudden hurry of violence and swearing horribly, he threw the bottle from him, and stooped; and I saw in his hand a stone hammer with a long heavy handle.

I shouted out with all my might, and

[1] **plummet** (plŭm'ĕt): a lead weight attached to a string, used by carpenters to test the straightness of a wall, etc. When the weight is dropped, the string becomes straight.

struggled with all my might. It was only my head and my legs that I could move, but to that extent I struggled with all the force that was within me. In the same instant I heard responsive shouts, saw figures and a gleam of light dash in at the door, heard voices and tumult, and saw Orlick emerge from a struggle of men, clear the table at a leap, and fly out into the night!

After a blank, I found that I was lying unbound on the floor, in the same place, with my head on someone's knee. My eyes were fixed on the ladder against the wall when there came between me and it, a face. The face of Trabb's boy!

"I think he's all right!" said Trabb's boy, in a sober voice. "But ain't he just pale, though!"

At these words, I recognized the face of him who supported me.

"Herbert! Great Heaven!"

"Softly," said Herbert. "Gently, Handel. Don't be too eager."

"And our old comrade, Startop!" I cried, as he too bent over me.

"Remember what he is going to assist us in," said Herbert, "and be calm."

The remembrance made me spring up, though I dropped again from the pain in my arm. "The time has not gone by, Herbert, has it? What night is tonight? How long have I been here?"

"The time has not gone by. It is still Monday night."

"Thank God!"

"And you have all tomorrow, Tuesday, to rest in," said Herbert. "Can you stand?"

"Yes, yes," said I, "I can walk. I have no hurt but in this throbbing arm."

They did what they could until we were able to get to town and obtain some cooling lotion to put upon it. Trabb's boy — Trabb's overgrown young man now — went before us with a lantern. But the moon was a good two hours higher than when I had last seen the sky, and the night though rainy was much lighter.

I learned from Herbert that I had in my hurry dropped the letter, open, in our chambers, where he, coming home to bring with him Startop, found it very soon after I was gone. Its tone made him uneasy, and he set off for the coach office with Startop. Finding that the afternoon coach was gone, he and Startop resolved to follow in a carriage. They arrived at the Blue Boar and, looking for someone to guide them out on the marshes, found Trabb's boy among the loungers under the Boar's archway. Thus Trabb's boy became their guide, and with him they went out to the sluice house. Herbert left his guide and Startop on the edge of the quarry, and went on by himself, and stole round the house two or three times. As he could hear nothing but indistinct sounds of one deep rough voice, he began to doubt whether I was there, when suddenly I cried out loudly, and he answered the cries, and rushed in, closely followed by the other two.

We relinquished all thoughts of pursuing Orlick at that time. For the present, under the circumstances, we deemed it prudent to make rather light of the matter to Trabb's boy. When we parted, I presented him with two guineas (which seemed to meet his views), and told him that I was sorry ever to have had an ill opinion of him (which made no impression on him at all).

It was daylight when we reached the Temple, and I went at once to bed, and lay in bed all day.

My terror, as I lay there, of falling ill and being unfitted for tomorrow, was so besetting that I wonder it did not disable me of itself. I started at every footstep and every sound, believing that

Provis was discovered and taken, and this was the messenger to tell me so. I persuaded myself that I knew he was taken. It happened sometimes that in the mere escape of a fatigued mind, I dozed for some moments or forgot; then I would say to myself with a start, "Now it has come, and I am turning delirious!"

They kept me very quiet all day, and kept my arm constantly dressed, and gave me cooling drinks. Whenever I fell asleep, I awoke with the notion I had had in the sluice house, that a long time had elapsed, and the opportunity to save him was gone. At last, from this self-exhausting fretfulness I was released, and I slept soundly.

Wednesday morning was dawning when I looked out of the window. Herbert lay asleep in his bed, and our old fellow student lay asleep on the sofa. I could not dress myself without help, but I made up the fire which was still burning, and got some coffee ready for them. In good time they too started up strong and well, and we admitted the sharp morning air at the windows, and looked at the tide that was still flowing toward us.

"When it turns at nine o'clock," said Herbert cheerfully, "look out for us, and stand ready, you over there at Mill Pond Bank!"

CHAPTER 38

An informer goes to his death.

It was one of those March days when the sun shines hot and the wind blows cold; when it is summer in the light, and winter in the shade. We had our thick woolen coats with us, and I took a bag. Of all my worldly possessions I took no more than the few necessaries that filled the bag. Where I might go, what I might do, or when I might return, were questions utterly unknown to me; nor did I vex my mind with them, for it was wholly set on Provis' safety. We loitered down to the Temple stairs, and stood loitering there, as if we were not quite decided to go upon the water at all. Of course I had taken care that the boat should be ready, and everything in order. After a while we went on board and cast off; Herbert in the bow, I steering. It was then about high water — half-past eight.

Our plan was this. The tide, beginning to run down at nine, and being with us until three, we intended still to creep on after it had turned, and row against it until dark. We should then be well in those long reaches below Gravesend,[1] where the river is broad and solitary, where the waterside inhabitants are very few, and where lone public houses are scattered here and there, of which we could choose one for a resting place. There, we meant to lie by all night. The steamer for Hamburg and the steamer for Rotterdam would start from London at about nine on Thursday morning. We should know at what time to expect them and would hail the first; so that if by any accident we were not taken aboard, we should have another chance. We knew the distinguishing marks of each vessel.

Old London Bridge was soon passed, and old Billingsgate market with its oyster boats and Dutchmen, and we were in among the tiers of shipping. Here were steamers, loading and unloading goods, and here, at her moorings, was tomorrow's steamer for Rotterdam, of which we took good notice; and here tomorrow's for Hamburg, under whose

[1] **Gravesend:** a section of Kent, about halfway between London and the North Sea coast.

bowsprit [1] we crossed. And now I, sitting in the stern, could see, with a faster beating heart, Mill Pond Bank and Mill Pond stairs.

"Is he there?" said Herbert.

"Not yet."

"Right! He was not to come down till he saw us. Can you see his signal?"

"Not well from here; but I think I see it. Now I see him! Pull both. Easy, Herbert. Oars!"

We touched the stairs lightly for a single moment, and he was on board and we were off again. He had a boat cloak with him, and a black canvas bag, and he looked as like a river pilot as my heart could have wished.

"Dear boy!" he said, putting his arm on my shoulder, as he took his seat. "Faithful dear boy, well done. Thank-'ee, thank'ee!"

Again among the tiers of shipping, in and out, avoiding rusty chain cables, frayed hempen hawsers,[2] and bobbing buoys, sinking for the moment floating broken baskets, scattering floating chips of wood and shaving, cleaving floating scum of coal in and out — upon the clearer river, where the ships' boys might take their fenders [3] in, no longer fishing in troubled waters with them over the side, and where the festooned sails might fly out to the wind.

At the stairs where we had taken him aboard, and ever since, I had looked warily for any token of our being suspected. I had seen none. He had his boat cloak on him, and looked, as I have said, a natural part of the scene. It was remarkable that he was the least anxious of any of us.

[1] **bowsprit** (bou'sprĭt): a pole or spar projecting from the bow or front of a ship.

[2] **hawsers** (hô'zĕrz): ropes.

[3] **fenders:** anything used as padding against the sides of ships, to protect them from damage in bumping against wharves or other ships.

"If you knowed, dear boy," he said to me, "what it is to sit here alonger my dear boy and have my smoke, arter having been day by day betwixt four walls, you'd envy me. But you don't know what it is."

"I think I know the delights of freedom," I answered.

"Ah," said he, shaking his head gravely. "But you don't know it equal to me. You must have been under lock and key, dear boy, to know it equal to me — but I ain't a-going to be low."

"If all goes well," said I, "you will be perfectly free and safe again, within a few hours."

"Well," he returned, drawing a long breath, "I hope so."

We made what way we could until the sun went down. At length we saw a light and a roof, and presently ran alongside a little causeway made of stones. I stepped ashore, and found the light to be in the window of a public house. It was a dirty place enough, and I dare say not unknown to smuggling adventurers; but there was a good fire in the kitchen, and there were eggs and bacon to eat. Also, there were two double-bedded rooms — "such as they were," the landlord said. No other company was in the house than the landlord, his wife, and a grizzled old "Jack" [4] who tended the little causeway.

With this assistant, I went down to the boat again, and we all came ashore, and brought out the oars, and rudder, and boat hook, and all else, and hauled her up for the night. We made a very good meal by the kitchen fire, and then apportioned the bedrooms: Herbert and Startop were to occupy one; I and our charge the other. We considered ourselves well off, for a more solitary place we could not have found.

[4] **Jack:** a sailor.

While we were comforting ourselves by the fire after our meal, the Jack asked me if we had seen a four-oared galley [1] going up with the tide. When I told him no, he said she must have gone down then, and yet she "took up too," when she left there.

"They must ha' thought better of it for some reason or another," said the Jack, "and gone down."

"A four-oared galley did you say?" said I.

"A four," said the Jack, "and two sitters."

"Did they come ashore here?"

"They put in with a stone two-gallon jar for some beer."

This information made us all uneasy, and me very uneasy. The dismal wind was muttering round the house, the tide was flapping at the shore, and I had a feeling that we were caged and threatened. A four-oared galley hovering about in so unusual a way as to attract this notice was an ugly circumstance that I could not get rid of. When I had induced Provis to go up to bed, I went outside with my two companions (Startop by this time knew the state of the case) and held council. On the whole we deemed it the better course to lie where we were, until within an hour or so of the steamer's time, and then to get out in her track, and drift easily with the tide. Having settled to do this, we returned into the house and went to bed.

I lay down with the greater part of my clothes on, and slept well for a few hours. When I awoke, the wind had risen. I looked out the window to where we had hauled up our boat, and I saw two men looking into her. They passed by under the window, looking at nothing else, and they did not go down to the landing place but struck across the

[1] **galley** (găl'ĭ): a large rowboat.

marshes. In that light, however, I soon lost them, and feeling very cold, lay down to think of the matter and fell asleep again.

We were up early, and I recounted what I had seen. Again our charge was the least anxious of the party. However, I proposed that he and I should walk away together to a distant point, and that the boat should take us aboard there. This being considered a good precaution, soon after breakfast he and I set forth, without saying anything at the tavern.

He smoked his pipe as we went along, and sometimes stopped to clap me on the shoulder. One would have supposed that it was I who was in danger, not he, and that he was reassuring me. We spoke very little.

We waited until we saw our boat coming round. We got aboard easily and rowed out into the track of the steamer. By that time it was ten minutes of one o'clock, and we began to look out for her smoke.

But it was half-past one before we saw her smoke, and soon after we saw behind it the smoke of another steamer. As they were coming on at full speed, we got the two bags ready, and took that opportunity of saying good-by to Herbert and Startop. We had all shaken hands cordially, and neither Herbert's eyes nor mine were quite dry, when I saw a four-oared galley shoot out from under the bank but a little way ahead of us, and row out into the same track.

I called to Herbert and Startop to keep before the tide, that the steamer might see us lying by for her, and begged Provis to sit quite still, wrapped in his cloak. He answered cheerily, "Trust to me, dear boy," and sat like a statue. Meantime the galley, which was skillfully handled, had crossed us, let us come up with her, and fallen alongside.

"You have a returned convict here," said the man. . . .

Leaving just room enough for the play of the oars, she kept alongside, drifting when we drifted, and pulling a stroke or two when we pulled. Of the two sitters, one held the rudder lines, and looked at us attentively — as did all the rowers; the other sitter was wrapped up, much as Provis was, and seemed to shrink and whisper some instruction to the steerer as he looked at us. Not a word was spoken in either boat.

Startop could make out, after a few minutes, which steamer was first, and gave me the word "Hamburg," in a low voice as we sat face to face. She was nearing us very fast, and the beating of her paddles grew louder and louder. I felt as if her shadow were absolutely upon us, when the galley hailed us. I answered.

"You have a returned convict here," said the man who held the lines. "That's the man, wrapped in the cloak. His name is Abel Magwitch, otherwise Provis. I arrest that man, and call upon him to surrender, and you to assist."

At the same moment, they pulled one stroke ahead, got their oars in, had run athwart us,[1] and were holding on to our side before we knew what they

[1] athwart (*a*·thwôrt′) us: crossed in front of us.

were doing. This caused great confusion on board of the steamer, and I heard them calling to us, and heard the order given to stop the paddles, and heard them stop, but felt her driving down upon us irresistibly. In the same moment, I saw the steersman of the galley lay his hand on his prisoner's shoulder, and saw that both boats were swinging round with the force of the tide, and saw that all hands on board the steamer were running forward frantically. Still in the same moment, I saw the prisoner start up, lean across his captor, and pull the cloak from the neck of the shrinking sitter in the galley. Still in the same moment, I saw that the face disclosed was the face of the other convict of long ago. Still in the same moment, I saw the face tilt backward with a white terror on it that I shall never forget, and heard a great cry on board the steamer and a loud splash in the water, and felt the boat sink from under me.

It was but for an instant that I seemed to struggle and then I was taken on board the galley. Herbert was there, and Startop was there; but our boat was gone, and the two convicts were gone.

What with the cries aboard the

steamer, and the furious blowing off of her steam, and her driving on, and our driving on, I could not at first distinguish sky from water or shore from shore; but the crew of the galley righted her with great skill, and, pulling with swift strong strokes ahead, lay upon their oars, every man looking silently and eagerly at the water astern.[1] Presently a dark object was seen in it, bearing toward us on the tide. No man spoke, but the steersman kept the boat straight and true before it. As it came nearer, I saw it to be Magwitch, swimming, but not freely. He was taken on board, and instantly chained at the wrists and ankles.

The galley was kept steady, and the silent eager lookout at the water was resumed. But the Rotterdam steamer now came up, and apparently not understanding what had happened, came on at speed. By the time she had been hailed and stopped, both steamers were drifting away from us, and we were rising and falling in a troubled wake of water. The lookout was kept for the other convict, long after all was still again and the two steamers were gone; but everybody knew that it was hopeless now.

At length we gave it up, and pulled under the shore toward the tavern we had lately left. Here, I was able to get some comforts for Magwitch — Provis no longer — who had received some very severe injury in the chest and a deep cut in the head.

He told me that he believed himself to have gone under the keel of the steamer, and to have been struck on the head in rising. The injury to his chest (which rendered his breathing extremely painful) he thought he had received against the side of the galley. He added that he did not know what

[1] astern (ȧ·stûrn'): backward; to the rear.

he might have done to Compeyson, but that in the moment of his laying his hand on his cloak to identify him, that villain had staggered up and back, and they had both gone overboard together. The sudden wrenching of Magwitch out of our boat had capsized us. He told me in a whisper that they had gone down, fiercely locked in each other's arms, and there had been a struggle underwater. He had disengaged himself, struck out, and swum away.

I never had any reason to doubt the exact truth of what he had told me. The officer who steered the galley gave the same account of their going overboard.

When I asked this officer's permission to change the prisoner's wet clothes by purchasing any spare garments I could get at the public house, he gave it readily, merely observing that he must take charge of everything his prisoner had about him. So the pocketbook which had once been in my hands passed into the officer's. He further gave me leave to accompany the prisoner to London, but declined to accord that grace to my two friends.

We remained at the public house until the tide turned, and then Magwitch was carried down to the galley and put on board. Herbert and Startop were to get to London by land, as soon as they could. We had a doleful parting, and when I took my place by Magwitch's side, I felt that that was my place henceforth while he lived.

For now my repugnance to him had all melted away, and in the hunted, wounded, shackled creature who held my hand in his, I only saw a man who had meant to be my benefactor, and who had felt affectionately, gratefully, and generously toward me with great constancy through a series of years. I only saw in him a much better man than I had been to Joe.

His breathing became more difficult and painful as the night drew on, and often he could not repress a groan. I tried to rest him on the arm I could use, in any easy position; but it was dreadful to think that I could not be sorry at heart for his being badly hurt, since it was unquestionably best that he should die. That there were, still living, people enough who were able and willing to identify him, I could not doubt. That he would be leniently treated, I could not hope — he who had been presented in the worst light at his trial, who had since broken prison and been tried again, who had returned from transportation under a life sentence, and who had occasioned the death of the man who was the cause of his arrest.

As we returned toward the setting sun we had yesterday left behind us, and as the stream of our hopes seemed all running back, I told him how grieved I was to think he had come home for my sake.

"Dear boy," he answered, "I'm quite content to take my chance. I've seen my boy, and he can be a gentleman without me."

No. I had thought about that while we had been there side by side. His hopes were in vain, for I foresaw that, being convicted, his possessions would be forfeited to the Crown.[1]

"Look'ee here, dear boy," said he. "It's best as a gentleman should not be knowed to belong to me now. Only come to see me as if you come by chance alonger Wemmick. Sit where I can see you when I am swore to, for the last o' many times, and I don't ask no more."

[1] **forfeited** (fôr'fĭt-ĕd) **to the Crown:** confiscated by the government, which had the legal right to the possessions of a prisoner in Magwitch's position.

"I will never stir from your side," said I, "when I am allowed to be near you. Please God, I will be as true to you as you have been to me!"

I felt his hand tremble as it held mine, and he turned his face away as he lay in the bottom of the boat, and I heard that old sound in his throat — softened now, like all the rest of him. It was a good thing that he had touched this point, for it put into my mind what I might not otherwise have thought of until too late: that he need never know how his hopes of enriching me had perished.

CHAPTER 39

Mr. Wemmick takes a walk.

MAGWITCH was taken to the Police Court next day, and would have been immediately committed for trial, but that it was necessary to send for an old officer of the prison ship from which he had once escaped, to speak to identify him. Nobody doubted it; but Compeyson, who would have sworn to it, was dead. I had gone direct to Mr. Jaggers at his private house, on my arrival overnight, to retain his assistance, but he told me that no power on earth could prevent its going against us.

I imparted to Mr. Jaggers my design of keeping Magwitch in ignorance of the fate of his wealth. Mr. Jaggers was angry with me for having "let it slip through my fingers." I understood very well that I had no claim, and I resolved that my heart should never be sickened with the hopeless task of attempting to establish one.

There appeared to be reason for supposing that the drowned informer had hoped for a reward, and had obtained some accurate knowledge of Magwitch's affairs. When his body was found, many miles from the scene of his death, notes were still legible, folded in a case he carried. Among these were the name of a banking house in New South Wales where there was a sum of money, and the description of certain lands of considerable value. Both those items were in a list that Magwitch, while in prison, gave to Mr. Jaggers, of the possessions he supposed I should inherit. His ignorance, poor fellow, at last served him; he never mistrusted but that my inheritance was quite safe, with Mr. Jaggers' aid.

After three days' delay, Magwitch was committed to take his trial at the next session, which would come on in a month.

It was at this dark time of my life that Herbert returned home one evening, a good deal cast down, and said:

"My dear Handel, I fear I shall soon have to leave you."

His partner having prepared me for that, I was less surprised than he thought.

"We shall lose a fine opportunity if I put off going to Cairo, and I am very much afraid I must go, Handel, when you most need me."

"Herbert, I shall always need you, because I shall always love you; but my need is no greater now than at another time."

"You will be so lonely."

"I have not leisure to think of that," said I. "You know that I am always with Magwitch to the full extent of the time allowed, and that I should be with him all day long, if I could. And when I come away from him, you know that my thoughts are with him."

"My dear fellow," said Herbert, "have you thought about yourself? Have you thought of your future? In this branch house of ours, Handel, we must have a — "

I saw that his delicacy was avoiding the right word, so I said, "A clerk."

"A clerk. I hope it is not at all unlikely that he may expand into a partner. Now, Handel — in short, my dear boy, will you come with me?"

There was something cordial and engaging in the manner in which he stretched out his honest hand. "Clara and I have talked about it again and again," Herbert pursued, "and she begged me only this evening to say that if only you will live with us when we are married, she will do her best to make you happy."

I thanked her heartily, and I thanked him heartily, but said I could not yet make sure of joining him.

"But if you thought, Herbert, that you could, without doing any injury to your business, leave the question open for a little while — "

"For any while," cried Herbert. "Six months, a year!"

"Not so long as that," said I. "Two or three months at most."

When we shook hands on this arrangement, he said he could now take courage to tell me that he believed he must go away at the end of the week.

On the Saturday in that same week, I took my leave of Herbert as he sat on one of the seaport mail coaches. I then went to my lonely home — if it deserved the name, for it was now no home to me, and I had no home anywhere.

On the stairs I encountered Wemmick. I had not seen him alone since the attempted escape; and he had come, in his private and personal capacity, to say a few words in reference to that failure.

"You don't blame me, I hope, Mr. Pip? I'm sure I tried to serve you, with all my heart."

"I am as sure of that, Wemmick, as you can be, and I thank you most earnestly for all your interest and friendship."

I invited Wemmick to come upstairs and refresh himself with a glass of grog before walking to Walworth. He accepted but appeared rather fidgety.

"What do you think of my meaning to take a holiday on Monday, Mr. Pip?"

"Why, I suppose you have not done such a thing these twelve months."

"These twelve years, more likely," said Wemmick. "Yes. I'm going to take a holiday. More than that; I'm going to take a walk. More than that; I'm going to ask you to take a walk with me. It ain't a long walk, and it's an early one. Say it might occupy you (including breakfast on the walk), from eight to twelve. Couldn't you stretch a point and manage it?"

He had done so much for me that this was very little to do for him. I said I could manage it — would manage it — and he was so very much pleased that I was pleased too.

Punctual to my appointment, I rang at the Castle gate on the Monday morning, and was received by Wemmick himself, who struck me as looking more precise than usual, and having a sleeker hat on.

When we had fortified ourselves with biscuits and were going out for that walk, I was considerably surprised to see Wemmick take up a fishing rod and put it over his shoulder. "Why, we are not going fishing!" said I. "No," returned Wemmick, "but I like to walk with one."

I thought this odd; however, I said nothing, and we set off. We went toward Camberwell Green, and when we were thereabouts, Wemmick said suddenly:

"Halloa! Here's a church!"

There was nothing very surprising in that; but again, I was rather surprised when he said, as if he were animated by a brilliant idea:

"Let's go in!"

We went in, Wemmick leaving his fishing rod in the porch, and looked all round. In the meantime, Wemmick was diving into his coat pockets and getting something out of paper there.

"Halloa!" said he. "Here's a couple of pair of gloves! Let's put 'em on!"

As the gloves were white kid gloves, I now began to have my strong suspicions. They were strengthened into certainty when I beheld the Aged enter at a side door, escorting a lady.

"Halloa!" said Wemmick. "Here's Miss Skiffins! Let's have a wedding."

The clerk and clergyman then appeared, and true to his notion of seeming to do it all without preparation, I heard Wemmick say to himself as he took something out of his waistcoat pocket before the service began, "Halloa! Here's a ring!"

I acted in the capacity [1] of best man to the bridegroom, while the responsibility of giving the lady away fell upon the Aged.

It was done, and we were out of the church. "Now, Mr. Pip," said Wemmick, triumphantly shouldering the fishing rod as we came out, "let me ask you whether anybody would suppose this to be a wedding party!"

Breakfast had been ordered at a pleasant little tavern a mile or so away. We had an excellent meal, and when anyone declined anything on the table, Wemmick said, "Provided by contract, you know; don't be afraid of it!" I drank

---

[1] **capacity** (ká·păs′ĭ·tĭ): position.

to the new couple, drank to the Aged, drank to the Castle, saluted the bride at parting, and made myself as agreeable as I could.

CHAPTER 40

Pip takes final leave of Magwitch.

MAGWITCH lay in prison very ill during the whole interval between his committal for trial and the coming round of the court sessions. He had broken two ribs, they had wounded one of his lungs, and he breathed with great pain and difficulty, which increased daily. Being far too ill to remain in the common prison, he was soon moved into the infirmary. This gave me opportunities of being with him that I could not otherwise have had. And but for his illness he would have been put into irons, for he was regarded as a determined prison breaker, and I know not what else.

Although I saw him every day, it was for only a short time. I do not recollect that I once saw any change in him for the better; he wasted and became slowly weaker and worse day by day from the day when the prison door closed upon him.

When the court sessions came round, Mr. Jaggers applied for the postponement of his trial but was refused. The trial came on at once, and when he was put to the bar, he was seated in a chair. No objection was made to my sitting outside the dock and holding the hand that he stretched out to me.

The trial was very short and very clear. Such things as could be said for him were said — how he had taken to industrious habits, and had thriven [1]

[1] **thriven** (thrĭv′ĕn): thrived; succeeded; prospered.

lawfully and reputably. But nothing could unsay the fact that he had returned, and was there in presence of the judge and jury. It was impossible not to try him for that, and do otherwise than find him guilty.

At that time it was the custom (as I learned from my terrible experience of that sessions) to devote a concluding day to the passing of sentences, and to make a finishing effect with the sentence of death. I saw two-and-thirty men and women put before the judge to receive that sentence together. Foremost among the two-and-thirty was he; seated, that he might get breath enough to keep life in him.

Penned in the dock, as I again stood outside it at the corner with his hand in mine, were the two-and-thirty men and women; some defiant, some stricken with terror, some sobbing and weeping, some covering their faces, some staring gloomily about. There had been shrieks from among the women convicts, but they had been stilled, and a hush had succeeded.

Then, the judge addressed them, and pronounced his sentence on Magwitch, with single attention to him as one who almost since infancy had been an offender against the laws. The appointed punishment for his return to the land that had cast him out being death, he must prepare himself to die.

The sun was striking in at the great windows of the court, through the glittering drops of rain upon the glass, and it made a broad shaft of light between the two-and-thirty and the judge. Rising for a moment, a distinct speck of face in this shaft of light, the prisoner said, "My Lord, I have received my sentence of death from the Almighty, but I bow to yours," and sat down again.

For several days and nights after he

"Thank'ee, dear boy. . . . You've never deserted me. . . ."

was sentenced I took no rest, except when I fell asleep in my chair. The daily visits I could make him were shortened now, and he was more strictly kept. Nobody was hard with him or with me. There was duty to be done, and it was done, but not harshly. Sometimes he was unable to speak; then, he would answer me with slight pressures on my hand, and I grew to understand his meaning very well.

The number of the days had risen to ten, when I saw a greater change in him than I had seen yet. His eyes were turned toward the door, and lighted up as I entered.

"Dear boy," he said, as I sat down by his bed, "I thought you was late. But I knowed you couldn't be that."

"It is just the time," said I. "I waited for it at the gate."

"You always waits at the gate; don't you, dear boy?"

"Yes. Not to lose a moment of the time."

"Thank'ee, dear boy, thank'ee. God bless you! You've never deserted me, dear boy."

I pressed his hand in silence, for I could not forget that I had once meant to desert him.

"And what's the best of all," he said, "you've been more comfortable alonger me since I was under a dark cloud, than when the sun shone. That's best of all."

He lay on his back, breathing with great difficulty. Do what he would, and love me though he did, the light left his face ever and again, and a film came over the placid look at the white ceiling.

"Are you in much pain today?"

"I don't complain of none, dear boy."

"You never do complain."

He had spoken his last words. He smiled, and I understood his touch to mean that he wished to lift my hand, and lay it on his breast. I laid it there, and he smiled again, and put both his hands upon it.

The allotted time ran out while we were thus; but, looking round, I found the governor of the prison standing near me, and he whispered, "You needn't go yet." I thanked him gratefully, and asked, "Might I speak to him, if he can hear me?"

The governor stepped aside and beckoned the officer away. The change, though it was made without noise, drew back the film from the placid look at the white ceiling, and he looked most affectionately at me.

"Dear Magwitch, I must tell you, now, at last. You understand what I say?"

A gentle pressure on my hand.

"You had a child once, whom you loved and lost."

A stronger pressure on my hand.

"She lived and found powerful

friends. She is living now. She is a lady and very beautiful. And I love her!"

With a last faint effort, which would have been powerless but for my yielding to it, and assisting it, he raised my hand to his lips. Then he gently let it sink upon his breast again, with his own hands lying on it. The placid look at the white ceiling came back, and passed away, and his head dropped quietly on his breast.

I thought of the two men who went up into the Temple to pray, and I knew there were no better words that I could say beside his bed than, "O Lord, be merciful to him, a sinner!"

CHAPTER 41

An old friend comes to Pip's rescue.

Now THAT I was left wholly to myself, I gave notice of my intention to quit the chambers in the Temple as soon as possible. I was in debt, and had scarcely any money, and I began to be seriously alarmed by the state of my affairs. Moreover, I was falling very ill. The late events had enabled me to put off illness, but not to put it away; I knew that it was coming on me now.

For a day or two I lay on the sofa, or on the floor — anywhere, according as I happened to sink down — with a heavy head and aching limbs, and no purpose, and no power. Then there came one night which appeared of great duration, and which teemed with anxiety and horror; and when in the morning I tried to sit up in my bed and think of it, I found I could not do so. Then I saw two men looking at me.

"What do you want?" I asked, starting. "I don't know you."

"Well, sir," returned one of them, bending down and touching me on the shoulder, "you're arrested."

"What is the debt?"

"Hundred and twenty-three pounds. Jeweler's account, I think."

I made some attempt to get up and dress myself. When I next noticed them, they were standing a little off from the bed, looking at me. I still lay there.

"You see my state," said I. "I would come with you if I could; but indeed I am quite unable. If you take me from here, I think I shall die by the way."

As they hang in my memory by only this one slender thread, I don't know what they did, except that they forbore to remove me.

That I had a fever and was avoided, that I suffered greatly, I know of my own remembrance, and did in some sort know at the time. I was delirious and sometimes struggled with real people, in the belief that they were murderers, but above all, I knew that there was a constant tendency in all these people to settle down into the likeness of Joe.

After I had turned the worst point of my illness, I opened my eyes in the night, and I saw in the great chair at the bedside, Joe. I opened my eyes in the day, and, sitting on the window seat, smoking his pipe in the shaded open window, still I saw Joe. I asked for cooling drink, and the dear hand that gave it to me was Joe's. I sank back on my pillow after drinking, and the face that looked so hopefully and tenderly upon me was the face of Joe.

At last one day I took courage, and said, "*Is* it Joe?"

And the dear old home voice answered, "Which it air, old chap."

"Oh, Joe, you break my heart! Look angry at me, Joe. Strike me, Joe. Tell me of my ingratitude. Don't be so good to me!"

For Joe had actually laid his head down on the pillow at my side and put his arm round my neck, in his joy that I knew him.

"Dear old Pip, old chap," said Joe, "you and me was ever friends. And when you're well enough to go out for a ride — what larks!"

After which, Joe withdrew to the window and stood with his back toward me, wiping his eyes. And as my extreme weakness prevented me from getting up and going to him, I lay there, penitently whispering, "O God, bless him! O God, bless this gentle, kindly man!"

Joe's eyes were red when I next found him beside me, but I was holding his hand and we both felt happy.

"Have you been here all the time, dear Joe?"

"Pretty nigh, old chap. For, as I says to Biddy when the news of your being ill were brought by letter, you might be amongst strangers, and you and me having been ever friends, a wisit at such a moment might not prove unacceptabobble. And Biddy, her word were, 'Go to him, without loss of time.'" There Joe cut himself off short, and informed me I was not to talk, and he proceeded to write a note to Biddy, with my love in it.

Evidently Biddy had taught Joe to write. As I lay in bed looking at him, it made me, in my weak state, cry with pleasure to see the pride with which he set about his letter. He got on very well indeed, and when he had signed his name, he viewed his work with unbounded satisfaction.

Not to make Joe uneasy by talking too much, even if I had been able to talk much, I deferred asking him about Miss Havisham until next day. He shook his head when I then asked him if she had recovered.

"Is she dead, Joe?"

"Why, you see, old chap," said Joe, and by way of getting at it by degrees, "I wouldn't go so far as to say that, for that's a deal to say; but she ain't living."

"Did she linger long, Joe?"

"About what you might call a week," said Joe, still determined, on my account, to come to everything by degrees.

"Dear Joe, have you heard what becomes of her property?"

"Well, old chap," said Joe, "it do appear that she had settled the most of it on Miss Estella. But she had wrote out a little coddleshell [1] in her own hand a day or two afore the accident, leaving a cool four thousand to Mr. Matthew Pocket. And why do you suppose, above all things, Pip, she left that cool four thousand unto him? 'Because of Pip's account of him.' I am told by Biddy, that air the writing," said Joe.

This account gave me great joy, as it perfected the only good thing I had done. I asked Joe whether any of the other relatives had any legacies.

"Miss Sarah," said Joe, "she has twenty-five pounds for to buy pills. Miss Georgiana, she has twenty, Mrs. —— what's the name of them wild beasts with humps?"

"Camels?" said I, wondering why he could want to know.

Joe nodded. "Mrs. Camels," by which I understood he meant Camilla, "she has five pounds to buy lights and cheer herself up when she wakes in the night. And now," said Joe, "you can take in one more shovelful today. Old Orlick's been a-bustin' open a dwelling 'ouse."

"Whose?" said I.

"Not, I grant you, but what his manners is given to blusterous. Still, an Englishman's 'ouse is his Castle, and

---

[1] **coddleshell**: Joe means *codicil* (kŏd′ĭ-sĭl), an item of instruction added to a will.

castles must not be busted 'cept when done in wartime. It was Pumblechook's, Pip. And they took his till, and they took his cashbox, and they drinked his wine, and they partook of his wittles, and they slapped his face, and they pulled his nose, and they tied him up to his bedpost, and they stuffed his mouth to perwent his crying out. But he knowed Orlick, and Orlick's in the county jail."

And with conversation like this, Joe became entirely free with me. I was slow to gain strength, but I did slowly and surely become less weak, and Joe stayed with me, and I fancied I was little Pip again.

For the tenderness of Joe was so beautifully proportioned to my need that I was like a child in his hands. There was no change whatever in Joe. Exactly what he had been in my eyes in the old days, he was in my eyes still, just as faithfully, just as simply right.

We looked forward to the day when I should go out for a ride. And when the day came, Joe wrapped me up, took me in his arms, and carried me down to an open carriage, as if I were still the small helpless creature of old. When we got back again and he carried me across the court and up the stairs, I thought of that eventful Christmas Day when he had carried me over the marshes. We had not yet made any mention of my change of fortune, nor did I know how much of my late history he was acquainted with.

"Have you heard, Joe," I asked him that evening, as he smoked his pipe at the window, "who my patron was?"

"I heared," returned Joe, "as it were not Miss Havisham, old chap."

"Did you hear who it was, Joe?"

"Well! I heared as it were a person who sent the person what give you the bank notes at the Jolly Bargemen, Pip."

"So it was."

"Astonishing!" said Joe.

"Did you hear that he was dead, Joe?"

"Which? Him as sent the bank notes, Pip?"

"Yes."

"I think," said Joe, after meditating a long time, and looking rather evasively at the window seat, "as I *did* hear tell that how he were something or another in a general way in that direction."

"Did you hear anything of his circumstances, Joe?"

"Not partickler, Pip."

"If you would like to hear, Joe — " I was beginning, when Joe got up and came to my sofa.

"Look'ee here, old chap," said Joe, bending over me. "Ever the best of friends; ain't us, Pip?"

I was ashamed to answer him.

"Wery good, then," said Joe, as if I *had* answered, "that's all right; that's agreed upon. Then why go into subjects, old chap, which as betwixt two sech must be forever unnecessary?"

The delicacy with which Joe dismissed this theme made a deep impression on my mind. But whether Joe knew how poor I was, and how my great expectations had all dissolved, like our own marsh mists before the sun, I could not understand.

Another thing in Joe that I could not understand when it first began to develop itself, was this. As I became stronger and better, Joe became a little less easy with me. In my weakness and entire dependence on him, the dear fellow had fallen into the old tone, and called me by the names, the dear "old Pip, old chap," that now were music in my ears. I too had fallen into the old ways, only happy and thankful that he let me. But though I held by them fast,

Joe's hold upon them began to slacken; and I soon began to understand that the fault of it was all mine.

I saw this change in him very plainly. One day we had been sitting in the bright warm sunlight, looking at the river, and I chanced to say as we got up:

"See, Joe! I can walk quite strongly. Now, you shall see me walk back by myself."

"Do not overdo it, Pip," said Joe; "but I shall be happy to see you able, sir."

The last word grated on me; but how could I complain! I walked no farther than the gate of the gardens, and then pretended to be weaker than I was, and asked Joe for his arm. Joe gave it to me, but was thoughtful.

I, for my part, was thoughtful too. I was ashamed to tell him exactly how I was placed. He would want to help me out of his little savings, I knew, and I knew that he ought not to help me, and that I must not permit him to do it.

It was a thoughtful evening with both of us. Before we went to bed, I had resolved that I would wait over to-morrow, tomorrow being Sunday, and would begin my new course with the new week. On Monday morning I would speak to Joe and tell him what I had in my thoughts.

We had a quiet day on the Sunday, and we rode out into the country, and then walked in the fields. At night, when I had gone to bed, Joe came into my room, as he had done all through my recovery. He asked me if I felt sure that I was as well as in the morning.

"Yes, dear Joe, quite."

"And are always a-getting stronger, old chap?"

"Yes, dear Joe, steadily."

Joe patted the coverlet on my shoulder with his great good hand and said, in what I thought a husky voice, "Good night!"

When I got up in the morning, refreshed and stronger yet, I was full of my resolution to tell Joe all, without delay. I went to his room, and he was not there. Not only was he not there, but his box was gone.

I hurried then to the breakfast table and on it found a letter. These were its brief contents.

Not wishful to intrude I have departured fur you are well again dear Pip and will do better without

Jo.

P.S. Ever the best of friends.

Enclosed in the letter was a receipt for the debt and costs on which I had been arrested. Down to that moment I had vainly supposed that my creditor had withdrawn until I should be quite recovered. I had never dreamed of Joe's having paid the money; but Joe had paid it, and the receipt was in his name.

What remained for me now, but to follow him to the dear old forge and there to beg his forgiveness and his old friendship, and to relieve my mind and heart of another idea, which had begun as a vague something lingering in my thoughts and had formed into a settled purpose.

The purpose was that I would go to Biddy, that I would show her how humbled and repentant I came back, that I would tell her how I had lost all I once hoped for. Then I would say to her, "Biddy, I think you once liked me very well, when my errant [1] heart, even while it strayed away from you, was quieter and better with you than it ever has been since. If you can like me only half as well once more, if you can take me with all my faults and disappointments on my head, if you can receive

---

[1] errant (ĕr′ănt): wandering.

me like a forgiven child, I hope I am a little worthier of you than I was — not much, but a little. And, Biddy, it shall rest with you to say whether I shall work at the forge with Joe, or whether I shall try for any different occupation down in this country, or whether we shall go away to a distant place where an opportunity awaits me which I set aside when it was offered, until I knew your answer. And now, dear Biddy, if you can tell me that you will go through the world with me, you will surely make it a better world for me, and me a better man for it, and I will try hard to make it a better world for you."

Such was my purpose. After three days more of recovery, I went down to the old place, to put it in execution. And how I sped in it is all I have left to tell.

CHAPTER 42

Biddy and Joe have news for Pip.

THE TIDINGS of my high fortunes having had a heavy fall had got down to my native place and its neighborhood before I got there. I found the Blue Boar in possession of the news, and I found that it made a great change in the Boar's demeanor.

It was evening when I arrived, much fatigued by the journey. The Boar could not put me into my usual bedroom, which was engaged (probably by someone who had expectations), and could only assign me a very poor chamber among the pigeons. I had as sound a sleep and the quality of my dreams was about the same as in the best bedroom.

Early in the morning I strolled round by Satis House. There were printed bills on the gate announcing a sale by auction of the household furniture and effects next week. The house itself was to be sold as old building materials, and pulled down. The ivy had been torn down, and much of it trailed low in the dust and was withered already. Stepping in for a moment at the open gate and looking around me with the uncomfortable air of a stranger who had no business there, I saw the auctioneer's clerk, pen in hand, making a temporary desk of the wheeled chair I had so often pushed along.

It was with pleasant relief that I turned my steps toward Biddy and Joe. I went toward them slowly, for my limbs were weak, but with a sense of increasing relief as I drew nearer to them, and a sense of leaving arrogance and untruthfulness farther and farther behind.

The June weather was delicious. The sky was blue, the larks were soaring high over the green corn. I thought all that countryside more beautiful and peaceful by far than I had ever known it to be. Many pleasant pictures of the life that I would lead there, and of the change for the better that would come over my character when I had a guiding spirit at my side whose simple faith and clear home wisdom I had proved, shortened my way. They awakened a tender emotion in me, for my heart was softened by my return, and such a change had come to pass that I felt like one who was toiling home barefoot from distant travel, and whose wanderings had lasted many years.

The schoolhouse where Biddy was mistress, I had never seen, but the little roundabout lane by which I entered the village for quietness' sake took me past it. I was disappointed to find that the day was a holiday; no children were there, and Biddy's house was closed.

Some hopeful notion of seeing her, busily engaged in her daily duties, before she saw me, had been in my mind and was defeated.

But the forge was a very short distance off, and I went toward it under the sweet green limes, listening for the clink of Joe's hammer. But the clink of Joe's hammer was not in the midsummer's wind.

Almost fearing without knowing why to come in view of the forge, I saw it at last, and saw that it was closed. No gleam of fire, no glittering shower of sparks, no roar of bellows; all shut up, and still.

But the house was not deserted, and the best parlor seemed to be in use, for there were white curtains fluttering in its window, and the window was open and gay with flowers. I went softly toward it, meaning to peep over the flowers, when Joe and Biddy stood before me, arm in arm.

At first Biddy gave a cry, as if she thought it was my ghost, but in another moment she was in my embrace. I wept to see her, and she wept to see me; I, because she looked so fresh and pleasant; she, because I looked so worn and white.

"But, dear Biddy, how fine you look!"

"Yes, dear Pip."

"And, Joe, how fine *you* look!"

"Yes, dear old Pip, old chap."

I looked at both of them, from one to the other, and then —

"It's my wedding day," cried Biddy, in a burst of happiness, "and I am married to Joe!"

They took me into the kitchen, and I laid my head down on the old deal table. Biddy held one of my hands to her lips, and Joe's restoring touch was on my shoulder. "He warn't strong enough, my dear, to be surprised," said Joe. And

Biddy said, "I ought to have thought of it, dear Joe, but I was too happy." They were both so overjoyed to see me, so proud to see me, so touched by my coming to them, so delighted that I should have come by accident to make their day complete!

My first thought was one of great thankfulness that I had never breathed my last hope to Joe. How often, while he was with me in my illness, had it risen to my lips.

"Dear Biddy," said I, "you have the best husband in the whole world, and if you could have seen him by my bed you would have — But no, you couldn't love him better than you do."

"No, I couldn't indeed," said Biddy.

"And, dear Joe, you have the best wife in the whole world, and she will make you as happy as even you deserve to be, you dear, good, noble Joe!"

Joe looked at me with a quivering lip, and put his sleeve before his eyes.

"And Joe and Biddy both, receive my humble thanks for all you have done for me, and all I have so ill repaid! I am going away within the hour, for I am soon going abroad, and I shall never rest until I have worked for the money with which you have kept me out of prison, and have sent it to you. Don't think, dear Joe and Biddy, that if I could repay it a thousand times over, I would suppose I could cancel a farthing of the debt I owe you."

They were both melted by these words, and both entreated me to say no more.

"But I must say more. Dear Joe, I hope you will have children to love, and that some little fellow will sit in this chimney corner of a winter night who may remind you of another little fellow gone out of it forever. Don't tell him, Joe, that I was thankless; don't tell him, Biddy, that I was ungenerous and unjust; only tell him that I honored you both, because you were both so good and true, and that, as your child, I said it would be natural to him to grow up a much better man than I did."

"I ain't a-going," said Joe, from behind his sleeve, "to tell him nothink like that, Pip. Nor Biddy ain't."

"And now, though I know you have already done it in your own kind hearts, pray tell me, both, that you forgive me! Pray let me hear you say the words, that I may carry the sound of them away with me, and then I shall be able to believe that you can trust me, and think better of me, in the time to come!"

"Oh, dear old Pip, old chap," said Joe. "God knows as I forgive you, if I have anythink to forgive!"

"Amen! And God knows I do!" echoed Biddy.

"Now let me go up and look at my old little room and rest there a few minutes by myself. And then when I have eaten with you, go with me as far as the end of the road, dear Joe and Biddy, before we say good-by!"

I sold all I had, and put aside as much as I could for my creditors — who gave me ample time to pay them in full — and I went out and joined Herbert. Within a month, I had left England, and within two months I was clerk to Clarriker and Co., and within four months I assumed my first undivided responsibility. For the beam across the parlor ceiling at Mill Pond Bank had then ceased to tremble under the old purser's growls and was at peace, and Herbert had gone away to marry Clara, and I was left in sole charge of the Eastern Branch until he brought her back.

Many a year went round before I was a third partner in the firm, but I lived happily with Herbert and his wife, and lived frugally, and paid my debts, and maintained a constant correspondence with Biddy and Joe. It was not until I became third in the firm that Clarriker betrayed me to Herbert; but he then declared that the secret of Herbert's partnership had been long enough upon his conscience, and he must tell it. So he told it, and Herbert was as much moved as amazed, and the dear fellow and I were not the worse friends for the long concealment. I must not leave it to be supposed that we were ever a great firm, or that we made mints of money. We were not in a grand way of business, but we had a good name, and worked for our profits, and did very well. We owed so much to Herbert's ever-cheerful industry and readiness that I often wondered how I had conceived that old idea of his inaptitude, until one day it occurred to me that perhaps the inaptitude had never been in him at all, but had been in me.

CHAPTER 43

Pip and Estella meet again.

FOR ELEVEN YEARS I had not seen Joe nor Biddy when, upon an evening in December, an hour or two after dark, I laid my hand softly on the latch of the old kitchen door. I touched it so softly that I was not heard, and I looked in unseen. There, smoking his pipe in the old place by the kitchen firelight, as hale and as strong as ever, though a little gray, sat Joe; and there, fenced into the corner with Joe's leg, and sitting on my own little stool looking at the fire, was — I again!

"We give him the name of Pip for your sake, dear old chap," said Joe, delighted when I took another stool by the child's side, "and we hoped he might grow a little bit like you, and we think he do."

I thought so too, and I took him out for a walk next morning, and we talked for a long time, understanding one another to perfection. And I took him down to the churchyard, and set him on a certain tombstone there, and he showed me from that elevation which stone was sacred to the memory of Philip Pirrip, late of this parish, and Georgiana, his wife.

"Biddy," said I, when I talked with her after dinner, as her little girl lay sleeping in her lap, "you must give Pip to me, one of these days; or lend him, at all events."

"No, no," said Biddy gently. "You must marry."

"So Herbert and Clara say, but I don't think I shall, Biddy. I have so settled down in their home that it's not at all likely. I am already quite an old bachelor."

Biddy looked down at her child, and put its little hand to her lips, and then put the good matronly hand with which she had touched it into mine. There was something in the action and in the light pressure of Biddy's wedding ring that had a very pretty eloquence.

"Dear Pip," said Biddy, "you are sure you don't fret for her?"

"Oh, no — I think not, Biddy."

"Tell me as an old friend. Have you quite forgotten her?"

"My dear Biddy, I have forgotten nothing in my life that ever had a foremost place there, and little that ever had any place there. But that poor dream, as I once used to call it, has all gone by, Biddy, all gone by!"

[Dickens originally wrote only two more paragraphs to end the story, but because some of his friends were dissatisfied with the conclusion, he changed it to what follows. You will find the original ending on page 719.]

Nevertheless, I knew while I said those words that I secretly intended to revisit the site of the old house that evening, alone, for her sake. Yes, even so. For Estella's sake.

I had heard of her as leading a most unhappy life, and as being separated from her husband, who had used her with great cruelty, and who had become quite renowned as a compound of pride, avarice, brutality, and meanness. And I had heard of the death of her husband, from an accident consequent on his ill treatment of a horse. This release had befallen her some two years before; for anything I knew she was married again.

The early dinner hour at Joe's left me time to walk over to the old spot before dark. There was no house now, no brewery, no building whatever left, but the wall of the old garden. The cleared space had been enclosed with a rough fence, and looking over it, I saw that some of the old ivy had struck root anew and was growing green on low quiet mounds of ruin. A gate in the fence standing ajar, I pushed it open and went in.

A cold silvery mist had veiled the afternoon, and the moon was not yet up to scatter it. But the stars were shining beyond the mist, and the moon was coming, and the evening was not dark. I could trace out where every part of the old house had been and was looking along the desolate garden walk, when I beheld a solitary figure in it.

The figure showed itself aware of me as I advanced. It had been moving toward me, but it stood still. As I drew nearer, I saw it to be the figure of a woman. Then, it faltered as if much

717

Pip and Estella meet again.

surprised, and uttered my name, and I cried out:

"Estella!"

"I am greatly changed. I wonder you know me."

The freshness of her beauty was indeed gone, but its majesty and its charm remained. Those attractions in it, I had seen before; what I had never seen before was the saddened softened light of the once proud eyes; what I had never felt before was the friendly touch of the once insensible hand.

We sat down on a bench that was near, and I said, "After so many years, it is strange that we should thus meet again, Estella, here where our first meeting was! Do you often come back?"

"I have never been here since."

"Nor I."

The moon began to rise, and I thought of the prisoner's placid look at the white ceiling, which had passed away. The moon began to rise, and I thought of the pressure on my hand when I had spoken the last words he had heard on earth.

Estella was the next to break the silence.

"I have very often hoped and intended to come back, but have been prevented by many circumstances. Poor, poor old place!"

The silvery mist was touched with the first rays of the moonlight, and the same rays touched the tears that dropped from her eyes. Not knowing that I saw them, and setting herself to get the better of them, she said quietly:

"Were you wondering, as you walked along, how it came to be left in this condition?"

"Yes, Estella."

"The ground belongs to me. It is the only possession I have not relinquished. Everything else has gone from me, little by little, but I have kept this. It was the subject of the only determined resistance I made in all the wretched years."

"Is it to be built on?"

"At last it is. I came here to take leave of it before its change. And you," she said, in a voice of touching interest to a wanderer, "you live abroad still."

"Still."

"And do well, I am sure?"

"I work pretty hard for a sufficient living, and therefore — yes, I do well!"

"I have often thought of you," said Estella.

"Have you?"

"Of late, very often."

"You have always held your place in *my* heart," I answered.

And we were silent again until she spoke.

"I little thought," said Estella, "that I should take leave of you in taking leave of this spot. I am very glad to do so."

"Glad to part again, Estella? To me, parting is a painful thing. To me, the remembrance of our last parting has been ever mournful and painful."

"But you said to me," returned Estella, very earnestly, " 'God bless you, God forgive you!' And if you could say that to me then, you will not hesitate to say that to me now — now, when suffering has been stronger than all other teaching, and has taught me to understand what your heart used to be. I have been bent and broken, but — I hope — into a better shape. Be as considerate and good to me as you were, and tell me we are friends."

"We are friends," said I, rising and bending over her, as she rose from the bench.

"And will continue friends apart," said Estella.

I took her hand in mine, and we went out of the ruined place; and as the morning mists had risen long ago when I first left the forge, so the evening mists were rising now, and in all the broad expanse of tranquil light they showed to me, I saw no shadow of another parting from her.

[The original ending, as it appeared in the first edition of *Great Expectations*, is as follows:]

It was two years more before I saw Estella. I had heard of her as leading a most unhappy life, and as being separated from her husband, who had used her with great cruelty, and who had become quite renowned as a compound of pride, brutality, and meanness. I had heard of the death of her husband from an accident consequent on ill treating a horse, and of her being married again to a Shropshire doctor who, against his interest, had once very manfully interposed on an occasion when he was in professional attendance upon Mr. Drummle, and had witnessed some outrageous treatment of her. I had heard that the Shropshire doctor was not rich, and that they lived on her own personal fortune. I was in England again — in London, and walking along Piccadilly with little Pip — when a servant came running after me to ask would I step back to a lady in a carriage who wished to speak to me. It was a little pony carriage which the lady was driving, and the lady and I looked sadly enough on one another.

"I am greatly changed, I know; but I thought you would like to shake hands with Estella too, Pip. Lift up that pretty child and let me kiss it!" (She supposed the child, I think, to be my child.) I was very glad afterward to have had the interview; for in her face and in her voice, and in her touch, she gave me the assurance that suffering had been stronger than Miss Havisham's teaching, and had given her a heart to understand what my heart used to be.

TYING TOGETHER THE THREADS OF THE PLOT

With the close of the Third Stage, the many secrets of the story are fully revealed. All the threads are firmly woven into place. We see that the novel has a central design, or plot, which reaches from Pip's childhood into his manhood, and like a fine, rich tapestry, it also has some bold small patterns in the form of minor plots. All are woven together artistically. We are now able to look at the story as a whole. To sharpen your observation, see whether you can tie together these threads of the plot:

1. What was Compeyson's relation to Magwitch *before* their imprisonment? *after* their escape? *after* their release from prison? How are Compeyson and Orlick connected in the story? Who was Arthur?

2. What was Miss Havisham's connection with Compeyson?

3. How did Magwitch happen to know Mr. Jaggers? Did he deliberately try to murder Compeyson at the end of the story? For what crime was he tried?

4. What held Molly under the influence of Mr. Jaggers? Was she aware of Magwitch's or Estella's whereabouts and activities?

5. What information did Pip keep from Herbert during their association in London? What information did he keep from Magwitch until the very end? Had this last piece of information been given to Magwitch earlier, would it have changed the basic plot in any way?

6. Would any good have been served if Estella had known about Molly?

SUMMING UP THE CHARACTERS

7. Now would be a good time to look over the list you made at the end of the Second Stage. Identifying the characters as "Good Influences" or "Bad Influences" helped to separate them for you, but perhaps reading the Third Stage has made you want to revise your list. By the close of the novel, what further changes have occurred in the people on your list? Magwitch has emerged as a basically good man, dealt with harshly by life. What changes have come to Estella? Herbert Pocket? What is your final opinion of each of these people who together helped to make a young boy into a man? Last, and most important, what is your judgment of that boy-into-man: Pip?

8. In the Third Stage of the book, your opinion of Pip must have undergone a change. What good traits appear in him when he has to make important decisions? These will readily be seen if you discuss the way he treats Magwitch, beginning with the opening scene of the Third Stage and ending with the man's death.

9. At what point in the Third Stage could it be said that Pip has finally come to know decisively what he values most in life? Pick out other events that show us that he has found himself and that his values are no longer confused.

IDEAS TO TALK OVER

10. Which one of the two endings do you prefer? Take a class vote to determine which is more popular. Students often like to "dream up" a third ending. Why not try it?

11. If the "happy" ending to the book is the one you prefer, explain why you think that the older, gentler Estella is an even better type of wife for Pip than Biddy might have been.

12. The phrase "great expectations" had one meaning at the beginning of the novel and perhaps another at the close. What, really, are the great expectations all of us share and value, as Pip learned to do?

FINDING DICKENS IN THE STORY

13. What scenes in the novel do you think might have been drawn from Charles Dickens' own experience, according to what you have read about him? What experience did Magwitch have in common with Dickens' own father? What would make you think that Mr. Jaggers is based on a character Dickens knew?

THE NOVEL AS A TYPE

14. Reading *Great Expectations* has placed before you some examples of the qualities and characteristics of the novel as a "type," in comparison with the short story. The novel has more characters, for instance, and their lives can be studied in greater detail than those of the characters in a short story. Can you make a list of the other differences? In making your list, keep in mind the elements of plot, character, setting, and time.

PEN AND PAPER

Here are some suggestions for composition topics:

A Character Study of Abel Magwitch
Joe Gargery and Mrs. Joe — an Odd but Happy Couple
What Is a Snob?
Pip's Most Courageous Decision
Estella Wasn't to Blame
You Can't Run Away from Your Problems
Today and Yesterday: Contrasting the Lives of Children in the Nineteenth and the Twentieth Centuries
What Is True Friendship?
Growing Up Is Never Too Easy

The Novel

SUGGESTIONS FOR FURTHER READING

Alcott, Louisa May, *Little Women*
First published in 1868, this is still a favorite with girls.

Annixter, Paul, *Swiftwater* (Wang, 1950)
During a family crisis, Bucky takes over his father's job as a trapper.

Baner, Skulda Vanadis, *First Parting* (Longmans, Green, 1960)
Girls will appreciate this story of a new teacher's experiences in a one-room schoolhouse on the prairies.

Bell, Margaret, *Watch for a Tall White Sail* (Morrow, 1948)
A girl faces new responsibility when she and her twin brother are stranded in an Alaskan seacoast town.

Buck, Pearl S., *The Good Earth* (John Day, 1949)
A Chinese peasant and his wife suffer poverty and wealth, joy and pain, as they work on the land they love.

Burchard, Peter, *Jed* (Coward-McCann, 1960)
A simple, moving story of a young sixteen-year-old Yankee soldier who finds a young Confederate in need of help.

Byrne, Donn, *Messer Marco Polo* *
A vivid retelling of Marco Polo's thirteenth-century journey to the mysterious empire of the Mongol ruler Kubla Khan.

Coleman, Pauline H., *The Different One* (Dodd, Mead, 1955)
After studying about heredity in biology class in school, a girl comes to the mistaken conclusion that she is adopted.

Cooper, James Fenimore, *The Last of the Mohicans*
Good readers who enjoy historical novels will find this classic filled with conflict and action.

Daly, Maureen, *Seventeenth Summer* (Dodd, Mead, 1948)
The successful, widely read novel about a seventeen-year-old girl.

Defoe, Daniel, *Robinson Crusoe*
The thrilling classic about an English castaway on a desert island.

Dickens, Charles, *David Copperfield* and *Dombey and Son*
"Must" reading for those who would deepen their friendship with this author.

Edmonds, Walter D., *Drums Along the Mohawk* (Little, Brown, 1951)
Indian warfare in the Mohawk Valley in Revolutionary times.

Ferber, Edna, *Cimarron* (Grosset & Dunlap, 1950)
The land rush in Oklahoma during the 1870's.

Freedman, Benedict and Nancy, *Mrs. Mike* (Coward-McCann, 1947)
A sixteen-year-old tubercular patient marries a sergeant of the Canadian Mounties. Their life at a Hudson Bay Post is eventful.

Gorsline, Douglas, *Farm Boy* (Viking, 1950)
Boys will enjoy this story of sixteen-year-old Johnny and how he deals with his problems.

Goudge, Elizabeth, *The Dean's Watch* (Coward-McCann, 1960)
Characters are painted sharply in this story set in a medieval cathedral town.

Hemingway, Ernest, *The Old Man and the Sea* (Scribner, 1952)
A remarkable tale of hardship, courage, and devotion.

Hudson, W. H., *Green Mansions* *
The forest wilderness of Venezuela is the background for this vividly imaginative adventure story.

Hugo, Victor, *Les Misérables* *
A stirring classic with characters you will not forget.

James, Will, *Smoky, the Cow Horse* (Scribner, 1926)
The classic story of a one-man horse.

Lane, Rose W., *Let the Hurricane Roar* (Longmans, Green, 1933)
You'll shiver while you read this one.

Lewis, Elizabeth, *To Beat a Tiger* (Holt, Rinehart & Winston, 1956)
Hunger and danger bind together sixteen boys who are separated from their families during the Japanese occupation of China.

* Included in *Four Novels for Adventure,* Fuller and Achtenhagen, eds. (Harcourt, Brace & World, 1960).

London, Jack, *The Call of the Wild* (Grosset & Dunlap, 1950) and *White Fang* (Arcadia, 1950)
Always favorites with boys and appealing to girls who like stories of adventure.
Nordhoff, C. B., and J. N. Hall, *Mutiny on the Bounty* (Little, Brown, 1932)
A captain drives his crew to mutiny.
O'Hara, Mary, *My Friend Flicka* (Lippincott, 1944)
Delightful story of Ken and the colt he brought up. Read *Green Grass of Wyoming* (Lippincott, 1946) too, and *Thunderhead* (Lippincott, 1943)
Orwell, George, *1984* (Harcourt, Brace & World, 1949)
A terrifying story of a society where individualism and privacy are destroyed by dictatorship.
Pease, Howard, *Bound for Singapore* (Doubleday, 1946), *Heart of Danger* (Doubleday, 1946), and *The Dark Adventure* (Doubleday, 1950)
Boys like these adventure stories and hunt for more by this popular author.
Pyle, Howard, *Men of Iron* (Harper, 1930)
A popular storyteller relates a tale of murder solved back in the days of knighthood.
Rasmussen, A. H., *Sea Fever* (Hastings House, 1960)
A good sea story involving a fifteen-year-old boy.
Rawlings, Marjorie K., *The Yearling* (Scribner, 1952)
A boy, his pet deer, and their problems.
Richter, Conrad, *Light in the Forest* (Knopf, 1953)
A white boy reared by Indians remains loyal to them and their ways.
Saroyan, William, *The Human Comedy* (Harcourt, Brace & World, 1943)
Humor and hard knocks help a boy grow up.
Schaefer, Jack, *Shane* (Houghton Mifflin, 1954)
A tense story of a mysterious man of power who takes the side of the Wyoming homesteaders and wins.
Scott, Sir Walter, *Ivanhoe*
No better story of the Middle Ages — knights, adventure, romance.
Speare, Elizabeth, *Witch of Blackbird Pond* (Houghton Mifflin, 1958)

A moving story set in Colonial Connecticut.
Stevenson, Robert Louis, *The Black Arrow*
Stirring tale of Old England by a master storyteller. *Kidnapped,* another favorite, has a Scottish background.
Tunis, John R., *All-American* (Harcourt, Brace & World, 1942), *The Iron Duke* (Harcourt, Brace & World, 1950) and *Schoolboy Johnson* (Morrow, 1958)
Stories for boys that emphasize sportsmanship at its best.
Twain, Mark, *The Prince and the Pauper* (World Publishing, 1948)
A prince changes places with a poor lad, and each meets adventure. *The Adventures of Tom Sawyer* and *The Adventures of Huckleberry Finn.* Both these novels are based on memories of the author's boyhood days in Missouri.
Verne, Jules, *Twenty Thousand Leagues Under the Sea* (World Publishing, 1946)
First published in 1896, this classic tale about a mystery submarine was once thought a wild flight into the imagination!
West, Jessamyn, *Cress Delahanty* (Harcourt, Brace & World, 1954) and *Friendly Persuasion* (Harcourt, Brace & World, 1945)
Both stories of happy home life.
Wyss, Johann D., *Swiss Family Robinson* (Dutton, 1957)
Another classic of shipwreck and castaways. This one concerns a family that takes every mishap in its stride.

BOOKS ABOUT DICKENS

Becker, May Lamberton, *Introducing Charles Dickens* (Dodd, Mead, 1940)
An excellent biography of Dickens, written especially for young readers.
Graham, Eleanor, *Story of Charles Dickens* (Abelard-Schuman, 1954)
This book stresses events in the life of Dickens which his writings reflect.
Priestley, J. B., *Charles Dickens: A Pictorial Biography* (Viking, 1962)
Illustrated account of the novelist's life.

FOR YOUR LISTENING

Scenes dramatized from *Great Expectations* are available on longplay record *Many Voices* 9B.

Frontispiece, Susan McCartney, courtesy The Metropolitan Museum of Art, Fletcher Fund, 1931; Page xiv, Susan McCartney, courtesy The Metropolitan Museum of Art, Purchase, 1929; 15, Ray Atkeson; 48, Frank Monaco; 49, British Travel Association; 59, Trans-World Airlines; 79, Emil Schultess from Black Star; 151, Courtesy of Mrs. Peter Benziger; 163, Photo Researchers; 164, drawing by James Thurber, permission *The New Yorker;* 166, California Institute of Technology; 170, Susan McCartney, courtesy The Metropolitan Museum of Art, Bequest of Benjamin Altman, 1913; 173, Pan American World Airways; 179, top, left; Shostal, right: Rapho-Guillumette, middle: Horst from Shostal, bottom: Ray Atkeson; 187, Culver; 192, Crown; 195, Photo Researchers; 197, Edith Reichmann; 198, Photo Researchers; 202, Rapho-Guillumette; 207, Susan McCartney; 209, British Information Services; 211, Boston Public Library; 214, Radio-Times Hulton; 223, top left: Radio-Times Hulton, bottom: Pix; 224, Brown Brothers; 228, New York Public Library; 231, Tulane University; 232, Museum of the City of New York; 239, Black and White, New York Public Library; Color, The Albright-Knox Art Gallery, Gift of the Julia R. and Estelle L. Foundation, Inc.; 240, Alfred Wertheimer; 247, Shostal; 255, Shostal; 258, Crane from Black Star; 267, T. Hatcher from Shostal; 271, Black Star; 279, Chicago Historical Society; 289, Hartmann from Magnum; 290, Culver; 294, Charles H. Habbell, courtesy of Thompson Ramo Woolridge, Inc.; 297, Bettmann Archive; 301, Bettmann Archive; 303, Edward Gray; 304, Schatz from Black Star; 306, Edward Gray; 308, Schatz from Black Star; 311, United States Air Force; 315,

National Aeronautical Services Association; 317, National Aeronautical Services Association; 319, National Aeronautical Services Association; 338, Louis Frohman, courtesy The Metropolitan Museum of Art, Fletcher Fund, 1956; 341, Haas from Magnum; 342, courtesy of Boston Museum of Fine Arts; 348, Boston Public Library, Rarebook Division; 355, Ehem. Staatl. Museen Berlin-Dahlem, Gemäldegalerie; 363, In the Collection of the Corcoran Gallery of Art; 365, Alwin Tolle; 369, Bibliotheque Nationale, Paris; 375, Hollyman from Photo Researchers; 378, courtesy of the Toledo Museum of Art, Gift of Edward Drummond Libbey, 1939; 380, The Lick Observatory; 383, Boston Museum of Fine Arts; 399, courtesy of Hall Park McCullaugh; 402, Shostal; 405, Bettmann Archive; 407, Hollyman from Photo Researchers; 411, Library of Congress; 412, Bettmann Archive; 414, Rollin Barrett; 415, © Arnold Newman; 416, Ansel Adams from Magnum; 418, Brown Brothers; 421, Photo Researchers; 426, Susan McCartney, courtesy Metropolitan Museum of Art, Rogers Fund, 1925; 445, Wagner International Photos; 469, Drawing C. Walter Hodges from *Globe Restored,* courtesy Ernest Benn, Ltd.; 518, Set Design by Claude Marks photo by Sedge Le Blang; 522, Susan McCartney, courtesy National Museum Athens; 551, New York Public Library Rarebook Division; 552, top: Boston Museum of Fine Arts, bottom, left: Boston Museum of Fine Arts, right: American Library color slide, courtesy National Gallery, London; 553, Alinari; 554, Susan McCartney, courtesy Josiah Wedgwood & Sons, Inc.; 556, Boston Public Library; 558, Victoria and Albert Museum; 559, Boston Public Library.

Special Indexes

READING SKILLS. Reading skills, when included in the study material accompanying a selection, are found on the opening page of the selection, under a separate heading at the bottom of the page, as listed below. A corresponding heading will be found in the study material that follows the selection; under this heading are study questions on the particular skill.

Anticipating outcome, 36, 118
Drawing conclusions, 80, 97, 214
Following the plot, 12, 429
Inferring character, 60, 152
Levels of meaning, 130
Noting an author's technique, 185
Reading with questions in mind, 90
Recognizing important details, 17, 258, 447
Recognizing main ideas, 290
Recognizing the nature of the conflict, 506
Relating character to plot, 5
Relating details to the main idea, 232, 327
Thematic reading, 289, 335
Tools of the poet, 352, 354, 365, 370, 395
Visualizing, 173

VOCABULARY DEVELOPMENT EXERCISES. The following vocabulary exercises appear under the heading *For Your Vocabulary* in the study material at the end of the selections.

Antonyms, 382
Context: using context clues, 47; words in context, 136, 191, 423
Contrast in character and language, 499
Interpreting and responding to language, 408
New words, 178
Playing with words, 387
Shades of meaning, 667
Suffixes: *–ive,* 150; *–some,* 78
Synonyms, 382
Using words in unusual ways, 385
Word families, 465
Word histories, 183, 278, 326, 366, 392, 403, 619
Word origins, 34

LITERARY TERMS AND TECHNIQUES. The following are the literary terms and techniques examined in connection with the study of the selections.

Allegory, 417
Alliteration, 353
Article, the, 172, 178
Biography, characteristics of, 208
Character: as an element in stories, 50; as developed in the drama, 447, 464–5, 480, 487, 499, 517; as developed in the novel, 666–7

Class reading, 347
Climax, as an element in plot, 3–4, 104
Conflict, 3–4; internal conflict, 506
Drama, characteristics of, 427–8
Epic, characteristics of, 523–4
Essay, the, 172, 183
Framework story, 137, 152, 162
Humor, techniques of, 34, 184, 393
Irony, 34; dramatic, 517
Lyric poetry, 365
Metaphor, 354
Onomatopoeia, 395
Plot 3–4: as developed in the drama, 429, 517; as developed in the novel, 618, 667, 719–20; complication, 3–4; steps 3–4
Poetry, characteristics of, 339–44; differences from prose, 369; in prose, 277; unusual sentence patterns in, 370
Question-mark story, 137
Research, techniques of, 51, 258, 278
Resolution, as an element in plot, 3–4, 517, 719–20
Science fiction, 168
Setting, 50
Short Story, characteristics of, 1, 3–4, 50, 96, 137
Short-short story, 137, 166
Simile, 354
Style, 94
Surprise-ending story, 137
Symbolism, 16
Theme, as developed in stories, 96

COMPOSITION EXERCISES. Suggestions for compositions are included in the study material under the heading *Pen and Paper*. Listed below are the pages on which the composition exercises appear, together with the selections they accompany.

Page:

ILLUSTRATIONS. Reproductions of famous paintings, prints, and sculpture appear as follows.

Commentary and study material relating to illustrations and to the selections that they accompany appear on the following pages.

AUTHORS' BIOGRAPHIES. Biographies of authors represented by selections in the book are to be found as follows.

Glossary

Listed below are words from the selections in the book that you will find useful to add to your vocabulary. The words are defined according to the context in which they appear in the selections. Proper names and words that are specialized, archaic, or not generally useful are not included in this glossary but have been footnoted, when appropriate, in the text.

a

abhorrence (ăb·hôr′ĕns). Disgust.
abjure (ăb·jŏŏr′). To renounce or reject.
abomination (ȧ·bŏm′ĭ·nā′shŭn). Horror; loathing.
abstracted (ăb·străkt′ĕd). Absent-minded.
accessible (ăk·sĕs′ĭ·b'l). Within reach.
acquire (ȧ·kwīr′). To gain or get.
adhesion (ăd·hē′zhŭn). A place where tissues have grown together.
adjust (ȧ·jŭst′). To set right.
administrator (ăd·mĭn′ĭs·trā′tĕr). An official.
adulation (ăd′ū·lā′shŭn). Great praise.
aggressive (ȧ·grĕs′ĭv). Likely to attack or quarrel.
agitate (ăj′ĭ·tāt). To disturb; to excite.
allege (ȧ·lĕj′). To claim.
allude (ȧ·lūd′). To refer indirectly.
amend (ȧ·mĕnd′). To change.
amiable (ā′mĭ·ȧ·b'l). Friendly.
amphitheater (ăm′fĭ·thē′ȧ·tĕr). An arena with raised tiers of seats in an oval or circular shape.
analyze (ăn′ȧ·līz). To reason out; to examine the parts or features of.
anatomy (ȧ·năt′ō·mĭ). Structure of a plant or animal.
anguish (ăng′gwĭsh). Extreme pain or distress.
animate (ăn′ĭ·māt). To inspire; to make lively.
anonymous (ȧ·nŏn′ĭ·mŭs). Unknown by name; unnamed.
anticipate (ăn·tĭs′ĭ·pāt). To expect.
apprehend (ăp′rē·hĕnd′). To understand.
aptitude (ăp′tĭ·tūd). Natural learning ability.
aquatic (ȧ·kwăt′ĭk). Water-dwelling.
arbitrary (är′bĭ·trĕr′ĭ). Unyielding; despotic.
arboreal (är·bō′rē·ăl). Of or like trees.
arch (ärch). Sly; mischievous.
arduous (är′dū·ŭs). Difficult.
arrogance (ăr′ō·găns). Haughtiness; pride. *adj.* **arrogant.**
aspirant (ăs·pīr′ănt). Hoper; seeker.

aspiration (ăs′pĭ·rā′shŭn). Hope; ambition.
assailant (ȧ·sāl′ănt). Attacker.
assent (ȧ·sĕnt′). To consent.
assurance (ȧ·shŏŏr′ăns). Certainty.
astute (ăs·tūt′). Keen; clever.
asunder (ȧ·sŭn′dĕr). Apart; separated.
audacity (ô·dăs′ĭ·tĭ). Boldness; impudence.
auditory (ô′dĭ·tō′rĭ). Pertaining to hearing.
august (ô·gŭst′). Majestic; impressive.
austerity (ôs·tĕr′ĭ·tĭ). Severity.
avarice (ăv′ȧ·rĭs). Greed for wealth.
averse (ȧ·vûrs′). Unwilling; opposed.

b

balance (băl′ăns). To equal.
betrothal (bē·trŏth′ăl). Engagement to be married.
blanch (blănch). To whiten.
blight (blīt). Any disease causing withering and decay in plants.
boisterous (bois′tĕr·ŭs). Noisy.
boorish (bŏŏr′ĭsh). Rude.
brine (brīn). Salt water.
brooch (brōch). An ornamental clasp with a pin or loop for attaching it.
brood (brŏŏd). To think moodily.
browse (brouz). To graze; to feed.
brusque (brŭsk). Abrupt; rough.

c

calculation (kăl′kū·lā′shŭn). Estimate.
calculus (kăl′kū·lŭs). A branch of higher mathematics.
callous (kăl′ŭs). Unfeeling.
canister (kăn′ĭs·tĕr). Container.
canny (kăn′ĭ). Shrewd.
canopy (kăn′ō·pĭ). Covering; top.
canyon (kăn′yŭn). A deep, rocky valley.
caper (kā′pĕr). To romp.
capitalize (kăp′ĭ·tăl·īz). To make money.

āpe, chãotic, bâre, ăt, ăttend, ärt, flásk, átop; ēke, mẽrely, ĕlect, ĕcho, prudĕnt, doẽr; ītem, ĭnn; rarĭty; ōde, ôpaque, fôr, dŏt, lôft, cŏnfide; sōon, tŏŏk; sour, toil; tūbe, ūnique, tûrn, sŭp, ŭntil.

caravan (kăr′a·văn). A company of travelers; a procession of cars, trucks, beasts of burden, etc.

careen (ka·rēn′). To sway.

cataract (kăt′a·răkt). A film over the lens of the eye.

catastrophe (ka·tăs′trŏ·fē). Calamity.

cavalcade (kăv′ăl·kād′). Procession.

celestial (sē·lĕs′chăl). Heavenly.

chaff (chăf). 1. Light husks of grain. 2. Anything light and worthless.

chaos (kā′ŏs). Confusion.

coherent (kŏ·hēr′ĕnt). Clearly connected or related.

collier (kŏl′yēr). A coal miner.

commendation (kŏm′ĕn·dā′shŭn). Recommendation; approval.

compassion (kŏm·păsh′ŭn). Pity or sympathy.

component (kŏm·pō′nĕnt). A part.

compound (kŏm′pound). Mixture.

comprehensive (kŏm′prē·hĕn′sĭv). Full; wide.

compromise (kŏm′prŏ·mīz). Settlement involving agreement by both sides to give up part of their demands.

computer (kŏm·pūt′ēr). Calculator.

congenital (kŏn·jĕn′ĭ·tăl). Present at birth.

consultation (kŏn′sŭl·tā′shŭn). Conference.

contemplation (kŏn′tĕm·plā′shŭn). Thought; study.

contemptuous (kŏn·tĕmp′·tū·ŭs). Scornful.

contiguous (kŏn·tĭg′ū·ŭs). Adjoining.

contort (kŏn·tôrt′). To twist.

controversy (kŏn′trŏ·vûr′sĭ). Disagreement.

copious (kō′pĭ·ŭs). Plentiful.

courier (kōōr′ĭ·ēr). Messenger.

courtier (kōr′tĭ·ēr). An attendant to a ruler.

crystallize (krĭs′tăl·īz). To make almost clear or transparent.

culprit (kŭl′prĭt). A criminal or person accused of crime or wrongdoing.

curate (kū′rāt). Clergyman.

curvature (kûr′va·tūr). Curving.

d

daft (dăft). Crazy.

dawdle (dô′d'l). To loiter; to waste time.

defer (dē·fûr′). 1. To yield. 2. To put off.

deference (dĕf′ēr·ens). Courtesy; respect.

definitiveness (dē·fĭn′ĭ·tĭv·nĕs). Decisiveness.

deject (dē·jĕkt′). To make gloomy; to cast down in spirit.

delegate (dĕl′ē·gāt). To assign.

delusion (dē·lū′zhŭn). False belief or opinion; misunderstanding or misconception.

demeanor (dē·mēn′ēr). Conduct; behavior.

denote (dē·nōt′). To signify.

deplorable (dē·plōr′a·b'l). Sad.

deprive (dē·prīv′). To rob; to keep from having.

derange (dē·rānj′). To upset; to make insane.

derision (dē·rĭzh′ŭn). Scorn.

desolate (dĕs′ō·lĭt). Barren; deserted.

destiny (dĕs′tĭ·nĭ). Fate.

dexterity (dĕks·tĕr′ĭ·tĭ). Skill.

diaphanous (dī·ăf′a·nŭs). Transparent.

diffuse (dĭ·fūs′). To spread out.

dilate (dī·lāt′). To enlarge.

dilemma (dĭ·lĕm′a). Difficult choice.

dire (dīr). Terrible.

discern (dĭ·zûrn′). To see; to understand.

disconsolate (dĭs·kŏn′sō·lĭt). Sorrowful.

discordant (dĭs·kôr′dănt). Harsh.

discourse (dĭs·kōrs′). Speech; conversation.

discretion (dĭs·krĕsh′ŭn). Good judgment. *adj.* **discreet** (dĭs·krēt′).

disdainful (dĭs·dān′fōol). Scornful; haughty.

dismal (dĭz′măl). Gloomy.

disreputable (dĭs·rĕp′ū·ta·b'l). Not respectable.

dissemble (dĭ·sĕm′b'l). To pretend.

distraught (dĭs·trôt′). Crazed; extremely upset.

divert (dī·vûrt′). To turn aside.

docile (dŏs′ĭl). Gentle; teachable; easily managed. *n.* **docility** (dŏ·sĭl′ĭ·tĭ).

doleful (dōl′fōol). Mournful.

dour (dōor). Stern.

douse (dous). To drench.

durable (dū′ra·b'l). Long-lasting.

e

earl (ûrl). Nobleman with rank corresponding to that of count.

eccentricity (ĕk′sĕn·trĭs′ĭ·tĭ). Oddness.

ecstasy (ĕk′sta·sĭ). Joy.

elation (ē·lā′shŭn). High spirits; high satisfaction.

embellish (ĕm·bĕl′ĭsh). To decorate.

emerge (ē·mûrj′). To come forth.

eminent (ĕm′ĭ·nĕnt). Clear; evident.

emit (ē·mĭt′). To give off.

emphatic (ĕm·făt′ĭk). Forceful; decisive.

engross (ĕn·grōs′). To interest deeply.

enjoin (ĕn·join′). To command; to bind by a promise.

enormity (ē·nôr′mĭ·tĭ). Wickedness.

enshroud (ĕn·shroud′). To cover as with a garment.

ensue (ĕn·sū′). To follow.

entrails (ĕn′trālz). Internal parts.

episode (ĕp′ĭ·sōd). Incident or set of incidents or events.

---

bar; church; dog; ardûous; fat; go; hear; jail; key; lame; meat; not; ring; pay; ran; see; shell; ten; there, thick; pastûre; vast; wind; yes; zoo, zh = z in azure.

epistle (ê·pǐs″l). Letter to a person.
epithet (ĕp′ĭ·thĕt). A descriptive expression.
equanimity (ē′kwȧ·nǐm′ĭ·tǐ). Calmness.
evasive (ê·vā′sǐv). Not frank.
exasperation (ĕg·zas′pēr·ā′shŭn). Anger; irritation.
exceed (ĕk·sēd′). To go beyond the limit; to surpass.
exhilarate (ĕg·zǐl′ȧ·rāt). To enliven.
exhort (ĕg·zôrt′). To advise; to urge.
exorbitant (ĕg·zôr′bǐ·tȧnt). Excessive; unreasonable.
extraneous (ĕks·trā′nê·ŭs). Nonessential.
extricate (ĕks′trǐ·kāt). To free or remove, as from difficulties.
exuberant (ĕg·zū′bēr·ȧnt). Abundant; lavish.
exultant (ĕg·zŭl′tȧnt). Triumphant.

f

facet (făs′ĕt). Side or aspect.
farthing (fär′thǐng). Small British coin worth less than a penny.
fathom (făth′ŭm). A measure of six feet.
feline (fē′līn). Cat; catlike.
felony (fĕl′ô·nǐ). A serious crime.
fervent (fûr′vĕnt). Warm; impassioned.
flinch (flǐnch). To dodge; to draw back.
fraudulent (frô·d′û·lĕnt). Deceitful.
frequent (frê·kwĕnt′) To visit often.
frugal (frōō′gȧl). Saving; economizing.
fugitive (fū′jǐ·tǐv). A person who runs away to escape the law.
furlough (fûr′lō). Leave of absence.
furtive (fûr′tǐv). Stealthy.

g

gall (gôl). To irritate.
gesticulation (jĕs·tǐk′û·lā′shŭn). Motion used for emphasis.
gesture (jĕs′tûr). Motion of the head, hands, etc.
glib (glǐb). Smooth-talking.
glider (glīd′ēr). An engineless aircraft.
gore (gōr). Triangular opening.
gratuitous (grȧ·tū′ǐ·tŭs). Uncalled for; free.
grievance (grēv′ȧns). Injustice; cause for complaint.
grimace (grǐ·mās′). To make a wry face.
grizzle (grǐz″l). To make grayish.
grovel (grŏv″l). To humble oneself in false submission or obedience.
grub (grŭb). To dig.
guttural (gŭt′ēr·ȧl). Harsh-sounding.

h

haphazard (hăp′hăz′ērd). Random; chance.
hapless (hăp′lĕs). Unlucky.
harass (hăr′ȧs). To annoy.
haunch (hônch). Leg and hip.
heathen (hē′thĕn). A nonreligious person.
hectic (hĕk′tǐk). Feverish.
homestead (hōm′stĕd). Home and land connected with it.
humid (hū′mǐd). Damp.
humiliate (hû·mǐl′ĭ·āt). To humble; to lower the self-respect of.
hummock (hŭm′ŭk). Knoll or hill.
hypocritical (hǐp′ô·krǐt′ǐ·kȧl). Insincere.

i

illustrious (ǐ·lŭs′trǐ·ŭs). Famous; renowned.
impartial (ǐm·pär′shȧl). Fair.
impediment (ǐm·pĕd′ǐ·mĕnt). Obstacle.
impenetrable (ǐm·pĕn′ê·trȧ·b′l). Too thick to be seen through or to pierce.
imperious (ǐm·pēr′ǐ·ŭs). Domineering; arrogant.
impetuous (ǐm·pĕt′û·ŭs). Rash.
implicate (ǐm′plǐ·kāt). To involve or entangle.
impressionable (ǐm·prĕsh′ŭn·ȧ·b′l). Capable of being influenced.
impromptu (ǐm·prŏmp′tū). Offhand; unrehearsed.
inaccessibility (ǐn′ăk·sĕs′ǐ·bǐl′ǐ·tǐ). Condition of being unreachable.
inarticulate (ǐn′är·tǐk′û·lȧt). Wordless; unable to speak or to be understood.
incarcerated (ǐn·kär′sēr·āt·ĕd). Confined; shut up in.
incentive (ǐn·sĕn′tǐv). Inducement; motive.
incessant (ǐn·sĕs′ȧnt). Unceasing.
incline (ǐn·klīn′). 1. To lean; to tend. 2. To slant or slope. *n.* **inclination** (ǐn′klǐ·nā′shŭn).
incognito (ǐn·kŏg′nǐ·tō). Disguised.
incomprehensible (ǐn′kŏm·prê·hĕn′sǐ·b′l). Not able to be understood. *n.* **incomprehensibility** (ǐn′kŏm·prê·hĕn′sǐ·bǐl′ǐ·tǐ).
incorruptible (ǐn′kŏ·rŭp′tǐ·b′l). Absolutely dependable; staunch. *adv.* **incorruptibly.**
incredible (ǐn·krĕd′ǐ·b′l). Unbelievable.
indifferent (ǐn·dǐf′ēr·ĕnt). Mediocre; ordinary.
indiscriminate (ǐn′dǐs·krǐm′ǐ·nǐt). Careless.
inestimable (ǐn·ĕs′tǐ·mȧ·b′l). Priceless.
inevitable (ǐn·ĕv′ǐ·tȧ·b′l). Unavoidable.
inexhaustible (ǐn′ĕg·zôs′tǐ·b′l). Limitless.
infallible (ǐn·făl′ǐ·b′l). Unerring; unfailing.
infer (ǐn·fûr′). To imply; to guess.

āpe, châotic, bâre, ăt, ȧttend, ärt, flăsk, ȧtop; ēke, mẹrely, ĕlect, ĕcho, prudĕnt, doẽr; ītem, ĭnn; rarĭty; ōde, ŏpaque, fôr, dŏt, lôft, cǒnfide; sōōn, tōōk; sour, toil; tūbe, ûnique, tûrn, sŭp, ŭntil.

infinite (ĭn'fĭ·nĭt). Endless.

infirmary (ĭn·fûr'má·rĭ). Room or building for treatment of the sick, especially in an institution.

inflexible (ĭn·flĕk'sĭ·b'l). Unyielding; stubborn.

ingrate (ĭn'grāt). Ungrateful person.

inherent (ĭn·hĕr'ĕnt). Existing naturally.

injunction (ĭn·jŭngk'shŭn). An order or direction, sometimes issued by a court.

innate (ĭn'nāt). Inborn; natural.

inshore (ĭn'shōr'). Toward shore.

insolent (ĭn'sō·lĕnt). Rude; insulting.

insoluble (ĭn·sŏl'û·b'l). Unsolvable.

insufferable (ĭn·sŭf'ēr·á·b'l). Not endurable.

intercept (ĭn'tēr·sĕpt'). To stop; hinder; seize.

interject (ĭn'tēr·jĕkt'). To throw in.

interminable (ĭn·tûr·mĭ·ná·b'l). Endless.

interposition (ĭn'tēr·pō·zĭsh'ŭn). Act of coming between; intervention.

interval (ĭn'tēr·văl). Pause.

intolerable (ĭn·tŏl'ēr·á·b'l). Unbearable. *adv.* **intolerably.**

intonation (ĭn'tō·nā'shŭn). Variation in pitch of the voice in speech.

irascible (ī·răs'ĭ·b'l). Cross; easily angered.

iridescent (ĭr'ĭ·dĕs'ĕnt). Shining with a rainbowlike effect.

irrelevant (ĭr·rĕl'ê·vănt). Unrelated; not to the point.

irreparable (ĭ·rĕp'á·rá·b'l). Hopeless; beyond repair.

irresistible (ĭr'rē·zĭs'tĭ·b'l). Overpowering.

isolate (ī'sō·lāt). To place apart.

j

joust (jŭst). To fight on horseback with lances.

jubilant (jōō'bĭ·lănt). Joyful.

l

labyrinth (lăb'ĭ·rĭnth). Maze.

lacerate (lăs'ēr·āt). To tear or cut roughly.

lackadaisical (lăk'á·dā'zĭ·kăl). Listless.

lair (lâr). Den or hiding place.

lament (lá·mĕnt'). To grieve; to mourn. *adj.* **lamentable** (lăm'ĕn·tá·b'l).

languid (lăng'gwĭd). Sluggish; without interest.

literal (lĭt'ēr·ăl). Real; accurate.

lucid (lū'sĭd). Clear.

luster (lŭs'tēr). Glow; brightness.

luxury (lŭk'shōō·rĭ). Extravagance.

m

malfunction (măl·fŭngk'shŭn). To work wrongly.

malice (măl'ĭs). Spite; ill will; strong dislike.

manifold (măn'ĭ·fōld). Many and different.

mar (mär). To spoil.

martyr (mär'tēr). Person who sacrifices his life or position for his beliefs.

maximum (măk'sĭ·mŭm). Greatest.

meager (mē'gēr). Small.

mete (mēt). To measure or give out shares.

metropolis (mē·trŏp'ō·lĭs). Large city.

mineralogist (mĭn'ēr·ăl'ō·jĭst). Specialist in minerals.

modify (mŏd'ĭ·fī). To change; to vary.

momentous (mō·mĕn'tŭs). Very important.

mortise (môr'tĭs). To join securely together.

mosaic (mō·zā'ĭk). Decoration made with inlaid tiles, stones, or other items.

musk (mŭsk). Substance obtained from a musk deer, used as a base for perfumes.

mute (mūt). To quiet.

mythical (mĭth'ĭ·kăl). Imaginary.

n

negligible (nĕg'lĭ·jĭ·b'l). Trifling.

nicety (nī'sĕ·tĭ). Luxury.

niggardly (nĭg'ērd·lĭ). Stingy; miserly.

nomadic (nō·măd'ĭk). Wandering.

nonconformist (nŏn'kŏn·fôr'mĭst). One who acts differently from his group.

nonentity (nŏn·ĕn'tĭ·tĭ). A nobody.

o

obituary (ō·bĭt'û·ĕr'ĭ). Written about a recent death.

oblivious (ŏb·lĭv'ĭ·ŭs). Forgetful.

opaque (ō·pāk'). Not letting light through.

opportune (ŏp'ōr·tūn'). Timely.

p

palatable (păl'ĭt·á·b'l). Tasty; pleasing.

patriarch (pā'trĭ·ärk). The father or head of a family or tribe.

penitent (pĕn'ĭ·tĕnt). Remorseful; repentant; sorry (for wrongdoing).

pensive (pĕn'sĭv). Thoughtful.

perceive (pēr·sēv'). 1. To see. 2. To understand. *n.* **perception** (pēr·sĕp'shŭn).

peripheral (pĕ·rĭf'ēr·ăl). External.

perjure (pûr'jēr). To falsify.

---

bar; church; dog; arduous; fat; go; hear; jail; key; lame; meat; not; ring; pay; ran; see; shell; ten; there, thick; pasture; vast; wind; yes; zoo, zh = z in azure.

perplex (pẽr·plĕks′). To puzzle; to confuse.
petrify (pĕt′rĭ·fī). To stupefy; to paralyze with fear or surprise.
pettish (pĕt′ĭsh). Cross; fretful.
petulant (pĕ·t′ụ·lănt). Peevish.
phenomenon (fē·nŏm′ē·nŏn). Unusual occurrence.
phosphorescence (fŏs′fō·rĕs′ĕns). Glow.
pilfer (pĭl′fẽr). To steal, especially small amounts.
pious (pī′ŭs). Showing religious devotion.
placid (plăs′ĭd). Calm; peaceful.
plague (plāg). To vex. n. scourge; nuisance; any form of evil.
poacher (pōch′ẽr). One who hunts or fishes illegally on someone else's land.
pomegranate (pŏm′grăn′ĭt). Tropical fruit, the size of an orange, with many seeds in a red pulp.
pompous (pŏmp′ŭs). Self-important.
portal (pōr′tăl). Gate; entrance; door.
posterity (pŏs·tĕr′ĭ·tĭ). Future generations.
posture (pŏs′tụr). Position; way of holding the body.
potent (pō′tĕnt). Powerful.
precise (prē·sīs′). Exact.
preferable (prĕf′ẽr·á·b'l). More desirable.
premature (prē′má·tūr′). Too early; untimely.
preoccupy (prē·ŏk′ụ·pī). To lose in thought; to take the attention of.
preposterous (prē·pŏs′tẽr·ŭs). Absurd.
presumptuous (prē·zŭmp′tụ·ŭs). Arrogant; overbold.
prevalent (prĕv′á·lĕnt). Widespread.
prey (prā). To feed upon.
procure (prō·kūr′). To obtain; to get.
profane (prō·fān′). To treat disrespectfully.
proficient (prō·fĭsh′ĕnt). Skilled.
profound (prō·found′). Deep.
promenade (prŏm′ē·näd). Walking place.
propeller (prō·pĕl′ẽr). Curved blade.
prophesy (prŏf′ē·sī). To predict; to foretell.
protract (prō·trăkt′). To prolong.
prudent (prōō′dĕnt). Wise; cautious.
purser (pûr′sẽr). Clerk who keeps accounts on a passenger ship.

r

raiment (rā′mĕnt). Clothing; garments.
rally (răl′ĭ). To revive or recover.
ravenous (răv′ĕn·ŭs). Hungry; greedy.
rebuff (rē·bŭf′). Sharp refusal; snub.
recapitulate (rē′ká·pĭt′ụ·lāt). To repeat.
recede (rē·sēd′). To move backward.
reconcile (rĕk′ŏn·sīl). 1. To restore to har-

mony. 2. To adjust. n. **reconciliation** (rĕk′ŏn·sĭl′ĭ·a′shŭn).
reconnoiter (rĕk′ŏ·noi′tẽr). To make a survey; to spy out.
reconstruction (rē′kŏn·strŭk′shŭn). Rebuilding.
recurrence (rē·kûr′ĕns). Return.
refraction (rē·frăk′shŭn). Bending, or deflection, of light rays.
refrain (rē·frān′). To hold back.
reiterative (rē·ĭt′ẽr·ā′tĭv). Repetitive.
reminiscence (rĕm′ĭ·nĭs′ĕns). Recollection; remembrance.
remonstrate (rē·mŏn′strāt). To complain; to plead.
remorseful (rē·môrs′fŏol). Filled with regret.
remote (rē·mōt′). Distant.
renegade (rĕn′ē·gād). Deserter.
reparation (rĕp′á·rā′shŭn). Compensation; act of making amends for a wrong.
repentance (rē·pĕn′tăns). Remorse or regret for sin or wrongdoing.
reproachful (rē·prōch′fŏol). Accusing.
repudiate (rē·pū′dĭ·āt). To cast off; to refuse.
repugnance (rē·pŭg′năns). Extreme dislike.
resplendent (rē·splĕn′dĕnt). Splendid.
restrain (rē·strān′). To counteract; to control.
retrieve (rē·trēv′). To bring back.
revel (rĕv′ĕl). To delight in.
reverberate (rē·vûr′bẽr·āt). To resound.
reverie (rĕv′ẽr·ĭ). Dreamlike or thoughtful state.
rigid (rĭj′ĭd). Severe; firm.
rigor (rĭg′ẽr). Harshness.
rite (rīt). Ceremony.
rueful (rōō′fŏol). Sad; regretting.
ruthless (rōōth′lĕs). Cruel.

S

sagacity (sá·găs′ĭ·tĭ). Wisdom.
sanitary (săn′ĭ·tẽr′ĭ). Clean; preventing disease.
saunter (sôn′tẽr). To stroll.
savanna (sá·văn′á). Treeless plain.
scrutinize (skrōō′tĭ·nīz). To examine carefully. n. **scrutiny** (skrōō′tĭ·nĭ).
seclusion (sē·klōō′zhŭn). Solitude; retirement from the world.
semibarbaric (sĕm′ĭ·bär·băr′ĭk). Half-civilized.
sequence (sē′kwĕns). Order; succession.
serrated (sĕr′āt·ĕd). Notched on the edge.
servile (sûr′vĭl). Servantlike.
sheath (shēth). Case for a dagger or sword.
shoal (shōl). Shallow.
shrewd (shrōōd). Sly; clever.

āpe, châotic, bâre, ăt, ăttend, ärt, flásk, átop; ēke, mẹrely, ělect, ĕcho, prudĕnt, doẽr; ītem, ĭnn; rarĭty; ōde, ŏpaque, fôr, dŏt, lŏft, cŏnfide; sōon, tŏok; sour, toil; tūbe, ūnique, tûrn, sŭp, ŭntil.

shroud (shroud). Garment in which a person is buried.

shun (shŭn). To avoid; to keep clear of.

simultaneous (sī′mŭl·tā·nē·ŭs). Coming at the same time.

singular (sĭng′gŭ·lẽr). Unusual.

skepticism (skĕp′tĭ·sĭz′m). Doubt.

skulk (skŭlk). To hide.

slander (slăn′dẽr). Evil deed; offense; disgraceful accusation.

smite (smīt). To strike; to cause suffering.

sodden (sŏd″n). Soaked.

solemnity (sō·lĕm′nĭ·tĭ). Formal occasion or event.

solemnize (sŏl′ĕm·nīz). To perform with solemn ceremony.

solicitude (sō·lĭs′ĭ·tūd). Concern.

sonorous (sō·nō′rŭs). Resonant; full in sound.

sophisticated (sō·fĭs′tĭ·kāt′ĕd). Worldly.

sparse (spärs). Scanty.

specification (spĕs′ĭ·fĭ·kā′shŭn). Requirement.

spectral (spĕk′trăl). Ghostly.

speculate (spĕk′û·lāt). To wonder; to guess. *n.* speculation (spĕk′û·lā′shŭn).

sphinxlike (sfĭngks′līk). Mysterious.

stamina (stăm′ĭ·nȧ). Vitality; endurance.

stance (stăns). 1. Way of standing. 2. In parachuting, the position of the jumper in mid-air.

stifle (stī′f′l). To smother.

stipulate (stĭp′û·lāt). To arrange or specify as a condition of agreement.

strategic (strȧ·tē′jĭk). Shrewd; clever.

stripling (strĭp′lĭng). A youth.

stylus (stī′lŭs). Pencil-like piece of metal.

suavity (swăv′ĭ·tĭ). Pleasantness; smoothness.

subdue (sŭb·dū′). To conquer.

subjugate (sŭb′jŏŏ·gāt). To subject; to subdue.

subsistence (sŭb·sĭs′tĕns). Livelihood.

substantial (sŭb·stăn′shăl). 1. Ample; large. 2. Real; actual.

suffuse (sŭ·fūz′). To overspread with a fluid or color.

superficial (sū′pẽr·fĭsh′ăl). Not thorough.

supposition (sŭp′ō·zĭsh′ŭn). Guess.

surmise (sûr·mīz′). Guess.

swarthy (swôr′thĭ). Dark-skinned.

symbol (sĭm′băl). Sign or letter.

symmetry (sĭm′ē·trĭ). Balanced shape; regularity.

t

terrain (tĕ·rān′). Region; physical environment.

thence (thĕns). From that place.

thither (thĭth′ẽr). To that place.

tolerable (tŏl′ẽr·ȧ·b′l). Fairly good.

tolerate (tŏl′ẽr·āt). To put up with.

tousle (tou′z′l). To rumple.

tract (trăkt). Stretch of land.

tradition (trȧ·dĭsh′ŭn). Custom.

transition (trăn·zĭsh′ŭn). Change.

transmit (trăns·mĭt′). To pass along.

transpire (trăn·spīr′). To happen; to take place.

traverse (trăv′ẽrs). To pass through.

treacherous (trĕch′ẽr·ŭs). 1. Dangerous. 2. Traitorous; untrustworthy.

trivial (trĭv′ĭ·ăl). Trifling.

tureen (tû·rēn′). Vessel from which soup is served.

turnkey (tûrn′kē′). Person in charge of the keys of a prison.

U

ultimate (ŭl′tĭ·mĭt). Final.

undistinguishable (ŭn′dĭs·tĭng′gwĭsh·ȧ·b′l). Not recognizable; not distinct.

unhallowed (ŭn·hăl′ōd). Unholy.

unintelligible (ŭn′ĭn·tĕl′ĭ·jĭ·b′l). Not clear.

unique (û·nēk′). Unequaled.

unorthodox (ŭn·ôr′thō·dŏks). Not customary.

unsullied (ŭn·sŭl′ĭd). Without tarnish or stain.

V

vehement (vē′ē·mĕnt). Violent.

vehicle (vē′ĭ·k′l). Conveyance.

velocity (vē·lŏs′ĭ·tĭ). Speed.

veritable (vĕr′ĭ·tȧ·b′l). Real; actual.

versatile (vûr′sȧ·tĭl). Many-sided.

vexation (vĕks·ā′shŭn). Annoyance.

vindictive (vĭn·dĭk′tĭv). Vengeful.

W

wharf (hwôrf). Pier or dock.

whelp (hwĕlp). Cub or pup; one of the young of a beast of prey.

wile (wīl). Trick.

wince (wĭns). To shrink from; to draw back suddenly.

wispy (wĭs′pĭ). Filmy.

wrangle (răng′g′l). To quarrel.

wreak (rēk). To inflict.

writhe (rīth). To twist.

Z

zeal (zēl). Active interest; enthusiasm.

---

bar; church; dog; ardŭous; fat; go; hear; jail; key; lame; meat; not; ring; pay; ran; see; shell; ten; there, thick; pastŭre; vast; wind; yes; zoo, zh = z in azure.

Index of Authors and Titles